STATISTICAL METHODS FOR BUSINESS DECISIONS

CHARLES T. CLARK

Associate Professor of Business Statistics
The University of Texas at Austin

LAWRENCE L. SCHKADE

Professor of Business Administration
The University of Texas at Arlington

SOUTH-WESTERN PUBLISHING CO.

Cincinnati ● Chicago ● Dallas ● Burlingame, Calif. ● New Rochelle, N. Y.
M25 ● Brighton, England

To our families . . .

Preface

Statistical Methods for Business Decisions has been written for use as a textbook in courses that present modern statistical techniques as they are applied to problems in business and industry. These methods range in degree of sophistication from elementary to advanced and comprise a significant portion of the methodology that is called quantitative methods in business. The level of presentation presumes no mathematical preparation beyond college algebra and no previous background in digital computers. The topics from mathematics and computer science that are more advanced than these basic levels are developed fully in the book.

There has been a dramatic increase in the use of statistical and other quantitative methods and the application of computers in the decision-making process in recent years. This book reflects the current trend by presenting statistical methods that are used frequently in making analyses as bases for business decisions and by illustrating how the calculations associated with the application of these methods can be accomplished with a digital computer. The availability of computers for problem-solving has led to the development of new statistical methods and to the modification of some of the traditional computational methods that were developed originally for use with manual calculators. A selection of these new statistical methods is included in this presentation. This book is designed as a textbook for students of statistical and operations analysis and as a reference book for managers who wish to use the statistical methods of management science in making decisions.

The style of presentation reflects an approach to the exposition of statistical methods that highlights clarity and understandability, based on more than two decades of combined teaching and consulting experience. The flow diagrams and other computer applications represent more than a decade of combined experience in teaching statistics and statistical applications in which a computer is used by the students to solve problems. It is not necessary, however, that a computer be available in conjunction with the use of this textbook, for the topical presentation is designed to be utilized either with or without a computer. Some of the statistical methods are very complicated and tedious to apply if calculations are done manually, and in these portions of the book computer use is stressed but not required. The use of flow diagrams divorces the computer discussion from any particular brand of computer or programming language.

v

The organization of this book is similar to that of *Introduction to Business and Economic Statistics*, Third Edition, by John R. Stockton. Principally, the symbols and notation in the two books, where coincident, are consistent with those recommended by the American Statistical Association. Also included in this book are study questions and problems, which appear at the end of each chapter. At the end of the book are a glossary of symbols, a list of formulas, and an extensive group of appendixes that include the statistical tables used most frequently. The examples and problems in this book have been selected to present understandable and realistic situations in business and industry. The study questions are designed to focus attention on important concepts and relationships developed in the discussions. Solutions to most of the odd-numbered problems are provided in the back of the book as reinforcements to the reader when solving the problems at the end of each chapter. The selected readings contain brief comments concerning other books that offer similar or more extensive presentations of the topics included in each of the chapters.

The authors are indebted to many persons for their interest and encouragement in the preparation of this manuscript. In particular, appreciation is expressed to Dr. John R. Stockton, who suggested the writing of this book; to Professors Vincent E. Cangelosi, A. Lee Cobb, and John P. Lymberopoulos for their helpful comments in reading portions of the manuscript; to Pearl Clark and Janette Schkade for their valuable assistance in editing the manuscript; to Kay Glass and Don Roger Robinson for assisting with problem solutions; to B. Lewis Keeling for his most valuable guidance, advice, and criticisms; and to Instituto Tecnologico de Monterrey, Mexico, for aiding indirectly in enhancing the completion of the manuscript.

The authors are also indebted to the Literary Executor of the late Sir Ronald A. Fisher, F.R.S., Cambridge, to Dr. Frank Yates, F.R.S., Rothamsted, and to Messrs. Oliver and Boyd, Ltd., Edinburgh, for their permission to reprint Tables III and IV from their book *Statistical Tables for Biological, Agricultural and Medical Research*, and Tables III and V-A from *Statistical Methods for Research Workers*; and to Dr. Stephen P. Shao, Old Dominion University, and the publisher for permission to reprint Table B from his book *Mathematics of Finance*.

C. T. C.
L. L. S.

Contents

Part IV Sampling

Part V Inference

Chapter 1

The Nature of Statistics

Within recent years it has become increasingly evident that the field of statistics is able to provide the businessman with one of his most valuable tools for decision making. It is the purpose of this book to review briefly the basic statistical techniques and to present some of the more advanced tools for statistical decision making that might be studied by the business student in a second course in business statistics. Much of the orientation of this book is to the digital computer, which now makes possible the use of statistical techniques often discussed in theory but seldom used in practice because of the arduous manual computation involved.

Today, the problems confronting the business manager are likely to be far more complex than they were a few years ago. The course of action he takes must often be selected from a vast number of alternative courses of action. The number of variables involved and the amount of quantitative data to be analyzed may be overwhelming unless a proper approach and the proper tools of analysis are used. For example, a personnel director who wishes to determine if the wage scales for his firm are in line with those paid by his competitors cannot compare directly the wages of the thousands of individual workers involved. He must have the statistical tools that enable him to summarize, analyze, and decide where he stands in the industry and what steps he needs to take to correct his problems and improve his ability to recruit and hold an effective work force.

Fortunately, the tools for analysis and decision making are more numerous and more powerful today than ever before. The computer makes possible their greatest use.

THE DECISION-MAKING PROCESS IN BUSINESS

The decision-making process in business follows essentially the same basic steps used for problem solving in physics, engineering, or chemistry.

1

In business and in the social sciences, the variables are often more numerous and more difficult to measure and control than in the physical sciences, but the steps are the same. They are:

1. Simplification
2. Building a decision model
3. Testing the model
4. Using the model to find a solution

Simplification

The ancient Greeks in the fourth, fifth, and sixth centuries before Christ made a great discovery. They learned how mathematical reasoning could be used to simplify and explain the things they observed in nature. When they saw that the heavenly bodies are spheres, the surfaces of lakes are flat, light travels in a straight line, and the sides of a house form a rectangle, they began to study lines, planes, circles, triangles, and rectangles as abstractions.

In their study of geometry the Greeks observed that certain basic facts are obvious. A straight line is the shortest distance between two points in a plane. Or, all the points on the circumference of a circle are equidistant from the center. They reasoned that if some new facts could be derived, these facts would apply to all those physical objects with the same basic properties. If the area of a triangle could be shown by reasoning to be one half the base times the altitude, then a carpenter could use this abstract idea to determine how much lumber he needed to enclose the end of a gable roof.

By dealing first with abstractions that strip away all the nonessential details of a situation, it is possible to reason with the remaining basic relationships and to use this reasoning to cover a multitude of complex cases. Better still, the basic reasoning may produce other meaningful information that is entirely unforeseen.

Building a Decision Model

Simplification is but the first step in the decision-making process. The decision maker next turns to the task of taking the essential factors in the problem and arranging them in a model. A *model* may be defined as a representation of reality designed to explain it and used to predict or to control it.

While the mathematician leads in the use of abstract concepts and models, mathematical ways of thinking about essential relationships have long been used by the physical scientist. This kind of thinking is rapidly being adopted by the social scientist and the businessman.

➤ *Example.* The mathematician who sees an object dropped from a tower can estimate with great accuracy the time it will take the object to reach the ground. He uses a simple model,

$$d = 16t^2$$

where d is the distance in feet from the top of the tower to the ground and t is the time in seconds it takes the object to fall. The mathematician disregards the resistance of air since the distance the object falls is not great. Further, he ignores the weight of the object as he knows that when air resistance is not considered, all objects fall at the same rate under the pull of gravity. The entire physical problem is now a simple problem of algebra; he needs only to insert a value for d in the equation and solve for t.

From the above-mentioned example, several characteristics of a model can be pointed out:

1. A model is a simplified representation of an actual situation.
2. It need not be complete or exact in all respects.
3. It concentrates on the most essential relationships and ignores the less essential ones.
4. It is more easily understood than the empirical situation and, hence, permits the problem to be more readily solved with a minimum of time and effort.
5. The model can be used again and again for like problems or can be modified if necessary to solve new ones with added complications.

The statistical formulas used in this book can be thought of as mathematical models capable of providing the decision maker with useful tools for his important and arduous task. Some of these models are quite simple, while others are complex.

A great deal of exciting work is being done on the frontiers of modern business decision making. Those individuals charged with the responsibility of guiding the destiny of large corporations have been faced with a growing problem in recent years. Too often they find that facts gathered in the traditional manner are so long in preparation that the decisions they are designed to guide must be made before all the facts are available. To solve this problem, research and planning personnel in many large organizations are working to develop complex models of their firm or industry, programmed for a large computer and capable of giving approximate answers to far-reaching questions long before these same answers could come through conventional organizational channels. This is model building in its most sophisticated form — simulation.

Testing the Model

The real test of any model is whether it predicts outcomes with usable accuracy. If the formula $d = 16t^2$ does not predict accurately the time it will take an object dropped from a tower to hit the ground, the formula must be replaced by one that can predict with the needed accuracy. An oversimplification of the empirical situation may have led to the development of a model that ignores elements essential to its functioning as a predictor. Even if all the essential elements have been identified, the model must be tested to see if the correct relationships between these essentials have been established. Certainly, as models become more complex, a great deal of testing may be necessary to establish that they will work.

Fortunately, in the field of statistics many of the models used are ones that have withstood the test of time and are known to be reliable within given limits. The task of the student is to understand what the limitations of a given model are and how it can be used to produce the required results. A simple model such as the arithmetic mean has been used for many years and its characteristics are well known. Some of the more sophisticated models are still being tested in order to learn what they will do.

Using the Model to Find a Solution

One of the difficulties encountered in a brief discussion of models is that there are many kinds of models and they have many uses. Further, they involve many different levels of abstraction. In statistics a model may be a simple descriptive measure of a frequency distribution or it may be used to accept or reject a sample as being drawn from a given universe. Such tests are necessary because, regardless of how precise a system of measurement may be, there are always elements of chance at work that introduce random variation.

The statistician may use a model to determine which variables are pertinent to changes occurring in some dependent variable and to what extent each shares in the process. At a higher level of abstraction, there are simulation models that operate on a problem-solving sequence in which the input for one stage is the output from a previous stage. Such problems are solved through the application of the so-called *Monte Carlo* methods.

The very nature of human thought is such that model building, model testing, and model application to solve problems are an integral part of any organized thought process.

WHAT IS STATISTICS?

Much of the confusion that arises in the public mind about statistics comes from the fact that the word *statistics* has two meanings.

1. When the businessman asks his secretary to secure for him the most recent statistics on population and housing for his state, he is asking for facts. These facts are in quantitative form and are, strictly speaking, *statistical data.*

2. When the businessman asks his quality control engineer to explain how statistics can be used to determine whether a shipment of parts should be accepted for use or returned to the supplier as unsatisfactory after inspecting only a few parts, he is asking about a *statistical method.*

All persons in modern-day life are bombarded by vast quantities of statistical data via newspapers, magazines, books, radio, TV, and in almost every phase of human activity.

To the scientist, the engineer, the businessman, or any other person engaged in problem-solving activities, the second sense of the word statistics is also important. It refers to the vast and ever-growing body of methods for collecting, summarizing, analyzing, and interpreting quantitative facts. These techniques are a part of the scientific method and can be applied in many fields of endeavor. In this book the prime emphasis will be on the application of statistical methods to the solution of business problems.

The word *statistic* should also be mentioned here for completeness. Throughout this text, when the word statistic is used in the singular, it will have a meaning completely different from the two just given. Statistic will be used to refer to an arithmetic mean, a median, a standard deviation, or some other descriptive measure computed from a sample. Of course, it is possible to use the word in the plural in this sense also.

Descriptive and Inductive Statistics

The word statistics has been defined as meaning both "statistical data" and "statistical methods." A further distinction is often made between descriptive statistics and inductive statistics. The term *descriptive statistics* is confined to the treatment of data for the purpose of describing their characteristics. This term is distinct from the term *inductive statistics*, which involves making forecasts, estimations, or judgments about some larger group of data than that actually observed or about some future happening based on a study of historical data. The arithmetic mean of a sample of observations is a descriptive measure, but if it is used to estimate the arithmetic mean of the universe from which the sample was drawn, inductive techniques are involved.

The foundation of inductive statistics is probability. When probability theory is used to estimate the likelihood that a sample has been drawn from a given universe, to forecast sales, or to predict the action of one variable based on its previous relationship with other variables, these are examples of inductive techniques. The whole idea of using probability theory to solve scientific or business problems on a formal, wide-scale basis is relatively recent but is of rapidly growing importance.

➤ *Example.* To point up the distinction between descriptive statistics and inductive statistics, imagine a manufacturer who is studying a report made by his quality control department of a shipment of parts received by the firm for an assembly operation. The shipment is from one of the manufacturer's regular suppliers and contains 10,000 parts. The inspectors have checked 200 of these parts drawn at random from the shipment.

The inspection shows 12 out of the 200 parts examined to be defective. This is 6% of the sample total. As long as the executive is interested only in this sample percent of defective parts, he is dealing with descriptive statistics.

Imagine further that there is a contract between the supplier and the manufacturer which states that the manufacturer will not accept any shipment of parts with more than 5% defective. Since the sample percent of defectives is 6%, the manufacturer may decide that the percent of defectives in the entire shipment is too high, and he may reject the entire lot. Just as soon as he generalizes about the proportion of defective parts of the entire shipment of 10,000 from the results obtained from an inspection of only 200 of the parts, he has moved into the domain of inductive statistics. He has generalized about the quality of the group when he has information about only a part of it.

The generalization that the manufacturer must make in the example above is not an easy one. He must recognize that his inspectors may have gotten a "bad" sample which has 6% defectives. If another sample of 200 parts were selected, "chance" might dictate that it would contain only 4% defectives. If the difference between the sample percent and the critical 5% for the whole shipment had been large, the decision might be easier to make. Also, if the sample had been much larger, it would be reasonable to assume that it might be more representative of the whole group. Finally, the way in which the sample was drawn is important. If only parts from the top of each box had been selected, these might be the ones most subject to damage. Only an experiment that is properly designed and carefully conducted can be used as the basis for generalization.

Statistical Laws

In discussing models, the formula

$$d = 16t^2$$

was used to describe an important law of falling bodies. Using Newton's laws of motion, one can compute exactly where the falling object would hit the ground beneath the tower. On the other hand, if a six-sided die is rolled on the table, there are no laws to predict whether the top face will stop as a one, two, three, four, five, or six. However, it is possible to predict that if the die is rolled a great many times, the one will appear on top about one sixth of the time. The distinction that is made between these two situations is the distinction between a *causal law* and a *statistical law.*

Even though the causal law permits an estimate of the exact spot where the object will fall, the problem is not that simple. If an experiment is carried out repeatedly, it will be observed that the actual hits will form a certain pattern about the predicted spot. Only if all physical conditions could be perfectly controlled in the empirical experiment would the dispersion of the actual hits be reduced to zero. The law is called "causal" because it is theoretically possible to control simultaneously all the physical conditions and to compute mathematically an exact answer.

In the case of the rolling die, the Newtonian laws of motion are still in effect, but the ability to predict the outcome of a single roll is not present. For one roll, or even a few rolls, the pattern of the outcomes is not predictable. It is necessary to fall back on the frequency with which different values occur in a great many trials to compute the probability that a one will occur in any one trial. The prediction in this case is based on a "statistical law."

In a sense there are statistical laws that allow for controlled conditions in such a manner that they permit the expression of a causal law. On the other hand, there are statistical laws, such as the laws for rolling a die, in which the conditions cannot be controlled. These laws must continue to be expressed as statistical laws. It is with the latter group that this book is concerned.

Populations and Samples

Another distinction that must be made early in a preliminary discussion of the field of statistics is the difference between a population and a sample. A *population* or a *universe* (the terms are used synonymously) can be defined as each and every member of some group. The group that constitutes a population can be determined in many ways. For example, the population of City A may be defined as all those persons living within the city limits. In this case a political boundary is used to designate the group. The population of sophomore students at College B may be defined as all the students having 30 or more but less than 60 hours of college course credit and registered in College B during the current semester. The definition of the population should be clear and complete.

Any descriptive measure of the characteristics of a population is called a *parameter*. For example, the total number of people living in City A or the average age of the sophomores registered in College B is a parameter.

Once the population has been defined, a *sample* can be described as some of the members of the population. Some of the residents of City A or some of the sophomores at College B would constitute a sample. There are, of course, many possible samples of a given size that might be drawn from any population of any size.

As has already been mentioned, a *statistic* is a descriptive measure of some characteristic of a sample. For example, the average age of a sample of sophomores from College B is a statistic.

Much of the work in inductive statistics is concerned with the problems involved in using a statistic to estimate a parameter.

VARIABLES

The basic building block with which the statistician deals is the variable. Statistical data are the result of successive observations of some characteristic of a group. The characteristic being observed is the *variable*. The observations, which are recorded as the corresponding magnitudes or numbers, are the *values of the variable*.

If the values of the variable can be counted, such as the number of rooms in a house or the number of automobiles sold during the month of August, the variable is said to be a *discrete variable*. The values of a discrete variable may be integers or other real numbers.

When the values of a variable are obtained by measuring from a continuous scale, the variable is said to be a *continuous variable*. Such measures as weight, time, distance, or volume involve measurement on a continuous scale. For any two measurements, no matter how close together, a third measurement can always be found that lies between the first two if a more precise measurement is taken. A continuous variable always has an infinite number of values that need not be whole numbers but which may be carried to as many decimal places as the accuracy of the measurement will justify.

A variable that is derived as a ratio of two other variables, such as income per capita, miles per hour, or units per day of production, is called a *derived variable*. Special problems may arise in dealing with these variables.[1]

The individual values of a variable in a population are designated by a capital X, and the number of observations is designated by a capital N. The N observations may be designated as

$$X_1, X_2, \ldots, X_N.$$

The values of a variable in a sample are designated by a lowercase x, and the number of observations is designated by a lowercase n. The n observations may be designated as

$$x_1, x_2, x_3, \ldots, x_n.$$

➤ *Example.* Six workers performing an assembly operation turn out 14, 16, 12, 10, 15, and 13 parts each in an hour. The variable X has six values, which can be denoted as follows:

$$X: X_1 = 14, X_2 = 16, X_3 = 12, X_4 = 10, X_5 = 15, \text{ and } X_6 = 13.$$

The group of six workers constitutes a universe, so capital X's have been used to denote each observation of the variable. Since only completed parts are counted, the variable is discrete.

Assume that a sample of three workers from the group is selected and the average time each worker takes to assemble one part is computed. If the times are 4.3, 3.7, and 4.6 minutes, the variable x has three values as follows:

$$x: x_1 = 4.3, x_2 = 3.7, x_3 = 4.6.$$

As the group of three workers constitutes a sample, lowercase x's have been used to denote each observation of the variable. The values of the variable are measured on a continuous scale, time, and the variable is continuous.

ACCURACY OF STATISTICAL DATA

The statistician is confronted with two problems in dealing with statistical data. He must be careful not to present quantitative facts in such a manner as to leave the impression that they are more accurate than they actually are. On the other hand, the statistician must be careful not to discard any accuracy that can be justified.

---

[1] See the discussion of the *harmonic mean* in Chapter 2.

➤ *Example.* If a news report states that unemployment during the past month increased by 257,115 persons as a result of a strike in the automobile industry, the reader is given the impression that the count is an exact one. Actually, it is probably an estimate compiled from new claims for unemployment compensation from several states, reports of layoffs made by the companies involved, and statements made by union officials. A statement to the effect that unemployment has risen approximately a quarter of a million persons would be more justified by the nature of the data. However, a statement by an official of the Texas Employment Commission in Austin that 23,121 new claims for unemployment compensation were filed during the past week would most likely be the result of an actual count made from reports from local offices of the commission. Even in this case it might be helpful to know that all the local offices reported so that no "estimates" had to be made by someone in Austin to fill in gaps in the report.

It must be recognized that additional accuracy in data is often secured only at additional cost, which may or may not be justified by the use to be made of the data. Many administrative decisions require only information that is approximate. The businessman may need to know only in a general way the changes that have occurred in inventories, sales, and employment, or the shifts that have been noted in consumer demand. Data that purport to be more accurate than they are, are not only deceptive but unnecessary as well.

Exact and Approximate Numbers

An *exact number* is one that results from the counting of distinct physical objects. The values of a discrete variable are exact numbers. While the concept of an exact number is simple, the mechanics of arriving at such a number may be complex. For example, census counts may be made of the population of a large city. Individuals are distinct units and can be counted, but, because they are constantly moving about and in and out of the city limits, the census count may be only a good approximation of the true population that is never known.

A datum which is arrived at by the measurement of some characteristic is always an *approximate number*. The fact that it is approximate does not mean it is inaccurate. If a student weighs himself on a drug store scales and finds his weight to be 174 pounds, the number 174 is an approximate number, rounded to the nearest full pound. It is an approximate number because the variable, weight, is a continuous variable. If the scales are reasonably accurate, so is the value of the observation. If the same student weighs himself on a very sensitive scales in the Physics Department and finds his weight to be 174.25 pounds, he may have a more accurate observation than before; but the number is still approximate.

Rounding

To avoid the impression of greater accuracy than actually exists, numbers are often rounded to drop unnecessary digits. If an estimate of a city's population is made from the number of water meter connections, it might be better to round an estimate of 121,144 to 120,000. The use of zeros implies that the number is approximate.

Rounding cannot always be accomplished by changing other digits to zeros, however. To do so might induce a downward bias in the data, as demonstrated in the following example.

➤ *Example.* If a company interested in the average age of its employees used the age at last birthday to compute the average, the average would undoubtedly be too small. It would be more accurate to round the age of each employee to his nearest birthday before computing the average. In some cases the age recorded for an employee would be less than his true age, and in other cases, more; but most of the inaccuracies would be canceled out in the final average.

The following rules are usually used in rounding:

1. *When the first of the digits to be rounded to zero is less than five, make no change in the last digit retained.*
2. *When the first of the digits to be rounded to zero is more than five, or five followed by some digits not all zero, increase the last digit retained by one.*
3. *When the first of the digits to be rounded to zero is five, or five followed by zeros only, make no change in the last digit retained if it is even, but increase it by one if it is odd.*

➤ *Example.* Given the following measurements, the rules for rounding would be applied as shown below to round to two digits in each case:

Rule	Original number	Number rounded to two digits
1	2.713	2.7
2	2.768	2.8
3	2.75	2.8
3	2.85	2.8
2	2.85001	2.9
3	2.850000	2.8
1	2.74995	2.7

Significant Digits

After rounding, any digit other than a zero is always *significant*. If sales for the month have been recorded as 3,427 units, each of the four digits is significant. This means that the only problem of significance is with zeros. The following rules may be used to determine if a zero is significant:

1. *A zero that falls between two significant digits is always significant.*
2. *A zero that falls after a significant digit is always significant if the number contains a decimal point.*
3. *A zero that falls before the first significant digit is not significant.*
4. *A zero that falls after the last significant digit of a whole number may or may not be significant. A dot placed above the last significant zero makes it and all the zeros that precede it significant.*

➤ *Example.* The rules of significant digits are used to interpret the zeros in the following numbers:

Rule	Number	Number of significant digits
2	12.740	5
3	0.00743	3
1	60,501	5
4	3,000	1 to 4
4	3,00$\dot{0}$	4
4	3,$\dot{0}$00	3
2	3,000.	4
1	609	3
4	60,900	3 to 5
2	1.2000	5
1	200.003	6

Computation with Rounded Numbers

Once the number of significant digits is determined for rounded numbers used in computation, two simple rules govern the number of significant digits that may be carried in the answer.

1. *In addition or subtraction, digits to the right of the place in which the last significant digit occurs in any of the numbers are not significant and should not be carried in the sum or remainder.*
2. *In multiplication or division, the product or quotient should contain no more significant digits than that number with the least number of significant digits used in the calculations.*

➤ **Example.** The rules for computation with rounded numbers are used to determine the proper number of significant digits in the following computations:

Rule	Computations	Answer to be shown as
1. (addition)	2.743 *172.6 14.76 ——— 190.103	190.1
1. (subtraction)	145.268 * 19.3 ——— 125.968	126.0
2. (multiplication)	172.43 * 1.2 ——— 34486 17243 ——— 206.916	210**
2. (division)	*3.1 ⟌ 47.12 ⟌ 15.2 31 —— 161 155 —— 62 62 ——	15

*This number determines the number of significant digits that may be carried in each answer.
**Although only two significant digits can be justified in the answer, it is necessary to add the zero, which is not significant, to keep from changing the value of the number.

ORGANIZATION OF DATA

Vast amounts of statistical data in their raw form almost defy comprehension. Thus, one of the first steps in dealing with statistical data is to organize the observations into some logical arrangement for analysis. This organization can take two basic forms: statistical tables and figures. A *statistical table* is a presentation of numbers in a logical arrangement, with some brief explanation to show what they are. A *figure* is a chart, graph, map, or other illustration designed to present statistical data in picture form. Even though a great deal of space could be devoted profitably to a discussion of these two forms, only the basic ideas needed in later chapters are presented here.

The Array

In an *array* the various values of the variable are arranged in order of magnitude with each individual value retaining its original identity. If a value appears more than once, it is listed separately each time it occurs. While the array is one of the simplest ways of organizing data, it has many useful applications in statistical analysis if the number of items is not too large.

➤ *Example.* Table 1.1 illustrates the arrangement of raw data into two types of arrays.

Table 1.1

NUMBER OF PARTS PRODUCED BY EACH OF SEVEN MACHINES
IN ONE HOUR

Machine	Number of parts produced per hour	Number of parts per hour shown as an array	
		Smallest to largest	Largest to smallest
A	132	127	141
B	134	131	137
C	141	132	134
D	131	132	132
E	127	134	132
F	132	137	131
G	137	141	127

The Frequency Distribution

When there are a great number of observations of a variable, it may be convenient to group them in some manner for further analysis. When the values of a variable result from the counting or measuring of some characteristic and when these observations are grouped into classes showing the number of observations in each class, the resulting table is called a *frequency distribution.*

➤ *Example.* A milk company clerk records the number of quarts of milk purchased by 64 families on a particular route during one month. The results are shown in Table 1.2.

To permit the clerk to understand better the meaning of his observations, these data might be arranged into a frequency distribution such as that shown in Table 1.3.

Table 1.2

NUMBER OF QUARTS OF MILK PURCHASED BY 64 FAMILIES
IN ONE MONTH

19	16	22	9	22	12	39	19
14	23	6	24	16	18	7	17
20	25	28	18	10	24	20	21
10	7	18	28	24	20	14	23
25	34	22	5	33	23	26	29
13	36	11	26	11	37	30	13
8	15	22	21	32	21	31	17
16	23	12	9	15	27	17	21

Table 1.3

NUMBER OF QUARTS OF MILK PURCHASED BY 64 FAMILIES
IN ONE MONTH

A frequency distribution

Number of quarts purchased	Number of families
5–9	7
10–14	10
15–19	13
20–24	18
25–29	8
30–34	5
35–39	3
Total	64

In the example above, the groupings 5–9, 10–14, . . . , 35–39, are called *class intervals*. The class interval is the width of each class and is five for each class in the foregoing example; *e.g.*, for the first class, the number of quarts can be 5, 6, 7, 8, or 9. The number of families recorded for each class, *i.e.*, 7, 10, . . . , are the *frequencies*. The *lower class limits* are the values 5, 10, . . . , and 35; the *upper class limits* are the values 9, 14, . . . , 39. The *class midpoints* are those values, such as 7, 12, . . . , 37, that fall halfway between the upper and the lower class limits.

It is also important to note that the values of the variable used in this example are discrete. Setting up a frequency distribution for discrete data is relatively simple as there is a definite break in the values of the variables since they are whole numbers.

The values of the observations of a continuous variable present some additional complications, as demonstrated by the following examples.

➤ *Example.* A milk company clerk makes a careful study of the length of time a driver spends making 64 deliveries on a new route. He records his observations in the following frequency distribution.

Table 1.4

TIME REQUIRED BY A MILKMAN TO MAKE
DELIVERIES TO 64 CUSTOMERS

(in minutes)

Time required to make a delivery	Number of deliveries
1 and under 2	12
2 and under 3	22
3 and under 4	13
4 and under 5	6
5 and under 6	5
6 and under 7	4
7 and under 8	2
Total	64

For the third class in this distribution:
The class interval is 3 and under 4 minutes, or 1 minute.
The frequency is 13 deliveries.
The lower class limit is 3 minutes.
The upper class limit is up to but not including 4 minutes.
The class midpoint is 3.5 minutes.

➤ *Example.* If the clerk making the study had rounded each observation to the nearest tenth of a minute and had then grouped his observations into a frequency distribution, his table might look like the one below.

Table 1.5

TIME REQUIRED BY A MILKMAN TO MAKE
DELIVERIES TO 64 CUSTOMERS

(in minutes)

Time required to make a delivery	Number of deliveries
1–1.9	11
2–2.9	23
3–3.9	12
4–4.9	7
5–6.9	5
7–9.9	3
10 and over	3
Total	64

For the third class in this distribution:
The class interval is 3 to 3.9 minutes.
The frequency is 12 deliveries.
The real lower class limit is 2.95 minutes, which is the shortest time that would be rounded to 3 minutes for inclusion in the third class.
The real upper class limit is a time just under 3.95 minutes, which would be rounded downward for inclusion in the third class.
The class midpoint is 3.45 minutes, halfway between the class limits of 3.95 and 2.95.

In the last example using continuous data, the class interval was not the same for all classes, and the last class, "10 and over," was written as an *open-end class*. While there are advantages to having all class intervals the same length and in not having open-end classes, it is not always possible to do this in dealing with economic and business data.

In setting up a frequency distribution, the most important consideration is the number of classes to be used. If there are too few classes, pertinent characteristics of the data are lost through too much summarization. If there are too many classes, the distribution is difficult to work with and there is not enough summarization.

It is logical to assume that the number of observations to be classified is an important factor in determining the number of classes. Judgment must also be used to secure logical class limits and a frequency distribution best designed to meet the needs for which it is intended.

The best rule of thumb for determining the number of classes is provided by a formula known as *Sturges' rule*, which is

$$k = 1 + 3.3 \log n \quad \ldots\ldots\ldots\ldots\ldots\ldots(1.1)$$

where,
k is the number of classes, when rounded to the nearest whole number
$\log n$ is the logarithm of the number of observations to be included in the distribution.

➤ *Example.* Four applications of Sturges' rule are shown below.

Number of observations	*Sturges' rule*	*Number of classes*
n is 50	$k = 1 + 3.3 \,(1.698970) = 1 + 5.6 =$	7
n is 500	$k = 1 + 3.3 \,(2.698970) = 1 + 8.9 =$	10
n is 5,000	$k = 1 + 3.3 \,(3.698970) = 1 + 12.2 =$	13
n is 50,000	$k = 1 + 3.3 \,(4.698970) = 1 + 15.5 =$	17

As the number of observations grows very large, there is a slight increase in the number of classes called for by Sturges' rule; but it is seldom that more than about 20 classes will be used.

A frequency distribution arranged to show the number of observations above or below a given figure is known as a *cumulative frequency distribution*. Such a distribution may take the shape of either a "more than" or a "less than" cumulative frequency distribution.

➤ *Example.* The observations shown in Table 1.3 are arranged below to demonstrate both forms of a cumulative frequency distribution.

Table 1.6

NUMBER OF QUARTS OF MILK PURCHASED BY 64 FAMILIES
IN ONE MONTH

Number of quarts purchased	Number of families	Number of quarts purchased	Number of families
Less than 10	7	More than 35	3
Less than 15	17	More than 30	8
Less than 20	30	More than 25	16
Less than 25	48	More than 20	34
Less than 30	56	More than 15	47
Less than 35	61	More than 10	57
Less than 40	64	More than 5	64

GRAPHIC PRESENTATION

All kinds of statistical data may be presented in graphic form. There are literally hundreds of different kinds of charts and graphs that can be used effectively to emphasize important facts and relationships in statistical data. The discussion in this book is limited to the histogram, the frequency polygon, and the ogive. These have the greatest application in later chapters. The selected readings at the end of this chapter give other sources of a more complete discussion of graphic presentation.

The Histogram

A *histogram* is a bar chart of continuous data that have been grouped into a frequency distribution. Since there are no gaps between the class limits, there are no gaps between the bars of the histogram. It is an accepted practice to use vertical bars in any chart of a frequency distribution.

➤ *Example.* The data in Table 1.4 are presented in Figure 1.1 as a histogram.

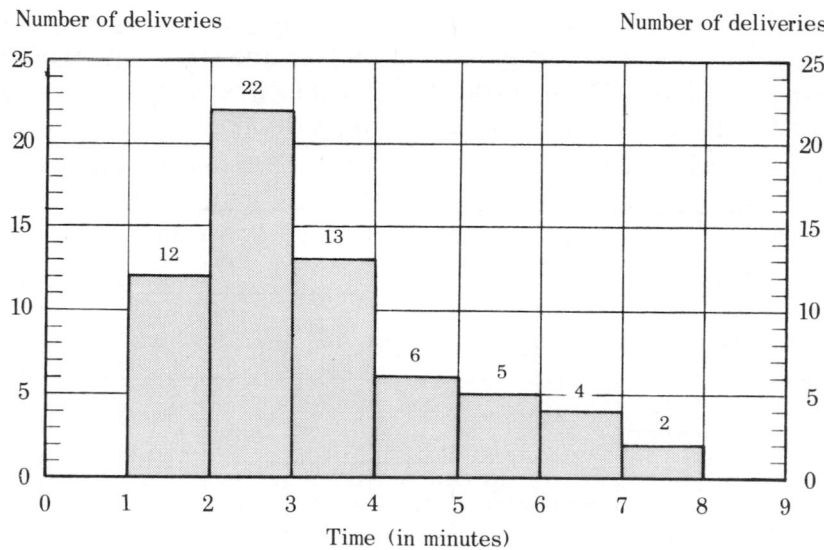

Figure 1.1

TIME REQUIRED BY A MILKMAN TO MAKE DELIVERIES
TO 64 CUSTOMERS

The bars have been plotted so that the height of each represents the frequency within that class. The tallest bar is the second one from the left, which shows that there were 22 deliveries that required between two and three minutes each. Since all the class intervals in this distribution are the same, all the bars have the same width.

The height of the bar may also be thought of in a slightly different way. Since the standard unit in this distribution is a class interval, the frequency per interval unit is referred to as the *frequency density*.

Suppose the distribution of delivery times has been arranged into classes of varying widths as shown below.

Table 1.7

TIME REQUIRED BY A MILKMAN TO MAKE DELIVERIES
TO 64 CUSTOMERS

(in minutes)

Time required to make a delivery	Number of deliveries	Frequency ÷ interval	Frequency density
1 and under 2	12	12 ÷ 1	12
2 and under 3	22	22 ÷ 1	22
3 and under 4	13	13 ÷ 1	13
4 and under 6	11	11 ÷ 2	5.5
6 and under 8	6	6 ÷ 2	3

When this distribution is plotted as a histogram in Figure 1.2, the frequency, which is the number of units in the class, represents the *area* of each bar. The frequency density, which is the number of units per minute, represents the *height* of the bar.

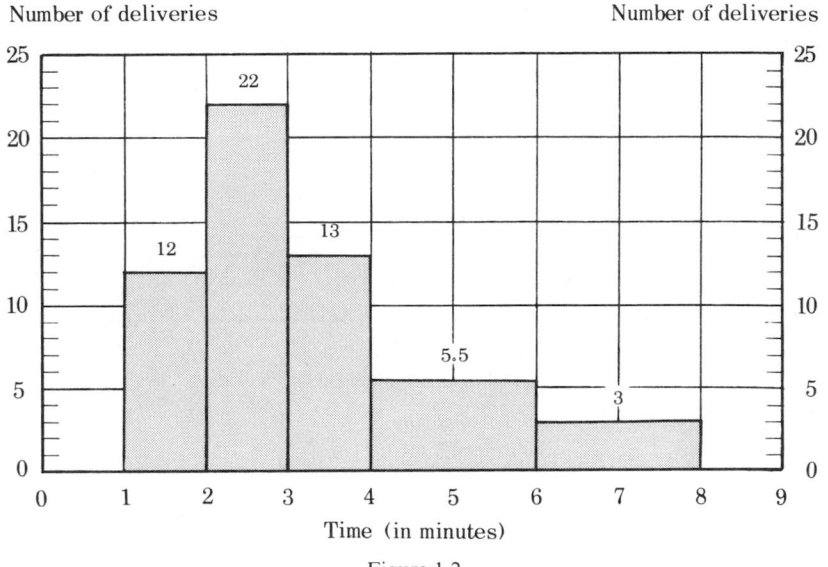

Figure 1.2

TIME REQUIRED BY A MILKMAN TO MAKE DELIVERIES
TO 64 CUSTOMERS

The Frequency Polygon

If the midpoints of the class intervals are connected by straight lines, and if the lines are brought to the base line in the vacant class at either end of the distribution, the resulting chart is a *frequency polygon.*

➤ *Example.* The histogram shown in Figure 1.1 has been converted into a frequency polygon in Figure 1.3.

The Ogive

In a line chart of a cumulative frequency distribution, the curve is called an *ogive.* An ogive is also referred to as a *cumulative frequency curve.* A chart of such a curve may be useful in estimating the number of units either above or below some given value in a distribution.

➤ *Example.* In Table 1.6 the number of quarts of milk purchased by 64 families in one month were shown in two cumulative frequency distributions. These same data are plotted as ogives in Figure 1.4.

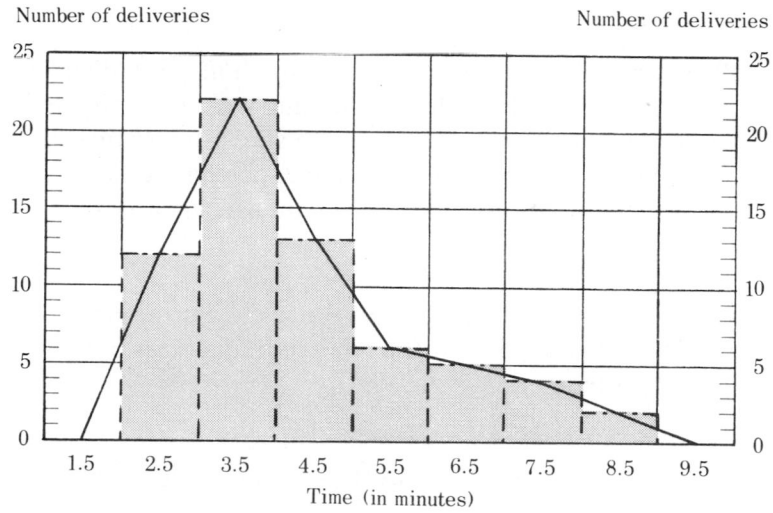

Figure 1.3

TIME REQUIRED BY A MILKMAN TO MAKE DELIVERIES
TO 64 CUSTOMERS

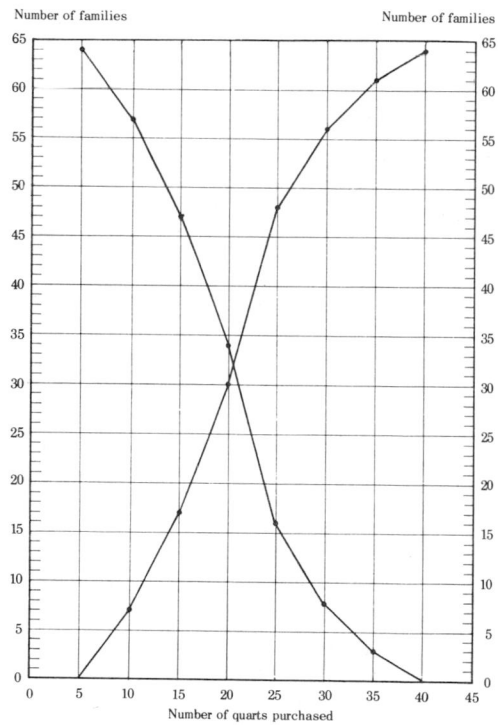

Figure 1.4

NUMBER OF QUARTS OF MILK PURCHASED BY 64 FAMILIES
IN ONE MONTH

Relative Frequencies

It will be important in later chapters to think of a distribution as having an area of one. In order to do this, it is necessary to convert frequency to relative frequency; that is, to show the frequency for each class of a frequency distribution as a decimal percent of the total number of units in the distribution. This is demonstrated in the following example.

➤ *Example.* The data from Table 1.4 are shown in terms of relative frequencies in Table 1.8, and the relative frequencies are plotted as a histogram in Figure 1.5.

Table 1.8

TIME REQUIRED BY A MILKMAN TO MAKE DELIVERIES
TO 64 CUSTOMERS

(in minutes)

Time required to make a delivery	Number of deliveries	Relative frequency (representing both height and area)
1 and under 2	12	0.188
2 and under 3	22	0.344
3 and under 4	13	0.203
4 and under 5	6	0.094
5 and under 6	5	0.078
6 and under 7	4	0.062
7 and under 8	2	0.031
Totals	64	1.000

In the foregoing example the class interval is the same for each class, and the relative frequency in each class represents both the height and the area for the bar for that class.

When the class interval is not the same for each class, the relative frequency represents only the area of the bar, which still has a total of one. The height of the bar must be computed as the relative frequency per unit of width, which is the frequency density.

➤ *Example.* The data from Table 1.8 are repeated in Table 1.9 with a different number of class intervals and showing the relative frequency per unit of width. The data are then presented in Figure 1.6 to emphasize the fact that the relative frequency represents the area of the bar, and the relative frequency per unit of width represents the height of the bar.

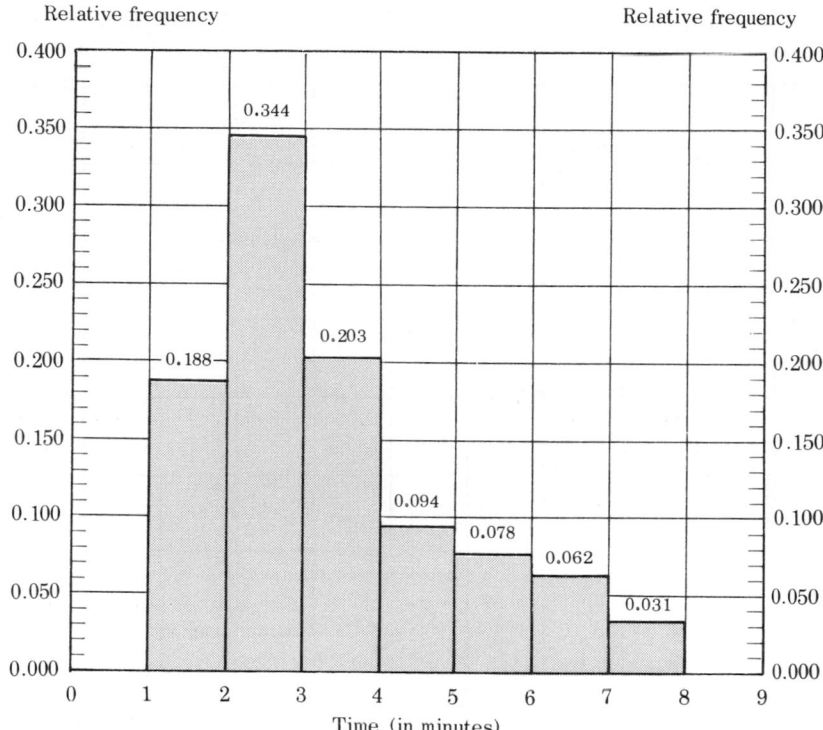

Figure 1.5

TIME REQUIRED BY A MILKMAN TO MAKE DELIVERIES
TO 64 CUSTOMERS

Table 1.9

TIME REQUIRED BY A MILKMAN TO MAKE DELIVERIES
TO 64 CUSTOMERS

(in minutes)

Time required to make a delivery	Number of deliveries	Relative frequency (area)	Width of class (minutes)	Relative frequency per unit of width (height)
1 and under 2	12	0.187	1	0.187
2 and under 3	22	0.344	1	0.344
3 and under 4	13	0.203	1	0.203
4 and under 6	11	0.172	2	0.086
6 and under 8	6	0.094	2	0.047
Totals	64	1.000		

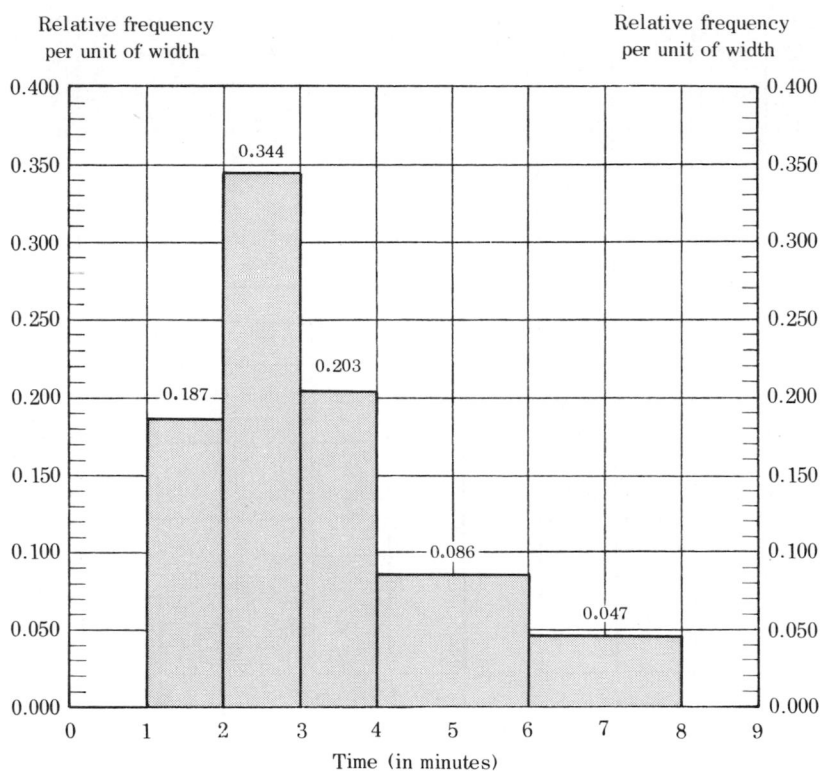

Figure 1.6

TIME REQUIRED BY A MILKMAN TO MAKE DELIVERIES
TO 64 CUSTOMERS

STUDY QUESTIONS

1-1. Explain briefly the meaning of each of the following terms:

a. model
b. Monte Carlo methods
c. statistics
d. statistical data
e. statistical method
f. statistic
g. descriptive statistics
h. inductive statistics
i. causal law
j. statistical law
k. population
l. universe
m. parameter
n. sample

o. variable
p. values of the variable
q. discrete variable
r. continuous variable
s. derived variable
t. exact number
u. approximate number
v. significant digit
w. array
x. frequency distribution
y. class interval
z. frequencies
aa. lower class limit
ab. upper class limit

ac. class midpoint
ad. open-end class
ae. Sturges' rule
af. cumulative frequency distribution
ag. histogram
ah. frequency density

ai. area of bar in a histogram
aj. height of bar in a histogram
ak. frequency polygon
al. ogive
am. cumulative frequency curve

1-2. Discuss the steps in the decision-making process. How does the application of these steps to business problems differ from their application to engineering problems?

1-3. Distinguish between the terms descriptive statistics and inductive statistics. Give two examples of each.

1-4. For the following variables distinguish between those that are continuous and those that are discrete:
  a. Number of absences students have in a history class
  b. Weight of castings in a foundry
  c. Time required to assemble 100 TV sets
  d. Grades on an accounting quiz
  e. Height of six-month-old fig bushes in a nursery
  f. Machines requiring repair in a factory in one day

1-5. Give three examples of a derived variable. What is the advantage of using a derived variable?

1-6. Discuss the difference between a population and a sample. Give examples of three populations, being careful that each is precisely and accurately defined.

1-7. If you wish to take a sample of dwelling units from the population of all dwelling units in a city, how would you define the term, "dwelling unit"? Why would it be necessary to have an exact definition?

1-8. Why is it necessary to distinguish between exact and approximate numbers in dealing with statistical data? Why is rounding necessary in dealing with approximate numbers? What is the danger of too much rounding?

1-9. What is a frequency distribution? When is it a useful way of organizing data? What problems are involved in determining the number of classes to be used?

1-10. What is a histogram? What advantages does its use provide in the analysis of statistical data?

1-11. Two frequency polygons can be compared with one another if they both have the same class intervals and the same total frequencies. If the class intervals are the same but the total frequencies are different for two distributions, can you suggest a way to compare them?

1-12. What is an ogive and what are its uses?

PROBLEMS

1-1. How many significant digits are there in each of the following numbers?
  a. 14,500   c. 0.0740   e. 1,700.0   g. 13,450.
  b. 0.0078   d. 78,002   f. 1,200   h. 1.0000

1-2. Round each of the following numbers so that it contains four significant digits:

a. 758,430   c. 178.000   e. 1,245,001   g. 433,500
b. 768,850   d. 0.078456   f. 333,499   h. 178,000

1-3. If all the numbers used in the following computations are approximate, round the results to the appropriate number of significant digits:

a. $\sqrt{2.73} = 1.6740416$ d. $1,748 \div 3 = 582.6666$

b. $(49)^2 = 2,401$ e. $(4,782)(3.8) = 18,171.6$

c.   742.37   f. 948.231
      22.4 $- 56.8$
   1,377.2379   891.431

   2,142.0079

1-4. The frequency distribution below shows the purchase orders for a small manufacturing plant during the month of October:

Size of order (in dollars)	Number of orders
under 10	23
10 and under 20	48
20 and under 30	60
30 and under 40	31
40 and under 50	24
50 and under 60	19
60 and under 70	12
70 and under 80	8
80 and under 90	5
Total	230

a. Would you estimate that the proper number of class intervals have been used?
b. For the class with the largest frequency find:
   (1) the class midpoint   (4) the upper class limit
   (2) the class frequency   (5) the class interval
   (3) the lower class limit
c. Make a "more than" cumulative frequency distribution. How many orders were $50 and greater?
d. Make a "less than" cumulative frequency distribution. How many orders were less than $60?
e. Draw a histogram of the frequency distribution.
f. Draw a frequency polygon. Since the first class begins with zero and there can be no vacant class at the beginning of the chart, bring the chart line to the base line at zero.
g. Draw ogives of the cumulative frequency distributions computed in (c) and (d). These may be drawn on the same chart.

1-5. The following distribution shows the number of miles (rounded to the nearest full mile) traveled by 85 city buses in one day of operation:

Distance traveled (in miles)	Number of buses
25–49	3
50–74	35
75–99	20
100–149	14
150–249	7
250–399	4
400–600	2
Total	85

a. Why was it best to set up this frequency distribution with unequal class intervals?

b. For the class with the largest frequency find:
   (1) the class midpoint   (4) the real upper class limit
   (2) the class frequency   (5) the class interval
   (3) the real lower class limit

c. Compute the relative frequency for each class. When this is plotted as a histogram, will the relative frequency for each class represent the area of that bar or the height of the bar?

d. Compute the relative frequency per unit of width (use 25 miles as the unit of width). What will this measure represent for each bar in the histogram?

e. Draw a histogram of the frequency distribution using the data computed in (c) and (d) in constructing the bars.

1-6. The distribution below shows the construction cost of 80 homes in a new subdivision:

$14,000	9,500	16,055	10,000	11,900	15,000	11,000	13,900
11,500	16,810	15,525	19,700	18,155	8,500	14,100	19,550
16,220	19,370	17,890	17,335	14,650	19,000	18,315	20,000
15,050	13,800	17,500	12,200	21,500	13,500	10,800	18,000
17,888	16,333	10,200	20,500	8,000	13,000	17,025	20,750
18,125	20,000	21,000	9,000	14,150	15,888	12,600	12,000
17,000	18,725	17,700	17,850	17,211	19,750	13,950	18,600
15,780	19,600	10,500	15,300	13,250	15,444	17,800	18,020
17,750	15,250	17,900	18,400	19,020	21,700	11,300	9,700
8,250	17,810	14,250	16,711	12,200	14,777	16,000	21,750

a. Use Sturges' rule to estimate the number of classes needed to organize these data in a frequency distribution.

b. Using the number of classes computed in (a), construct a frequency distribution with equal class intervals beginning with $8,000 and under $10,000, etc.

c. Draw a histogram of the distribution.

d. Draw a frequency polygon.

e. Draw a cumulative frequency curve (ogive) showing the number of houses costing "$20,000 and more," etc.

   f. Draw a cumulative frequency curve showing the number of houses "less than $10,000," etc.

   g. Using the curve drawn in either (e) or (f), estimate the cost which divides the distribution in half so that 40 of the houses cost less than that amount and 40 cost more.

   h. Compute the frequency in each class as a percent of total and plot the results as a histogram.

1-7. The following distribution shows the amount of the hospital bills for 64 patients discharged from a hospital during a three-day period.

$107.77	301.74	49.25	98.10	38.00	49.75	331.18	99.82
42.18	142.00	132.00	179.00	187.72	164.92	82.78	211.80
399.45	193.02	109.50	55.00	122.23	24.87	294.15	850.07
241.11	26.50	2,743.80	150.25	197.50	356.08	612.12	119.54
127.70	566.67	250.01	381.11	133.37	47.75	252.22	401.17
180.93	45.00	632.08	67.88	177.87	798.50	375.02	264.50
483.33	1,500.63	148.18	275.98	70.90	95.03	62.12	342.00
152.78	125.77	195.17	32.80	124.00	97.18	714.88	202.00

   a. Classify the observations into a frequency distribution with an appropriate number of classes using unequal class intervals. Begin with the class "$25–49," and end with "$800 and over." Be careful to design a distribution that best shows the characteristics of the data.

   b. Set up two cumulative frequency distributions and plot them both as cumulative frequency curves on the same chart. How would you evaluate that spot on the chart where the curves cross?

SELECTED READINGS

Spear, Mary Eleanor. *Charting Statistics.* New York: McGraw-Hill Book Company, Inc., 1952.

   This is an excellent book on practical graphic presentation of statistical data. It presents many types of charts, and sources are given throughout for the convenience of the student who may wish to obtain further information.

Stockton, John R. *Introduction to Business and Economic Statistics.* 3d ed. Cincinnati: South-Western Publishing Company, 1966.

   Most of the basic ideas presented in this chapter are discussed more extensively in Chapters 1 through 4.

Walker, Helen M. *Mathematics Essential for Elementary Statistics.* Rev. ed. New York: Henry Holt and Company, 1951.

   This is a self-teaching manual of great value to the student who wishes to review the elementary mathematical concepts necessary to an understanding of statistics.

Chapter 2

Descriptive Statistics: Averages

The word "average" is a part of almost everyone's vocabulary. One speaks of the "average student" or the "average starting salary," often without being very specific as to exactly what he means. He uses the word "average" in an attempt to find one single figure to describe a whole group of figures.

Since there are several different kinds of averages in statistics, there is a need to be very precise in the use of terminology. Each average must be clearly defined and labeled to avoid ambiguity and confusion. This chapter deals with such measures of central tendency as the arithmetic mean, geometric mean, harmonic mean, median, and mode. Also, the measures of location known as quartiles, deciles, and percentiles are discussed.

USES OF AN AVERAGE

Averages are more widely used than any other statistical measures, largely because they are easily computed and have many applications. While any list of uses may overlap or overlook some special use, at least three uses of an average can be listed:

1. An average provides a "summary" of the data. It represents an attempt to find one figure that tells more about the characteristics of the distribution than any other. For example, a firm that hires several hundred clerks a year has an average monthly starting salary of $270. This one figure summarizes the hiring policy for clerks as far as beginning pay is concerned.
2. An average provides a "common denominator" for comparing two groups of data. If the average monthly sales of Department A are compared with the average monthly sales of Department B, a quick and easy comparison of the sales of the two departments can be made.
3. An average can provide a measure of "typical size." For example, if the income of a family is compared with the average income of all families in the community, a judgment can be made as to whether the family income under study is above or below the average and by how much.

ARITHMETIC MEAN

Because it is the best known, easily understood, and most useful, the arithmetic mean is the most often used average in statistics. The *arithmetic mean* can be defined as the sum of the values of a variable divided by the number of values. To compute the mean of the values of some variable X, such as $X_1, X_2, X_3, \ldots, X_N$, the following equation can be used:

$$\mu = \frac{\Sigma X}{N} \quad \dots\dots\dots\dots\dots\dots\dots\dots\dots\dots(2.1)$$

where,
  μ is the arithmetic mean
  X is the value of an individual observation of the variable
  ΣX is "the sum of" the values of the variable[1]
  N is the number of values being averaged.

➤ *Example.* If a car owner purchases gasoline six times during the month in the following amounts, 5.4, 9.8, 7.6, 8.2, 8.7, and 10.1 gallons, the arithmetic mean of his purchases is:

$$\mu = \frac{5.4 + 9.8 + 7.6 + 8.2 + 8.7 + 10.1}{6} = \frac{49.8}{6} = 8.3 \text{ gallons.}$$

The arithmetic mean has an additional advantage that if the total is known, together with the number of values being averaged, it is not necessary to know the values of the individual items to compute the mean.

➤ *Example.* If the total payroll for a retail store with 43 employees is $14,308.25, then:

$$\mu = \frac{\$14,308.25}{43} = \$332.75.$$

The fact that an arithmetic mean can be computed does not always imply that it is a useful average.

➤ *Example.* If five salesmen travel 25, 35, 28, 850, and 32 miles in visiting customers one week:

$$\mu = \frac{25 + 35 + 28 + 850 + 32}{5} = 194 \text{ miles.}$$

---

[1]See Technical Note No. 1 at the end of this chapter.

This figure is neither typical of the distance traveled by the salesmen who make all of their calls in a single district of town, nor is it
typical of the one salesman who travels throughout the state to visit
his customers. The arithmetic mean has the one weakness of being
unduly influenced by unusually large or unusually small values in a
distribution.

The arithmetic mean has another quality that is familiar to students
of mechanics. It is one that will have useful implications in Chapter 3
in the discussion of moments about the arithmetic mean as a way to
measure the skewness (lack of symmetry) and peakedness of a distribution of values.

The sum of the deviations of the values less than the mean will be
equal to the sum of the deviations of the values greater than the mean.
Or stated another way, the sum of the deviations of the values from their
mean is zero.

➤ *Example.* For the following values the arithmetic mean is 8, and the
sum of the values about 8 is 0.

Values of X	$X - \mu$	
2	−6	
4	−4	
4	−4	$\mu = \dfrac{72}{9} = 8$
6	−2	
10	2	
10	2	$\Sigma(X - \mu) = 0$
12	4	
12	4	
12	4	
$\overline{72}$	$\overline{0}$	

This characteristic is illustrated graphically in Figure 2.1, where
blocks of equal weight are distributed along a bar (assumed to have no
weight) marked with a scale of all possible values of the variable.
When the bar is placed on a fulcrum, it will be in balance only if the
fulcrum is located at that spot on the scale whose value is the arithmetic mean of the values represented by the weights.

Weighted Arithmetic Mean

Formula 2.1 assumes that the values being averaged are all of equal
importance. This is not always the case, however. For example, the grade
on a three-hour final examination is more important than the grade on a

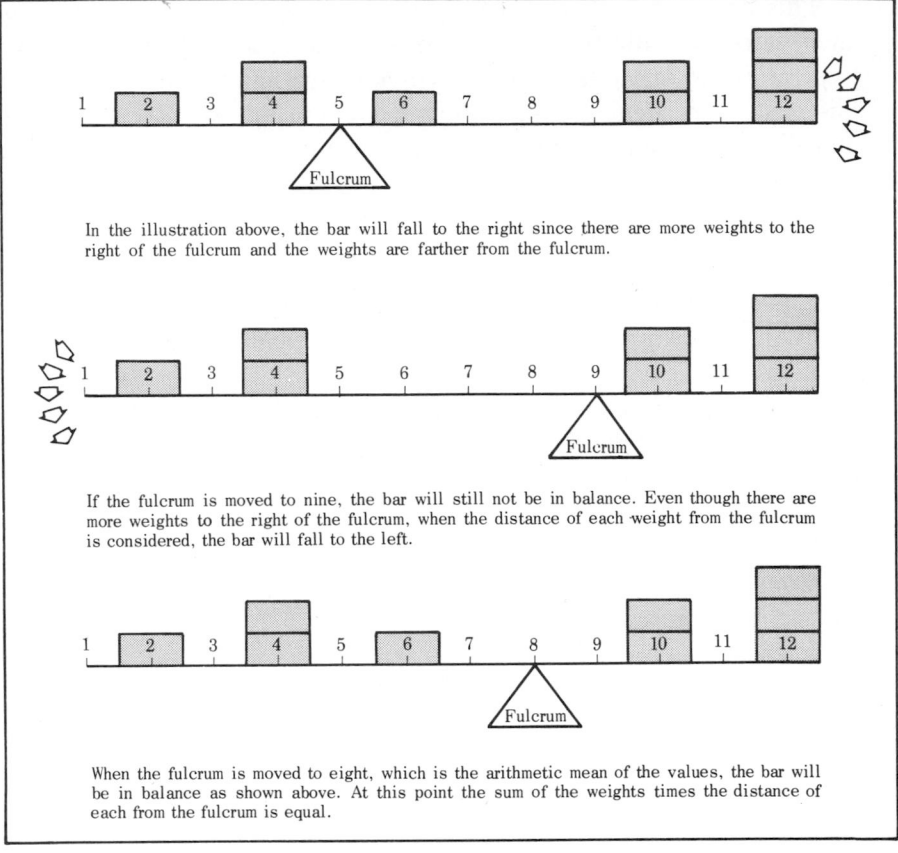

In the illustration above, the bar will fall to the right since there are more weights to the right of the fulcrum and the weights are farther from the fulcrum.

If the fulcrum is moved to nine, the bar will still not be in balance. Even though there are more weights to the right of the fulcrum, when the distance of each weight from the fulcrum is considered, the bar will fall to the left.

When the fulcrum is moved to eight, which is the arithmetic mean of the values, the bar will be in balance as shown above. At this point the sum of the weights times the distance of each from the fulcrum is equal.

Figure 2.1

THE ARITHMETIC MEAN OF A SET OF
POINTS IS ITS BALANCE POINT.

one-hour quiz in determining the final grade in a course. To compute the mean of the values of the variable X when each value has an assigned weight, such as $w_1 X_1$, $w_2 X_2$, $w_3 X_3$, . . . , $w_N X_N$, the following equation can be used:

$$\mu = \frac{\Sigma w X}{\Sigma w} \quad \text{.............................(2.2)}$$

where,

w is the weight assigned each value of X.

➤ **Example.** In the case of a student's final grade, the weighted arithmetic mean might be computed as shown in the following table:

Table 2.1

COMPUTATION OF WEIGHTED ARITHMETIC MEAN
Semester Grades of One Student

Work	Grade X	Weight w	wX
Homework problems	79	5	395
Laboratory reports	85	10	850
First hour quiz	72	15	1,080
Second hour quiz	68	15	1,020
Third hour quiz	81	15	1,215
Term report	89	10	890
Final examination	75	30	2,250
Total	...	100	7,700

$$\mu = \frac{\Sigma wX}{\Sigma w} = \frac{7,700}{100} = 77.$$

In order to simplify the arithmetic involved, it is customary to assign weights so that they total either 1 or 100. This is not a requirement, however.

Arithmetic Mean, Grouped Data

When there are a great number of values of a variable to be considered, one may wish to group them into a frequency distribution as a more effective way of dealing with them. In some instances, the statistician may have to work with data already grouped by someone else. Where data have been grouped, the exact value of each item is no longer known; thus, while an estimate can be made of the arithmetic mean, it is still only an estimate. The availability of a digital computer to do the tedious calculation limits somewhat, but probably will never eliminate, the use of the frequency distribution as a way of handling data. Grouping observations into a frequency distribution makes it possible to present them in a table, or as a histogram or a frequency polygon when charts are used.

The following formula can be used to compute the arithmetic mean of grouped data:

$$\mu = \frac{\Sigma fm}{N} \quad \dots\dots\dots\dots\dots\dots\dots\dots\dots(2.3)$$

where,

f is the number of items in each class
m is the midpoint of each class interval
N is the total number of items in the distribution.

➤ *Example.* Table 2.2 is a frequency distribution of the size of gasoline purchases made by 256 customers at a service station.

Table 2.2

COMPUTATION OF THE ARITHMETIC MEAN, GROUPED DATA

Purchases of Gasoline by 256 Customers

Purchases of gasoline (in gallons)	Number of purchases f	Gallons purchased (midpoint) m	fm
0.0–1.9	9	0.95	8.55
2.0–3.9	22	2.95	64.90
4.0–5.9	57	4.95	282.15
6.0–7.9	64	6.95	444.80
8.0–9.9	46	8.95	411.70
10.0–11.9	33	10.95	361.35
12.0–13.9	18	12.95	233.10
14.0–15.9	7	14.95	104.65
Total	256	...	1,911.20

$$\mu = \frac{1,911.20}{256} = 7.47 \text{ gallons.}$$

In computing the mean of this frequency distribution, it is assumed that the midpoint of each class is representative of the items in that class. While some items will be larger and some smaller, it is logical to assume a uniform distribution of items within each interval.

The formula for grouped data is actually a weighted arithmetic mean with the class midpoint, m, representing X for all the items in that class, and the frequency, f, for each class being used as the weight, w, for that class.

The preceding method can be used to estimate the mean regardless of whether the class intervals are the same for all classes. If, however, the frequency distribution has an open-end class such as "14.0 and over," it is impossible to estimate the mean unless the values of the individual items in that class are known. In an open-end class there is no way to determine the midpoint. Since many economic data are classified in open-end frequency distributions, the statistician is forced to refer to the original data before they were grouped, or he must use some other average.

When the class intervals of a frequency distribution are all the same size, a shortcut method of estimating the arithmetic mean is available through use of the following formula:

$$\mu = A + \frac{\Sigma fd'}{N} i \ldots\ldots\ldots\ldots\ldots\ldots\ldots\ldots\ldots.(2.4)$$

where,

A is the midpoint of some arbitrarily selected class interval

f is the frequency of each class

d' is the deviation in class interval units from A

N is the sum of f

i is the class interval of a frequency distribution having classes all the same size.

While the value of A may be the midpoint of any class interval, it should be chosen near the middle of the distribution to keep the arithmetic as simple as possible.

➤ *Example.* The data in Table 2.2 are used again in Table 2.3 to illustrate the shortcut method of estimating the arithmetic mean. The answer is the same as that obtained by using Formula 2.3.

Table 2.3

COMPUTATION OF THE ARITHMETIC MEAN FROM GROUPED
DATA USING THE SHORTCUT METHOD

Purchases of Gasoline by 256 Customers

Purchases of gasoline (in gallons)	Number of purchases f	d'	fd'
0.0–1.9	9	−3	−27
2.0–3.9	22	−2	−44
4.0–5.9	57	−1	−57
6.0–7.9	64	0	0
8.0–9.9	46	1	46
10.0–11.9	33	2	66
12.0–13.9	18	3	54
14.0–15.9	7	4	28
Total	256	...	66

$$\mu = 6.95 + \frac{66}{256} 2 = 6.95 + 0.52 = 7.47 \text{ gallons.}$$

The value of "A" may be thought of as an "estimated mean." If this value is less than the true arithmetic mean, μ, the value of the term "$\frac{\Sigma fd'}{N} i$" (which is a correction factor for the difference between A and μ) will be positive. When the correction factor is added to the value of A, it will increase its value to μ. If, on the other hand, A is taken as a value greater than μ, the value of the correction factor will be negative and when added to A, will reduce it to the value of μ.

Another way to think of A is to imagine it as a fulcrum upon which the distribution (in the form of a histogram) is placed. The distribution will be in balance only if A is the same value as the mean. If A is not the same as the mean and if the fulcrum is moved, right or left, by the amount of the correction factor, the fulcrum will then be located at the mean and the histogram will be in balance as shown in Figure 2.2.

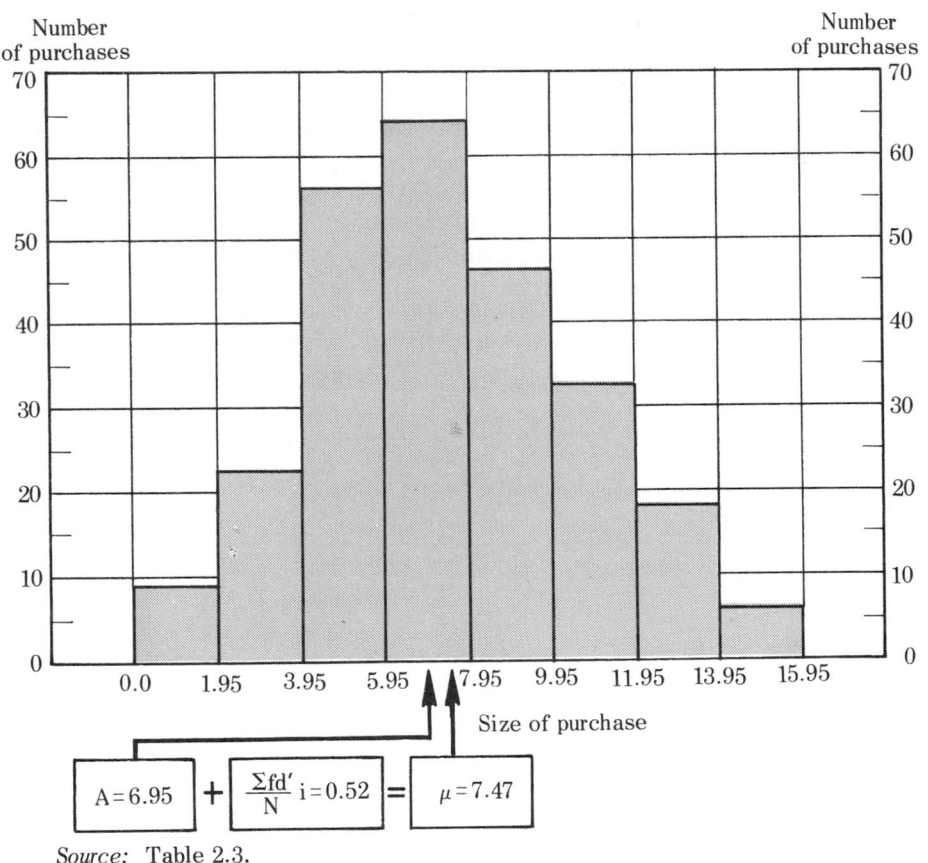

$$A=6.95 \quad + \quad \frac{\Sigma fd'}{N}\, i=0.52 \quad = \quad \mu=7.47$$

Source: Table 2.3.

Figure 2.2

THE ARITHMETIC MEAN OF A FREQUENCY
DISTRIBUTION IS ITS BALANCE POINT.

GEOMETRIC MEAN

The geometric mean is a measure used to average ratios and percents, and is particularly valuable in computing index numbers. The *geometric mean* can be defined as the Nth root of the product of N values of a variable. If the variable X has values $X_1, X_2, X_3, \ldots, X_N$, the geometric mean of these values can be computed as follows:

$$G = \sqrt[N]{X_1 \cdot X_2 \cdot X_3 \cdot \ldots \cdot X_N} \ldots\ldots\ldots\ldots\ldots(2.5)$$

where,

G is the geometric mean

X is the value of the individual observation of the variable

N is the number of values being averaged.

When N is more than two, the geometric mean can be most easily computed by using logarithms and the following formula:

$$\log G = \frac{\Sigma \log X}{N} \ldots\ldots\ldots\ldots\ldots\ldots(2.6)$$

➤ *Example.* Table 2.4 shows the computation of the geometric mean of four ratios. Each ratio shows the population of Houston, Texas, as a percent of the figure 10 years before.

Table 2.4

COMPUTATION OF THE GEOMETRIC MEAN

Percentage Change from Previous 10 years of Population
in Houston, Texas, 1920–1960

Year	Population (in thousands)	Percent of previous 10 years X	Log X
1920	138	...	...
1930	292	211.6	2.325516
1940	385	131.8	2.119915
1950	596	154.8	2.189771
1960	938	157.4	2.197005
Total	...	...	8.832207

Source: United States Bureau of Census.

$$\log G = \frac{\Sigma \log X}{N} = \frac{8.832207}{4} = 2.208052$$

$$\text{antilog } 2.208052 = 161.46$$

$$G = 161.46$$

$$\text{Average rate of increase} = 161.46\% - 100.00\%$$

$$= 61.46\%.$$

If an arithmetic mean is computed for the four percentages:

$$\mu = \frac{211.6 + 131.8 + 154.8 + 157.4}{4} = \frac{655.6}{4} = 163.9.$$

In Table 2.5 the population of Houston for 1920 is multiplied by 163.9 percent every 10 years, resulting in a total of 995,840 persons by 1960. It will be noted that this figure is too large by 57,840 persons. On the other hand, when the geometric mean of 161.46 is used every 10 years, the figure for 1960 is 937,840 persons, which would round to 938,000, showing the geometric mean to be the appropriate average to use in this case.

Table 2.5

USE OF GEOMETRIC MEAN VS. ARITHMETIC MEAN
IN AVERAGING RATES OF CHANGE

Percentage Change from Previous 10 Years of Population of
Houston, Texas, 1920–1960

Year	Population (in thousands) Actual figures	Estimates of population for 1960 from 1920 figures	
		Using μ of 163.9	Using G of 161.46
1920	138	...	...
1930	292	(226.18)	(222.81)
1940	385	(370.71)	(359.75)
1950	596	(607.59)	(580.85)
1960	938	(995.84)	(937.84)

Source: Table 2.4.

The geometric mean is also used in computing the average rate of increase between any two time periods, such as the average annual rate of increase in gross national product between two dates or the rate of increase in a sum of money at compound interest. If the beginning and ending figures for a series are known and if it is desired to determine the average rate of growth, the rate can be computed using the following formula:

$$r = \sqrt[N]{\frac{P_N}{P_o}} - 1 \quad \dots\dots\dots\dots\dots\dots\dots(2.7)$$

where,
   r is the rate of increase
   P_N is the value at the end of the period
   P_o is the value at the beginning of the period
   N is the number of time periods.

➤ *Example.* In the case of the population of Houston, if P_N is taken as the population in 1960, P_o is the population in 1920, and N is four, which is the number of 10-year time periods:

$$r = \sqrt[4]{\frac{938}{138}} - 1 = \text{antilog}\left(\frac{\log 6.797}{4}\right) - 1$$

$$r = 1.6146 - 1 = 0.6146.$$

To express this value as a percent:

$$0.6146 \times 100 = 61.46\% \text{ per 10 years.}$$

If it is desirable to know the annual rate of increase in population for Houston, Texas, for the 40-year period from 1920 to 1960, this can be found as follows:

$$r = \sqrt[40]{\frac{938}{138}} - 1 = \frac{\log 6.797}{40} - 1$$

$$r = 1.0491 - 1 = 0.0491$$

$$\text{or } .0491 \times 100 = 4.91\% \text{ each year.}$$

The nature of the formula for the geometric mean (see Formula 2.5) is such that if any of the values being averaged is zero, the product of the values will be zero, and the geometric mean cannot be computed. It is also meaningless to compute the geometric mean if negative values are involved. The arithmetic mean is handicapped by neither of these short-comings. These difficulties can usually be overcome, however, by using care in selecting the way in which the values are expressed when they are to be averaged using the geometric mean.

While the geometric mean can be computed from grouped data, this is seldom necessary and will not be discussed in this book.

HARMONIC MEAN

The *harmonic mean* is another of the specialized averages which is useful in solving problems that involve variables expressed as time rates such as miles per hour, number of units produced per day, or number of contracts completed per year. It also can be used in handling certain types of price data such as units per dollar.

If the variable X has values $X_1, X_2, X_3, \ldots, X_N$, the harmonic mean of these values can be computed as:

$$H = \frac{N}{\sum\frac{1}{X}} \quad\ldots\ldots\ldots\ldots\ldots\ldots\text{(2.8)}$$

where,

H is the harmonic mean

$\dfrac{1}{X}$ is the reciprocal of the value of an individual observation of the variable

N is the number of values being averaged.

The need for this average can be shown best through an example.

➤ *Example.* If four machines in a machine shop are used to produce the same part, but they work at different rates of speed, it might be useful to know the average rate of speed in planning production or estimating costs. The figures below show the minutes required by each machine to produce one part and the average time required per machine.

Machine	Minutes required to make one part	Number of parts produced per hour
A	2.5	24
B	2.0	30
C	1.5	40
D	6.0	10
Total	12.0	104

$$\mu = \frac{12.0}{4} = 3.0 \text{ minutes.}$$

If the four machines work for one hour, and if each machine requires on the average three minutes per part, the machines would produce an average of 20 parts each, or 80 parts in total. One of the characteristics of the arithmetic mean is that if it is substituted for each value in the series, the sum of the values will remain unchanged. For this example the total number of parts produced by the four machines in one hour should be figured in another way.

The average first computed tells us that only 80 parts per hour can be produced by the four machines, but when the number of parts is computed separately for each machine, the total jumps to 104. This leads to the conclusion that the average (arithmetic mean) is inappropriate. If, instead, the harmonic mean is used:

$$H = \frac{4}{\dfrac{1}{2.5} + \dfrac{1}{2.0} + \dfrac{1}{1.5} + \dfrac{1}{6.0}} = \frac{4}{0.400 + 0.500 + 0.667 + 0.167}$$

$$= 2.31 \text{ minutes.}$$

Since four machines running for one hour represent 240 minutes operating time, then

$$240 \div 2.31 \text{ will produce } 104 \text{ parts.}$$

Thus, the harmonic mean of 2.31 minutes per part is the proper average to use.

The arithmetic mean would have also given the same result if it had been computed as a weighted mean using as weights the number of parts produced per hour. These computations are shown below.

Machine	Minutes required per part (X)	Number of parts per hour (w)	wX
A	2.5	24	60.0
B	2.0	30	60.0
C	1.5	40	60.0
D	6.0	10	60.0
Total		104	240.0

$$\mu = \frac{\Sigma wX}{\Sigma w} = \frac{240.0}{104} = 2.31 \text{ minutes.}$$

The chief advantage of using the harmonic mean rather than a weighted arithmetic mean is that the harmonic mean requires no system of weights and thus avoids the problem of determining what the proper weights should be.

MEDIAN

The *median* is defined as the value of the middle item of a group of values when they are arranged in an array from smallest to largest. The median is an average of position. While its value is affected by the position of each item in the series, it is not unduly influenced by a few very large or very small items as is the arithmetic mean.

Median, Ungrouped Data

Finding the median for ungrouped data is a matter of arranging the items in an array and then finding the middle item. This can be a tedious job if the number of items is large.

➤ *Example.* The following shows the location of the median time required by five workers to perform an assembly operation:

Worker	Time (in minutes)	Time (arranged in array)
1	25	23
2	26	25
3	30	26 → Median
4	23	28
5	28	30

A strict application of the definition of the median leads to two problems that need special consideration because, technically, the median is indeterminate. The first of these problems arises when there are an even number of items. The second problem appears when two or more items in the center of the array have the same value. These special cases are discussed in the following two examples.

➤ Example.
An even number
of items:

Time
(in minutes)
23
25
26
28 → Median $= \dfrac{26 + 28}{2} = 27$ minutes
30
31

When there are an even number of items in the distribution, the median is taken as a value halfway between the middle two.

➤ Example.
An odd number
of items with identical
items at the center:

Time
(in minutes)
23
25
26 → Median $= 26$ minutes
26
28

In the example above, the value 26 is taken as the median even though two of the values are smaller and one is larger than the median value.

Median, Grouped Data

When a large number of items are involved, the mechanical job of sorting the items into an array can be extremely tedious and time consuming. Under these conditions, it may be much more expedient first to classify the items in a frequency distribution and then to estimate the median. If the data to be analyzed have already been grouped by someone else, the statistician may have no choice but to make such an estimate.

The median can be estimated for data in a frequency distribution by use of the following formula:

$$Md = L_{Md} + \frac{\frac{N}{2} - F_{LMd}}{f_{Md}} i_{Md} \dots\dots\dots\dots\dots(2.9)$$

where,

Md is the median

L_{Md} is the real lower limit of the median class

F_{LMd} is the cumulative frequency less than the real lower limit of the median class

f_{Md} is the frequency of the median class

i_{Md} is the class interval of the median class

N is the number of items in the distribution.

➤ *Example.* The data in Table 2.6 are used to demonstrate how to estimate the median from a frequency distribution.

Table 2.6

LOCATION OF THE MEDIAN, GROUPED DATA

Wage Increases in Manufacturing, 1962
(Number in thousands)

Increases in wages (in cents per hour)	Number f	Cumulative number F
Under 2	74	74
2 and under 4	430	504
4 and under 6	1,702	2,206
6 and under 8	2,095	4,301
8 and under 10	1,751	6,052
10 and under 12	879	6,931
12 and under 15	279	7,210
15 and under 19	174	7,384
19 and over	58	7,442
Total	7,442	...

Source: Wage Developments in Manufacturing, 1962 (Washington: U.S. Department of Labor, Bureau of Labor Statistics, 1963), p. 10.

$$Md = 6 + \frac{\frac{7,442}{2} - 2,206}{2,095} 2$$

$$Md = 6 + 1.45 = 7.45 \text{ cents.}$$

The first step is to determine the class within which the median falls. This determination is easy if a cumulative frequency column is added to the work sheet to show for each class the number of items in that class and all preceding classes. As there are 7,442 items in the distribution, the middle item is found to be

$$\frac{N}{2} = \frac{7,442}{2} = 3,721.$$

Since there are an even number of items in the distribution, the value of the item that represents the median lies halfway between items number 3,721 and 3,722. As there are 2,206 items in the first three classes and 4,301 items in the first four, the fourth class will contain the median and is called the "median class."

Under certain conditions the median has two distinct advantages over the arithmetic mean. The median is a more representative average than the mean for a distribution that is badly skewed, and it can be located in a frequency distribution that has an open-end class, *i.e.*, "19 and over." Many distributions of economic data have both of these characteristics.

MODE

The *mode* can be defined as the most frequently occurring value. Since the word "mode" means "most fashionable," it may be the most representative average that describes an entire distribution of the values of some variable.

➤ *Example.* If the starting salaries made by 10 graduating seniors on their first jobs were in the following amounts, the fact that the greatest number started at $500 per month would make that figure the mode:

Name	Starting salary	Starting salary (array)	
Anderson	$625	$460	
Black	500	480	
Cleveland	480	500	
Dawson	500	500	← Mode = $500
Emerson	460	500	
Franklin	500	500	
George	575	525	
Harris	530	530	
Ives	525	575	
Jackson	500	625	

When there are only a few values in a distribution, it is quite possible that there will be no two of them alike; hence, there will be no mode. It is also possible that there may be two or more modes. In these cases, it is clear that the mode cannot be used as a measure of central tendency.

Empirical Mode

When the mean and the median of a distribution are known, it is possible to estimate the mode using the other two averages. This measure is called the *empirical mode*. It is defined as the value of the arithmetic mean minus three times the difference between the mean and the median. The formula is shown below:

$$Mo_E = \mu - 3(\mu - Md) \quad \dots\dots\dots\dots\dots(2.10)$$

where,
Mo_E is the empirical mode
μ is the arithmetic mean
Md is the median.

➤*Example.* If it is known that the arithmetic mean of a distribution of values is 38.2 and the median is 41.6, the empirical mode can be calculated as follows:

$$Mo_E = 38.2 - 3(38.2 - 41.6) = 48.4.$$

The formula is based on a very simple relationship that exists between the three averages. A symmetrical distribution will have a mean, a median, and a mode that are all the same. When the distribution is skewed, however, the averages tend to pull apart, with the mode located at the highest point in the distribution and the mean moving farthest in the direction of the tail. The median should lie approximately two thirds of the distance from the mode to the mean. This relationship is shown in Figure 2.3.

The relationship will not hold exactly for all distributions, particularly for ones with only a few items or ones that are badly skewed. For this reason the formula, which applies to both grouped and ungrouped data, should be used with caution and only when the mode cannot be arrived at directly from the data themselves.

Mode, Grouped Data

When data are grouped in a frequency distribution, the class with the greatest number of items is the *modal class*. If the data are plotted as a histogram, the modal class will be represented by the tallest bar.

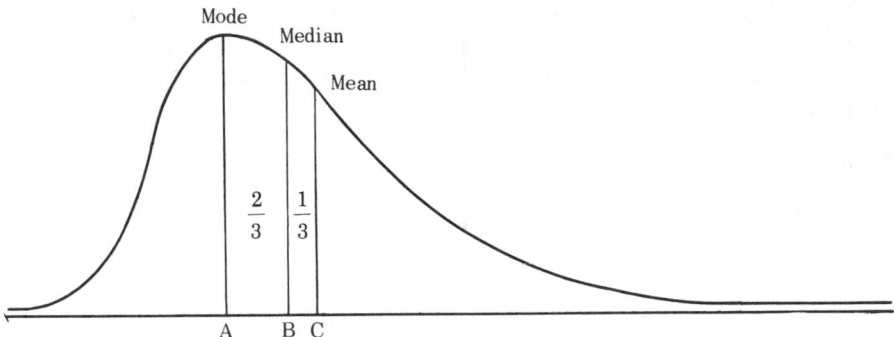

The distance from A to B is approximately $\frac{2}{3}$ of the distance from A to C.

Figure 2.3

THE RELATIONSHIP BETWEEN MEAN, MEDIAN, AND
MODE IN AN ASYMMETRICAL DISTRIBUTION

The easiest way to arrive at one figure to represent the mode is to take the midpoint of the modal class. This is called the *crude mode.* Where the frequencies of the two classes lying immediately on either side of the modal class are approximately equal, the crude mode is probably a good estimate and can be arrived at by inspection. When one of the classes adjacent to the modal class has substantially more items than the class immediately on the other side of the modal class, it is reasonable to expect that the mode will not be centered in the modal class but will be drawn in the direction of the adjacent class with the most items. In the example shown in Table 2.7, the modal class is clearly that of "age 30–39," but it should be greater than the midpoint of that class as there are more life insurance salesmen represented in the "40–49" age bracket than in the "20–29" age group.

The following formula can be used to locate the mode in a frequency distribution:

$$Mo = L_{Mo} + \frac{d_1}{d_1 + d_2} \, i_{Mo} \quad \dots\dots\dots\dots\dots\dots(2.11)$$

where,

Mo is the mode

L_{Mo} is the real lower limit of the modal class

d_1 is the difference between the number of items in the modal class and the class that immediately precedes it

d_2 is the difference between the number of items in the modal class and the class that immediately follows it

i_{Mo} is the class interval of the modal class.

The mode can be located in an open-end frequency distribution since it is necessary to know only the number of items in the extremes of the distribution and not their values.

➤*Example.* The following table illustrates the location of the mode:

Table 2.7

LOCATION OF THE MODE, GROUPED DATA

Ages of Life Insurance Salesmen in
a Midwestern Company

Age (years)	Number of salesmen
20–29	24
30–39	60
40–49	42
50–59	31
60 or older	19
Total	176

Source: Hypothetical data.

$$d_1 = 60 - 24 = 36$$
$$d_2 = 60 - 42 = 18$$
$$Mo = 29.5 + \frac{36}{36 + 18} 10 = 29.5 + 6.7$$
$$Mo = 36.2 \text{ years.}$$

Mode, Graphic Interpolation

The mode can also be approximated graphically by drawing lines diagonally from the upper corners of the tallest bar of a histogram to the upper corners of the adjacent bars. These lines intersect at the point above the X axis which is the mode.

➤*Example.* Figure 2.4 uses the same data on the ages of life insurance salesmen shown in Table 2.7. The data are displayed as a histogram and the mode is estimated by the graphic method.

QUARTILES, DECILES, AND PERCENTILES

Quartiles, deciles, and percentiles are other summary measures of a distribution that are important as locators. Just as the median is a value that divides a distribution so that half of the items are smaller and the other half are larger than the median, the quartiles divide the distribution into quarters; the deciles divide it into tenths; and the percentiles divide it into hundredths.

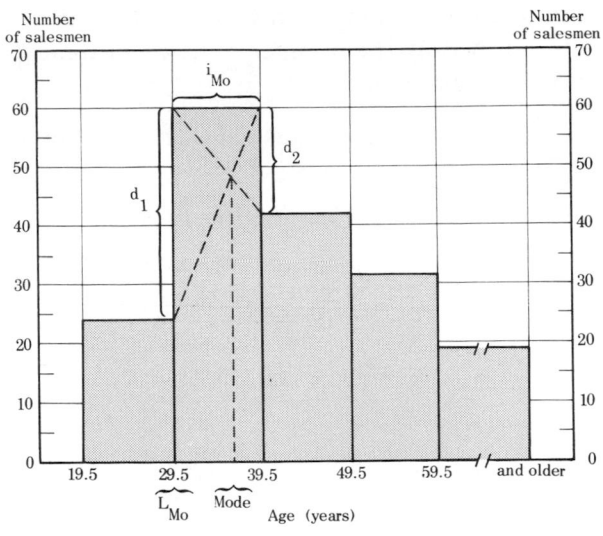

Source: Table 2.7.

Figure 2.4

LOCATION OF THE MODE, GRAPHIC METHOD

Quartiles

To calculate quartiles of ungrouped data, the items must be in an array. The *second quartile* is the same as the median and is found in exactly the same manner. The *first quartile* (Q_1) is that value which divides the items less than the median in half. The *third quartile* (Q_3) is that value which divides the items greater than the median in half.

➤*Example.* The location of quartiles for ungrouped data is shown below:

Salaries *(Array)*		*Salaries* *(Array)*	
\$420		\$420	
430		428	$Q_1 = \dfrac{428 + 432}{2} = \$430$
435 ← Q_1 First Quartile = \$435		432	
438		438	$Md = \dfrac{438 + 440}{2} = \$439$
441		440	
445 ← Q_2 Second Quartile or Median = \$445		445	$Q_3 = \dfrac{445 + 449}{2} = \$447$
447		449	
490		450	
500 ← Q_3 Third Quartile = \$500			
510			
515			

When the data are classified in a frequency distribution, the first and third quartiles can be located using formulas that are modifications of the formula for the median:

$$Q_1 = L_{Q_1} + \frac{\frac{N}{4} - F_{L_{Q_1}}}{f_{Q_1}} i_{Q_1} \dots\dots\dots\dots\dots(2.12)$$

$$Q_3 = L_{Q_3} + \frac{\frac{3N}{4} - F_{L_{Q_3}}}{f_{Q_3}} i_{Q_3} \dots\dots\dots\dots(2.13)$$

where,

Q_1 is the first quartile

Q_3 is the third quartile

L_{Q_1} is the real lower limit of the first quartile class

L_{Q_3} is the real lower limit of the third quartile class

$F_{L_{Q_1}}$ is the cumulative frequency less than the lower limit of the first quartile class

$F_{L_{Q_3}}$ is the cumulative frequency less than the lower limit of the third quartile class

f_{Q_1} is the frequency of the first quartile class

f_{Q_3} is the frequency of the third quartile class

i_{Q_1} is the class interval of the first quartile class

i_{Q_3} is the class interval of the third quartile class

N is the number of items in the distribution.

➤*Example.* For the data in Table 2.6 (page 43),

$$\frac{N}{4} \text{ is } \frac{7,442}{4} = 1,860.5,$$

As there are 504 items in the first two classes and 2,206 items in the first three classes, the third class is the first quartile class. The value of the first quartile is computed as follows:

$$Q_1 = 4 + \frac{\frac{7,442}{4} - 504}{1,702} 2 = 4 + 1.59$$

$$Q_1 = 5.59 \text{ cents.}$$

In the same manner and using the same frequency distribution, the third quartile is found to lie in the fifth class. The value of the third quartile is computed as follows:

$$Q_3 = 8 + \cfrac{\cfrac{3(7,442)}{4} - 4,301}{1,751} 2 = 8 + 1.46$$

$$Q_3 = 9.46 \text{ cents.}$$

From these measures it is estimated that in 1962 one fourth of all the wage increases in manufacturing in the United States were less than 5.59 cents per hour; one half were between 5.59 and 9.46 cents; and the remaining one fourth were greater than 9.46 cents. Salary data or other wage information expressed in this form are particularly useful to personnel officers or others responsible for wage and salary administration in business.

Deciles and Percentiles

An array of values can be divided into ten equal parts or a hundred equal parts following the same rules used to divide it into four equal parts. These measures are seldom used except for distributions with a great number of values. They are very useful, however, in such situations as locating a student's test score in relation to thousands of other students who may have taken the same test. For example, it is possible to say that John Jones is in the upper tenth of his graduating class or that his score on a college entrance examination was in the upper 5% of those taking the test.

To calculate deciles and percentiles from ungrouped data, the items are first placed in an array. A value is then located which divides the array of items so that a given proportion of the items are smaller and a given proportion larger than that value. The procedure used to locate the strategic value, which is the wanted decile or percentile, is precisely that used to locate the median or a quartile. The only difference is the proportion of items falling above or below the value selected.

Calculating deciles and percentiles for data in a frequency distribution can be accomplished by using one of the following formulas as it stands or with an appropriate modification. For example, the formula to be used in estimating the third decile is:

$$D_3 = L_{D_3} + \frac{\frac{3N}{10} - F_{L_{D_3}}}{f_{D_3}} i_{D_3} \quad \text{.................} \textbf{(2.14)}$$

where,

D_3 is the third decile

L_{D_3} is the real lower limit of the third decile class

$F_{L_{D_3}}$ is the cumulative frequency less than the lower limit of the third decile class

f_{D_3} is the frequency of the third decile class

N is the number of items in the distribution

i_{D_3} is the class interval of the third decile class.

➤ *Example.* For the data in Table 2.6, the class containing the third decile can be located by taking $\dfrac{3N}{10}$ or $\dfrac{3(7,442)}{10}$, which is 2,232.6. There are 2,206 items in the first three classes and 4,301 items in the first four; so the fourth class contains the third decile, which can be located as follows:

$$D_3 = 6 + \frac{\dfrac{3(7,442)}{10} - 2,206}{2,095} \, 2 = 6 + \frac{53.2}{2,095}$$

$$D_3 = 6 + 0.03 = 6.03 \text{ cents.}$$

Formula 2.14 can be modified slightly to give a formula for the 75th percentile:

$$P_{75} = L_{P_{75}} + \frac{\dfrac{75N}{100} - F_{L_{P_{75}}}}{f_{P_{75}}} \, i_{P_{75}} \ldots \ldots \ldots \ldots (2.15)$$

where,

P_{75} is the 75th percentile

$L_{P_{75}}$ is the real lower limit of the 75th percentile class

$F_{L_{P_{75}}}$ is the cumulative frequency less than the lower limit of the 75th percentile class

$f_{P_{75}}$ is the frequency of the 75th percentile class

N is the number of items in the distribution

$i_{P_{75}}$ is the class interval of the 75th percentile class.

➤ *Example.* Using again the data in Table 2.6, the class containing the 75th percentile can be located by taking $\dfrac{75N}{100}$ or $\dfrac{75(7,442)}{100}$, which is 5,581.5. This value, which falls into the fifth class, can be estimated as follows:

$$P_{75} = 8 + \frac{\dfrac{75(7,442)}{100} - 4,301}{1,751} \, 2 = 8 + \frac{2,561}{1,751}$$

$$P_{75} = 8 + 1.46 = 9.46 \text{ cents.}$$

TECHNICAL NOTE NO. 1: Subscripts and Summations

Statistical formulas are written with two objectives in mind:

1. To provide a symbolic notation for expressing relationships clearly and concisely with a minimum of writing.
2. To present a general form that can be used with many different kinds of data.

As in mathematics, the first letters of the alphabet such as *a, b,* and *c* are used to represent constants. The last letters of the alphabet such as *x, y,* and *z* are used to represent variables.

If the statistician is interested in the hourly rates of machine-tool operators, he may let X represent the rate, which is a variable and which can take on as many values as there are operators. If there are four operators, he may refer to their rates as $X_1, X_2, X_3,$ and X_4. If he wishes to refer to a rate in general from this group, he might use X_i, where i is a variable subscript that can take on any one of the four values of X (*i.e.,* $X_1, X_2, X_3,$ or X_4).

There are several advantages to this arrangement. For example, if the statistician wishes to indicate the sum of the values of the variable, he may write this as

$$\sum_{i=1}^{4} X_i$$

which is the total of the four rates, where X_i goes from X_1 through X_4. The Greek capital letter Σ (sigma) is used to denote sum.

This can be written in more general terms as

$$\sum_{i=1}^{n} X_i$$

which refers to the total of all the values of the variable, where X_i goes from X_1 through the last value of X_n, whatever it may be.

The notation

$$\sum_{i=3}^{n-2} X_i$$

can be used to indicate the sum of the values of the variable beginning with the third one and including all but the last two.

In a problem dealing with a rectangular array of values such as that shown on the next page:

Ratings of Service Stations by Professional Shoppers

	Rater A	Rater B	Rater C	Rater D
Station 1	47	78	82	61
Station 2	62	50	75	94
Station 3	59	63	92	76
Station 4	57	88	77	80

the variable price can be represented by a double subscript notation in which the first subscript denotes the row, and the second subscript, the column. Such a rectangular array of entries appearing in rows and columns is called a *matrix*.

Ratings of Service Stations by Professional Shoppers

	Rater A	Rater B	Rater C	Rater D
Station 1	X_{11}	X_{12}	X_{13}	X_{14}
Station 2	X_{21}	X_{22}	X_{23}	X_{24}
Station 3	X_{31}	X_{32}	X_{33}	X_{34}
Station 4	X_{41}	X_{42}	X_{43}	X_{44}

When the statistician refers to the value of the variable represented by X_{23}, he is referring to the rating of Station 2 made by Rater C, which is 75 points. If he wishes to refer to a rating in general, he can use the notation X_{ij}, where i stands for the ith row, and j stands for the jth column. The sum of all the ratings for Station 3 can be written as

$$\sum_{j=1}^{4} X_{3j} = 59 + 63 + 92 + 76 = 290.$$

The sum of all the ratings made by Rater D can be written as

$$\sum_{i=1}^{4} X_{i4} = 61 + 94 + 76 + 80 = 311.$$

The sum of all the ratings made on all four stations can be written as

$$\sum_{i=1,}^{4} \sum_{j=1}^{4} X_{ij} = 47+78+82+61+ \\ 62+50+75+94+ \\ 59+63+92+76+ \\ 57+88+77+80 = 1{,}141.$$

A matrix with m rows and n columns can be written as

$$X_{11}\ X_{12}\ \ldots\ X_{1n} \\ X_{21}\ X_{22}\ \ldots\ X_{2n} \\ .\qquad.\quad \ldots\quad . \\ X_{m1}\ X_{m2}\ \ldots\ X_{mn}$$

and its sum can be written as

$$\sum_{i=1}^{m} \sum_{j=1}^{n} X_{ij}$$

STUDY QUESTIONS

2-1. Explain briefly the meaning of each of the following statistical measures:

a. arithmetic mean	h. modal class
b. weighted arithmetic mean	i. crude mode
c. geometric mean	j. second quartile
d. harmonic mean	k. first quartile
e. median	l. third quartile
f. mode	m. seventh decile
g. empirical mode	n. sixty-seventh percentile

2-2. Under what conditions would you use each of the following averages?
   a. arithmetic mean
   b. geometric mean
   c. harmonic mean

2-3. Under what conditions would each of the following be the most appropriate average to use to describe a distribution?
   a. arithmetic mean
   b. median
   c. mode

2-4. Under what conditions would you use an empirical mode?

2-5. Why is an arithmetic mean computed from a frequency distribution only an estimate of the true value? Under what conditions can it not be computed at all? What other averages can you use when you cannot estimate the mean?

2-6. What is the greatest weakness of each of the following averages?
   a. arithmetic mean
   b. mode
   c. geometric mean

2-7. If a frequency distribution is skewed positively (to the right), what is the normal relationship between the arithmetic mean, the median, and the mode? What statistical average can be estimated from this relationship?

2-8. Is it possible to compute an average rate of growth per year for a city between the years 1900 and 1960 if we know only the population figures for those two years and know nothing of what happened to the population during the 60 years in between? Explain.

PROBLEMS

2-1. You are given the following observations: 2, 2, 4, 5, 5, and 25.
   a. Compute the arithmetic mean.
   b. Compute the geometric mean.
   c. Compute the median.
   d. Is there a mode? If so, what is it?

2-2. Mary can type a standard form letter in 15 minutes. Jane can type the same letter in 12 minutes, but it takes Sue 20 minutes to do the same job.
   a. What is the average number of minutes required to type the form letter?
   b. What is the average number of letters typed per hour per girl?

2-3. The work of four bus boys in a large cafeteria is studied to determine how long it takes each boy, on the average, to clear the dishes from a table in his assigned area. Some boys work faster than others and some are assigned tables further from the kitchen and have to walk farther than others. The results of the study are shown below:

AVERAGE TIME REQUIRED BY FOUR
BUS BOYS TO CLEAR ONE TABLE

Bus boy	Time (in minutes)
1	2.5
2	1.6
3	2.0
4	3.2

a. Compute the overall average time it takes to clear one table, using the harmonic mean. Can you prove that the harmonic mean is an appropriate average in this case?

b. Compute the overall average time it takes to clear one table, using a weighted arithmetic mean. Is your answer the same as in (a)?

2-4. The following table gives the number of master policies for group life insurance in force in the United States for selected years for the period 1920 through 1960.

a. Compute the geometric mean of the percentages to determine the average percent change for each year over the value 10 years before.

b. Is the geometric mean the proper average to use in this problem? Support your answer.

c. Assume that the number of master policies in 1965 is 200,000. Use this figure and the 1920 figure to compute the average rate of growth per five years between 1920 and 1965.

NUMBER OF MASTER POLICIES FOR GROUP LIFE INSURANCE
IN FORCE FOR THE UNITED STATES
FOR SELECTED YEARS, 1920–1960

Year	Number of master policies (in thousands)	Percentage of number of master policies of previous 10 years
1920	6	...
1930	19	316.7
1940	23	121.1
1950	56	243.5
1960	169	301.8

Source: 1963 *Life Insurance Fact Book* (New York: Institute of Life Insurance, 1964), p. 27.

2-5. An index of livestock prices is composed of the prices of cattle, sheep, and hogs. Prices of cattle on January 1, 1967, are 112% of the base year, prices of sheep are 120%, and prices of hogs are 98% of the base period.

    a. Each series of items in the index is considered to be of equal importance. Find the index for January 1, 1967, by computing the geometric mean of the price relatives.

    b. Find the same index called for in (a) by computing the unweighted mean of the price relatives. Is the arithmetic mean larger or smaller than the geometric mean? Will this always be true?

    c. Assume that, in the index, cattle are considered to be twice as important as hogs, and hogs are three times as important as sheep. Use a weighted arithmetic mean of the price relatives to compute the index.

2-6. The arithmetic mean of a frequency distribution is known to be 97.2 and the median is 95.4. Compute the empirical mode. In which direction is the distribution skewed? If the known values for the mean and the median were reversed, what effect would this change have on the value of the empirical mode?

2-7. The table below contains the results of 60 observations:

    a. Compute the arithmetic mean.

    b. Compute the median.

    c. Compute the mode.

    d. Compute the first quartile.

    e. Compute the third quartile.

MEASUREMENTS OF A CRITICAL DIMENSION OF SIXTY PARTS
Unit: .001 inches in excess of 6.500 inches

15.4	5.2	12.3	18.1	19.0	12.0
10.4	15.1	19.8	21.5	24.6	13.3
5.5	11.2	6.8	25.3	9.8	22.0
21.7	24.8	13.7	21.9	24.9	19.7
7.1	22.5	26.7	30.7	22.4	18.6
15.3	18.2	19.5	7.0	14.8	11.3
8.4	27.2	32.6	27.8	16.5	29.3
23.3	10.6	14.0	17.8	20.1	16.7
16.2	34.5	11.8	18.0	14.7	23.4
19.5	20.8	24.9	17.4	19.5	17.2

2-8. The table at the top of the next page gives the distribution of licensed automobile drivers in the United States by age.

    a. Compute the arithmetic mean.

    b. Compute the median.

    c. Compute the mode (interpolation within the modal class).

    d. Compute the empirical mode. How does it compare with that computed in (c)?

    e. Compute the first and the third quartiles.

    f. Compute the fourth decile.

    g. Compute the thirty-second percentile.

DISTRIBUTION OF LICENSED DRIVERS
IN THE UNITED STATES BY AGE, 1962

Age in years	Number in hundreds of thousands
14–15	2
16–20	60
21–29	157
30–39	219
40–49	176
50–59	118
60–69	63
70–90	21
Total	816

Source: Automobile Facts and Figures
(1963 Edition, Automobile Manufacturer's
Association), p. 42.

2-9. The following table shows the number of automobiles in the United States
in 1962 by age.

    a. What figure divides the distribution so that half the cars are newer and the
other half older? What is this measure called?

    b. What percent of the cars are between three and six years old?

    c. Seventy-five percent of the cars are newer than what age?

    d. Eight tenths of the cars are older than what age?

    e. What two ages include the middle 50% of the cars in terms of age?

ESTIMATED AGE OF PASSENGER CARS IN THE
UNITED STATES IN 1962

Age in years	Number in thousands
Under 1	4,500
1–2	5,600
2–3	6,180
3–4	5,800
4–5	4,290
5–6	5,850
6–7	5,580
7–8	5,990
8–9	3,700
9–10	4,000
10–11	1,990
11–12	2,210
12–13	2,090
13–14	1,120
14 and older	1,660
Total	60,560

Source: Automobile Facts and Figures
(1963 Edition, Automobile Manufacturer's
Association), p. 22.

SELECTED READINGS

Mills, Frederick C. *Statistical Methods.* 3d ed. New York: Henry Holt and Company, 1955.

>   Chapter 4 discusses such measures of central tendency as the arithmetic mean, median, mode, geometric mean, and harmonic mean.

Neter, John, and William Wasserman. *Fundamental Statistics for Business and Industry.* 2d ed. Boston: Allyn and Bacon, Inc., 1961.

>   The first half of Chapter 7 discusses shortcuts to the description of frequency distributions and the calculation of the arithmetic mean, median, and percentiles.

Richmond, Samuel B. *Statistical Analysis.* 2d ed. New York: The Ronald Press Company, 1964.

>   Chapter 3 discusses the arithmetic mean, and Chapter 4 discusses the median, quartiles, mode, geometric mean, and harmonic mean. There is also a discussion of the comparative uses of the arithmetic, geometric, and harmonic means.

Stockton, John R. *Introduction to Business and Economic Statistics.* 3d ed. Cincinnati: South-Western Publishing Company, 1966.

>   Chapter 5 discusses the definition, computation, use, and chief characteristics of the principal averages.

Chapter 3

Descriptive Statistics: Other Measures

An average consists of one value designed to describe most accurately the values of a distribution. Other measures are also needed to summarize the characteristics of a distribution or to compare two distributions with one another. It is often important to know if the items in a distribution are concentrated or widely dispersed, and how the shape of the distribution compares with that of a normal distribution.

The purpose of this chapter is to discuss the following most commonly used measures of the shape of a distribution:

1. Measures of absolute dispersion
2. Measures of relative dispersion
3. Measures of skewness
4. Measures of kurtosis

The measures discussed are all a part of the kit of tools needed for statistical problem-solving methods that are presented in later chapters.

MEASURES OF ABSOLUTE DISPERSION

Measures of dispersion are measures of scatter about an average. Measures of *absolute* dispersion, as distinguished from measures of *relative* dispersion, are in the same units as the data whose scatter they measure. For example, the scatter of salaries about an average is measured in dollars and cents, and the variation of time required for workers to do an assembly operation is measured in minutes and seconds. Measures of absolute dispersion cannot be used to compare the scatter in one distribution with that in another distribution when the averages of the distributions differ in size or the units of measure differ in kind.

The following measures of absolute dispersion are discussed here:

1. Range
2. Interquartile range
3. Quartile deviation
4. Average (mean) deviation
5. Variance and standard deviation

Range

The *range* is the simplest of all measures of dispersion. It can be defined either as:

1. The difference between the largest and the smallest values of some variable, or
2. The largest and the smallest values themselves.

For example, a firm has 25 accountants on its payroll, and the monthly salaries of these accountants vary from a low of $450 to a high of $850. The range can be defined as either $400 or $450 to $850 per month. The latter expression gives more information, however.

While the range is familiar and easy to compute, its advantages stop there. It tells nothing about what lies in between the largest and the smallest values. Thus, for example, in the case of the accountants' salaries, 24 of them might be earning $450 per month and the remaining one, $850. Or there might be only one earning $450 and the other 24 earning $850. The average salary in each case would be quite different.

Interquartile Range

The *interquartile range* measures the scatter of the middle 50% of the values in a distribution. As shown below, this type of range is defined as the distance between the first and the third quartiles:

$$QR = Q_3 - Q_1 \quad \text{...........................(3.1)}$$

where,

QR is the interquartile range.

➤ *Example.* If a personnel director is making a study of salaries paid secretaries in a community, he may find the range an unusable measure as it will be influenced by the extremes at both the high and the low ends of the distribution. Some very low-paid secretaries probably have the title, but their skills are inadequate. At the top end of the scale, however, he may find jobs requiring much more ability and training than normally required of a secretary; hence, these secretaries will be better paid. The interquartile range is not influenced by the extremes of very high or very low salaries. It measures, instead, the spread in salaries of the most significant group, that which lies in the middle of the distribution.

Quartile Deviation

The *quartile deviation* is defined as one half the distance between the first and the third quartiles. Its formula is:

$$Q = \frac{Q_3 - Q_1}{2} \quad \text{...........................(3.2)}$$

where,

Q is the quartile deviation.

The quartile deviation can be computed from a frequency distribution with an open-end class when it might not be possible to compute other types of measures.

Average (Mean) Deviation

Average deviation is the average amount of scatter of the items in a distribution from either the mean or the median, ignoring the signs of the deviations. The average that is taken of the scatter is an arithmetic mean, which accounts for the fact that this measure is often called the *mean deviation.*

The concept of average deviation is a simple one. If a rifleman shoots at a target, and if the mean distance that the shots miss the center of the bull's-eye is computed, this mean is the average deviation. It is important to note that the concern is with the distance of the hit from the bull's-eye and not with whether the hit was high, low, at the right, or at the left.

Average Deviation, Ungrouped Data. Average deviation is defined for ungrouped data in either of two ways:

$$AD = \frac{\Sigma |X - Md|}{N} \quad \text{.......................(3.3)}$$

or

$$AD = \frac{\Sigma |X - \mu|}{N} \quad \text{.......................(3.4)}$$

where,

AD is the average deviation

$|X - Md|$ is the absolute difference between the value of the variable and the median, disregarding signs

$|X - \mu|$ is the absolute difference between the value of the variable and the arithmetic mean, disregarding signs

N is the number of values of X.

Unless the distribution of the values of X is symmetrical, the average deviation will be smaller when computed from the median than when it is computed from the mean. The use of the median in computing the average deviation is generally preferred.

➤ *Example.* Table 3.1 is used to illustrate the computation of the average deviation from ungrouped data.

Table 3.1

COMPUTATION OF AVERAGE DEVIATION, UNGROUPED DATA

Size of Truck Fleets Operated by Nine Oil Companies
in the United States, 1962

Company	Number of trucks X	$\|X - Md\|$ (Md is 500)	$\|X - \mu\|$ (μ is 502)
Texaco	285	215	217
Skelly	310	190	192
Carter-Humble	317	183	185
Continental	371	129	131
Standard (Ohio)	500	0	2
Ashland	563	63	61
Sunray DX	690	190	188
Richfield	710	210	208
Esso-Humble	772	272	270
Total	...	1,452	1,454

Source: Motor Truck Facts (Detroit: Automobile Manufacturers Association, Inc., 1963), p. 30.

$$AD = \frac{\Sigma \, |\, X - Md \,|}{N} = \frac{1{,}452}{9} = 161.33 \text{ trucks, or}$$

$$AD = \frac{\Sigma \, |\, X - \mu \,|}{N} = \frac{1{,}454}{9} = 161.56 \text{ trucks.}$$

Average Deviation, Grouped Data. The average deviation can be estimated from a frequency distribution by using the following formula:

$$AD = \frac{\Sigma f \, |\, m - Md \,|}{N} \quad \dots\dots\dots\dots\dots\dots(3.5)$$

where,
f is the frequency for each class
N is Σf
$|\, m - Md \,|$ is the absolute difference between the midpoint of each
class interval and the median, disregarding signs.

The average deviation of grouped data, as with ungrouped data, can be measured about the mean as well as about the median. However, it cannot be computed from a frequency distribution with an open-end class unless the values of the items in that class are known.

Variance and Standard Deviation

The most useful measures of dispersion and those with the most desirable mathematical properties are variance and standard deviation. *Variance* may be defined as the arithmetic mean of the squared deviations of the individual items from their arithmetic mean. Analysis of variance is a valuable statistical tool and is discussed in Chapter 14.

The square root of variance is called *standard deviation*. This measure is particularly useful when dealing with the normal distribution (see Chapter 8) since any normal distribution can be completely determined when its mean and standard deviation are known.

Standard Deviation, Ungrouped Data. For ungrouped data, the formulas for standard deviation and variance are written as follows:

$$\sigma = \sqrt{\frac{\Sigma(X - \mu)^2}{N}} \quad \dots\dots\dots\dots\dots\dots\dots(3.6)$$

$$\sigma^2 = \frac{\Sigma(X - \mu)^2}{N} \quad \dots\dots\dots\dots\dots\dots\dots(3.7)$$

where,
σ is the standard deviation of a universe[1]
σ^2 is the variance of a universe.

Algebraic manipulation of Formulas 3.6 and 3.7 gives the ones shown below, which are equally correct and often easier to use:

$$\sigma = \sqrt{\frac{\Sigma X^2}{N} - \left(\frac{\Sigma X}{N}\right)^2} \quad \dots\dots\dots\dots\dots(3.8)$$

$$\sigma^2 = \frac{\Sigma X^2}{N} - \left(\frac{\Sigma X}{N}\right)^2 \quad \dots\dots\dots\dots\dots(3.9)$$

➤ *Example.* Both Formulas 3.6 and 3.8 are used in Table 3.2 on page 64 to illustrate the computation of the standard deviation for ungrouped data.

Standard Deviation, Grouped Data. There are two methods of computing the standard deviation from grouped data. The longer of the two methods can be used in all cases regardless of whether the class intervals

---

[1] The Greek lower-case sigma (σ) is used to denote the standard deviation of a universe of items. The letter *s* is used to denote the standard deviation of a sample. The relationship between σ and *s* is discussed in detail in Chapter 9, which deals with sampling distributions.

Table 3.2

COMPUTATION OF STANDARD DEVIATION, UNGROUPED DATA

Length of Life of Eight Experimental Light Bulbs

Bulb	Length of life (thousands of hours) X	$X - \mu$	$(X - \mu)^2$	X^2
1	2.9	− 1.3	1.69	8.41
2	5.6	1.4	1.96	31.36
3	4.2	0	0	17.64
4	3.3	− .9	.81	10.89
5	4.8	.6	.36	23.04
6	5.0	.8	.64	25.00
7	3.7	− .5	.25	13.69
8	4.1	− .1	.01	16.81
Total	33.6	0	5.72	146.84

Formula 3.6:

$$\mu = \frac{33.6}{8} = 4.2$$

$$\sigma = \sqrt{\frac{\Sigma(X - \mu)^2}{N}} = \sqrt{\frac{5.72}{8}} = \sqrt{0.715}$$

$$\sigma = \sqrt{0.715} = 0.846 \text{ or } 846 \text{ hours.}$$

Formula 3.8:

$$\sigma = \sqrt{\frac{\Sigma X^2}{N} - \left(\frac{\Sigma X}{N}\right)^2} = \sqrt{\frac{146.84}{8} - \left(\frac{33.6}{8}\right)^2} = \sqrt{0.715}$$

$$\sigma = \sqrt{0.715} = 0.846 \text{ or } 846 \text{ hours.}$$

are the same for all classes. The standard deviation has the same limitation as the mean and the average deviation; it cannot be computed from a frequency distribution with an open-end class.

The long formula is written as follows:

$$\sigma = \sqrt{\frac{\Sigma f(m - \mu)^2}{N}} \quad \dots\dots\dots\dots\dots\dots\dots\text{(3.10)}$$

where,
    f is the frequency of each class μ is the arithmetic mean
    m is the midpoint of each class interval N is the sum of f.

➤ *Example.* Table 3.3 shows the computation of the standard deviation of grouped data using the so-called long method.

Table 3.3

COMPUTATION OF STANDARD DEVIATION
(LONG METHOD FOR GROUPED DATA)

Length of Life of Eighty Experimental Light Bulbs

Length of life (thousands of hours)	Number of bulbs f	Class midpoint m	$m-\mu$	$(m-\mu)^2$	$f(m-\mu)^2$
2 and under 3	4	2.5	−2.125	4.516	18.064
3 and under 4	16	3.5	−1.125	1.266	20.256
4 and under 5	33	4.5	−0.125	0.016	0.528
5 and under 6	20	5.5	0.875	0.766	15.320
6 and under 7	7	6.5	1.875	3.516	24.612
Total	80	...	...	...	78.780

Note: The μ of the above distribution is 4.625.

$$\sigma = \sqrt{\frac{\Sigma f(m-\mu)^2}{N}} = \sqrt{\frac{78.780}{80}} = \sqrt{0.98475}$$

$$\sigma = 0.992 \text{ or } 992 \text{ hours.}$$

When data are grouped into a frequency distribution with equal class intervals, a shortcut method of computation is available in which the standard deviation and the variance can be estimated without first computing the arithmetic mean. Deviations are taken in class-interval units from some arbitrary origin, A, as shown in the following formula:

$$\sigma = i\sqrt{\frac{\Sigma f(d')^2}{N} - \left(\frac{\Sigma fd'}{N}\right)^2} \quad \dots\dots\dots\dots\dots\text{(3.11)}$$

where,
  σ is the standard deviation
  i is the class interval for all classes
  f is the frequency of each class
  d' is the deviation in class-interval units from A, where A is the mid-point of some arbitrarily chosen class interval
  N is the sum of f.

➤ *Example.* Table 3.4 shows the computation of the standard deviation of grouped data using the so-called shortcut method.

Table 3.4

COMPUTATION OF STANDARD DEVIATION (SHORTCUT METHOD FOR GROUPED DATA, UNIFORM CLASS INTERVAL)

Length of Life of Eighty Experimental Light Bulbs

Length of life (thousands of hours)	Number of bulbs f	d'	fd'	$f(d')^2$
2 and under 3	4	−2	−8	16
3 and under 4	16	−1	−16	16
4 and under 5	33	0	0	0
5 and under 6	20	1	20	20
6 and under 7	7	2	14	28
Total	80	...	10	80

Note: $A = 4.5$.

$$\sigma = i \sqrt{\frac{\Sigma f(d')^2}{N} - \left(\frac{\Sigma fd'}{N}\right)^2}$$

$$\sigma = 1 \sqrt{\frac{80}{80} - \left(\frac{10}{80}\right)^2}$$

$$\sigma = 1 \sqrt{0.9844} = 0.992 \text{ or } 992 \text{ hours.}$$

The standard deviation is more appropriate mathematically than the average deviation since the negative signs are removed by squaring the deviations rather than by ignoring the signs as is done in computing the average deviation. The many useful properties of the standard deviation become apparent later in this book in the study of the normal probability distribution.

MEASURES OF RELATIVE DISPERSION

Measures of relative dispersion show some measure of scatter as a percent of the average about which they are computed. They are normally used to compare the scatter in one distribution with the scatter in another.

➤ *Example.* An investor, trying to decide between one of two stocks, wishes to select the one with less fluctuation in price. He computes the standard deviation of closing prices for each stock for one month and obtains the following results:

Stock	A	B
Standard deviation in prices for one month	$1.50	$12.00

With no further information, the investor might purchase stock *A*, for its price shows the smaller variation.

While there are many measures of relative dispersion, the *coefficient of variation* is the most commonly used. It shows the standard deviation as a percent of the arithmetic mean. The formula is written as:

$$V = \frac{\sigma}{\mu} \cdot 100 \quad \dots\dots\dots\dots\dots\dots\dots\dots(3.12)$$

where,
σ is the standard deviation
μ is the arithmetic mean.

➤ *Example.* Assume, in the preceding stock example, that stock *A* had an average (mean) price of $5 a share and stock *B* had an average price of $75 a share. As shown below, the computation of the coefficient of variation for each stock might cause the investor to purchase *B* rather than *A*.

$$V \text{ (for stock } A) = \frac{1.50}{5.00} \cdot 100 = 30\%$$

$$V \text{ (for stock } B) = \frac{12.00}{75.00} \cdot 100 = 16\%.$$

If data are badly skewed or are grouped in a frequency distribution with an open-end class, the following formula for the coefficient of variation is more useful:

$$V = \frac{Q}{Md} \cdot 100 \quad \dots\dots\dots\dots\dots\dots\dots\dots(3.13)$$

where,
Q is the quartile deviation
Md is the median.

Another useful measure is the *coefficient of quartile variation*:

$$V_Q = \frac{Q_3 - Q_1}{Q_3 + Q_1} \cdot 100 \quad \dots\dots\dots\dots\dots\dots(3.14)$$

where,
Q_1 is the first quartile
Q_3 is the third quartile.

MEASURES OF SKEWNESS

In addition to knowing the average value of a distribution and some measure of scatter about that average, it is often important to know whether or not a distribution is symmetrical. If it is not symmetrical, it is said to be *skewed*.

Pearsonian Coefficients of Skewness

There are two formulas for measuring skewness, both of which are named after the statistician, Karl Pearson. These formulas are based on the knowledge that with a symmetrical distribution, the values of the mean, the median, and the mode are the same. As the distribution becomes skewed, however, these measures pull apart, with the arithmetic mean drawn farthest in the direction of the extreme values in the tail. The mode remains with the greatest concentration of items, and the median falls roughly two thirds of the distance from the mode to the mean. These relationships are illustrated in Figure 3.1.

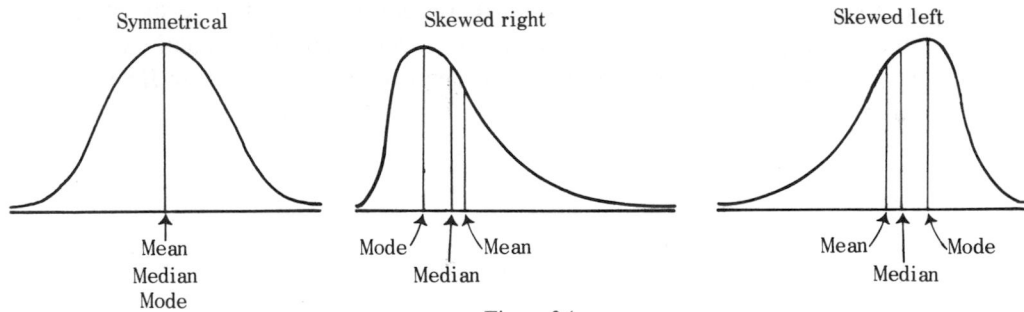

Figure 3.1

RELATIONSHIP OF THE MEAN, MEDIAN, AND MODE AS DETERMINED
BY THE DIRECTION OF THE SKEWNESS

The formulas for computing the coefficients of skewness are:

$$Sk = \frac{\mu - Mo}{\sigma} \dots\dots\dots\dots\dots\dots\dots\dots(3.15)$$

$$Sk = \frac{3(\mu - Md)}{\sigma} \dots\dots\dots\dots\dots\dots\dots(3.16)$$

where,
    Sk is the coefficient of skewness
    μ is the arithmetic mean
    Mo is the mode
    Md is the median
    σ is the standard deviation.

➤ **Example.** A distribution has the following values:

$$\mu = 17.2 \qquad Md = 19.4$$
$$Mo = 23.7 \qquad \sigma = 10.6.$$

The coefficient of skewness is computed as:

$$Sk = \frac{17.2 - 23.7}{10.6} = -0.61$$

or as:
$$Sk = \frac{3(17.2 - 19.4)}{10.6} = -0.62.$$

The negative sign indicates that the tail of this distribution is to the left and the distribution is skewed to the smaller values. If the sign had been positive, the distribution would be skewed to the right. The fact that the two measures are not exactly the same indicates that the pattern of relationships between the three averages is not always the same, and the coefficients are, at best, estimates of the degree of skewness.

Use of Moments to Measure Skewness

The term "moment" in mechanics refers to the measure of a force with reference to its tendency to produce rotation. The strength of the tendency is dependent upon the amount of the force and the distance from the origin at which the force is applied.

In the discussion of the arithmetic mean in Chapter 2 it was shown that the arithmetic mean is a point of balance. The tendency of a bar to rotate to the right or to the left due to weights distributed along its length is zero when the bar is balanced on a fulcrum located at the mean. At this point the values of the weights in terms of distance along the scale on the bar are equal on both sides of the fulcrum. The arithmetic mean is the first moment about the origin.

In addition to moments about the origin, there is a series of four moments measured about the arithmetic mean that are of value to the statistician.[2]

The *first moment* is:

$$M_1 = \frac{\Sigma(X - \mu)}{N} \quad \dots\dots\dots\dots\dots(3.17)$$

and its value is always zero.

The *second moment* is:

$$M_2 = \frac{\Sigma(X - \mu)^2}{N} \quad \dots\dots\dots\dots\dots(3.18)$$

---

[2]See the discussion on moments in Chapter 7.

The second moment is also the variance. Its square root, the standard deviation, is the best measure of the absolute dispersion in a distribution.

From the concepts of the first and the second moments, the *third moment*, which is the arithmetic mean of the deviations about the mean cubed, can be developed. It is written:

$$M_3 = \frac{\Sigma(X - \mu)^3}{N} \quad \ldots\ldots\ldots\ldots\ldots\ldots(3.19)$$

The third moment provides a measure of absolute skewness. The sign tells the direction of the skewness, and the value of M_3 tells the amount of skewness in terms of the units of measure of the data themselves. If M_3 is zero, the distribution is symmetrical.

Measures of absolute skewness are generally not so valuable as those that measure relative skewness. A ratio of the third moment squared to the second moment cubed gives a measure of relative skewness known as β_1 (beta one):

$$\beta_1 = \frac{M_3^2}{M_2^3} \quad \ldots\ldots\ldots\ldots\ldots\ldots\ldots(3.20)$$

Another measure of skewness is α_3 (alpha three), which is:

$$\alpha_3 = \sqrt{\beta_1} = \frac{M_3}{\sqrt{M_2^3}} \quad \ldots\ldots\ldots\ldots\ldots(3.21)$$

For both measures, β_1 and α_3, a zero shows that the distribution is symmetrical. A negative sign for the third moment indicates that the distribution is skewed to the left, and a positive sign shows it to be skewed to the right. The larger the value, the greater the degree of skewness.

Moments, Ungrouped Data. With the aid of a digital computer, computing the moments of a distribution can be accomplished quite simply without need for first arranging the values in a frequency distribution. Without the help of a computer, the job is formidable if there are many values with which to work.

➤*Example.* The computation of the first three moments for ungrouped data and the use of these measures to compute β_1 and α_3 are shown in Table 3.5. The table also contains a column of figures at the extreme right that are not used for this example but will be used later in computing the fourth moment.

Table 3.5

COMPUTATION OF MOMENTS FROM UNGROUPED DATA

Number of Defective Parts Produced by Six Machines
in One Hour of Operation

Machine*	Number of defective parts X	$X-\mu$	$(X-\mu)^2$	$(X-\mu)^3$	$(X-\mu)^{4**}$
B	14	−6	36	−216	1,296
E	16	−4	16	−64	256
A	18	−2	4	−8	16
D	20	0	0	0	0
F	25	+5	25	+125	625
C	27	+7	49	+343	2,401
Total	120	0	130	180	4,594

*In order of number of defective parts.
**The data in this column will be used in a later example.

$$\mu = \frac{120}{6} = 20$$

$$M_1 = \frac{\Sigma(X - \mu)}{N} = 0$$

$$M_2 = \frac{\Sigma(X - \mu)^2}{N} = \frac{130}{6} = 21.667$$

$$M_3 = \frac{\Sigma(X - \mu)^3}{N} = \frac{180}{6} = 30$$

$$\beta_1 = \frac{M_3^2}{M_2^3} = \frac{30^2}{21.667^3} = \frac{900}{10,171.766} = 0.088$$

$$\alpha_3 = \sqrt{0.088} = 0.297.$$

Moments, Grouped Data. If data are grouped into classes with unequal class intervals, the second and the third moments can be computed by using the following formulas:

$$M_2 = \frac{\Sigma f(m - \mu)^2}{N} = \sigma^2 \quad \dots\dots\dots\dots(3.22)$$

$$M_3 = \frac{\Sigma f(m - \mu)^3}{N} \quad \dots\dots\dots\dots\dots(3.23)$$

Where the class interval is the same for all classes, the following short-cut formulas are quicker and easier to use:

$$M_2 = M_2' - (M_1')^2 \dots \dots \dots \dots \dots \dots \dots \dots \dots (3.24)$$
$$M_3 = M_3' - 3(M_1')(M_2') + 2(M_1')^3 \dots \dots \dots (3.25)$$

where,

$$M_1' \text{ is } \frac{\Sigma f d'}{N}$$

$$M_2' \text{ is } \frac{\Sigma f(d')^2}{N}$$

$$M_3' \text{ is } \frac{\Sigma f(d')^3}{N}.$$

→ **Example.** The computation of β_1 and α_3 from grouped data is shown in Table 3.6. Again, the table contains one column of figures that will be used in a later example.

Table 3.6

COMPUTATION OF MOMENTS FROM GROUPED DATA

Purchases of Gasoline by 256 Customers

Purchases of gasoline (in gallons)	Number of purchases f	d'	fd'	$f(d')^2$	$f(d')^3$	$f(d')^4*$
0.0–1.9	9	−3	−27	81	−243	729
2.0–3.9	22	−2	−44	88	−176	352
4.0–5.9	57	−1	−57	57	−57	57
6.0–7.9	64	0	0	0	0	0
8.0–9.9	46	1	46	46	46	46
10.0–11.9	33	2	66	132	264	528
12.0–13.9	18	3	54	162	486	1,458
14.0–15.9	7	4	28	112	448	1,792
Total	256		66	678	768	4,962

Source: Table 2.3.
*The data in this column will be used in a later example.

$$M_1' = \frac{\Sigma f d'}{N} = \frac{66}{256} = 0.2578$$

$$M_2' = \frac{\Sigma f(d')^2}{N} = \frac{678}{256} = 2.6484$$

$$M_3' = \frac{\Sigma f(d')^3}{N} = \frac{768}{256} = 3.0000$$

$$M_2 = M_2' - (M_1')^2 = 2.6484 - (0.2578)^2 = 2.5819$$
$$M_3 = M_3' - 3(M_1')(M_2') + 2(M_1')^3$$
$$M_3 = 3 - 3(0.2578)(2.6484) + 2(0.2578)^3 = 0.9860$$
$$\beta_1 = \frac{M_3^2}{M_2^3} = \frac{(0.9860)^2}{(2.5819)^3} = 0.056$$
$$\alpha_3 = \sqrt{\beta_1} = \sqrt{0.056} = 0.237.$$

The distribution is skewed slightly to the right.

MEASURES OF KURTOSIS

Kurtosis is that property of a distribution which expresses its relative peakedness. It is normally measured by β_2 (beta two) or by α_4 (alpha four). The values of these two measures are the same and are expressed by the following formulas:

$$\beta_2 = \alpha_4 = \frac{M_4}{M_2^2} \qquad \dots\dots\dots\dots\dots\dots\text{(3.26)}$$

where,
  M_4 is the *fourth moment*:

$$M_4 = \frac{\Sigma(X - \mu)^4}{N} \qquad \dots\dots\dots\dots\dots\text{(3.27)}$$

for ungrouped data.

The greater the value of β_2, the more peaked the distribution. A normal distribution has a β_2 of 3 and is called *mesokurtic*. If β_2 is greater than 3, the distribution is *leptokurtic*; and if β_2 is less than 3, the distribution is *platykurtic*. Each of these types of distribution is illustrated in Figure 3.2.

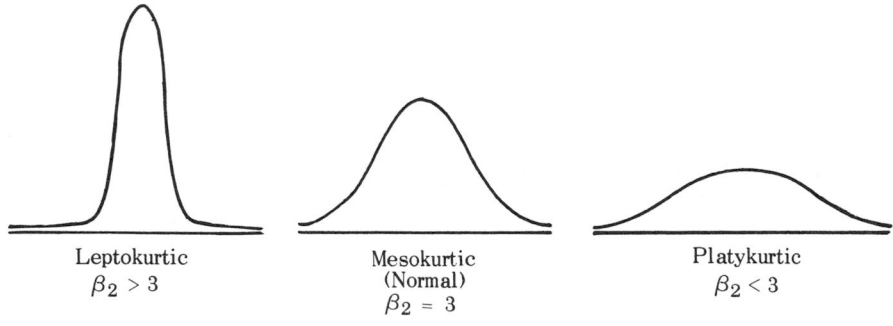

Leptokurtic	Mesokurtic	Platykurtic
$\beta_2 > 3$	(Normal)	$\beta_2 < 3$
	$\beta_2 = 3$	

Figure 3.2

CLASSIFICATION OF DISTRIBUTIONS BASED ON
DEGREE OF PEAKEDNESS

➤*Example.* The kurtosis for the distribution of six items shown in Table 3.5 is:

$$M_4 = \frac{4,594}{6} = 765.667$$

M_2 has already been computed as 21.667.

Then, $$\beta_2 = \frac{M_4}{M_2^2} = \frac{765.667}{(21.667)^2} = 1.63.$$

This distribution is platykurtic.

If the data are grouped in a frequency distribution, β_2 and α_4 can be computed by using the following formula for the fourth moment:

$$M_4 = \frac{\Sigma f(m - \mu)^4}{N} \dots\dots\dots\dots\dots\dots\dots\dots\dots\dots\dots\dots(3.28)$$

or if the class intervals are all the same,

$$M_4 = M_4' - 4(M_1')(M_3') + 6(M_1')^2(M_2') - 3(M_1')^4 \dots(3.29)$$

where,

$$M_4' = \frac{\Sigma f(d')^4}{N}.$$

➤*Example.* In the example shown in Table 3.6, the kurtosis can be computed as:

$$M_4' = \frac{4,962}{256} = 19.3828$$

and

$$M_4 = 19.3828 - 4(0.2578)(3) + 6(0.2578)^2(2.6484) - 3(0.2578)^4$$
$$M_4 = 17.3327$$
$$\beta_2 = \frac{M_4}{M_2^2} = \frac{17.3327}{(2.5819)^2} = 2.6.$$

This distribution is slightly platykurtic.

STUDY QUESTIONS

3-1. Explain briefly the meaning of each of the following statistical measures:

a. measures of dispersion
b. measures of absolute dispersion
c. measures of relative dispersion
d. range
e. interquartile range
f. quartile deviation
g. average deviation
h. mean deviation
i. variance

j. standard deviation
k. coefficient of variation
l. coefficient of quartile variation
m. skewness
n. kurtosis
o. mesokurtic
p. leptokurtic
q. platykurtic

3-2. What advantage does the interquartile range have over the range as a measure of dispersion?

3-3. Of what practical use are measures of absolute dispersion? Give two examples.

3-4. When is it preferable to use measures of relative dispersion when considering scatter? Give two examples.

3-5. If a frequency distribution has an open-end class, what measures of absolute and relative dispersion can be computed? Is it possible to measure skewness and kurtosis for such a distribution?

3-6. Give an example of a distribution that would normally be negatively skewed and give an example of a distribution that would normally be positively skewed. Into which category would you expect most economic data to fall?

3-7. Under what conditions would it be necessary to use one of the Pearsonian measures of skewness and impossible to use moments to compute a measure of skewness?

3-8. Which moment can be used as a measure of absolute skewness? How is the same moment used and with what other values to measure relative skewness?

3-9. What does the second moment of a frequency distribution measure?

3-10. If a distribution has a β_1 value of -0.004 and a β_2 value of 2.58, what general statements can be made about its shape?

3-11. If a distribution has an α_3 value of 0.25 and an α_4 value of 4.00, what can be said about its shape?

PROBLEMS

3-1. The number of minutes that each of 10 women spent while shopping in a supermarket was noted by the assistant manager. The times, recorded to the nearest minute, were 17, 25, 6, 8, 14, 32, 37, 22, 20, and 11 minutes.

a. Find the range.
b. Find the interquartile range.
c. Compute the quartile deviation.

d. Compute the average deviation about the median.

e. Compute the standard deviation.

f. Compute the coefficient of variation using the mean and the standard deviation.

g. Compute the coefficient of variation using the quartile deviation and the median.

h. Compute the coefficient of quartile variation.

3-2. A carefully kept record of the height of 160 tomato plants in an experimental plot reveals the following distribution:

HEIGHT OF 160 TOMATO PLANTS
IN AN EXPERIMENTAL PLOT

Height of plants (in inches)	Number of plants
20 and under 25	12
25 and under 30	54
30 and under 35	49
35 and under 40	37
40 and under 45	8
Total	160

a. Compute the Pearsonian coefficient of skewness using the mean, the mode, and the standard deviation. What does this measure tell about the shape of the distribution?

b. Compute the same measure using the median rather than the mode. Is the answer the same as in (a)? If not, how do you account for the difference?

c. Compute β_1. What does this measure reveal about the shape of the distribution? Do you think this measure is better than those computed in (a) and (b)?

d. Compute β_2 and tell what information it gives about the distribution.

3-3. Below is a frequency distribution of the salaries paid clerk-typists working in the home office of an insurance company.

SALARIES PAID 200 CLERK-TYPISTS
BY AN INSURANCE COMPANY

Monthly salary (in dollars)	Number of clerk-typists
$175–224	24
225–274	36
275–324	58
325–374	45
375–424	22
425–474	15
Total	200

a. Compute the interquartile range and the quartile deviation of the distribution of salaries. Explain what these measures mean.
b. Compute the average deviation about the median salary, which is $309.
c. Compute the standard deviation:
   (1) Using the long method. (2) Using the shortcut method.
d. A distribution of the salaries paid 250 file clerks in the same company has an arithmetic mean of $264 and a standard deviation of $25. Use the coefficient of variation to compare the relative dispersion of file clerks' salaries with those of clerk-typists. Why cannot the two standard deviations be compared directly?

3-4. A college dormitory housing 250 girls has a telephone switchboard that is manned by two operators between the hours of 6 p.m. and 10 p.m. The number of incoming calls during the evenings of one semester is shown below.

NUMBER OF INCOMING CALLS TO A
DORMITORY SWITCHBOARD

Number of calls per night	Number of nights
150–199	3
200–249	9
250–299	13
300–349	38
350–399	15
400 and over	7
Total	85

a. Compute a measure of absolute dispersion of the distribution of telephone calls.
b. Compute a measure of relative dispersion.

Note: The fact that this distribution has an open-end class narrows the choice of measures which can be computed.

3-5. A record was kept over a period of three months by a sales manager to determine the average number of calls made per work day by his six salesmen. The results are shown below:

RECORD OF AVERAGE NUMBER OF CALLS
PER DAY MADE BY SIX SALESMEN

Salesman	Average number of calls per day
Mr. Black	4
Mr. Brown	8
Mr. Green	7
Mr. Red	9
Mr. White	10
Mr. Yellow	10

a. Compute α_3 as a measure of skewness of this distribution of six values. Is the distribution symmetrical? If not, in which direction is it skewed?

b. Compute α_4 as a measure of kurtosis of the distribution. What does this measure mean?

SELECTED READINGS

Croxton, Frederick E., and Dudley J. Cowden. *Applied General Statistics.* 2d ed. Englewood Cliffs, N. J.: Prentice-Hall, Inc., 1955.

Chapter 10 has a discussion of dispersion, skewness, and kurtosis, including a discussion of the use of moments.

Freund, John E., and Frank J. Williams. *Modern Business Statistics.* Englewood Cliffs, N. J.: Prentice-Hall, Inc., 1958.

Chapter 4 discusses measures of variation, and Chapter 5 discusses measures of symmetry and skewness and measures of peakedness.

Mills, Frederick C. *Statistical Methods.* 3d ed. New York: Henry Holt and Company, 1955.

Chapter 5 contains a discussion of measures of variation, including their relationships and chief characteristics. It also discusses measures of relative variation and skewness.

Stockton, John R. *Introduction to Business and Economic Statistics.* 3d ed. Cincinnati: South-Western Publishing Company, 1966.

Chapter 6 contains a discussion of measures of dispersion, skewness, and kurtosis.

Chapter 4

The Nature and Impact of the Computer

THE COMPUTER REVOLUTION

Few developments in our time have so captured the imagination of the public or have had such widespread implications for business as the electronic computer. Ralph J. Cordiner, when president of General Electric Corporation, predicted, "When the history of our age is written, I think it will record three profoundly important technological developments:

Nuclear energy, which vastly increases the energy to do work;
Automation, which greatly increases man's ability to use tools;
and
Computers, which multiply man's ability to do mental work."[1]

Ray Eppert, president of Burroughs Corporation, was quoted in *Fortune* magazine as saying, "The electronic computer has a more beneficial potential for the human race than any other invention in history."[2] Many other equally competent people share these views.

Historical Development

The electronic digital computer is a development of twentieth-century electronics, but for centuries man has been intrigued with the idea of machines to do his arithmetic. In 1617 John Napier described a machine to aid in multiplication; in 1642 the celebrated mathematician, Blaise Pascal, invented the first adding machine equipped with a number wheel and capable of carrying a digit from one digit position to the next.

Another mathematician, Gottfried Wilhelm Leibniz, invented the Leibniz wheel, which made possible multiplication by means of repeated

---

[1]From the testimony given by Mr. Cordiner before the Subcommittee on Economic Stabilization, Joint Congressional Committee on the Economic Report, in Washington, D.C., on October 26, 1955.

[2]Gilbert Burck, "The Boundless Age of the Computer," *Fortune*, Vol. XVIII, No. 3 (March, 1964), pp. 101–113.

addition. This principle was used in the manufacture of the Thomas machine in 1822. From these developments have come the modern-day electric calculator now in widespread use.

The basic concepts of the modern computer were first developed by a British mathematician, Charles Babbage. In 1822 Babbage demonstrated a small working model of a machine he called a *difference engine*. This device was designed to build up tables of mathematical functions from their successive differences. While still working on this machine, Babbage also developed what he called an *analytic engine*. If he had had the engineering know-how to make it work, this analytic engine would have been a universal computer, sufficiently complex to handle any finite computation.

Many of Babbage's ideas were used by Howard Aiken in the development of the first relay computer known as the MARK I. This computer was built with the help of International Business Machines Corporation (IBM) and was demonstrated in 1944. A similar machine using relays as computing elements was developed about the same time by George Stibitz at the Bell Telephone Laboratories.

The first large-scale electronic computer was the ENIAC, which was built at the Moore School of Electrical Engineering at the University of Pennsylvania. It was developed during the period from 1942 to 1945 and was designed primarily to perform calculations required in the preparation of ballistics tables. The acronym, ENIAC, was contracted from Electronic Numerical Integrator and Calculator. It was composed of 18,000 tubes and could count by adding electronic pulses generated at the rate of 100,000 per second. It was slow and inflexible by modern standards. What it did, however, was to demonstrate that the electron could be harnessed to compute, and its speed challenged mathematicians to use it in other ways. The ENIAC was followed by the EDVAC, EDSAC, and several other similar machines.

It took the technical advances brought about by World War II to make it possible to build a completely successful electronic computer. By the end of the war, industry had overcome many of the problems involved in producing reliable electronic components.

The first large machine built for commercial sale was the UNIVAC (Universal Automatic Calculator). It was manufactured by the Sperry Rand Corporation and was intended for use in the 1950 decennial census of the United States.

The Whirlwind computer developed at the Massachusetts Institute of Technology was the first computer to use magnetic core storage. In the early 1950's IBM completed its 701 computer with electrostatic storage and its 650 computer using a rotating magnetic drum for storage.

Developments in the last 10 years have been too numerous to recount here. In addition to a complete line of computers produced by IBM, other industrial giants now marketing computers include General Electric, Radio Corporation of America, Burroughs, National Cash Register, Minneapolis-Honeywell, Control Data, and the Univac Division of Sperry Rand. There is no reason to believe that the revolution will slow up any time soon. On the contrary, it can be expected that the future will bring even more powerful and useful machines to solve the growing problems of government, science, and business.

The Nature of the Computer Revolution

The impact of the computer revolution has already been felt in many areas. In the field of government, the computer has been able to improve greatly the efficiency and productivity of bureaucracy. For example, in 1960 the Bureau of the Census was able to do twice as much work with 2,250 employees and the help of computers as it had been able to do with 4,500 employees 10 years before when it had just begun its computer program.

The federal government, including the Defense Department and the Atomic Energy Commission, is one of the largest users of computers. The Air Force uses computers to direct its SAGE (Semi-Automatic Ground Environment) System as a protection against a surprise air attack. These computers, working as a system, are able to keep track of every aircraft flying over the United States and Canada; can identify each as friend or foe; and can assign planes or missiles to intercept an enemy raider.

To the engineer and the scientist, the computer has come as a colossal technological advance. The very fact that a computer can manipulate symbols a million times faster than a man with a pencil and paper eliminates the drudgery of computation, increases the accuracy of results, and reduces considerably the time it takes to solve problems. But this is not all. If a rocket were being sent to the moon, only a computer has the capability to analyze fast enough the data returned to earth by the instruments aboard the rocket in order to control the flight of the missile. Thus, it is not just a case of being able to do things faster, but of being able to do things never before possible.

The nature of the computer is such that to use it in solving problems, one is forced to think clearly and precisely about what he intends to do. He cannot successfully instruct a computer to work for him until he has first determined clearly in his own mind what he wants done. In this respect the computer has been responsible for a whole new way of thinking about how problems may be approached and solved. It has brought about a revolution in thinking as well as a revolution in technology.

THE IMPORTANCE OF THE COMPUTER TO BUSINESS

The importance of the computer to the business community is no less than that in government and the sciences. A Sperry Rand UNIVAC installed in a General Electric plant in Louisville in 1954 was the first computer used by a private company. In the 10 years that followed, many thousands of computers were put to work in plants, factories, warehouses, and home offices of American businesses. The job of training skilled technicians to use and maintain the new machines was exceeded only by the number of problems faced by thousands of business executives who had to adjust their thinking to the tremendous potential of the new tool.

The adjustment of businessmen to the new ways of thinking brought about by the computer has been phenomenal. Unlike many great innovations of the past, the computer has become an accepted tool within a decade rather than within the century or more often required of a technological revolution.

Data Processing

The first applications of the computer in business were largely confined to routine data processing. This included such tasks as preparing payrolls and writing salary checks, keeping track of inventories, preparing bills, sorting checks in banks, and gathering vast amounts of data for annual and special reports. In a large organization, such as an insurance company, the job of transferring company records to punched cards or to magnetic tape was a monumental task requiring two to three years in some cases. But once the switch was made, the benefits were immense, not only in doing the old job better, but also in having available a great deal of new information never before practical to assemble. There were mistakes made, to be certain. Many companies purchased equipment far too expensive for their needs, while others did not know how to utilize their installations to the fullest extent. Many of these problems are being solved, and since computers are now far more reliable mechanically than in the past, the unit costs of using a computer are declining steadily.

Problem Solving

At the same time that data processing was speeding up paper work in the office, the engineers and scientists in large business organizations were using computers to solve scientific and engineering problems. In 1953 Lockheed Aircraft Company was using computers in calculating trajectories and designing space vehicles. Other companies have used computers to solve production problems, to design bridges, and to point the way to new products.

Simulation

An important new area of computer application — simulation by means of computer models — has opened in recent years and holds great promise for the future. The use of models in business planning is not new. Mock-ups, pilot plants, blueprints, and many other types of models have been used for many years. Before computers were available, it was necessary to construct many models slowly and laboriously and to compare them carefully with one another to determine which was the most likely to succeed.

The computer can make excellent use of simulation models in the form of mathematical equations to help the businessman understand the changing relationships of facts. He can simulate part or all of his firm's operations in a computer and test to see how each course of action might affect dozens of different situations.

For example, one major oil company, with the help of several mathematicians, has developed a model of its firm to help find answers to such questions as, "Would it be better to concentrate all our service stations in a few states rather than spread them out over several states?" or "Would it be profitable for us to supply our distributors from tank trucks rather than by rail?" The management of this company had found that it often took so long to answer complicated questions such as these by conventional methods that decisions had to be made before all the facts could be gathered. Simulation on a computer is one way to solve such problems.

In Chapter 1 it was pointed out that models can be modified and improved with experience. As the businessman works with a model, he corrects its weaknesses and adds refinements to make it more realistic. As he continues to work with his model, it gets better and better and his computer simulation grows in effectiveness. He soon finds he can test hundreds of possible plans of action and get approximate answers as to how well each will work out. These answers come in a matter of minutes rather than weeks. Continued work should lead to the point where he can tell with a high degree of accuracy what is happening, what should be happening, and what will probably happen in the future.

Real Time Computer Systems

The digital computer available to the businessman today enables him to control his business and to understand its environment as never before. The computer allows him to get relevant facts about his business almost at the time they happen, and it is possible for him to understand the changing relationships of these facts. These new techniques are called "on line" or "real time" systems. Several applications of these techniques are now found in American business, and many computer experts predict that by 1970 nearly all new electronic data-processing systems will be real time systems.

The meaning of the term "real time" can be explained best with an example such as SABRE, which is the name of the system used by American Airlines to handle seat reservations. Airline officials decided several years ago that their most difficult economic problem was the proper handling of seat reservations. They wanted to fly with as many seats filled as possible but without selling the same seat to more than one person. As tickets were sold in many offices miles apart, keeping track of reservations was a difficult problem. With more planes, more lines, and more offices, the problem got worse; and the handling of each reservation became more costly. The SABRE system was developed by IBM for American Airlines at a cost of $30 million. It connects all American Airline ticket offices with one centralized computer system which handles information so fast that if anyone anywhere on the system cancels a seat reservation, that same seat can be sold to someone else a few seconds later at another American Airlines office a thousand miles away. To be on the safe side, the system includes another computer which is "offline" but ready to cut in instantly to take over the SABRE system if there is a failure in the regular computer. This standby computer can be used to solve special problems fed it while it is not needed to handle reservations. The savings in staff, increased load factors on planes, and more efficient flight plans are expected to amount to several million dollars a year in the near future. This system is able to supply the company with facts that are "on line," *i.e.*, as soon as they exist and in "real time," *i.e.*, in sufficient numbers to act upon them by making immediate decisions.

Other examples of real time systems are those used by Westinghouse Electric and Lockheed Missiles & Space, Inc. Work is now going forward to provide such a system for American railroads to improve the handling of freight cars.

WHAT IS A COMPUTER?

A computer is many different things to many people. To the engineer who designed it, it is a complicated piece of electronic equipment using the most advanced techniques in circuitry. It is built to do the fastest, most accurate job of computing while requiring a minimum of space and maintenance. To the mathematician or the physical scientist, it is a device for solving long, complicated mathematical problems involving millions of separate calculations. To the businessman, it may be a way of doing tedious bookkeeping and inventory chores. Certainly, to the statistician, the computer is a means for carrying out statistical analysis of a type that was never practical to do by hand or on an electric calculator. The machine adds nothing to the body of statistical theory, but it adds much to the means of putting that theory to work on practical problems.

In general, a *computer* can be defined as an electronic machine that accepts input data, processes the data, and makes available the results as answers. The *program* is a detailed set of instructions that shows step by step how the data are to be processed. The program is prepared by a person called the *programmer*.

Some computers are designed as *special-purpose* machines. That is, they are built to do a particular job over and over again, but cannot be readily converted to other uses. On the other hand, *general-purpose* machines can be used for any kind of data processing. Such a machine may handle the task of designing a bridge for the engineering department in the morning and may process the payroll for the accounting department that afternoon. However, the general-purpose machine has less speed and efficiency due to its greater flexibility of purpose.

Kinds of Computers

Based on their internal method of operation, there are two broad classes of computers, *digital* and *analog*. The statistician is concerned almost entirely with the use of digital computers.

The digital computer handles numbers in much the same way as a desk calculator. It computes in discrete steps and with discrete symbols of information. It cannot handle a continuous real function, but only the value of the function at discrete points. For example, to represent all the values of the interval between plus and minus one would require an infinite storage that no digital computer could have. It can only compute and store a finite number of values. The manipulation of numbers is performed under the arbitrary rules of arithmetic, and the precision of the digital operations is determined by the number of digits used in computation. The necessity to work with approximations is not necessarily inaccurate, since the approximation error can be made so small as to be negligible.

Calculating with digits is not the only way in which a computer can work. An analog computer computes by combining quantities rather than digits. Some physical quantities such as electric current or voltage are considered analogous to the numbers involved. A simple analog device familiar to most students is the slide rule. The slide rule has numbers represented by lengths proportional to their logarithms. Numbers can be multiplied on a slide rule by adding their corresponding lengths. Electronic analog computers use electrical voltages as analogs for numbers and can add, subtract, multiply, or divide these quantities. By combining circuits into simple networks, highly complex calculations can be performed very rapidly. Such machines are particularly useful in the solution of problems involving the use of ordinary differential equations.

Programming an analog computer requires an understanding of electronics in order to be able to translate mathematical expressions into circuit combinations. While the programmer need not understand all the electronic features of his machine, he should understand the mathematics of signal analysis and have a knowledge of the machine's logic.

The analog computer has the advantages of lower cost and higher speed in obtaining final answers. It is, however, less flexible than the digital computer. Its precision depends on its construction, maintenance, and the ability of its user to read and interpret its results. Precision is usually restricted to about one tenth of one percent.

The advantages of the digital computer, with its stored program and its greater precision, have led to its increased use over the analog computer in most situations.

Functional Units of a Computer

All general-purpose digital computer systems can be divided into five component parts: input units, storage unit, arithmetic-logic unit, control unit, and output units. In some cases an input-output unit is one unit, and often the arithmetic-logic unit and the control unit are thought of as one, the central processing unit. The relationship of these units to one another is shown in Figure 4.1.

Input. It is necessary for the programmer to communicate with the computer in two ways. He must be able to tell it what to do, and he must give it the data with which he wishes it to work. This communication takes place through the input units of the computer.

Input units are able to read instructions and data that are in a rigidly prescribed form and to make this information available to the computer. The information may be carried in the form of punched cards, punched paper tape, magnetic tape, or characters printed in magnetic ink on paper documents, such as checks. Very limited inputs may be made from a typewriter or switches on the computer console. In an "on-line" type of system, data may flow directly from some operation, such as a refinery flow, to the computer without any intermediate handling by man.

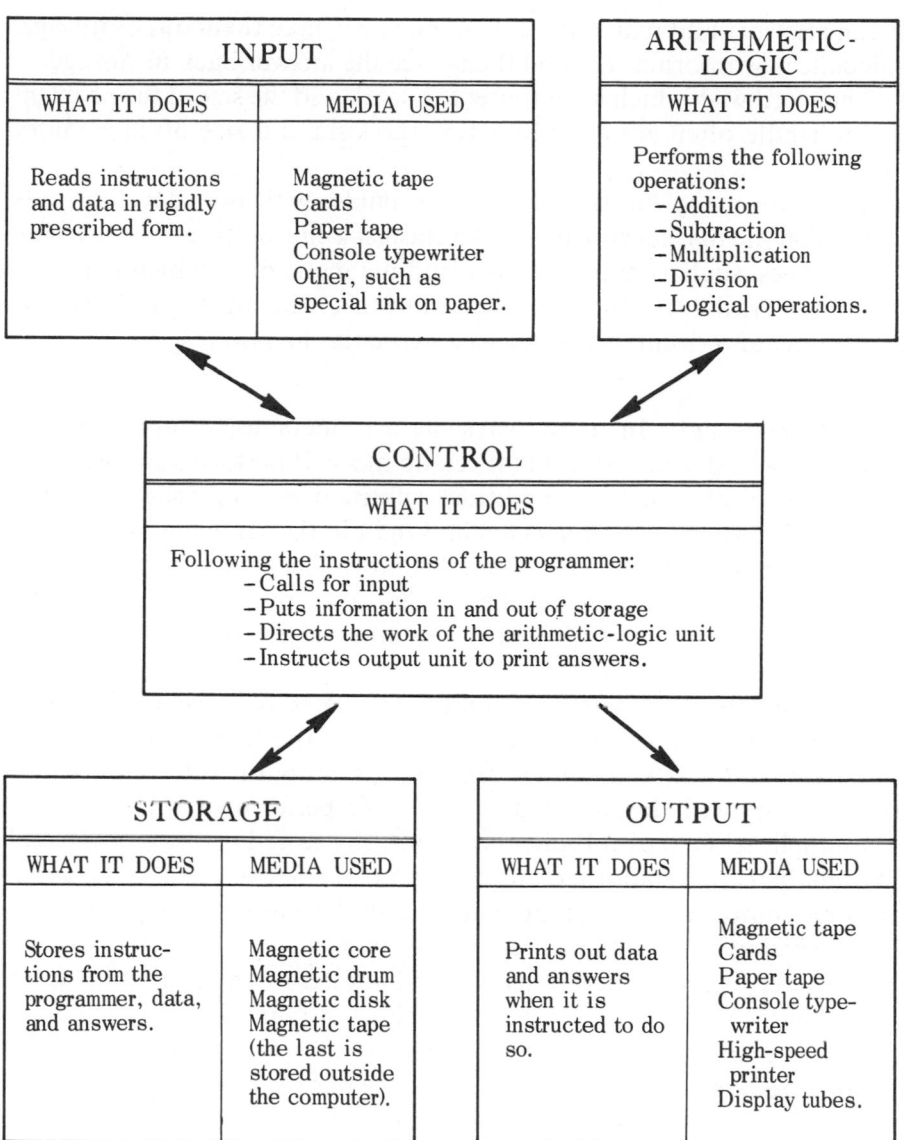

Figure 4.1

FUNCTIONAL UNITS OF A COMPUTER

Storage. The storage unit may be thought of as a large number of tiny storage boxes, each with its own box number. Both instructions and data can be electronically stored in these memory locations until ready for use by the computer. The computer has the ability to plan how the storage space will be utilized and can "remember" what is stored in each location.

It can also sort and rearrange data in memory, take them out of storage, calculate new information, and then place the answer back in storage.

The speed with which a computer can work and the size of the problem it can handle often are determined by the kind and size of its memory unit.

There are many kinds of storage available, with new developments coming on the market constantly. The fastest kinds of storage are *random access* types, such as magnetic core and magnetic disk, which make information available without any delay due to sorting through a long tape or waiting for a drum to revolve to a particular location.

Arithmetic-Logic. In many ways the arithmetic-logic unit functions much like a desk calculator, but it can do more. It performs simple arithmetic operations such as addition, subtraction, multiplication, and division. It also shifts numbers left and right in the same manner that an operator shifts the carriage on a calculator. The term, "logic," comes from the ability of the unit to make simple, logical decisions such as determining, after examination, whether a number is zero or not; or whether it is positive or negative.

Basically, the arithmetic-logic unit is composed of registers. The main register, called the *accumulator*, is much like the long dial on a desk calculator and acts as a storage register. Names of the other one or two registers vary with the particular machine. To perform an operation such as multiplication, the multiplier is temporarily stored in one register, and the multiplicand in another; the product is then developed in the third. In some computers one register can be used for more than one purpose, thus reducing the number of registers to two.

Only very simple operations can be handled by the arithmetic-logic unit. Thus, the user who wishes to perform a complicated calculation must resort to the techniques of numerical analysis that permit such a problem to be solved by the repetition of the basic operations of addition, subtraction, multiplication, and division.

Control. As with any complicated organization, there must be centralized direction and control of the entire operation. In the digital computer, this function is performed by the control unit, which acts as the brain for the system. This unit has all the circuitry necessary to perform all operations throughout the computing system. Its duties include such activities as calling for input, putting information in and taking information out of storage, directing arithmetic operations, and commanding the output of answers.

Each operation of the control unit is a two-step cycle. The unit first secures an instruction from the memory unit, decodes it, and issues orders to the other components of the computer. The second step involves doing something with the results of the work directed in the first step, usually storing the result in memory for future use.

Output. The output unit provides the means for the computer to communicate with the user. Any information stored in memory may be brought out for examination in one of many ways. Output devices produce information from the computer as holes punched in cards or in paper tape, as magnetized spots along the length of magnetic tape, or as printed information on paper. In recent years devices called display tubes have been developed that will present information in the form of charts, graphs, or even animated engineering blueprints.

Special data conversion equipment is available to convert data from one form to another. For example, information on punched cards can be transcribed automatically into magnetic tape or vice versa. When this operation takes place utilizing the computer itself, the devices are said to be *on-line*. When the operations take place independently of the computer, they are called *off-line*.

HOW THE COMPUTER WORKS

The job of the computer is to receive, process, and print out data, both numbers and instructions. The data must be handled by electronic components such as transistors, magnetic cores, and wires. These devices both store and move the data by means of electronic signals. The presence or absence of a signal in a specific component is the method by which a bit of information is recorded.

Binary Operations

The computer can deal with only *two* states or conditions, the presence or the absence of a signal. Thus, the computer is said to function in a *binary mode*. The word *binary* means composed of two elements. This can be thought of as "off" or "on" in the case of a lamp; "closed" or "open" in the case of a switch; "conducting" or "not conducting" current in the case of a wire; or as being "magnetized" with one of two opposite polarities in the case of a magnetic element. Because electronic components need only two stable states, they can be made to operate not only exceedingly rapidly but also very reliably. These are necessary qualities of a computer.

Binary digits can be used to represent any kind of information. This is done within the computer by assigning or associating specific values to a group of binary positions such as those shown in Figure 4.2. If each of the four panels in this figure is thought of as a row of eight tiny light bulbs on a computer console, the value of any number from one through 255 can be indicated by adding the values represented by each bulb in that panel which is lighted. The size of the number that can be represented may be increased by adding additional light bulbs to the panel.

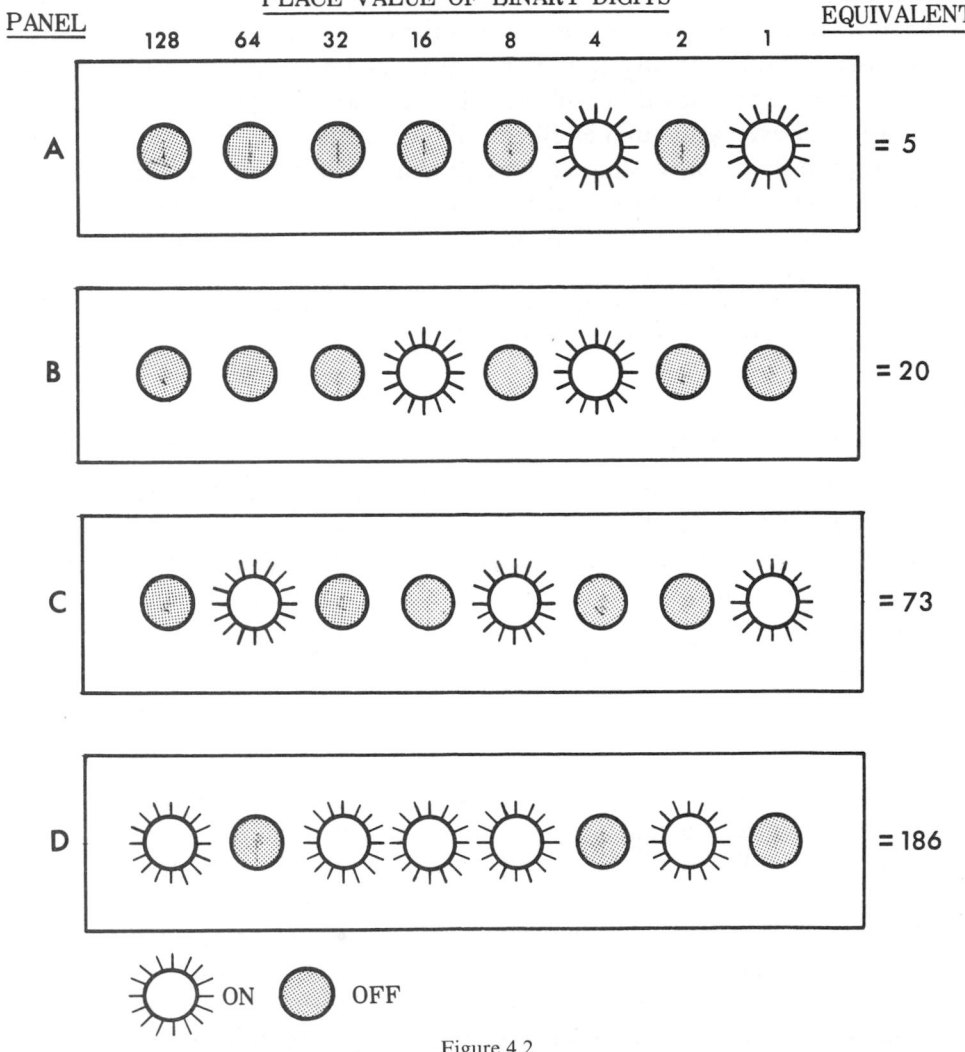

Figure 4.2

REPRESENTING BINARY NUMBERS WITH LIGHTS
ON A COMPUTER CONSOLE

The binary system of notation uses only two symbols. The zero (0) is used to represent the absence of an assigned value, and the one (1) is used to represent the presence of an assigned value. In the illustration in Figure 4.2, if the light is on, this fact would be represented by a one (1); and if the light is off, this fact would be represented by a zero (0). The binary numbers can now be written symbolically as follows:

Panel	Binary	Decimal
A	101	5
B	10100	20
C	1001001	73
D	10111010	186

All computers use binary digits rather than decimal digits to represent stored information. While the computer user normally does not need to work directly with the binary system, the method of representing values using the binary system is helpful in understanding the general concept of data representation.

The binary notation one (1) is called a *bit*, and the notation zero (0) is called a *no bit*. For example, the binary expression 10100 is said to have a bit in positions 4 and 16. There are no bits in positions 1, 2, and 8.

In decimal notation the place value of digits represents units, 10's, 100's, 1,000's, and so forth. The decimal number 1,084 can be thought of as one 1,000, no 100, eight 10's, and four units. These are often called *base-10 numbers* and can be written in mathematical notation as $(1 \times 10^3) + (0 \times 10^2) + (8 \times 10^1) + (4 \times 10^0)$.

Binary numbers are *base-two numbers* and the binary number 10100 has the same meaning as $(1 \times 2^4) + (0 \times 2^3) + (1 \times 2^2) + (0 \times 2^1) + (0 \times 2^0)$ which is $16 + 0 + 4 + 0 + 0 = 20$. Table 4.1 shows the binary numbers that can be represented in a three-bit address. An *address*

Table 4.1

RELATIONSHIP BETWEEN BINARY AND DECIMAL NUMBERS

Binary	Value computed as:	Decimal equivalent
000	$(0 \times 2^2) + (0 \times 2^1) + (0 \times 2^0) =$	0
001	$(0 \times 2^2) + (0 \times 2^1) + (1 \times 2^0) =$	1
010	$(0 \times 2^2) + (1 \times 2^1) + (0 \times 2^0) =$	2
011	$(0 \times 2^2) + (1 \times 2^1) + (1 \times 2^0) =$	3
100	$(1 \times 2^2) + (0 \times 2^1) + (0 \times 2^0) =$	4
101	$(1 \times 2^2) + (0 \times 2^1) + (1 \times 2^0) =$	5
110	$(1 \times 2^2) + (1 \times 2^1) + (0 \times 2^0) =$	6
111	$(1 \times 2^2) + (1 \times 2^1) + (1 \times 2^0) =$	7

identifies the storage location. A 10-bit address will handle a binary number as large as 1,023, and 12 bits will handle a number as large as 4,095.

There are rules for adding, subtracting, multiplying, and dividing binary numbers. These rules are not presented in this book, but references to them may be found in the selected readings at the end of this chapter.

In addition to the binary system of handling numbers, the computer can also represent alphabetic characters and special symbols in binary. The codes used differ with the machine, but the fundamental principles are the same. The computer codes also have built-in methods of checking the validity of coded information to insure the accuracy of computations.

Can a Computer Think?

The answer to the question, "Can a computer think?," is not so easy as one might suppose. In the final analysis it probably depends on how "thinking" is defined. If one defines thinking as "something which is mysterious and mystical and which is exclusively reserved as a human activity," the definition automatically excludes the computer. The answer to the question has to be "No."

On the other hand, the popular conception that a computer is merely a high-speed number calculator is too restrictive. It has already been pointed out in this chapter that computers can be instructed to make logical decisions and to solve problems. If thinking is defined as "a process which leads to intelligent behavior," then there are those who feel that it is possible to construct eventually computer programs that can cause a computer to "think" within the meaning of this more positive definition. This field of research is called *artificial intelligence*, and while it is still a relatively new area, rapid strides have already been made here.

The type of computer program which can cause a computer to "think" is not one that is restricted to highly stereotyped or routine tasks. It must be a program which causes the computer to be sensitive to the environment in which it operates. The computer must be able to analyze its own performance, recognize its own weaknesses, and modify its own program in such a way as to "learn" from past experience. This learning, then, will make its future performance more effective. At this point the answer to the question, "Can a computer think?," may be "Yes."

Programs have already been written to teach a computer to play checkers, to solve symbolic integration problems in calculus, to learn foreign langues for purposes of translation, and to demonstrate many other types of artificial intelligence. These are only steps toward the final goal of a "thinking" computer, but many of them represent long steps in that direction.

Approaches to Problem Solving

One of the purposes of this book is to examine ways in which the computer can be used effectively to solve problems in business statistics. In approaching this subject it will be helpful to examine briefly those problem-solving techniques that lend themselves to computer applications.

Brute-Force Approach. Because computers can work so fast, there are those who take the point of view that the computer can "think of everything" and can select from all possible choices the best solution to a problem. This may be possible in some limited situations, but certainly not in all. For example, if a large manufacturer were faced with the problem of locating a new warehouse somewhere in the United States, could he program a computer to consider all possible sites from the standpoint of cost, convenience, transportation, sales, etc., to give him the one best location? The answer is "Probably not." The number of possible alternatives would be far too numerous ever to be considered all at one time by any computer now in existence. It seems clear that the number of possible alternatives must be limited in some fashion to permit a practical computer solution.

The limitations of the brute-force approach are further illustrated by the fact that computers are still not unbeatable champions at chess. The size of the chess maze is so enormous that it is not possible to program a computer to play optimum chess by considering every possible move by both players. There are too many alternatives for the computer to consider them all within its limited memory capacity.

Heuristic Approach. It has already been noted that, for a computer program to be effective, it must be able to approach the maze of all possible solutions to a problem in some highly selective manner so that it can explore only those alternatives that offer the greatest chance of success and ignore the others. The word *heuristic* means "to discover." A *heuristic method* is one that uses some kind of strategy designed to limit the search for solutions in a large problem space. This strategy may be a rule of thumb or other simplified approach that it is hoped will lead to a solution to some complex problem. It is also hoped that the solution will be "good enough" if not optimal. For example, one heuristic approach used by humans is to apply the rule of thumb that, "A new problem may be solved by using the same methods that have solved similar problems in the past." This method is no guarantee of success, but it often works.

As another example, a businessman wishing to solve an extremely complex production problem by means of a heuristic method might divide the big problem into relatively independent subproblems. Each subproblem might be subject to a computer solution by some optimizing technique, and the resulting solutions combined into a possible solution to the overall problem.

Much progress has been made in the heuristic approach to problem solving on the computer, and the future seems to hold great promise. However, a great deal more study is needed in this area before heuristically oriented problem solvers will be able to make maximum use of the computer.

Algorithmic Approach. This method is often contrasted to the heuristic approach. An *algorithm* is defined as a sequence of numerical operations that will lead to the solution of a particular problem. Most of the equations and formulas used in statistics are ideal for solution by a computer since they can be treated as algorithms, and a step-by-step solution is possible. Much of the discussion in the following chapters is directed at developing the algorithms of statistics, showing how they can be used in helping to solve business problems, and picturing the solution steps in flow diagrams. The major shortcoming of the algorithmic approach is that many of the most complex problems one would like to attack via the computer have no known algorithms available for an overall solution. In such cases it may take a combination of heuristics and algorithms to provide the solution.

Simulation Approach. Computer simulation has been discussed earlier in this chapter, but the technique may be appropriately mentioned again here for completeness. This technique offers a way of arriving at approximate solutions to complex problems using the digital computer. It is an approach that seems certain of greater use as simulation models become more numerous and more accurately portray the real relationships of facts to one another.

PUTTING THE COMPUTER TO WORK

The job of putting the computer to work to solve problems is thought of in its most general sense as *programming*. The steps to be followed in programming any problem are:

1. Analyzing the problem to set forth the method of solution.
2. Coding the problem into a sequence of instructions for the computer.
3. Operating the computer to solve the problem.

Some of the general approaches to problem solving have already been discussed in this chapter. Chapter 5 describes in detail the use of flow diagrams as one of the most effective methods of analyzing a problem and determining a step-by-step method of solution.

The coding of the problem into a language that can be understood by the computer is discussed briefly in this section. Problems involved in the physical operation of a computer are not a part of this book.

In speaking of a computer system, there are two general areas that must be considered:

1. The physical configuration of equipment in the computer system, generally known as the *hardware* phase of the system.
2. The many techniques developed for the most efficient use of the computer hardware such as computer languages, compilers, assembly systems, and library subroutines, all known as the *software* phase of the system.

The primary concern here is with the software package of programming aids that is offered by manufacturers to make it possible for users to operate computers effectively. The importance of the software in any computer system rivals the hardware, and the two areas have developed with equal rapidity in recent years.

Machine Language Programming

The most tedious and difficult programming is that in which the program is written in actual machine code, or machine language. This was the method used by all programmers in the early days of computer development. In this kind of programming, the problem must be analyzed in terms of the individual operations that the computer can perform; and the instructions must be kept in the exact sequence in which they are to be executed. The programmer must understand the computer in complete detail, and he must bear the full burden of logic, program organization, and allocation of all memory storage. This is a demanding and an inefficient way to write a program. It is also difficult to train programmers to do this kind of coding.

Symbolic Codes

As the use of computers became more widespread, the shortage of competent programmers became acute. This problem, together with the many difficulties of machine language programming, led to the development of more advanced systems of program writing. It was learned that a computer can be programmed to recognize instructions written in other languages and to translate those instructions into machine language. The first of these new languages permitted the programmer to use symbols, such as ADD for addition and SUB for subtraction, to stand for the same machine instructions. These symbolic codes, called *mnemonics*, permitted one-for-one translation; *i.e.*, one symbol for one machine language instruction.

Macro-Instruction Codes

The next big breakthrough in programming languages came with *macro-instructions*. A single one of these instructions could be used by the programmer to produce a whole series of machine language instructions. It was soon possible for the programmer to write a few instructions in a language much like English which could be translated by the machine itself into a program that might perform thousands of calculations. Further, it was possible to assign to the computer the job of keeping track of all its own memory locations, thus relieving the programmer of this serious headache. With these and other developments, the power of programming languages was becoming very striking, and the time required to train qualified programmers was substantially reduced.

It is neither possible nor necessary here to describe the many software languages that have been developed to make the job of the programmer more efficient and less arduous. There have been dozens of such languages, and any modern-day computer has available one or more of them to aid its user.

It should also be pointed out that in addition to the language, with its associated rules of grammar, the computer manufacturer also provides the user with a machine language program called a *compiler*. The compiler is used to translate the language used by the programmer into the language (machine) used by the computer. There are many other aids such as library programs and subroutines also provided by the computer manufacturer to simplify the task of the person who is preparing a problem for computer solution.

Data Processing Languages

A basic distinction is often made between so-called *data processing languages* and *scientific languages*. In general, the former are designed primarily for handling large flows of business data where relatively little computation is required. The scientific languages are more appropriate for use where data inputs are relatively small but where more sophisticated computation is needed.

The first data processing language was developed by Remington Rand Univac and was called FLOW-MATIC. It provided the businessman with a programming language that had a vocabulary very nearly the same as his own. This made it easy for systems analysts, accountants, and operating managers to use the UNIVAC computer with a minimum of training in computer programming.

In 1959 a voluntary committee of government users and computer manufacturers developed a data processing language known as COBOL (COmmon Business Oriented Language). It was an effort to produce an English-like programming language that could be used on many different types of processing systems. Several computer manufacturers now have machine language compilers that provide for the translation of COBOL programs into machine language programs on their computers. It is hoped by many that compilers will be developed for additional machines in the future so that COBOL will eventually become a "universal" data processing language for business and government.

Scientific Languages

Of the many languages developed primarily for scientific and engineering work, the most widely used is FORTRAN (FORmula TRANslation), which was developed by IBM. As the name implies, the language is designed to resemble the language of mathematics. It is particularly suited for solving the kinds of equations used by the mathematician, the physical scientist, the engineer, and the statistician. The person who knows mathematical symbols can write a program, using the symbols with very little change and without bothering to learn anything about the machine language of the computer. This language has been so successful that several other manufacturers have developed FORTRAN compiler programs for their own equipment.

Another mathematical language, ALGOL (ALGOrithmic Language) was developed in 1958 and was revised in 1960. ALGOL has features similar to FORTRAN but is supposed to be even more powerful. The developers of ALGOL intended it to become the universal scientific language in the same way that COBOL was designed to be the universal business language. In actual practice, however, ALGOL is used far less frequently than FORTRAN.

IMPACT OF THE COMPUTER ON THE FIELD OF STATISTICS

The question might be asked, "Why should a student of statistics be concerned with a discussion of the computer in a book on business statistics?" Many books on statistics have been written in the past with no mention of the computer or, at the most, only a cursory glance at electronic data processing as a way of handling large amounts of data very rapidly. Practically no thought has been given to the impact of the computer on the field of statistics itself.

The computer is more than just a tool to work problems faster and with less effort. It is, in a sense, a new way of thinking about how to solve problems. It has already made obsolete many statistical techniques cherished for years by statisticians, and it is daily making possible the development of new techniques that were impractical a few years ago. In some cases the computer may even become an integral part of a research program when the researcher is involved in a project such as simulation research.

Many Established Statistical Techniques Now Obsolete

For many years the frequency distribution has been used as a convenient way of grouping data to make it easier to examine their characteristics. Statisticians have been proud of the many so called "shortcut" methods devised to make it possible to estimate such measures as the arithmetic mean or the standard deviation of a distribution. Before the advent of the electric calculator, and even afterwards, the amount of sheer arithmetic involved in computing the standard deviation of 1,000 items using the following basic formula (3.6) was very extensive:

$$\sigma = \sqrt{\frac{\Sigma(X - \mu)^2}{N}}.$$

It was necessary to add all the 1,000 items; compute the arithmetic mean; calculate 1,000 differences from the mean; square each of the differences; divide the total by 1,000; and take the square root of the quotient. Extreme care had to be exercised at each step to prevent error.

It is easy to see why the statistician was agreeable to the sacrifice of some accuracy if he could reduce substantially the amount of calculation in such a problem. The following shortcut formula for the standard deviation (3.11), which was discussed in Chapter 3, provides a good example of the compromise:

$$\sigma = i\sqrt{\frac{\Sigma f(d')^2}{N} - \left(\frac{\Sigma fd'}{N}\right)^2}.$$

The data were grouped into classes all having the same width of class interval so that the midpoint of each class could be counted as a certain number of class interval units from some arbitrary origin. No arithmetic mean had to be computed, and hence no deviations about the mean had to be measured. It was assumed that all the items in a given class were equally distributed throughout that class. It was hoped that most errors would be offsetting so that total error would be small. The amount of arithmetic was greatly reduced and the result was reasonably accurate. The use of the shortcut method was dependent upon whether the data could be logically arranged into classes of equal size, and no open-end class was permitted.

The use of a digital computer to compute the standard deviation of the 1,000 items eliminates the arduous work of repetitive computation; it practically removes the chance of mathematical error; and because it is no longer necessary to group data into frequency distributions, it is more accurate. In brief, the use of the computer makes obsolete almost all shortcut methods devised over the past 50 years to reduce the drudgery of computation.

Some Statistical Techniques Made More Effective

The impact of the computer on the field of statistics has been important in other ways. In general, it can be said that in any problem situation in which the amount of data to be processed is very large or the amount of computation to be performed is very extensive, the computer will provide a solution more quickly, more accurately, and more economically than conventional methods.

Examples of techniques that were well developed in theory, but difficult to use in practice without a computer, come to mind by the dozens to instructors who have taught statistics in the classroom.

➤ *Example.* If a manufacturer were trying to examine the relationship between some variable such as hardness (X_1) of a manufactured part and nine other variables used in the hardening process $(X_2, X_3, X_4, \ldots, X_{10})$, he might gather 500 sets of observations of these variables and try to use multiple regression analysis (see Chapter 18) to find the equation of average relationship. Statistical theory tells him how this should be done, but to find the solution, he must solve 10 simultaneous equations with 10 unknowns.

The story is told of a group of statisticians who became engaged in an argument several years ago about the best way to solve 10 simultaneous equations. There are several acceptable methods of solution. Since the group could settle the argument in no other way, they agreed to a contest in which each was to solve a given problem of this nature using his favorite method. After several days of hard work, they all gave up without a solution. For all practical purposes the problem was beyond their ability to compute — regardless of the method used.

Examples of computer solutions to multiple regression problems using 30 or more variables are now common. Not only can the computer be used to compute the regression equation and any desired coefficients, but it can also be used to apply tests of significance to each independent variable to determine how significant a part it plays in the variations of the dependent variable. All this work can be done accurately in a few seconds on a fast computer, whereas the task could not be accomplished at all, even after days of work, on an electric calculator.

Other examples of the tremendous power of the computer to solve problems, never before practical to tackle, can be found in the areas of analysis of variance, experimental design, statistical quality control, and the application of statistical theory to macro programs such as those found in large inventory control problems. Many of these ideas will be presented in more detail in later chapters.

New Statistical Techniques Being Generated

Not only does the computer make it practical to apply techniques already developed in theory, but its use is also leading to the development of much new statistical theory.

One of the first examples appeared in 1958 with the publication of a technical paper by the National Bureau of Economic Research on "Seasonal Adjustments by Electronic Computer Methods."[3] In this paper the authors pointed out that the use of electronic computers, by forcing them to make explicit their assumptions at each stage of the work and by enabling them to make comprehensive tests of results, has thrown considerable light on the technical problems of making seasonal adjustments. In many cases the new knowledge led to improvements over techniques previously used to do this kind of work.

In Chapter 9, which deals with sampling distributions, it is shown how tables of random digits can be used to simulate sampling experiments. In recent years similar techniques known as *Monte Carlo simulation methods* have been devised to attack a variety of problems both in the sciences and in business. These problems are ones that cannot be solved by direct means because of limitations of time or cost. The point here is that, in long and complex problems, the computer becomes a necessary part of these simulations. If 100,000 random numbers are needed, these can be generated on a computer in any one of several statistically acceptable ways and applied to the problem as needed.

It is possible to create within the computer an artificial population that is a model of a physical system. The model can be tested at relatively little expense. This type of simulation makes it possible to avoid the cost

---

[3]Julius Shiskin and Harry Eisenpress, *Seasonal Adjustments by Electronic Computer Methods*, Technical Paper 12 (New York: National Bureau of Economic Research, 1958), p. 416.

of building and operating expensive physical equipment that would otherwise be necessary. Work of this type has been done, for example, in the study of the collision of photons with electrons in physics and in the study of complex waiting-line problems in industry.

Almost every new application of the computer to a highly complex problem of this type brings a better understanding of these powerful new tools of analysis and adds something to the growing body of statistical theory.

STUDY QUESTIONS

4-1. Explain briefly the meaning of each of the following terms:

a. difference engine	h. accumulator	n. programming
b. analytic engine	i. on-line	o. hardware
c. data processing	j. off-line	p. software
d. on-line in real-time	k. binary	q. mnemonics
e. computer	l. bit	r. macro-instructions
f. program	m. algorithm	s. compiler
g. random access		

4-2. Distinguish between a general-purpose and a special-purpose computer.

4-3. Distinguish between an analog computer and a digital computer. Which type is of more use to the statistician? Why?

4-4. Discuss the meaning of the term "artificial intelligence" as applied to computers. Why is this area of research of interest to the businessman?

4-5. What are the shortcomings of machine-language programming?

4-6. In your opinion how large should a problem be before you could justify the use of a computer to solve it? Discuss the criteria you might use to make such a decision.

4-7. Distinguish between a scientific language and a data-processing language for writing a computer program. Do you think it might be possible to develop one language to do both jobs?

4-8. Discuss the relationship between machine language and binary mode in computer programming.

4-9. How do you explain the fact that mathematicians did not invent the computer many years sooner than they did?

4-10. What is the purpose of SAGE?

4-11. What kinds of input and output devices enable man to communicate with the computer?

4-12. What are the advantages of modern programming languages to computer users?

4-13. What is random access storage? What types of media are used to provide random access storage?

4-14. What kinds of logical decisions can a computer make?

4-15. Distinguish between COBOL and FORTRAN. Which would provide the more efficient program to solve a series of simultaneous equations? Why?

PROBLEMS

4-1. Explain how the binary number 11011011 can be converted to its decimal equivalent. What is its value?

4-2. Write the following decimal numbers in binary:

a. 7	c. 52	e. 500	g. 999
b. 26	d. 238	f. 847	h. 1,286

4-3. Convert the following binary numbers to their decimal equivalents:

a. 1101	e. 10101011
b. 10111	f. 111001000
c. 11000	g. 1011000111
d. 100001	h. 11111110111

4-4. Devise your own binary system, using six binary digits, to represent the 26 letters of the alphabet. How many unused combinations would you have left to use for special characters?

4-5. Assume you wish to find the standard deviation of 1,000 values of the variable X using Formula 3.6. Draw a diagram that sets forth step by step the instructions you would tell the computer to follow in solving this problem. You may devise any logical system of diagramming you wish in order to do the job.

SELECTED READINGS

Anderson, Decima M. *Basic Computer Programming*. New York: Appleton-Century-Crofts, 1964.

> This is a beginner's learning manual with many excellent illustrations. It is designed to take the student through every step necessary to write computer programs in FORTRAN for an IBM 1620 computer.

Feigenbaum, Edward A., and Julian Feldman (eds.). *Computers and Thought*. New York: McGraw-Hill Book Company, Inc., 1963.

> A very thought-provoking series of articles by 28 authors who have written of their research and thinking in the area of artificial intelligence and computers.

Gregory, Robert H., and Richard L. Van Horn. *Automatic Data-Processing Systems, Principles and Procedures* (2d ed.). Belmont, California: Wadsworth Publishing Company, Inc., 1963.

> One of the most complete books available to introduce the student to business data processing.

Kemeny, John G., Arthur Schleifer, Jr., J. Laurie Snell, and Gerald L. Thompson. *Finite Mathematics with Business Applications*. Englewood Cliffs, N. J.: Prentice-Hall, Inc., 1962.

> This book carries a discussion of binary numbers and binary arithmetic on pages 44–47. Monte Carlo simulation is discussed on pages 199–215.

Saxon, James A. *COBOL, A Self-Instructional Manual*. Englewood Cliffs, N. J.: Prentice-Hall, Inc., 1963.

> This is a good self-instructional manual developed to teach the beginner the fundamentals of COBOL programming.

Chapter 5

Flow Diagrams for Statistical Methods

Before any problem can be solved, a method of solution, an algorithm, must be determined. The solution of statistical problems by numerical methods is accomplished by performing a series of elementary arithmetic or algebraic operations. For example, the arithmetic mean of a frequency distribution is found by simple summation, counting, and division. The equation $\mu = \dfrac{\Sigma X}{N}$ is a symbolic statement which summarizes the basic operations that must be performed to find the mean of a series of values.

Other statistical methods are much more complex computationally, but each of these algorithms consists of a sequence of numerical operations. A detailed presentation, in graphic form, of the logical sequence of the basic numerical operations of an algorithm is valuable as a learning device and particularly useful in the preparation of a set of instructions for the solution of the problem on a computer.

FLOW DIAGRAMS AND PROBLEM LOGIC

A graphic device for presenting a logical sequence of computational steps is called a *flow diagram*. A flow diagram presents the procedure for problem solving in greater detail than traditional symbolic methods. Anyone familiar with basic numerical operations can follow the computational sequence presented by a flow diagram and perform the necessary calculations.

Problem Analysis and Flow Diagrams

The preparation of a flow diagram offers advantages to the analyst in formulating an algorithm. The relative degree of detail presented by a flow diagram requires that the approach to the problem be outlined in terms of elementary arithmetic or algebraic operations. The process of preparing such an outline helps one to avoid errors in logic, to detect omissions, and to eliminate unnecessary steps.

The preparation of a flow diagram helps the analyst to visualize a sequence of operations and to relate one phase of a solution sequence to another. Visual inspection of a tentative succession of operations provides a useful perspective that can help to point out discrepancies in logic or completeness. By means of a flow diagram, one can experiment with alternative approaches to a problem to determine which algorithm is most efficient computationally. A completed flow diagram should show clearly and correctly all major phases of an algorithm, including a sufficient amount of detailed information so that all necessary steps can be determined.

Flow Diagrams and Computer Programs

Before any problem can be solved by a computer, someone must analyze the computational nature of the problem, prepare a detailed sequence of computational steps, and translate these steps into a program — a series of instructions written in a suitable computer language. In many business firms there is a division of labor between problem analysis and computer programming. Problem analyses, frequently in the form of flow diagrams, are prepared by systems analysts, and the computer programs adapted from the flow diagrams are written by programmers. The necessity for effective communications between analyst and programmer is clear, and good technique in the preparation of flow diagrams is particularly important.

The division of labor between problem analysis and programming offers an advantage to the statistician who is not a programmer. The statistician can obtain a computer solution to his problem by preparing an understandable flow diagram and giving it to a professional programmer for translation into a computer program. In this manner, one who has limited knowledge of computers can gain access to the tremendous arithmetic speed and capacity of computers for solving problems. A knowledge of flow diagramming also helps one to understand programs that have been prepared for the solution of a wide variety of standard types of statistical problems. These programs are called *library programs*, and most computer installations maintain files of these programs, including descriptive material that explains the computational nature of the programs and the procedure for using the programs.

ELEMENTS OF FLOW DIAGRAMS

A flow diagram, also called a flow chart, is a collection of boxes, arrows, lines, and other graphic symbols that indicate the sequence of activities to be performed. While there is some variation in the number and type of symbols used in the preparation of flow diagrams, some standardization of symbol use has been achieved in recent years. The important point is that the use of symbols be consistent within the flow diagram. The connotation given to symbols introduced in this presentation is in general agreement with standard practice in the computer industry.

Flow Direction

The *flow direction* symbol is a solid line with an arrowhead that indicates the direction of the next step in the computational procedure of an algorithm. It is customary to read flow diagrams from top to bottom and from left to right. Flow direction arrows connect the various other symbols, indicating the sequence of operations to be performed. Problem solution techniques frequently involve the repetition of a given arithmetic operation or subsequence of operations. A repetitive or iterative sequence is called a *loop* and frequently results in a direction of flow contrary to the top to bottom or left to right conventions. Examples of flow direction symbols are shown in Figure 5.1.

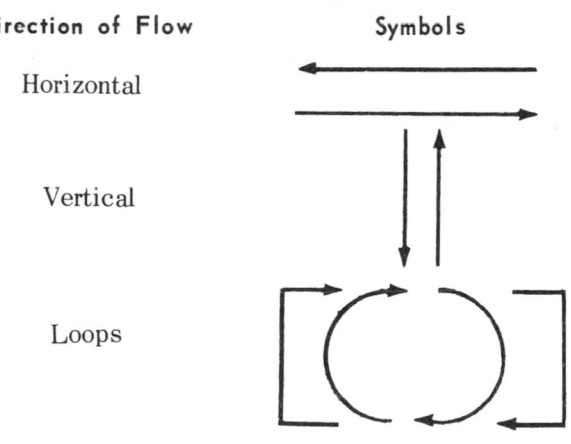

Figure 5.1

FLOW DIRECTION SYMBOLS

Arithmetic Statements

The symbol denoting an arithmetic statement is a rectangular box, which encloses an arithmetic relationship. This symbol most often represents a *command*, which states that an arithmetic operation is to be performed. For example, the box

$$Y = X + 5$$

states that the variable Y should take on a value which is to be determined by finding the sum of a value of the variable X (which has been defined or computed previously) and the constant five.

An arithmetic statement may take the form of a definition rather than a command. A *definition* simply states that a given arithmetic relationship holds. For example,

$$Z = 6$$

defines the variable Z as having a value of six, and no arithmetic operation is required. In practice, arithmetic statements that constitute commands occur much more frequently on flow diagrams than do definition statements. Definition statements are normally used to establish initial and interim conditions of a problem solution method.

➤*Example.* A portion of a flow diagram is to be written to show the calculation of the value of $y_c = a + bx$ for the defined constants a and b and a series of values of x. The partial algorithm is shown in Figure 5.2. The flow direction symbols denote the sequence of operations to be followed and the arithmetic statements give the necessary definitions and commands. The subscript of the variable x denotes the ith value from the series of x values which is substituted to obtain y_c.

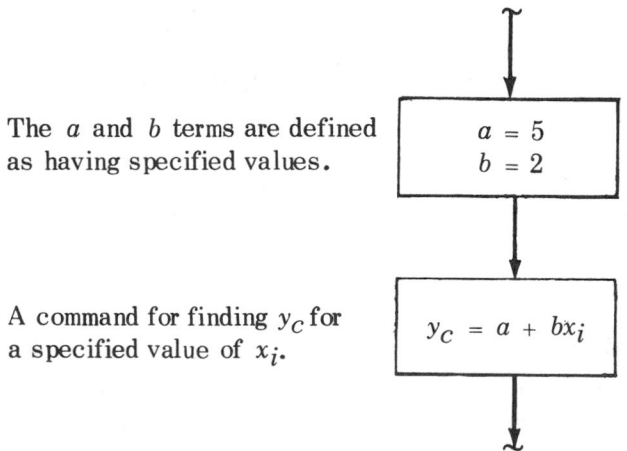

The a and b terms are defined as having specified values.

$$a = 5$$
$$b = 2$$

A command for finding y_c for a specified value of x_i.

$$y_c = a + bx_i$$

Figure 5.2

A PARTIAL ALGORITHM FOR FINDING VALUES OF $y_c = a + bx_i$

Decision Statements

A *decision statement* is used in a flow diagram to indicate which of the alternate directions of flow are to be taken as determined by the relationship between two values. A decision symbol, shown as a diamond, includes a question that asks if a certain relationship is true. For example,

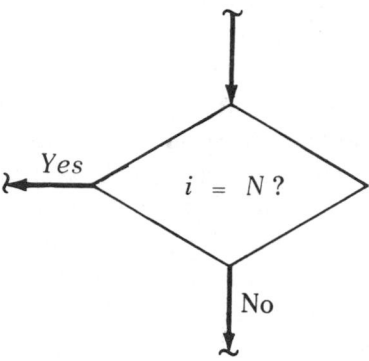

designates a decision statement that asks if the value of i is equal to the value of N, where i has assumed one of a possible range of values during an iterative process.

The possible flow directions that can be taken from the decision statement are called *branches*. There are some instances in which more than two branches may be logical possibilities at a decision point in a flow diagram. For example, if the value of one quantity is less than another, a given flow direction is indicated; if the values are equal, a second flow direction results; and if the former is greater than the latter value, still another branch is indicated. A decision statement of this type is shown below, where the X and the Y values are compared. Any of three possible flow directions can be taken, depending upon the relationship of X and Y.

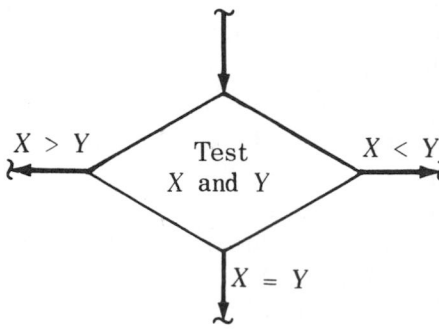

Iterative Loops

Many statistical methods, such as the algorithms for finding the standard deviation of a series of ungrouped data, involve the repetition of an arithmetic sequence. For example, in computing the standard deviation, $(X - \mu)^2$ is determined for all values of X so that the sum of the squared deviations can be found. This repetitive type of operation, in which the same arithmetic sequence is performed for each of a series of values, is called a *loop*. Each repetition of the arithmetic sequence is called an *iteration*. An *iterative process* is an orderly progression through a series of values, where the same sequence of numerical operations is performed for each value of the series. For example, $Z = \Sigma X^2 + \Sigma X^3$ is to be found for 10 values of the variable X. Writing the expression in the form $Z = (X_1^2 + X_2^2 + \ldots + X_{10}^2) + (X_1^3 + X_2^3 + \ldots + X_{10}^3)$ indicates that the solution can be found by an iterative process consisting of squaring, cubing, and summing the values of X.

The progression through the series of X values is determined by *incrementing*, in which the value of the subscript is successively increased by a uniform amount. For example, let i denote the value of the subscript of X. A value of $i = 1$ corresponds to the item X_1; $i = 2$ denotes the item X_2; $\ldots$; and $i = 10$ denotes the item X_{10}. The progression through the series of X values is achieved by giving i an initial value of, say, zero and by increasing or incrementing the value of i by one for each iteration. An application of an incremented subscript is discussed below.

➤ *Example.* A flow diagram is to be written to show the method for finding the sum of a series of 100 values of a variable X. The series is denoted $X_1, X_2, \ldots, X_{100}$, and an arbitrarily selected value of the variable is denoted X_i. The first statement of the partial algorithm in Figure 5.3 is a definition that sets the basic variables ΣX and i equal to zero, and N equal to 100. This step, referred to as *initializing*, defines the initial conditions for the sequence of arithmetic operations. With these variables defined, the next step is the decision statement, which asks if i is equal to 100. Since $i = 0$ at this point, the answer is "No" and the flow is vertically downward from the decision statement to an arithmetic statement. The expression in this statement is a command requiring that the subscript i take on a value equal to its present (initial) value plus one. In this manner, i is incremented so that $i = 0 + 1 = 1$. Next, the flow is to an arithmetic statement which requires that the variable ΣX take on a value equal to its present (initial) value plus the value of item X_i. To best illustrate the change in value of the variable ΣX, assume that first several items in the series have the following values:

Item	Value
X_1	12
X_2	8
X_3	16
X_4	5
X_5	11
.	.
.	.
.	.
X_{100}	18

For the first iteration through the loop, $i = 1$; therefore, the term X_i refers to X_1. The new value of the variable ΣX is the sum: $\Sigma X + X_1 = 0 + 12 = 12$. Following this addition, the first iteration is complete as the flow returns to the decision statement and i is compared with N. Since $i = 1$ is less than $N = 100$, another iteration is indicated and the corresponding branch leads vertically downward. In the next step the subscript i takes on the value $i = 1 + 1 = 2$. After i is incremented, the variable ΣX takes on the value $\Sigma X = \Sigma X + X_2 = 12 + 8 = 20$.

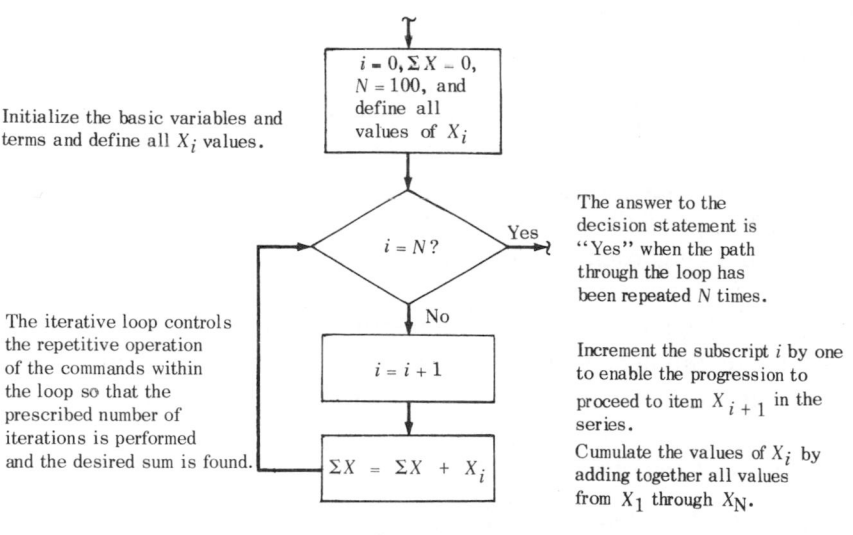

Initialize the basic variables and terms and define all X_i values.

$i = 0, \Sigma X = 0,$ $N = 100$, and define all values of X_i

$i = N?$

The answer to the decision statement is "Yes" when the path through the loop has been repeated N times.

The iterative loop controls the repetitive operation of the commands within the loop so that the prescribed number of iterations is performed and the desired sum is found.

$i = i + 1$

$\Sigma X = \Sigma X + X_i$

Increment the subscript i by one to enable the progression to proceed to item X_{i+1} in the series.

Cumulate the values of X_i by adding together all values from X_1 through X_N.

Figure 5.3

A PARTIAL ALGORITHM FOR FINDING THE THE SUM
OF 100 VALUES OF X

Following this operation, the flow returns to the decision statement and the second iteration is complete as i is compared with N and the appropriate branch is taken.

Iterations are continued until $i = N$ and the "Yes" branch leads the flow of the sequence away from the loop. On the final or N^{th} iteration through the loop, i takes on a value of N, and the value of item X_N is added to the value of the variable ΣX so that in the final iteration, $\Sigma X = 0 + X_1 + X_2 + \ldots + X_{100} = 0 + 12 + 8 + 16 + 5 + 11 + \ldots + 18$. With the addition of the X_{100} item to the previous values in the series, the sum of the items is obtained, and the progression through the series is complete.

The process by which a variable such as ΣX takes on a series of values until the desired value is obtained is perhaps better understood if it is related to what takes place in the memory of a computer on which the algorithm is programmed. The name of a variable corresponds to a position or a section of the memory of a computer. In this fashion the variable name is the address or location of the portion of memory in which a numerical value is to be stored. In the process of performing the sequence of arithmetic operations, the performance of a command such as "$\Sigma X = \Sigma X + X_i$" is interpreted as "Store in the memory location designated ΣX the sum of the numerical value presently in that location and the value in the memory location designated X_i, where i has a specified value for each iteration or stage of the sequence." In this manner, during the fourth iteration in the foregoing example the execution of the command, "$\Sigma X = \Sigma X + X_i$," results in the value stored in memory location X_4 being added to the numerical value stored in memory location denoted ΣX. As the result of the first three iterations, the value accumulated in memory position ΣX is $12 + 8 + 16 = 36$. On the fourth iteration, the value 5 is added to the sum 36 and the result, 41, is stored in the memory location designated ΣX. The value stored in this location is changed during each iteration until the sum of all X_i values has been found.

The iterative loop is one of the most powerful and versatile concepts of modern computers. It makes possible the performance of many arithmetic operations of a repetitive nature with just a handful of commands.

Terminals and Connectors

Terminals. The beginning and the end of a flow diagram are denoted by a symbol called a *terminal*. This symbol, shaped like a rectangle with rounded ends, is used to mark the start of a computational sequence or to indicate that a solution has been reached.

➤ *Example.* The arithmetic mean of a series of 100 values of the variable X is to be determined from the equation

$$\mu = \frac{\Sigma X}{N}.$$

The partial algorithm in Figure 5.3 shows the sequence for finding the sum of a series of values of X. After all the necessary steps are determined, the complete flow diagram for finding the mean is shown in Figure 5.4. (The special symbol used to designate the summation sequence is explained fully in the next section.)

Connectors. Flow diagrams for complex algorithms are lengthy and cannot be shown easily on a single page. The end of one portion of a flow diagram and the beginning of the next portion are designated by a circle called a *connector*. Each connector should be identified by a symbol within the circle. For example, the *exit* from, or the end of, the first portion of a flow diagram may be designated by the connector

The *entry* to, or the resumption of, the flow diagram is denoted by the connector

for which the symbol in the entry connector matches the exit connector.

Subroutines

A substantial number of statistical methods can be viewed, from a computational standpoint, as a collection of basic subsequences, with each method being a combination of certain subsequences. For example, the flow diagram in Figure 5.4 makes use of the summation subsequence shown in Figure 5.3. Summations are a basic part of a number of statistical methods. Having developed the detailed steps for finding a summation, one can use a single symbol to refer to a basic predetermined subsequence, as in Figure 5.4. A basic subsequence is called a *subroutine*. Some of the more common subroutines, used in conjunction with numerical methods, are subsequences for finding square roots, factorials, trigonometric values, logarithms, reciprocals, and exponentials.

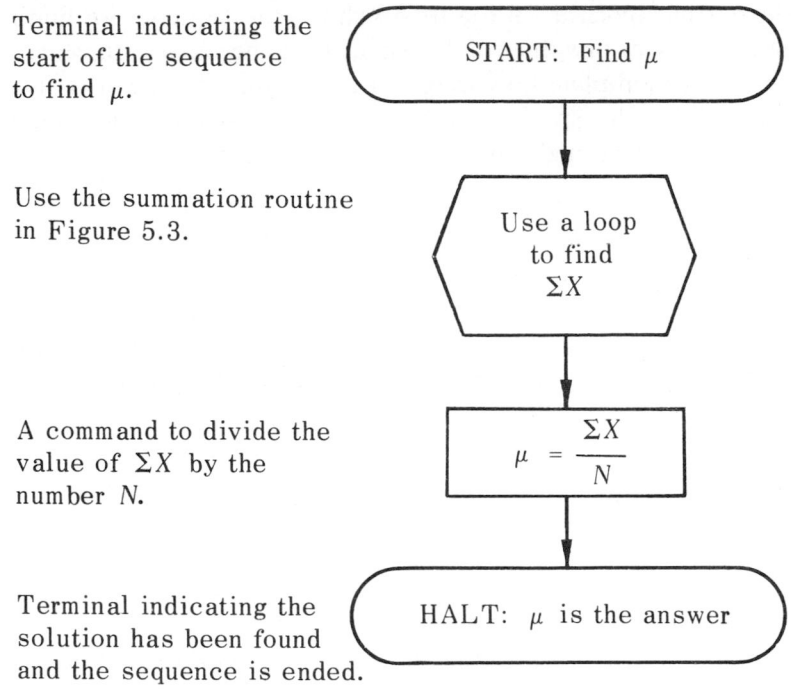

Terminal indicating the start of the sequence to find μ.

Use the summation routine in Figure 5.3.

A command to divide the value of ΣX by the number N.

Terminal indicating the solution has been found and the sequence is ended.

START: Find μ

Use a loop to find ΣX

$\mu = \dfrac{\Sigma X}{N}$

HALT: μ is the answer

Figure 5.4

A FLOW DIAGRAM OF AN ALGORITHM FOR FINDING THE MEAN OF 100 VALUES OF X

The symbol for a subroutine or a predetermined subsequence is a hexagon. For example,

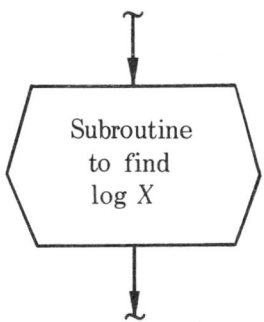

Subroutine to find $\log X$

denotes the sequence of steps necessary for finding the logarithm of a value of the variable X.

➤ *Example.* A subroutine for finding the square root of a number can be written as an iterative procedure, which makes successive approximations until the answer is sufficiently accurate. The relationship for finding the square root of a number x is given by

$$y_{i+1} = \tfrac{1}{2}\left(y_i + \frac{x}{y_i}\right)$$

where y_{i+1} and y_i are approximations of the square root of x. Assume that x is greater than one and an initial guess, y_0, at the square root is made. Successive approximations are to be made until the absolute value of $y_{i+1} - y_i$ is less than some minimum specified value. Let E denote the maximum allowable difference or error in successive approximations.

Assume that an approximation of $\sqrt{3}$ is desired so that the estimate is accurate to four decimal places. The values of the basic terms for this case are $x = 3$, and $E = 0.0001$. Since $\sqrt{3}$ is greater than one, the initial estimate is arbitrarily assumed to be $y_0 = 1$. An estimate of $\sqrt{3}$ is sufficiently accurate if $|y_{i+1} - y_i| < E$.

The sequence of arithmetic operations for finding $\sqrt{x}$ is shown in Figure 5.5 and the values of the various terms for each iteration are shown in Table 5.1. For instance, the estimate of $\sqrt{3}$ obtained by the first iteration of the algorithm, for which $i = 0$ and $i + 1 = 1$, is found by solving

$$y_1 - \tfrac{1}{2}\left(y_0 + \frac{x}{y_0}\right) = \tfrac{1}{2}\left(1.000000 + \frac{3.000000}{1.000000}\right) = 2.000000.$$

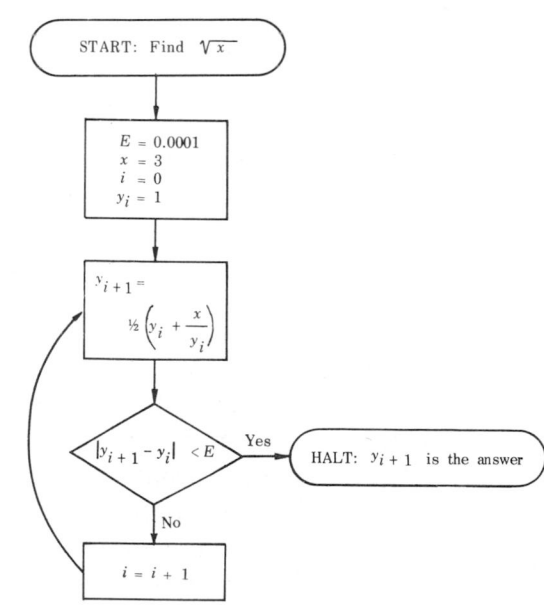

Initialize the algorithm by assigning values to the basic terms.

A command to find the value of the y_{i+1} approximation of $\sqrt{x}$

A decision statement to determine if the y_{i+1} approximation is within the acceptable error range.

Increment the subscript of y so that y_i will now take on the value formerly called y_{i+1}.

START: Find $\sqrt{x}$

$E = 0.0001$
$x = 3$
$i = 0$
$y_i = 1$

$y_{i+1} = \tfrac{1}{2}\left(y_i + \frac{x}{y_i}\right)$

$|y_{i+1} - y_i| < E$ Yes → HALT: y_{i+1} is the answer

No

$i = i + 1$

Figure 5.5

A SUBROUTINE FOR FINDING AN ESTIMATE OF $\sqrt{x}$

Table 5.1

VALUES OF THE BASIC TERMS FOR THE ITERATIONS

FOR APPROXIMATING $\sqrt{3}$

Iteration (i)	Current estimate (y_i)	New estimate (y_{i+1})	Approximation error $\|y_{i+1} - y_i\|$
0	1.000000	2.000000	1.000000
1	2.000000	1.750000	0.250000
2	1.750000	1.732143	0.017857
3	1.732143	1.732051	0.000092

The new approximation is compared with the current estimate to determine if the difference is within the allowable degree of error by computing

$$\|y_{i+1} - y_i\| = \|2.000000 - 1.000000\| = 1.000000.$$

Since the difference in the estimates of $\sqrt{3}$ is greater than E, an additional iteration is indicated. The estimate obtained by the second iteration, for which $i = 1$ and $i + 1 = 2$, is obtained by solving

$$y_2 = \tfrac{1}{2}\left(y_1 + \frac{x}{y_1}\right) = \tfrac{1}{2}\left(2.000000 + \frac{3.000000}{2.000000}\right) = 1.750000.$$

The desired estimate of $\sqrt{3}$ is obtained on the iteration for which the absolute value of the difference between the third and the fourth computed estimates is less than E, or $0.000092 < 0.000100$, as seen in Table 5.1.

➤ *Example.* The value of $n! = n(n - 1)(n - 2)\ldots(n - n + 1)$, read "$n$ factorial," can be determined as a subroutine. The flow diagram shown in Figure 5.6 shows the method of finding 25!

The algorithm in Figure 5.6 begins with a terminal statement which specifies that the value of $n!$ is to be computed, and proceeds to define the initial values of the basic terms. The next logical step consists of determining whether n is equal to zero. If so, the value of $n!$ is equal to one by definition. In this example, $n = 25$; consequently, the answer to $n = 0?$ is "No," and the corresponding branch indicates the next step. This step is a decision statement that asks if the current value of the variable i is equal to n. Since i currently has a value of one, the answer is "No" and the next step is indicated by the respective branch.

The next logical step consists of incrementing the value of i by one. This is done to allow an orderly progression of the value of i from its initial value to the value of n. For each value of i, the corresponding factorial is computed, so that when $i = n$, the desired factorial is obtained.

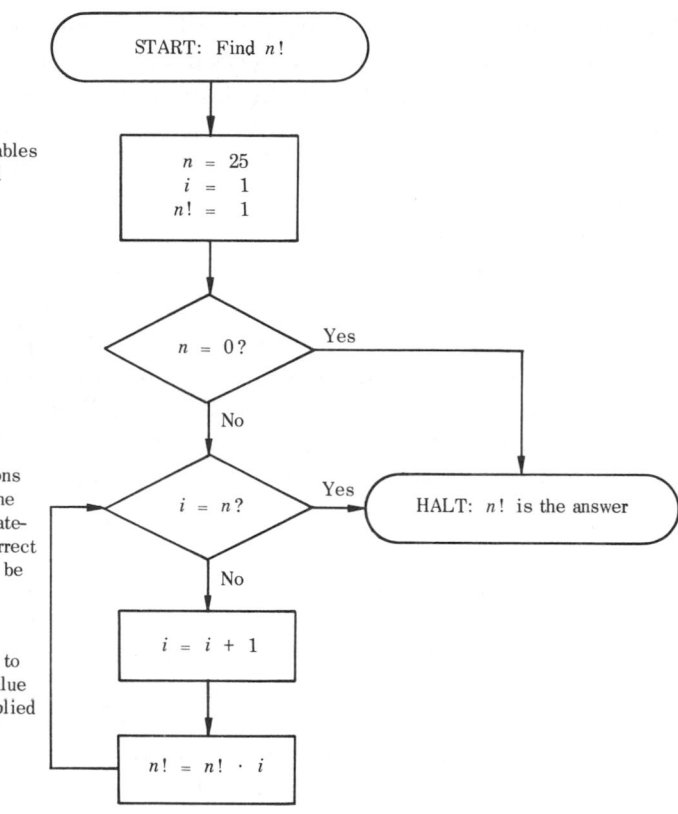

Initialize the basic variables by giving specific initial values.

The decision statement determines if the value of n is zero; if so, $n! = 1$ is the answer.

If $n \neq 0$, then n iterations are to be made through the loop and the decision statement assures that the correct number of iterations will be made.

Increment the value of i to obtain the next higher value in the sequence of multiplied values to find $n!$

Figure 5.6

A SUBROUTINE FOR FINDING $n!$

The first time i is incremented, it is defined as taking on the new value $i = 1 + 1 = 2$. The next logical step is an arithmetic statement that calls for the computation $n! \cdot i = 1 \cdot 2 = 2$. At this stage a value of $n!$ has been obtained, but since i is less than 25, the factorial that has been computed is not the desired value. The computation just performed is equivalent to computing $2! = 2 \cdot 1 = 2$. After a value of $n!$ has been found, the flow of logic proceeds to the decision statement to ask if "$i = n?$" Now the first iteration of the loop is completed. Since $i = 2$ at this point, the answer is "No," and the flow of logic proceeds downwards a second time. On the second iteration, i takes on a value of $i = 2 + 1 = 3$ and the value of $n!$ is computed by multiplying the previous value of $n!$ by the current value of i. In this manner, $n!$ takes on the value $n! = n! \cdot i = 2 \cdot 3 = 6$. Notice that $n!$ is the factorial of the current value of the variable i and the computation of this value is equivalent to finding $3! = 3 \cdot 2 \cdot 1 = 6$.

Succeeding values of $n!$ are found by continuing the iterations in the loop until the condition $i = n$ is satisfied, at which time the desired value of $n!$ is obtained and the loop is terminated. For example, suppose that the iterations have progressed to the point that $i = 24$. Since 24 is less than the defined value of n, the logical sequence proceeds to the arithmetic statement for incrementing i so that i takes on the value of $i = 24 + 1 = 25$. A new value of $n!$ is then computed by multiplying the current value of $n!$ by the incremented value of i, or $n! = 24! \cdot 25 = 25!$ The new value of $n!$ is equivalent to the product, $1 \cdot 2 \cdot 3 \cdot \ldots \cdot 23 \cdot 24 \cdot 25 = 25!$ The desired value of $n!$ is obtained, in effect, by multiplying all the values of i together by successive iterations. Finally, the decision statement controlling the loop is reached again. This time, however, the answer to the question "$i = n$?" is positive. Thus, the loop is terminated as the flow of logic proceeds to the terminal signaling a halt to the computations.

➤ *Example.* The smallest of a series of n numbers, denoted X_1, $X_2, \ldots, X_n$, is to be determined. While the smallest value of X in the series may occur more than once, this value nevertheless is unique and is to be determined. The process consists of starting with the first of a series of numbers and comparing it with succeeding values until a smaller value of X is found. The smaller value is then compared with the remaining values in the series, and so forth, until the minimum value is found. This logical sequence is shown as a subroutine in Figure 5.7 for $n = 100$ values of X.

With one slight modification, the subroutine in Figure 5.7 can be used to find the maximum value in a series of numbers. The necessary change is made in the decision statement, which asks is $X_i < X_{\min}$? By reversing the inequality at this point so that the decision statement appears as

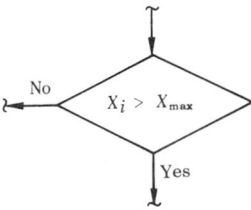

the maximum value of a sequence can then be found.

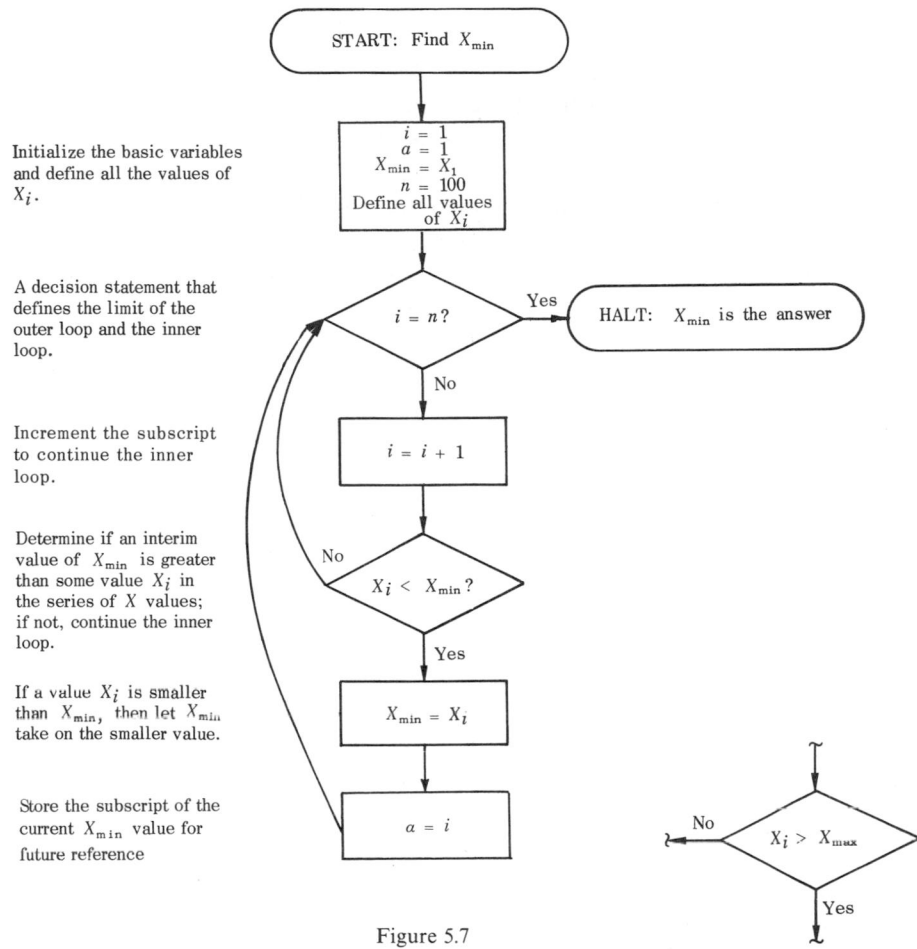

Figure 5.7

A SUBROUTINE FOR FINDING THE MINIMUM OF A SERIES OF VALUES

FLOW DIAGRAMS OF SOME STATISTICAL METHODS

The computational techniques of some statistical methods, such as the shortcut methods for finding the arithmetic mean, the standard deviation, and the coefficient of correlation for grouped data, are specially designed to facilitate manual calculations. These methods have become obsolete in view of the computational capability of computers, but there are many useful applications of data arrangement or grouping in conjunction with computer solution of problems.

In this section, flow diagrams are illustrated for several selected statistical methods that are presented in this text.

Statistical Array

The degree of variation or range in a series of observations of a variable cannot be discerned readily if the data are ordered randomly. Raw data do not indicate clearly the nature of the distribution of items between the largest and the smallest values of a series. An array, a special arrangement of items usually in ascending order of magnitude, is useful for visualizing the pattern of variation in a series of data.

A flow diagram of a procedure for placing a random sequence of N values of a variable X into an ascending array is shown in Figure 5.8.

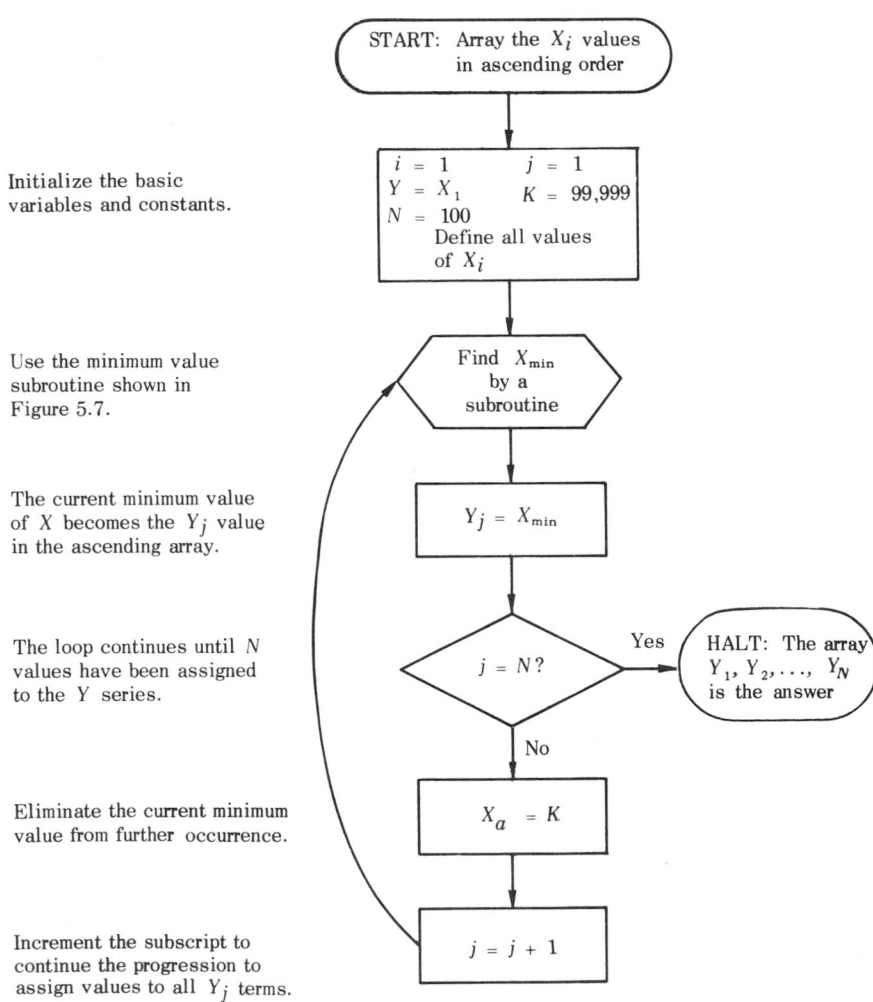

Figure 5.8

AN ALGORITHM FOR MAKING AN ARRAY OF VALUES IN ASCENDING ORDER

The technique for making the array begins by utilizing the subroutine for finding the minimum value of a series, as shown in Figure 5.7. The minimum value of the random sequence is determined by the subroutine and is designated as the first value Y_1 of the array. Since this smallest value has been determined and should not be considered again, its value is changed to a very large positive number K such as 99,999, which is larger than any X value in the series. The subroutine is again employed to find the minimum value of the remainder of the original random series, and this value is designated as the second value Y_2 in the ascending array. The X_i value corresponding to Y_2 is set equal to K, and the loop is repeated until Y_N has been determined.

The power and the versatility of the use of loops are demonstrated in this application. One loop is used to determine the minimum value of a series and a second loop is employed to assign each of the values in the random series to an appropriate position in the ascending array. Perhaps, aside from the incredible arithmetic speed of computers, the use of loops within loops best demonstrates why computers are used for solving problems of any significant size or complexity.

Frequency Distribution

A flow diagram of constructing a frequency distribution demonstrates the use of a compound sequence of decision statements. While the determination of the frequency distribution of a single group of data is usually a manual operation, the use of a computer might be justified if many different distributions are to be determined.

If the class limits of a frequency distribution have been determined previously, then the frequencies of each class can be found in a straight-forward fashion as seen in Figure 5.9. Assume there are n items to be classified into five class intervals, with upper limits denoted $L_1, L_2, \ldots, L_5$. The frequencies are found by comparing each of the items, a value of the variable X, with the class limits, beginning with the smallest of the limits. By successive comparison, the correct interval is found for the observation. In this manner, a distribution with class limits of the type "equal to but under" is developed.

If the class limits are not given, a frequency distribution can be found by use of Sturges' Rule[1] for determining the number of classes, by setting the class limits, and by utilizing the sequence in Figure 5.9. A detailed flow chart of this procedure is left as an exercise.

---

[1]Sturges' Rule for determining the number of classes is explained on page 17 of Chapter 1.

START: Find the frequencies of a distribution

Initialize the basic variables and constants and define the values of X_i.

$i = 1$	
$f_1 = 0$	The values of
$f_2 = 0$	$L_1, L_2, \ldots, L_5$
$f_3 = 0$	are specified and
$f_4 = 0$	the values of X_i
$f_5 = 0$	and n are defined.

Determine if X_i is an item in the first interval; if so, add one to the frequency. If not, continue the loop by making a series of similar decisions until the X_i value corresponds to one of the intervals and the corresponding frequency is incremented.

$X_i < L_1$? —Yes→ $f_1 = f_1 + 1$

No

$X_i < L_2$? —Yes→ $f_2 = f_2 + 1$

No

$X_i < L_3$? —Yes→ $f_3 = f_3 + 1$

No

$X_i < L_4$? —Yes→ $f_4 = f_4 + 1$

No

$f_5 = f_5 + 1$

Increment the subscript to continue the loop.

$i = i + 1$

Terminate the loop when all n values have been assigned to the proper intervals.

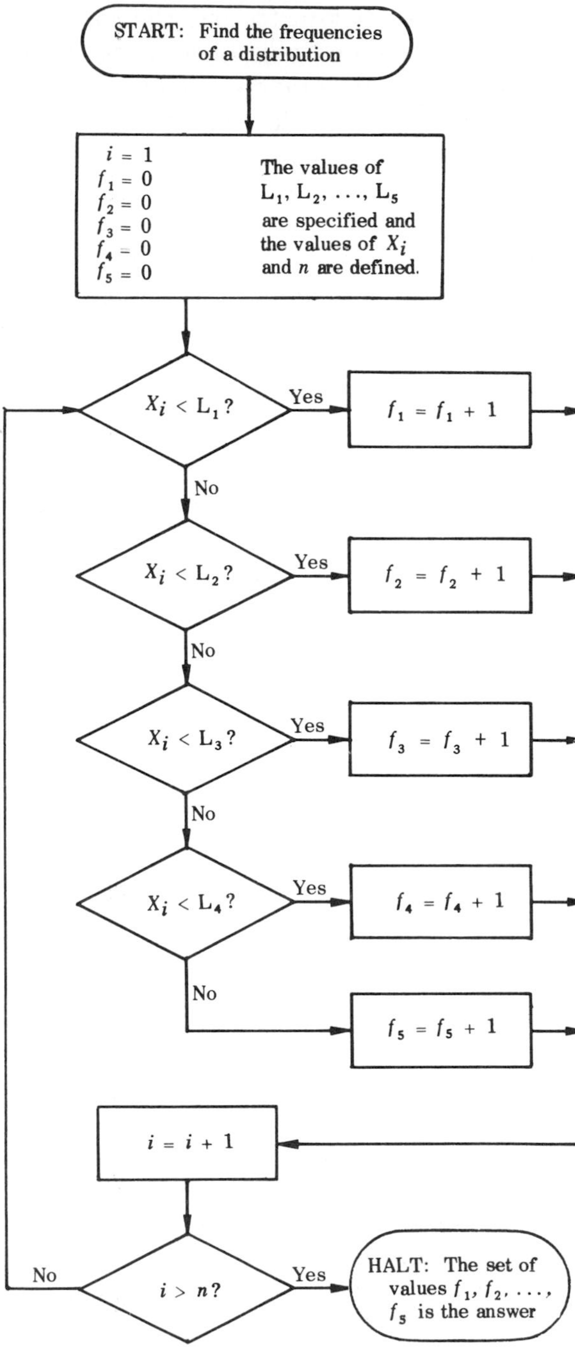

No ← $i > n$? —Yes→ HALT: The set of values $f_1, f_2, \ldots, f_5$ is the answer

Figure 5.9

AN ALGORITHM FOR FINDING THE FREQUENCIES
OF FIVE CLASS INTERVALS

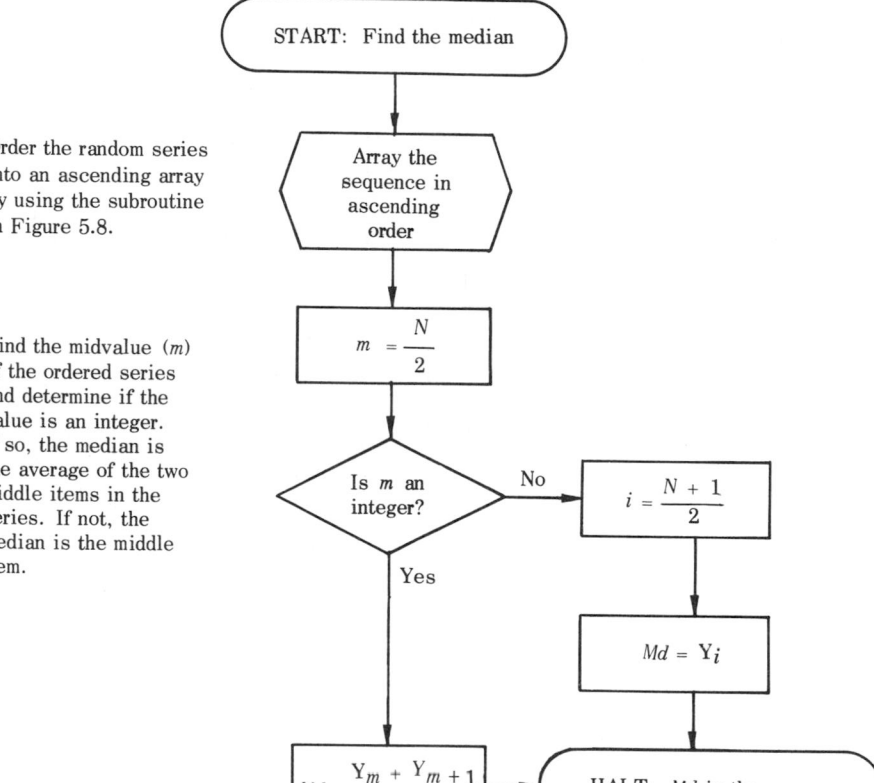

Order the random series into an ascending array by using the subroutine in Figure 5.8.

Find the midvalue (m) of the ordered series and determine if the value is an integer. If so, the median is the average of the two middle items in the series. If not, the median is the middle item.

Figure 5.10

AN ALGORITHM FOR FINDING THE MEDIAN OF A RANDOM SERIES

Median

The median of a random sequence of N values of a variable X can be found by using a procedure such as that shown in the flow diagram in Figure 5.10. The data are first arrayed as shown in the subroutine of Figure 5.8. The next step is to determine if N is odd or even. If N is odd, then $\frac{N}{2}$ is not an integer, and the middle value of the array is the median. For an even value of N, $\frac{N}{2}$ is an integer, and the value of the median is determined as the average of the two middle values of the array.

Moments

The moments of a frequency distribution are useful for describing the dispersion, skewness, or peakedness of the distribution. The values of

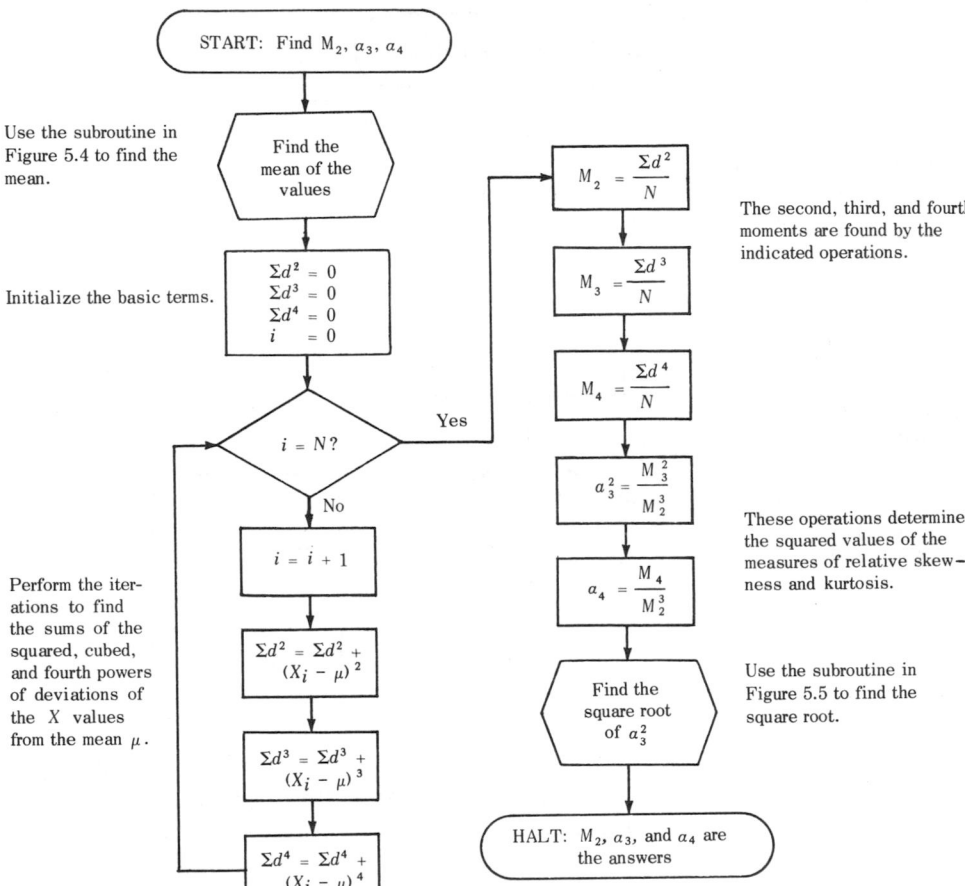

Figure 5.11

AN ALGORITHM FOR FINDING MEASURES OF VARIANCE, SKEWNESS,
AND KURTOSIS

M_2, α_3, and α_4 (see Formulas 3.18, 3.21, and 3.26) can be determined by the operational sequence chart shown by the flow chart in Figure 5.11. The procedure to be followed is to find the arithmetic mean and then the sum of the squared, cubed, and fourth powers of the deviations from the mean. The sums are averaged, and the measures of relative skewness and kurtosis are determined as the square roots of the ratios of the squares or cubes of the absolute measures.

Polynomials

The analysis of trends in time series data, discussed in Chapter 19, utilizes polynomials for expressing the pattern of change in a series of data over a period of time. In a somewhat similar fashion, regression analysis of the variation of two variables, a principal topic of Chapter 16, leads to the development of a relationship expressed as a polynomial. The polynomial that best expresses the relationship between variables may be of the first order (the linear case) or higher (curvilinear). For purposes of the present discussion, only first-order polynomials relating two variables are considered.

A first-order polynomial is expressed in general form by $y_c = a + bx$, where a and b are constants, y_c is the computed value of the dependent variable, and x is the independent variable. The values of a and b are determined by the method of least squares, which assures that the line defined by the constants is the best linear expression of the average relationship between y and x. The method for finding the values of a and b is derived in Chapter 16, in which the linear equations

$$\Sigma y = na + b\Sigma x$$

$$\Sigma xy = a\Sigma x + b\Sigma x^2$$

are solved in terms of a and b. In this manner,

$$a = \frac{\Sigma y \Sigma x^2 - \Sigma xy \Sigma x}{n\Sigma x^2 - (\Sigma x)^2} \quad \text{and} \quad b = \frac{n\Sigma xy - \Sigma x \Sigma y}{n\Sigma x^2 - (\Sigma x)^2}.$$

A linear trend may be computed for a series of data, say the gross sales of a business, y, for a period of n years, x. Given the sales data and the respective years, a trend in sales of the form $y_c = a + bx$ can be computed by the procedure shown in Figure 5.12. The appropriate sums, squares, sums of squares, and products are determined so that the constants of the equation may be found.

Since the linear trend or regression line is an average relationship, the equation $y_c = a + bx$ is not expected to determine a calculated value of y_c that corresponds exactly to the observed value of y for a given paired value of x. The standard deviation of the differences between y_c and y for the values of x is of considerable value in expressing the degree of precision with which y_c, on the average, tends to estimate y. Figure 5.13 shows a flow diagram for substituting the observed values of x into the equation $y_c = a + bx$, determining $(y - y_c)^2$, and finding the standard deviation of the differences, sometimes called the standard error of estimate, $S_{y \cdot x}$.

Methods for finding the constants of polynomials of a higher order than one require the simultaneous solution of as many linear equations as there are unknowns in the polynomial expression. The techniques of matrix algebra, which are especially useful for facilitating these calculations, are discussed in the following section.

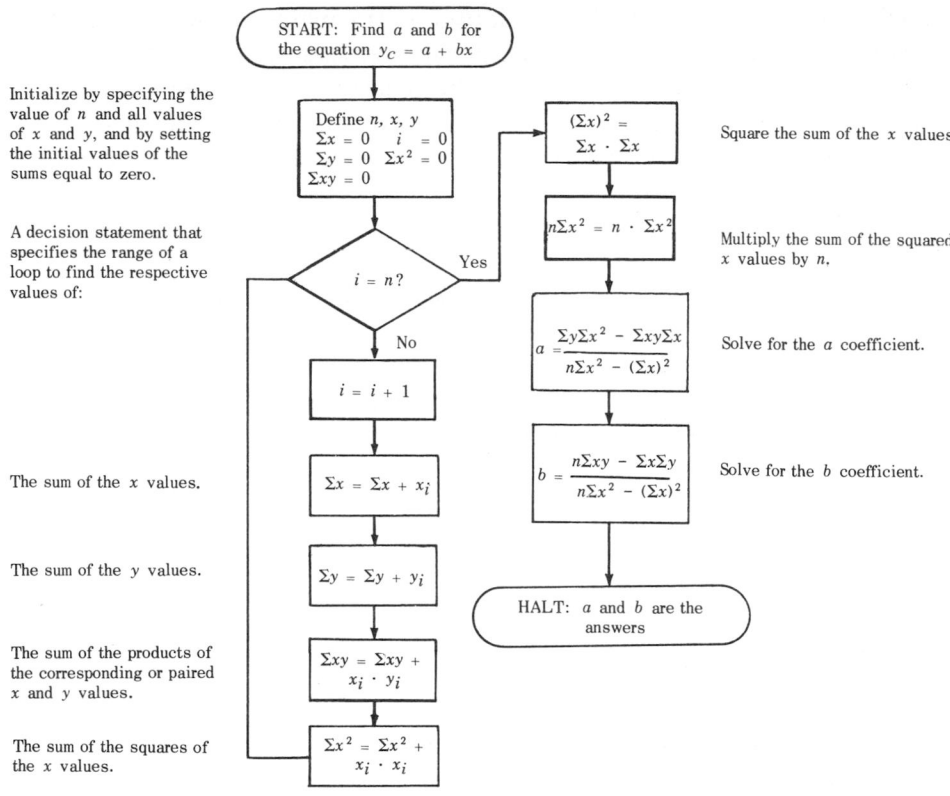

Initialize by specifying the value of n and all values of x and y, and by setting the initial values of the sums equal to zero.

A decision statement that specifies the range of a loop to find the respective values of:

The sum of the x values.

The sum of the y values.

The sum of the products of the corresponding or paired x and y values.

The sum of the squares of the x values.

Square the sum of the x values.

Multiply the sum of the squared x values by n.

Solve for the a coefficient.

Solve for the b coefficient.

Figure 5.12

AN ALGORITHM FOR FINDING THE COEFFICIENTS OF A FIRST-ORDER POLYNOMIAL BY THE METHOD OF LEAST SQUARES

Computations Involving a Matrix of Data

Several statistical methods involve data arranged in a rectangular array called a *matrix*. A matrix consists of data arranged in rows and columns as a means of presenting categories of data in a convenient form.

➤ *Example.* The values obtained in selecting a sample of nine parts produced by each of eight identical machines and measuring the diameter of the parts are shown in matrix form in Table 5.2. This table is shown in general form where x_{ij} denotes any selected sample observation, i designates a selected row (sample item), and j identifies a selected column (sample) in which the selected observation occurs. The subscript i, in this example, may take on a value in the range from one to nine, inclusive. The subscript j can assume any value in the range from one to eight, inclusive.

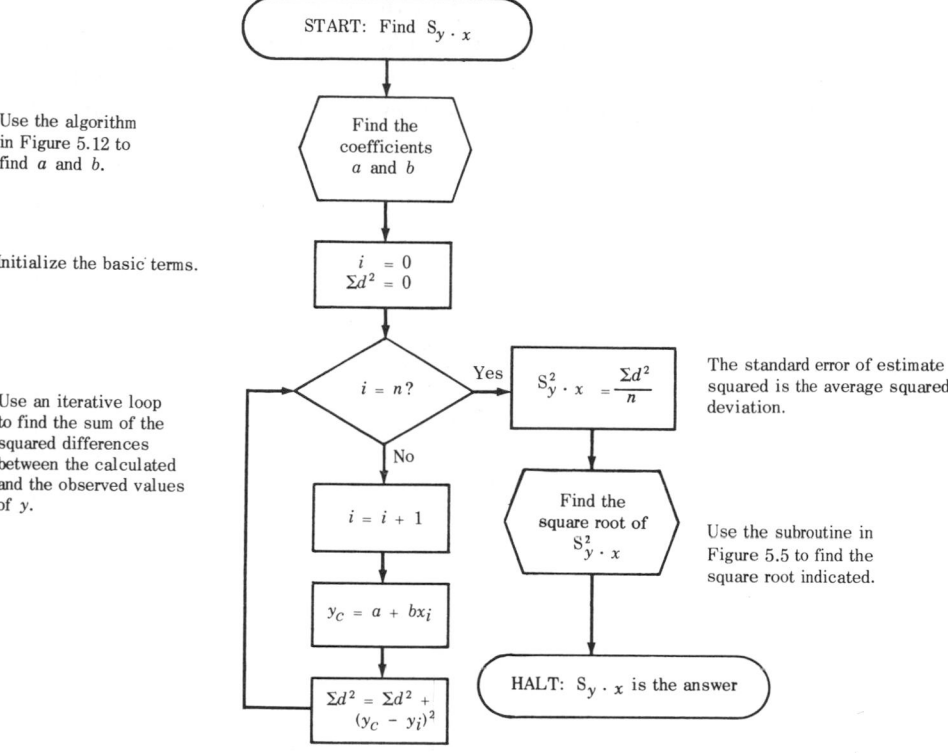

Use the algorithm
in Figure 5.12 to
find *a* and *b*.

Initialize the basic terms.

Use an iterative loop
to find the sum of the
squared differences
between the calculated
and the observed values
of *y*.

The standard error of estimate
squared is the average squared
deviation.

Use the subroutine in
Figure 5.5 to find the
square root indicated.

Figure 5.13

AN ALGORITHM FOR FINDING THE STANDARD ERROR OF ESTIMATE

Table 5.2

A GENERAL FORM OF A MATRIX OF DATA
OF SEVERAL SAMPLES

Sample item	Sample number						
	1	2	3	...	j	...	8
1	x_{11}	x_{12}	x_{13}	...	x_{1j}	...	x_{18}
2	x_{21}	x_{22}	x_{23}	...	x_{2j}	...	x_{28}
3	x_{31}	x_{32}	x_{33}	...	x_{3j}	...	x_{38}
.	.	.	.	...	.	...	.
.	.	.	.	...	.	...	.
.	.	.	.	...	.	...	.
i	x_{i1}	x_{i2}	x_{i3}	...	x_{ij}	...	x_{i8}
.	.	.	.	...	.	...	.
.	.	.	.	...	.	...	.
9	x_{91}	x_{92}	x_{93}	...	x_{9j}	...	x_{98}
TOTALS	$\sum_i x_{i1}$	$\sum_i x_{i2}$	$\sum_i x_{i3}$	...	$\sum_i x_{ij}$	...	$\sum_i x_{i8}$

Some representative arithmetic operations that might be applied to the matrix of observations shown in Table 5.2 include the computation of the mean of each sample (column) and the grand mean (all sampled items). The algorithm for computing these statistics, shown in Figure 5.14, demonstrates a very important use of loops.

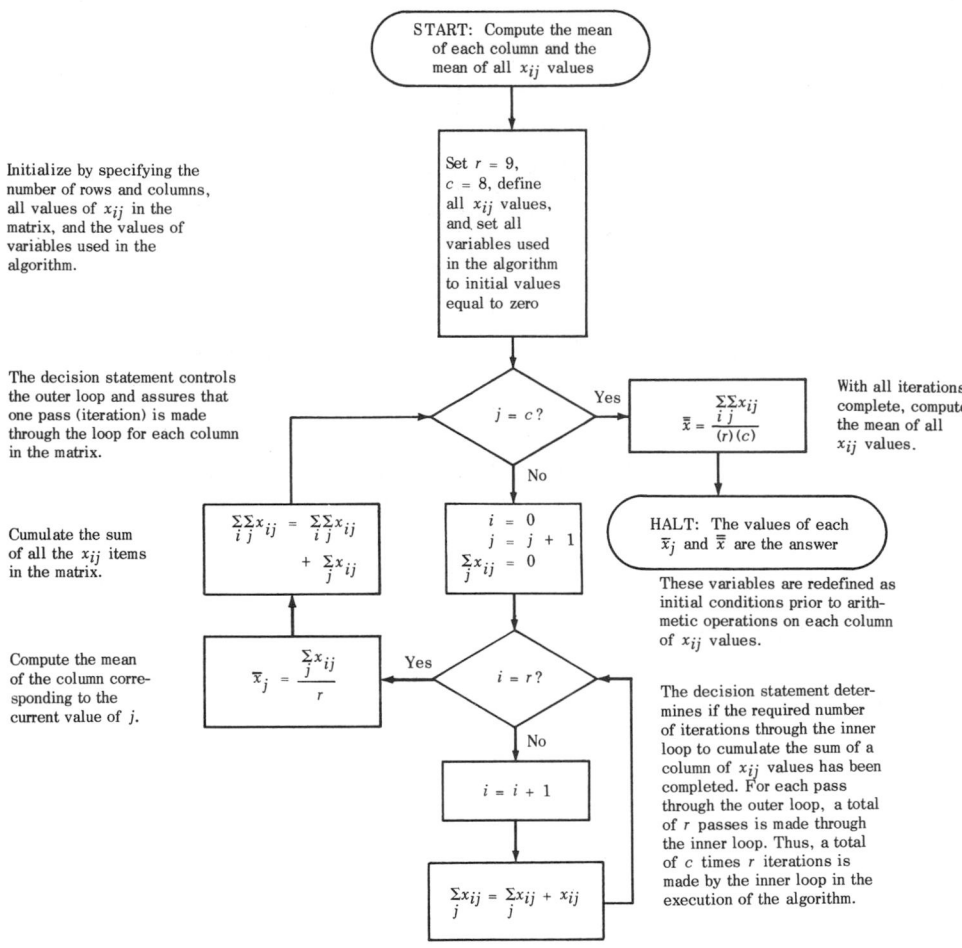

Figure 5.14

AN ALGORITHM FOR COMPUTING THE COLUMN MEANS AND THE
MEAN OF ALL THE VALUES IN A MATRIX OF NINE ROWS AND
EIGHT COLUMNS

In computing the column means manually, one procedure might be to sum the items in each column and divide by the number of items in the column. Next, the grand mean can be found by adding the column sums and dividing the total number of items in all samples. This approach is shown in Figure 5.14. The inner loop, controlled by the decision statement "$i = r$?", provides for the accumulation of a column sum. The outer loop is controlled by the decision statement "$j = c$?" and shows the steps for computing each column mean and the accumulation of the sum of all sampled items.

With the initial conditions defined, the first iteration through the outer loop begins with $j = 0$. Therefore, the response to the decision statement is "No," and the flow of logic follows the corresponding branch. The next step consists of an arithmetic statement that increments the subscript j and sets two basic variables equal to zero as initial conditions for iterations in the inner loop. Next, the subscript i is compared with r. Since the quantities are not equal, the flow of logic is via the "No" branch to the arithmetic statement in which i is incremented. At this point $i = 1$ and $j = 1$. Proceeding to the next arithmetic statement in the inner loop, the value of the item of data denoted x_{11} is added to the value of the variable designated $\sum_j x_{ij}$, which now takes on the value $\sum_j x_{ij} = 0 + x_{11}$. The first iteration through the inner loop is complete as the flow of logic returns to the decision statement that asks if "$i = r$?" For a value of r greater than one, the answer is negative and the second iteration is begun by incrementing i so that $i = 1 + 1 = 2$. At this stage, $i = 2$ and $j = 1$. Proceeding to the next arithmetic statement, the variable $\sum_j x_{ij}$ takes on a value equal to the sum of the first two items in the first column, or $\sum_j x_{ij} = x_{11} + x_{21}$.

In a similar manner, the sum of all the items in column one of Table 5.2 is found when $i = r$, the required number of iterations through the inner loop is complete, and the computational sequence follows the "Yes" branch to the outer loop.

The first arithmetic statement calls for the computation of the mean of the first column. In the next statement a variable denoted $\sum_i \sum_j x_{ij}$ takes on a value equal to its present (initial) value plus the sum of the items in the first column so that $\sum_i \sum_j x_{ij} = \sum_i \sum_j x_{ij} + \sum_j x_{ij} = 0 + \sum_1 x_{ij}$. Following this computation, the first iteration through the outer loop is complete. Since $j = 1$ at this stage and is less than c, a second iteration is indicated. The computational sequence is continued by incrementing j, so that $j = 1 + 1 = 2$, and setting i and $\sum x_{ij}$ equal to zero. The latter variables are again set to zero since the sum of the items in the second column is to be computed. Successive iterations are made through the inner loop until $i = r$ and the flow of logic proceeds to the outer loop, where the mean of the items in the second column is computed. Next, the sum of the items in the second column is added to the current value of the

variable $\Sigma\Sigma x_{ij}$, which now takes on a value equal to the sum of the items
　　　　$i\ j$
in the first two columns, or $\underset{i\ j}{\Sigma\Sigma} x_{ij} = \underset{1}{\Sigma} x_{ij} + \underset{2}{\Sigma} x_{ij}$.

The second iteration through the outer loop is complete as the flow again reaches the decision statement.

Iterations are continued through the outer loop until $j = c$. For each iteration through the outer loop, a total of r iterations is completed in the inner loop. The double-loop arrangement insures that the desired arithmetic operations are performed with each of the total number (r times c) of x_{ij} values in the matrix.

By use of multiple loops, a very large number of calculations can be performed with relatively few statements. The use of multiple loops provides one of the best insights into the versatility and capacity of computers for performing extensive arithmetic operations for solving problems.

NUMERICAL ANALYSIS

Numerical analysis is a rapidly developing branch of mathematics that is concerned with finding solutions to problems by successive approximations. Many of the recent developments in science and engineering involve problems that can best be solved by approximation methods. Exact solutions are not available for some problems, while for other problems it is more efficient to find the solution each time it is needed rather than to store and search for desired values.

Numerical analysis has been utilized since the beginning of applied science, but the most significant period of use began with the digital computer. In the past, potential applications of numerical methods were unfeasible because of prohibitive manual calculations. With access to the prodigious computational capability of modern computers, more numerical methods are now feasible, and in many instances are looked upon as basic methods that are commonly used.

Methods of numerical analysis are computational sequences that involve the repeated application of the four basic arithmetic operations. For this reason, flow diagrams are especially useful for presenting the logic of these methods. One of these methods is presented in Figure 5.5, which shows a method for finding the square root of a number by repetitive application of some elementary operations. The derivation of a polynomial equation by the method of least squares involves the solution of simultaneous linear equations. This procedure is one of the fundamental methods of numerical analysis.

Techniques of numerical analysis touch on a broad range of mathematical topics, and a substantial number of these methods are useful in the solution of statistical problems. Conversely, statistical methods are especially useful when experimental data are limited or expensive to obtain. Sample data provide descriptive statistics for use as parameter estimates in problem formulations. The reliability of inferences concerning the relationships between variables can be determined from statistical data. Experimental design, regression methods, and analysis of variances are powerful tools for examining the complex relationships between two or more variables. These statistical models are implemented by numerical methods. The results obtained may be substituted into other expressions that are, in turn, solved by successive approximations. The area of interaction between numerical analysis and statistics is sure to grow rapidly with continued research and development.

STUDY QUESTIONS

5-1. Explain briefly the meaning of each of the following terms:

        a. algorithm
        b. flow diagram
        c. library program
        d. flow direction symbol
        e. command
        f. definition
        g. decision statement
        h. branches
        i. loop
        j. iteration
        k. iterative process
        l. incrementing
        m. initializing
        n. terminal
        o. connector
        p. subroutine
        q. matrix
        r. numerical analysis

5-2. Identify the basic components of a flow diagram.

5-3. What are the advantages of using flow diagrams?

5-4. How are computer programs related to flow diagrams?

5-5. What is the function of a decision statement in a loop?

5-6. List three mathematical operations that you feel would be useful as subroutines. Use examples other than those cited in the chapter.

5-7. Compare and contrast statistical methods and numerical analysis.

5-8. Give an example of a problem that would involve three loops, where the first loop is the outer loop, the second loop lies within the outer loop, and the third loop lies within the second loop.

PROBLEMS

5-1. In a survey, data were compiled of the wages of workers X in various classifications and the number of workers in each class k. Prepare a flow diagram to find the weighted mean wage paid all surveyed personnel.

5-2. How can Sturges' Rule be applied to Figure 5.9 to make the algorithm of a more general nature and find the frequencies of any number of class intervals?

5-3. In Figure 5.10, the decision is made whether $m = \dfrac{N}{2}$ is an integer. Write a subroutine to determine if a number is an integer.

5-4. The trigonometric function sine x can be found by the approximating series

$$\text{sine } x = x - \frac{x^3}{3!} + \frac{x^5}{5!} - \frac{x^7}{7!} + \frac{x^9}{9!} - \frac{x^{11}}{11!} + \cdots$$

Write a flow diagram to find the sine of value of $x = 0.50$. The maximum allowable error is $E = 0.0001$.

5-5. Prepare a flow diagram of a subroutine to find the mean and the variance of a series of values of X.

5-6. An economic analyst wishes to average the rates of growth in the manufacturing sector of the economy for a period of years. Prepare a flow diagram for the appropriate algorithm to find the average.

5-7. The United States Bureau of the Census determines the median annual income for households for all counties in each state. Assume that the income data are grouped into class intervals such as "\$0 and under \$1,000," "\$1,000 and under \$2,000," and "\$2,000 and under \$3,000" and that all class intervals are equal. Prepare a flow diagram for an algorithm to find the median income per household.

5-8. The number of different five-card poker hands that can be dealt from a deck of cards is given by the expression

$$\frac{n!}{r!(n-r)!} = \frac{52!}{5!\,47!}.$$

Write a flow diagram to find the number of different possible poker hands.

5-9. A coin is tossed, and for each toss the outcome of a head is just as likely to occur as a tail. If the coin is tossed 10 times, the likelihood that heads will turn up six times is

$$P = \frac{10!}{6!(10 - 6)!} (.50)^6 (.50)^4.$$

Prepare a flow diagram to find P.

5-10. The number of vehicles passing a point on a turnpike is reported in hourly totals by a machine. The data for a six-week period are to be summarized by computing:
 a. The average number of vehicles per week.
 b. The average number of vehicles by day of the week.
Prepare an algorithm and a flow diagram to find these averages.

5-11. The president of a chain of cafeterias wishes a summary report made of the annual sales of each of the 20 cafeterias in the chain. The sales are reported in daily totals and the following averages are to be computed:
 a. Average sales per month per cafeteria.
 b. Average sales per week per cafeteria.
 c. Average sales per day of the week per cafeteria.
Prepare an algorithm and a flow chart to find these averages.

SELECTED READINGS

Carnahan, Brice, H. A. Luther, and James O. Wilkes. *Applied Numerical Methods*, Vol. II. Preliminary Edition. New York: John Wiley and Sons, 1964.
    An extensive list of statistical methods is presented in Chapter 8, along with discussions, example programs, and flow diagrams.
Kemeny, John G., Arthur Schleifer, Jr., J. Laurie Snell, and Gerald L. Thompson. *Finite Mathematics with Business Applications*. Englewood Cliffs, N. J.: Prentice-Hall, Inc., 1962.
    Concepts of flow diagrams, including types of statements illustrated by a number of example algorithms, are discussed in Chapter 3. Flow diagrams of more sophisticated problems are included in Chapter 4.
Ledley, Robert S. *Programming and Utilizing Digital Computers*. New York: McGraw-Hill Book Company, Inc., 1962.
    Excellent discussions of decisions, flow diagrams, loops, and subroutines are found in Chapter 2. An overview of numerical methods is presented in Chapter 9.
McCormick, John M., and Mario G. Salvadori. *Numerical Methods in FOR-TRAN*. Englewood Cliffs, N. J.: Prentice-Hall, Inc., 1964.
    The latter half of this book presents a large number of example programs in the FORTRAN algebraic language, flow diagrams, and discussions of applications of numerical methods.

McCracken, Daniel D., Harold Weiss, and Tsai-Hwa Lee. *Programming Business Computers*. 4th ed. New York: John Wiley and Sons, 1963.

    Flow charting notation for computer-oriented data processing problems is presented in Chapter 3.

Schmidt, Richard N., and William E. Meyers. *Electronic Business Data Processing*. New York: Holt, Rinehart, and Winston, 1963.

    An amplification of flow diagrams for data processing problems is presented in Chapters 16 and 17.

Chapter 6

Probability and Incremental Inventory Analysis

PROBABILITY AND STATISTICS

The descriptive statistics reviewed in Chapters 2 and 3 provide measures for summarizing a body of data. As mentioned earlier, a descriptive measure computed for a universe of data is known as a parameter; a descriptive measure calculated from a sample of data drawn from a universe is called a statistic. When complete data are not available, a sample statistic is used to estimate a universe parameter. The process of making estimates or inferences concerning the universe parameters is called *statistical inference*. Making an estimate of a universe parameter from a sample statistic involves uncertainty, for although the sample characteristics tend to reflect those of the universe, the estimate is not exact and some degree of error is expected. The risk of a specified degree of error in estimation is expressed in terms of a numerical probability. Similarly, if an inference concerning the universe is made from a sample statistic, the risk of a given degree of error can be expressed as a numerical probability.

Statistical inference, which is discussed in Part V, draws heavily upon the theory of probability, that link which relates the properties of a sample to those of the universe from which the sample is drawn. In order to consider statistical inference effectively, therefore, some knowledge of probability theory is necessary. Generally, probability theory enables one to draw conclusions about the probable composition of a sample of data based on a mathematical model of the universe. Statistical inference, on the other hand, is concerned with making an inference about a mathematical model of the composition of a universe on the basis of a sample statistic.

In essence, the study of probability poses three kinds of problems: (1) defining and interpreting what is meant by probability; (2) utilizing known probabilities to calculate others; and (3) obtaining numerical probabilities. This discussion is limited to a consideration of the first two problems; the third is discussed later in the chapters on estimation and inference. The scope of the present discussion is further limited to those topics of probability theory that are most helpful in understanding statistical inference. The focus is upon the meaning of probability and making deductions from the rules of probability. After some methods of counting are reviewed, probability theory — including topics from set theory, rules for calculating probabilities, revision of probabilities, and mathematical expectation — is presented in detail.

METHODS OF COUNTING

The elementary process of counting is very familiar, for frequently a businessman has occasion to count the number of items of a given kind of merchandise to determine whether to place an order for additional stock; a salesman may make a count of the number of calls made in a week to complete a report; or a foreman may count the number of machines in working order to schedule production. In each of these instances the items are arranged or listed so that a count may be made. While the process of counting used in many applications may be quite simple, it is nonetheless important, for the most sophisticated computations performed by a digital computer involve simple counting.

Counting becomes more complex, however, where the number of ways of arranging a set of items is to be determined. This type of counting problem is especially important in the study of probability. In this section we shall consider the general principles and shortcut methods for efficiently counting the arrangements of a set of items.

Permutations

The term *arrangement* is commonly used to describe a combination or a disposition of objects or things such as a floral arrangement, an arrangement of furniture, or the arrangements for a meeting. Of interest in this discussion, however, is a special kind of arrangement called a *permutation*, which may be defined as any ordered sequence of a group of things.

> ➤ *Example.* An automobile dealer wishing to place three new cars in a row in a display window wants to know the number of ways the cars, denoted *A*, *B*, and *C*, can be arranged. One method of solving this problem is to list and count all possible arrangements of the cars. The six possible arrangements or permutations are: *ABC*, *ACB*, *BAC*, *BCA*, *CAB*, and *CBA*.

An especially useful graphic means of presenting arrangements in an organized manner is called a *tree diagram*. A tree diagram of the previous example, as seen in Figure 6.1, shows the possible arrangements as

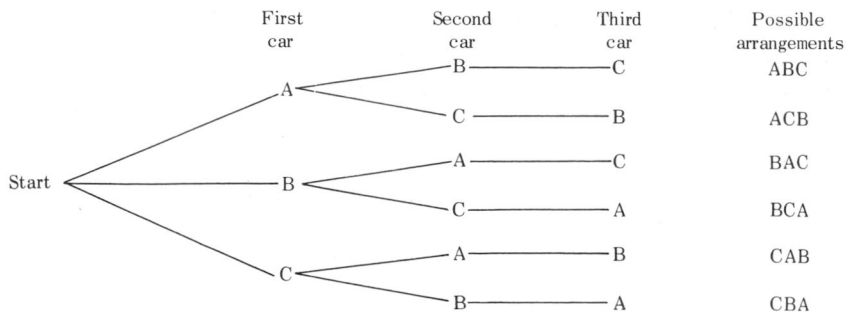

Figure 6.1

TREE DIAGRAM SHOWING THE PERMUTATIONS OF *ABC*

branches. Notice that the tree diagram shows every order in which the cars can be placed, and each change in order constitutes a different arrangement.

The Multiplication Principle. The number of permutations of three cars can be determined by an alternative method by considering the choices available at each step in selecting the cars. The tree diagram in Figure 6.1 indicates that there are three possible choices for selecting a car in the first step. Corresponding to each of the three ways for selecting the first car are two choices available in the second step, since either of the two remaining cars may be chosen. Thus, there are $3 \cdot 2 = 6$ ways of choosing the first two cars, as shown in Figure 6.1 under the column "Second car." After two cars have been selected, only one car remains for the third step. In summary, there are three ways of performing the first step, two ways of performing the second step, and one way of performing the third step. Thus, there are $3 \cdot 2 \cdot 1 = 6$ permutations or ways of selecting the cars.

Many counting problems involve more than three steps and the computation of the number of permutations requires considerable labor in listing and counting. Generalizing the results of the previous example, however, provides a convenient method for computing permutations. This method is expressed by the *multiplication principle*, which states:

If the first step in an operation can be performed in n_1 ways, the second in n_2 ways, the third in n_3 ways, and so on for k steps, then the total of k steps can be performed in $n_1 \cdot n_2 \cdot n_3 \cdot, \ldots, \cdot n_k$ ways.

For example, the luncheon menu of a restaurant offers a choice of four appetizers, five entrees, three types of beverages, and six desserts. The total number of ways one can order a different assortment of these luncheon items is $4 \cdot 5 \cdot 3 \cdot 6 = 360$.

Some Simplified Methods of Computation. The problem of computing the number of permutations of a set of objects can be solved by using the multiplication principle, but in certain important kinds of problems the method can be shortened. One problem of this type involves a calculation of the number of permutations of a set of objects with all objects being included in each permutation. That is, how many different arrangements can be made by using all the objects in the set in each arrangement? For this special case of the multiplication principle, it may be stated that *for n distinct objects with all being used each time, there are n! possible different permutations.* The term $n!$ is read as "n factorial" and equals $n(n - 1)(n - 2) \ldots (n - n + 1)$. For example, $3! = 3 \cdot 2 \cdot 1 = 6$; $4! = 4 \cdot 3 \cdot 2 \cdot 1 = 24$; and $6! = 6 \cdot 5 \cdot 4 \cdot 3 \cdot 2 \cdot 1 = 720$. The number of permutations for n objects with all objects included each time, all taken together, is denoted by $_nP_n$ and

$$_nP_n = n! \quad \dots\dots\dots\dots\dots\dots\dots\dots\dots(6.1)$$

➤ *Example.* Five workers are to be assigned to five different jobs. There are five possible ways of assigning the first worker, four ways of assigning the second, and so on. Therefore, there are $_5P_5 = 5! = 5 \cdot 4 \cdot 3 \cdot 2 \cdot 1 = 120$ different ways of assigning all five workers to each of the five jobs.

For some counting problems it is necessary to determine the number of possible permutations of a set of n different objects in which only a portion of the objects is included in each arrangement. Suppose a set has a total of n objects and r of these objects are taken at a time, where r is less than n. *The number of possible permutations of n different things taken r at a time, denoted by $_nP_r$, is*

$$_nP_r = \frac{n!}{(n - r)!} \quad \dots\dots\dots\dots\dots\dots\dots\dots(6.2)$$

The expression, $_nP_r$, is derived from the application of the multiplication principle where $_nP_r = n(n - 1)(n - 2) \ldots (n - r + 1)$. Multiplying by $\dfrac{(n - r)!}{(n - r)!}$, the result is $\dfrac{n!}{(n - r)!}$.

➤ *Example.* Teams of two salesmen each are to be selected from a total of six men in the sales force of a company and assigned to two sales territories. The number of possible assignments of salesmen is

$$_6P_2 = \frac{6 \cdot 5 \cdot 4 \cdot 3 \cdot 2 \cdot 1}{4 \cdot 3 \cdot 2 \cdot 1} = 30 \text{ different teams of two salesmen each.}$$

An algorithm for computing permutations is shown in Figure 6.2. This algorithm is an extension of the one shown in Figure 5.6, page 115, where the added features arise from the need for finding the value of $(n - r)!$ in addition to finding $n!$ The computational sequence of this algorithm provides for finding the factorial of all numbers in the range from $i = 1$ to $i = n$. Since $(n - r)$ is less than or equal to n, at some point the value of i will equal $(n - r)$ and the corresponding factorial obtained on that iteration will equal $(n - r)!$ When the value of $(n - r)!$ has been found, it is retained for use in the final arithmetic statement in the algorithm in which $_nP_r$ is computed.

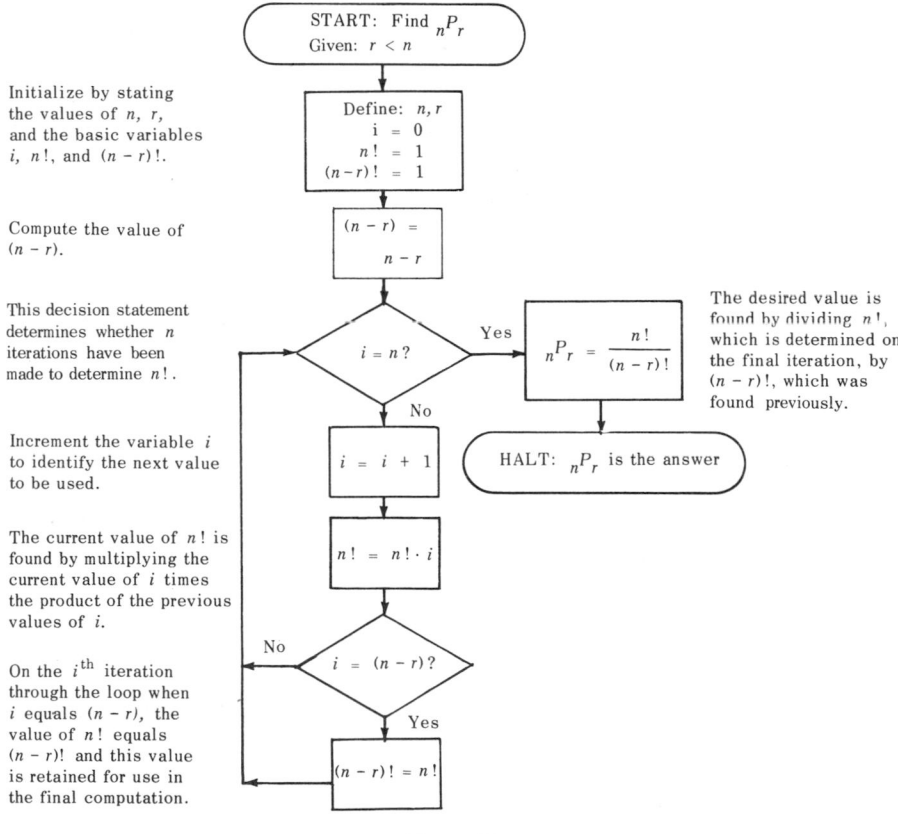

Figure 6.2

AN ALGORITHM FOR FINDING VALUES OF $_nP_r$

The method for finding $(n - r)!$ is shown in Figure 6.2, which begins with initializing the basic variables and values and the computation of $(n - r)$. The iterations for finding $n!$ are begun with the decision statement that asks if "$i = n?$". Since the answer is "No" for n greater than zero, the flow is downward. Next, i is incremented and an interim value of $n!$ is computed. This value is the factorial of the current value of i. If $i = (n - r)$, the interim value of $n!$ is the desired value of $(n - r)!$; if not, the iterations are continued. Should $(n - r) = 0$, the answer to "$i = (n - r)$?" is negative for all iterations and $(n - r)!$ retains its initial value of zero, and $0! = 1$ by mathematical definition.

Suppose one wishes to find the value of $_5P_2$, where $n = 5, r = 2$, and $(n - r) = 3$. Following the iterations in Figure 6.2, i will range from zero to five, and when $i = 3$, the interim value $n! = 3!$ will have been computed. Since $i = (n - r)$ for $i = 3$, then $(n - r)! = 3!$. This factorial is therefore retained for use in the final computation. The iterations will continue until $i = n$, at which time $n! = 5!$, and the desired value of $n!$ will have been computed. The computational sequence is then completed with the calculation of $_5P_2$.

The Addition Principle. Some counting problems are concerned with determining the permutations of each of two operations, where the use of one operation precludes the use of the other. Operations with this property are said to be *mutually exclusive.* The *addition principle* states:

For two mutually exclusive operations, where the first may be performed in m ways, and the second in n ways, then one or the other of the operations can be performed in m + n ways.

➤ *Example.* An automobile salesman tells a customer that the standard model of his brand of cars is available in three body styles, six colors, and two kinds of transmissions, while the sports model is available in two body styles, five colors, and two types of transmissions. The customer has a total of $m + n = 3 \cdot 6 \cdot 2 + 2 \cdot 5 \cdot 2 = 56$ different choices in his selection of an automobile.

The addition principle can be easily generalized to include any finite number of mutually exclusive operations.

The multiplication principle, including the special cases, and the addition principle offer methods for calculating the number of possible arrangements of a set of objects, but not all counting problems can be solved by the straightforward substitution into one of the formulas presented in this section. Rather, some problems may necessitate the use of a combination of the principles presented here or a specially designed counting method appropriate to the unusual properties of the problem.

Combinations

The permutations of a set of objects are based on the *order* of the arrangements, where each change in order constitutes a different arrangement. However, if one wishes to determine how many different selections of objects can be made, *where order is not of consequence*, a different problem is posed. A selection of objects for which order is not of consequence is called a *combination*. Thus, the number of possible combinations of a set of *n* objects taken all together is one, since order does not count and there is only one way of including all the objects in the combination. If, however, groups of *r* objects are taken from a set of *n* distinct objects, then more than one combination is possible.

➤ *Example.* The letters *A, B,* and *C,* if taken as a group, constitute just one combination, since order does not matter. However, these letters taken all together can be arranged to form $3! = 6$ permutations.

➤ *Example.* An accountant has four problems, denoted by *W, X, Y,* and *Z,* to be solved on an electronic computer. The problems require equal amounts of computation time on the computer. There is, however, only enough time available to solve three of the four problems. The possible combinations and permutations of three of the four problems are listed in Table 6.1.

Table 6.1

COMBINATIONS AND PERMUTATIONS OF THE FOUR ITEMS
W, X, Y, AND *Z*

Combinations	Permutations
WXY	*WXY, WYX, XWY, XYW, YWX, YXW*
WXZ	*WXZ, WZX, XWZ, XZW, ZWX, ZXW*
WYZ	*WYZ, WZY, YWZ, YZW, ZWY, ZYW*
XYZ	*XYZ, XZY, YXZ, YZX, ZXY, ZYX*

The number of combinations is denoted by $_nC_r$. From Table 6.1 it is seen that there are only four different combinations, while the number of permutations $_4P_3$ totals 24. For each of the four combinations, there are $r!$ or $3 \cdot 2 \cdot 1 = 6$ permutations. Dividing the total number of permutations $\dfrac{n!}{(n-r)!}$ by the number of permutations per combination, $r!$, gives the number of combinations, or

$$_nC_r = \binom{n}{r} = \frac{n!}{r!(n-r)!} \quad \dots\dots\dots\dots\dots(6.3)$$

where $\binom{n}{r}$ is an alternative way of denoting the number of combinations for $r \leq n$.

➤ *Example.* A display manager wishes to place four different colors of a style of women's spring dresses in a display window. If there are six colors from which to choose, the number of combinations of four different colors is

$$_6C_4 = \binom{6}{4} = \frac{6!}{4!(6-4)!} = 15.$$

The mathematician Blaise Pascal developed a useful method for determining the number of combinations of n things taken r at a time. This method is expressed by the following rule:

$$\binom{n+1}{r} = \binom{n}{r-1} + \binom{n}{r} \dots\dots\dots\dots\dots(6.4)$$

where $1 \leq r \leq n$. This rule can be verified by rewriting it in terms of factorial symbols and simplifying the expression.

The value of the rule lies in providing a simple means of constructing a table for the values of $\binom{n}{r}$. This table is known as *Pascal's triangle*. A portion of this table showing the values of $\binom{n}{r}$ for n and r from 0 through 10 is presented in Table 6.2. The numbers in the body of the table are the combinations of n things (rows) taken r (columns) at a time.

Table 6.2

A TABLE OF VALUES OF $\binom{n}{r}$ FOR n AND r FROM 0 TO 10

r \\ n	0	1	2	3	4	5	6	7	8	9	10
0	1										
1	1	1									
2	1	2	1								
3	1	3	3	1							
4	1	4	6	4	1						
5	1	5	10	10	5	1					
6	1	6	15	20	15	6	1				
7	1	7	21	35	35	21	7	1			
8	1	8	28	56	70	56	28	8	1		
9	1	9	36	84	126	126	84	36	9	1	
10	1	10	45	120	210	252	210	120	45	10	1

➤ *Example.* If a florist has seven different kinds of cut flowers in stock, how many combinations of four kinds of flowers can be made? In Table 6.2 where row 7 intersects column 4, the corresponding value indicates that 35 combinations are possible.

The methods of counting discussed in the foregoing sections provide general rules and shortcut methods for determining the number of possible permutations or combinations of a finite set of objects. An understanding of these concepts is important, for in the following sections of this chapter the concepts that have been introduced serve as a part of the basis for presenting the theory of probability and methods of calculating probabilities.

THE MEANING OF PROBABILITY

The concept of probability is particularly useful in business as well as in personal life when a decision or judgment is made concerning a situation for which the outcome is uncertain. A businessman may decide that the chances are excellent that a new product will succeed; a manager reflects on past experience to estimate the completion date of a research project; a construction foreman schedules work crews based on his judgment that rain is not likely on a given day. Each of these situations involves uncertainty and each of the decisions is essentially a prediction of an outcome, made with some degree of confidence that the prediction will be substantiated. Probability theory offers a means for mathematically formulating predictions of uncertain outcomes, and it is important to distinguish between some interpretations of probability and the mathematical deductions obtained from the postulates of probability.

Preliminary Ideas

Before taking up a discussion of the meaning of probability, a few basic concepts will be introduced to facilitate the presentation of a formal definition of probability.

The first of these concepts is that of an experiment. In order to apply the concepts of probability and statistics to business problems, it is necessary to obtain data for analysis. Any process of observation is called an *experiment*. Thus, tossing dice, observing the percent of defective items in a lot of manufactured articles, or recording the arrivals of customers at a supermarket check-out counter may be looked upon as experiments.

In these instances the numbers that turn up on the dice, the condition of a manufactured product as being acceptable or defective, or the number of arrivals at a check-out counter per time unit are called the possible outcomes of experiments. Each of the outcomes that can occur in a single trial of an experiment is called an *elementary event*.

➤ *Example.* A trial of an experiment consists of tossing a die. The elementary events or outcomes of a toss of a die are the numbers 1 through 6 on the faces of the die. Any one of the events can occur in a single trial.

The die-tossing example points to an important concept in that the numbers 1 through 6 comprise the complete list of possible events. A group of events that constitutes a complete list of possible events which can occur, one of which is bound to occur in a trial of an experiment, is said to be *collectively exhaustive.* If the occurrence of any one of the events on the list of possible events precludes the occurrence of any other, the possible events are *mutually exclusive.*

➤ *Example.* A supermarket has five counters for checking out customers. The check-out process at any one of the counters constitutes an event that must be performed at any one (collectively exhaustive) but only one (mutually exclusive) of the counters.

Associated with each of the elementary events is an entity called an *elementary unit* or an *observation.* The totality of elementary units is termed the *universe* or the *population.* Consider a bin of mass-produced parts that contains a mixture of acceptable and defective items. A trial of an experiment is performed by selecting a part at random from the bin, observing whether the part is acceptable or defective, and replacing the part in the bin. The simple events are the two possible outcomes— acceptable or defective. The universe of elementary units includes all the parts in the bin. Associated with each elementary unit are two possible outcomes—acceptable or defective.

Experiments involve making a limited number of trials when more extensive experimentation is impossible, impractical, or uneconomical. The process of making a finite number of trials by randomly selecting elementary units from a universe is called *simple random sampling.* Data obtained from simple random samples are frequently used to calculate averages or measures of dispersion. A statistic thus computed serves as the basis for estimating a universe parameter or making an inference about the composition or characteristics of the universe.

➤ *Example.* A sample is taken from a large inventory of one-pound boxes of granulated sugar. A trial is performed by randomly selecting a box of sugar (elementary unit), weighing the contents, and recording the weight (elementary event). A total of $n = 50$ trials is made and the average weight of the sampled boxes is found to be 16.1 ounces, or slightly more than the intended weight of 16.0 ounces for the universe of inventory items. Management is now faced with the problem of deciding whether the average weight of all boxes is more than 16.0 ounces.

➤ *Example.* A marketing research team, seeking to determine what percent of customers in an area prefers their firm's brand of detergent, randomly selects 400 housewives and asks each of them which brand she prefers. The tabulation shows that 15% of the sampled customers favor the firm's brand. The sample percent serves as an estimate of the percent of all customers in the area who prefer this brand of detergent.

Objective Probability

The *objective* interpretation of probability is based on two different approaches to the meaning of probability, which employ abstract reasoning or experience to determine probabilities.

Equiprobable Events. The concept of *equiprobable events*, also called the *principle of insufficient reason*, suggests that if there is no reason to favor any one of the possible outcomes of a situation to any other, then the outcomes should be considered equally likely to occur.

➤ *Example.* A fair coin is tossed and an individual is asked to state the probability that a head will appear. The answer will most likely be $\frac{1}{2}$ if there is no evidence to suggest that the sides of the coin are not equally likely to occur.

But what is the basis for stating that a side of a fair coin will turn up with a probability of $\frac{1}{2}$? There are two possible outcomes of a toss of a fair coin, but only one of the outcomes is desired. The ratio of the number of ways in which the desired outcome can occur to the total number of possible outcomes is $\frac{1}{2}$, the probability of the desired outcome.

The determination of this probability does not require that one toss the coin many times to gain experience, for the symmetry of the probabilities of the outcomes is seen intuitively from the assumption of a fair coin. Probabilities determined by using intuitive judgment or abstract reasoning are determined by what is called the *a priori method* of calculating probabilities.

The application of the concept of equiprobable outcomes is limited to situations where symmetrical probabilities can be assumed, such as drawing from a fair deck of cards or tossing a fair die. For these situations probabilities can be determined by the a priori method, and extensive experimental data are not required.

Relative Frequency. It is apparent that the probabilistic model based on equiprobable events is appropriate for a special class of problems. In many instances experience indicates that even if an experiment is performed under *uniform conditions*, the outcomes of the trials will occur with differing frequencies.

➤ *Example.* In a game played with a standard deck of playing cards, a player observes that a face card denoted F (ace, king, queen, or jack) is dealt on a single draw from a full deck of cards less often than a non-face card denoted N. For 100 trials of the experiment, each consisting of randomly drawing a card from a full deck of well-shuffled cards, the player obtains the results shown in groups of 10 draws in Table 6.3. The columns in the table show the number of face cards F for each group of 10 draws, the cumulative totals of face cards $\Sigma F = m$, the cumulative number of trials n, and the relative frequency of drawing face cards $\dfrac{m}{n}$.

Table 6.3

RESULTS OF 100 RANDOM DRAWS FROM A STANDARD DECK
OF PLAYING CARDS

Trial numbers	Events	Number of face cards F	Cumulative number of face cards $\Sigma F = m$	Cumulative number of trials n	Relative frequency $\dfrac{m}{n}$
1–10	$F\ N\ N\ N\ N\ F\ N\ N\ N\ N$	2	2	10	0.200
11–20	$F\ F\ F\ N\ N\ N\ F\ N\ N\ F$	5	7	20	0.350
21–30	$N\ N\ F\ N\ F\ N\ N\ F\ N\ F$	4	11	30	0.367
31–40	$N\ N\ N\ N\ N\ N\ F\ N\ N\ N$	1	12	40	0.300
41–50	$N\ F\ F\ N\ N\ N\ N\ N\ N\ N$	2	14	50	0.280
51–60	$N\ N\ F\ N\ F\ N\ N\ \hat{F}\ N\ F$	4	18	60	0.300
61–70	$F\ F\ N\ F\ N\ F\ N\ F\ F\ N$	6	24	70	0.343
71–80	$N\ N\ N\ N\ F\ N\ N\ N\ F\ N$	2	26	80	0.325
81–90	$N\ F\ F\ N\ N\ N\ F\ N\ N\ N$	3	29	90	0.322
91–100	$N\ N\ N\ F\ N\ N\ N\ N\ N\ N$	1	30	100	0.300

An important property of the example above is illustrated in Figure 6.3 by the horizontal line drawn at a relative frequency of $\dfrac{16}{52} = 0.308$, the proportion of a deck of cards consisting of face cards. As n, the number of trials, becomes large, the deviations of the relative frequencies about

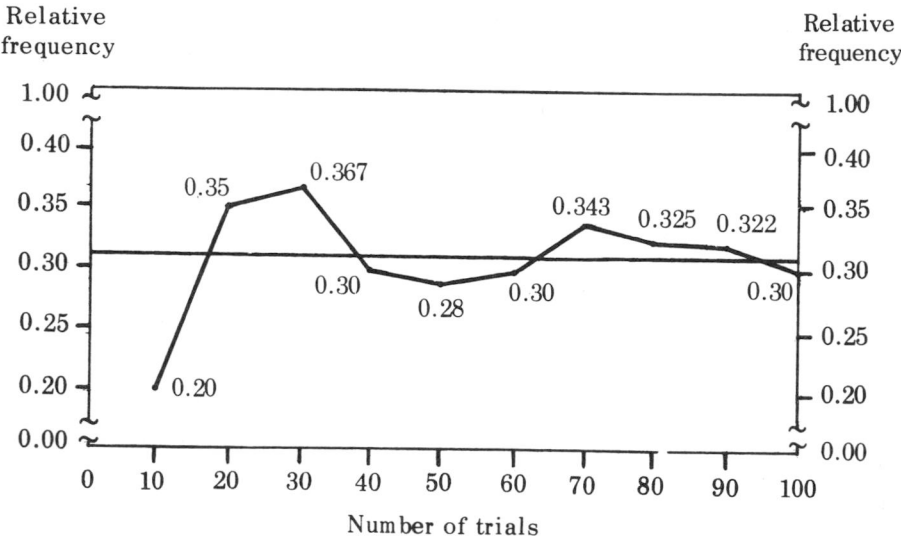

Figure 6.3

RELATIVE FREQUENCY OF DRAWING FACE CARDS
IN CUMULATIVE TRIALS

the horizontal line at 0.308 tend to decrease. This tendency for the relative frequencies to converge on the proportion 0.308, that is, for the fluctuations to decrease as *n* becomes large, illustrates what is called *statistical regularity*. Thus, for a very large *n*, the relative frequency would very closely approximate a number *P*, the probability of the occurrence of an event. For the previous problem the event, drawing a face card, is denoted by *F*; *P(F)* is the probability of drawing a face card; and *P(F)* = 0.308.

The relative frequency $\frac{m}{n}$ determined from 100 trials of the experiment of drawing cards is 0.300 and closely approximates *P(F)* = 0.308. In this particular example *P(F)* is calculated a priori since the number of face cards and the total number of cards are known. But it is not possible to calculate a priori probabilities for every experiment; in fact, many experiments are performed to estimate the probability of an event by determining the relative frequency. The relative frequency determined from a finite number of trials provides a numerical value with which to estimate the probability of an event. Although relative frequencies are sometimes used as probabilities, the values of the two quantities *P(F)* and $\frac{m}{n}$ are not necessarily the same.

➤ *Example.* A marketing analyst uses simple random sampling to estimate what proportion of customers who enter a department store buys appliances. Of 100 customers sampled, eight purchased appliances. The estimate of the probability that a customer entering the store will purchase an appliance is $\dfrac{m}{n} = \dfrac{8}{100} = 0.08$, assuming the universe proportion remains constant while the sample is drawn (statistical regularity).

Viewing a relative frequency or probability as a proportion suggests three basic properties of these measures of uncertainty. First, the ratio of the number of occurrences to the number of trials cannot be less than zero or more than one. It follows that the probability of an event A, which is one of the set of mutually exclusive and collectively exhaustive events of an experiment, is in the range

$$0 \le P(A) \le 1 \quad\ldots\ldots\ldots\ldots\ldots\ldots\ldots\ldots\ldots\text{(6.5)}$$

Second, since the events are collectively exhaustive, one of the elementary events must occur on a trial. The probability that the event which occurs is not A is

$$P(A') = 1 - P(A) \quad\ldots\ldots\ldots\ldots\ldots\ldots\ldots\text{(6.6)}$$

A third property is illustrated by examining the nature of the event A'. Suppose the event A denotes an elementary event from a list of several mutually exclusive and collectively exhaustive events. Then A' denotes an event composed of the group of mutually exclusive events other than A and is called a *compound event*. The occurrence of any of the events other than A constitutes the nonoccurrence of A, that is, the occurrence of A'. Thus, $P(A')$ is the sum of the probabilities of all the elementary events except A.

➤ *Example.* A businessman who sells appliances in a variety of colors finds that, on the average, 60% of his customers purchase white; 20% buy brown; 10% buy green; and 10% buy yellow. The probability that a customer selected at random will buy a white appliance is $P(W) = 0.60$. The probability that the customer will select a color other than white, $P(W')$, is the sum of the probabilities for the remaining elementary events, or $P(B) + P(G) + P(Y) = 0.20 + 0.10 + 0.10$. The probability of the compound event nonwhite is $P(W') = 0.40$.

These three important properties are summarized by the following axioms of probability theory:

1. A probability is a number between 0 and 1 that is assigned to an event.
2. The sum of the probabilities of the mutually exclusive and collectively exhaustive events of an experiment must total 1.
3. The probability of an event composed of a group of mutually exclusive events is equal to the sum of the probabilities of the events.

A probability or a relative frequency of zero is interpreted to mean that the occurrence of an event is highly unlikely rather than strictly impossible. At the other extreme of $P(A) = 1$, a similar interpretation is made in that an event is not assumed to be strictly certain to occur; but for all practical purposes, certainty is a reasonable assumption.

The relative frequency approach to probability is summarized by four principal characteristics: (1) the assumption of a large number of trials of an experiment; (2) the presumption of statistical regularity; (3) the use of empirical information gained from experience; and (4) the use of a relative frequency to estimate probability. For certain kinds of problems, the first two characteristics become limitations. In some situations probabilities are estimated before trials can be made. In this manner, subjective estimates are assigned as probabilities to events for which there is no actual or reliable experience. For example, a manufacturer wishes to experiment with a new process and makes a decision to undertake the untried process on the basis of an 80–20 chance estimate that the process will be profitable.

The Limit of a Relative Frequency. The relative frequency approach to probability utilizes the ratio $\dfrac{m}{n}$ as an estimate of the probability $P(A)$ of an event A for a large value of n. This approach is modified by the limit of the relative frequency concept, which states that the probability $P(A)$ of an event A exists and that

$$\lim_{n \to \infty} \frac{m}{n} = P(A),$$

which is read: the probability $P(A)$ is the limit of the relative frequency $\dfrac{m}{n}$ as the number of trials n becomes very large.

The relative frequency approach, upon which much of probability theory is based, will be used extensively in the following discussion. The limit concept does, however, offer a more rigorous definition that frequently appears in statistical literature.

Subjective Probability

The view that the concept of probability has meaning only in instances when trials of an experiment can be repeated under uniform conditions presently enjoys considerable favor. But how does one deal with problems for which repeated trials are impossible, impractical, or uneconomical? Are probabilities pertinent in such situations? The *subjective* or *personalistic* interpretation of probability is a view of probability as a numerical expression of personal judgment or belief with respect to a particular proposition. Also, with practice, a "rational" individual can think abstractly about his beliefs concerning the elements of a situation that are not certain, regardless of how he may feel about any other aspects of the situation. Further, if different "rational" individuals are confronted with the same information, their degree of belief and personal probability estimates for the same event may be different.

This is not to say, however, that a "rational" individual will assign probabilities arbitrarily. Rather, probabilities are assigned to real world events on the basis of experience with such events and, in general, "rational" individuals with similar experiences for given events will assign roughly the same probability. Thus, if an individual appraising the probability of an event feels that the event would occur with a relative frequency p for many trials made under uniform conditions, he will assign a probability p to the event.

➤ *Example.* A veteran contractor submits a proposal for constructing an office building and believes he has a 50–50 chance of being awarded the contract. Thus, he assigns a subjective probability of $p = 0.50$ to the event that the contract will be received.

The subjective approach to probability uses probabilities as "weights" that are assigned to events. In this manner an individual expresses his degree of belief in the likelihood of the outcomes of a situation, one and only one of which is certain to occur.

➤ *Example.* An industrial relations manager expresses his belief in the likelihood of each of the possible outcomes of current labor negotiations by weighting each of the outcomes. Reflecting on his past experiences in similar negotiations, he assigns the following subjective probabilities as weights:

Event	*Probability*
Settlement	0.60
Arbitration	0.30
Strike	0.10
	1.00

The nature of some business problems is such that historical frequencies of outcomes are not available or are impossible to obtain. If a product is to be marketed for the first time, there is no past experience of selling the product with which to determine the likelihood of success. However, it is possible to visualize the probabilities involved as relative frequencies in an imaginary series of trials, even if it is not possible to perform repeated trials. Where, historically, there is no precedent for assigning probabilities, but subsequent trials are possible, an initial probability estimate can be made subjectively and later modified in terms of experience. This technique of revising probabilities will be considered in a later discussion of Bayes' Theorem. With successive revisions, the long-run probabilities obtained subjectively will approximate those determined solely from objective data.

SETS, RANDOM VARIABLES, AND PROBABILITY

The objective and subjective interpretations of probability provide useful approaches for obtaining probabilities from relative frequencies or subjective estimates. The role of probability in statistical inference and other statistical decision problems is subtle and complex. The concept of sets, however, offers a very useful mathematical model with which to present probability at a slightly more advanced level. In this section, set theory is introduced to amplify the concepts of probability previously discussed and to provide insight into the relationships among events, sample spaces, random variables, axioms of probability, and Bayes' Theorem.

Sets and Events

Sets. The idea of a set was introduced in the discussion of the permutations or combinations of a group of objects. The concept of a set has great significance in the study of probability, for all mathematics can be developed from this fundamental notion. In general, a *set* is a well-defined collection of entities, whether real or imaginary. By this definition, the employees of a firm form a set. Similarly, we may speak of the set of the theories of the origin of the universe, the set of insured automobiles in an area, or the set of outcomes of an experiment. These illustrations are examples of *discrete* sets, since each collection of entities is comprised of a finite number of elements. This discussion will be essentially limited to the consideration of discrete sets.

A set can be identified in two different ways. The elements of a set can be designated by means of a *description*, where, by means of a rule, it can be determined whether a given object is in a set. Alternatively, a set can be identified by a *listing*, which enumerates all the elements of the set.

➤ **Example.** A set of elementary units is described by a rule stating that the set consists of pieces of pasteboard or plastic which are a deck of playing cards. Another set is defined by listing the four suits of a deck of cards, the set of elementary events.

A listing of a set is customarily enclosed with braces. For the latter example above, the listing is {clubs, diamonds, hearts, spades}. The set of elementary events of an experiment is called a *universal set*.

Set Operations. In many instances only a particular portion of the elements of a universal set is of interest. Any part of a universal set is called a *subset*. Any subset of a universal set of outcomes of an experiment is called an *event*.

➤ **Example.** The set of all possible outcomes of a trial of an experiment consisting of a toss of a fair die is the universal set {1, 2, 3, 4, 5, 6}.

➤ **Example.** There are 36 possible elementary events that can occur in a trial of an experiment in which a pair of fair dice are tossed. The subset of elementary events in which the sum of the numbers on the faces of the dice is seven is {(1, 6), (2, 5), (3, 4), (4, 3), (5, 2), (6, 1)}.

Subsets of a universal set are sometimes easier to visualize if presented graphically. One form of graphic presentation is the *Venn diagram*, in which the universal set is represented by a rectangle and the subsets are shown as circular portions of the rectangle. See Figure 6.4.

➤ **Example.** Consider the universal set S as a deck of 52 playing cards with a subset of hearts H and a subset of kings K. The set of all cards is represented by the rectangle and the subset of cards that are either hearts or kings is represented by the areas enclosed by the circles H and K in Figure 6.4.

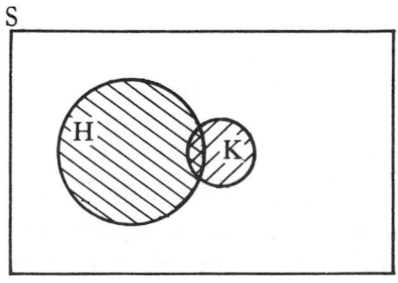

Figure 6.4

VENN DIAGRAM OF THE SUBSETS OF
HEARTS AND KINGS

The subset of elements that are in either H or K is the shaded area in Figure 6.4. This area is called the *union* of H and K and is denoted by $H \cup K$, which is read "H cup K," "H or K," or "H union K." The doubly crosshatched portion, where the circles H and K overlap, represents elements that are in both subsets. This portion is called the *intersection* of H and K and is denoted by $H \cap K$, which is read "H cap K," "H and K," or "H intersection K." For the previous example, $H \cap K$ consists of a single element, the king of hearts. Subsets containing only one element are called *unit sets*.

Subsets from a universal set can be designated so that the subsets contain no common elements. When shown graphically, these sets do not intersect, since the occurrence of an element in one subset precludes its presence in the other. Sets that contain only elements which are not common (mutually exclusive) to another set are called *disjoint*. To complete the designation of the areas in a diagram, the elements in a universal set S that are not included in one or more subsets of interest are denoted by S', which is called the *complement*.

➤ *Example.* The subsets of hearts and diamonds from a set of playing cards S are shown by the areas H and D in Figure 6.5. These areas do not overlap since a card must be either a heart or a diamond and cannot be both. The cards in the deck that are not hearts or diamonds, $S - H \cup D$, are represented by the shaded portion S' in the rectangle.

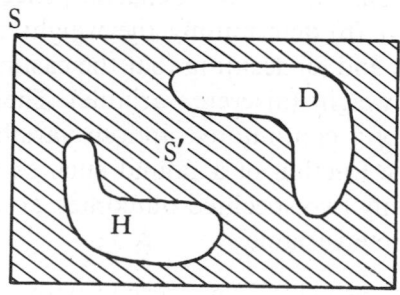

Figure 6.5

DIAGRAM OF DISJOINT SUBSETS H AND D, AND S',
THE COMPLEMENT OF THE SUBSETS

The presentation of sets by means of diagrams is useful for suggesting the relationships that exist in the combination of two or more sets in terms of unions, intersections, and complements. Proofs of the results, however, are based on the algebra of sets involving a series of theorems that are beyond the scope of this discussion.

Random Variables and Functions

Random Variables. The concept of a *variable* was introduced in Chapter 1 and in a general way in the review of descriptive statistics. In these discussions a variable was associated with a series of values that express observed characteristics of elementary units and provide the basis for computing a summary statistic, such as an average or a measure of dispersion. Similarly, in this chapter the idea of a variable is suggested by observing values such as those obtained by tossing dice, sampling the weights of boxes of sugar, or randomly selecting customers in a survey. In each of these instances the specific outcome of a trial is not known in advance, but some information is available concerning the relative frequency of each outcome. Trials made from processes of this type where the events are not identical nor individually predictable with certainty are termed *stochastic processes* or *chance processes*. Making repeated trials of an experiment involving stochastic processes yields results or events. A quantity that takes on a definite value or property for every possible elementary event is called a *random variable*, also referred to as a *chance variable* or a *stochastic variable*. Random variables are of two types: *continuous* and *discrete*. A continuous variable can assume an infinite number of values, while a discrete variable can take on only a specified finite number of values.

➤ *Example.* An experiment is performed where the trials consist of: (a) taking a random sample (a stochastic process) of metal castings (elementary units), (b) determining the weight of each casting (continuous variable), and (c) deciding that the casting is of an acceptable or unacceptable weight (discrete variable). The weight of a casting (observed value of a continuous random variable, an event) can be determined to the fraction of a pound such as 5.61825 . . . pounds, while there are only two specified outcomes, acceptable or unacceptable, for the discrete variable.

This discussion is principally concerned with discrete random variables, although in later chapters continuous variables will be applied or utilized as approximations for discrete variables.

Sets and Functions. The concept of a discrete variable can be related to that of sets by stating that a variable is a range of values, each of which can be associated with a set of objects.

➤ *Example.* Consider the outcome of an experiment in which two fair dice are tossed. The value three of a discrete variable is associated with the elementary events {1, 2} or {2, 1}. The value three of the discrete variable is also associated with the compound event $\{(1, 2), (2, 1)\}$. The set of all values for the random variable is the numbers associated with the universal set of events $\{2, 3, 4, 5, 6, 7, 8, 9, 10, 11, 12\}$. Remembering that the elementary outcomes of a toss of two fair dice have equal probabilities of $\frac{1}{36}$ and that the probability corresponding to a compound event is equal to the sum of the probabilities of the component elementary events, the probability associated with the event $\{(1, 2), (2, 1)\}$ is $\frac{1}{36} + \frac{1}{36} = \frac{1}{18}$. For the possible events corresponding to a trial of an experiment, there is a set of probabilities such that for each event (subset) there is a corresponding numerical probability.

The relationship between the elements of one set and those of another can be described by a rule called a *function*. The rule can be expressed verbally or in mathematical terms.

➤ *Example.* If a worker is paid under a piecework incentive plan, one might consider his wage as a function of his output. Accordingly, a "high wage" corresponds to "high output" and a "low wage" is associated with "low output" in terms of a function, which in this case is a verbal rule.

The set of all possible levels of output that a worker can achieve is called the *domain*. For each output level there is a corresponding wage, and the set of wage amounts forms a set called the *range*. If the worker's wage is different for each level of output, then the relationship between the sets is called a *point function*, which assigns a value or an element in the range of each "point" or element in the domain.

➤ *Example.* An incentive plan states that a worker is paid $0.05 for each unit of output he produces. The function or transformation relating a worker's wage W with output P is the set function $W = \$0.05P$, and is shown graphically in Figure 6.6.

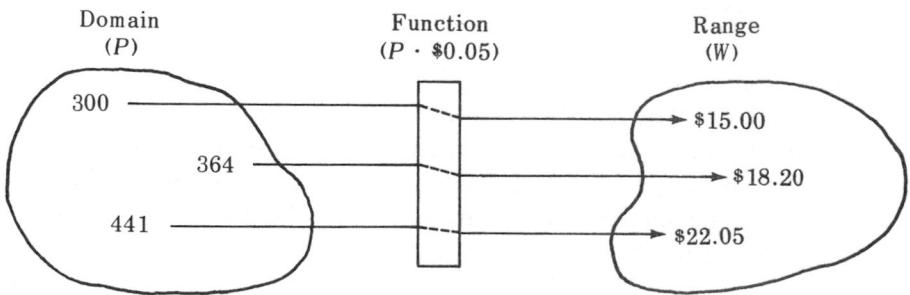

Figure 6.6

A POINT FUNCTION RELATING WORKER OUTPUT
AND WAGES

There are many situations where the domain consists of one or more sets rather than single points or elements, and the corresponding range is one or more real numbers. A function with a domain and a range of this type is called a *set function*.

➤ *Example.* The amount of income tax withheld from an employee's wage depends upon the number of exemptions claimed and the bracket in which the wage falls. For this example, consider employees who claim two exemptions. Let Y be the set of all monthly wage amounts up to $1,000 and the subsets of Y be the wage amounts in each of the withholding brackets. One set function whose domain is all the subsets of Y is the function $F(Y)$, which gives the amount of withholding for any subset. This set function is illustrated in Figure 6.7.

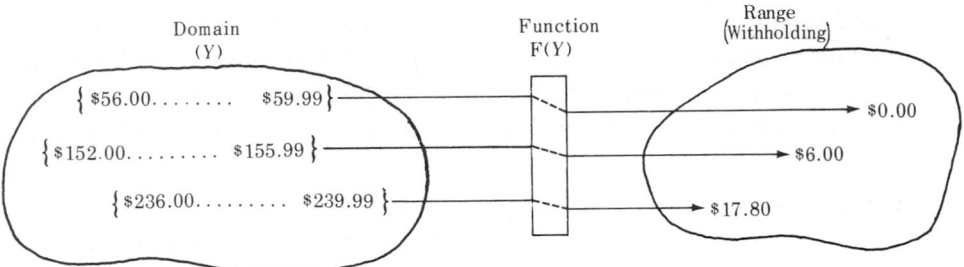

Figure 6.7

A SET FUNCTION RELATING INCOME BRACKETS
AND WITHHOLDING TAX

Sample Space. A fundamental concept in the theory of sampling is the identification of the elementary events or *sample points* from which sample observations can be selected. A *sample space* of an experiment is defined as the set of sample points so that each point corresponds to one and only one possible elementary event.

➤ *Example.* In an experiment a fair coin is tossed twice, and for each toss, one of two possible outcomes, a head H or a tail T occurs. The sample space or domain of elementary events is the universal set of sample points $\{(H, H), (H, T), (T, H), (T, T)\}$. The number of tails T that can be obtained is the range $\{0, 1, 2\}$ of a discrete random variable. The elements of the range correspond to the subsets $\{(H, H)\}$, $\{(H, T), (T, H)\}$, and $\{(T, T)\}$.

Note in the example that each number of tails which can be obtained in two tosses of the coin corresponds to a subset of events. The sample space of the example experiment is shown graphically in the left-hand diagram in Figure 6.8, and the range corresponding to the sample space is in the right-hand diagram. The subset of the two sample points $\{(T, H), (H, T)\}$ enclosed by the dotted line corresponds to the unit subset $\{1\}$ from the range of the number of tails obtained. The lines associating these subsets in Figure 6.8 represent a counting rule — a function.

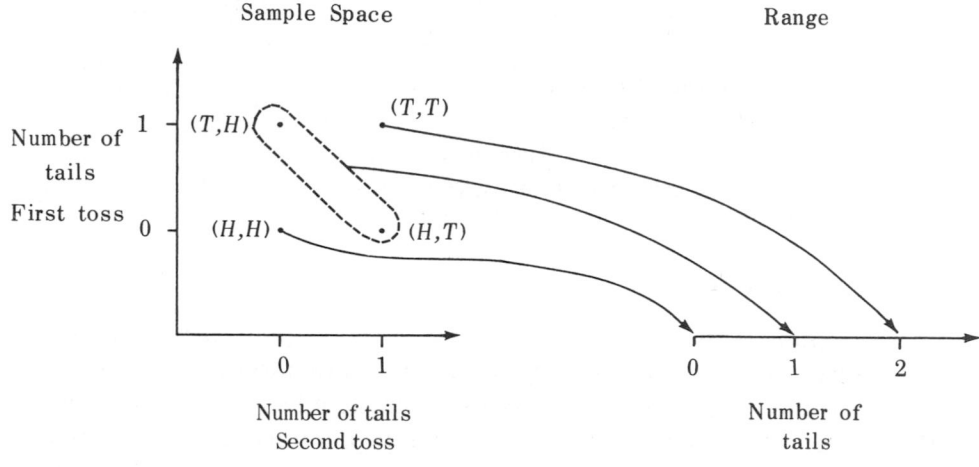

Figure 6.8

SAMPLE SPACE AND RANGE OF TOSSES OF A FAIR COIN

Another function of greater interest here is that which associates the subsets of outcomes with probabilities. The function can be evaluated a priori by comparing the number of sample points in a subset with the number of points in the sample space. Thus, the fraction of outcomes in which one tail occurs is $\frac{2}{4} = \frac{1}{2}$. Similarly, the fraction of outcomes giving no tails is $\frac{1}{4}$; for two tails, the ratio is $\frac{1}{4}$. The function that transforms subsets of a sample space into probabilities is represented by the rectangle in Figure 6.9. This function can be expressed mathematically in general form by $P(r) = \binom{n}{r} p^r (1 - p)^{n-r}$. This expression denotes binomial probabilities, which are discussed in detail in Chapter 7.

The correspondence between subsets of the sample space of an experiment and values of a random variable can be expressed by selecting an appropriate function. The principal objective in many statistics problems is that of discovering what function should be assigned to a sample space.

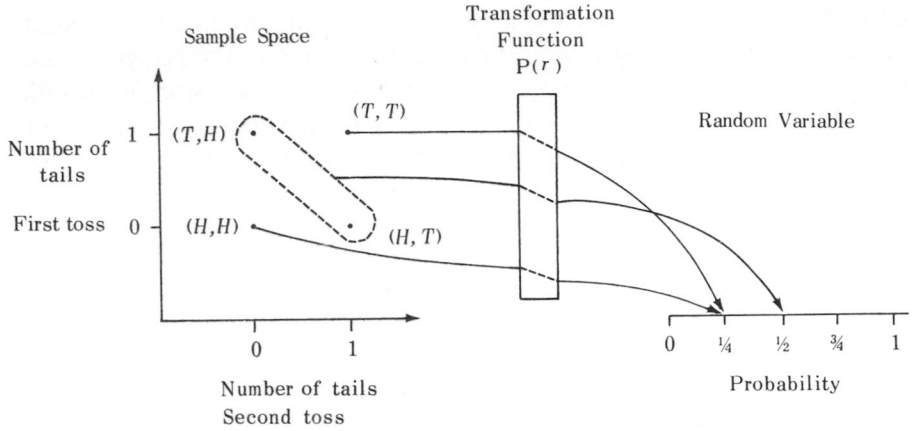

Figure 6.9

TRANSFORMATION OF SUBSETS OF A SAMPLE SPACE
TO PROBABILITIES

RULES OF PROBABILITY

The axioms of probability introduced in the section on preliminary ideas serve as a basis for considering the interpretation of probability. These axioms do not, however, provide a sufficient basis for formulating the wide spectrum of probability problems encountered in business, but in this section additional rules are presented to provide a more comprehensive approach to calculating probabilities.

By way of review, the axioms previously introduced are associated with concepts of sets in the following example.

➤ **Example.** Consider an experiment consisting of two tosses of a fair coin. The points of the sample space and the related probabilities are listed as follows:

Sample points	Event	*A priori* probability
(H, H)	A_1	$P(A_1) = \frac{1}{4}$
(H, T)	A_2	$P(A_2) = \frac{1}{4}$
(T, H)	A_3	$P(A_3) = \frac{1}{4}$
(T, T)	A_4	$P(A_4) = \frac{1}{4}$
		1.0

The a priori probabilities are expressed by the probability set function, $P(A_i) = \frac{1}{4}$. Thus, $P(A_1) = \frac{1}{4}$ and $P(A'_1) = 1 - P(A_1) = 1 - \frac{1}{4} = \frac{3}{4}$. Let B_1 denote the event "head on first toss," and $P(B_1) = P(A_1 \cup A_2) = P(A_1) + P(A_2) = \frac{1}{4} + \frac{1}{4} = \frac{1}{2}$.

The example illustrates the axioms of probability previously introduced. These are summarized as follows:

$$\text{I. } 0 \leq P(A_i) \leq 1$$
$$\text{II. } P(A_1) + P(A_2) + \ldots + P(A_k) = 1$$
$$\text{III. } P(A_1') = 1 - P(A_1)$$

The Special Rule of Addition

A fourth axiom is illustrated by the result $P(B_1) = P(A_1) + P(A_2)$ of the foregoing example. This axiom, known as the *Special Rule of Addition*, states:

For k mutually exclusive events

$$P(A_1 \cup A_2 \cup \ldots \cup A_k) = P(A_1) + P(A_2) + \ldots + P(A_k)\ldots\textbf{(6.7)}$$

➤ *Example.* A bin contains 400 identical parts of which 120 were produced by Machine A, 80 by Machine B, 96 by Machine C, and 104 by Machine D. If a part is selected at random from the bin, the probability that it was produced by Machine A or B or D is $P(A \cup B \cup D)$ $= P(A) + P(B) + P(D) = \frac{120}{400} + \frac{80}{400} + \frac{104}{400} = \frac{76}{100} = 0.76$. The selection of a part at random implies that each of the 400 parts in the bin has an equal chance of $\frac{1}{400}$ of being selected. Suppose we are interested in the selection of a part produced by Machine A. The selection of any one of the parts produced by Machine A constitutes the occurrence of the event of interest. Thus, the probability of the event is the sum of the probabilities for the 120 parts or $P(A) = 120(\frac{1}{400}) = \frac{120}{400} = 0.30$.

In many instances experimental events are not mutually exclusive, for the subsets corresponding to the events may have common elements.

➤ *Example.* The probability of either the event B_1 "head on first toss" or the event B_2 "head on second toss" in two tosses of a fair coin is $P(B_1 \cup B_2) = \frac{1}{2} + \frac{1}{2} - \frac{1}{4} = \frac{3}{4}$, for $\{(H, H)\}$ is the intersection $B_1 \cap B_2$ of the subsets as shown in Figure 6.10.

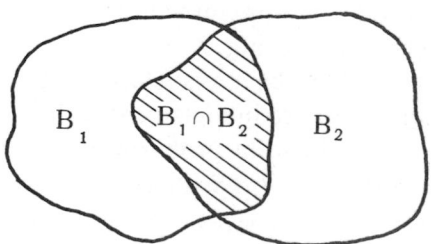

Figure 6.10

DIAGRAM OF INTERSECTING SUBSETS

The General Rule of Addition

It is apparent from Figure 6.10 that $P(B_1 \cup B_2)$ does not equal $P(B_1)$ + $P(B_2)$, for B_1 and B_2 have a common element $\{(H, H)\}$ whose probability should not be added twice. These results can be summarized by the *General Rule of Addition*, which states:

If B_1 and B_2 are events, then

$$P(B_1 \cup B_2) = P(B_1) + P(B_2) - P(B_1 \cap B_2)\ldots\ldots\ldots(6.8)$$

This rule applies to the addition of probabilities whether the events are mutually exclusive or not. If events are mutually exclusive, then the corresponding subsets are disjoint and the last term $P(B_1 \cap B_2)$ is zero. For events not mutually exclusive, $P(B_1 \cap B_2)$ is greater than zero and less than or equal to one.

The Special Rule of Multiplication

The rules of addition provide the basis for finding the probability of a compound event where the occurrence of *any one* of the component elementary events constitutes the occurrence of the compound event. But not all probability problems are of this nature, since one may wish to determine the probability of a *succession* of elementary events. This type of probability is called a *joint* probability.

➤ *Example.* A production supervisor randomly assigns five operators to five machines. From experience it is known that, on the average, each of the operators spends about one tenth of his time waiting for raw material. The operators include two men and three women. The probability that at any moment during the working day the operator of a randomly selected machine will be *both* male and waiting for material is $P(\text{male}) \cdot P(\text{waiting}) = \left(\frac{2}{5}\right) \cdot \left(\frac{1}{10}\right) = \frac{2}{50}$, as shown by the probability tree in Figure 6.11.

Before generalizing the results in Figure 6.11, it is important to make clear an assumption that is implicit in the example; namely, that the selection of a male or a female operator in no way influences the likelihood that the worker is operating a machine or waiting for material. Events of this type are said to be *statistically independent*. Similarly, the outcomes of tosses of a coin are independent if the coin is a fair one.

A general statement of the joint probability of independent events is given by the *Special Rule of Multiplication*, which states:

For k independent events $A_1, A_2, \ldots, A_k$, the probability that all these events will occur is

$$P(A_1 \cap A_2 \cap \ldots \cap A_k) = P(A_1) \cdot P(A_2) \cdot \ldots \cdot P(A_k) \ \ldots\ldots(6.9)$$

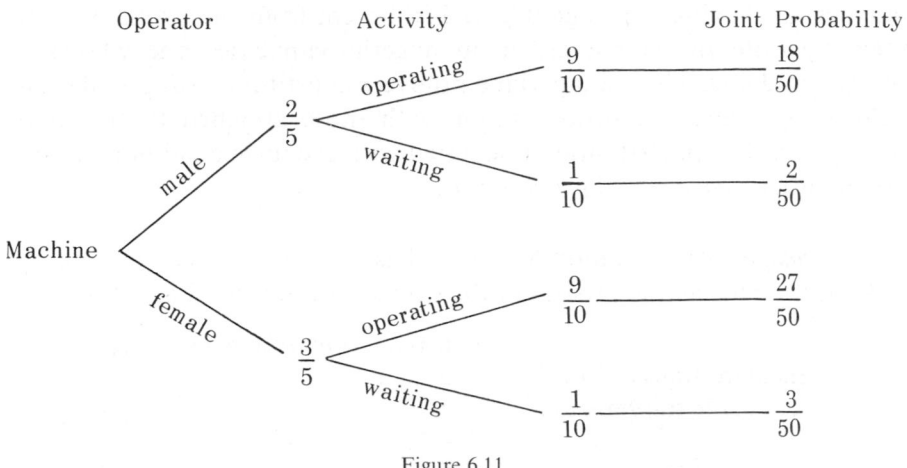

Figure 6.11

TREE DIAGRAM SHOWING CALCULATION
OF JOINT PROBABILITIES

➤ *Example.* Records of an airline indicate that $\frac{1}{3}$ of its stewardesses are blondes, $\frac{1}{2}$ are college graduates, and $\frac{3}{4}$ have more than one year of service. The probability that a randomly selected stewardess is blonde *and* a college graduate *and* has more than a year of service is, assuming independence, $\left(\frac{1}{3}\right) \cdot \left(\frac{1}{2}\right) \cdot \left(\frac{3}{4}\right) = \frac{1}{8}$.

It is important that mutually exclusive events not be confused with independent events. Consider the outcomes of a toss of a fair coin where A denotes the event "head" and B denotes the occurrence of a tail. The events A and B are collectively exhaustive and mutually exclusive (cannot occur simultaneously), which implies $P(A \cap B) = 0$. But Formula 6.9 states that if these are independent events, then

$$P(A \cap B) = P(A) \cdot P(B), \text{ but } 0 \neq \left(\tfrac{1}{2}\right) \cdot \left(\tfrac{1}{2}\right)$$

and, therefore, A and B are not independent. It follows that independent events must have nonzero probabilities and correspond to sets with a common point, that is, a nonzero intersection.

In reality, business problems often involve statistical dependence, in which the probability of one event is conditional upon the occurrence of another. The following section takes up problems of this type.

Conditional Probability

Problems frequently arise that deal with the probabilities for only a portion of instead of the complete sample space. Thus, the probability of an event depends upon what portion of the sample space is considered. The probability of randomly selecting from the population of all em-

ployees one having a college degree is different from the probability of
selecting from the employees in managerial capacities one who is a
college graduate. The managerial employees constitute a subpopulation
defined by special conditions along with those attached to the total
population. The probabilities associated with events in a subpopulation
are defined as *conditional probabilities*.

➤ *Example.* An automobile dealer has 10 cars for use as demon-
strators. The characteristics of the cars are summarized as follows:

	Sedans	Station wagons	Total
Standard transmission	2	1	3
Automatic transmission	4	3	7
Total	6	4	10

If all the cars are available for use, the sample space S is 10 for the
random selection of a vehicle. The probability of an event A, the
selection of a car with an automatic transmission, is $P(A) = \frac{7}{10}$; the
probability of event B, the random choice of a station wagon, is
$P(B) = \frac{4}{10}$. Now assume that a customer asks to drive a station wagon.
The sample space is reduced from $S = 10$ to the subpopulation $B = 4$.
The conditional probability of A (a car with an automatic transmission) given that the car is a station wagon is $P(A \mid B) = \frac{3}{4}$, the
probability of A associated with the reduced sample space B. The term
$P(A \mid B)$ is read: the probability that an event A will occur, given the
condition that event B has already occurred. The original sample space
S is depicted in Figure 6.12 by the rectangle shown in two parts. The
reduced sample space B is represented by the right-hand portion of
the rectangle. The shaded portion of the rectangle is the subset of
vehicles with automatic transmissions.

The result $P(A \mid B) = \frac{3}{4}$ is verified by considering that $P(A \mid B)$ is
equal to $P(A \cap B)$, the proportion of all cars that are station wagons
with automatic transmissions divided by $P(B)$, the proportion of cars
that are station wagons. Thus,

$$P(A \mid B) = \frac{P(A \cap B)}{P(B)} = \frac{\frac{3}{10}}{\frac{4}{10}}.$$

More formally, the *conditional probability* of an event A relative to an
event B, given that A and B are events from the same sample space and
$P(A) \neq 0$, is expressed by

$$P(A \mid B) = \frac{P(A \cap B)}{P(B)} \quad \dots \dots \dots \dots \dots \dots \text{(6.10)}$$

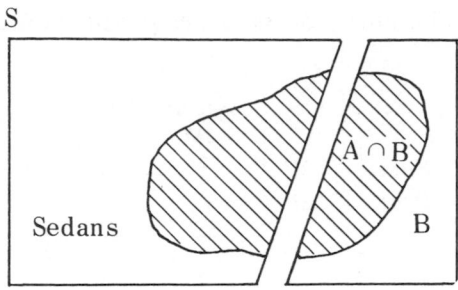

Figure 6.12

DIAGRAM OF AN ORIGINAL AND REDUCED
SAMPLE SPACE

An assumption of the foregoing example was that the sample points had equal probabilities, but this assumption is not a requirement. Conditional probabilities can be very usefully applied to more general problems of assigning probabilities in a sample space. Another important general use of conditional probability is made in ascertaining the validity of various alternative hypotheses that may be based on experimental outcomes.

The General Rule of Multiplication

Probabilities can be assigned to a sample space by means of a rearrangement of the terms in Formula 6.10 as illustrated by the following examples.

➤ *Example.* In the toolroom of a plant there are six identical power drills, four of which are in working order (W) and two of which are defective (D). The toolroom clerk receives a requisition for two drills and the drills are selected randomly and issued. The sample space S for the experiment is

$$S = \{(W, W), (W, D), (D, W), (D, D)\}$$

representing the possible outcomes of selecting two drills. The probability of issuing two drills in working order is $P(W_1) = \frac{4}{6}$ for the first selection and $\frac{3}{5}$ for the second selection, and from Formula 6.10:

$$P(W_2 \mid W_1) = \frac{P(W_1 \cap W_2)}{P(W_1)}$$

$$\frac{3}{5} = \frac{P(W_1 \cap W_2)}{\frac{4}{6}}$$

and

$$P(W_1 \cap W_2) = \left(\tfrac{3}{5}\right)\left(\tfrac{4}{6}\right) = \tfrac{2}{5}.$$

Similarly, the probabilities of the other possible outcomes are shown as follows:

		Second Drill		
		W	D	
First	W	$\frac{2}{5}$	$\frac{4}{15}$	$\frac{2}{3}$
Drill	D	$\frac{4}{15}$	$\frac{1}{15}$	$\frac{1}{3}$
		$\frac{2}{3}$	$\frac{1}{3}$	1

➤ **Example.** A contractor submits separate contract bids for the plumbing and heating of a building. The contractor estimates subjectively that he has a $\frac{1}{2}$ chance of being awarded the plumbing contract, event A. Further, he estimates that there is a $\frac{2}{3}$ chance of also receiving the heating contract, event B, if the plumbing contract is received. Should the contractor not receive the plumbing contract, he nevertheless feels that he has a $\frac{1}{4}$ chance of receiving the heating contract. The probabilities for the intermediate and the final events are shown in Figure 6.13.

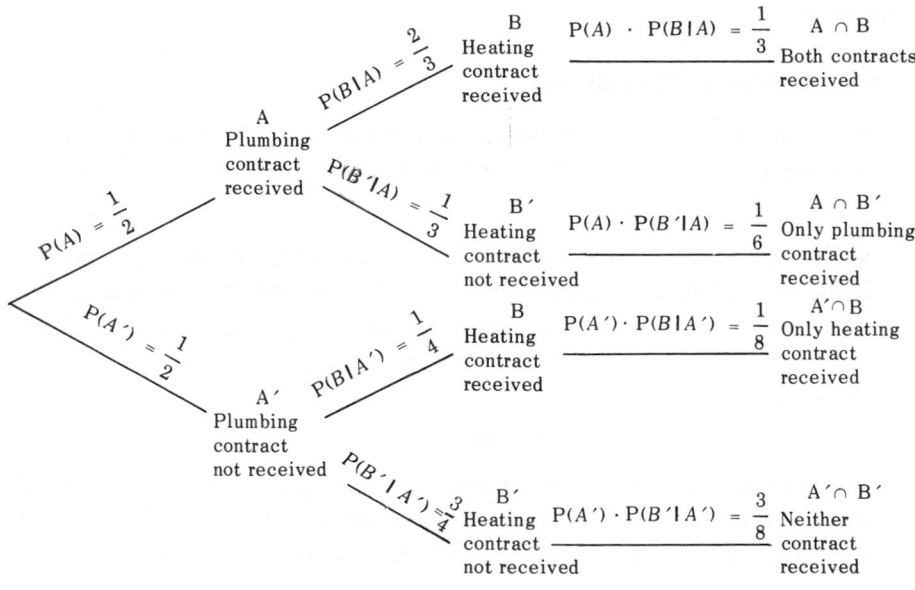

Figure 6.13

TREE DIAGRAM OF SEQUENTIAL EVENTS INVOLVING
CONDITIONAL PROBABILITIES

The foregoing example provides an intuitive illustration of the *General Rule of Multiplication*, which states:

If A and B are dependent events, the probability that A will occur, given that B has occurred, is expressed by

$$P(A \cap B) = P(B) \cdot P(A \mid B) \dots\dots\dots\dots\dots(6.11)$$

and it is also true that

$$P(A \cap B) = P(A) \cdot P(B \mid A).$$

In the previous example the probability that the heating contract will be received (given that the plumbing contract was not received) is $P(A' \cap B) = P(A') \cdot P(B \mid A') = \left(\frac{1}{2}\right) \cdot \left(\frac{1}{4}\right) = \frac{1}{8}$.

The Rule of Elimination

Suppose the contractor in the preceding example wishes to determine the probability of receiving the heating contract whether or not the plumbing contract is received. There are two conditions in which the heating contract can be received, and the probability of either of these outcomes occurring is the sum of the joint probabilities $P(A) \cdot P(B \mid A) + P(A') \cdot P(B \mid A') = \left(\frac{1}{2}\right)\left(\frac{2}{3}\right) + \left(\frac{1}{2}\right)\left(\frac{1}{4}\right) = \frac{11}{24}$.

The general form of this type of calculation is given by the *Rule of Elimination*, which states:

If $A_1, A_2, \ldots, A_k$ are mutually exclusive events, then

$$P(B) = P(A_1) \cdot P(B \mid A_1) + P(A_2) \cdot P(B \mid A_2) + \ldots + P(A_k) \cdot P(B \mid A_k)$$
$$\dots\dots\dots\dots\dots(6.12)$$

The Rule of Elimination provides a general approach for determining the total probability of the occurrence of an event that can conditionally occur in each of several ways. The total probability of an event is illustrated in the foregoing example. Following the branches of the tree diagram in Figure 6.13, the event B can occur in either of two ways, after event A or after event A'.

Bayes' Theorem and the Revision of Probabilities

In the example dealing with the awarding of plumbing and heating contracts, there were two ways in which the contractor could receive the heating contract. The probability of receiving the heating contract in each of the two ways is dependent upon whether the plumbing contract is received. Suppose the contractor learns that he has been awarded the heating contract, but the decision concerning the plumbing contract has not been announced. The contractor now asks, "What is the probability that the plumbing contract will not be received?" This is to ask, "What is $P(A' \mid B)$?"

Bayes' Theorem. Before the announcement of either of the contracts, it was estimated that the probability of the contractor's receiving the plumbing contract is $P(A) = \frac{1}{2}$ and the probability of his not receiving the contract is $P(A') = \frac{1}{2}$. These probabilities, determined before any experimental information is obtained, are called *prior* probabilities. The conditional probability associated with each outcome of awarding the plumbing contract is known prior to any contract announcement and is sometimes called the *likelihood*. Once the receipt of the heating contract is learned, that is, experimental data are available, it is possible to estimate whether the plumbing contract was also received. This estimate is expressed as a numerical probability and is called the *posterior* probability, since this probability is determined after the result of an experiment is known. Thus, $P(A' \mid B)$ is the posterior probability estimate that the plumbing contract was not received.

The total probability of receiving the heating contract is the sum of the probabilities on the two corresponding branches of the tree diagram in Figure 6.13, or

$$P(B) = P(A) \cdot P(B \mid A) + P(A') \cdot P(B \mid A') = \frac{1}{3} + \frac{1}{8} = \frac{11}{24}.$$

The posterior probability $P(A' \mid B)$ is calculated by determining what proportion of the total probability of B is attributed to the occurrence of B, given A'. In other words, B can occur in more than one way and the total probability of B occurring is the sum of the probabilities of each of the ways in which B can occur. It follows that the probability that B occurred in one *particular* way is the ratio of the probability of B occurring in that particular way to the total probability of B happening at all. Thus,

$$P(A' \mid B) = \frac{P(A') \cdot P(B \mid A')}{P(A) \cdot P(B \mid A) + P(A') \cdot P(B \mid A')} = \frac{\left(\frac{1}{2}\right)\left(\frac{1}{4}\right)}{\left(\frac{1}{2}\right)\left(\frac{2}{3}\right) + \left(\frac{1}{2}\right)\left(\frac{1}{4}\right)} = \frac{\frac{1}{8}}{\frac{11}{24}}$$

$$= \frac{3}{11}.$$

➤ *Example.* In a manufacturing plant, Machine I produces 40% of the output, Machine II produces 25%, and Machine III produces 35%. One and one-half percent of the output of Machine I is defective; Machine II produces 1.2% defective items; and 2.0% of the output of Machine III is defective. A day's output from the machines consists of a large number of items. An item selected randomly from a day's output is found to be defective. A production supervisor wishes to know the respective probabilities that the item was produced by Machine I, Machine II, or Machine III. Let E designate the event of the random selection of a defective item and H_1, H_2, and H_3 denote, respectively, the event of the item having been produced by Machines I, II, and III. The various events and probabilities are shown in Table 6.4.

Table 6.4

CALCULATION OF POSTERIOR PROBABILITIES

Event	Prior $P(H_i)$	Conditional $P(E \mid H_i)$	Joint $P(H_i \cap E)$	Posterior $P(H_i \mid E)$
Machine I (H_1)	0.40	0.015	0.006	0.3750
Machine II (H_2)	0.25	0.012	0.003	0.1875
Machine III (H_3)	0.35	0.020	0.007	0.4375
		$P(E)$ =	0.016	

The posterior probability $P(H_1 \mid E)$ that the defective item was produced by Machine I is calculated by dividing the joint probability $P(H_1 \cap E)$ of the event that the item was produced by Machine I *and* defective by the total probability $P(E)$. The probability that the defective item was produced by Machine I is

$$P(H_1 \mid E) = \frac{P(H_1 \cap E)}{P(E)} - \frac{0.006}{0.016} = 0.3750,$$

where $P(H_1 \cap E) = P(H_1) \cdot P(E \mid H_1)$ and $P(E) = P(H_1 \cap E) + P(H_2 \cap E) + P(H_3 \cap E)$. The posterior probabilities for Machines II and III are calculated in a similar manner:

$$P(H_2 \mid E) = \frac{P(H_2 \cap E)}{P(E)} = \frac{0.003}{0.016} = 0.1875$$

and

$$P(H_3 \mid E) = \frac{P(H_3 \cap E)}{P(E)} = \frac{0.007}{0.016} = 0.4375.$$

This example is shown graphically in Figure 6.14 where the rectangle is the set S of a day's output of items; the portions H_1, H_2, and H_3 are the subsets of items produced by Machines I, II, and III, respectively; and the shaded portion E is the subset of defective items.

These results above are expressed in general form by *Bayes' Theorem,* which states:

If H_1, H_2, . . . , H_k *are mutually exclusive and collectively exhaustive events with nonzero probabilities, the posterior probability of an event H_i is:*

$$P(H_i \mid E) = \frac{P(H_i \cap E)}{P(H_1 \cap E) + P(H_2 \cap E) + \ldots + P(H_k \cap E)} \quad \ldots (6.13)$$

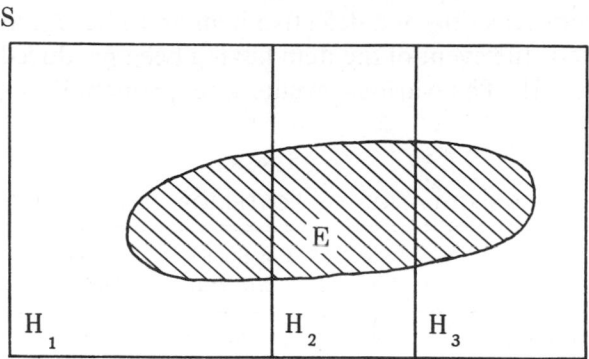

Figure 6.14

DIAGRAM OF THE OUTPUT OF THREE MACHINES

Revision of Probabilities. The application of Bayes' Theorem provides an important result in that the posterior probabilities constitute modifications of the prior probabilities based on experimental evidence. In the preceding example a defective item was selected, but the three machines differ in the proportion of defective items produced. Therefore, it follows that the probability of selecting a defective item from the production of a given machine should be proportional to the fraction of the total number of defective items produced by that machine. This modification is illustrated by comparing the prior and the posterior probabilities as follows:

Probability	*Machine*		
	I	II	III
Prior — before the item is known to be defective	0.4000	0.2500	0.3500
Posterior — after the item is known to be defective	0.3750	0.1875	0.4375

On any successive random selection, the probability of obtaining an acceptable *or* defective item from the output of Machine I is the prior probability $P(H_1) = 0.40$; but if an item is selected that is found to be defective, the probability that it belongs to the output of Machine I is $P(H_1 \mid E) = 0.3750$.

The revision of probabilities may also be applied to problems for which repeated experimental trials are possible and successive revisions of prior probabilities are made to verify a hypothesis concerning an event. For each successive revision, the posterior probability of the preceding trial becomes the prior probability of the following trial.

➤ *Example.* In a warehouse are two unmarked bins of parts, one of which is known to contain 80% defective items and the other 20% defective items. But it is not known which bin contains the larger percent of defective parts. Equal prior probabilities are assigned on the basis of insufficient reason. A part is selected from a bin in which the items are assumed to be 80% defective. The part turns out to be defective, denoted E, and the posterior probabilities are calculated. A second part, also defective, is chosen from the same bin, and the posterior probabilities are calculated to estimate the probability that Bin I contains 80% defective parts. The calculations are shown in Table 6.5. Notice that the posterior probabilities based on the outcome of the first trial are the prior probabilities of the second trial. The probability of the hypothesis that Bin I contains 80% defective items is 0.94, the posterior probability based on the two experimental outcomes.

Table 6.5

CALCULATION OF POSTERIOR PROBABILITIES FROM
EXPERIMENTAL DATA

Trial	Event	Prior $P(H_i)$	Conditional $P(E \mid H_i)$	Joint $P(H_i \cap E)$	Posterior $P(H_i \mid E)$
First	Bin I (H_1)	0.50	0.80	0.40	0.80
	Bin II (H_2)	0.50	0.20	0.10	0.20
			$P(E)$ =	0.50	
Second	Bin I (H_1)	0.80	0.80	0.64	0.94
	Bin II (H_2)	0.20	0.20	0.04	0.06
			$P(E)$ =	0.68	

In reality, a sample of more than two items would provide greater reliability, but the use of larger samples would require a great many steps in revising probabilities if it were done for each sample item. Sampling theory, however, provides convenient, shortcut methods for formulating such problems and these will be considered in Chapter 7.

MATHEMATICAL EXPECTATION

In the discussions that follow, the concept of a mathematical expectation will be used frequently and it is important to relate this idea to concepts of probability already presented. The *mathematical expectation*, also called the *expected value*, of a variable is the weighted arithmetic mean of the variable. The weights used to find the mathematical expectation are all the respective probabilities of the values that the variable can possibly assume.

➤ *Example.* In a game of chance, a player is offered an amount of money in dollars equal to the value that turns up on the toss of a fair

die. The sample space of a discrete variable X is the set of outcomes
{$1, $2, $3, $4, $5, $6} and associated with each sample point is an
equal probability of $\frac{1}{6}$. The weighted arithmetic mean or mathematical
expectation of the amount paid to the player is $\frac{1}{6}($1) + \frac{1}{6}($2) + \frac{1}{6}($3)$
$+ \frac{1}{6}($4) + \frac{1}{6}($5) + \frac{1}{6}($6) = 3.50.

Summarizing the results above more formally, let X denote a variable
with outcomes $X_1, X_2, \ldots, X_n$ that occur with probabilities $P(X_1)$,
$P(X_2), \ldots, P(X_n)$. The mathematical expectation of X is written $E(X)$,
and

$$E(X) = X_1 P(X_1) + X_2 P(X_2) + \ldots + X_n P(X_n) \ldots\ldots(6.14)$$

Note that the mathematical expectation of $3.50 in the preceding
example is not a value of the variable X that can actually occur. Rather,
the expected value of the variable X is the long-run average of payments
for many repeated trials of the game expressed as the probability-
weighted mean of the values of the variable.

➤ *Example.* A player pays $2 to play a game of chance. If on a single
draw from a standard deck of cards the ace of spades is drawn, the
player is paid $15. The player is paid $1 if any other spade is drawn.
The expected value of the game for the player is

$$E(X) = \tfrac{1}{52}($13) + \tfrac{12}{52}(-$1) + \tfrac{39}{52}(-$2) = -$1.48.$$

The game is not a fair one, for the long-run expectation of the player
is a loss of $1.48 for each play of the game. To make the game a fair
gamble, the cost of playing the game should be reduced to $0.69 rather
than the original cost of $2.

The use of a mathematical expectation was originally applied to games
of chance and lotteries, but the notion of an expected value has become
more generally applied and is now a common term in everyday parlance.
Business decisions frequently involve the consideration of expected
values in evaluating alternative courses of action.

INCREMENTAL INVENTORY MODELS

Probability concepts may be applied to business decisions in which
the outcomes of events are uncertain. The inventory models considered
in this discussion are based on the assumption that decisions are made
in terms of expected monetary values.

An Inventory Decision Problem

A type of inventory problem that occurs frequently in business in which one must decide how many units of inventory should be stocked and the number of units that will be required or demanded is a random variable. In this type of problem, a discrete set of acts or alternatives is available from which a choice can be made and the monetary outcome of a particular choice or act is uncertain. It is assumed that expected monetary value is the criterion used in making the inventory decision. The selection of the best of available acts can be determined by computing the expected monetary value associated with each of the available choices.

➤ *Example.* A department store manager must decide how many dresses of a given style to stock for the coming season. Dresses can be purchased from the manufacturer in lots of 10 dozen dresses. The profit per dozen dresses is $100 and dresses not sold by the end of the season are sold at a loss of $75 per dozen. Assume that unsatisfied demand will not result in any loss of future sales. The manager estimates that there is a 0.30 probability of selling 50 dozen dresses, a 0.50 probability of selling 60 dozen dresses, and a 0.20 probability of selling 70 dozen dresses. The conditional profit for each possible action is found by calculating the gross profit and subtracting any loss. For instance, if 50 dozen dresses are demanded and 60 dozen were stocked, the gross profit is (50)($100) = $5,000. At the end of the season 60 − 50 = 10 dozen dresses that must be sold at a loss of 10($75) = $750. The net profit of stocking 60 dozen dresses, given the *condition* that 50 are demanded, is $5,000 − $750 = $4,250 as seen in Table 6.6 under the heading "Act: Stock 60 dozen."

Table 6.6

CALCULATION OF THE MAXIMUM EXPECTED PROFIT

Event (Demand in dozens)	Probability	Act: Stock 50 dozen		Act: Stock 60 dozen		Act: Stock 70 dozen	
		Conditional profit	Expected profit	Conditional profit	Expected profit	Conditional profit	Expected profit
50	0.30	$5,000	$1,500	$4,250	$1,275	$3,500	$1,050
60	0.50	5,000	2,500	6,000	3,000	5,250	2,625
70	0.20	5,000	1,000	6,000	1,200	7,000	1,400
Total expected profit			$5,000		$5,475		$5,075

A demand of 50 dozen dresses is expected with a 0.30 probability, and the expected profit from stocking 60 dozen dresses is ($4,250)(0.30) = $1,275.

The best act is to stock 60 dozen dresses, for the expected profit is $5,475, the maximum expected profit of all three acts.

Incremental Analysis

The foregoing example illustrates the technique of computing the expected monetary value of respective alternatives and choosing the specific act for which the expected value is a maximum. An alternative approach may be utilized in which the decision procedure may be viewed as a sequence of steps in which the inventory level is increased successively by one unit in each step. The profitability of each additional unit is evaluated in terms of expected profitability. Units are added to inventory until the point is reached where the addition of one more unit decreases expected profit. This approach to the inventory decision problem is called *incremental analysis*.

➤ *Example.* A bookstore manager must decide how many copies of the current edition of a tax law book should be stocked. Since some of the tax laws change from year to year, a new edition of the book is published each year and old editions become obsolete. The bookstore purchases the books for $8 per copy and the books retail at $10 per copy. Books not sold in the year while the edition is current must be sold for $3 per copy. Sales records indicate that the probability of demand for tax books is as follows:

Demand (units)	Probability
10	0.05
11	0.15
12	0.35
13	0.25
14	0.15
15	0.05
	1.00

The conditional profit of each of the acts and the corresponding demand levels is shown as follows:

Table 6.7

CONDITIONAL PROFIT FOR VARIOUS STOCKING DECISIONS
AND LEVELS OF DEMAND

Demand			Stock			
(units)	10	11	12	13	14	15
10	$20	$15	$10	$5	$0	$ − 5
11	20	22	17	12	7	2
12	20	22	24	19	14	9
13	20	22	24	26	21	16
14	20	22	24	26	28	23
15	20	22	24	26	28	30

The expected profit of each of the acts and the corresponding levels
of demand is shown as follows:

Table 6.8

PROBABILITY WEIGHTED CONDITIONAL PROFITS FOR VARIOUS
STOCKING DECISIONS AND LEVELS OF DEMAND

		Expected profits					
Demand				Stock			
(units)	Probability	10	11	12	13	14	15
10	0.05	$1.00	$0.75	$0.50	$0.25	$0.00	$ −0.25
11	0.15	3.00	3.30	2.55	1.80	1.05	0.30
12	0.35	7.00	7.70	8.40	6.65	4.90	3.15
13	0.25	5.00	5.50	6.00	6.50	5.25	4.00
14	0.15	3.00	3.30	3.60	3.90	4.20	3.45
15	0.05	1.00	1.10	1.20	1.30	1.40	1.50
Total	1.00	$20.00	$21.65	$22.25	$20.40	$16.80	$12.15

The optimum act in this example is to stock 12 units, for the expected profit is a maximum.

The incremental character of this type of analysis is perhaps grasped
more readily by considering a stepwise presentation. This approach
begins with considering the profitability of stocking 10 units. The
expected profit is computed as:

Event	Probability	Conditional profit	Expected profit
Demand < 10	0.00	$0.00	$0.00
Demand ≥ 10	1.00	20.00	20.00
	1.00		$20.00

The probability that the demand level will be greater than or equal to 10 is the sum of the probabilities for all demand levels of 10 or more.

The incremental expected profit of adding one more unit (the 11th) to the stock level is computed as:

Event	Probability	Conditional profit	Expected profit
Demand < 11	0.05	$ − 5.00	$ − 0.25
Demand ≥ 11	0.95	2.00	1.90
	1.00		$1.65

The expected profit of increasing the stock level from 10 to 11 units is $1.65. The total expected profit of stocking 11 units is found by adding the expected profit for stocking 10 units and the expected profit for stocking the 11th unit, or

Stock 10 units		Add an 11th unit		Stock 11 units
$20.00	+	$1.65	=	$21.65

This value is the same as that obtained for the act "Stock 11" in Table 6.8.

The incremental expected profit of increasing the stock level by an additional unit (the 12th) is computed as:

Event	Probability	Conditional profit	Expected profit
Demand < 12	0.20	$ − 5.00	$ − 1.00
Demand ≥ 12	0.80	2.00	1.60
	1.00		$0.60

The probability that demand will be less than 12 units is the probability of demand of 10 plus the probability of a demand of 11 units, or

$$0.05 + 0.15 = 0.20.$$

Correspondingly, the probability that demand will be 12 or more units is computed as:

$$0.95 − 0.15 = 0.80.$$

The incremental expected profit of increasing the stock level from 11 to 12 units is found by adding the expected profit for stocking 11 units and the expected profit for stocking the 12th unit, or

Stock 11 units		Add a 12th unit		Stock 12 units
$21.65	+	$0.60	=	$22.25

This value is the same as that obtained for the act "Stock 12" in Table 6.8.

If an increment, consisting of a 13th unit, is added to the stock level of 12 units, the expected profit is computed to be:

Event	Probability	Conditional profit	Expected profit
Demand < 13	0.55	$ − 5.00	$ − 2.75
Demand ≥ 13	0.45	2.00	0.90
	1.00		$ − 1.85

The incremental expected profit of adding a 13th unit is $ − 1.85. Since the incremental marginal profit is negative, the act "Stock 13" is not the optimal choice. This is seen by computing the total expected profit of stocking 13 units as follows:

Stock 12 units		Add a 13th unit		Stock 13 units
$22.25	−	$1.85	=	$20.40

The expected profit for stocking 13 is less than the expected profit for stocking 12 units. The expected profit for stocking either 14 or 15 units is also less than that for the act "Stock 12," as seen in Table 6.8.

Analysis Using Marginal Expected Values

The application of incremental analysis can be tedious if a large number of available acts and possible levels of demand are involved in an inventory decision problem. The amount of computation can be reduced by utilizing a significant concept in microeconomic theory. On the basis of this concept, the optimal economic choice is that for which the marginal revenue is equal to the marginal cost. This concept is extended to apply to situations involving uncertainty, in which case the optimal choice is that for which the expected marginal revenue is equal to the expected marginal cost.

The class of incremental inventory problems presented in this discussion are discrete in nature. It may happen that the equivalence of marginal revenue and marginal cost corresponds to an act that is not practical, such as "Stock $11\frac{1}{2}$ units." The most profitable available act can, however, be obtained by marginal analysis.

The marginal revenue in the foregoing example is:

$$MR = \text{Sales price} - \text{Dealer cost} = \$10 - \$8 = \$2.$$

The marginal cost in this example is the cost sustained when units are no longer current and must be sold at a loss. For this reason, marginal cost will be termed marginal loss and it is computed as:

$$ML = \text{Sales price} - \text{Dealer cost} = \$3 - \$8 = \$ - 5.$$

The expected marginal revenue is written pMR, where p is the probability that an additional (incremental) unit will be sold and the incremental profit (MR) will be earned. The expected marginal loss is written $(1 - p)ML$, where $(1 - p)$ is the probability that an additional (incremental) unit will not be sold and the incremental loss (ML) will be incurred. Total expected profit is a maximum for the act for which the respective expected marginal values are equal, or

$$pMR = (1 - p)ML \qquad ....(6.15)$$

Formula 6.15 is solved for p to obtain

$$p_c = \frac{ML}{ML + MR} \qquad ....(6.16)$$

where p_c is the computed probability that an incremental unit will be sold. The value of p_c for the foregoing example is computed by Formula 6.16 as follows:

$$p_c = \frac{ML}{ML + MR} = \frac{5}{5 + 2} = 0.71.$$

The application of the value $p_c = 0.71$ in selecting the optimal act is illustrated by summarizing the results of the incremental analysis. This summary is presented in Table 6.9.

Table 6.9
SUMMARY OF AN INCREMENTAL ANALYSIS OF AN
INVENTORY PROBLEM

Demand D (1)	Probability that less than D units will be demanded (2)	Probability that D or more units will be demanded (3)	Expected incremental profit (4)	Total expected profit (5)
10	0.00	1.00	0.00($0) + 1.00($2) = $2.00	$20.00
11	0.05	0.95	0.05($-5) + 0.95($2) = $1.65	21.65
12	0.20	0.80	0.20($-5) + 0.80($2) = $0.60	22.25
13	0.55	0.45	0.55($-5) + 0.45($2) = $-1.85	20.40
14	0.80	0.20	0.80($-5) + 0.20($2) = $-3.60	16.80
15	0.95	0.05	0.95($-5) + 0.05($2) = $-4.65	12.15

The value $p_c = 0.71$ can be used to select the optimal act by comparing this computed value with the probabilities in column (3) of Table 6.9. The probabilities in column (3) reflect the likelihood that the level of demand will be equal to or greater than some selected value D. The computed value $p_c = 0.71$ does not occur in column (3) of Table 6.9 because of the discrete character of the problem. The optimal inventory decision is found, however, by comparing the probabilities in column (3) with $p_c = 0.71$. The inventory level should be increased incrementally as long as the probability in column (3) is not less than the computed value p_c. In this example, the inventory level is increased to a level of 12 units. At this level $p_c = 0.71 < 0.80$. For an inventory level of 13, $p_c = 0.71 > 0.45$, and the choice is not optimal since the probability of selling the additional incremental unit is less than the computed value p_c.

STUDY QUESTIONS

6-1. Explain briefly the meaning of each of the following terms:

a. statistical inference	x. Venn diagram
b. arrangement	y. union
c. permutation	z. intersection
d. tree diagram	aa. unit set
e. combination	ab. disjoint set
f. Pascal's triangle	ac. complement
g. experiment	ad. stochastic processes
h. elementary event	ae. random variable
i. collectively exhaustive event	af. function
j. mutually exclusive event	ag. domain
k. elementary unit	ah. range
l. universe	ai. point function
m. simple random sampling	aj. set function
n. equiprobable events	ak. sample space
o. a priori probability	al. joint probability
p. statistical regularity	am. statistically independent events
q. compound event	an. conditional probability
r. subjective probability	ao. prior probability
s. set	ap. posterior probability
t. discrete set	aq. revised probability
u. universal set	ar. mathematical expectation
v. subset	as. incremental analysis
w. event	

6-2. What are the mutually exclusive and collectively exhaustive events for the following experiments?

a. The number of heads in a toss of two coins

b. The combined value of the faces in a toss of a pair of dice

c. The number of spades or kings in a hand of five cards dealt from a deck of 52 playing cards

6-3. What assumptions must be made so that the outcomes of each of the following experiments may be considered equiprobable?

    a. Tossing a coin

    b. A salesman attempting to sell an automobile to a customer

    c. The price of a common stock one month from now.

6-4. In an experiment two hands of 12 cards each are dealt from a deck of 52 playing cards. Hand A is dealt, with replacement, from the deck and contains five spades. Hand B is dealt without replacement and contains four spades. How are the following concepts related to the samples represented by hands A and B?

    a. statistical regularity   d. compound event

    b. uniform conditions   e. a priori probability

    c. relative frequency   f. conditional probability

6-5. The consumers in a marketing area may be classified by a variety of criteria, such as annual income, occupation, and education. Write a description for each of two subsets that:

    a. Identify consumers with a common characteristic

    b. Are disjoint

    c. Have an intersection

    d. Are the complements of other subsets

6-6. An electronic component of a computer is mass produced by a firm. The component is judged to be of acceptable quality if its voltage rating lies within a specified range. Random samples of components are drawn hourly from the process and, if the sample contains no defective units, production is continued. If a defective component is drawn in the sample, the process is stopped and adjustments are made. Relate the characteristics of this example to each of the following concepts:

    a. Discrete random variable   c. Stochastic variable   e. Subset

    b. Continuous random variable   d. Sample space

6-7. Draw a diagram of the sample space of an experiment consisting of one toss of three coins. Relate graphically the subsets of the sample space with the range, expressed in terms of the number of heads that can occur.

6-8. A space capsule is to be launched to orbit the planet Jupiter and to transmit data reflecting conditions on the planet. The probability that the capsule will remain on course during the launch period is A. The probability that the capsule will drift from the designated course while in flight is designated B. Probability C denotes the likelihood that corrections can be made in flight to correct any deviations from the desired trajectory and course. Express each of the following probabilities in words:

    a. $P(B \mid A)$ c. $P(C \mid A')$ e. $P(A \cup B)$

    b. $P(C \cap B \mid A)$ d. $P(A \cap B')$ f. $P(C \mid A \cup B)$

6-9. Draw a tree diagram of the situation described in Question 6-8.

6-10. Considering the situation given in Question 6-8:

    a. Which probabilities are independent?

    b. How are the rules of addition or multiplication of probabilities related to this situation?

6-11. What is the logical basis of Bayes' Theorem?

PROBLEMS

6-1. The letters R, S, T, and U are to be used as prefixes of inventory numbers for the items in a warehouse.
    a. How many different prefixes can be arranged with the four letters?
    b. If only two letters are to be used, how many different prefixes can be arranged?

6-2. Using the letters W, X, Y, and Z:
    a. Compute the number of different sequences of four letters that can be arranged.
    b. Find the number of different sequences of three letters that can be arranged from the four letters.

6-3. Evaluate:
    a. $_5P_2$
    b. $_8P_6$
    c. $_9P_4$

6-4. Evaluate:
    a. $_6P_1$
    b. $_5P_2$
    c. $_{10}P_3$

6-5. How many different telephone numbers can be arranged from a three-digit area code and a seven-digit local number?

6-6. How many different telephone numbers, consisting of a two-letter alphabetical prefix and a five-digit number, can be formed provided the letters I and O do not appear as the first letter of a prefix and a prefix is not a repetition of any letter?

6-7. A firm has an inventory of five identical mechanisms in stock, one of which is defective.
    a. How many different groups of three mechanisms can be selected?
    b. How many different groups of three mechanisms can be selected that do not include the defective item?

6-8. If a firm has 10 salesmen, in how many ways can the salesmen be divided into:
    a. Two groups of six and four salesmen?
    b. Two groups of seven and three salesmen?

6-9. A machine shop has six work orders that require lathe work and four work orders that require milling work. If the shop has three lathes and two milling machines, in how many different ways can the work orders be assigned to the machines?

6-10. The standby repair crew of a shipyard consists of four electricians and five pipe fitters. There are repair calls pending, six of which require electrical repair and eight require pipe repairs. In how many different ways can the calls be assigned to the workmen?

6-11. Perform an experiment in which a thumbtack is shaken in a container, tossed onto a surface, and observed whether the tack lands with its point upward or downward. Repeat this procedure for a total of 50 trials. Use the relative frequency to estimate the probability that the tack will land point up on a trial of the experiment.

6-12. Perform an experiment in which random draws, with replacement, are made from a deck of cards. Remove six spades and six clubs from a standard deck of playing cards. Shuffle the remaining 40 cards, deal a card from the deck, observe whether it is a black card, replace the card, and shuffle the deck. Repeat this procedure 50 times. Compare the relative frequency and the probability of drawing a black card on a single draw from the deck.

6-13. If A and B are independent events, $P(A) = 0.30$, and $P(B) = 0.60$, evaluate:

   a. $P(A \cup B)$
   b. $P(A \cap B)$
   c. $P(B \mid A)$
   d. $P(A \cap B')$

6-14. If X, Y, and Z are independent events, evaluate:

   a. $P(Z)$ if $P(X \cap Z) = \frac{1}{2}$ and $P(X) = \frac{3}{4}$
   b. $P(Z)$ if $P(Y \cup Z) = \frac{3}{4}$ and $P(Y) = \frac{1}{6}$
   c. $P(Z \mid X \cap Y)$ if $P(X) = \frac{1}{5}$, $P(Y) = \frac{1}{4}$, and $P(Z) = \frac{1}{2}$
   d. $P(Z)$ if $P(X \cup Y \cup Z) = \frac{3}{4}$, $P(X) = \frac{1}{2}$, and $P(Y) = \frac{1}{8}$

6-15. An auditor selects accounts for inspection at random from the file of accounts receivable. Accounts that are less than six months old are termed new accounts. The accounts are classified as follows:

	Current	*Delinquent*
New accounts	108	12
Old accounts	792	88

Let N denote the event of the selection of a new account, and C, an account that is current. Evaluate the following:

   a. $P(N \mid C)$ e. $P(C' \mid N)$
   b. $P(N \cap C)$ f. $P(C \mid N')$
   c. $P(N \cup C')$ g. $P(C' \cap N')$
   d. $P(N' \cap C)$ h. $P(N \mid C \cup C')$

6-16. Incoming telephone calls to two exchanges during a one-hour period were recorded and classified as follows:

	Local	*Long distance*
GReenwood exchange	256	64
HOmewood exchange	144	36

Let G denote a call to the Greenwood exchange; H, a call to the Homewood exchange; L, a local call; and D, a long-distance call. Evaluate:

   a. $P(H \cap D)$ e. $P(L \mid G \cup H)$
   b. $P(G \cup L)$ f. $P(G \mid L \cup D)$
   c. $P(H \mid L)$ g. $P(G \cap H)$
   d. $P(D \mid H)$ h. $P(H \cup G \mid D)$

6-17. A contractor in the building-wrecking business has observed that his major competitor submits bids on about 60% of the jobs on which the contractor bids. The contractor has observed that he has been awarded jobs about 15% of the time when his major competitor also submitted a bid, and about 30% of the time when the competitor did not bid on the job. If the contractor submits a bid and does not receive the contract for the job, what is the probability that the major competitor also submitted a bid?

6-18. An oil-well drilling company must decide whether to drill a well at a location that the company has leased. On the basis of geological reports, there is a 0.40 probability that a formation of type *A* lies beneath the prospective well site, a 0.35 probability of a formation of type *B*, and a 0.25 probability of a type *C* formation. Company records show that 20% of the time oil is discovered in type *A* formations, 40% in type *B*, and 30% in type *C* formations. What is the probability that:

    a. If the well produces oil, it comes from a type *B* formation?

    b. If the well proves to be a dry hole, a type *C* formation lies beneath the well site?

6-19. An individual is offered an opportunity to bet $5 on the outcome of a roll of a pair of dice. If the dice turn up so that the sum of the faces totals seven or 11, the individual wins $15. For any other outcome the bet is lost. What is the expected value of the game for the individual?

6-20. An owner of a department store in a desirable downtown business location has an opportunity to sell his business for $500,000. He estimates that if he operates the store and business remains good, he can realize $900,000. If, however, there is a substantial shift of consumer shopping to the suburbs, he will realize only $200,000.

    a. If the probability of continued good business is 0.60, what is his optimum act?

    b. For what probability for continued good business would the building owner be indifferent to selling his business?

6-21. A baker has studied his records and notices that for the past 300 days the demand for his product has varied as follows:

Demand (units)	Number of days
10,000	18
11,000	90
12,000	120
13,000	60
14,000	12
	300

    a. What is the expected demand for his product?

    b. If production cost is $0.15 per unit, wholesale price is $0.20 per unit, and units not sold at the end of a day can be sold for only $0.10 per unit, what is the optimum daily output for the bakery? (Compute the optimum act for demand in terms of the nearest thousand units.)

6-22. A sporting goods dealer must decide how many outboard motorboats of a particular type to stock for the coming season. The probability distribution for levels of demand are as follows:

Demand (units)	Probability
5	0.05
6	0.10
7	0.20
8	0.30
9	0.15
10	0.10
11	0.10

The boats cost the dealer $800 each and the retail price during the season is $1,000 each. Boats not sold during the season must be marked down to $750.

   a. Compute the marginal expected profit of increasing the stock of boats from seven to eight units.
   b. Find the expected profit of the optimum act.

6-23. Draw a flow diagram for computing the values of $_nC_r$.

6-24. Draw a flow diagram for finding the coefficients of Pascal's triangle.

SELECTED READINGS

Feller, William. *An Introduction to Probability Theory and Its Applications.* 2d ed. New York: John Wiley and Sons, 1957.

> Chapters 1 and 2 present concise discussions of the nature of probability and its applications to various disciplines.

Kozelka, Robert M. *Elements of Statistical Inference.* Reading, Mass.: Addison-Wesley Publishing Company, Inc., 1961.

> Sets, counting, probability, and functions as the basis for statistical inference are presented in the first two chapters of this readable text.

Schlaifer, Robert. *Probability and Statistics for Business Decisions.* New York: McGraw-Hill Book Company, Inc., 1959.

> A discussion of the meaning and application of probability for business decisions is included in Chapter 1. An amplified presentation of conditional and joint probabilities can be found in Chapter 9.

Yamane, Taro. *Statistics, An Introductory Analysis.* New York: Harper and Row, 1964.

> Alternate approaches to probability are introduced in Chapter 5 and are amplified in Chapter 16.

Chapter 7

Discrete Probability Distributions

Many practical business problems involve an analysis of the fluctuations of significant variables such as variations in sales, demand for inventory items, characteristics of manufactured products, and production costs. An important step in the analysis of a variable consists of grouping or classifying observations into a frequency distribution. The distribution of the relative frequencies with empirical values serves as the basis for determining the expectation of future values of a variable. In this manner, a distribution of expectations or probabilities serves as a model of an actual distribution of values.

The notion of expectation associated with relative frequencies is akin to the interpretation of probabilities, as discussed in the preceding chapter. A relative frequency is not in itself a probability, but an approximation of a probability. In many real situations, with no other significant information available, it is useful to assign probabilities that are numerically equal to the relative frequencies with which the values of a random variable have occurred. A theoretical model of the relative frequencies of a finite number of observations of a variable is called a *probability distribution*. It is a systematic arrangement of the probabilities associated with the mutually exclusive and collectively exhaustive elementary events of an experiment.

The principal objective of many statistical problems is the selection of an appropriate probability distribution with which to describe a random variable. In some situations, a variable is of such a nature that the probability distribution can be determined *a priori*.

➤ *Example.* It is known that half of the items in an inventory of screws of a given size were bought (B), while the other half were manufactured (M) by the firm having the inventory. The screws were thoroughly mixed as they were placed in a bin. A sample of four screws is to be drawn randomly from the bin. The number of manufactured screws that the sample can contain is defined as the random variable X. The probabilities associated with the elementary events of the experiment are computed *a priori* in Table 7.1 and systematically arranged as a probability distribution in Figure 7.1.

Table 7.1

THE *A PRIORI* PROBABILITIES OF THE OUTCOMES
OF AN EXPERIMENT

No. of mfg'd. parts X	Elementary events	Probability $P(X)$
0	(B, B, B, B)	$\left(\frac{1}{2} \cdot \frac{1}{2} \cdot \frac{1}{2} \cdot \frac{1}{2}\right) = \frac{1}{16}$
1	$(M, B, B, B), (B, M, B, B),$ $(B, B, M, B), (B, B, B, M)$	$4\left(\frac{1}{2} \cdot \frac{1}{2} \cdot \frac{1}{2} \cdot \frac{1}{2}\right) = \frac{1}{4}$
2	$(M, M, B, B), (M, B, M, B),$ $(M, B, B, M), (B, M, M, B),$ $(B, M, B, M), (B, B, M, M)$	$6\left(\frac{1}{2} \cdot \frac{1}{2} \cdot \frac{1}{2} \cdot \frac{1}{2}\right) = \frac{3}{8}$
3	$(M, M, M, B), (M, M, B, M),$ $(M, B, M, M), (B, M, M, M)$	$4\left(\frac{1}{2} \cdot \frac{1}{2} \cdot \frac{1}{2} \cdot \frac{1}{2}\right) = \frac{1}{4}$
4	(M, M, M, M)	$\left(\frac{1}{2} \cdot \frac{1}{2} \cdot \frac{1}{2} \cdot \frac{1}{2}\right) = \frac{1}{16}$

In other instances there is limited information available concerning the pattern of variation of a variable, and it is not feasible to determine theoretically the probability distribution of a variable. It is possible, however, that a theoretical probability distribution may provide a reasonably good expression or a model of a frequency distribution of observed values.

➤ *Example.* A study of the arrivals of trucks at a loading dock of a freight warehouse was made in which the number of trucks X arriving every half-hour period was observed. The results are summarized in Table 7.2. The distribution of arrivals was compared with a theoretical distribution that was judged to be a good description of the data. The empirical results and the theoretical approximation are shown in Figure 7.2.

Table 7.2

OBSERVED ARRIVALS OF TRUCKS
AT A LOADING DOCK

Number of arrivals per half-hour period	Number of periods
0	22
1	35
2	27
3	8
4	4
5	3
6	1
Total	100

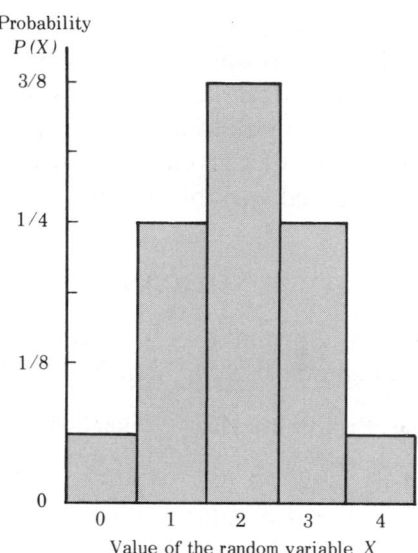

Figure 7.1

PROBABILITY DISTRIBUTION OF THE
OUTCOMES FOR SAMPLES OF FOUR SCREWS

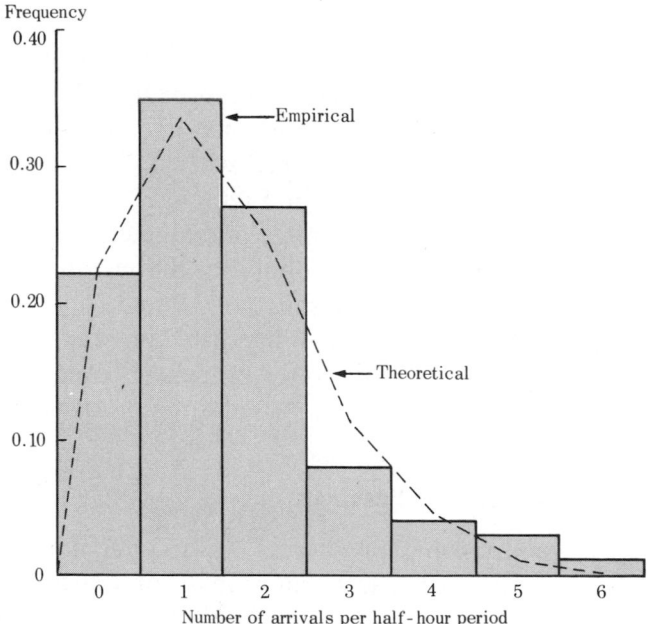

Figure 7.2

EMPIRICAL AND THEORETICAL DISTRIBUTIONS OF ARRIVALS
OF TRUCKS AT A LOADING DOCK

This chapter focuses upon some of the theoretical probability distributions that have most frequent applications to business problems. The emphasis is upon the theoretical basis of these distributions and the methods of determining probabilities. The statistical techniques for assessing the appropriateness of a given theoretical probability distribution as a model of an observed variable are discussed in Chapter 13.

PROBABILITY DENSITY FUNCTIONS

A function that assigns a probability to each of the elementary events of an experiment is called a *probability density function.*

Discrete and Continuous Probability Density Functions

A probability density function, abbreviated *pdf,* may be either discrete or continuous. A *discrete pdf* is a point function that is defined over a finite sample space, and takes on only a finite number of values. For example, a discrete *pdf* is defined over a sample space of an experiment consisting of the outcomes of drawing a sample of 25 accounts from the charge-account records of a large department store. It is known that 10% of all accounts are delinquent. The *pdf* assigns a probability to each of the elementary events, the number of delinquent accounts that can be drawn in the sample.

A *continuous pdf* is a set function that expresses a distribution in which a probability is assigned to a given range of values. For example, an automatic machine produces bearings that average three inches in diameter. The bearings may be produced with any diameter within the possible range of values as shown in Figure 7.3. The continuous *pdf* assigns a probability to any given range of diameters. The shaded area in Figure 7.3 corresponds to the probability that a randomly selected bearing will have a diameter in the range of 3.0 to 3.1 inches.

A *pdf* is distinguished from a probability distribution in that the former is a rule for assigning a probability to the elementary events of an experiment, while the latter is a systematic presentation or arrangement of the probabilities.

Cumulative Probability Density Functions

In the process of solving problems, one is often interested in the probability of all values less than or more than some specified value of a random variable rather than in the probability of an individual value. For instance, the manager of the freight warehouse in the example presented in Table 7.2 and Figure 7.2 may be interested in the probability of *more than two* trucks arriving in a half-hour period.

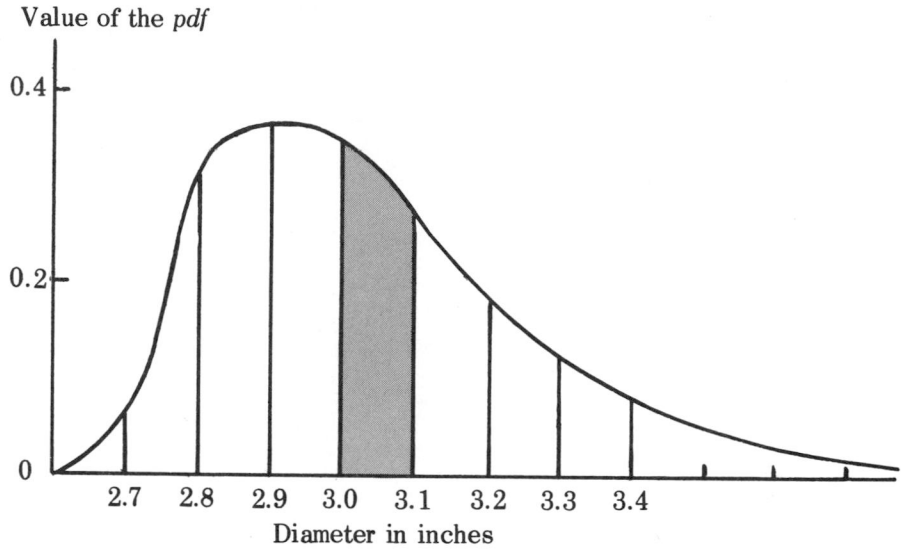

Figure 7.3

PROBABILITY DISTRIBUTION OF THE DIAMETERS OF BEARINGS

Viewing the relative frequencies as probabilities, the probability of more than two trucks arriving in a half-hour period is obtained by cumulating the values of the *pdf* for the respective events, or 0.09 + 0.03 + 0.02 + 0.01 = 0.15. Proceeding systematically in a similar fashion, the values of a discrete *cumulative probability density function* are obtained. The results are shown in Table 7.3 and Figure 7.4. For example, the cumulative probability is 0.74 for one or more arrivals during a half-hour period.

Table 7.3

PROBABILITIES OF SPECIFIED NUMBERS OF TRUCK ARRIVALS
PER HALF-HOUR PERIODS

Value of the random variable	Value of the *pdf*	Value of the cumulative *pdf*
0	0.26	1.00
1	0.35	0.74
2	0.24	0.39
3	0.09	0.15
4	0.03	0.06
5	0.02	0.03
6	0.01	0.01
	1.00	

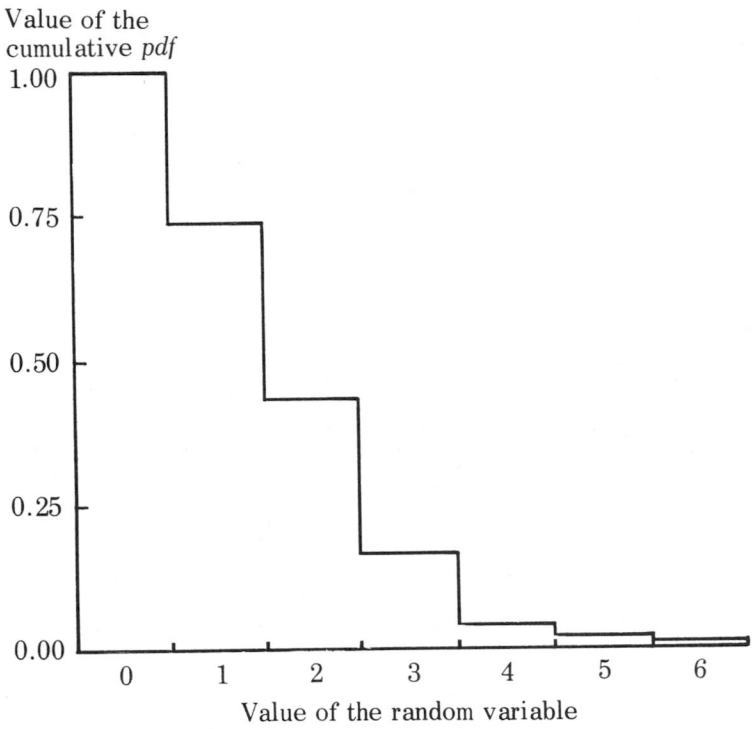

Figure 7.4

CUMULATIVE *pdf* OF A SPECIFIED NUMBER OF TRUCKS OR MORE
ARRIVING PER HALF-HOUR PERIOD

The height of each of the segments of the graph in Figure 7.4 corresponds to a cumulative area, or the *tail* of the distribution in Figure 7.2. The value 0.15 of the discrete cumulative *pdf* in Figure 7.4 represents the probability of three or more arrivals and is equal to the area of the right-hand tail of the distribution in Figure 7.2, which corresponds to the probability of three or more arrivals during a half-hour period.

A continuous cumulative *pdf* takes a form similar to the function in Figure 7.4, except that it is a smooth curve. The characteristics of a continuous cumulative *pdf* are discussed more fully in the following chapter.

MOMENTS

The expected value or the arithmetic mean of a random variable is defined by Formula 6.14 (page 168) as the weighted sum of the values of the variable, where the weights are the respective values of the probability density function. The expected value or mathematical expectation of other functions of a random variable can also be computed. An important class of these functions is termed *moments*. Some of the moments about the origin and the mathematical expectation of a variable have particular significance in statistical analysis.

Moments about the Origin

Expressed in general form, the kth *order moment about the origin of a random variable X* is defined as the mathematical expectation of the kth power of X, written M'_k. The kth moment (where k is some integer) of a discrete variable X, which may take on the values $X_1, X_2, \ldots, X_n$ with respective probabilities $P_1, P_2, \ldots, P_n$ assigned by a density function $P(X)$, is given by

$$M'_k = E(X^k) = \Sigma X_i^k P_i \quad \ldots\ldots\ldots\ldots\ldots\ldots\ldots\ldots(7.1)$$

Two of the moments about the origin of a random variable, the zero-order and the first-order moments, are important statistically. Applying Formula 7.1, the zero-order moment for the random variable X is

$$M'_0 = E(X^0) = \Sigma X_i^0 P_i = 1,$$

the total area of the probability distribution of X. The first-order moment of X is written as

$$M'_1 = E(X^1) = \Sigma X_i^1 P_i = \mu,$$

the expected value or arithmetic mean of the distribution of X.

➤ *Example.* The probability distribution of a discrete random variable X and the computation of the zero- and the first-order moments about the origin are shown in Table 7.4. The zero-order moment about the origin is one; the first-order moment is the mean of the distribution, $\mu = 1.60$.

Table 7.4

COMPUTATION OF THE EXPECTED VALUE OF A
DISCRETE RANDOM VARIABLE

Value of the random variable X_i	P_i	$X_i^0 P_i$	$X_i^1 P_i$
0	0.10	$(1)(.10) = 0.10$	$(0)(.10) = 0.00$
1	0.30	$(1)(.30) = 0.30$	$(1)(.30) = 0.30$
2	0.50	$(1)(.50) = 0.50$	$(2)(.50) = 1.00$
3	0.10	$(1)(.10) = 0.10$	$(3)(.10) = 0.30$
Totals	$\Sigma P_i = 1.00$	$\Sigma X_i^0 P_i = 1.00$	$\Sigma X_i^1 P_i = 1.60$

Moments about the Mathematical Expectation

A second important class of moments consists of the moments about the arithmetic mean, or the mathematical expectation of a random variable. The kth *moment of a discrete random variable X about* $E(X)$ is defined as the mathematical expectation of the kth power of the deviations of the values of X from μ and is written

$$M_k = E(X_i - \mu)^k = \Sigma(X_i - \mu)^k P_i \quad \dots\dots\dots\dots\dots\dots(7.2)$$

The first zero-order moment of a discrete random variable X about μ is given by

$$M_0 = E(X_i - \mu)^0 = \Sigma(X_i - \mu)^0 P_i = E(1) = 1,$$

the total area of the probability distribution. The first-order moment is written

$$M_1 = E(X_i - \mu)^1 = \Sigma(X_i - \mu)^1 P_i = 0,$$

which states that the sum of the deviations about the mean is zero. This expression is similar to Formula 3.17 (page 69), which is based on the relative frequency rather than on the probability of the occurrence of the values of a random variable.

The second-order moment of a discrete random variable X about μ is

$$M_2 = E(X_i - \mu)^2 = \Sigma(X_i - \mu)^2 P_i = \sigma^2,$$

the variance of the distribution of X, and is similar to Formula 3.18, page 69.

➤ *Example.* The mathematical expectation of a discrete random variable X is computed from the probability distribution in Table 7.5.

Table 7.5

COMPUTATION OF THE EXPECTED VALUE OF μ
FOR THE RANDOM VARIABLE X

Value of the random variable X_i	Probability $P(X_i)$	$X_i P_i$
0	0.10	$0(.10) = 0.00$
1	0.20	$1(.20) = 0.20$
2	0.40	$2(.40) = 0.80$
3	0.20	$3(.20) = 0.60$
4	0.10	$4(.10) = 0.40$
Totals	1.00	$\Sigma X_i P_i = \mu = 2.00$

The computation of the zero-, first-, and second-order moments about the mathematical expectation of the random variable X is shown in Table 7.6. The algorithm for finding these moments is shown in Figure 7.5. The standard deviation of the values of the random variable is the square root of the variance, or $\sqrt{1.2000} = 1.0954$.

The third and fourth moments about the mathematical expectation provide measures of absolute skewness and kurtosis. The application of these measures is discussed in Chapter 3.

Table 7.6

COMPUTATION OF THE ZERO-, FIRST-, AND SECOND-ORDER MOMENTS
ABOUT THE MEAN

X_i	$P(X_i)$	$(X_i - \mu)^0 P_i$	$(X_i - \mu)^1 P_i$	$(X_i - \mu)^2 P_i$
0	0.10	$(0 - 2.00)^0 (.10)$ $= 0.10$	$(0 - 2.00)^1 (.10)$ $= -0.20$	$(0 - 2.00)^2 (.10)$ $= 0.40$
1	0.20	$(1 - 2.00)^0 (.20)$ $= 0.20$	$(1 - 2.00)^1 (.20)$ $= -0.20$	$(1 - 2.00)^2 (.20)$ $= 0.20$
2	0.40	$(2 - 2.00)^0 (.40)$ $= 0.40$	$(2 - 2.00)^1 (.40)$ $- 0.00$	$(2 - 2.00)^2 (.40)$ $= 0.00$
3	0.20	$(3 - 2.00)^0 (.20)$ $= 0.20$	$(3 - 2.00)^1 (.20)$ $= 0.20$	$(3 - 2.00)^2 (.20)$ $= 0.20$
4	0.10	$(4 - 2.00)^0 (.10)$ $= 0.10$	$(4 - 2.00)^1 (.10)$ $= 0.20$	$(4 - 2.00)^2 (.10)$ $= 0.40$
Totals	1.00	$E(X_i - \mu)^0 = 1.00$	$E(X_i - \mu)^1 = 0.00$	$E(X_i - \mu)^2 = 1.20$

THE BINOMIAL PROBABILITY DISTRIBUTION

An important class of business problems involves random processes for which there are only two possible outcomes. The outcomes occur without any fixed pattern, and the probability of either outcome remains unchanged for each trial. Processes with these characteristics are called *Bernoulli processes*. For example, the parts produced by a machine are classified as being "acceptable" or "defective," and the probability of selecting either type of part remains unchanged for each trial. Similarly, in a survey, consumers are asked if they prefer a particular brand of product to other similar brands. The likelihood of eliciting either response remains unchanged, regardless of how many customers are queried.

In order to simplify the expression of the characteristics of Bernoulli processes, a specified or desired outcome of a trial will be termed a *success*. The proportion, or the long-run fraction, of successes obtained

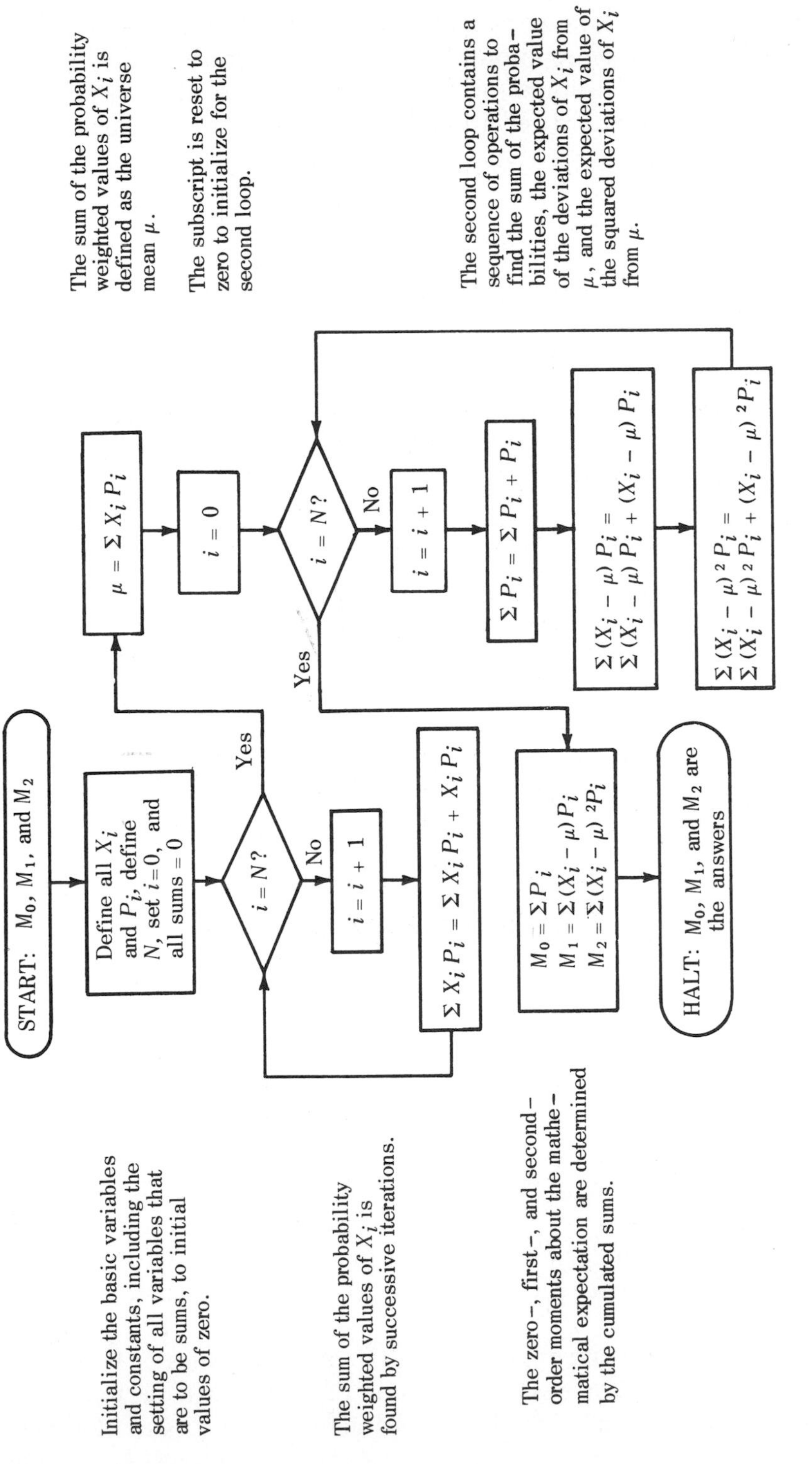

Figure 7.5

A FLOW DIAGRAM OF AN ALGORITHM FOR FINDING M_0, M_1, AND M_2

from a very large number of trials of a Bernoulli process is called a *parameter*. In some instances the proportion of trials that yields successes is known with certainty. Whatever the results of a finite number of trials, the acceptance of the validity of this long-run fraction is unchanged.

Binomial Probability Density Function

Consider an experiment in which a die is tossed four times and the number of sixes occurring is recorded. The number of ways in which a given number of sixes can be obtained is found by means of the rule for computing combinations. Thus, the number of ways of getting three sixes in four tosses of the die is

$$\binom{n}{r} = \binom{4}{3} = \frac{4!}{3!\,(4-3)!} = 4 \text{ ways.}$$

The probability that any one of the four ways will occur is obtained by using the rule for multiplying probabilities. For instance, the probability of obtaining a sequence consisting of three sixes (S) and one nonsix (N) is

$$P(SSSN) = \left(\tfrac{1}{6} \cdot \tfrac{1}{6} \cdot \tfrac{1}{6} \cdot \tfrac{5}{6}\right) = \tfrac{5}{1,296}.$$

The probability of getting three sixes in four tosses of a die is

$$4\left(\tfrac{5}{1,296}\right) = \tfrac{5}{324}.$$

These results can be generalized by viewing the occurrence of a six as a success where the probability of a success is p. Let q denote a nonsix, or a *failure*, where $q = 1 - p$. The probability that r successes and $n - r$ failures will be obtained in a particular sequence is given by

$$\underset{r \text{ successes}\quad n - r \text{ failures}}{(p \cdot p \cdot p \cdots p)(q \cdot q \cdot q \cdots q)} = p^r q^{n-r}$$

The number of ways in which r successes can be obtained in n trials is given by $\binom{n}{r}$. The generalized expression of the function describing the probability of obtaining exactly r successes in n trials of an experiment is

$$P(r \mid n, p) = \binom{n}{r} p^r q^{n-r} \quad\ldots\ldots\ldots\ldots\ldots\ldots(7.3)$$

and is called the *binomial probability density function*.

➤ *Example.* A large shipment of purchased parts is received at a warehouse, and 10 parts are randomly selected and checked for quality. The parts are the output of a machine that consistently produces 5% defective items. The probability that the sample of 10 parts will include one defective is equal to the value of the binomial probability density function of the random variable r, where $r = 1, n = 10$, and $p = 0.05$. This probability is expressed by

$$P(r = 1 \mid n = 10, p = .05) = \binom{10}{1} (.05)^1 (.95)^9 = \frac{10!}{1!\,9!} (.05)(.63)$$

$$= 0.32$$

The general expression, $P(r \mid n, p)$, is read "the probability of r successes, given the binomial density function defined by the values of n and p."

The term binomial arises from the fact that the value of Formula 7.3 for specified values of n, r, and p is equivalent to the corresponding term of the expansion of the binomial expression $(p + q)^n$.

➤ *Example.* Forty percent of the employees of a large plant are male and a random sample of two employees is taken. The probability that the sample will contain 0, 1, or 2 male employees can be determined by evaluating the terms of the expansion of

$$(.40 + .60)^2 = (.40)^0 (.60)^2 + 2(.40)^1 (.60)^1 + (.40)^2 (.60)^0$$

$$= 0.36 + 0.48 + 0.16.$$

These three terms correspond to the probabilities of zero, one, and two successes. Similarly, the probability of obtaining one male in the sample of two employees is

$$P(r = 1 \mid n = 2, p = .40) = \binom{2}{1} (.40)^1 (.60)^1 = \frac{2!}{1!\,1!} (.40)(.60)$$

$$= 0.48.$$

This result is identical with the second term of the expansion of the binomial $(.40 + .60)^2$.

Determining Binomial Probabilities

The generalized expression of the binomial probability density function $P(r) = \binom{n}{r} p^r q^{n-r}$ provides the means for computing the probability of every possible number of successes in a given number of trials. A systematic arrangement of these probabilities is called a *binomial probability distribution.* Consequently, the binomial probability density function defines a whole series of distributions, one for every possible combination of values of n and p, the parameters of the respective distributions.

Some of the binomial probability distributions, presented as histograms in Figure 7.6, illustrate the characteristics of the distributions for selected values of n and p. While only the distributions corresponding to values of $p = 0.50$ are symmetric, the distributions for small values of p are reasonably symmetric, especially for large values of n. This property enables one to employ the symmetric normal curve as a useful approximation, as discussed in the next chapter.

In many situations one may wish to determine the probability of r or more successes, or of r or less successes, in a given number of trials. In effect, what is desired is the probability corresponding to the area of a tail of a binomial distribution. This probability can be determined by adding the binomial probabilities for the respective events. For experiments with a sizable number of trials, the cumulation of probabilities can be arduous, especially if r is not approximately equal to zero or n. Binomial probabilities can be readily obtained from published tables that give the tail areas for a considerable range of values of n and p, and all the corresponding values of r. Because of the cumulative nature of these tables, individual probabilities can also be readily obtained by making the appropriate subtractions.

The cumulative probabilities for a limited number of binomial distributions are given in Appendix D. The table values correspond to the areas of the right-hand tails of the distributions, the probabilities of r or more successes for given values of n and p. Since the total area of any binomial distribution is one, the area of any left-hand tail, the probability of less than r successes, is one minus the probability of r or more successes.

➤ *Example.* Given the values $n = 8$ and $p = 0.40$, the probability of four or more successes $P(r \geq 4 \mid n = 8, p = 0.40)$ is 0.4059 as seen in Appendix D, opposite $r = 4$. This probability is shown as the right-hand tail (shaded portion) in Figure 7.7. Similarly, the probability of more than four successes, $P(r > 4 \mid n = 8, p = 0.40)$, is 0.1737 and is found opposite $r = 5$ for $n = 8$ and $p = 0.40$. To find $P(r < 4 \mid n = 8, p = 0.40)$, the probability of less than four successes is $1 - P(r \geq 4)$. This is found by reading 0.4059 opposite $r = 4$ and computing $1 - P(r \geq 4) = 1 - 0.4059 = 0.5941$. The probability of exactly four successes $P(r = 4 \mid n = 8, p = 0.40)$ is found by computing $P(r \geq 4) - P(r \geq 5)$; 0.4059 is read opposite $r = 4$, and 0.1737, opposite $r = 5$. The difference is $0.4059 - 0.1737 = 0.2322$.

The problem of computing probabilities for values of $p > 0.50$ is slightly more involved, since Appendix D does not reflect values of p larger than 0.50. The table may be used for $p > 0.50$ by recasting the problem in terms of $q = 1 - p$.

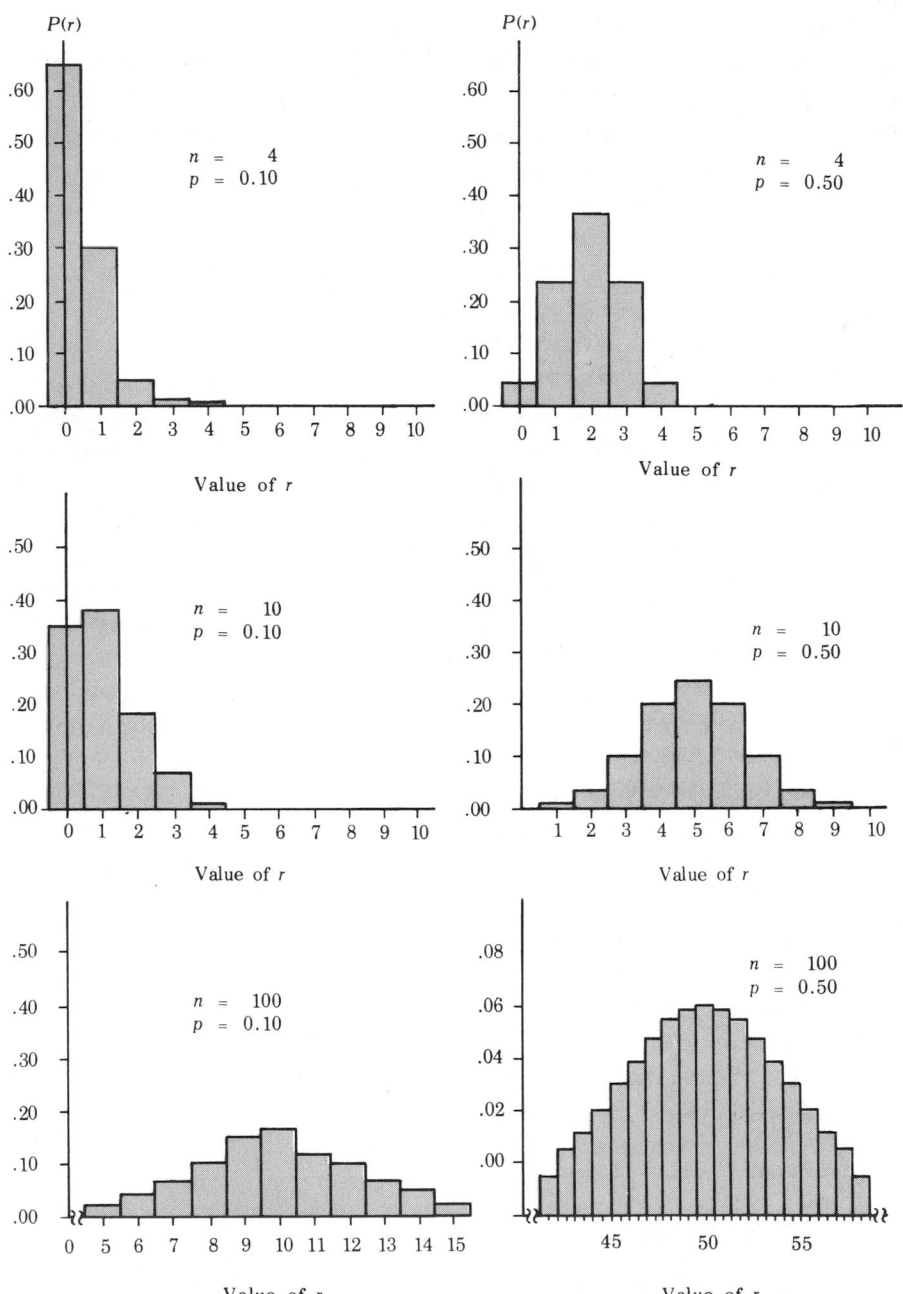

Figure 7.6

BINOMIAL PROBABILITY DISTRIBUTIONS FOR SELECTED VALUES
OF n AND p

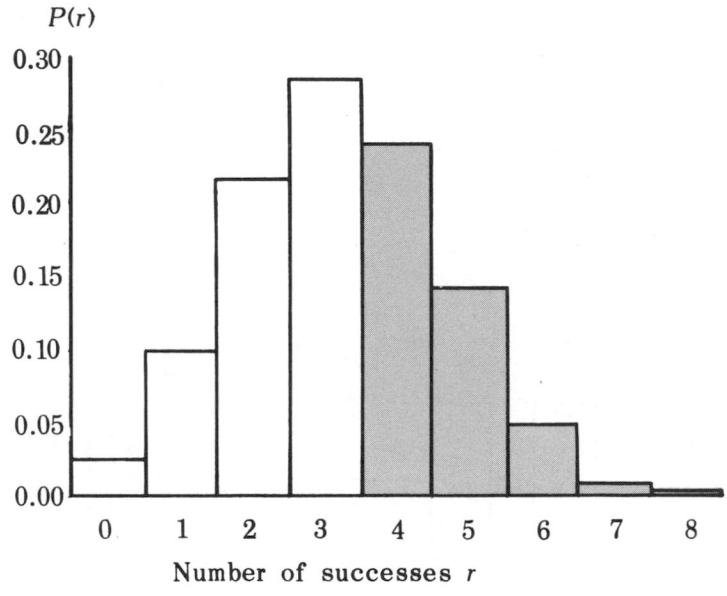

Figure 7.7

PROBABILITY DISTRIBUTION OF $P(r \mid n = 8, p = 0.40)$

➤ **Example.** Given the values $n = 8$ and $p = 0.60$. The probability of five or more successes $P(r \geq 5 \mid n = 8, p = 0.60)$ is written equivalently as $1 - P(r \geq n - r + 1 \mid n, q) = 1 - P(r \geq 8 - 5 + 1 \mid n = 8, q = 0.40)$. Reading from Appendix D, the appropriate value is 0.4059 and the probability is computed $1 - 0.4059 = 0.5491$.

The binomial probabilities in Appendix C can be computed by means of the algorithm shown in Figure 7.8. In practice, this algorithm can serve as a subroutine in a computer program, where it is more economical to compute a desired probability than to store a large number of probabilities and search for the desired value.

Descriptive Measures of the Binomial Distribution

The general expression of the binomial distribution describes a series of distributions. Each of these distributions is defined by a unique combination of the parameters n and p. In practice, the value of the long-run fraction of successes is rarely known with certainty, except in a situation where it can be computed *a priori*. More often, n and p are properties of a sample drawn from a universe, and p serves as an estimate of the parameter π, the long-run fraction of successes. Whether the parameters of a binomial distribution are known or estimated, the descriptive measures of the corresponding distribution are of considerable value in the formulation and solution of certain problems.

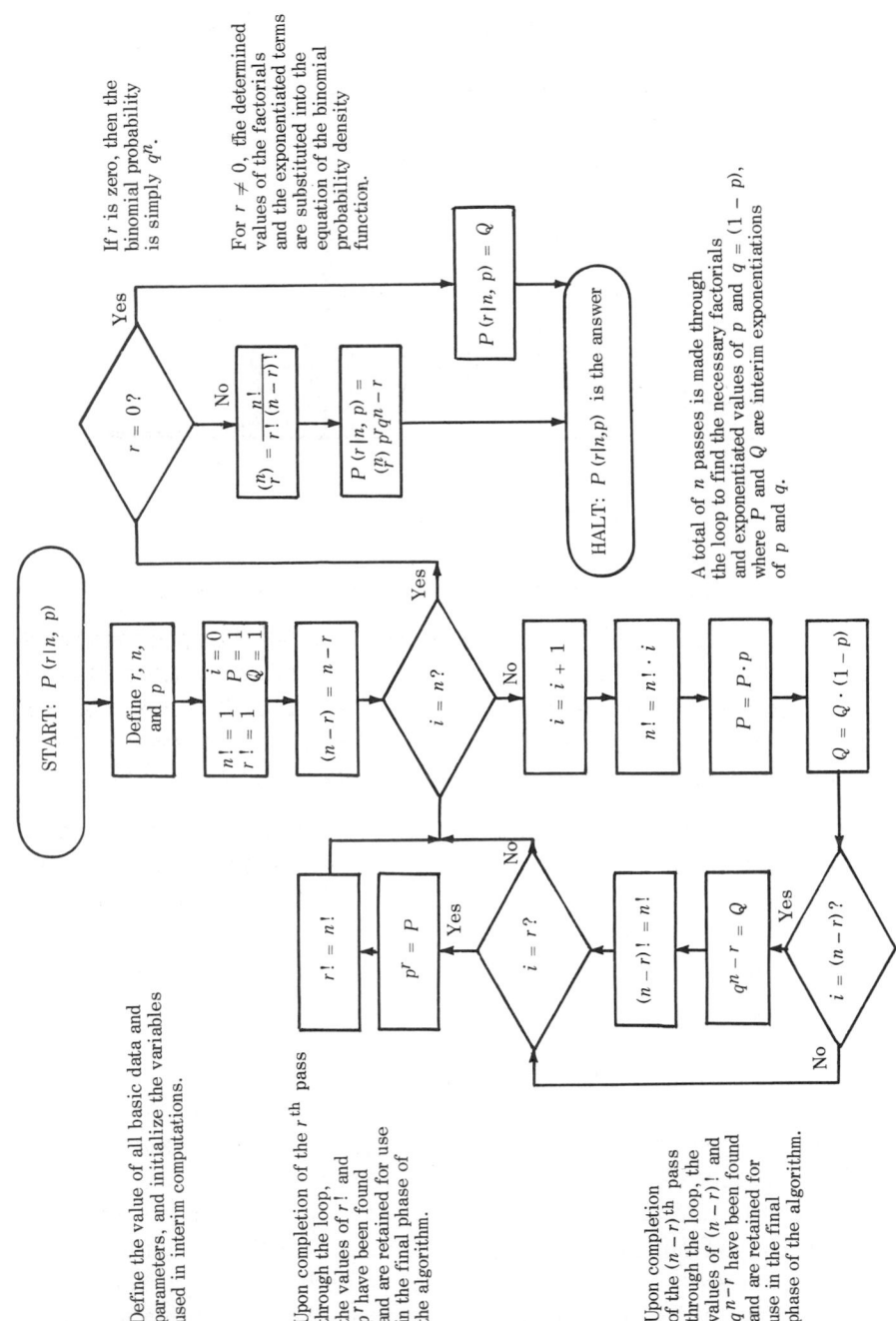

If r is zero, then the binomial probability is simply q^n.

For $r \neq 0$, the determined values of the factorials and the exponentiated terms are substituted into the equation of the binomial probability density function.

A total of n passes is made through the loop to find the necessary factorials and exponentiated values of p and $q = (1 - p)$, where P and Q are interim exponentiations of p and q.

Define the value of all basic data and parameters, and initialize the variables used in interim computations.

Upon completion of the rth pass through the loop, the values of $r!$ and p^r have been found and are retained for use in the final phase of the algorithm.

Upon completion of the $(n - r)^{\text{th}}$ pass through the loop, the values of $(n - r)!$ and q^{n-r} have been found and are retained for use in the final phase of the algorithm.

The Mean and the Variance of a Bernoulli Process. The derivation of some of the moments of the binomial distribution is made easier because Bernoulli trials may be viewed in more than one fashion. Consider an experiment in which two parts are drawn, with replacement, from a bin in which half of the parts are Brand *A* and the remaining parts are Brand *B*. The total number of parts in the bin is denoted by *N* and the proportion of parts that are Brand *A* is defined as

$$\frac{A}{N} = \pi.$$

For the experiment, the probability of drawing a unit of Brand *A*, viewed as a success, is $\pi = \frac{1}{2}$. The probability of selecting a unit of Brand *B* is $1 - \pi = \frac{1}{2}$. The probability of obtaining a specified number of successes *r* in *n* trials is given by the density function

$$P(r \mid n, \pi) = \binom{n}{r} \pi^r (1 - \pi)^{n-r} \dots\dots\dots\dots\dots(7.4)$$

The derivation of the mean and the variance of a binomial distribution are more readily seen by taking a slightly different view of Bernoulli trials. Assume that a sample of *n* items is drawn from the bin of parts and consider a discrete variable *X* that takes on a value of one for a success (obtaining a unit of Brand *A*) and a value of zero for a failure. In this manner, *n* independent random variables, $X_1, X_2, X_3, \dots, X_n$, are defined, one for each of the individual trials.

For example, suppose a sample of six items is drawn randomly with the set of outcomes $\{B, B, A, B, A, B\}$. The trials, outcomes, and defined variables are shown in Table 7.7.

Table 7.7
THE RESULTS OF A RANDOM SAMPLE
OF SIX ITEMS

Trial	Outcome	Value of *X*	Variable defined
1	*B*	0	X_1
2	*B*	0	X_2
3	*A*	1	X_3
4	*B*	0	X_4
5	*A*	1	X_5
6	*B*	0	X_6

The mathematical expectation of the variable *X* is determined by

$$E(X) = \Sigma X P(X) = (1)(\pi) + (0)(1 - \pi) = \pi.$$

The variance is derived as

$$\text{Var}(X) = E(X - \pi)^2 = \Sigma(X - \pi)^2 P(X) = (1 - \pi)^2\pi + (0 - \pi)^2(1 - \pi)$$
$$= \pi(1 - \pi).$$

The number of successes for n trials is the sum

$$r = X_1 + X_2 + \ldots + X_n,$$

and it follows[1] that for $n = 6$, the expected value of r is

$$E(r) = E(X_1) + E(X_2) + \ldots + E(X_6) = \pi + \pi + \ldots + \pi$$

or

$$E(r) = n\pi \quad\ldots\ldots\ldots\ldots\ldots\ldots\ldots\ldots\ldots\ldots\ldots\ldots(7.5)$$

Similarly, the variance of r is given by

$$\text{Var}(r) = \pi(1 - \pi) + \pi(1 - \pi) + \ldots + \pi(1 - \pi)$$

or

$$\text{Var}(r) = n\pi(1 - \pi) \quad\ldots\ldots\ldots\ldots\ldots\ldots\ldots(7.6)$$

The standard deviation of the distribution is written

$$\sigma_r = \sqrt{n\pi(1 - \pi)} \quad\ldots\ldots\ldots\ldots\ldots\ldots\ldots(7.7)$$

➤ *Example.* Consider the possible distinct samples of two items that can be drawn from a bin of parts, 10% of which are defective. The selection of a defective part is denoted as S and a value of one is taken on by the variable X. Similarly, F denotes a failure and X takes on the value of zero. The possible outcomes and the corresponding expected values are listed in Table 7.8.

Table 7.8

COMPUTATION OF $E(r)$

Sample outcomes	Value of X_i	Probability of the outcomes	Expected value of the sample
SS	1, 1	$(.10)(.10) = 0.01$	$2(.01) = 0.02$
SF	1, 0	$(.10)(.90) = 0.09$	$1(.09) = 0.09$
FS	0, 1	$(.90)(.10) = 0.09$	$1(.09) = 0.09$
FF	0, 0	$(.90)(.90) = 0.81$	$0(.81) = 0.00$
Totals		1.00	0.20

[1] These relationships are based on a theorem, which is given without proof, that if r is the sum of n independent random variables, all having the same probability distribution, then $E(r)$ is equal to the expected value of the sum, and the variance of r is equal to the variance of the sum.

The expected value of the number of successes r per sample of two items is

$$E(r) = n\pi = (2)(0.1) = 0.20.$$

The variance of r for $n = 2$ is

$$\text{Var}(r) = n\pi(1 - \pi) = 2(.10)(.90) = 0.18,$$

and the standard deviation is $\sqrt{.18} = 0.424$.

The Characteristics of the Distribution of Sample Proportions. The foregoing example reflects the fact that samples of the same size drawn from a population can yield different results in terms of the number or the proportion of successes obtained. Each of the distinct samples that can be drawn from a population defines a sample point. The probability of obtaining a success on any one of the trials of a sample is π; the probability of a failure is $1 - \pi$. The probability of a sample point is given by the density function $\pi^r(1 - \pi)^{n-r}$, where r is the number of successes corresponding to the sample point and n is the sample size.

The number of ways that r successes can be obtained in n trials is given by the combinatorial expression $\binom{n}{r}$, and the value of this expression indicates the number of sample points that satisfy the event "r successes in n trials." It follows that, given π, the probability of obtaining r successes in a sample of n trials is the binomial probability

$$P(r \mid n, \pi) = \binom{n}{r} \pi^r(1 - \pi)^{n-r}.$$

The fraction of successes in n trials is $p = \dfrac{r}{n}$ and is defined as the *sample proportion*. Expressing the number of successes r as a fraction of n, the sample size, the corresponding binomial probabilities are unchanged and

$$P(r \mid n, \pi) = P\left(\frac{r}{n}\right) = \binom{n}{r} \pi^r(1 - \pi)^{n-r}.$$

Thus, the sampling distribution of p is a binomial distribution. Recalling that $E(r) = n\pi$ and $\text{Var}(r) = n\pi(1 - \pi)$, the expression of the sample proportion $p = \dfrac{r}{n}$ may be substituted for r to obtain the mean, the variance, and the standard deviation of the sampling distribution, where

$$E(p) = \pi \quad \dots\dots\dots\dots\dots\dots\dots\dots(7.8)$$

$$\text{Var}(p) = \frac{\pi(1 - \pi)}{n} \quad \dots\dots\dots\dots\dots\dots(7.9)$$

$$\sigma_p = \sqrt{\frac{\pi(1 - \pi)}{n}} \quad \dots\dots\dots\dots(7.10)$$

➤ **Example.** In a large marketing area, 0.40 of the consumers prefer an upright to a chest-type freezer. A sample of $n = 5$ consumers is to be drawn. Let r denote the number of consumers in the sample who prefer an upright freezer. The values of r that can occur in the sample are $r = 0, 1, 2, \dots, 5$. The number of successes r may be expressed as a sample proportion $p = \dfrac{r}{n}$, which can take on the values $\frac{0}{5}$, $\frac{1}{5}$, $\frac{2}{5}$, $\dots$, $\frac{5}{5}$, each with a corresponding binomial probability $P\left(\dfrac{r}{n}\right) = \binom{5}{r}(0.40)^r(0.60)^{5-r}$. These probabilities are listed as follows:

Table 7.9

VALUES OF $P\left(p = \dfrac{r}{5}\right)$ FOR ALL POSSIBLE VALUES OF r

$$P(p = \tfrac{0}{5}) = 0.0778$$
$$P(p = \tfrac{1}{5}) = 0.2592$$
$$P(p = \tfrac{2}{5}) = 0.3456$$
$$P(p = \tfrac{3}{5}) = 0.2304$$
$$P(p = \tfrac{4}{5}) = 0.0768$$
$$P(p = \tfrac{5}{5}) = 0.0102$$

$$1.0000$$

The probability distribution of p is shown in Figure 7.9, where the heights of the bars of the histogram correspond to the probability of drawing a sample with given values of p. The mean, the variance, and the standard deviation of the distribution are computed as

$$E(p) = \pi = 0.40,$$

$$\text{Var}(p) = \frac{\pi(1 - \pi)}{n} = \frac{0.24}{5} = 0.048$$

$$\sigma_p = \sqrt{\frac{\pi(1 - \pi)}{n}} = \sqrt{0.048} = 0.219.$$

An alternative interpretation of the probability distribution may be made in terms of the number of successes. The probability that a single

Probability density

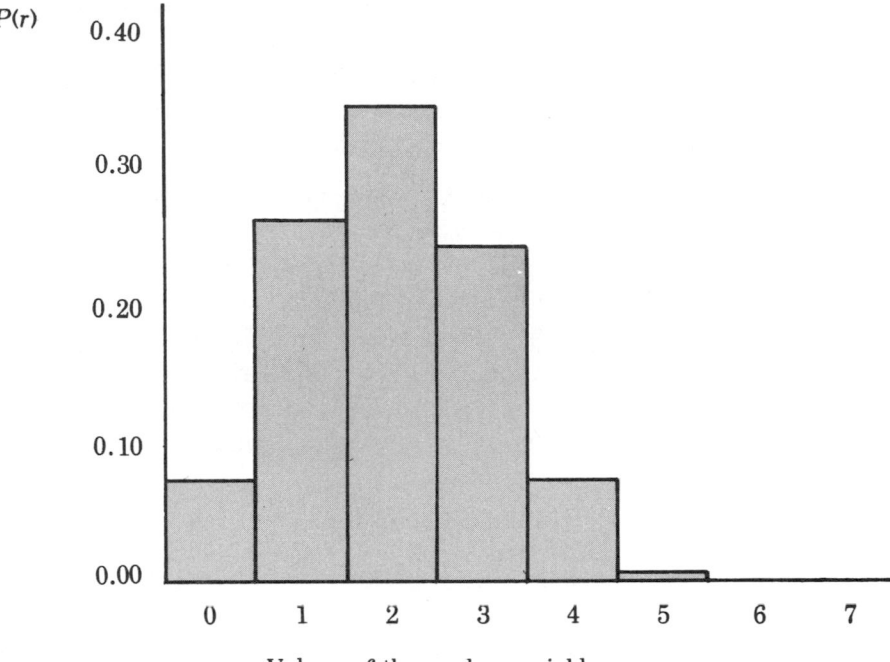

Figure 7.9

VALUES OF $P\left(p = \dfrac{r}{5}\right)$ FOR ALL POSSIBLE VALUES OF r

sample will have three successes, or $p = 0.60$, is $P(p = 0.60) = 0.2304$. Alternatively, if many samples of five consumers were randomly drawn, the expectation is that 2,304 out of 10,000 samples would have three successes.

The probability distribution of sample proportions provides the basis for testing hypotheses about parameters on the basis of sample data. These important applications are taken up more fully in the discussion of sampling distributions and tests of significance in Chapters 9 and 12.

THE POISSON PROBABILITY DISTRIBUTION

An important class of business problems is characterized by the small probability of a success for any one of many trials of an experiment. Problems of this type include applications in insurance involving the number of deaths in a time period, the analysis of the formation of waiting lines at service facilities, the demand for inventory items, and counting the number of defects in a manufactured item. The *Poisson probability distribution* is a mathematical model with properties suitable for expressing this type of problem. This model can be viewed either as the limiting form of the binomial distribution or as a distribution in its own right, which describes a Poisson process. These approaches and their applications are discussed in the following sections.

The Poisson Probability Distribution: A Limiting Form of the Binomial Distribution

The computation of probabilities for a Bernoulli process, where n is large and p is small, can be laborious; but these computations can be simplified by use of a limiting form of the binomial distribution, the Poisson probability distribution. Although, in a strict sense, a Poisson process is not characterized by trials with two possible outcomes and a constant probability of success, by employing suitable definitions, a Poisson process can be viewed as being Bernoulli.

For example, a manufacturing process continuously extrudes metal tubing and the thickness of the tubing wall is occasionally below minimum quality standards. In a sample of 1,000 feet of extruded tubing, 20 defective places were detected, or an average of two defects per 100 feet. The defects occur randomly over the tubing. If the probability of finding a specified number of defects in a length of tubing remains constant, this Poisson process may be considered Bernoulli by viewing a very short length of tubing as an independent trial with an outcome of zero or more successes.

Binomial Probabilities and the Poisson Distribution. By definition, a Bernoulli trial has only two possible outcomes, success or failure. For example, this definition is illustrated by viewing a 100-foot length of tubing as being subdivided into 10 pieces. The probability of a defect in a 10-foot segment is 0.20. Now let the 100 feet be divided into one-foot lengths and $p = 0.02$. Note that $np = (10)(.20) = (100)(.02) = 2$ for each case. Continuing in this manner, the 100-foot length can be divided into any n number of smaller units so that np is constant for all cases. As n becomes large, the probability of more than one defect per subunit becomes very small. The difference between the binomial probability distribution and its limiting form, the Poisson probability distribution, becomes negligible. This relationship is seen in Figure 7.10, which shows the binomial and the Poisson distributions for a value of $np = 0.50$.

In a Bernoulli process, probabilities are associated with the probability p of a success for each independent trial and r number of successes in n trials. For a Poisson process, probabilities are related to a given number of successes k per unit of space (e.g., a small length of tubing) and

Probability density

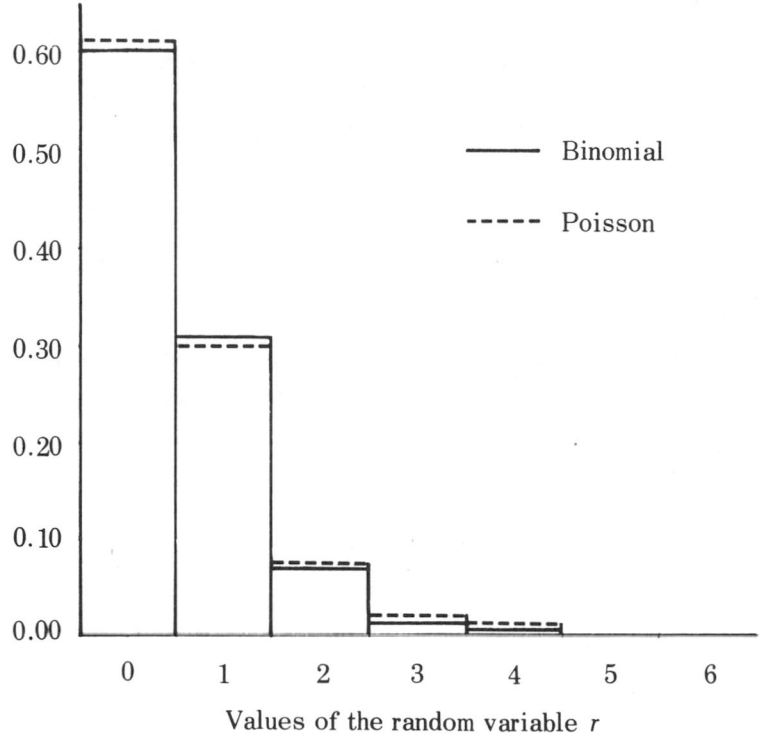

Figure 7.10
THE PROBABILITY DISTRIBUTION OF $P(r \mid n = 10, p = 0.05)$ AND
THE POISSON APPROXIMATION FOR $np = 0.50$

the number of successes t in a given amount of space. The terms p and k are analogous as are r and t. The expected number of successes np for a Bernoulli process corresponds to

$$\lambda = kt,$$

the expected number of successes in a given amount of space for a Poisson process.

➤ *Example.* In a study of the arrivals of trucks at a warehouse, the probability of an arrival during any given minute (a trial) was determined to be $p = 0.0333$. The expected number of arrivals per half hour is $np = (30)(0.0333) = 1$. Viewing a minute as a unit of space k and a half hour as the given amount of space t, then $\lambda = (0.0333)(30) = 1$.

Binomial probabilities for r successes in n trials are computed by use of the expression $P(r \mid n, p) = \binom{n}{r} p^r (1 - p)^{n-r}$. For small values of p, the

the resulting probability distribution for the possible values of r forms a very skewed distribution. For very small values of p and correspondingly large values of n, so long as np remains constant, the limit of the binomial probability is the Poisson probability, as expressed by

$$\lim_{\substack{n \to \infty \\ p \to 0}} P(r \mid n, p) = \frac{(np)^r}{r!} \, e^{-np},$$

where e is the base of natural logarithms with the value 2.718282. Expressing the Poisson probability density function in terms of $np = \lambda$,

$$P(r \mid \lambda) = \frac{\lambda^r}{r!} \, e^{-\lambda} \dots\dots\dots\dots\dots\dots(7.11)$$

From Formula 7.11 it may be seen that the Poisson distribution has one parameter and that the entire distribution can be determined, given the value of λ.

➤ *Example.* A machine produces large quantities of items and from past experience it is known that an average of one item in a hundred is defective. A sample of 20 items is drawn from a large number of produced items. The binomial probability of obtaining two defective units is

$$P(r = 2 \mid n = 20, p = 0.01) = \binom{20}{2} (0.01)^2 (0.99)^{18} = 0.0159,$$

which can be read from Appendix C for $n = 20$, $p = 0.01$, and $r = 2$. The Poisson approximation of this probability is found by computing

$$\lambda = np = (20)(0.01) = 0.20 \text{ and}$$

$$P(r = 2 \mid \lambda = 0.20) = \frac{0.20^2}{2!} (2.718282)^{-0.20} = \frac{0.04}{2} (0.81873)$$

$$= 0.0164.$$

The small difference between the exact binomial probability and its approximated value, the corresponding Poisson probability, arises from the number of trials and the sample size. For larger values of n and constant values of $np = \lambda$, the difference becomes smaller, approaching zero as n increases without limit.

The Table of Poisson Probabilities. The time-consuming task of computing Poisson probabilities manually by means of Formula 7.11 can be avoided by use of Appendix G, which presents the cumulative probability of r or more successes for various values of λ. Appendix G gives the probability corresponding to the right-hand tail of the Poisson distribution in much the same manner as Appendix D indicates the cumulative binomial probabilities for values of n, p, and r or more successes.

➤ ***Example.*** From past experience it has been determined that, on the average, three out of every 100 data cards read into a computer contain a numerical mistake. A sample of 50 data cards is selected at random from a large number of cards on file. The binomial and the Poisson probabilities for the possible number of cards containing errors are presented in Table 7.10 and shown as histograms in Figure 7.11. The dotted lines denote the Poisson probabilities, and the solid lines, the binomial probabilities. The values in Table 7.10 are read from Appendix D for values of $n = 50$ and $p = 0.03$, and from Appendix G for values of $\lambda = (50)(0.03) = 1.5$. The term r' denotes a specified value that the random variable r may assume.

Table 7.10

BINOMIAL AND POISSON PROBABILITIES FOR VALUES OF r'

Number of successes r'	Binomial $P(r \geq r' \mid n = 50, p = 0.03)$	$P(r = r' \mid n = 50, p = 0.03)$	Poisson $P(r \geq r' \mid \lambda = 1.50)$	$P(r = r' \mid \lambda = 1.50)$
0	1.0000	0.2181	1.0000	0.2231
1	0.7819	0.3372	0.7769	0.3347
2	0.4447	0.2555	0.4422	0.2510
3	0.1892	0.1264	0.1912	0.1256
4	0.0628	0.0460	0.0656	0.0470
5	0.0168	0.0131	0.0186	0.0141
6	0.0037	0.0030	0.0045	0.0036
7	0.0007	0.0006	0.0009	0.0007
8	0.0001	0.0001	0.0002	0.0002

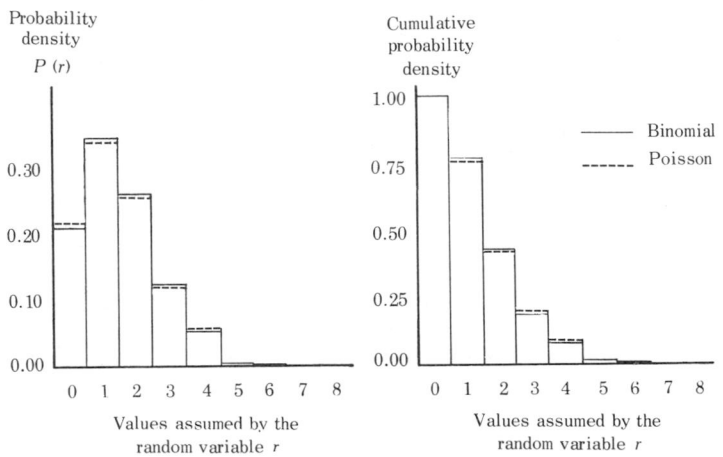

Figure 7.11

BINOMIAL AND POISSON DISTRIBUTIONS SHOWING INDIVIDUAL AND CUMULATIVE PROBABILITIES FOR $P(r \mid n = 50, p = 0.03)$ and $P(r \mid \lambda = 1.50)$

The Poisson probabilities in Appendix F can be computed by means of the algorithm shown in Figure 7.12. An algorithm of this type can be used as a subroutine in a computer program to compute a desired Poisson probability, to a desired number of decimal places, rather than storing a large number of probabilities and searching for the desired value.

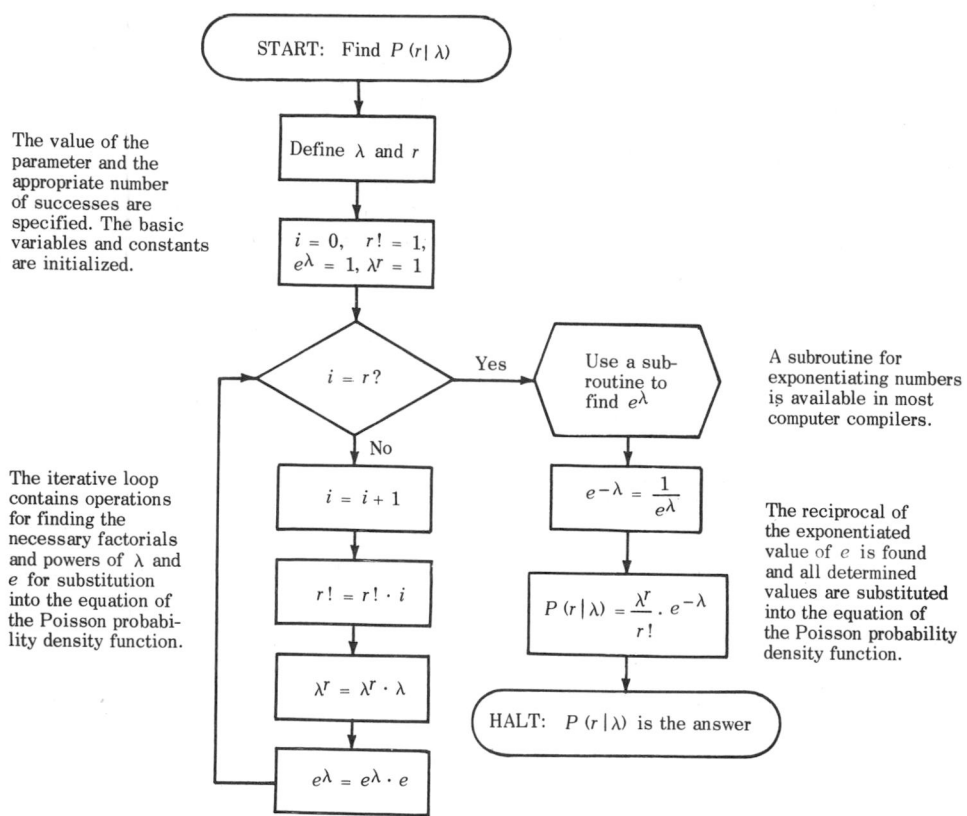

The value of the parameter and the appropriate number of successes are specified. The basic variables and constants are initialized.

The iterative loop contains operations for finding the necessary factorials and powers of λ and e for substitution into the equation of the Poisson probability density function.

A subroutine for exponentiating numbers is available in most computer compilers.

The reciprocal of the exponentiated value of e is found and all determined values are substituted into the equation of the Poisson probability density function.

Figure 7.12
AN ALGORITHM FOR FINDING POISSON PROBABILITIES

The Poisson Probability Distribution: A Model of a Poisson Process

The binomial and the Poisson distributions have basic requirements in common — statistical stability and independent trials. But the notion of a "trial" for a Poisson distribution requires the special definition of a continuum of time, space, or some other dimension as being divided into sufficiently small units so that the likelihood of more than one success per unit is extremely small. In this manner, each small unit is a trial, and not more than one success will occur in a given trial. Further, the probability of a success is the same for all trials and is independent of the outcomes of any previous or future trials. Any phenomenon which can be expressed as an experiment with trials that satisfy the conditions above is called a *Poisson process*.

For example, the occurrence of accidental explosions in a refinery can be viewed as a Poisson process. Fortunately, safety measures help to reduce the frequency of these events. The probability of an explosion during a time period, say a month, is small, and the probability of more than one explosion in a given month is extremely small. To be viewed properly as a Poisson process, the occurrence of any given explosion must be independent of any past explosions and the probability of an explosion during any randomly selected month must be the same as for all other months.

A Poisson Process As the Sum of Several Processes. A binomial distribution can be looked upon as the sum of *n* Bernoulli processes. In a similar manner, a Poisson process may be the result of the interaction of several processes that may or may not be Poisson in nature. Consider a situation in which a shipyard has a tool crib from which several identical welding machines are issued to workers as needed. The demand for the machines varies as does the number of hours of use each month. The maintenance supervisor is interested in the distribution of the number of times each month a machine is out of service because of a faulty regulator. The expected number of times this type of repair is required varies with the hours of use and thus is not constant from month to month, but may be constant on a per-hour-of-use basis. For such a case, the frequency of repairs each month is not statistically stable. Stability is also impaired by the tendency of a greater frequency of repairs with increased age of the equipment and, conversely, the absence of any additional breakdowns while the machine is awaiting repair or being repaired.

The independence of the incidence of the need for repairs holds only if the known factors inducing breakdowns are taken into account and the resulting average failure rate remains constant. Considering the problems of stability and independence cited above, the incidence of repairs for a single machine could hardly be looked upon as a Poisson process. The pattern of regulator breakdowns for a number of machines is much more likely to be Poisson distributed, even though the incidence of regulator repairs for individual welding machines is not a Poisson process. The important point suggested by this example is that while the expected number of repairs each month may fluctuate for individual machines, the frequency of need for regulator repairs for all machines may be stable. The larger the number of machines involved, the greater the tendency for individual fluctuations in repair rates to average out. It can be proved that if the monthly rates for regulator repair for individual machines are considered to be Poisson processes, the aggregate regulator repair rate for all machines must equal the sum of the individual rates.

Moments of the Poisson Distribution. The mathematical expectation of a Poisson distribution is the first moment about the origin. A comparison of the binomial and the Poisson distributions demonstrates that the mean of binomial distributions np is equal to λ, the mean of the Poisson distributions. Stated more formally, the expected value of the number of successes of a Poisson distributed random variable r is

$$E(r) = \lambda \quad \ldots\ldots\ldots\ldots\ldots\ldots\ldots\ldots\ldots(7.12)$$

The variance and the standard deviation of a Poisson distribution can be derived from the variance of the binomial $\mathrm{Var}(r) = np(1 - p)$. The Poisson distribution is the limit of the binomial distribution, as n increases without limit and the value of p becomes correspondingly small, so that $np = \lambda$ remains constant. Thus, $np(1 - p)$ approaches $np = \lambda$ as $p(1 - p)$ approaches one and

$$\mathrm{Var}(r) = \lambda \quad \ldots\ldots\ldots\ldots\ldots\ldots\ldots\ldots(7.13)$$

and the standard deviation is

$$\sigma_r = \sqrt{\lambda} \quad \ldots\ldots\ldots\ldots\ldots\ldots\ldots\ldots(7.14)$$

➤ *Example.* In an inspection operation, 300-foot lengths of electrical cable are checked for defects in the exterior sheathing, and the number of defects for each length of cable is recorded. From past experience, the number of defects per length of cable is considered a Poisson process. The results of the inspection of a sample of 20 lengths of cable from current production are shown in Table 7.11. The distribution of the number of inspected lengths in the sample having a specified number of defects is not exactly a Poisson distribution, due to the random selection of the sampled lengths and the limited size of the sample. The moments of the sample provide good estimates of the process parameters, as shown in Table 7.12. The average number of defects per length of cable in the sample is

$$\frac{\text{Total number of defects}}{\text{Total units inspected}} = \frac{10}{20} = 0.50.$$

The sample average is an estimate of λ, the process average (denoted $\bar{c}$ in the literature of statistical quality control). The variance of the process is estimated by $\lambda = 0.50$. The values of the moments of the sample, based on Poisson probabilities for values of r, are calculated in Table 7.12 and verify the results obtained from the sample data.

The Poisson distribution has important applications in statistical quality control and in waiting-line problems. These topics are considered at greater length in Chapters 8 and 9.

Table 7.11

RESULTS OF THE INSPECTION OF 20 LENGTHS
OF ELECTRICAL CABLE

Sample item	Number of defects	Sample item	Number of defects
1	1	11	1
2	0	12	0
3	0	13	1
4	1	14	2
5	0	15	0
6	2	16	1
7	0	17	1
8	0	18	0
9	0	19	0
10	0	20	0
		Total	10

Table 7.12

OBSERVED AND EXPECTED VALUES OF A SAMPLE OF 20 LENGTHS OF CABLE
ASSUMING A POISSON PROCESS WITH $\lambda = 0.50$

Number of defects per cable	Number of cables	Poisson probability $P(r = r' \mid \lambda = 0.50)$	Expected number of cables $(20)P(r = r' \mid \lambda = 0.50)$	Expected values of r $(r)P(r = r' \mid \lambda = 0.50)$	Expected values of $(r - \lambda)^2$ $(r - \lambda)^2 P(r = r' \mid \lambda = 0.50)$
0	12	0.6065	12.130	0.0000	0.1516
1	6	0.3033	6.066	0.3033	0.0758
2	2	0.0758	1.516	0.1516	0.1706
3	0	0.0126	0.252	0.0378	0.0790
4	0	0.0016	0.032	0.0064	0.0196
5	0	0.0002	0.004	0.0009*	0.0034*
Totals	20	1.0000	20.000	$E(r) = 0.5000$	$Var(r) = 0.5000$

*Corrected for rounding error.

THE HYPERGEOMETRIC PROBABILITY DISTRIBUTION

The binomial probability distribution is an exact model of a Bernoulli process, for which the probabilities of the two possible outcomes remain constant for all trials. In some experiments, however, trials are made so that the sample space is reduced and the corresponding probabilities of a success or failure are changed from trial to trial. A systematic arrangement of the probabilities associated with the two outcomes, success or failure, of a process characterized by the reduction of a finite sample space and a corresponding change in probabilities from trial to trial is defined as a *hypergeometric probability distribution*. For example, if cards are drawn without replacement, the probability of drawing a spade on any given draw is conditional upon the outcomes of previous draws, and the sample space is reduced for each card drawn.

The principal application of the hypergeometric probability distribution in business pertains to sampling from a finite universe. This subject is one of the major topics of statistical quality control, which is discussed in Chapter 9.

The Basic Concepts of the Hypergeometric Probability Distribution

Consider a lot of 10 manufactured parts, two of which are defective. A random sample of two items is drawn without replacement from the lot. The total number of distinct samples of two items that can be drawn is the set of combinations of 10 parts taken two at a time, or

$$\binom{10}{2} = \frac{10!}{2!\,8!} = 45.$$

Each of the possible combinations has an equal probability of being selected. The set of all combinations is classified into subsets, and the members of each subset consist of a combination with a given number of defective parts.

The probability of selecting a sample with a specified number of defectives is the proportion of all possible samples containing that specified number of defectives. Thus, the probability of selecting a sample with zero defectives is the possible number of samples which can be drawn that include no defectives expressed as a fraction of all possible samples. A sample of two with no defectives must be drawn exclusively from the eight acceptable items in the lot (universe). The number of such samples is the subset of combinations that total

$$\binom{8}{2} = \frac{8!}{2!\,6!} = 28.$$

The probability of selecting a sample with no defectives is the *a priori* probability

$$\frac{\binom{8}{2}}{\binom{10}{2}} = \frac{28}{45} = 0.622.$$

A sample with one defective will include one of the eight acceptable items and one of the two defective items from the lot. There are $\binom{8}{1} = 8$ ways of selecting an acceptable item, and for each of these ways there are $\binom{2}{1} = 2$ ways of combining a defective item with an acceptable item in a sample of two items. In this manner, the number of possible samples of two items, which include one acceptable and one defective item, is the set of combinations that total

$$\binom{8}{1}\binom{2}{1} = \frac{8!}{1!\,7!} \cdot \frac{2!}{1!\,1!} = 16.$$

The probability of drawing a sample with one defective is

$$\frac{\binom{8}{1}\binom{2}{1}}{\binom{10}{2}} = \frac{16}{45} = 0.356.$$

A sample with two defectives can be drawn in only one way since

$$\binom{8}{0}\binom{2}{2} = \frac{8!}{0!\,8!} \cdot \frac{2!}{0!\,2!} = 1.$$

The probability of drawing this sample is

$$\frac{\binom{8}{0}\binom{2}{2}}{\binom{10}{2}} = \frac{1}{45} = 0.022.$$

The sample results are mutually exclusive and collectively exhaustive, and for the previous example, the probabilities are $P(c \mid N, r, n)$:

$$P(0 \mid 10, 2, 2) = 0.622$$
$$P(1 \mid 10, 2, 2) = 0.356$$
$$P(2 \mid 10, 2, 2) = 0.022$$
$$\overline{ 1.000}$$

Generalizing these results, let N denote the population size, r the total number of defective units, c the number of defectives (successes) in a sample, and n the sample size. The hypergeometric probability of c successes in n trials, given finite values of N and r, is expressed by

$$P(c \mid N, r, n) = \frac{\binom{N-r}{n-c}\binom{r}{c}}{\binom{N}{n}} \qquad \dots\dots\dots\dots\dots(7.15)$$

Hypergeometric probabilities can be computed by means of the algorithm shown in Figure 7.13. An algorithm of this type can be used to compute tables of values of $P(c \mid N, r, n)$ or to compute individual values as a subroutine in a computer program.

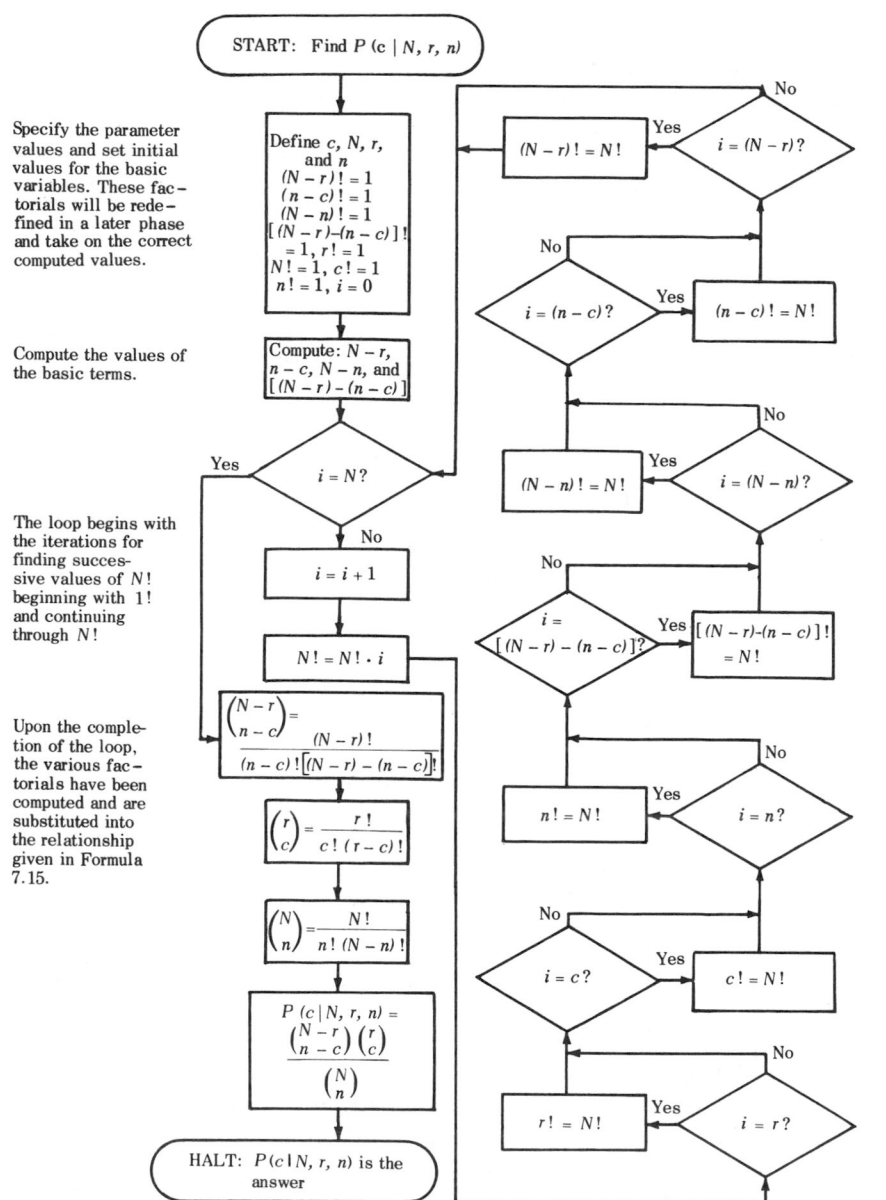

Specify the parameter values and set initial values for the basic variables. These factorials will be redefined in a later phase and take on the correct computed values.

Compute the values of the basic terms.

The loop begins with the iterations for finding successive values of $N!$ beginning with $1!$ and continuing through $N!$

Upon the completion of the loop, the various factorials have been computed and are substituted into the relationship given in Formula 7.15.

The loop generates values of $N!$ for all values from one through N. Since all the other basic terms are less than or equal to N, then at some point $N!$ takes on the value of the factorial of each of the basic terms in Formula 7.15. When each of these factorials is equal to $N!$, the value of that factorial is defined and the loop continues until the factorials of all the basic terms, including $N!$, have been determined.

Figure 7.13

AN ALGORITHM FOR FINDING HYPERGEOMETRIC PROBABILITIES

Binomial Approximations of Hypergeometric Probabilities

The hypergeometric distribution is an exact model of sampling from a finite universe. Unless N is very small, the binomial distribution provides good approximations of hypergeometric probabilities, since the probability of a success changes only slightly for successive trials.

➤ *Example.* A bin of 50 parts contains three defective units. A sample of five units is drawn randomly from the bin. The proportion of defective units in the finite universe is $p = \frac{3}{50} = 0.06$. The value of p is assumed to be constant for all trials, which is equivalent to assuming an infinite lot size. The computation of the binomial approximations of the hypergeometric probabilities is shown in Table 7.13.

Table 7.13

EXACT AND APPROXIMATE PROBABILITIES OF THE RESULTS OF
A SAMPLE OF FIVE DRAWN FROM A UNIVERSE OF 50 ITEMS
THREE OF WHICH ARE DEFECTIVE

Number of defectives	Hypergeometric probability $P(c \mid N, r, n)$	Binomial probability $P(r \mid n, p)$
0	$\dfrac{\binom{47}{5}\binom{3}{0}}{\binom{50}{5}} = 0.7239$	$\binom{5}{0}(0.06)^0(0.94)^5 = 0.7339$
1	$\dfrac{\binom{47}{4}\binom{3}{1}}{\binom{50}{5}} = 0.2526$	$\binom{5}{1}(0.06)^1(0.94)^4 = 0.2342$
2	$\dfrac{\binom{47}{3}\binom{3}{2}}{\binom{50}{5}} = 0.0230$	$\binom{5}{2}(0.06)^2(0.94)^3 = 0.0299$
3	$\dfrac{\binom{47}{2}\binom{3}{3}}{\binom{50}{5}} = 0.0005$	$\binom{5}{3}(0.06)^3(0.94)^2 = 0.0019$

The probabilities in Table 7.13 indicate that the binomial distribution provides close approximations of the exact probabilities of the sample results. Calculating exact probabilities for large finite universes is somewhat facilitated by the use of the logarithms of factorials, but even these calculations can be time consuming. For a great many practical problems in statistical quality control, the binomial approximations of exact probabilities are satisfactory. A small sample drawn from a finite universe does not substantially exhaust the universe, and binomial probabilities offer close estimates of exact probabilities. The larger the sample, the greater the tendency to exhaust a finite universe and the greater the disparity between the corresponding exact and approximate probabilities.

THE MULTINOMIAL DISTRIBUTION

An extension of the binomial distribution can be used to consider experimental trials for which more than two outcomes are possible. The likelihood that a specified number of each of multiple outcomes will be obtained in n trials, for which the probability of the outcome of each is constant from trial to trial, is called a *multinomial probability*.

Suppose it is known that in an area and in terms of overall programming, 40% of TV viewers prefer channel A; 25% prefer channel B; and 35% prefer channel C. A sample of six viewers is selected randomly and each is asked to give his preference. The likelihood that the preferences will be two for A, three for B, and one for C may be computed as a multinomial probability.

The number of ways in which the two viewers who prefer A can be selected in the sample of six is

$$\binom{n}{n_1} = \binom{6}{2} = 15,$$

where n_1 is the number of items in the A group. Given that the first group has been selected, the second group which prefers B may be selected from the $6 - 2 = 4$ remaining viewers in the sample. The number of ways in which the viewers who prefer B can be selected is

$$\binom{n - n_1}{n_2} = \binom{4}{3} = 4,$$

where n_2 is the number of items in the B group. Finally, the viewer who prefers C is selected from the sample item remaining and the number of ways in which this can be accomplished is

$$\binom{n - n_1 - n_2}{n_3} = \binom{6 - 2 - 3}{1} = 1,$$

where n_3 is the number of items in the C group.

The number of ways in which the three groups can be selected is written symbolically

$$\binom{n}{n_1}\binom{n - n_1}{n_2}\binom{n - n_1 - n_2}{n_3} =$$

$$= \frac{n!}{n_1!(n - n_1)!} \cdot \frac{(n - n_1)!}{n_2!(n - n_1 - n_2)!} \cdot \frac{(n - n_1 - n_2)!}{n_3!(n - n_1 - n_2 - n_3)!}.$$

Reducing this expression algebraically and substituting the appropriate values gives

$$\frac{n!}{n_1!\, n_2!\, n_3!} = \frac{6!}{2!\, 3!\, 1!} = 60.$$

One sequence in which the six viewers could be selected is *BABBCA*. The probability of obtaining this particular sequence is

$$(p_2)(p_1)(p_2)(p_2)(p_3)(p_1) = (p_1)^2(p_2)^3(p_3)^1$$
$$= (.40)^2(.25)^3(.35)^1$$
$$= 0.000775$$

where p_1, p_2, and p_3, respectively, are the probabilities of the occurrence of *A*, *B*, or *C*. This result may be generalized as the probability of obtaining any single sequence of six items in which a group of two items are from the universe *A*, three are from universe *B*, and one from universe *C*. The general expression is this probability

$$(p_1)^{n_1}(p_2)^{n_2}(p_3)^{n_3}.$$

A sequence with this probability may be obtained in any of $\dfrac{n!}{n_1!\, n_2!\, n_3!}$ ways. The multinomial probability that in *n* trials event E_1 occurs n_1 times, event E_2 occurs n_2 times, ..., event E_k occurs n_k times is written

$$\frac{n!}{n_1!\, n_2!\, \ldots\, n_k!}\, p_1{}^{n_1}\, p_2{}^{n_2} \cdots \cdots p_k{}^{n_k} \quad\ldots\ldots\ldots\ldots\ldots(7.16)$$

The probability of drawing a sample of six viewers of whom two prefer channel *A*, three prefer *B*, and one prefers *C* is computed by Formula 7.16 as

$$\frac{6!}{2!\, 3!\, 1!}(.40)^2(.25)^3(.35)^1 = (60)(.000775) = 0.0465.$$

The probability of drawing a sample of six viewers such that three prefer channel *A*, one prefers *B*, and two prefer *C* is computed as

$$\frac{6!}{3!\, 1!\, 2!}(.40)^3(.25)^1(.35)^2 = (60)(.00196) = 0.158.$$

➤ *Example.* In a nationwide survey, a marketing research group of a firm determines that 45% of customers prefer a new package design, 30% prefer the old design, and the remainder are undecided. If a random sample of 10 supermarket customers is selected at random, the probability that five will prefer the new design, three will not, and two will be undecided is the multinomial probability

$$\frac{10!}{5!\, 3!\, 2!}(.45)^5(.30)^3(.25)^2 = (2{,}520)(.000030375) = 0.077.$$

THE PASCAL PROBABILITY DISTRIBUTION

A binomial probability expresses the likelihood of obtaining a specified number of successes in a given number of Bernoulli trials. There are
situations in which one may wish to know the likelihood of what might
be called the inverse of the binomial case. One might ask what the probability is that a specified number of Bernoulli trials will be required to
obtain a given number of successes. A probability of this type, for which
the values of r and p are given, is called a *Pascal probability*.

The Nature of Pascal Probabilities

Consider a situation in which two types of metal parts, consisting of
shafts and bushings are fitted together in an assembly operation. Inspection records indicate that if the shafts and bushings are assembled
randomly, the assembled clearance between the shaft and the bushing of
10% of the finished assemblies will be too large and the assembly is considered defective. Suppose a production manager wishes to know the
probability that of six assemblies selected at random, two will be defective and the second defective unit will be the sixth assembly selected.

Denoting acceptable assemblies as A and defective assemblies as D,
one possible sequence that can occur in the random selection is $ADAAAD$.
The probability of obtaining this sequence is

$$P = \left(\tfrac{9}{10}\right)\left(\tfrac{1}{10}\right)\left(\tfrac{9}{10}\right)\left(\tfrac{9}{10}\right)\left(\tfrac{9}{10}\right)\left(\tfrac{1}{10}\right) = \frac{6,561}{1,000,000} = 0.006561.$$

The number of ways in which two defectives can be obtained in a sample
of six assemblies is $\binom{6}{2} = 15$ ways. But the problem at hand has the
special qualification that the sixth selection yield a defective assembly.
In such a case, only five sequences satisfy all the conditions.

These sequences are:

Sequence	Probability
$DAAAAD$	$\left(\tfrac{1}{10}\right)\left(\tfrac{9}{10}\right)\left(\tfrac{9}{10}\right)\left(\tfrac{9}{10}\right)\left(\tfrac{9}{10}\right)\left(\tfrac{1}{10}\right) = 0.006561$
$ADAAAD$	$\left(\tfrac{1}{10}\right)\left(\tfrac{9}{10}\right)\left(\tfrac{9}{10}\right)\left(\tfrac{9}{10}\right)\left(\tfrac{9}{10}\right)\left(\tfrac{1}{10}\right) = 0.006561$
$AADAAD$	$\left(\tfrac{1}{10}\right)\left(\tfrac{9}{10}\right)\left(\tfrac{9}{10}\right)\left(\tfrac{9}{10}\right)\left(\tfrac{9}{10}\right)\left(\tfrac{1}{10}\right) = 0.006561$
$AAADAD$	$\left(\tfrac{1}{10}\right)\left(\tfrac{9}{10}\right)\left(\tfrac{9}{10}\right)\left(\tfrac{9}{10}\right)\left(\tfrac{9}{10}\right)\left(\tfrac{1}{10}\right) = 0.006561$
$AAAADD$	$\left(\tfrac{1}{10}\right)\left(\tfrac{9}{10}\right)\left(\tfrac{9}{10}\right)\left(\tfrac{9}{10}\right)\left(\tfrac{9}{10}\right)\left(\tfrac{1}{10}\right) = 0.006561$
Total	0.032805

The probability of obtaining any one of the mutually exclusive sequences
is 0.006561. The probability of randomly drawing six assemblies, of

which two are defective and the second defective assembly is obtained on the sixth draw, is the sum of the probabilities of the five events, which totals 0.032805.

Generalizing this result, in a manner similar to the derivation of binomial probabilities, the probability that n Bernoulli trials will be required to obtain r successes in a particular order is written

$$\underbrace{(p \cdot p \cdot p \cdot \ldots \cdot p)}_{r \text{ successes}} \underbrace{(q \cdot q \cdot q \cdot \ldots \cdot q)}_{n - r \text{ failures}} = p^r q^{n-r}$$

In the type of problem being considered, the rth success must occur on the nth trial. The number of possible sequences that satisfy the conditions of the problem is determined by the number of ways in which $r - 1$ successes can be obtained in $n - 1$ trials. This number is expressed by $\binom{n-1}{r-1}$. The probability that precisely n trials will be required to obtain the rth success is a Pascal probability written

$$P(n \mid r, p) = \binom{n-1}{r-1} p^r (1 - p)^{n-r} \quad \ldots \ldots \ldots \ldots (7.17)$$

➤ *Example.* A refinery maintains a large inventory of different types of parts for maintenance and repairs. Some types of parts are needed infrequently, and in a typical week, one or more units of only about 30% of the different types of parts are used. The use of these parts is recorded as withdrawals by the accounting department. In making a tabulation of the inventory items used in a given week, a search is made through the inventory accounts to determine whether a type of part was used and to record the number of units withdrawn. The accounts are recorded serially (in order by inventory number) on magnetic tape. The ordering of the sequence of accounts is independent of the frequency of usage of the type of part. The probability that a computer must examine five accounts in order to encounter one which reflects a withdrawal during a week is a Pascal probability written

$$P(n = 5 \mid r = 1, p = 0.30) = \binom{5-1}{1-1} (0.30)^1 (0.70)^{5-1}$$

$$= \frac{(5-1)!}{0! \, (5-1)!} (0.30)(0.24)$$

$$= 0.072.$$

➤ *Example.* A real estate salesman estimates that 80% of the customers with whom he deals can qualify financially for a mortgage loan for the house of their choice. The probability that six loan applications will be processed by the salesman before four approvals are obtained is a Pascal probability written

$$P(n = 6 \mid r = 4, p = 0.80) = \begin{pmatrix} 6 - 1 \\ 4 - 1 \end{pmatrix} (0.80)^4 (0.20)^2$$

$$= \frac{5!}{3! \, 2!} (0.41)(0.04)$$

$$= 0.16.$$

Pascal and Binomial Probabilities

Computing Pascal probabilities by means of Formula 7.17, as illustrated in the foregoing example, becomes increasingly tedious as n becomes large. A table of Pascal probabilities can be prepared, but the values that would appear in such a table can be obtained from a table of binomial probabilities. The relationship between binomial and Pascal probabilities is described by the following reasoning. If n Bernoulli trials yield r or more successes, it follows that n or fewer trials were required to obtain the rth successes. Expressed symbolically,

$$\underset{\text{Pascal}}{P(n \leq \tilde{n} \mid r, p)} = \underset{\text{binomial}}{P(r \geq \tilde{r} \mid n, p)} \quad \ldots\ldots\ldots\ldots(7.18)$$

where $\tilde{n}$ and $\tilde{r}$ are specified values of n and r. The converse also holds such that if in n Bernoulli trials there are fewer than r successes, it follows that in order to obtain r successes, more than n trials are necessary. A symbolic expression of this relationship is written

$$\underset{\text{Pascal}}{P(n > \tilde{n} \mid r, p)} = \underset{\text{binomial}}{P(r < \tilde{r} \mid n, p)} \quad \ldots\ldots\ldots\ldots(7.19)$$

➤ *Example.* The manager of an automobile rental agency in an airport terminal observes that about 25% of his customers ask to rent economy cars to take advantage of lower rental rates. On a given afternoon there are only three economy cars that are available. The likelihood that all three of these vehicles will be rented by the next 12 or fewer customers served is the probability

$$\underset{\text{Pascal}}{P(n \leq 12 \mid r = 3, p = 0.25)} = \underset{\text{binomial}}{P(r \geq 3 \mid n = 12, p = 0.25)}.$$

This probability may be read in Appendix D as 0.6093, which appears opposite $r = 3$ for $p = 0.25$ and $n = 12$.

➤ *Example.* The manager of maintenance for data processing equipment in a large city observes that only four units of a type of electronic component are in inventory. Records indicate that the replacement of this type of component is required on about 12% of all service calls. At the present time, a total of 20 service calls is on the roster to be completed. The likelihood that more than 20 calls will be completed before all four of the available components are used is the probability

$$\underset{\text{Pascal}}{P(n > 20 \mid r = 4, p = 0.12)} = \underset{\text{binomial}}{P(r < 4 \mid n = 20, p = 0.12)}.$$

The value in Appendix D opposite $r = 4$ for $p = 0.12$ and $n = 20$ is 0.2127. This is the probability that 20 or fewer calls will be completed before the inventory is depleted. The desired probability therefore is $1 - 0.2127 = 0.7873$.

STUDY QUESTIONS

7-1. Explain briefly the meaning of each of the following terms:
  a. probability distribution
  b. probability density function
  c. discrete *pdf*
  d. continuous *pdf*
  e. cumulative *pdf*
  f. moment about the origin
  g. moment about the mathematical expectation
  h. Bernoulli processes
  i. success
  j. parameter
  k. binomial *pdf*
  l. binomial probability distribution
  m. sample proportion
  n. Poisson probability distribution
  o. Poisson process
  p. hypergeometric probability distribution
  q. multinomial probability
  r. Pascal probability

7-2. What is the relationship between a frequency distribution and a probability distribution?

7-3. What is the difference between a probability density function and a probability distribution?

7-4. Why does a discrete *pdf* take the form of a step function?

7-5. Of what significance are the moments of a random variable?

7-6. Which of the following can be considered Bernoulli processes?
  a. Tossing a fair coin
  b. Tossing an unfair (biased) coin
  c. Dealing cards from a deck
  d. Determining whether produced parts are acceptable or defective

7-7. What definition is necessary in order to consider a Poisson process as being Bernoulli?

7-8. Explain why the sum of several random processes, which are not individually Poisson, can be a Poisson process.

7-9. What is the principal reason for approximating hypergeometric probabilities with binomial probabilities?

7-10. Distinguish between the hypergeometric distribution and the multinomial distribution.

7-11. Describe briefly the relationship between the Pascal and the binomial probabilities.

PROBLEMS

7-1. What is the probability of getting:
  a. Two fives on three tosses of a single fair die?
  b. Four heads on nine tosses of a fair coin?

7-2. Find the probability of obtaining:
  a. Twenty-five heads on a single toss of 50 fair coins
  b. Six fives on a single toss of 10 fair dice

7-3. A machine produces parts that are consistently 10% defective. A sample of 20 items is selected randomly from the output of the machine. What is the probability of getting:
  a. Two defective parts?
  b. Three or more defective parts?

7-4. Using the information given in Problem 7-3, compute the probability of getting:
  a. Fewer than four defective parts
  b. Three or four defective parts

7-5. Compute the mean and the standard deviation for the distribution described in Problem 7-3.

7-6. Ten items are selected at random from a large inventory of items, 25% of which are purchased and the remainder are produced by the firm that has the inventory. Compute the first moment about the origin and the second moment about the mathematical expectation of the probability distribution of the number of purchased parts that can be obtained in a sample of 10 items.

7-7. From experience it is known that in a given suburb of a city, 60% of the TV viewers watch a particular program on Friday nights. A researcher randomly selects 20 families from the area and calls to ask if the program in question is being viewed. What is the probability that the number of families who respond affirmatively will be:

a. 10 or more?   c. exactly 15?

b. less than 12?   d. either 16 or 17?

7-8. In controlling the quality of output of a machine, an inspector selects samples of 10 items. If the sample contains one or more defective units, the machine is adjusted. What is the probability that production will be stopped and the machine adjusted if the output is:

a. 80% acceptable?   c. 90% acceptable?

b. 60% acceptable?   d. 99% acceptable?

7-9. Production records of a process indicate that the percent of defective items produced has had a stable pattern of variation as follows:

Proportion defective	Frequency
0.01	0.20
0.03	0.50
0.05	0.30
	———
	1.00

These frequencies are assumed to be good estimates of prior probabilities. A sample of 20 items is taken from the process and it contains one defective item. Compute the revised probabilities in view of the sample information.

7-10. A company purchases manufactured parts in carload lots. The inspection records kept on all incoming lots indicate that carload lots with specified percents of faulty units have been received with the following frequencies:

Proportion of faulty units	Frequency
0.01	0.20
0.02	0.50
0.03	0.20
0.04	0.10
	———
	1.00

Samples of 20 items are drawn from incoming lots. If a sample contains no faulty items, the entire lot is accepted; if it contains one or more faulty items, the lot is inspected in detail.

    a. If a sample is drawn from an incoming lot that contains 3% faulty items, what is the probability that the lot will be accepted?

    b. If a sample is drawn and contains one faulty item, what is the probability that the lot contains 4% faulty items? 1%?

7-11. An airline has determined from experience that, on an average, on one in 100 flights an aircraft will experience a minor equipment failure. What is the Poisson approximation of the probability that in the next 100 flights the number of failures will be:

    a. exactly two?

    b. less than one?

    c. more than one?

    d. either one or two?

7-12. The probability that any single component of a missile will malfunction is 0.001. The missile has 500 components.

    a. What is the probability that the missile will not function properly if fired?

    b. What level of reliability of the components must be achieved (by improved design or production methods) to give a 0.90 probability that the missile will not malfunction when fired?

7-13. An automatic machine makes paper clips from coils of wire. On the average, one in 500 paper clips is defective. If the paper clips are packed in boxes of 100, what is the probability that any given box of clips will contain:

    a. no defectives?

    b. one or more defectives?

    c. less than two defectives?

    d. less than one defective?

7-14. The number of defects per yard of cotton material produced on a machine is considered a Poisson process. The output of the machine varies in terms of the average number of defects per foot, and the frequency with which various levels of defects have occurred are listed as follows:

Defects per foot	Frequency
0.001	0.50
0.003	0.40
0.005	0.10
	——
	1.00

    If a sample of 100 feet of material is inspected and one or more defects is found, the machine is adjusted; otherwise, the machine is allowed to run.

a. If a sample is taken from the production of the machine as it is averaging 0.003 defects per foot, what is the probability that the machine will be adjusted on the basis of the sample results?
b. If a sample of 100 feet of material contains two defects, what is the probability that the machine averaged 0.005 defects per foot?

7-15. Defective guidance mechanisms were mistakenly mounted on two of a group of 10 rockets. It is not known which rockets have the defective mechanisms, and a sample of three rockets is selected for testing.
    a. What is the probability that the sample will include: no defective mechanisms? both defective mechanisms?
    b. Compute the binomial approximations for (a).

7-16. If a bridge hand of 13 cards is dealt from a standard deck of cards, what is the probability of its containing:
    a. 4 hearts?
    b. 2 or more kings?

7-17. A digital computer manufacturer leases computers to customers and provides engineering maintenance. Service call records made by engineers indicate that 65% of the service calls involve failures in input-output equipment, 25% result from operation errors, and 10% arise from failures in the processing unit (internal memory, arithmetic unit, registers, etc.). If service calls vary randomly with respect to the source of failure, what is the probability that of the next seven service calls three will involve input-output units, three will result from operation error, and one will originate from a faulty processing unit?

7-18. The student body of a university consists of the following groups:

Group	Percent
Freshmen	35
Sophomores	24
Juniors	18
Seniors	13
Graduates	10
	100

A random sample of 10 students is selected. Compute the probability that the sample will include four freshmen, two sophomores, no juniors, two seniors, and two graduate students.

7-19. Using the grouping characteristics in Problem 7-18, compute the probability that a sample of six students must be selected to obtain two juniors.

7-20. Using the grouping characteristics in Problem 7-18, compute the probability that a sample of 10 or fewer must be selected to obtain three sophomores.

7-21. Draw a flow diagram of an algorithm to generate a five-place table of binomial probabilities for the range from n equals one through 100, and p equals 0.01 through 0.50 for all values of n.

7-22. Draw a flow diagram of an algorithm to generate a five-place table of Poisson probabilities for values of λ equal to 0.1 through λ equal to 25.0. Values of $P(r \mid \lambda)$ of less than 0.000001 should not be included in the table.

SELECTED READINGS

Ekeblad, Frederick A. *The Statistical Method, Applications of Probability and Inference to Business and Other Problems.* New York: John Wiley and Sons, Inc., 1962.
   A good discussion of the relationship between the binomial and the Poisson distributions is presented in Chapter 5.
Grant, Eugene L. *Statistical Quality Control.* 3d ed. New York: McGraw-Hill Book Company, Inc., 1964.
   A lucid comparison of the binomial, the Poisson, and the hypergeometric probability distributions is presented in Chapter 9.
Schlaifer, Robert. *Probability and Statistics for Business Decisions.* New York: McGraw-Hill Book Company, Inc., 1959.
   The revision of probabilities using theoretical distributions of conditional probabilities is clearly presented in Chapters 21 through 23.

Chapter 8

Continuous Probability Distributions

Probability distributions associated with continuous variables are highly significant in the study of statistical inference. The theoretical basis and the practical value of some of the more widely used distributions are discussed in this chapter and in Part V, "Inference."

SAMPLE SPACE, PROBABILITIES, AND CONTINUOUS VARIABLES

A continuous variable, which is defined over a given range, may take on any of the values in the range. In the process of determining the value of a continuous variable, it is rare that measurements can be made on a continuous scale. More often, the precision of measurement is limited, and only a finite number of values can be determined accurately. For example, consider a process in which boxes of sugar are filled. The desired weight is one pound, but the actual weights of the filled boxes vary over a given range. The actual weights of the filled boxes are a continuous variable, defined for all possible weights, to the smallest fraction of an ounce. In the process of weighing, the scale is capable of measuring weights to the nearest tenth of an ounce, the minimum interval of measurement. The distribution of the discrete weights of the boxes of sugar recorded in a production run is an approximation of the continuous distribution of the actual weights of the filled boxes.

A distribution of the weights of boxes of sugar filled by the process is shown in Figure 8.1. All the weights are included in the range from 15.5 ounces to 16.5 ounces. For purposes of this discussion, it is assumed that any value in this range is a possible weight of a filled box. Following this approach, it is particularly useful to think of the set of elementary outcomes of an experiment as being an interval of the range of the continuous random variable, where any point in the interval is a possible outcome. In this manner, the sample space of the variable is any interval of possible outcomes or the union of such intervals.

For example, the range of weights of the boxes in Figure 8.1 is divided into intervals of 0.1 ounces. These intervals serve as the basis for the sample space of the variable. The possible outcomes of the variable W are defined as the set $S = \{15.5 \leq W \leq 16.5\}$, where any weight from 15.5 ounces to 16.5 ounces can occur. The sample space of the random variable W is the set S. For any subset E of S there is a corresponding probability that is assigned by a probability density function (a set function). In Figure 8.1, for each interval (subset E) of the range (set S) there is a corresponding probability (area under the curve over the interval).

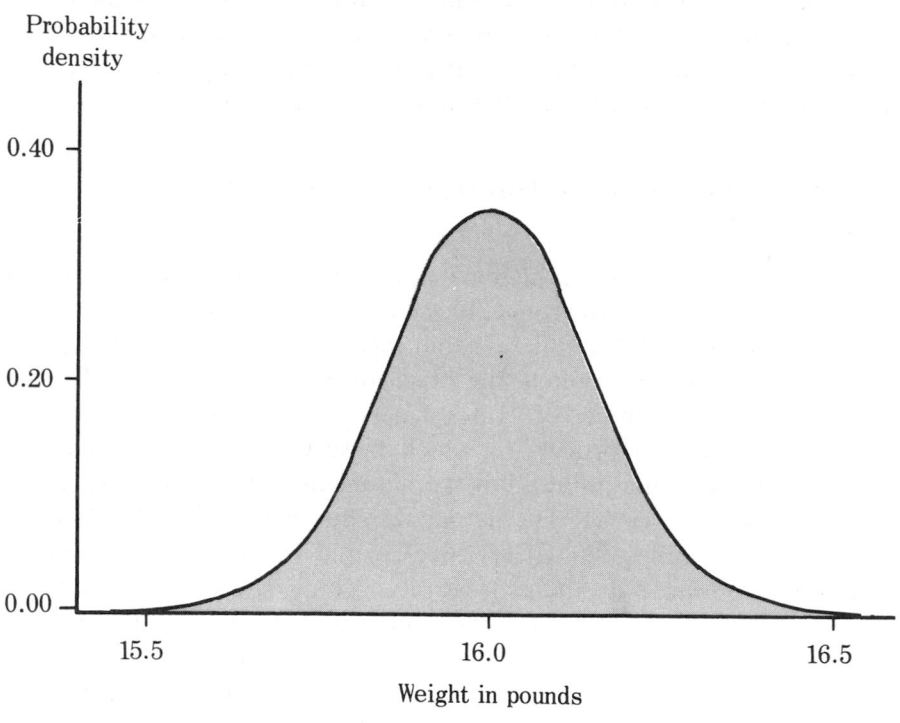

Figure 8.1

PROBABILITY DISTRIBUTION OF WEIGHTS OF BOXES OF SUGAR

A grouped frequency distribution is a device for dividing the range of a continuous variable into intervals and associating a frequency with each interval. The intervals are disjoint, but the union of all of them is the set $S = E_1 \cup E_2 \cup E_3 \cup \ldots \cup E_n$. The partitioning intervals are usually the same size, and the considerations for determining the number and size of intervals are discussed in Chapter 1.

The probability distribution of a continuous variable is similar to that of a discrete variable. The areas under the curve for selected intervals from the range of a continuous variable are analogous to the areas of the bars of the histogram of a discrete probability distribution. The probability density associated with any single value of a continuous variable is expressed graphically by the height of the curve corresponding to that value.

In practice, the principal application of continuous probability distributions lies in their use as approximations of discrete distributions. Much of the theoretical development of statistical methods has been prompted by a need for approximating methods. Several of the more useful continuous distributions are presented in the discussion that follows.

THE UNIFORM DISTRIBUTION

The simplest probability distribution of a continuous variable is expressed by the *uniform density function*. For example, a function of this type is expressed by

$$f(X) = \frac{1}{B - A} \text{ if } A \leq X \leq B,$$

and

$$f(X) = 0 \text{ for all other values of } X.$$

A density function for $f(X) = \frac{1}{4}$ is shown in Figure 8.2. The probability that the variable X will take on a value in any specified interval is

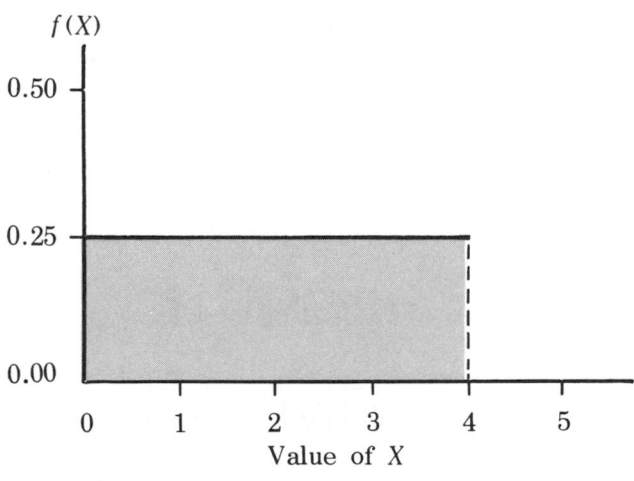

Figure 8.2

UNIFORM PROBABILITY DISTRIBUTION OF THE
CONTINUOUS VARIABLE X

represented by the area under the curve (in this case a line) over the interval. The probability of X over the interval from one to three is written $P(1 < X < 3)$ and corresponds to the area under the curve $y = f(X)$ for the interval.

Areas under curves are used widely in statistics, and an area is commonly expressed as an *integral*. An integral is written

$$\int_a^b f(X)dX \dots\dots\dots\dots\dots\dots\dots\dots\dots(8.1)$$

and is read "the area under the curve (density function) $y = f(X)$ over the interval from a to b," where $\int$ is called the *integral symbol* and a and b are numbers that express the limits of the interval. Relating the integral in Formula 8.1 to areas under the curve in Figure 8.2, it can be seen that the following relationships are true:

Integral	*Area defined*
$\int_1^1 f(X)dX = 0$	area over any point is zero.
$\int_1^2 f(X)dX + \int_2^3 f(X)dX = \int_1^3 f(X)dX$	area over the interval one to two plus the area from two to three equals the area from one to three.
$\int_0^4 f(X)dX - \int_0^2 f(X)dX = \int_2^4 f(X)dX$	area from zero to four less the area from zero to two equals the area from two to four.

By similar reasoning, the expression $\int_{-\infty}^a f(X)dX$ is read "area under the curve $y = f(X)$ over the interval where X is less than or equal to a," and $\int_a^\infty f(X)dX$ represents the area under $y = f(X)$ where X is equal to or greater than a, and $\int_{-\infty}^\infty f(X)dX$ is the integral for the values of X from minus infinity to infinity. Evaluating these expressions in terms of Figure 8.2 for a value of $a = 3$ yields:

$$\int_{-\infty}^3 f(X)dX = \tfrac{3}{4}, \int_3^\infty f(X)dX = \tfrac{1}{4}, \text{ and } \int_{-\infty}^\infty f(X)dX = 1, \text{ where values}$$

of X less than zero and greater than four are not defined.

The area under the curve of a probability density function over an interval from a to b is equal to the probability corresponding to the interval, and $\int_a^b f(X)dX = P(a < X < b)$. It is relatively easy to evaluate areas under simple density functions, but the areas under the density functions to be presented in the following discussions are difficult to evaluate even with the benefit of the methods of calculus. For this reason tables of the areas under these functions have been computed and are provided in the appendixes at the end of the text.

THE EXPONENTIAL DISTRIBUTION

Some of the assumptions basic to Pascal or Poisson probabilities are particularly useful for introducing the basis of the exponential distribution. A Pascal probability, as presented in Chapter 7, expresses the likelihood that n trials will be required to obtain r successes. In the previous chapter, a Poisson probability is related to the likelihood of the occurrence of a specified number of successes (r) in a finite interval of time or space, where the number of successes is the random variable. For this discussion, the roles of these quantities are reversed and the interval of space or time will be viewed as the random variable t, and the probability distribution for a specified number of successes will be determined.

The Time or Distance Required to Obtain a Success

A continuous time period or physical object may be looked upon as being divided into intervals, and the expected number of successes per interval may be computed. This technique, described in the presentation of the Poisson processes in Chapter 7, will be used in the following discussion.

Assume that a utility company maintains standby crews for making emergency repairs on service facilities, and that the service calls are Poisson distributed with time. In the past period of 5,000 service hours there has been a total of 417 emergency service calls, an average of two every 24-hour period. If a trial is viewed as an eight-hour interval (a third of a day), the expected number of successes per trial is $\frac{2}{3} = 0.67$. The probability that n eight-hour periods (trials) will be required to obtain a success is expressed by $P(n) = p^1 q^{n-1}$. The probabilities for various values of n are summarized by the Pascal distribution for $r = 1$ and $p = 0.67$.

If a trial is viewed as a six-hour period (a fourth of a day), the corresponding probabilities are found to be Pascal distributed for $r = 1$ and $p = 0.50$. For a trial consisting of a three-hour period (an eighth of a day), the respective Pascal distribution is $r = 1$ and $p = 0.25$. The probabilities for various values of n and p are shown in Table 8.1. These probabilities are used to determine the area of the bars in the histograms in Figure 8.3. The width of a bar corresponds to the fractional part of a 24-hour day, and its height is such that the area (width times height) is equal to the respective Pascal probability. Note that the height of the first bar in each histogram (reading left to right) is two, the expected number of calls per day. Thus, the vertical scale corresponds to probability density, and the area under the curve for a specified interval relates to probability.

Table 8.1

PASCAL PROBABILITIES FOR SELECTED VALUES
OF n AND p

Number of trials n	Probability of one success in n trials $P(n) = p^r q^{n-r}$	Total elapsed time (hours)
	Eight-Hour Periods $r = 1, p = 0.67$	
1	$(.67)(.33)^0 = 0.667$	8
2	$(.67)(.33)^1 = 0.222$	16
3	$(.67)(.33)^2 = 0.074$	24
4	$(.67)(.33)^3 = 0.025$	32
5	$(.67)(.33)^4 = 0.008$	40
6	$(.67)(.33)^5 = 0.003$	48
	Six-Hour Periods $r = 1, p = 0.50$	
1	$(.50)(.50)^0 = 0.500$	6
2	$(.50)(.50)^1 = 0.250$	12
3	$(.50)(.50)^2 = 0.125$	18
4	$(.50)(.50)^3 = 0.062$	24
5	$(.50)(.50)^4 = 0.031$	30
6	$(.50)(.50)^5 = 0.016$	36
	Three-Hour Periods $r = 1, p = 0.25$	
1	$(.25)(.75)^0 = 0.250$	3
2	$(.25)(.75)^1 = 0.187$	6
3	$(.25)(.75)^2 = 0.141$	9
4	$(.25)(.75)^3 = 0.105$	12
5	$(.25)(.75)^4 = 0.079$	15
6	$(.25)(.75)^5 = 0.059$	18

Characteristics of the Exponential Distribution

An identical continuous curve is plotted for each of the histograms in Figure 8.3. The smaller the division of the horizontal scale, the closer the

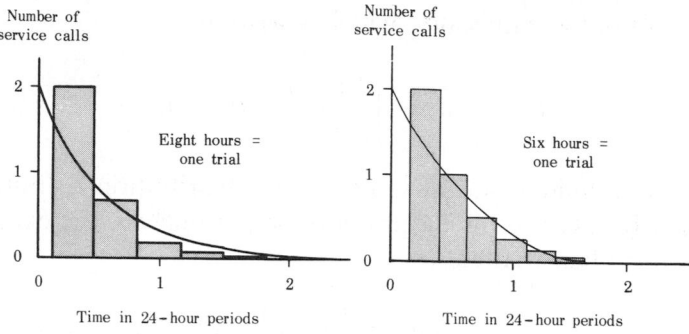

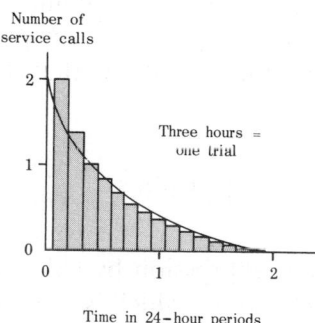

Figure 8.3

HISTOGRAMS OF PASCAL PROBABILITIES WITH AN EXPONENTIAL CURVE
AS THE LIMIT

histogram approaches the curve. It can be proved mathematically that the histogram approaches the smooth curve as a limit as the number of divisions increases without limit. The limiting curve is called the *exponential density function*, which may be written

$$f(t) = \frac{1}{\beta} e^{-\left(\frac{t}{\beta}\right)}$$

where β is the reciprocal of the average number of successes per interval (unit of space); e is 2.7183, the base of natural logarithms; and t is the number of intervals and is greater than zero. The *exponential distribution* has a single parameter, β; and, given the value of this factor, the entire distribution can be determined.

The mean of the exponential distribution is equal to the probability-weighted sum of the values of t, which is written

$$E(t) = \mu = \int_0^\infty \frac{1}{\beta} e^{-\left(\frac{t}{\beta}\right)} dt = \beta.$$

By a similar technique the variance of this distribution is found to be equal to β^2. Because of the nature of these parameters, the exponential distribution is often written

$$f(t) = \frac{1}{\beta} e^{-\left(\frac{t}{\beta}\right)} \dots\dots\dots\dots\dots\dots\dots \textbf{(8.2)}$$

This form will be used in the following discussion.

Probabilities associated with a random variable having an exponential distribution may be found by obtaining the appropriate area under the density function. It is simpler, however, to compute the probability that a success will not be obtained in t intervals. The probability that a success will not occur is one minus the probability that the event will occur. This relationship is written

$$P(t) = 1 - \int_0^t f(t)dt = \int_t^\infty \frac{1}{\beta} e^{-\left(\frac{t}{\beta}\right)} dt.$$

Integrating the right-hand expression by calculus gives the area under the density function from t to ∞, which is written

$$P(t) = e^{-\left(\frac{t}{\beta}\right)} \dots\dots\dots\dots\dots\dots\dots \textbf{(8.3)}$$

Formula 8.3 expresses the probability that a success will not be obtained prior to the interval t.

➤ *Example.* A manufacturer's advertisement states that his brand of electronic equipment is very reliable, with an average of only two failures every 100,000 hours of use. The failures are Poisson distributed. A firm that is considering the purchase of a unit of this equipment is interested in the probability distribution of the length of time a unit is expected to operate before a failure occurs. Ordinates (heights) of the curve at selected values of t are computed in Table 8.2, and the entire curve is plotted in Figure 8.4. The probability that the equipment will not fail prior to the end of the first 100,000-hour period is shown by the shaded portion of Figure 8.4. This probability is written

$$P(t) = e^{-\left(\frac{1}{.5}\right)} = 0.13534$$

and may be read in Appendix E for $\lambda = 2$. The probability that the equipment will not fail in the first 50,000 hours is written

$$P(t) = e^{-\left(\frac{.5}{.5}\right)} = 0.36788,$$

which corresponds to $e^{-\lambda}$ where $\lambda = 1$ in Appendix E.

Table 8.2

SELECTED ORDINATES OF AN EXPONENTIAL DISTRIBUTION
FOR $\beta = 0.5$

Interval (periods of 100,000 hours) t	Ordinate $f(t) = 2(2.7183)^{-\left(\frac{t}{.5}\right)}$	Total elapsed time (hours)
0.0	$2(2.7183)^{-(.0/.5)} = 2.00000$	0
0.5	$2(2.7183)^{-(.5/.5)} = 0.73576$	50,000
1.0	$2(2.7183)^{-(1.0/.5)} = 0.27068$	100,000
1.5	$2(2.7183)^{-(1.5/.5)} = 0.09958$	150,000
2.0	$2(2.7183)^{-(2.0/.5)} = 0.03664$	200,000

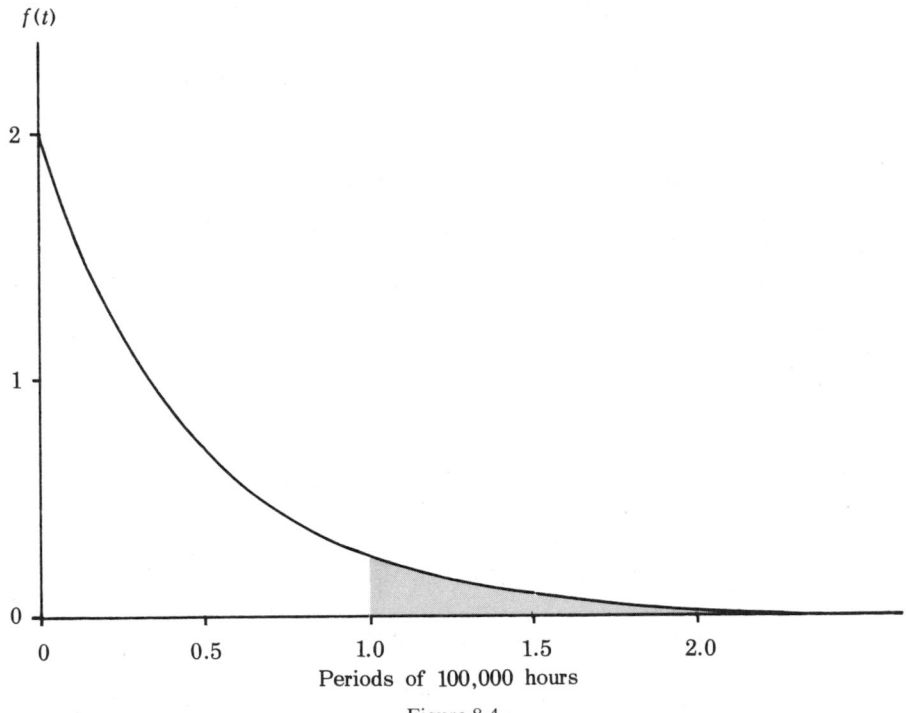

Periods of 100,000 hours

Figure 8.4

EXPONENTIAL DISTRIBUTION OF EQUIPMENT FAILURES

The exponential distribution provides a useful means of approximating either a Pascal or a Poisson distribution for which p is extremely small. In a discussion in the latter part of this chapter, the exponential distribution is related to a more general form, the gamma distribution.

THE NORMAL DISTRIBUTION

Perhaps the best known and most important of all probability distributions is the symmetric curve called the *normal distribution*. The normal distribution is also known as the *Gaussian curve* or the *normal curve of error*. The normal distribution is significant because it provides close approximations for a number of real distributions of considerable practical value. Also, the normal distribution has mathematical properties that simplify its application.

The Normal Distribution As the Limit of the Binomial Distribution

The distributions in Figure 8.5 illustrate the significant fact that the histogram of a binomial distribution becomes smoother as n increases. For very large values of n, the binomial distribution approaches its limit, a continuous curve. It can be proved that a sufficiently large value of n can be selected so that the difference between a discrete binomial distribution and its limit, a continuous curve, is less than some arbitrarily selected value, however small. The continuous curve that is the limit of the binomial curve as n increases without limit is called the *normal probability distribution*. The normal curve is symmetrical about the mean and it is the limit of a binomial distribution even for $p \neq 0.50$, as shown in Figure 8.5.

As is true of the binomial distribution, the normal distribution is defined by two parameters. These parameters are μ, the mathematical expectation, and σ, the standard deviation. Each combination of values of μ and σ defines a different normal distribution, although all of these distributions have characteristics in common. These features will be discussed more fully in the topics that follow.

The Normal Density Function. The limit of the binomial density function

$$P(r \mid n, p) = \binom{n}{r} p^r (1 - p)^{n-r}$$

as n increases without limit is the *normal density function*. This function is written

$$f(r) = \frac{1}{\sigma_r \sqrt{2\pi}} \, e^{-\frac{1}{2}\left(\frac{r - E(r)}{\sigma_r}\right)^2} \dots\dots\dots\dots\dots\dots(8.4)$$

where π is the constant 3.1416 and e is 2.7183, the base of natural logarithms. Notice that the normal density function is of a form similar to the exponential distribution where a constant is multiplied times e raised to a negative exponent.

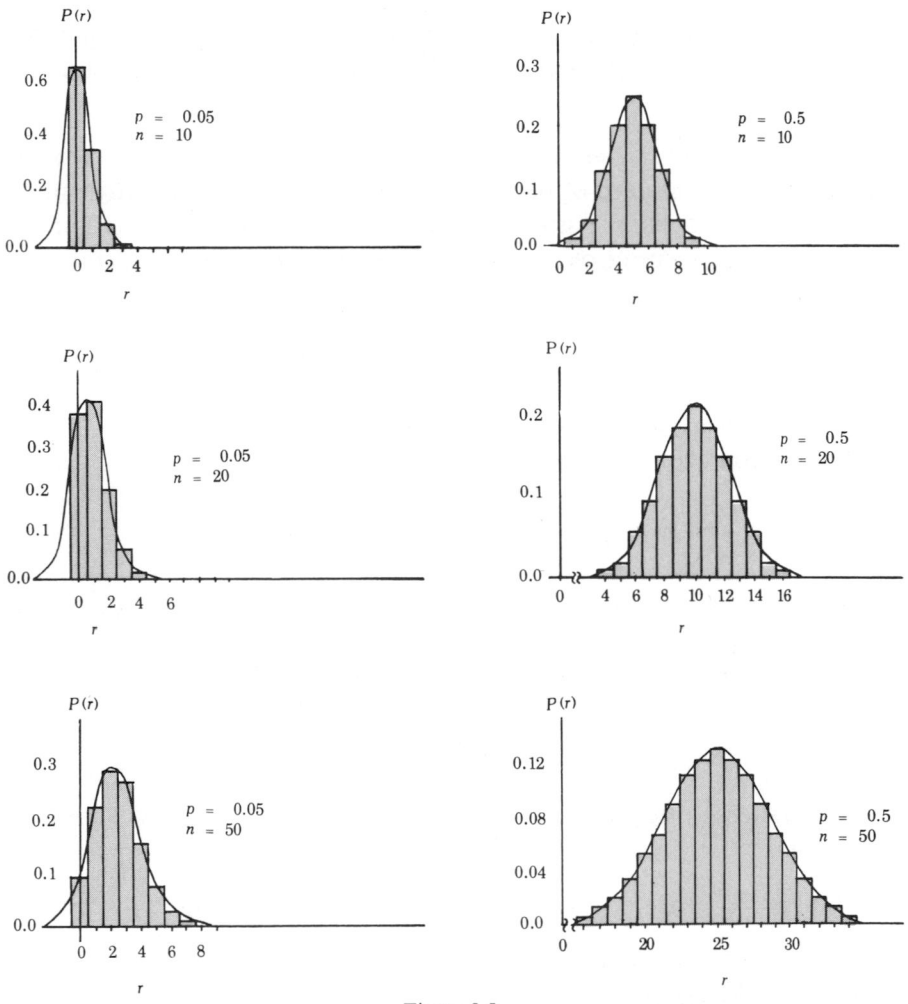

Figure 8.5

BINOMIAL DISTRIBUTIONS FOR SELECTED VALUES OF n AND p AND
THE NORMAL CURVE AS A LIMIT

The distribution described by the normal density function is continuous. Whereas $P(r \mid n, p)$ expresses the area of the bar of a histogram at $r, f(r)$ is the area of a bar that approaches zero in width, and therefore is simply the ordinate of the normal curve at a value r. Since r takes on the properties of a continuous variable as n becomes very large, it is helpful to describe the normal density function in terms of a continuous variable X. The normal distribution may be expressed alternatively as

$$f(X) = \frac{1}{\sigma\sqrt{2\pi}}\, e^{-\frac{1}{2}\left(\frac{X-\mu}{\sigma}\right)^2} \dots\dots\dots\dots\dots(8.5)$$

where $f(X)$ is the ordinate of the normal distribution for a specified value of X, μ is the mathematical expectation, and σ is the standard deviation.

Moments of the Normal Distribution. Several of the moments of the normal distribution are of particular value in applying this distribution to empirical frequency distributions and other probability distributions.

The first moment about the origin, the mathematical expectation, is written

$$E(X) = \int_{-\infty}^{\infty} Xf(X)dX = \mu,$$

where μ is the expected value of the random variable X.

The second moment about the mean is expressed by

$$E(var) = \int_{-\infty}^{\infty} (X - \mu)^2 f(X)dX = \sigma^2,$$

where σ^2 is the variance or the expected value of the squared deviations about the mean.

The third moment about the mean is written

$$M_3 = \int_{-\infty}^{\infty} (X - \mu)^3 f(X)dX,$$

which expresses the absolute skewness of a distribution, and is zero for the normal distribution. The relative skewness is expressed by Formula 3.20, page 70, where $\beta_1 = \frac{M_3^2}{(\sigma^2)^3}$. A distribution having a β_1 value of zero does not provide a clue to the shape of the distribution other than that it may be symmetric.

The fourth moment about the mean of the normal distribution

$$M_4 = \int_{-\infty}^{\infty} (X - \mu)^4 f(X)dX$$

is an expression of absolute kurtosis. Relative kurtosis is expressed by Formula 3.26, page 73, where $\beta_2 = \frac{M_4}{(\sigma^2)^2}$. A normal distribution is mesokurtic and $\beta_2 = 3$.

A single moment may reveal relatively little information about a distribution, but in combination, the whole set of moments will usually determine a distribution exactly. In the discussions that follow, the moments of the normal distribution will be used as aids in judging whether a normal distribution is a reasonably good model of another distribution.

The Normal Frequency Function. A normal curve can be fitted to a finite universe by computing the ordinate of the normal curve in terms of frequencies. Consider a population of N items grouped into intervals, where i is the value of the width of each interval. The ordinate of the fitted normal curve at any point X can be computed by substituting appropriate values into the equation of the *normal frequency function*, which is written

$$Y = \frac{Ni}{\sigma\sqrt{2\pi}}\, e^{-\frac{1}{2}\left(\frac{X-\mu}{\sigma}\right)^2} \dots\dots\dots\dots\dots(8.6)$$

A normal frequency distribution is strictly determined if μ and σ are known and N and i are given. Since $f(X)$ is implicit for all normal density and frequency distributions, these curves have common properties and the same relative shape.

The maximum ordinate Y_0, the height of the normal frequency curve at the mean, is

$$Y_0 = \frac{Ni}{\sigma\sqrt{2\pi}}\, e^{-\frac{1}{2}\left(\frac{0}{\sigma}\right)^2} = \frac{Ni}{\sigma\sqrt{2\pi}},$$

since $e^{-0} = 1$. The normal frequency at any other value of X may be determined relative to Y_0 by employing the general expression

$$Y = Y_0 e^{-\frac{1}{2}\left(\frac{X-\mu}{\sigma}\right)^2} \dots\dots\dots\dots\dots(8.7)$$

The calculation of ordinates is simplified somewhat by using the values of

$$\frac{1}{\sqrt{2\pi}}\, e^{-\frac{1}{2}\left(\frac{X-\mu}{\sigma}\right)^2},$$

which are given in Appendix H. Any desired frequency can be computed by multiplying $\dfrac{Ni}{\sigma}$ by the corresponding value in Appendix H.

➤ *Example.* Iron castings are produced by a process in which the weights of the castings are normally distributed, with a mean of 300 pounds and a standard deviation of 10 pounds. The weights of 1,000 castings are recorded and grouped into a frequency distribution in

Table 8.3. The weights are approximately normally distributed. The normal curve frequency at the mean is

$$Y_0 = \frac{Ni}{\sigma} \frac{1}{\sqrt{2\pi}} e^{-\frac{1}{2}\left(\frac{X-\mu}{\sigma}\right)^2} = \frac{(1{,}000)(5)}{10}(0.39894) = 199.47,$$

where the value 0.39894 is read from Appendix H opposite $z = \frac{X-\mu}{\sigma}$ $= 0$. For the value $X = 307.5$ pounds, the normal curve frequency is found by utilizing the value in Appendix H for $z = \frac{(307.5 - 300.0)}{10}$ $= 0.75$. The frequency $X = 307.5$ is computed as

$$Y_{307.5} = \frac{(1{,}000)(5)}{10}(0.30114) = 150.56.$$

Table 8.3

OBSERVED AND THEORETICAL FREQUENCIES OF
WEIGHTS OF 1,000 CASTINGS

Class limits (pounds)	Observed frequency	Normal curve frequency (ordinates method)
Under 265	0.00	0.23
265 and under 270	1.00	1.01
270 and under 275	5.00	4.54
275 and under 280	17.00	15.87
280 and under 285	44.00	43.14
285 and under 290	92.00	91.32
290 and under 295	149.00	150.56
295 and under 300	192.00	193.33
300 and under 305	192.00	193.33
305 and under 310	149.00	150.56
310 and under 315	92.00	91.32
315 and under 320	44.00	43.14
320 and under 325	17.00	15.87
325 and under 330	5.00	4.54
330 and under 335	1.00	1.01
Over 335	0.00	0.23
	1,000.00	1,000.00

This result differs slightly from the frequency of 149 at the midpoint of the interval "305 and under 310" in Table 8.3. The slight difference between the values is the result of the grouping error of the discrete distribution. The frequencies of the discrete and the continuous distributions are presented in Figure 8.6, which illustrates the close correspondence of the two distributions. If the size of the interval were reduced sufficiently, the two distributions would be identical.

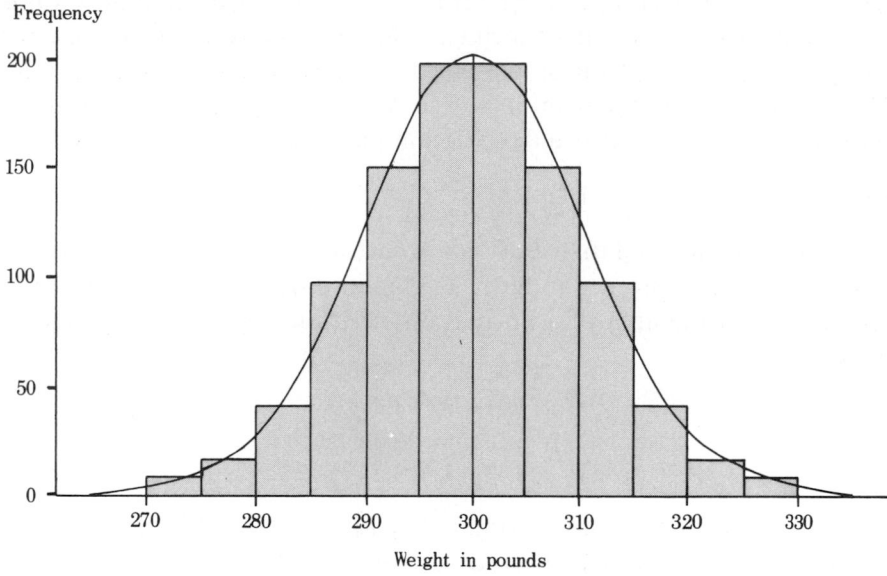

Figure 8.6

OBSERVED AND THEORETICAL DISTRIBUTION OF WEIGHTS
OF 1,000 CASTINGS

Normal Probabilities

Probabilities associated with a random variable having a normal distribution may be found by obtaining the appropriate area under the density function. The probability that the random variable X will take on a value in a specified range between a and b is written

$$P(a < X < b) = \int_a^b f(X)dX$$

where $f(X)$ is the normal density function.

In theory, the range of the normal distribution is infinite and the density function is asymptotic to the X axis. The total area under the curve represents the set of collectively exhaustive events and

$$\int_{-\infty}^{\infty} f(X)dX = 1.$$

Normal probabilities are not easily found by use of the normal density function, but approximations can be computed by numerical methods.

Approximations for a wide range of areas are presented in Appendix H. These values correspond to the probability that X will take on a value in a range from μ to some specified value. It is convenient to view the range as a deviation from μ expressed in terms of standard deviations. For example, the range from $\mu = 5$ to $X = 8$ for a normal distribution with $\sigma = 2$ is expressed as a deviation in terms of the standard deviation by $\dfrac{X - \mu}{\sigma} = \dfrac{8 - 5}{2} = 1.5\sigma.$

Areas of the normal distribution are customarily related to deviations from the mean, expressed in terms of standard deviations. For example, the percent of the area of a normal distribution over selected ranges is as follows:

$$\mu \pm 1\sigma = 68.27\%$$
$$\mu \pm 2\sigma = 95.45\%$$
$$\mu \pm 3\sigma = 99.73\%.$$

These relationships are approximated in Table 8.3 and Figure 8.6 by the normal curve fitted to the discrete distribution of weights of castings as follows:

$$\mu \pm 1\sigma = 300 \pm (1)(10) = \frac{687.98}{1,000.00} = 68.798\%$$

$$\mu \pm 2\sigma = 300 \pm (2)(10) = \frac{956.70}{1,000.00} = 95.670\%$$

$$\mu \pm 3\sigma = 300 \pm (3)(10) = \frac{997.52}{1,000.00} = 99.752\%.$$

The slight deviations from the theoretical values are the result of the discrete nature of rounding error.

Values for areas of the normal curve for selected ranges are found in Appendix H. Since a normal distribution is symmetric, the table reflects values for only one side of the distribution. The area corresponding to $\mu \pm 1\sigma$ is found opposite $z = \dfrac{X - \mu}{\sigma} = 1.0\sigma.$ In Appendix H this value is read as 0.34134. Since it corresponds to only one side of the distribution, the desired area is $(2)(0.34134) = 0.68268$. Similarly, the area over the range $\mu \pm 2\sigma$ is read opposite $z = \dfrac{X - \mu}{\sigma} = 2.0\sigma$ in Appendix H as 0.47725, and $(2)(0.47725) = 95.450$.

➤ *Example.* In the past, the demand in the month of March for denim slacks produced by a firm has been normally distributed, with a mean of 10,000 pairs and a standard deviation of 500 pairs. The plant manager wishes to know the probability that demand will be in the range from 8,500 to 10,625 pairs. The range overlaps both sides of the distribution, but not symmetrically. Consequently, the problem must be solved in parts. The area over the portion of the range

$$z = \frac{X - \mu}{\sigma} = \frac{8,500 - 10,000}{500} = -3.00\sigma,$$

where the negative sign denotes direction. Reading from Appendix H, the corresponding value is 0.49865. The area over the partial range

$$z = \frac{X - \mu}{\sigma} = \frac{10,625 - 10,000}{500} = 1.25\sigma$$

is read as 0.39435. The area over the total range is

$$\int_{8,500}^{10,000} f(X)dX + \int_{10,000}^{10,625} f(X)dX = 0.49865 + 0.39435 = 0.89300,$$

which is shown as the shaded portion of the left-hand curve in Figure 8.7.

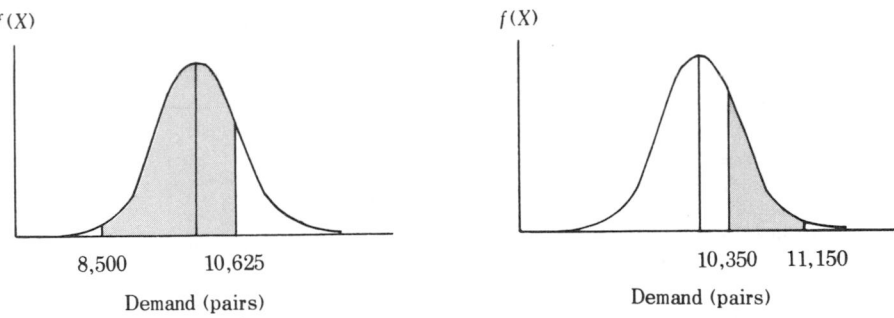

Figure 8.7

PROBABILITIES FOR SELECTED RANGES OF A NORMAL
RANDOM VARIABLE

Now suppose the plant manager wishes to find the probability that demand will be between 10,350 and 11,150 pairs, as shown in the shaded portion of the right-hand curve in Figure 8.7. The area in question is found by determining the area over the range

$$z = \frac{X - \mu}{\sigma} = \frac{11,150 - 10,000}{500} = 2.3\sigma.$$

The corresponding value in Appendix H is 0.48928.

The area over the range

$$z = \frac{X - \mu}{\sigma} = \frac{10,350 - 10,000}{500} = 0.7\sigma$$

is read as 0.25804. The desired probability is

$$\int_{10,000}^{11,150} f(X)dX - \int_{10,000}^{10,350} f(X)dX = 0.48928 - 0.25804 = 0.23124.$$

Areas of the normal curve may be used as an alternative method for fitting a normal curve to a frequency distribution.

➤ *Example.* A sample of 100 parts of a particular type produced by a machine is taken. The diameters of the parts are measured in terms of deviations in thousandths of an inch from a specified dimension. These deviations are grouped into a frequency distribution, which is used as an estimate of the universe distribution of all parts produced. The distribution and related values are shown in Table 8.4.

Table 8.4

OBSERVED AND EXPECTED FREQUENCIES OF DIAMETERS OF 100 PARTS

Class limits (deviations in 0.001")	Observed frequency f	d'	fd'	fd'^2	Expected normal frequency
Less than 0.5	0	-4	0	0	0.1
0.5 and under 1.0	1	-3	-3	9	0.7
1.0 and under 1.5	3	-2	-6	12	4.4
1.5 and under 2.0	16	-1	-16	16	15.0
2.0 and under 2.5	27	0	0	0	28.2
2.5 and under 3.0	35	1	35	35	28.8
3.0 and under 3.5	12	2	24	48	16.4
3.5 and under 4.0	4	3	12	36	5.5
4.0 and under 4.5	2	4	8	32	0.8
More than 4.5	0	5	0	0	0.1
Total	100		54	188	100.0

$$\bar{x} = A + \frac{\Sigma fd'}{n} i$$

$$= 2.25 + \left(\frac{54}{100}\right)0.5$$

$$= 2.52$$

$$s = i \sqrt{\frac{\Sigma f(d')^2}{n} - \left(\frac{\Sigma fd'}{n}\right)^2}$$

$$= 0.5 \sqrt{\frac{188}{100} - (0.54)^2}$$

$$= 0.5 \sqrt{1.88 - 0.29}$$

$$= 0.63.$$

The expected frequencies are obtained by using the sample statistics as estimates of the universe mean and of the standard deviation and applying the normal curve areas. The expected frequency of the interval "2.5 and under 3.0" is computed in two parts, since $\bar{x}$ lies in this interval. The required calculations are:

$$\frac{X - \mu}{\sigma} = \frac{2.50 - 2.52}{0.63} = -0.032\sigma$$

$$\frac{X - \mu}{\sigma} = \frac{3.00 - 2.52}{0.63} = 0.760\sigma.$$

The appropriate normal curve areas read from Appendix H are 0.01205 and 0.27637, respectively. The sum of these values 0.28842 multiplied by $n = 100$ yields the expected normal frequency for the interval shown in Table 8.4. The expected frequency for the interval "3.0 and under 3.5" is computed similarly as follows:

$$\frac{X - \mu}{\sigma} = \frac{3.00 - 2.52}{0.63} = 0.76\sigma$$

$$\frac{X - \mu}{\sigma} = \frac{3.50 - 2.52}{0.63} = 1.56\sigma.$$

The corresponding areas read from Appendix H are 0.27637 and 0.44062, respectively. The desired area is found by subtracting these values, $0.44062 - 0.27637 = 0.16425$, and multiplying the result by 100 to give the expected frequency 16.425. The remaining expected frequencies are computed similarly, and the results are shown in Table 8.4. The observed frequencies are shown by a histogram and the expected frequencies are shown by a frequency polygon in Figure 8.8, page 244.

The Unit or Standard Normal Distribution

The technique of expressing a range of a continuous variable in terms of standard deviations provides the basis of a standardized form of the normal distribution. Let U denote a deviation written $\dfrac{r - E(r)}{\sigma_r}$. Substitute this relationship in Formula 8.4 and multiply the equation by σ_r to keep the area of each bar of the histogram unchanged. The resulting expression

$$f(U) = \frac{1}{\sqrt{2\pi}} e^{-\frac{1}{2}U^2} \quad\quad\quad\text{...........................(8.8)}$$

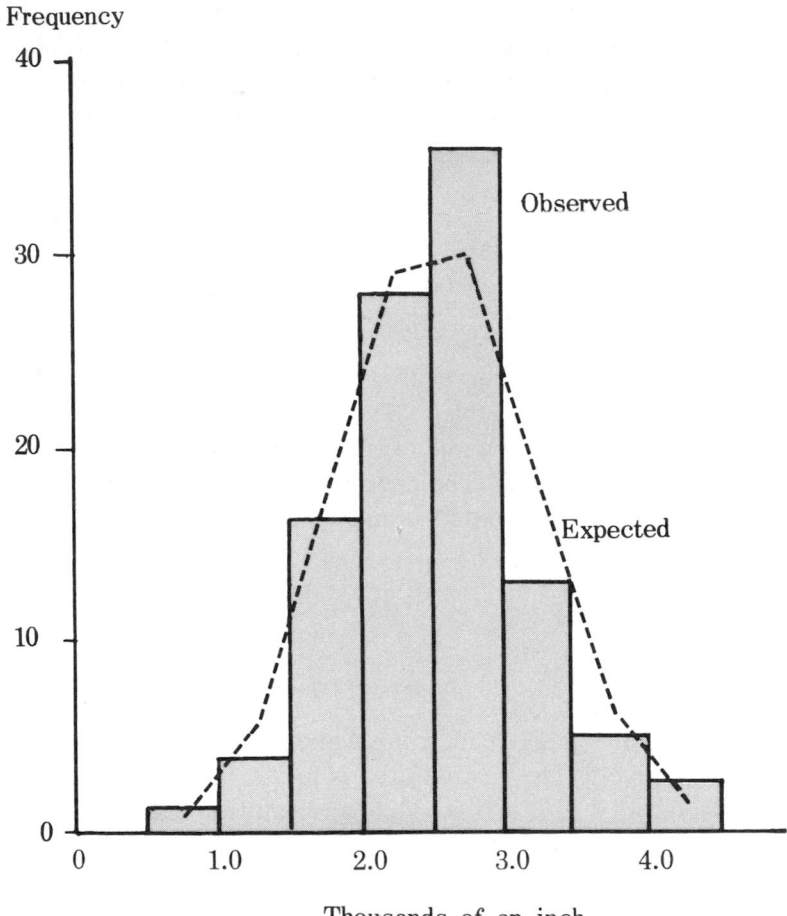

Figure 8.8

OBSERVED AND EXPECTED FREQUENCIES OF PARTS PRODUCED
BY A MACHINE

is the equation of the *standard* or *unit normal density function*. This distribution has no parameters since the random variable is standardized in terms of deviations and the mean $E(U) = \mu = 0$. Further, the standard deviation $\sigma_U = 1$; hence, the name, unit normal distribution. Areas under the standard normal density function are read from Appendix H. The usefulness of this distribution is demonstrated in Part V in the presentation of statistical inference.

The transformation of binomial distributions into unit normal form is seen in Figure 8.9. This conversion is accomplished by expressing the bars of the histogram of the binomial distribution in terms of σ_r units instead of units of one. The width of each of the bars in the binomial

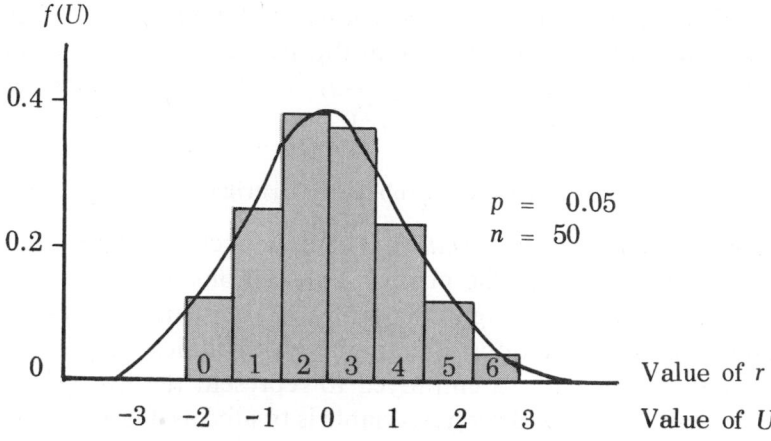

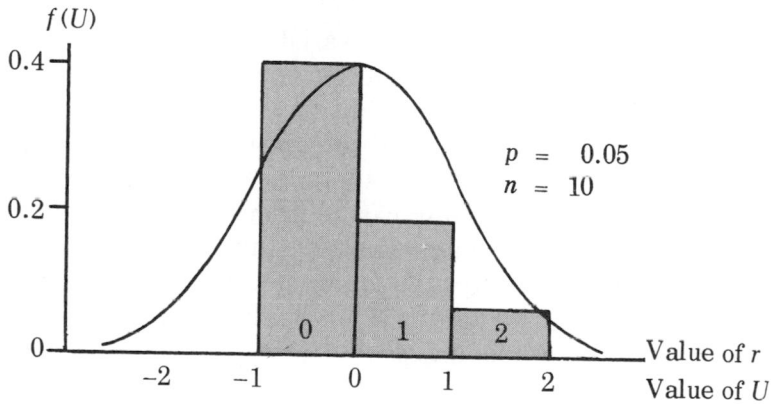

Figure 8.9

STANDARDIZED BINOMIAL DISTRIBUTIONS FOR SELECTED VALUES OF
n AND *p* AND UNIT NORMAL DISTRIBUTIONS FITTED TO THE DATA

histogram is one, but in the transformation to unit normal form, each width is expressed in standard deviation units. Therefore, the width of each bar is $\dfrac{1}{\sigma_r}$. In order to keep the area of the bars unchanged, the height of each bar of the binomial histogram is multiplied by σ_r.

For example, consider the binomial distribution in Figure 8.5, page 235, where $n = 50$ and $p = 0.05$. The area of the bar for $r = 3$ is 0.2199, which is the probability read from Appendix C. The conversion to unit normal form is accomplished by computing the transformed width of the bar as $\dfrac{1}{\sqrt{(50)(0.05)(0.95)}} = \dfrac{1}{1.54} = 0.649$ standard deviation units. The height of the bar is transformed by multiplying $(0.2199)(1.54) = 0.339$.

A bar with these transformed dimensions is plotted for $r = 3$ in the upper diagram of Figure 8.9. Note that the area of the bar is unchanged by the transformation since $(0.339)(0.649) = 0.220$, the rounded equivalent of the value read from Appendix C.

Normal Approximations of Discrete Probability Distributions

Normal and Binomial Probabilities. There is a close correspondence between the binomial and the normal distributions for finite values of n and $p \neq 0.50$, as seen in Figure 8.5. In some problems it is convenient to use normal approximations of binomial probabilities. In this manner, a continuous distribution is employed to represent the histogram of a discrete variable, and the discrete variable is treated as if it were continuous.

A bar of the histogram of a discrete variable corresponds to a single value of the variable. Since only integer (whole number) values are usually defined for this type of variable, the bar is assumed to extend halfway to the integer preceding and the integer following the central value. For example, the bar of a histogram centered on the value 15 of a discrete variable is assumed to extend from 14.5 to 15.5. The extension of the histogram in this manner is called the *continuity correction.* Areas under the normal density function are found in terms of deviations from the mean, and a similar approach is used to find normal areas to approximate binomial probabilities.

➤ *Example.* A sample of 20 items is selected randomly from a process for which $p = 0.40$. The probability of obtaining exactly 5 defectives is found by solving

$$P(r = 5 \mid n = 20, p = 0.40) = \binom{20}{5} (0.40)^5 (0.60)^{15} = 0.0746,$$

which is shown as the shaded portion of Figure 8.10. The normal curve approximation of this binomial probability is found by solving for σ_r and $E(r)$ and employing these to obtain the appropriate normal area.

For this example,

$$E(r) = np = (20)(0.40) = 8.00$$

and

$$\sigma_r = \sqrt{npq} = \sqrt{20(0.40)(0.60)} = 2.19.$$

The histogram at $r = 5$ extends from 4.5 to 5.5, and the normal approximation is found by expressing these values as deviations from

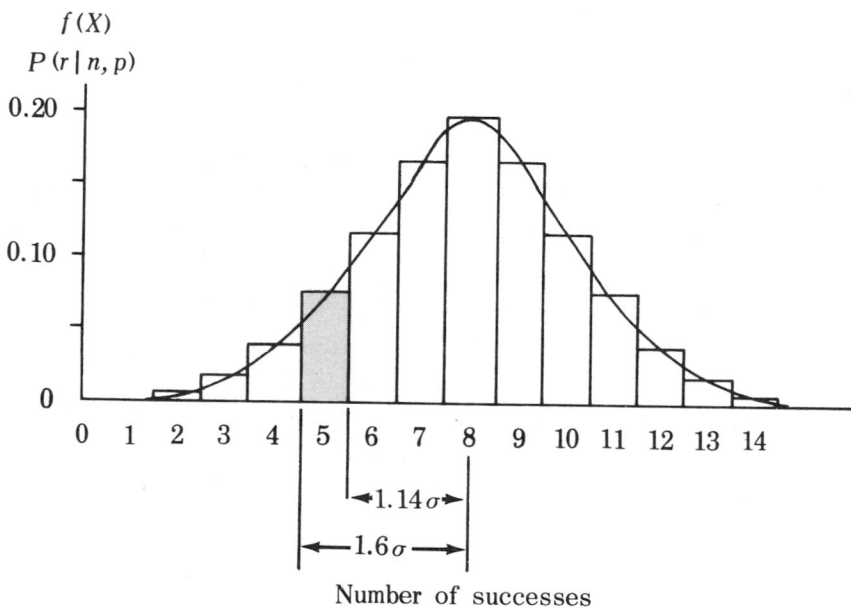

Figure 8.10

NORMAL APPROXIMATION OF BINOMIAL PROBABILITIES

$E(r)$ in terms of standard deviations. These values are obtained by writing

$$z = \frac{r - E(r)}{\sigma_r} = \frac{4.5 - 8}{2.19} = -1.60\sigma$$

and

$$z = \frac{r - E(r)}{\sigma_r} = \frac{5.5 - 8}{2.19} = -1.14\sigma.$$

These values of z are read in Appendix H as 0.44520 and 0.37286, respectively. The normal approximation of this binomial probability is $0.44520 - 0.37286 = 0.07234$, which compares very favorably with the exact probability of 0.0746.

Applying the properties of the unit normal distribution, the approximate binomial probability can be found by computing the area of the bar of the histogram. The width of any bar of the histogram is equal to $\frac{1}{\sigma_r}$, since the normal density function is multiplied by σ if it is transformed to a unit normal distribution. The height of the unit normal curve at $r = 5$ is the value of $f(X)$ for

$$z = \frac{r - E(r)}{\sigma_r} = \frac{5 - 8}{2.19} = -1.37\sigma.$$

The ordinate $f(X)$ for $z = -1.37\sigma$ is read from Appendix H as approximately 0.1563. The area of the bar is found by multiplying the width times the approximate height at the center of the bar. This is written

$$P(r \mid n, p) = \frac{1}{\sigma_r} \cdot f(X) = \frac{1}{2.19}(.1563) = 0.0714.$$

The normal density function is the limit of the binomial as n becomes very large; consequently, the normal approximation of binomial probabilities improves as n becomes larger. For finite values of n, the normal approximation is poorer in the tails of the binomial than nearer the expected value.

Normal and Poisson Probabilities. The expected number of successes in a Poisson process is denoted by λ, which is analogous to $E(r)$. Similarly, $\sqrt{\lambda}$ corresponds to σ_r. The normal approximation of a Poisson probability is computed by utilizing the correction and solving for

$$z = \frac{r - \lambda}{\sqrt{\lambda}}.$$

➤ *Example.* A study of the customer arrivals at the appliance department of a store revealed that the probability of an arrival during the period of one minute is 0.033. The expected number of arrivals every half hour is $np = \lambda = (30)(0.033) = 1$. The Poisson probability of exactly two arrivals during a half-hour period is computed as follows:

$$P(r \mid \lambda) = \frac{\lambda^r}{r!} e^{-\lambda} = \left(\frac{1}{2}\right)(e^{-1}) = 0.1839.$$

The normal approximation is computed by solving

$$z = \frac{r - \lambda}{\sqrt{\lambda}} = \frac{2.5 - 1}{1} = 1.5\sigma, \quad z = \frac{r - \lambda}{\sqrt{\lambda}} = \frac{1.5 - 1}{1} = 0.5\sigma.$$

Reading the values of the corresponding areas from Appendix H gives 0.43319 and 0.19146, respectively. The normal approximation is the difference $0.43319 - 0.19146 = 0.24173$, which is shown as the shaded area in Figure 8.11.

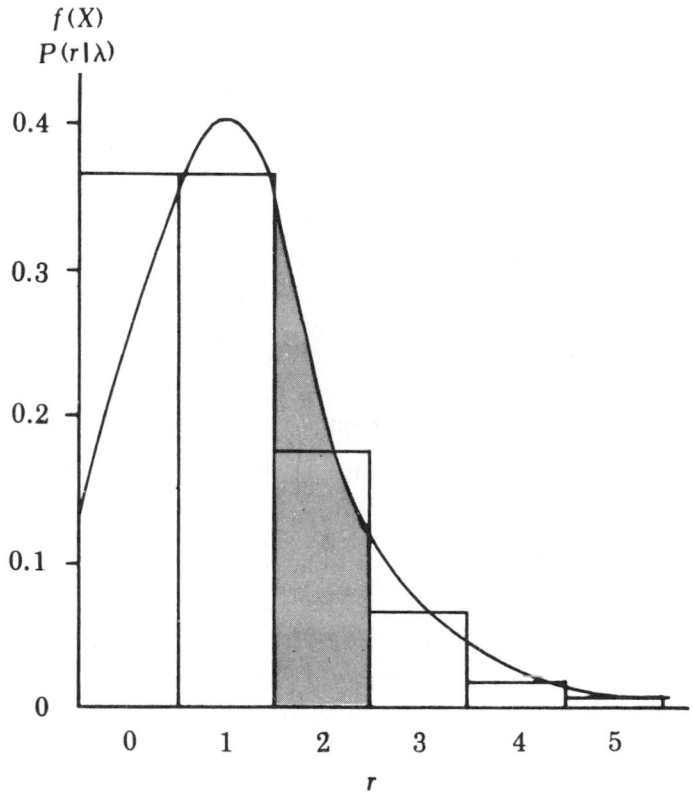

Figure 8.11

NORMAL APPROXIMATION OF POISSON PROBABILITIES

Normal and Pascal Probabilities. Pascal probabilities relate to the number of Bernoulli trials required to obtain r successes. In this manner r successes is the sum of r random variables, where a number of trials are required to achieve a success. As a consequence, the Pascal distribution of the required number of trials for obtaining a success approaches a normal distribution as r becomes very large. A normal approximation can be obtained by employing the moments of the Pascal distribution.

➤ *Example.* The probability that more than 50 trials will be required to obtain 12 successes if $p = 0.30$ is expressed by

$$P(n > 50 \mid r = 12, p = 0.30) = P(r < 12 \mid n = 50, p = 0.30)$$
$$= 1 - 0.8610 = 0.1390$$

where the value of 0.8610 is read from Appendix D. The normal approximation is found by substituting n for r and computing

$$z = \frac{n - E(n)}{\sigma_n} = \frac{50.5 - \dfrac{12}{0.30}}{\sqrt{\dfrac{(12)(0.70)}{(0.30)^2}}} = \frac{10.5}{9.7} = 1.08\sigma$$

and subtracting the corresponding value in Appendix H from one half to obtain $0.50000 - 0.35993 = 0.14007$.

Normal approximations can be usefully applied to several other distributions. Normal approximations of these types of probabilities can be computed in a manner similar to that outlined in the foregoing discussions.

The Significance of the Normal Distribution

The normal distribution is dominant among theoretical distributions in the study and application of statistics. The preeminence of this distribution is the result of its mathematical characteristics and its suitability as a mode of expression for many phenomena.

The derivation of the moments of the binomial distribution in Chapter 7 utilizes the notion of a variable X that takes on a value of one or zero, depending upon whether a success or a failure is obtained on a trial. In this fashion, the probability of a success is constant for all trials, and each trial is an independent binary (two-valued) random variable. The sum of these variables is the binomial distribution, and the mean and the variance of the binomial are the sums of the expected values and the variances, respectively, of the independent variables. As the number of variables (n) becomes large, the sum approaches the normal distribution as a limit.

This important result is generalized further by some theorems, which are given without proof. The first theorem states that:

If each of n independent random variables has an identical probability distribution, the sum of these distributions approaches a normal distribution as n becomes large. It is significant that this is true whatever the nature of the probability distribution, unless a distribution has an infinite mean or standard deviation.

A second theorem states that:

For certain specified conditions, the normal limit extends to sums of independent random variables for which the probability distributions are not all alike.

The importance of the normal distribution in statistical theory is also predicated by the fact that, by proper transformation, any continuous distribution can be converted into a normal distribution. The prominence of the normal distribution also results from the frequent occurrence of variables, in the analysis of business problems, which are sums of independent random variables with very similar, if not identical, probability distributions. This fact will be amplified further in the discussion of the central limit theorem in Chapter 9.

The suitability of the normal distribution as an approximating form of the probability distributions of various random variables is seen in the computation of normal approximations in preceding portions of this chapter. The fact that sums of random variables tend to approach normality as *n* increases, implies that the larger the value of *n*, the better the normal approximation. For many practical problems, unless exact probabilities are required, normal approximations are utilized, especially when *n* is not small.

The theorems described above apply to sums of independent random variables, for which the number of variables and the nature of the identical probability distributions are known. It is fairly common for a business problem to involve a variable that is the sum of random variables, the number and the probability distributions of which are unknown, and which may or may not be completely independent. While the precise nature and relationship of the component variables may be unknown, many empirical distributions appear reasonably normal when plotted. For these cases the "fitting" of a normal curve to historical data enables one to use the normal curve as a reasonably good model and to take advantage of the considerable amount of information that is known about this model.

Methods for appraising the appropriateness of the fit of a normal curve to empirical data are discussed in Chapter 13, "Chi-Square and Other Nonparametric Methods."

THE GAMMA DISTRIBUTION

A Poisson distribution expresses the likelihood of *r* successes per unit of space. The probability density function of the interval for *r* Poisson successes, or for the interval between Poisson successes, is called the *gamma density function*. This function may be written

$$f(t) = \frac{\left(\dfrac{t}{\mu}\right)^{r-1} e^{-\left(\frac{t}{\mu}\right)}}{(r-1)!} \quad \dots\dots\dots\dots\dots\dots(8.9)$$

where *r* is the number of successes, *t* is the number of intervals, and μ is the reciprocal of the average number of successes per interval. The gamma distribution is related to a Poisson process in a fashion similar to the relationship between the Pascal and the binomial distributions.

Table 8.5

CHARACTERISTICS OF SELECTED DISTRIBUTIONS

DISCRETE DISTRIBUTIONS

Distribution	Density function	Parameters	Probability or frequency	Limiting form or limit of	Approximate or alternate distributions	Applications
Binomial	$\binom{n}{r} p^r (1-p)^{n-r}$	n, p	$P(r)$ = probability of r successes in n Bernoulli trials, given a constant value of p. (Formula 7.3)	Normal and Poisson (if p is small and n is large)	Normal and Poisson	Sampling from a Bernoulli process.
Poisson	$\dfrac{\lambda^r}{r!} e^{-\lambda}$	λ	$P(r)$ = probability of r successes in many trials, given a constant value of λ. (Formula 7.11)	Poisson	Normal and exponential (if p is small)	Sampling from a process considered Bernoulli, where n is large, p is small, and np is constant.
Hypergeometric	$\dfrac{\binom{N-r}{n-c}\binom{r}{c}}{\binom{N}{n}}$	N, n, c	$P(r)$ = probability of r successes in n Bernoulli trials from a finite universe of size N, given the total possible number of successes c. (Formula 7.15)	Hypergeometric	Binomial, Poisson, and normal	Sampling from a finite universe containing a given number of successes and where p changes from trial to trial.
Pascal	$\binom{n-1}{r-1} p^r (1-p)^{n-r}$	r, p	$P(n)$ = probability that n Bernoulli trials will be required to obtain r successes, given a constant value of p. (Formula 7.17)	Exponential (for $r = 1$)	Binomial, normal, and exponential (if p is small)	Determining the probability that n Bernoulli trials will be needed to obtain a desired number of successes.

Distribution	Formula	Parameters	Probability statement			Primary use
Uniform	$\dfrac{1}{B-A}$	None	$P(a < X < b)$ = the probability that X will take on a value in the interval from a to b.			Primarily of theoretical value.
Exponential	$\dfrac{1}{\beta}e^{-\left(\frac{t}{\beta}\right)}$	β	$P(t)$ = probability that if trials are Bernoulli, a success will not occur in time period t. (Formula 8.3)	Pascal (for $r = 1$)	Gamma (for $r = 1$), Poisson, and Pascal	Determining the probability that a given space or time interval will be required to obtain a success.
Normal probability	$\dfrac{1}{\sigma\sqrt{2\pi}}e^{-\frac{1}{2}\left(\frac{X-\mu}{\sigma}\right)^2}$	μ, σ	$P(a < X < b)$ = probability the random variable X will take on a value in the interval from a to b, given μ and σ. (Formula 8.5)	Binomial		Describing continuous and certain discrete variables and sums of random variables that may be considered normal.
Normal frequency	$\dfrac{Ni}{\sigma\sqrt{2\pi}}e^{-\frac{1}{2}\left(\frac{X-\mu}{\sigma}\right)^2}$	N, i, μ, σ	Y = theoretical normal frequency of a distribution given N, i, μ, and σ. (Formula 8.6)	Unit normal		Provides a normal approximation for a frequency distribution.
Unit normal	$\dfrac{1}{\sqrt{2\pi}}e^{-\frac{1}{2}U^2}$	None	$P(a < U < b)$ = probability the random variable $U = \pm\dfrac{(X-\mu)}{\sigma}$ will take on a value in the interval from a to b. (Formula 8.8)		Standard form into which all normal distributions can be transformed	Valuable for describing any normal distribution, especially those related to statistical inference.
Gamma	$\dfrac{\left(\frac{t}{\mu}\right)^{r-1}e^{-\left(\frac{t}{\mu}\right)}}{(r-1)!}$	$r, \dfrac{1}{\mu}$ (α, β)	$P\left(\dfrac{t}{\mu} < \dfrac{\tilde{t}}{\tilde{\mu}}\right)$ = probability that if successes are Poisson distributed, less than time t will be required to obtain r successes, given r and $\dfrac{1}{\mu}$. (Formula 8.9)	Exponential (for $r = 1$)		Determining the probability that t or less time will be required to obtain a success.

The exponential distribution is a special case of the gamma distribution, for which $r = 1$.

A family of distributions is defined by the gamma density function for various values of the two parameters r and $\left(\dfrac{t}{\mu}\right)$. In statistical literature the gamma distribution often appears in a form where r is denoted α and $\left(\dfrac{t}{\mu}\right)$ is designated as β.

Probabilities associated with the gamma distribution may be obtained by calculus, but these methods are very complicated. For instance, unless r is a positive integer, the value of the integral of the density function must be evaluated by numerical methods. There is a relationship between the gamma and the Poisson probabilities that somewhat facilitates the application of the gamma distribution. The relationship of the cumulative gamma and the Poisson probabilities is written

$$P\left[\left(\frac{t}{\mu}\right) < \left(\frac{\tilde{t}}{\tilde{\mu}}\right) \mid r\right] = P\left[r \geq \tilde{r} \mid \lambda = \left(\frac{\tilde{t}}{\tilde{\mu}}\right)\right],$$

$$\text{gamma} \qquad\qquad\qquad \text{Poisson}$$

where $\tilde{t}$ and $\tilde{\mu}$ are specified values of t and μ. These probabilities may be read from Appendix G.

> ➤ *Example.* Customers arriving at a check-out counter of a super-market are Poisson distributed at a rate of one every two minutes. The probability that the total time interval required for three customers to arrive is less than 10 minutes is computed for $r = 3$, $\tilde{t} = 10$, and $\tilde{\mu} = 2$. Reading from Appendix G opposite $r = 3$ and $\lambda = \dfrac{\tilde{t}}{\tilde{\mu}} = \dfrac{10}{2} = 5$, the probability is 0.8753.

Another special case of the gamma distribution is significant in the study of statistics. The gamma density function for which the value of $r = \dfrac{d.f.}{2}$, where *d.f.* equals the degrees of freedom, and $\mu = 2$, is called the *Chi-square distribution*. This distribution is discussed in Chapter 13.

COMPARISON OF SELECTED PROBABILITY DISTRIBUTIONS

The distributions considered in Chapters 7 and 8 are more or less related, depending upon the nature of the random variables involved. The basic characteristics of each of these distributions are summarized in Table 8.5 to provide additional insight into the nature of the individual distributions and the relationships that exist among distributions.

WAITING-LINE MODELS

The necessity of standing in line for service is an experience that occurs commonly. The statistical and economic considerations in the buildup of waiting lines are significant in many business problems. A *waiting line* or a *queue* is defined as a formation of inputs that wait for service or processing at a facility in a system. Some examples of familiar types of waiting lines are shown in Table 8.6.

Table 8.6

EXAMPLES OF SYSTEMS INVOLVING WAITING LINES

System	Input unit	Service or processing facility
Calls made at a coin-operated telephone	Individual approaching telephone to place a call	Telephone circuits and operator
Automobile service station	Vehicle is driving into station for fuel and other service	Attendant, gasoline pump, and other equipment
Supermarket	Customer seeking to have the amount of purchase tabulated and to pay for the purchase	Clerk, cash register, and bagging operation at a check-out counter
"Five-minute" car wash	Automobiles arriving to be washed	Attendants and automatic car-washing apparatus
Medical clinic	Patients entering to receive medical attention	Physician, nurse and clerical staff, and related equipment and drugs

Basic Types of Waiting-Line Systems

Each example in Table 8.6 describes a system in which units of input arrive randomly for service or processing. An input that appears at a facility for service is called an *arrival*. The number of input units that arrive during a time period (hour, day, minute, etc.) is a random variable. The average number of arrivals per unit of time is called the *arrival rate*.

The length of time required to process or to serve an incoming unit is called the *service time* or the *holding time*. The average number of units processed or served per unit of time is called the *service rate*. The service time may be constant (as in a "five-minute" car wash) or a random variable. The interaction of varying numbers of arrivals per unit of time with random service times required to process inputs is described in terms such as the average length of the waiting line, the average waiting time of a unit, and the probability that an arriving input unit will have to wait for service.

The simplest system in which waiting lines occur involves inputs that arrive at a single service facility, form a waiting line from time to time, and a "first-come first-served" rule determines the priority with which units are served. More complex systems may involve multiple-service facilities (or channels) in a parallel or series configuration. An input in a system consisting of a parallel arrangement of identical service facilities (or channels) may be served on a "first-come first-served" basis by any of the facilities.

Another type of system consists of a multiple phase or series arrangement of facilities (not necessarily identical), in which the output of one service facility constitutes the input of a succeeding stage. A fourth basic type of service facility configuration consists of a series-parallel combination, which is shown in Figure 8.12. Waiting lines may also involve more complex service priority rules that govern the precedence of entry of inputs into a service facility. This discussion, however, is limited to the simplest types of waiting-line systems and priority rules.

The relevant factors and assumptions required to define and analyze a system involving a waiting line are summarized as follows:

1. The arrival rate of inputs is a random variable described by a probability distribution.
2. The times required to service or process inputs is a constant or a random variable described by a probability distribution.
3. The number and configuration of service facilities is known.
4. The priority for the precedence of input units for being serviced is specified by a priority rule.
5. The source of input units is known to be infinite or finite.

Mathematical formulation of waiting-line buildup is feasible only in very restricted cases. This discussion presents some of the waiting-line models that can be formulated and analyzed statistically. A technique for obtaining solutions for more complex models is presented in the discussion of the Monte Carlo method in Chapter 9.

Selected Arrival and Service Time Distributions

Waiting lines in servicing systems, which are characterized by a Poisson distribution of arrivals and constant or exponentially distributed service times, can be formulated statistically to determine certain characteristics of the system. These assumptions concerning the distributions of arrivals and service times are applicable to many business problems.

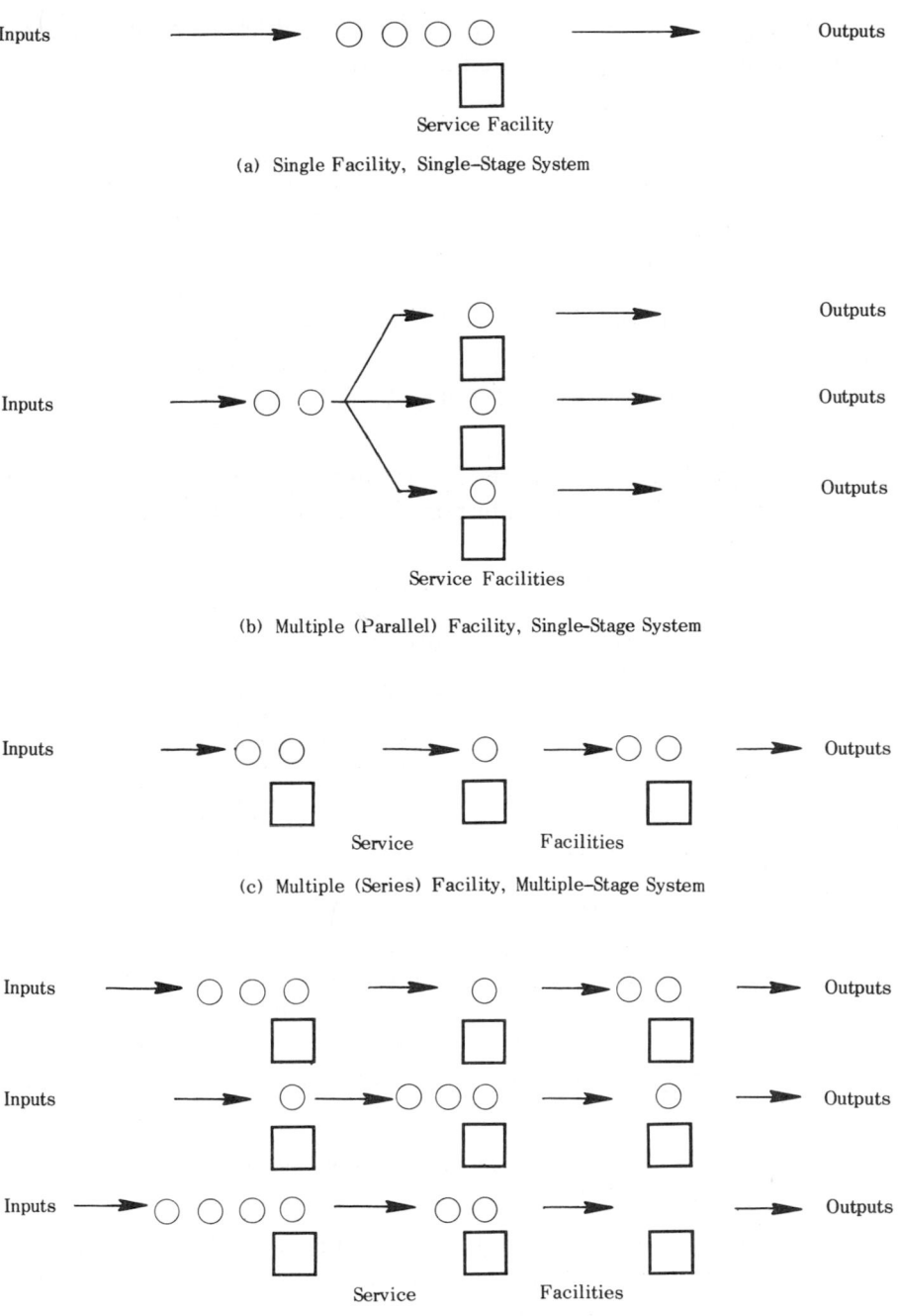

(a) Single Facility, Single–Stage System

(b) Multiple (Parallel) Facility, Single-Stage System

(c) Multiple (Series) Facility, Multiple–Stage System

(d) Multiple (Series–Parallel) Facilities, Multiple–Stage System

Figure 8.12

SELECTED TYPES OF WAITING-LINE SYSTEMS

➤ **Example.** Arrivals of ships at the loading dock of a refinery for a period of two months are listed as follows:

	Week							
Day	1	2	3	4	5	6	7	8
Sunday	0	2	1	0	2	2	3	1
Monday	0	2	1	0	3	1	0	1
Tuesday	1	1	0	2	0	0	1	3
Wednesday	2	1	4	1	2	1	0	0
Thursday	3	1	1	0	1	1	3	0
Friday	2	0	1	0	1	0	2	1
Saturday	1	1	0	2	0	1	1	1

The distribution of arrivals per day is found by tabulating the number of days in which specified numbers of arrivals occur. The results are summarized as follows:

Number of ships arriving per day	Observed frequency f_o	Expected frequency f_e
0	17	18.6
1	23	20.6
2	10	11.3
3	5	4.1
4	1	1.1
5 or more	0	0.3
Total	56	56.0

Expected frequencies are based on the Poisson distribution for which λ is approximately equal to the mean of the observed frequency distribution. In this example,

$$\text{Mean arrival rate} = \frac{0(17) + (1)(23) + (2)(10) + (3)(5) + (4)(1) + (5)(0)}{56}$$

$$= \frac{62}{56} = 1.11 \text{ arrivals per day.}$$

The value of λ in Appendix F that is closest to the mean value is $\lambda = 1.10$. The probabilities corresponding to $\lambda = 1.10$ are used to compute the expected frequencies. The expected frequency for zero arrivals is computed

$$f_e = (0.3329)(56)$$
$$= 18.6 \text{ days.}$$

The remaining expected frequencies are computed similarly. The observed and expected frequencies are plotted in Figure 8.13. This figure indicates that the distribution of arrivals of ships is approximated closely by the Poisson distribution for $\lambda = 1.10$.

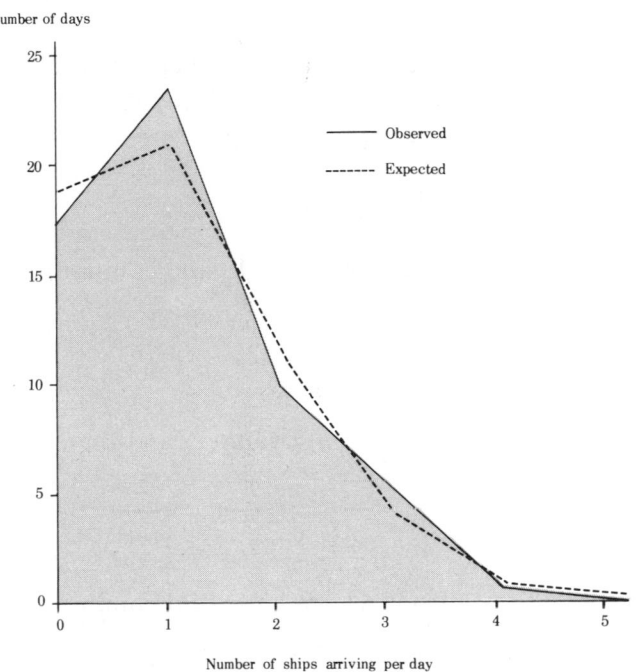

Figure 8.13

DISTRIBUTION OF THE ARRIVALS OF SHIPS AT A LOADING DOCK

➤ *Example.* The service times required to load ships at a loading dock (described in the foregoing example) are summarized by the following distribution:

Service time (days)	Observed frequency f_o	Expected frequency f_e
0.0 and under 0.5	38	37.9
0.5 and under 1.0	16	14.0
1.0 and under 1.5	4	5.1
1.5 and under 2.0	2	1.9
2.0 or more	0	1.1
Total	60	60.0

The mean service time, denoted μ, is computed as follows:

$$\mu = \frac{0.25(38) + 0.75(16) + 1.25(4) + 1.75(2)}{60}$$

$$= \frac{30}{60} = 0.5.$$

The expected frequencies are based on exponential probabilities computed by use of Appendix E. The expected frequency of service times less than 0.5 days is computed by writing

$$e^{-\left(\frac{t}{\mu}\right)} = e^{-\left(\frac{0.5}{0.5}\right)} = e^{-1},$$

reading $e^{-1} = 0.36788$ from Appendix E, and computing

$$f_e = 60(1 - 0.36788)$$
$$= 60(0.63212)$$
$$= 37.9 \text{ ships.}$$

The expected frequency for the interval "0.5 and under 1.0" is computed by writing

$$e^{-\left(\frac{1.0}{0.5}\right)} = e^{-2},$$

reading $e^{-2} = 0.13534$ from Appendix E, and computing

$$f_e = 60(0.36788 - 0.13534)$$
$$= 60(0.23254)$$
$$= 14.0 \text{ ships.}$$

The remaining expected frequencies are computed similarly. The observed and expected frequencies are plotted in Figure 8.14. The service times are approximated closely by an exponental distribution defined by $\mu = 0.5$.

Single Facility Waiting-Line Models with Infinite Input Sources

The characteristics of single facility waiting-line models with Poisson arrival distributions, constant or exponential service times, and an infinite source of inputs can be formulated. Both the Poisson and the exponential distributions are defined by single parameters, and formulas for computing waiting-line formation characteristics can be derived. The resulting expressions are not complex.

The class of waiting-line models described in this discussion is based on the assumption of the possibility (however remote) of an infinite

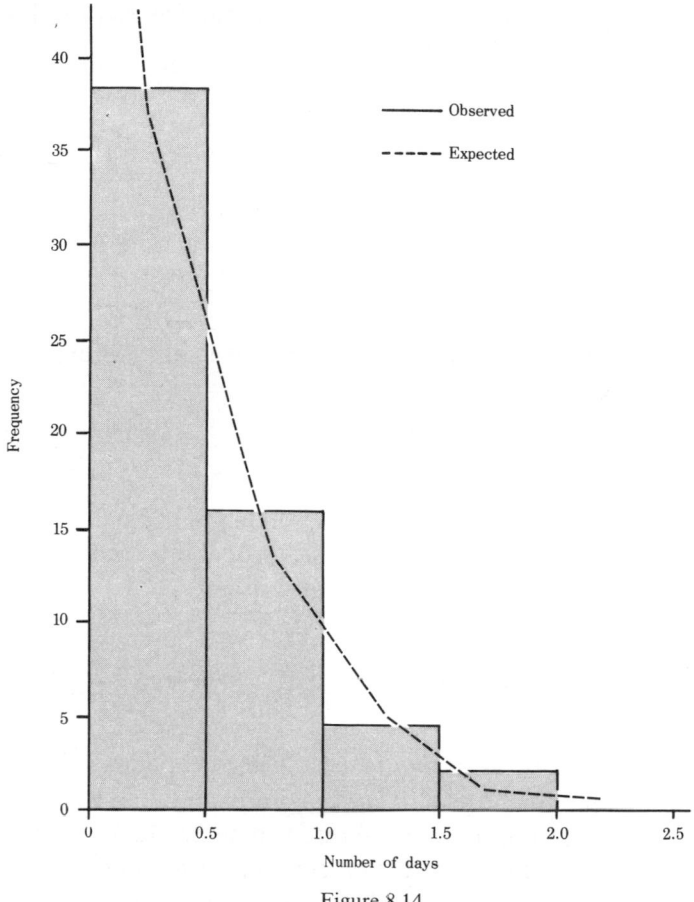

Figure 8.14

DISTRIBUTION OF THE SERVICE TIMES FOR LOADING SHIPS

buildup of waiting lines. Waiting lines that have a finite maximum length may also be formulated. For instance, a maintenance engineer services eight identical units of data processing equipment. The maximum possible waiting-line length is eight machines.

Poisson Arrivals and Constant Service Times. This type of waiting-line model is based on the assumption of Poisson distributed arrivals and constant service times. The average arrival rate indicates the average number of units arriving per unit time. This average rate is denoted a, where $a = \lambda$ for Poisson distributed arrivals.

The service rate, denoted s, expresses the average number of units processed or served per unit time. The service rate must exceed the arrival rate for this type of model or the waiting-line buildup will be infinite. Given the assumptions of this model, the average waiting-line length and average waiting time per unit may be computed. The required formulas are written:

Expected length of the waiting line

$$E(L_w) = \frac{a^2}{2s(s - a)} \quad \dots\dots\dots\dots\dots\dots(8.10)$$

Expected waiting time of a unit

$$E(T_w) = \frac{a}{2s(s - a)} \quad \dots\dots\dots\dots\dots\dots(8.11)$$

The proportion of the time that the service facility is expected to be utilized is written:

Expected utilization of the facility

$$E(U) = \frac{a}{s} \dots\dots\dots\dots\dots\dots\dots\dots\dots(8.12)$$

and is called the *utilization factor*. The probability that a unit which arrives will not have to wait for service is written:

Probability of no delay

$$P(D) = 1 - \frac{a}{s} \dots\dots\dots\dots\dots\dots\dots\dots(8.13)$$

➤ *Example.* Customers arrive to use a large capacity, coin-operated dry cleaning machine in a self-service laundromat in a Poisson distributed manner. The average arrival rate is nine per 12-hour period. The processing cycle time of the dry cleaning machine is 40 minutes. Customers typically process only one load of clothing per trip to the laundromat. The average number of arrivals is computed

$$a = \frac{9}{12} = 0.75 \text{ units per hour.}$$

The average service rate, in terms of customers processed, is computed

$$s = \frac{60}{40} = 1.50 \text{ units per hour.}$$

The expected length of the waiting line is computed

$$E(L_w) = \frac{a^2}{2s(s - a)}$$

$$= \frac{(0.75)^2}{(2)(1.50)(1.50 - 0.75)} = \frac{0.56}{2.25}$$

$$= 0.25 \text{ units.}$$

The expected waiting time of a customer is computed

$$E(T_w) = \frac{a}{2s(s - a)}$$

$$= \frac{0.75}{(2)(1.50)(1.50 - 0.75)} = \frac{0.75}{2.25}$$

$$= 0.33 \text{ hours.}$$

The proportion of the time the machine is expected to be in use is computed

$$E(U) = \frac{a}{s}$$

$$= \frac{0.75}{1.50} = 0.50.$$

The probability that a customer arriving in the laundromat to use the machine will not have to wait for service is computed

$$P(D) = 1 - \frac{a}{s}$$

$$= 1 - 0.50 = 0.50.$$

Poisson Arrivals and Exponential Service Times. This class of waiting-line models assumes that arrivals are Poisson distributed, service times are distributed exponentially, the arrival rate is less than the service rate, there is an infinite source of units, and the service priority is "first-come first-served." Given these assumptions, the service system characteristics are as follows:

Expected length of the waiting line

$$E(L_w) = \frac{a^2}{s(s - a)} \quad \text{.............................(8.14)}$$

Expected number of units in the service system (including the one being served)

$$E(L_s) = \frac{a}{s - a} = E(L_w) + \frac{a}{s} \quad \text{..............(8.15)}$$

Expected waiting time

$$E(T_w) = \frac{a}{s(s - a)} = \frac{E(L_w)}{a} \quad \text{...................(8.16)}$$

Expected total time in the system (waiting time plus service)

$$E(T_s) = \frac{1}{s - a} = E(T_w) + \frac{1}{s} \quad \dots\dots\dots\dots(8.17)$$

Probability that n units will be in the system

$$P(n) = \left(1 - \frac{a}{s}\right)\left(\frac{a}{s}\right)^n \quad \dots\dots\dots\dots\dots(8.18)$$

The formulas for the utilization factor and the probability of delay are the same as Formulas 8.12 and 8.13 for the constant service-time model.

➤ **Example.** The arrivals of ships at the loading dock of a refinery are Poisson distributed. The average arrival rate is 1.10 ships per day. The service (loading) times of the ships are distributed exponentially with an average service time of 0.50 days per ship. The average service rate is two ships per day. The characteristics of the service system are computed as follows:

Expected length of the waiting line

$$E(L_w) = \frac{a^2}{s(s - a)}$$

$$= \frac{(1.10)^2}{2(2 - 1.10)} = \frac{1.21}{1.80} = 0.67 \text{ units.}$$

Expected number of units in the service system

$$E(L_s) = \frac{a}{s - a} = E(L_w) + \frac{a}{s}$$

$$= \frac{1.10}{0.90} = 0.67 + \frac{1.10}{2}$$

$$= 1.22 \text{ units.}$$

Expected waiting time

$$E(T_w) = \frac{a}{s(s - a)} = \frac{E(L_w)}{a}$$

$$= \frac{1.10}{2(2 - 1.10)} = \frac{0.67}{1.10}$$

$$= \frac{1.10}{1.80} = 0.61 \text{ days.}$$

Expected total time of a unit in the system

$$E(T_s) = \frac{1}{s-a} = E(T_w) + \frac{1}{s}$$

$$= \frac{1}{2 - 1.10} = 0.61 + \frac{1}{2}$$

$$= 1.11 \text{ days.}$$

Probability that $n = 2$ units will be in the system

$$P(n = 2) = \left(1 - \frac{a}{s}\right)\left(\frac{a}{s}\right)^n$$

$$= \left(1 - \frac{1.10}{2}\right)\left(\frac{1.10}{2}\right)^2$$

$$= (0.45)(0.55)^2 = 0.14.$$

Utilization factor

$$E(U) = \frac{a}{s}$$

$$= \frac{1.10}{2} = 0.55.$$

Probability of no delay

$$P(D) = 1 - \frac{a}{s}$$

$$= 1 - \frac{1.10}{2} = 0.45.$$

Multiple Service Facility Waiting-Line Models with Infinite Input Sources

The characteristics of a multiple service facility waiting-line model with Poisson arrival distributions and exponentially distributed service times are formulated on the basis of the assumptions implicit in the single facility models, except that multiple identical facilities are available. The service rate for a multiple service facility system is sM, where M is the number of facilities or channels. The service rate sM must exceed a, the arrival rate. It is also assumed that if all M channels are occupied, a single waiting line will be formed.

The waiting-line characteristics involve the probability that no units will be in the system. This probability, denoted $P(0)$, is computed by the relationship

$$P(0) = \cfrac{1}{\left[\cfrac{\left(\dfrac{a}{s}\right)^M}{M!\left[1 - \dfrac{\left(\dfrac{a}{s}\right)}{M}\right]} + 1 + \cfrac{\left(\dfrac{a}{s}\right)^1}{1!} + \cfrac{\left(\dfrac{a}{s}\right)^2}{2!} + \cdots + \cfrac{\left(\dfrac{a}{s}\right)^{M-1}}{(M-1)!} \right]} \quad (8.19)$$

for $\left(\dfrac{a}{s}\right) < M$. Waiting-line characteristics may be computed by the following formulas:

Expected length of the waiting line

$$E(L_w) = \cfrac{\left(\dfrac{a}{s}\right)^{M+1}}{(M-1)!\left[M - \left(\dfrac{a}{s}\right)\right]^2} P(0)\ldots\ldots\ldots(8.20)$$

Expected number of units in the system (including the units being served)

$$E(L_s) = E(L_w) + \left(\dfrac{a}{s}\right) \ldots\ldots\ldots\ldots\ldots\ldots\ldots(8.21)$$

Expected waiting time

$$E(T_w) = \cfrac{E(L_w)}{a} \ldots\ldots\ldots\ldots\ldots\ldots\ldots\ldots(8.22)$$

Expected total time in the system (waiting time plus service)

$$E(T_s) = E(T_w) + \dfrac{1}{s} = \dfrac{E(L_s)}{a} \ldots\ldots\ldots\ldots(8.23)$$

Expected utilization of the system

$$E(U) = \dfrac{a}{sM} \ldots\ldots\ldots\ldots\ldots\ldots\ldots\ldots(8.24)$$

Probability of no delay

$$P(D) = 1 - \dfrac{a}{sM} \ldots\ldots\ldots\ldots\ldots\ldots(8.25)$$

➤ *Example.* A utility company has four crews for making emergency electrical repairs. Calls for service arrive in a Poisson distribution. The average arrival rate is 3.6 calls per hour. Repair times are distributed exponentially, with an average service time of 50 minutes. The mean service rate is

$$s = \frac{60}{50} = 1.2 \text{ units per hour.}$$

The probability $P(0)$ of no units in the system is computed

$$P(0) = \cfrac{1}{\left[\cfrac{\left(\frac{3.6}{1.2}\right)^4}{4!\left[1 - \cfrac{\left(\frac{3.6}{1.2}\right)}{4}\right]} + 1 + \cfrac{\left(\frac{3.6}{1.2}\right)^1}{1!} + \cfrac{\left(\frac{3.6}{1.2}\right)^2}{2!} + \cfrac{\left(\frac{3.6}{1.2}\right)^3}{3!} \right]}$$

$$= \cfrac{1}{\left[\cfrac{81}{24(1 - 0.75)} + 1 + 3 + \cfrac{9}{2} + \cfrac{27}{6} \right]}$$

$$= \frac{1}{13.5 + 1 + 3 + 4.5 + 4.5} = 0.0377.$$

The waiting-line characteristics are computed as follows:

Expected length of waiting line

$$E(L_w) = \cfrac{\left(\frac{3.6}{1.2}\right)^5}{(4 - 1)!\left[4 - \left(\frac{3.6}{1.2}\right)\right]^2}(0.0377)$$

$$= \frac{243}{6(1)^2}(0.0377) = 1.53 \text{ units.}$$

Expected number of units in the system

$$E(L_s) = 1.53 + \frac{3.6}{1.2} = 4.53 \text{ units.}$$

Expected waiting time

$$E(T_w) = \frac{1.53}{3.6} = 0.425 \text{ hours.}$$

Expected total time of a unit in the system

$$E(T_s) = 0.425 + \frac{1}{1.2}$$

$$= 1.258 \text{ hours.}$$

Expected utilization of the system

$$E(U) = \frac{3.6}{1.2(4)} = 0.75.$$

Probability of no delay

$$P(D) = 1 - \frac{3.6}{1.2(4)} = 0.25.$$

Single Service Facility Systems with Finite Input Sources

The waiting-line characteristics of service systems with Poisson distributed arrivals, exponentially distributed service times, an arrival rate that is less than the service rate, a finite source of units, and a "first-come first-served" service priority can be formulated. This type of system is characterized by a single service facility (such as a single repairman) that serves a finite number of units (machines). Given these assumptions, the principal characteristics may be computed as follows:

Probability that all m units are waiting or being served

$$P(m) = \frac{1}{\left[1 + \frac{1}{1!}\left(\frac{s}{a}\right)^1 + \frac{1}{2!}\left(\frac{s}{a}\right)^2 + \cdots \frac{1}{m!}\left(\frac{s}{a}\right)^m\right]} \quad \ldots(8.26)$$

Probability of m − k units waiting or being served

$$P(m - k) = \frac{1}{k!}\left(\frac{s}{a}\right)^k P(m) \quad \ldots\ldots\ldots\ldots\ldots\ldots\ldots\ldots\ldots\ldots(8.27)$$

Expected length of the waiting line

$$E(L_w) = m - \frac{a + s}{a}[1 - P(0)] \quad \ldots\ldots\ldots\ldots\ldots(8.28)$$

Expected waiting time

$$E(T_w) = \frac{1}{s}\left[\frac{m}{1 - P(0)} - \frac{a + s}{a}\right] \quad \ldots\ldots\ldots\ldots\ldots(8.29)$$

➤*Example.* A repairman provides maintenance for four identical machines. Calls for service average four per eight-hour day and are Poisson distributed in occurrence. The average repair time is 15 minutes and service times are distributed exponentially. The waiting-line characteristics are computed as follows:

Arrival rate

$$a = \frac{4}{8} = 0.5 \text{ units per hour.}$$

Service rate

$$s = \frac{60}{15} = 4 \text{ units per hour.}$$

Probability that all four units are waiting or being served

$$P(m = 4) = \frac{1}{\left[1 + \frac{1}{1!}\left(\frac{4}{0.5}\right)^1 + \frac{1}{2!}\left(\frac{4}{0.5}\right)^2 + \frac{1}{3!}\left(\frac{4}{0.5}\right)^3 + \frac{1}{4!}\left(\frac{4}{0.5}\right)^4\right]}$$

$$= \frac{1}{\left[1 + 8 + \frac{64}{2} + \frac{512}{6} + \frac{4,096}{24}\right]}$$

$$= \frac{1}{1 + 8 + 32 + 85.3 + 170.7}$$

$$= \frac{1}{297}$$

$$= 0.00337.$$

Probability of one unit waiting or being served $(m - k = 4 - 3 = 1)$

$$P(m - 3) = \frac{1}{3!}\left[\frac{4}{0.5}\right]^3 (0.00337)$$

$$= \frac{1}{6}(512)(0.00337)$$

$$= 0.29.$$

Expected length of the waiting line

$$E(L_w) = 4 - \frac{0.5 + 4}{0.5}\left[1 - \frac{1}{4!}\left(\frac{4}{0.5}\right)^4 (0.00337)\right]$$

$$= 4 - 9\left[1 - \frac{4,096}{24}(0.00337)\right]$$

$$= 4 - 9(1 - 0.575)$$

$$= 4 - 3.825$$

$$= 0.175 \text{ units.}$$

Expected waiting time

$$E(T_w) = \frac{1}{4}\left[\frac{4}{1 - 0.575} - \frac{0.5 + 4}{0.5}\right]$$

$$= \frac{1}{4}[9.41 - 9]$$

$$= \frac{0.41}{4} = 0.10 \text{ hours.}$$

STUDY QUESTIONS

8-1. Explain briefly the meaning of each of the following terms:

a. continuous variable

b. uniform density function

c. integral

d. exponential distribution

e. exponential density function

f. normal distribution

g. normal probability distribution

h. normal density function

i. normal frequency function

j. unit normal distribution

k. continuity correction

l. gamma distribution

m. gamma density function

n. waiting line

o. arrival

p. arrival rate

q. service time

r. service rate

s. utilization factor

8-2. Relate the following concepts to a continuous random variable:

a. sample space

b. set function

c. probability density function

8-3. A continuous variable has a density function of $f(X) = \frac{1}{2}$, for $0 \le X \le 2$. What are the probabilities corresponding to the following areas:

a. $\int_0^{\frac{1}{2}} f(X)dX$

c. $\int_{\frac{1}{4}}^{\frac{3}{2}} f(X)dX$

b. $\int_1^2 f(X)dX$

d. $\int_{-\infty}^{\infty} f(X)dX$

8-4. Express the following probabilities in integral form if $f(X)$ is the density function of a continuous random variable:

a. $P(2 < X < 4)$

c. $P(0 < X)$

b. $P(a < X < b)$

d. $P(X < a)$

8-5. Is a continuous density function the same thing as a probability distribution? Explain.

8-6. Explain the relationship of the exponential distribution to Pascal probabilities.

8-7. Of what value are the moments of the normal distribution?

8-8. What is the theoretical and practical significance of the normal distribution?

8-9. Describe the value of the gamma distribution to the study of statistics.

PROBLEMS

8-1. The lengths of telephone calls are exponentially distributed, with a mean of four minutes. What is the probability that a call will last more than two minutes? less than three minutes?

8-2. The processing times of computer programs were recorded as follows:

Time (Seconds)	Number of programs
15	61
30	29
45	14
60	9
75	2
	115

In terms of processing times, the programs are entered randomly into the computer. Compute the probability that a program entering the computer will require 30 or more seconds of processing time on the basis of:
  a. historical data
  b. Pascal probability density (Hint: Base the probability on a five-second interval as one trial.)
  c. exponential probability density
  Fit an exponential curve to the historical data given above and plot the results.

8-3. The length of time customers spend per shopping trip in a supermarket is normally distributed, with a mean of 30 minutes and a standard deviation of 10 minutes. The shopping times of 200 customers are recorded and grouped. Use the ordinates of the normal curve to find the expected frequency of the following intervals:
  a. 15 but less than 20 minutes
  b. 37.5 but less than 45.0 minutes

8-4. The fuel consumption of a fleet of 150 trucks is normally distributed, with a mean of 15 miles per gallon and a standard deviation of 1.5 miles per gallon. Use normal curve ordinates to find the expected number of trucks that average:
  a. 13 but less than 14 miles per gallon
  b. 14.5 but less than 15.5 miles per gallon

8-5. A total of 10,000 lengths of pipe extruded by a process are normally distributed, with a mean of 20.0 feet and a standard deviation of 0.2 feet.
  a. How many lengths are between 20.0 and 20.4 feet?
  b. What portion of lengths are between 19.7 and 20.2 feet?
  c. What percent of lengths are more than 20.3 feet long?

8-6. Plastic bags used for packaging produce are received in bulk from a supplier. The breaking strength of the bags averages 5.0 pounds per square inch. If the strength of bags is normally distributed, what is the value of the standard deviation if:
   a. 34% of the bags have a breaking strength between 5.0 and 6.1 pounds per square inch?
   b. Half of the bags have a breaking strength between 4.5 and 5.5 pounds per square inch?
   c. One fourth of the bags have a breaking strength of 4.2 pounds or less?

8-7. Solve Problem 8-3 by use of normal curve areas.

8-8. Solve Problem 8-4 by use of normal curve areas.

8-9. An automobile dealer has determined that 30% of his customers buy station wagons. For the next 10 customers selected at random:
   a. Find the probability that four will buy station wagons.
   b. Compute the normal curve approximation of the probability that four will buy station wagons.

8-10. A machine produces parts that are boxed in lots of 100 parts. If there has been an average of five defective parts per box:
   a. What is the binomial probability that a box will contain two defective parts?
   b. What is the normal curve approximation of the probability that a box will contain two defective parts?

8-11. Maintenance records indicate that only one in 100 new automobiles of a given brand has a major transmission failure within the warranty period. Records are to be kept on the next 50 new vehicles that are sold. Compute:
   a. The binomial probability that no new automobiles will have a major transmission failure.
   b. The normal curve approximation of the probability that no new automobiles will have a major transmission failure.

8-12. A clothing store manager has observed that 40% of his customers wear shirts designated "medium" in size. Compute:
   a. The probability that more than 20 shirt sales will be required to sell 10 medium-size shirts.
   b. The normal curve approximation of (a).

8-13. Fire-loss records for a large chemical plant indicate that there is an average of one major fire every four years. Find the probability that there will be two major fires in less than six years, if the occurrence of fires is Poisson distributed.

8-14. A firm stocks a special type of pressure-relief valve in its inventory of items for plant maintenance. An analysis of the demand for this part over a period of time revealed the following data:

Number of valves required	Number of months
0	6
1	14
2	13
3	10
4	5
5	2
	50

What is the probability that five valves will be demanded in less than three months?

8-15. Customers arrive at an automatic car wash establishment in a Poisson distributed manner at a rate of 10 per hour. A car can enter the car wash every four minutes. Compute:
  a. The expected length of the waiting line.
  b. The expected waiting time per customer.
  c. The probability that an arriving customer will have to wait.

8-16. An escalator has the capacity for transporting up to 30 persons per minute from one floor to another in a building. At rush periods during the day, people arrive at the escalator in a Poisson manner at an average rate of one person every three and a half seconds. Compute:
  a. The expected length of the waiting line.
  b. The expected waiting time per person.
  c. The expected utilization of the escalator.

8-17. The times required to transact business with patrons at a special delivery window in a post office are distributed exponentially, with a mean of two minutes. Customer arrivals are Poisson distributed with a mean rate of 18 per hour. Compute:
  a. The expected length of the waiting line.
  b. The expected time a customer will be in the system.

8-18. The arrivals of customers at a telephone booth are considered to be Poisson distributed, and the average length of time between arrivals is 15 minutes. Calls average four minutes and are distributed exponentially. Compute:
  a. The expected number of customers in the system.
  b. The expected waiting time of a customer.
  c. The probability that two units will be in the system.

8-19. The credit department of a clothing store has three clerks that serve customers. The times required to serve customers average eight minutes and are distributed exponentially. If customers arrive in a Poisson distribution at the rate of 12 persons per hour, find:
  a. The expected length of the waiting line.
  b. The expected waiting time.
  c. The expected utilization of the system.

8-20. A television repair shop has a staff of four repairmen. The times required to repair television sets average two hours and are distributed exponentially. An average of 12 sets per eight-hour day is received and the arrivals are distributed in a Poisson manner. Compute:
  a. The expected length of the waiting line.
  b. The expected waiting time.
  c. The expected total number of units in the system.

8-21. The engineering maintenance representative of a computer manufacturer services three identical computers. Records indicate that the average time per service call is 1.6 hours and that the lengths of service calls are distributed exponentially. Calls for service arrive at the rate two per eight-hour day. Find:
  a. The probability that one of the computers is waiting or being served.
  b. The expected waiting time.

8-22. A distributor has four trucks that are used to make local deliveries to customers. The trucks are loaded at a single dock, and loading times are exponentially distributed, with a mean of 20 minutes. The average time required for a delivery is 1.2 hours and these times are Poisson distributed. Find:
  a. The probability that a truck will not have to wait to be loaded.
  b. The expected length of the waiting line.

SELECTED READINGS

Freund, John E. *Mathematical Statistics.* Englewood Cliffs, N. J.: Prentice-Hall, Inc., 1962.
  A readable description of various density functions is represented in Chapter 5.
Sasieni, Maurice, Arthur Yaspan and Lawrence Friedman. *Operations Research, Methods and Problems.* New York: John Wiley & Sons, Inc., 1963.
  Chapter 6 presents a derivation of some simple classes of waiting-line formulations.
Schlaifer, Robert. *Probability and Statistics for Business Decisions.* New York: McGraw-Hill Book Company, Inc., 1959.
  Detailed discussions of the exponential and the gamma distributions are presented in Chapter 14.

Chapter 9

Sample Distributions and Estimation

Descriptive statistics, probability, and probability distributions provide the conceptual basis for relating sample statistics, as estimators, to universe parameters. Following a presentation of the characteristics of random samples and the properties of estimators, probability distributions of sample statistics and estimating methods are considered.

SIMPLE RANDOM SAMPLING

A group of items drawn randomly from a universe constitutes a small-scale replica of the universe. Each statistic computed from the sampled items provides an estimate of a parameter of the parent universe. As the number of items drawn becomes large, a sample statistic approximates more closely a universe parameter.

The question of what constitutes a properly drawn sample hinges upon the nature of the universe. Of immediate interest is the simplest case, a *simple random sample*, also called a *probability sample*. This type of sampling consists of selecting items at random from a universe of units that are essentially homogeneous in terms of some characteristic. For example, a simple random sample may be drawn from the universe of employed people, who are assumed to be homogeneous except for differences in income. Actually, these people can be classified into sub-groups by type of employment or other characteristics. Sampling techniques for more complex situations are considered in Chapter 10.

Distinct Samples Drawn from a Universe

Random sampling is based on the concept of equiprobable outcomes; the sample space, as defined on page 154, consists of the universe of items or outcomes, each of which has an equal chance of being selected.

Suppose that a sample of items is to be selected from a universe and the selection of each item in the universe is equiprobable. If the size of the sample is smaller than the universe, all the items in the universe cannot appear in the sample. As a result, a number of different samples can be drawn. For example, a sample of three alphabetical characters is to be selected randomly from a universe consisting of the letters W, X, Y, and Z. The number of distinct samples is the number of combinations $\binom{4}{3} = 4$, as seen in Table 6.1, page 139. If samples of three items are drawn from an infinite universe, the number of distinct samples is infinite.

Random Numbers

The practical problem of selecting a random sample from a universe of items arises frequently in statistical analysis. Equiprobable items may be viewed as a uniformly distributed random variable that takes on values over its defined range. Thus, a universe of N items is looked upon as a uniform distribution described by the density function $f(X) = \dfrac{1}{N}$.

Consider a situation in which an auditor wishes to select a random sample of 10 from a large number of accounts. Assume that the accounts are numbered serially from one through N. A sample can be selected randomly by choosing numbers in a random manner from the range one through N and selecting the accounts that correspond to the numbers. The random selecting of numbers is facilitated by the use of either of several methods.

The Middle-Square Method. A sequence of numbers generated by a uniformly distributed random variable is called a table of *random numbers*. Random numbers can be generated by any of several techniques, one of which is the *middle-square method*. For example, this method may be used to generate a random sequence of four-digit random numbers. The first step consists of taking an initial four-digit integer and finding its square. The highest and the lowest order digits of the square are eliminated, leaving the four "middle" digits, which are the second random number in the sequence. The third random number is found by squaring the second random number and eliminating the highest and the lowest order digits of the square.

➤ *Example.* A sequence of 10 random numbers of four digits is to be determined. An initial integer 4163 is selected as the first random number. This value is squared to give $(4163)^2 = 17330569$. The high-order digits 17 and the low-order digits 69 are eliminated to yield 3305, the second four-digit random number. This technique is repeated until all 10 values are obtained, as shown in Table 9.1.

The random numbers in Table 9.1 may be applied to the selection of a random sample of 10 accounts in the previous auditing example, if the total number of accounts is 10,000. The first item of the sample is the 4,163rd account in the serially numbered series. The second sample item is the 3,305th account, the third is the 9,230th account, and so forth. The accounts drawn in this manner are random selections, for the numbers 0,000 through 9,999 are equiprobable.

Table 9.1

A SEQUENCE OF 10 FOUR-DIGIT RANDOM NUMBERS
GENERATED BY THE "MIDDLE-SQUARE" METHOD

Iteration	High-order digits	Four-digit random numbers	Low-order digits
1		4163	
2	17	3305	69
3	10	9230	25
4	85	1929	00
5	03	7210	41
6	51	9841	00
7	96	8452	81
8	71	4363	04
9	19	0357	69
10	00	1274	49

Suppose the accounts total 6,310. A random sample of 10 can be selected by use of the four-digit number series, except that all numbers greater than 6310 are not used. For example, the third random number in Table 9.1 is 9230, which is greater than 6310. This number is not used for selecting a sample item, but is used to compute the next random number.

The middle-square method has the advantage of simplicity in generating random numbers. The method possesses an inherent disadvantage, however, in that if long series of numbers are generated, the series tend to converge to zero. An alternative method may be used to obtain series of numbers that are random for as many as several million digits.

Lehmer's Method. A technique for generating series of numbers that are random for up to several million digits is called *Lehmer's method*. This method consists of beginning with an initial eight-digit random number. This number is multiplied by the prime number 23. The product of this multiplication is a number with as many as 10 digits. The two high-order digits are subtracted from the two low-order digits of the product. The eight low-order digits of the difference of this subtraction are an eight-digit random number. A second random number is obtained by multiplying this eight-digit random number by the prime 23 and subtracting the two high-order digits from the two low-order digits of the product to obtain another eight-digit random number. Since the digits of this number are random, any two, three, and up to eight digits may be selected, depending upon how many random digits are desired.

➤ *Example.* A sequence of five random numbers of four digits each is obtained by use of Lehmer's method. An initial eight-digit random number 98418452 is selected. This number is multiplied by the prime 23 to give a 10-digit product 2263624396. The two high-order digits are subtracted from the two low-order digits to give the difference 2263624374. Eliminating the two high-order digits gives 63624374. Selecting the middle four digits gives the four-digit random number 6243. A second random number is obtained by multiplying the random number 63624374 by the prime 23 to give 1463360602; subtracting the two high-order digits from the two low-order digits of the product to yield 1463360588; eliminating the two high-order digits to obtain 63360588; and selecting the middle four digits 3605. This technique is repeated until all five values are found, as shown in Table 9.2. The procedure for finding random numbers by Lehmer's method is shown graphically in Figure 9.1.

Table 9.2

A SERIES OF FIVE FOUR-DIGIT RANDOM NUMBERS GENERATED
BY THE USE OF LEHMER'S METHOD

Iteration	Initial random number	Product	Difference	Eight-digit random number	Four-digit random number
1	98418452	2263624396	2263624374	63624374	6243
2	63624374	1463360602	1463360588	63360588	3605
3	63360588	1457293524	1457293510	57293510	2935
4	57293510	1317750730	1317750717	17750717	7507
5	17750717	0408266491	0408266487	08266487	2664

Random number generators have been developed that generate numbers that have exponential, Poisson, normal, gamma, or other distributions. These series are obtained by transforming uniformly distributed random numbers by an appropriate density function. Com-

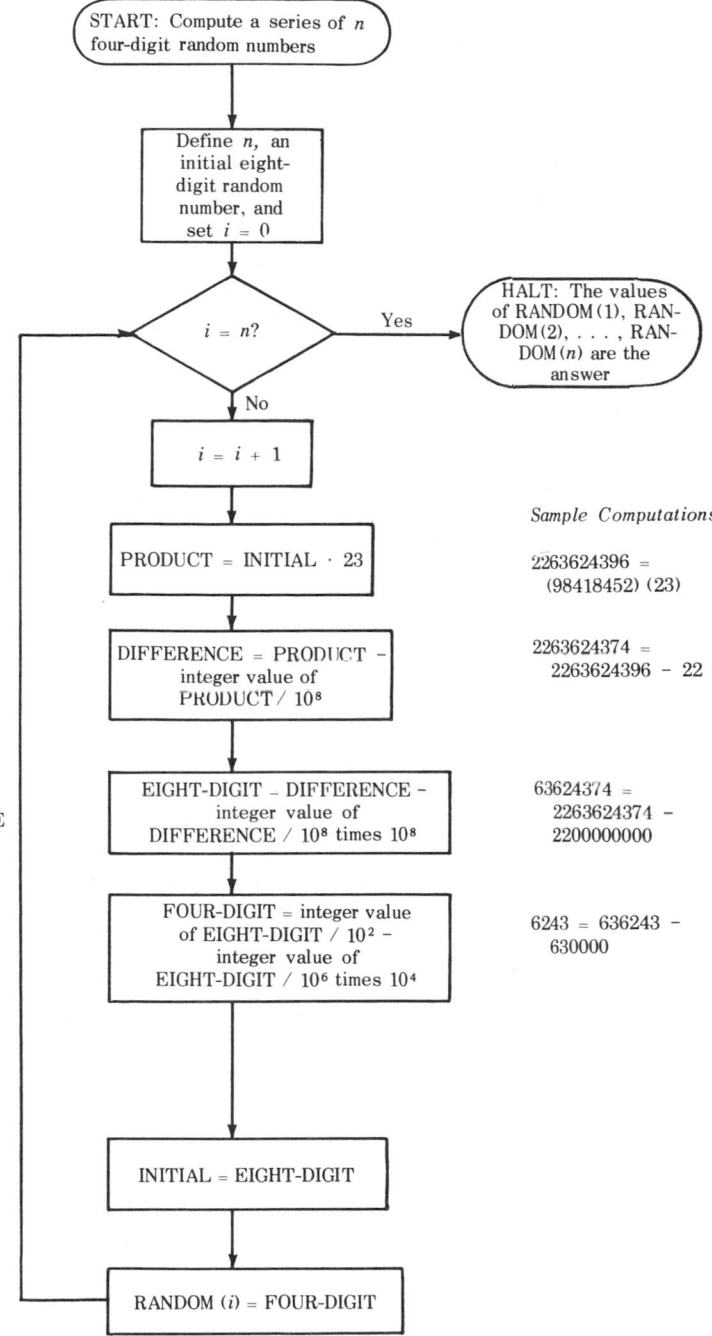

Initialize the conditions by defining the required values of n, INITIAL, and the variable i.

Compare the current value of i with the total number of random numbers to be generated to determine if the required iterations have been completed.

Increment the subscript.

Compute the product of an eight-digit random number times the prime number 23.

Subtract from PRODUCT the quotient of PRODUCT divided by 10^8, for which the decimal fraction has been truncated.

Subtract from DIFFERENCE the quotient of DIFFERENCE divided by 10^8, with the decimal fraction truncated and the resulting integer multiplied by 10^8.

Divide EIGHT-DIGIT by 10^2, truncate the decimal part, and subtract from this integer EIGHT-DIGIT divided by 10^6 with the fractional part truncated and the remaining integer multiplied by 10^4.

Set INITIAL equal to the value of the eight-digit number generated in the current iteration for use in future iterations.

Assign the current value of i as a subscript to aid in future identification.

START: Compute a series of n four-digit random numbers

Define n, an initial eight-digit random number, and set $i = 0$

$i = n$?　　Yes　　HALT: The values of RANDOM(1), RAN-DOM(2), . . . , RAN-DOM(n) are the answer

No

$i = i + 1$

PRODUCT = INITIAL · 23

DIFFERENCE = PRODUCT – integer value of PRODUCT / 10^8

EIGHT-DIGIT = DIFFERENCE – integer value of DIFFERENCE / 10^8 times 10^8

FOUR-DIGIT = integer value of EIGHT-DIGIT / 10^2 – integer value of EIGHT-DIGIT / 10^6 times 10^4

INITIAL = EIGHT-DIGIT

RANDOM (i) = FOUR-DIGIT

Sample Computations

$2263624396 =$
$(98418452) (23)$

$2263624374 =$
$2263624396 - 22$

$63624374 =$
$2263624374 -$
2200000000

$6243 = 636243 -$
630000

Figure 9.1

A FLOW DIAGRAM FOR FINDING FOUR-DIGIT RANDOM NUMBERS
BY LEHMER'S METHOD

puter programs for finding random numbers with various distributions are described in a source listed in the selected bibliography at the end of this chapter.

Table of Random Numbers. A table of six-digit random numbers is presented in Appendix N. Any series read across or down the table is random. For example, if one wishes a series of five random numbers of three digits each, these can be obtained by reading down the table from the upper left-hand part of the first page: 345, 549, 423, 554, and 797. A five-number series may also be found by reading across the table to obtain 345, 457, 576, 769, and 699.

It is important to remember that it is the method of drawing a sample, not the sample itself, which is random. For this reason a random sample is sometimes referred to as a "properly drawn" sample or a sample "drawn by a random method." Random numbers provide a method for selecting sample items so that the probabilities associated with any point in the sample space are not changed by any of the values of the sample.

Monte Carlo Method. The random selection of cards from a well-shuffled deck is a familiar experiment for obtaining equiprobable outcomes. A probability distribution corresponding to the random selection of cards may be defined by associating certain outcomes with specified events. For example, a uniform distribution with four intervals may be defined in terms of the four suits of the deck. Other discrete distributions can be defined by grouping outcomes and designating these groups or subsets as corresponding to specified events.

➤ *Example.* A discrete probability distribution may be defined by grouping the outcomes of random draws from a deck of playing cards (with replacement and repeated shuffling) and identifying the outcomes with specified events. A distribution of this type is defined by associating the pip value of cards with events that have the following probabilities:

Outcomes	Event	Probability
A	0	1/13
2, 3, 4	1	3/13
5, 6, 7, 8, 9	2	5/13
10, J, Q	3	3/13
K	4	1/13
		———
		1.0

Simple random sampling from this distribution is accomplished by drawing a card from a well-shuffled deck, associating the pip value of the card with the corresponding event, replacing the card, shuffling the deck, and repeating the process.

The technique described in the foregoing example is a process for generating data artificially. A process of generating events by use of random numbers is called the *Monte Carlo method*. The name of this method is derived from the random outcomes of the roulette wheels observed at the famed gambling casino.

Suppose one wishes to generate randomly events that have a Poisson distribution defined by $\lambda = 0.1$. This distribution is described as follows:

Event	Probability
0	0.905
1	0.090
2	0.005
	1.000

A deck of 52 playing cards is not a suitable device for generating these events with the specified frequencies, for there are a limited number of cards in the deck. For example, one cannot readily associate the event "2" with the outcome of a draw from the deck.

The Monte Carlo method and random numbers can be used to generate the desired events. Equiprobable three-digit random numbers provide the sample space for generating the events. The numbers are grouped proportionately as follows:

Random numbers	Event	Probability	Cumulative probability
000–904	0	0.905	0.905
905–994	1	0.090	0.995
995–999	2	0.005	1.000
		1.000	

The generation of events by use of random numbers is seen most clearly by the relationship between the number of random numbers in each group and the cumulative probability associated with that group. The group of random numbers (000–904) associated with event "0" includes a total of 905 distinct numbers. This corresponds directly to the probability 0.905. The group of random numbers (905–994) related to event "1" includes 90 different numbers. The probability of event "1" and the increase in the cumulative probability is 0.090. Similarly, the number of random numbers in the third group (995–999) is directly proportional to the probability of event "2" and the increase in the cumulative probability. This proportionality is seen by comparing the five random numbers in the third group with the probability of the occurrence of the event "2," which is 0.005 or five chances out of a thousand.

Simple random sampling from this Poisson distribution is achieved artificially, or *simulated*, by selecting a three-digit random number, relating the number to one of the groups, and associating the occurrence of the number with the corresponding event. For example, the random number 543 is between 000 and 904. It is related to the first group and the occurrence of event "0." Similarly, the random number 997, which is between 995 and 999, is associated with the event "2." If many equi-probable three-digit random numbers are related to the groupings and associated events, the events are expected to "occur" with frequencies equal to the theoretical probabilities.

The use of the Monte Carlo method is illustrated by another example in which a manufacturer produces an assembly that may be described simply as a shaft and a bushing.[1] A cylindrical shaft is the male portion of the assembly that is fitted into a matching recess in a bushing, the female part. The relationship of the parts is such that, when assembled, it is impossible to gauge physically the assembled clearance. The assembled clearance between the parts is a principal determinant of the quality of the assembly. The production management staff wishes to determine the distribution of assembled clearances that would be obtained from the assembly of many parts randomly.

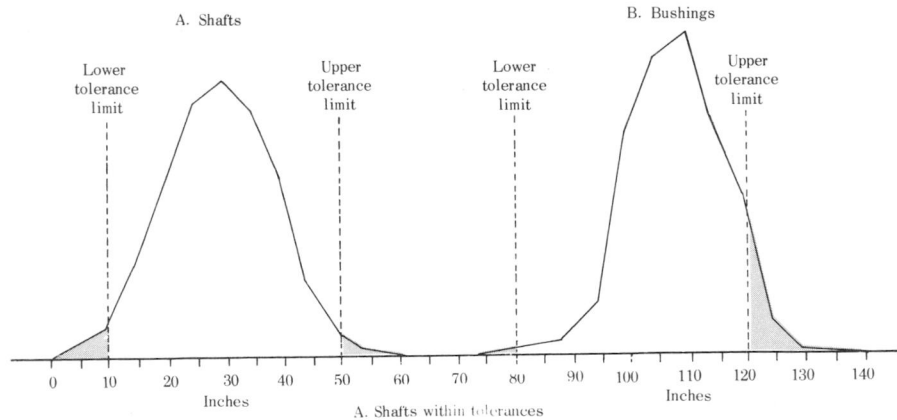

Figure 9.2

FREQUENCY DISTRIBUTIONS OF SHAFT AND BUSHING DIAMETERS,
IN DEVIATIONS FROM A NOMINAL DIMENSION
(.0000 OMITTED)

[1]Adapted from Lawrence L. Schkade, "Estimation and Simulation of the Interaction of Truncated Distributions," *Southwestern Social Science Quarterly*, Vol. 47, No. 1 (June, 1966), pp. 51–58. Reprinted by permission.

Not all shafts and bushings manufactured meet specifications, and these defective parts are excluded from assembly. The defective parts are shown by the shaded portions of the distributions in Figure 9.2. The distribution of clearances between assembled parts, which cannot be observed directly, can be generated by simple random sampling from the distributions of shafts and bushings. A shaft is selected by the Monte Carlo method, a bushing is chosen similarly, and the difference between the diameters of the two sampled parts is the assembled clearance. This clearance is entered as an observation in the distribution of assembled clearances. The process is repeated many times to obtain this distribution.

The simulation of the random assembly of parts is achieved by expressing the distributions of shaft and bushing diameters in cumulative density form, using random numbers to simulate the selection of the parts, and computing the assembled clearance between mated parts. These operations are accomplished readily with the aid of a digital computer, whereas manual computation for a large number of iterations is very time consuming.

The simulation procedure is illustrated in Figure 9.3. A random number is generated by means of a subroutine in the computer program and is used to select a shaft for assembly. For example, the selection of a shaft is simulated by generating a two-digit random number, say 55, and locating that value on the vertical scale of the cumulative probability distribution of shafts in Figure 9.3A. The selected value on the vertical scale is then projected horizontally to intersect the cumulative probability curve. The point of intersection with the probability curve is then projected vertically downward to the horizontal scale of shaft diameters. In this instance, the number 55 corresponds to the selection of a shaft with a diameter of 30.

The selection of a bushing dimension is simulated similarly by generating another random number, say 31, associationg it with the cumulative probability curve in Figure 9.3B, and noting the diameter (100) corresponding to the intersection of the horizontal projection of the random number to the probability curve. Having randomly selected a pair of shafts and bushing diameters, the assembled clearance is found by obtaining the difference between the two selected diameters, $100 - 30 = 70$. This difference is recorded as the first entry in the simulated distribution of assembled clearances and the first iteration is complete.

A large number of iterations is required to provide accurate estimates of the proportion of items in intervals in the distribution. The distribution of clearances in Figure 9.4 shows the results of 30,000 iterations of the simulated assembly of shafts and bushings.

A. Shafts within tolerances

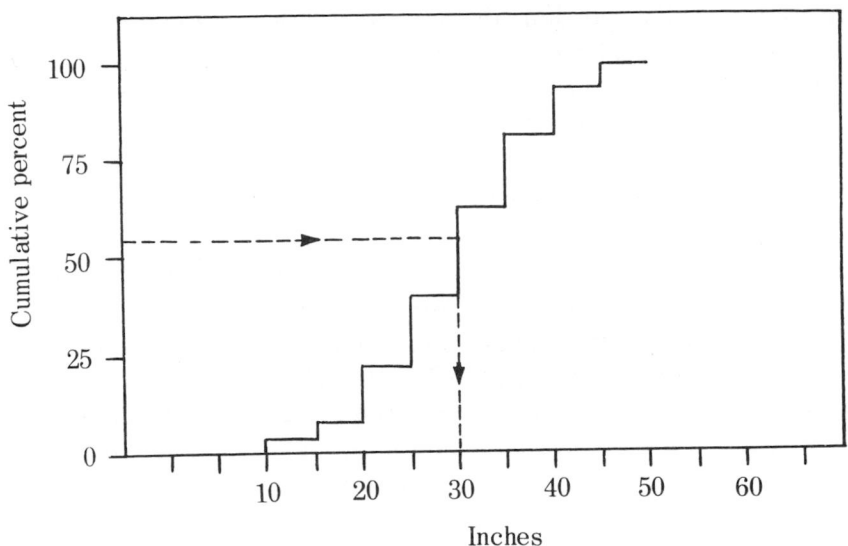

B. Bushings within tolerances

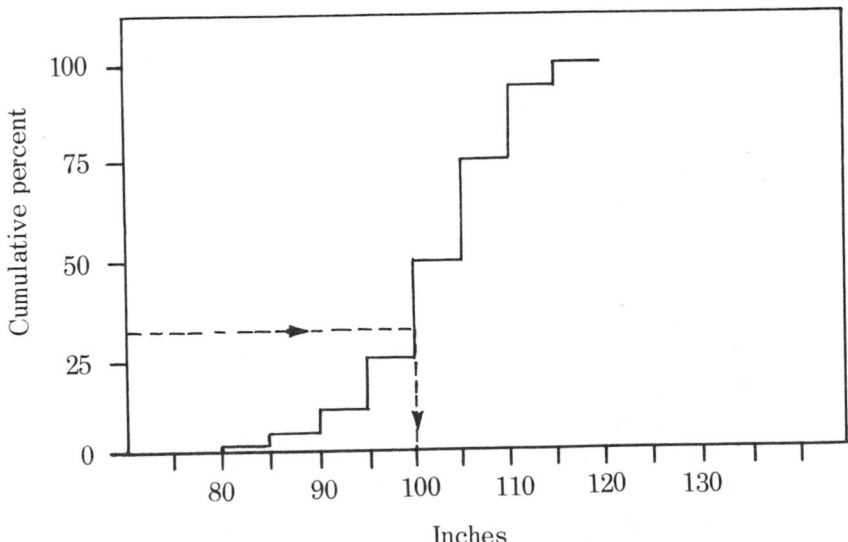

Figure 9.3

CUMULATIVE PROBABILITY DISTRIBUTION OF SHAFT AND BUSHING
DIAMETERS, IN DEVIATIONS FROM A NOMINAL DIMENSION
(.0000 OMITTED)

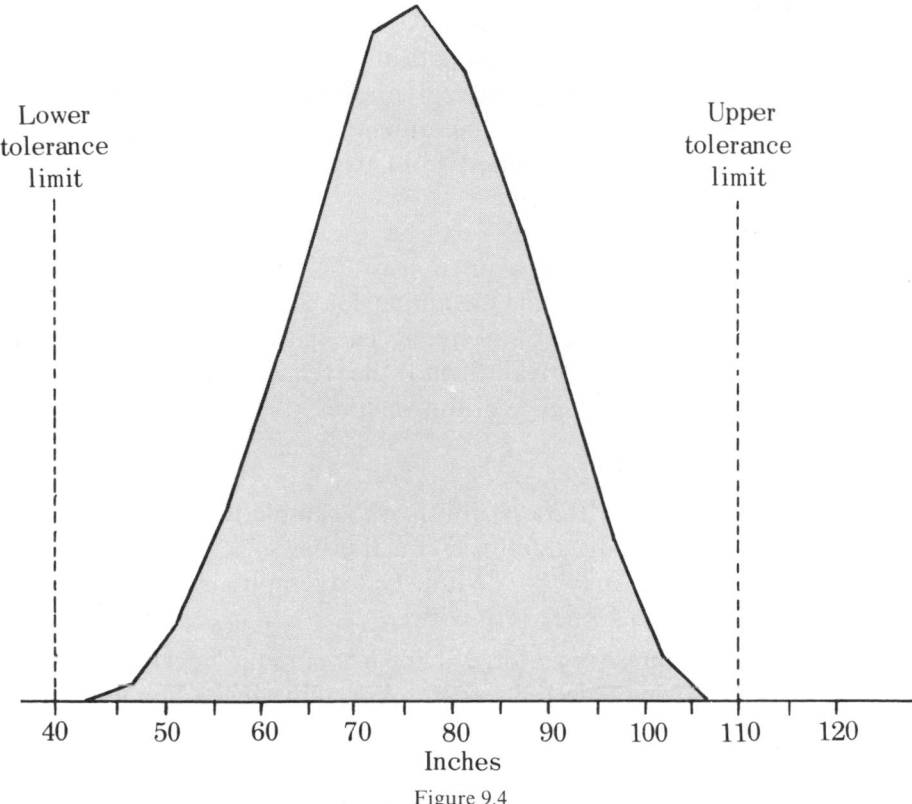

Figure 9.4

SIMULATED DISTRIBUTION OF ASSEMBLED CLEARANCES
(.0000 OMITTED)

The Monte Carlo method is especially useful in simulating the operation of complex multiple-stage and multiple-facility systems, which are simulated by use of random numbers in conjunction with the corresponding distributions of arrivals and service times. This simulation technique is used to estimate expected waiting-line length, average waiting time of units, utilization ratios, and other desired values. The procedure for finding these estimates is similar, although more complex than the simulation of the interaction of the distributions described in the foregoing example.

DISTRIBUTIONS OF SAMPLE STATISTICS

The basis of scientific inquiry lies in the motivation to discover and determine the nature of phenomena. Descriptive statistics provide a form of expression used frequently to describe phenomena that are random variables. Suppose that one wishes to discover the statistical nature of the fuel consumption of a new model automobile or determine the statistical characteristics of the burning life of a type of mercury-vapor lamp. Clearly, it is uneconomical to test all automobiles produced, and the process of testing lamps is destructive. If one is to obtain any information concerning the nature of these phenomena, the obvious alternative is sampling. Each statistic computed from the sample data provides an estimate of a universe parameter.

Recalling that distinct samples can be drawn from a universe as the result of random selection or chance, it is apparent that the computed statistics will differ from sample to sample, for each sample is a different subset of the universe or set of all items. The nature of these variations is highly significant statistically, and the related distributions and theorems constitute the essence of this chapter.

Distribution of Sample Means

The characteristics of the distribution of sample means play a very important role in making inferences on the basis of sample statistics. These characteristics may be demonstrated empirically by drawing random samples from a known universe.

➤ *Example.* A universe is formed from a standard deck of playing cards by removing selected cards to produce the following distribution:

Universe elements	Frequency	Element value
Ace	4	1
2	4	2
3	4	3
4	3	4
5	3	5
6	3	6
7	2	7
8	2	8
9	2	9
10	1	10
Jack	1	11
Queen	1	12
King	1	13
Total	31	

An experiment is performed by drawing randomly, with replacement, a total of 308 samples of 10 cards each. The frequency distribution of the mean, median, and standard deviation of each of the samples is shown in Table 9.3. The distributions of the sample means and the parent universe are plotted in Figure 9.5 in terms of frequency density.

Table 9.3

SUMMARY OF THE SAMPLE STATISTICS OF 308 SAMPLES
OF 10 ITEMS

Sample value	Number		
	Means $\bar{x}$	Medians Md	Standard deviations s
1.0 and under 1.5			2
1.5 and under 2.0			19
2.0 and under 2.5		2	81
2.5 and under 3.0	2	8	87
3.0 and under 3.5	8	23	63
3.5 and under 4.0	23	36	35
4.0 and under 4.5	33	41	11
4.5 and under 5.0	53	49	6
5.0 and under 5.5	65	51	3
5.5 and under 6.0	60	42	1
6.0 and under 6.5	36	23	
6.5 and under 7.0	21	16	
7.0 and under 7.5	6	11	
7.5 and under 8.0	1	3	
8.0 and under 8.5		2	
8.5 and under 9.0		1	
Totals	308	308	308

Summary:

Average $\quad\quad\quad\quad \bar{\bar{x}} = 5.25 \quad\quad Md_{Md} = 4.95 \quad\quad \bar{s} = 3.03$

Standard deviation $\quad s_{\bar{x}} = 0.94 \quad\quad s_{Md} = 1.18 \quad\quad s_s = 0.73$

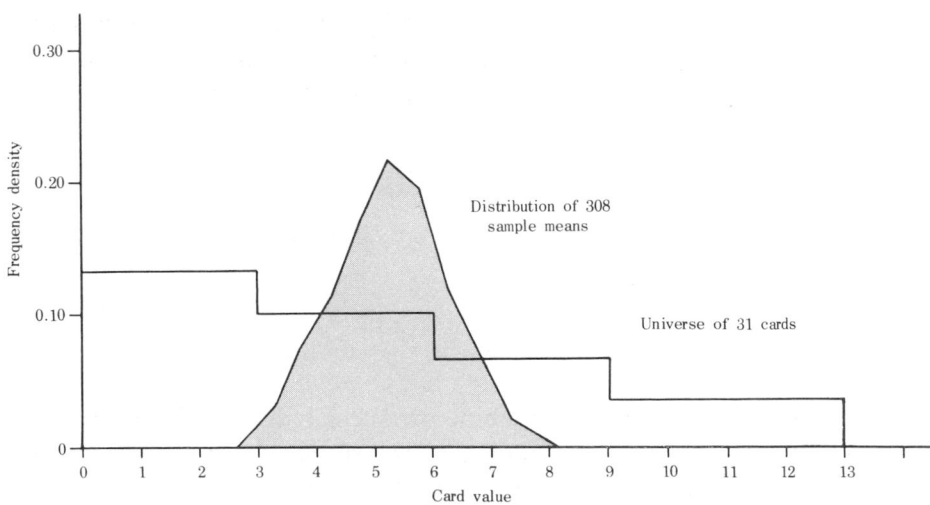

Figure 9.5

DISTRIBUTIONS OF A UNIVERSE OF 31 CARDS AND THE SAMPLE MEANS
OF 308 SAMPLES

For example, the frequency density of aces in the universe of cards is computed as $\frac{4}{31} = 0.13$. The mean of the sample means is denoted $\bar{\bar{x}}$; the standard deviation of the distribution of sample means is $s_{\bar{x}}$; and μ and σ are the mean and the standard deviation, respectively, of the universe.

Tchebycheff's Inequality. The distribution of sample means in this example demonstrates experimentally some important statistical concepts. As shown in Table 9.3, the sample means are approximately centered about the universe mean and almost normally distributed. The distribution of sample means becomes more concentrated about the universe mean as the sample size becomes larger. This relationship is based on what is called the *law of large numbers.*

A more precise statement of this law is expressed by *Tchebycheff's inequality,* which may be written

$$P(\,|\,x - \mu\,| \geq k\sigma) \leq \frac{1}{k^2} \qu\dots\dots\dots\dots\dots(9.1)$$

This relationship states the probability that a randomly selected value which differs from the universe mean by more than k standard deviations will not exceed $\frac{1}{k^2}$. This relationship holds, whatever the form of the distribution.

➤ *Example.* A dry-cell battery is selected at random from a large number of identical batteries produced by a process. The probability that the voltage x produced by this battery will differ from the universe mean voltage μ by 1.5 or more standard deviations is written

$$P(\,|\,x - \mu\,| \geq 1.5\sigma) \leq \frac{1}{(1.5)^2}.$$

The probability that $\bar{x}$ deviates from μ by 1.5σ or more is less than or equal to

$$\frac{1}{(1.5)^2} = 0.44.$$

➤ *Example.* An automatic machine produces ball bearings that vary in diameter, but the distribution of the diameters is unknown. A sample of ball bearings is drawn randomly from the production of the machine and the mean of the sample $\bar{x}$ is computed. The probability that $\bar{x}$ differs from μ, the universe mean diameter, by two standard deviations of sample means or more is written

$$P(\,|\,\bar{x} - \mu\,| \geq 2\sigma_{\bar{x}}) \leq \frac{1}{(2)^2} = 0.25.$$

The converse implication of Tchebycheff's inequality is also of considerable value. In this manner one might say that the minimum proportion of a distribution included in the range of k standard deviations about the mean is $1 - \left(\dfrac{1}{k^2}\right)$. For example, for $k = 3$, the minimum proportion of any distribution, whatever its shape, included in the range of three standard deviations about the mean is $1 - \dfrac{1}{(3)^2} \geq 0.89$. The normal distribution with more than 99 % of its area in the range of three standard deviations is well within the limit of the inequality. If one has no information whatever concerning the shape of a distribution, the provisions of Tchebycheff's inequality can be most beneficial.

Central Limit Theorem. A statement of the law of large numbers that is even more precise is given by what is called the *central limit theorem*. This most important theorem in statistics states that:

If a universe has a mean μ and a finite standard deviation σ, then the distribution of sample means approaches a normal distribution with a mean μ and a standard deviation $\dfrac{\sigma}{\sqrt{n}}$ as the sample size increases.

This theorem is verified in Technical Note No. 1 at the end of this chapter, where it is demonstrated that the expected value of a sample mean is the universe mean. This relationship is written

$$E(\bar{x}) = \mu \quad \dotfill (9.2)$$

It is also shown that the expected value of the variance of sample means is $\text{var}(\bar{x}) = \dfrac{\sigma^2}{n}$. The standard deviation of sample means, called the *standard error of the mean*, is the square root of the variance of means and is written

$$\sigma_{\bar{x}} = \frac{\sigma}{\sqrt{n}} \quad \dotfill (9.3)$$

Estimates of parameters based on sample results in the example above tend to confirm the relationships in Formulas 9.2 and 9.3. The mean of the 308 sample means is $\bar{x} = 5.25$, a very good estimate of $\mu = 5.26$. The standard deviation of the 308 sample means is $s_{\bar{x}} = 0.94$, a reasonably good estimate of the theoretical value of the standard error of the mean

$$\sigma_{\bar{x}} = \frac{3.36}{\sqrt{10}} = 1.06.$$

The fact that the estimate $s_{\bar{x}}$ is less than $\sigma_{\bar{x}}$ is in part the result of an inherent downward bias. This relationship will be discussed in greater detail in a section that follows.

For a constant value of σ, the standard error of the mean varies inversely with sample size. This is to say that, on the average, the mean of a large sample is expected to provide a more reliable estimate of μ than would the mean of a smaller sample. For example, if samples of 25 are drawn with replacement from the universe of cards in Figure 9.5, the standard error of the mean is

$$\sigma_{\bar{x}} = \frac{3.36}{\sqrt{25}} = 0.672.$$

If samples of 100 items are drawn, the standard error of the mean is

$$\sigma_{\bar{x}} = \frac{3.36}{\sqrt{100}} = 0.336.$$

Notice that the standard error for a sample size of 25 is twice the standard error for a sample of 100 items, as shown in Figure 9.6. Thus, if the expected sampling error is to be cut in half, the sample size must be increased four times. For a very large sample, the standard error approaches zero as the sample size n increases without limit.

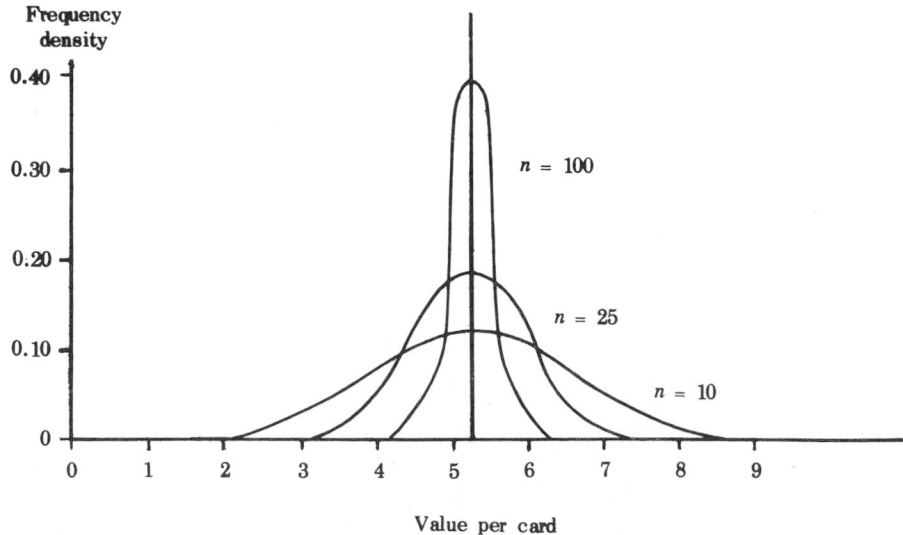

Figure 9.6

DISTRIBUTIONS OF SAMPLE MEANS FOR SELECTED SAMPLE SIZES

The distribution of sample means for large samples is distributed normally whatever the shape of the universe, provided σ is finite. Many populations encountered in practice are normal or very nearly so. It can be shown that:

If a universe is normal, the distribution of sample means is normal, even if the sample size is small.

Samples of 30 or more items are frequently considered large for statistical purposes. The importance of the normal distribution is made very clear by the central limit theorem and related theorems. The application of these concepts to making estimates of parameters and inferences about universes is considered in the latter part of this chapter and in Chapter 10.

Distribution of Sample Medians

The median is a position measure equal to the mean if a distribution is symmetric. If samples are drawn randomly from a normally distributed universe, the distribution of sample medians can be described theoretically. This distribution is expressed by a theorem that states:

If a universe is large and can be approximated closely by a normal distribution, with a mean μ and a standard deviation σ, the medians of random samples of size n are distributed with a mean μ and a standard deviation $1.25 \dfrac{\sigma}{\sqrt{n}}$, and the distribution of sample medians is nearly normal if n is large.

The standard deviation of the distribution of sample medians is called the *standard error of the median* and is denoted

$$\sigma_{Md} = 1.25 \frac{\sigma}{\sqrt{n}} \dotfill (9.4)$$

➤ *Example.* An aptitude test is administered to a large number of job applicants. The distribution of scores is approximately normal, with a mean of 50 and a standard deviation of 10. If a random sample of 25 applicants is selected, the corresponding value of the standard error of the median is computed

$$\sigma_{Md} = 1.25 \cdot \frac{10}{\sqrt{25}} = 2.50.$$

The relationship between $\sigma_{\bar{x}}$ and σ_{Md} is seen in Figure 9.7, which shows the frequency distributions of the means and medians of 308 samples as presented in Table 9.3. The distribution of these sample medians is more

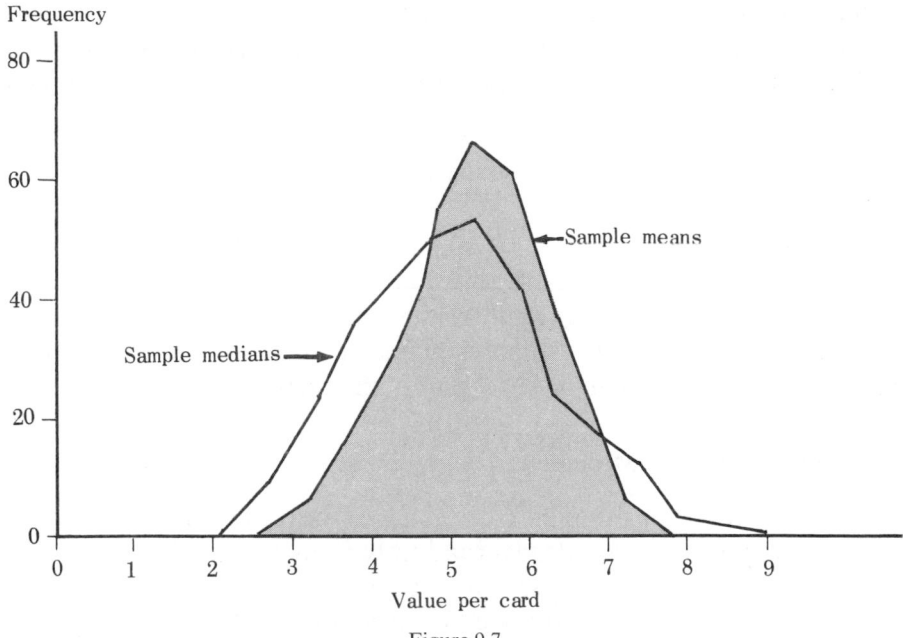

Figure 9.7

FREQUENCY DISTRIBUTIONS OF THE MEANS AND THE MEDIANS
OF 308 SAMPLES

widely dispersed than the distribution of means. The standard deviations
of these distributions have a ratio of

$$\frac{s_{Md}}{s_{\bar{x}}} = \frac{1.18}{0.94} = 1.26.$$

This result closely approximates the theoretical result in Formula 9.4;
which states that the expected ratio is

$$\frac{\sigma_{Md}}{\sigma_{\bar{x}}} = 1.25.$$

The difference between the experimental and the theoretical results is
attributed to random variation in the selection of the samples.

Distributions of Sample Standard Deviations and Variances

In the analysis of random variables relevant to business problems, it is
common that the standard deviation of the universe is unknown. In such
a case σ must be estimated by the sample standard deviation, if a complete enumeration of the universe is infeasible. The distribution of sample
standard deviations is of considerable interest, for it provides an insight
into the reliability of a sample estimate of universe variation.

The Distribution of Sample Standard Deviations. This distribution is defined by a theorem that states:

If a universe is large and normally distributed with a standard deviation of σ, the standard deviations of random samples of size n, where n is large, are closely approximated by a normal distribution with a standard deviation $\dfrac{\sigma}{\sqrt{2n}}$.

The standard deviation of the distribution of standard deviations of samples drawn from a normal universe is called the *standard error of the standard deviation* and is denoted

$$\sigma_s = \frac{\sigma}{\sqrt{2n}} \quad\dots\dots\dots\dots\dots\dots\dots\dots\dots\dots\dots\dots(9.5)$$

The distribution of standard deviations of large samples drawn randomly from a nonnormal universe with a standard deviation σ approaches normality if the sample size is large. The standard error of the standard deviations for this case is written

$$\sigma_s = \sqrt{\frac{M_4 - M_2^2}{4M_2 \cdot n}} \quad\dots\dots\dots\dots\dots\dots\dots(9.6)$$

A sample may be considered large if $n > 100$, and in many instances $n > 30$ is viewed to be sufficiently large to assume normality.

The standard deviations of the 308 samples in Table 9.3 are plotted in Figure 9.8. This distribution is skewed positively. The average standard

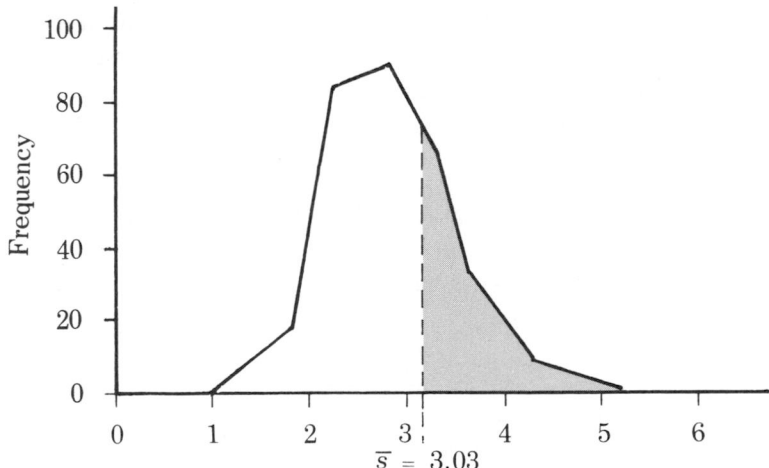

$\bar{s} = 3.03$

Value of the sample standard deviation s

Figure 9.8

FREQUENCY DISTRIBUTION OF THE STANDARD DEVIATIONS
OF 308 SAMPLES

deviation, $\bar{s} = 3.03$, indicates the tendency toward downward bias, for $\sigma = 3.36$. The standard deviation of the sample standard deviations $s_s = 0.73$ compares favorably with the theoretical value of $\sigma_s = 0.75$ computed by use of Formula 9.6.

The Expected Value of a Sample Variance. The expected value of the variance s^2 of a sample is derived to illustrate an important fact. The variance utilizes Formula 3.8 and is written:

$$E(s^2) = E\left[\frac{\sum\limits_{1}^{n} x_i^2}{n} - \left(\frac{\sum\limits_{1}^{n} x_i}{n}\right)^2\right]$$

$$= \frac{1}{n} \sum_{1}^{n} E(x_i^2) - E(\bar{x}^2).$$

It can be shown that $E(x_i^2) = \sigma^2 + \mu^2$ and $E(\bar{x})^2 = \dfrac{\sigma^2}{n} + \mu^2$ by using a corollary of the derivation of the variance of sample means. Substituting these values gives

$$E(s^2) = \sigma^2 + \mu^2 - \frac{\sigma^2}{n} - \mu^2.$$

Simplifying this expression gives

$$E(s^2) = \frac{n-1}{n} \sigma^2 \dotfill (9.7)$$

This result demonstrates the important fact that, on the average, a sample variance, as an estimator, understates the universe variance. Consequently, if an estimate of the dispersion of a universe is to be made on the basis of a sample, a correction for downward bias should be applied.

Correction for Bias in an Estimate of Universe Dispersion. One technique that is frequently used consists of making a correction in computing the sample variance. This value is computed by the expression

$$s^2 = \frac{\sum\limits_{1}^{n}(x_i - \bar{x})^2}{n} \dotfill (9.8)$$

Since s^2, and therefore s, is biased, a correction is applied to obtain an unbiased estimate of σ^2. This *unbiased estimate of universe variance* is written

$$\hat{\sigma}^2 = \frac{n}{n-1} s^2 \dotfill (9.9)$$

where the correction for small sample bias is made by use of the ratio $\dfrac{n}{n-1}$ derived in Formula 9.7. The relationship in Formula 9.9 is confirmed by the experimental results in Table 9.3. Substituting the average standard deviation for s and $n = 10$,

$$\hat{\sigma}^2 = \frac{10}{10-1}(3.03)^2 = 10.20,$$

which compares favorably with the known universe variance $\sigma^2 = (3.36)^2 = 11.29$.

Another technique for correcting for small sample bias consists of computing

$$s^2 = \frac{\sum\limits_{1}^{n}(x_i - \bar{x})^2}{n-1}$$

and stating that s^2 is the sample variance and an unbiased estimate of σ^2. This is not what is defined as the sample variance in Formula 9.8. However, the above definition does occur commonly in statistical literature. The expression above is equivalent to $\hat{\sigma}^2$, the unbiased estimate of σ^2. It follows that an unbiased estimate of σ may be obtained by computing

$$\hat{\sigma} = \sqrt{\frac{\sum\limits_{1}^{n}(x_i - \bar{x})^2}{n-1}} \quad \text{.........................(9.10)}$$

Formula 9.10 may be written alternatively as

$$\hat{\sigma} = \sqrt{\frac{n}{n-1}}\, s \quad \text{.........................(9.11)}$$

➤ *Example.* A sample of five tires of a given type is drawn from the output of a process. The weights of the tires, in pounds, are as follows: 15.2, 14.9, 15.0, 14.8, and 15.1. The mean weight is 15.0 pounds. The sample standard deviation is computed as follows:

$(15.2 - 15.0)^2 = 0.04$
$(14.9 - 15.0)^2 = 0.01$
$(15.0 - 15.0)^2 = 0.00$
$(14.8 - 15.0)^2 = 0.04$
$(15.1 - 15.0)^2 = 0.01$

Total $\qquad$ 0.10

$$s = \sqrt{\frac{\sum\limits_{1}^{n}(x_i - \bar{x})^2}{n}}$$

$$= \sqrt{\frac{0.10}{5}} = 0.1414.$$

The unbiased estimate of the universe standard deviation is computed

$$\hat{\sigma} = \sqrt{\frac{\sum\limits_{1}^{n}(x_i - \bar{x})^2}{n-1}} = \sqrt{\frac{0.10}{5-1}} = 0.1581$$

and expressed in alternative form

$$\hat{\sigma} = \sqrt{\frac{n}{n-1}}\, s = \sqrt{\frac{5}{4}}\,(0.1414) = 0.1581.$$

An Unbiased Estimate of the Standard Error of the Mean. If a sample of items is drawn from a universe for which σ is unknown, the standard error of the mean must be estimated from the sample or a complete enumeration of the universe must be made. The latter course of action is impractical or impossible in many instances. For such a case, the sample standard deviation can be corrected for small sample bias and used as an estimate of σ. Formula 9.3 can be rewritten to utilize the result of Formula 9.10 and to obtain an expression of the desired estimate written

$$\hat{\sigma}_{\bar{x}} = \frac{\hat{\sigma}}{\sqrt{n}} \qquad \dots\dots\dots\dots\dots\dots\dots\dots(9.12)$$

Multiplying the numerator and the denominator of Formula 9.12 by $\sqrt{\dfrac{n-1}{n}}$ provides an alternative expression of an unbiased estimate of $\sigma_{\bar{x}}$. This estimate is given by

$$\hat{\sigma}_{\bar{x}} = \frac{s}{\sqrt{n-1}} \qquad \dots\dots\dots\dots\dots\dots\dots(9.13)$$

➤ *Example.* Four trucks are tested to estimate the average fuel consumption per truck for a fleet of trucks. The fuel consumption for the four trucks, in miles per gallon, for a 5,000-mile test run is as follows: 12.1, 11.8, 12.4, and 11.7. The average consumption rate is 12.0 miles per gallon. An estimate of the standard error of the mean is computed as follows:

$$(12.1 - 12.0)^2 = 0.01$$
$$(11.8 - 12.0)^2 = 0.04$$
$$(12.4 - 12.0)^2 = 0.16$$
$$(11.7 - 12.0)^2 = 0.09$$

Total   0.30

$$\hat{\sigma}_{\bar{x}} = \frac{\hat{\sigma}}{\sqrt{n}} = \frac{\sqrt{\dfrac{0.30}{4-1}}}{\sqrt{4}}$$

$$= \frac{0.316}{2} = 0.158.$$

The estimate of the standard error of the mean is also computed by:

$$\hat{\sigma}_{\bar{x}} = \frac{s}{\sqrt{n-1}} = \frac{\sqrt{\dfrac{0.30}{4}}}{\sqrt{4-1}} = \frac{0.274}{1.732} = 0.158.$$

A Distribution Computed from Sample Variances. The chi-square distribution is introduced in Chapter 8 as a special case of the gamma distribution. The chi-square distribution has many useful applications, a number of which are based on a theorem that states:

If s^2 is the variance of a sample of n items drawn randomly from a normal universe, then $\dfrac{ns^2}{\sigma^2}$ has a chi-square distribution with $n-1$ degrees of freedom.

This theorem is introduced in this section to indicate the nature of a sampling distribution involving variances. A more detailed discussion of this theorem is given in Chapter 13.

Distribution of Sample Proportions

The characteristics of the distribution are introduced in Chapter 7, where the density function, the mean, and the standard deviation are derived. These are, respectively,

Formula 7.4 $\qquad P(r \mid n, p) = \binom{n}{r} \pi^r (1 - \pi)^{n-r}$

Formula 7.8 $\qquad E(p) = \pi$

Formula 7.10 $\qquad \sigma_p = \sqrt{\dfrac{\pi(1 - \pi)}{n}}.$

The distribution of sample proportions, introduced in Chapter 7, is shown to be binomially distributed with a density function given by Formula 7.4.

Expected Value of a Sample Proportion. The expected value of a sample proportion $E(p)$ is the universe proportion π, as stated by Formula 7.8. This relationship is an expression of one form of the law of large numbers. Suppose that m is the number of successes in n Bernoulli trials, π is the universe proportion, and $\dfrac{m}{n}$ is the average number of successes p. If an arbitrarily small number ε is selected and n increases without limit, then:

$$\lim_{n \to \infty} P \left[\left| \frac{m}{n} - \pi \right| > \varepsilon \right] = 0 \quad \ldots\ldots\ldots\ldots\ldots(9.14)$$

Formula 9.14 states that as n becomes large, the probability that $\frac{m}{n}$ differs from π by more than an arbitrarily small value ε approaches zero as a limit.

The Standard Error of a Sample Proportion. The standard deviation of proportions of samples drawn from a universe with a known value of π is expressed by Formula 7.10. This expression is termed the *standard error of the proportion* and indicates the extent to which a sample proportion can be expected to deviate from the universe proportion. Viewed in this manner, the standard error of the proportion σ_p is analogous to the standard error of the mean $\sigma_{\bar{x}}$.

The variance of the distribution of sample proportions is written

$$\text{var}(p) = \frac{\pi(1 - \pi)}{n} = \frac{\sigma^2}{n}$$

and the variance of a sample in terms of its proportion is written

$$s^2 = p(1 - p).$$

The analogous relationship of the properties of the distribution of sample means and proportions may be employed to derive the expression of an unbiased estimate of the standard error of the proportion.

Utilizing the unbiased estimate of universe variance expressed by Formula 9.9, a similar expression in terms of proportion may be written

$$\hat{\sigma}^2 = \frac{n}{n - 1} s^2$$

$$= \frac{n}{n - 1} p(1 - p).$$

The estimate of the standard error of the proportion employs this result, and substituting p for $\bar{x}$,

$$\hat{\sigma}_p^2 = \frac{\hat{\sigma}^2}{n} = \frac{\dfrac{n}{n - 1} p(1 - p)}{n} = \frac{p(1 - p)}{n - 1}.$$

The unbiased estimate of the standard error of the proportion is

$$\hat{\sigma}_p = \sqrt{\frac{p(1 - p)}{n - 1}} \quad \ldots\ldots\ldots\ldots\ldots\ldots(9.15)$$

➤ *Example.* A department store has a large inventory of identical items, of which 40% are Brand A and the remainder are Brand B. A sample of 10 items is to be selected. The expected proportion of units of Brand A included in the sample is

$$E(p) = \pi = 0.40.$$

The standard error of the mean, a measure of the degree to which p for the sample of 10 items is expected to deviate from π, is computed

$$\sigma_p = \sqrt{\frac{\pi(1 - \pi)}{n}} = \sqrt{\frac{(0.40)(1 - 0.40)}{10}} = 0.155.$$

➤ *Example.* A chemical process produces polyethylene containers. It is known that some defective items are produced by the process. A sample of 26 items, selected at random, includes two defective items. Since the value of π is unknown, it is estimated by p, which is computed

$$p = \frac{m}{n} = \frac{2}{26} = 0.077.$$

The estimated standard error is computed

$$\hat{\sigma}_p = \sqrt{\frac{p(1 - p)}{n - 1}} = \sqrt{\frac{(0.077)(0.923)}{26 - 1}} = 0.053.$$

ESTIMATION OF INFINITE UNIVERSE PARAMETERS

A number of remarks are made in the discussions of probability and probability distributions that point to the value of these concepts in making estimates of universe parameters on the basis of sample results. Statistical estimation is a part of statistical inference, which is the process of making estimates or inferences concerning infinite universe parameters. For example, if the average annual expenditure for entertainment per family in a geographic area is unknown, an estimate can be obtained from a sample. The estimate of the average expenditure of all families is obtained from the sample mean. This type of estimate that consists of a single value is called a *point estimate*. The concept of the standard error of the mean indicates, however, that the dispersion of sample means about the universe mean can be predicted and a more informative type of estimate called an *interval estimate* can be made. This type of estimate states in terms of probability the likelihood that the universe mean will occur in a specified range expressed in terms of the standard error of the mean.

Point Estimates

If a sample proportion is used to estimate the universe proportion, the statistic p as a random variable is called an *estimator* of the parameter π. The value this variable takes on is called the *point estimate*. While the expected value of a sample proportion is $E(p) = \pi$, the discussion of the distribution of sample proportions indicates that the value of the estimate p is not likely to be precisely the same value as π. While point estimation does have limitations, it is a valuable tool for decision making.

If one must rely on a single value as an estimate of a parameter, it is desirable to select the random variable that is expected to provide the most dependable estimate. For example, if the universe proportion is to be estimated, why not use $\left(\dfrac{m}{n}\right)^2$, $\sqrt{\dfrac{m}{n}}$, or some other variable as the estimate of π? Any random variable with a range from zero to one could be used as an estimator. The problem is to decide which variable is the best estimator.

The best estimator is the one that is most suitable to a given problem, most likely to give the desired result, is the least risky, or has other desirable properties. The statistical properties of estimators may be analyzed by four criteria that are termed *consistency*, *efficiency*, *unbiasedness*, and *sufficiency*. These properties are considered in the discussions that follow.

Properties of Good Estimators. Returning to the question concerning the use of $\left(\dfrac{m}{n}\right)^2$, $\sqrt{\dfrac{m}{n}}$, or some other variable as an estimate of π, consider the case in which one can sample the entire universe. If the entire universe is examined, the sample size is N, the number of items in the universe and neither $\left(\dfrac{m}{N}\right)^2$ nor $\sqrt{\dfrac{m}{N}}$ is equal to π, unless π is zero or one. However, the value of the variable $\dfrac{m}{n}$, for which $n = N$, is precisely the value of π.

This result demonstrates an important property of a good estimator. If a variable is a good estimator of a universe parameter, and if a large sample is taken, the estimate should differ only slightly from, if not be precisely equal to, the parameter. An estimate with these properties is said to be *consistent* and conforms to the following definition:

A random variable $\hat{\theta}$ is a consistent estimator of θ if, for a sample size n,
$$\lim_{n \to \infty} P(\,|\,\hat{\theta} - \theta\,| > \varepsilon) = 0,$$
where ε is an arbitrarily small number.

In other words, as the sample size becomes large, the probability that the estimate will differ from the parameter value by even some small amount approaches zero as a limit. On the basis of the foregoing definition, which is based on Tchebycheff's theorem, it follows that $\bar{x}$ is a consistent estimator of μ, and p is a consistent estimator of π. The median is a consistent estimator of μ for a symmetric universe, but other properties of the median make it a much less desirable estimator than $\bar{x}$.

A second property of a good estimator is illustrated by means of an example. Consider a plant that has two automatic machines which produce identical parts. The machines can be adjusted so that each produces parts with the same average dimension, except that the dispersion of the items produced by the older of the machines is considerably more than the newer one. Suppose that one day the machines are producing parts with the same but unknown average dimension.

In order to determine the average dimension of the produced parts, a sample is to be taken from the production of one of the machines. Which of the machines is expected to provide the better information? The standard error of the mean is $\sigma_{\bar{x}} = \dfrac{\sigma}{\sqrt{n}}$. The degree to which a sample mean can be expected to deviate from μ is a function of σ, if the sample size is constant. Consequently, the mean of a sample taken from the output of the machine with the smallest degree of dispersion is expected to produce an estimate that is said to be the most *efficient*. This property is stated formally by the following definition:

A random variable θ_1 is an efficient estimator of θ if the variance of θ_1 is less than the variance of any other variable θ_2.

It follows from this definition that the mean of a sample is a relatively more efficient estimator of μ than is the sample median. By use of Formula 9.4, the variance of the mean is less than that of the median since
$$\sigma_{Md} = 1.25\sigma_{\bar{x}}.$$
The discussion of the properties of the distribution of sample standard deviations indicates the bias inherent in estimating universe dispersion on the basis of sample data. Formula 9.7 indicates that $E(s^2) = \dfrac{n-1}{n}\sigma^2$, and s^2 is a biased estimator of σ^2. A good estimator must be *unbiased*, and an estimator with this property is defined as follows:

An estimator $\hat{\theta}$ is an unbiased estimator of θ if $E(\hat{\theta}) = \theta$ for any sample size n and for all values of θ.

On the basis of the definition above, $\dfrac{n}{n-1}s^2$ is an unbiased estimator of σ^2, for all values of σ^2.

A fourth property of a good estimator requires that the estimator be *sufficient*. The condition of sufficiency is defined as follows:

An estimator $\hat{\theta}$ is a sufficient estimator of θ if it utilizes all the information in a sample that is relevant to estimating θ.

Examples of sufficient statistics are $\bar{x}$ and p, which are estimators of μ and π, respectively. These estimators are sufficient since, given the value of these statistics, no additional information can be obtained from a sample that is of any benefit in estimating μ or π. In other words, if the value of the sufficient estimator $\hat{\theta}$ is known, the individual sample values as such do not provide any additional information about the value of the parameter θ.

It is desirable that an estimator have all the properties discussed in the foregoing section, but it is not always possible to determine such an estimator. A general method for finding good estimators is described in the section that follows.

Maximum Likelihood Estimators. A general method for determining good estimators is called the *method of maximum likelihood*. This method yields consistent and sufficient estimators if such statistics exist, and such a variable also tends to be the most efficient as the sample size becomes large. In addition, this technique most often produces estimators that are unbiased. Stated formally:

If a parameter θ is viewed as a variable, the method of maximum likelihood leads to the selection of a value of θ such that the likelihood (probability) of randomly obtaining a set of sample values is a maximum.

The logic of this method is perhaps more easily grasped by means of an example. Random sampling is based on the assumption that a sample, as a small-scale replica of the universe, will tend to reflect the properties of the universe. If descriptive statistics, such as the mean and the variance, are computed, it is assumed that these will in some degree reflect the characteristics of the respective parameters. For example, suppose a random sample of the weights of 40 parts is selected from the production of a process and the sample mean is 25 pounds. What is the most likely value of μ in view of the sample result? The conclusion is that the most likely value of μ is $\bar{x} = 25$ pounds, and not 35 pounds, 20 pounds, or some other value. The value of μ is indeed a definite, fixed value; but the method of maximum likelihood views μ as if it were a variable such that the most likely value of μ is $\bar{x}$, its *maximum likelihood estimator*.

➤ *Example.* The shipping department of a wholesale distributor packages customer orders for shipment. Through oversight, the name and address labels were omitted from three packages, whose contents differ. Each of the packages contains a large number of flashlights that are identical except for color. It is known from the customer order sheets that the packages should contain the following proportions of red and blue flashlights:

Package	Proportions
X	0.8 R, 0.2 B
Y	0.5 R, 0.5 B
Z	0.1 R, 0.9 B

One of the packages is opened, a sample of two flashlights is drawn, and it contains one red and one blue flashlight. The question now is: What is the most likely proportion of red and blue flashlights in the package?

The probability of drawing a sample with one red and one blue flashlight from each of the packages is:

Package	Probability (red and blue)
X	$P(R)P(B) = (.8)(.2) = 0.16$
Y	$P(R)P(B) = (.5)(.5) = 0.25$
Z	$P(R)P(B) = (.1)(.9) = 0.09$

Clearly, the sample result would most frequently be obtained from package Y, since the probability of obtaining the sample result is the maximum of the three values. Stated another way, of the three packages, package Y will most often produce samples of two consisting of one item of each color.

The foregoing example illustrates that p is the maximum likelihood estimator of π. This result is verified mathematically by defining a *likelihood function* or "the probability density of a parameter." This idea is used in Technical Note No. 2 at the end of this chapter to obtain an estimator θ, the parameter of a binomial distribution.

The method of maximum likelihood may be applied to derive maximum likelihood estimators of parameters of density functions that are most often applied to business problems. This method most often produces unbiased estimators, but the most notable exception is the estimator of σ^2. As seen in Formula 9.7, $E(s^2)$ is a biased estimator of universe variance. The use of the correction shown in Formula 9.9 gives an unbiased estimator, which is written

$$E\left[\frac{n}{n-1}s^2\right] = \sigma^2.$$

Some examples of the more commonly used maximum likelihood estimators include:

Parameter	Estimator
μ	$\bar{x}$
π	$\dfrac{r}{n}$
σ	$\sqrt{\dfrac{n}{n-1}}\, s$
σ_p	$\sqrt{\dfrac{p(1-p)}{n-1}}$
λ	np
β	$\dfrac{1}{r}$

Interval Estimates

The process of making point estimates of parameters by use of maximum likelihood estimators provides valuable information for making judgments concerning the value of a parameter. A moment's reflection on the nature of the distributions of sample statistics enables one to see that even the best point estimate may deviate enough from the parameter value to make the estimate unsatisfactory. For this reason it is common practice to estimate a parameter in terms of an interval.

Interval Estimates for Means. The properties of the distribution of sample means are especially useful in demonstrating the concept of using an interval to estimate a parameter. The central limit theorem provides that the distribution of sample means can be considered normal even if the universe is not normal or symmetric. As a consequence, one can say that if a sample of n items is drawn from a universe with a mean μ and a variance σ^2, the probability is 0.95 that the mean of the sample will have a value in the interval from $\mu - 1.96\sigma_{\bar{x}}$ to $\mu + 1.96\sigma_{\bar{x}}$. This probability may be written as

$$P(\mu - 1.96\sigma_{\bar{x}} < \bar{x} < \mu + 1.96\sigma_{\bar{x}}) = 0.95.$$

➤ *Example.* The average unit cost of producing a product is $\mu = \$5.00$, with a standard deviation of $\sigma = \$0.10$. The product is produced in batches of 25 units. A batch is selected and is considered to be a random sample. The average unit cost for the 25 items is unknown, but the probability is 0.95 that the sample mean $\bar{x}$ has a value in the interval

$$\mu - 1.96\frac{\sigma}{\sqrt{n}} < \bar{x} < \mu + 1.96\frac{\sigma}{\sqrt{n}}.$$

This is expressed numerically as

$$5.00 - 1.96 \frac{0.10}{\sqrt{25}} < \bar{x} < 5.00 + 1.96 \frac{0.10}{\sqrt{25}}$$

or

$$\$4.96 < \bar{x} < \$5.04.$$

If a *single item* x is selected randomly from the production process and if the cost per unit is normally distributed, the probability is 0.95 that the cost of the selected item is

$$\mu - 1.96\sigma < x < \mu + 1.96\sigma.$$

Expressed numerically, this interval is

$$5.00 - 1.96(0.10) < x < 5.00 + 1.96(0.10)$$

or

$$\$4.80 < x < \$5.20.$$

The foregoing example illustrates the interval within which the values of $\bar{x}$ or x are expected to occur, given the values of μ and σ. It is common that μ is unknown and must be estimated. The best point estimate of the parameter is $\bar{x}$, but $\bar{x}$ may deviate somewhat from μ. The best estimate of μ therefore consists of the point estimate plus an expression of the interval about $\bar{x}$ within which μ may be expected to occur with a given prob-ability. This type of estimate is called an *interval estimate*.

One of the characteristics of the normal distribution is that it becomes asymptotic for values of the normal variable which differ extensively from the mean. The distribution of sample means tends to be normal, and, theoretically, a sample mean may take on *any* value as the result of the random selection of sample items. Consequently, it is not possible to "draw the line" on sampling error, and one cannot say that it is certain that chance in the form of sampling error will not produce a sample mean which is larger than some upper limit or smaller than some lower limit. It is possible to state in terms of probability the likelihood that a mean will take on a value in a specified interval. This type of interval is called a *confidence interval* and is defined formally as follows:

If t is an estimator of θ, then given the density function of t, it is possible to find two values t_1 and t_2 such that

$$P(t_1 < \theta < t_2) = \phi$$

where ϕ is a fixed probability, and the set of values of t between t_1 and t_2 is the confidence interval of θ.

The general form of an interval estimate of μ is written

$$\bar{x} - z_\alpha \sigma_{\bar{x}} < \mu < \bar{x} + z_\alpha \sigma_{\bar{x}} \dots\dots\dots\dots\dots\dots(9.16)$$

where z is expressed in standard deviation units and α is the probability that μ will exceed a specified limit.

➤ *Example.* A sample of 400 sales invoices is drawn randomly from a large number of invoices, and the mean value per invoice is $2,485. The standard deviation of the universe of invoices is estimated to be $800. The sample mean provides a point estimate of the universe mean, but management wishes to have a confidence interval estimate of μ such that the probability is 0.98 that μ has a value in the interval. The 98 % confidence interval estimate of μ is written

$$\bar{x} - z_{.01}\sigma_{\bar{x}} < \mu < \bar{x} + z_{.01}\sigma_{\bar{x}}$$

and computed

$$\$2{,}485 - 2.33\,\frac{800}{\sqrt{400}} < \mu < \$2{,}485 + 2.33\,\frac{800}{\sqrt{400}}$$

to equal

$$\$2{,}391.80 < \mu < \$2{,}578.20.$$

The value of $z_{.01}$ is found in Appendix H corresponding to the value in the body of the table that is closest to 0.490. The interval estimate for this example is presented in Figure 9.9.

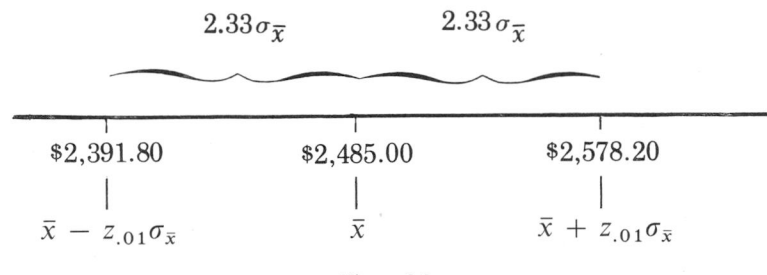

Figure 9.9

A 98% CONFIDENCE INTERVAL ESTIMATE OF μ

➤ *Example.* From experience, it is known that a grinding machine produces items with a universe standard deviation of 0.100 inches. In the course of a working day, the machine has a breakdown which requires that the machine be reset. With this new setting, it is not certain what the mean dimension of the finished items may be. In order to be sure that the items produced will meet specifications, a sample of 36 items is taken randomly from those produced after the new setting. These items have a mean of 2.100 inches, the point estimate of μ. The probability is 0.95 that μ has a value in the confidence interval

$$2.100 - 1.96\frac{0.100}{\sqrt{36}} < \mu < 2.100 + 1.96\frac{0.100}{\sqrt{36}}$$

or

$$2.067 < \mu < 2.133.$$

This interval is seen in Figure 9.10. The halves of two curves are shown in this figure as an alternative way of viewing a confidence interval. In this manner, the probability is 95% that $\bar{x}$ will not differ from μ by more than $1.96\sigma_{\bar{x}}$ if μ is as small as 2.067 inches or as large as 2.133 inches.

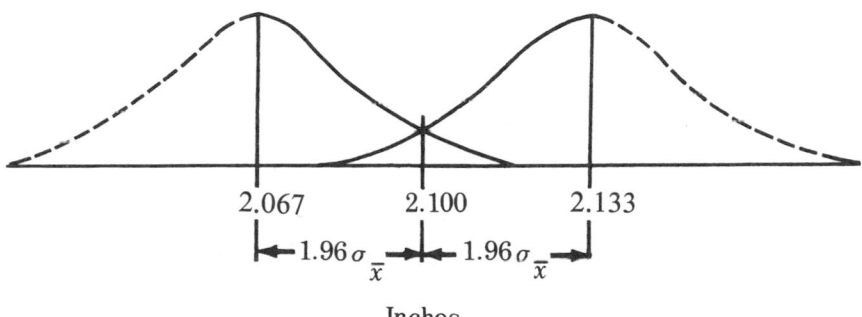

Inches

Figure 9.10

A 95% CONFIDENCE INTERVAL OF μ FOR SPECIFIED VALUES OF
σ, n, AND $\bar{x}$

The probability associated with a confidence interval is termed the *level of confidence* or the *confidence coefficient*. From the foregoing discussion, it follows that an interval estimate with a 100% level of confidence is infinitely large. To be meaningful, one must settle for something less than certainty in making interval estimates. A major point to be considered is that it is impossible to prove that a parameter lies in any finite interval.

A one-sided confidence interval may be computed for the case in which just one limit is desired. Suppose this limit is the lower limit of an interval for estimating μ. The interval is written

$$\bar{x} - z_\alpha \sigma_{\bar{x}} < \mu \quad \ldots\ldots\ldots\ldots\ldots\ldots\ldots\text{(9.17)}$$

where the confidence interval extends to infinity.

➤ *Example.* A trucking firm is considering a contract for the purchase of tires for a fleet of trucks. The firm is particularly interested in the average mileage that can be obtained per tire. A sample of 100 tires is tested and the average mileage per sampled tire is 25,000 miles. The standard deviation for all tires is 2,000 miles. The firm is concerned with avoiding the purchase of tires for which the average mileage is low. Consequently, a one-sided interval estimate is to be made. A 95% confidence interval estimate of μ is written

$$\bar{x} - z_{.05}\sigma_{\bar{x}} < \mu$$

and computed

$$25,000 - 1.64 \, \frac{2,000}{\sqrt{100}} < \mu$$

or

$$24,672 < \mu.$$

The value of $z = 1.64$ is obtained from Appendix H for a probability of $0.50 - 0.05 = 0.45$.

   In this example $z_{.05}$ implies that the area is in one tail of the curve, since a one-sided interval is computed. This type of problem is illustrated in Figure 9.11. The area to the left of the lower limit is 5%, and the value of z is 1.64. The 95% confidence interval estimate of μ is the unshaded portion of the curve. In other words, it may be stated with 95% confidence that μ is *at least as large* as the lower limit of the interval.

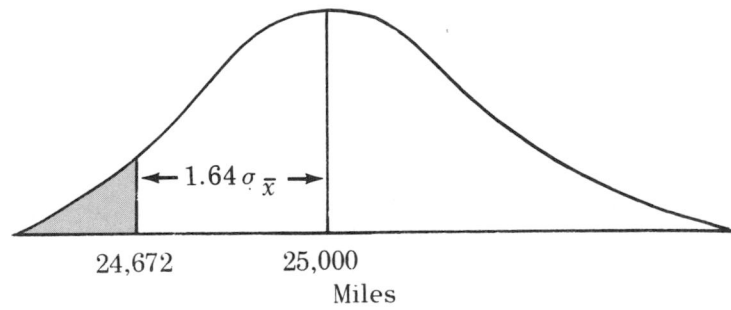

Figure 9.11

A ONE-SIDED INTERVAL ESTIMATE OF μ WITH A LEVEL OF
CONFIDENCE OF 95%

Interval Estimate of the Universe Proportion. The technique of making an interval estimate of the universe percent is applied in much the same fashion as in the case of estimating the universe mean. A confidence interval for a universe proportion is written

$$p - z_\alpha \sigma_p < \pi < p + z_\alpha \sigma_p \dots\dots\dots\dots\dots\dots(9.18)$$

where p is the point estimate of π, the value of α is related to the level of confidence, and σ_p is the standard error of the proportion for a known value of π.

A problem arises in computing the confidence interval, for given a constant sample size, the standard error varies with the value of π. A confidence interval is not symmetrical about p unless $p = 0.50$. For example, assume that $n = 100$. The standard error of the proportion for $\pi = 0.50$ is

$$\sigma_p = \sqrt{\frac{\pi(1 - \pi)}{n}} = \sqrt{\frac{(0.50)(1.00 - 0.50)}{100}} = 0.05.$$

For a value of $\pi = .20$, the standard error is

$$\sigma_p = \sqrt{\frac{(0.20)(1.00 - 0.20)}{100}} = 0.04.$$

The exact range of a confidence interval is determined by solving a quadratic equation for the values of π at the limits of the interval. For example, a 95% confidence interval is to be computed about a given value of p. The interval is written

$$p - \pi = \pm 1.96 \sqrt{\frac{\pi(1 - \pi)}{n}}.$$

The desired values of π are found by squaring both sides of the expression above and solving the quadratic for its roots. Squaring the expression gives

$$p^2 - 2p\pi + \pi^2 = \frac{3.84[\pi(1 - \pi)]}{n}.$$

For a value of $p = 0.20$ and $n = 40$, the quadratic expression is written

$$(0.20)^2 - 2(0.20)\pi + \pi^2 = \frac{3.84(\pi - \pi^2)}{40}$$

$$0.04 - 0.40\pi + \pi^2 = 0.096\pi - 0.096\pi^2$$

$$1.096\pi^2 - 0.496\pi + 0.04 = 0.$$

Solving for the roots by means of the quadratic formula gives

$$= \frac{0.496 \pm \sqrt{(0.496)^2 - 4(1.096)(0.04)}}{2(1.096)}$$

$$= \frac{0.496 \pm \sqrt{0.246 - 0.175}}{2.19}$$

$$= \frac{0.496 \pm 0.265}{2.19}$$

$$= 0.226 \pm 0.121.$$

The 95% confidence interval of π is 0.105 to 0.347, and is shown in Figure 9.12. The figure shows the asymmetric nature of the confidence interval which results from the fact that σ_p varies with the value of π.

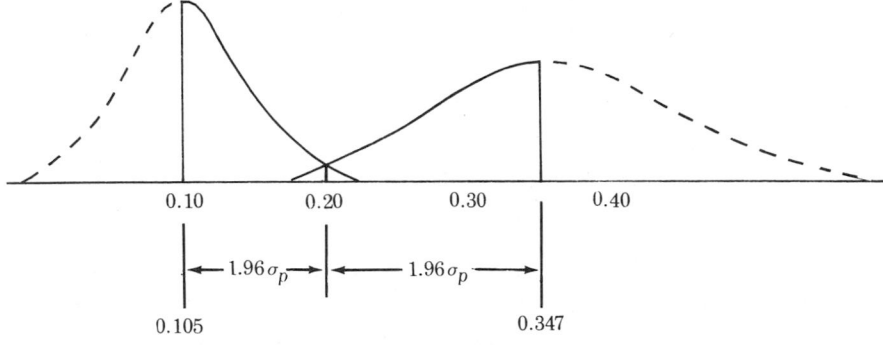

Figure 9.12

A 95% CONFIDENCE INTERVAL ESTIMATE OF π ABOUT $p = 0.20$

As a practical matter, an approximation of the confidence interval often provides sufficient accuracy for estimating π. One approximation is obtained by assuming that the interval is symmetric and employing the value of σ_p corresponding to the point estimate. For example, if $p = 0.20$ and $n = 40$, the approximation of the interval estimate of π is as follows:

$$\text{confidence interval} = 0.20 \pm 1.96 \sqrt{\frac{(0.20)(0.80)}{40}}$$

$$= 0.20 \pm 1.96 \sqrt{0.004}$$

$$= 0.20 \pm 0.123.$$

The limits of the interval are 0.077 to 0.323, which compare favorably with the exact limits computed previously.

Interval Estimate of the Universe Percent. The calculation of interval estimates for proportions involves decimals, which are moderately troublesome computationally if squares or square roots are involved. For this reason, the universe percent is often used in calculations. The conversion from proportion to percent is accomplished by multiplying by a factor of 100. For example, for $\pi = 0.60$ and $n = 49$, the corresponding values of the universe percent and the standard error of the percent are

$$\text{universe percent} = 100\pi = 100(0.60) = 60$$

$$\sigma \text{ percent} = \sqrt{\frac{100\pi(100 - 100\pi)}{49}} = \sqrt{\frac{(60)(40)}{49}} = 7\%.$$

The 95% confidence interval based on a percent of 60 and a sample size of 49 is computed

$$60 \pm 1.96 \sqrt{\frac{(60)(40)}{49}}$$

$$60 \pm 1.96(7).$$

The confidence limits are 46.3% and 73.7%.
  The corresponding result using a proportion is computed

$$0.60 \pm 1.96 \sqrt{\frac{(0.60)(0.40)}{49}}$$

$$0.60 \pm 1.96(0.07).$$

The confidence limits are 0.463 and 0.737. The two methods give the same results, as long as one is consistent in substituting π or 100π in the formulations.

Interval Estimates and Sample Size

The size of an interval estimate depends upon both the level of confidence chosen and the sample size. The effect of each of these factors is introduced in preceding sections. This concept is considered in more detail in this section to provide a basis for determining the sample size needed to produce an interval estimate with a specified range.

Sample Size for an Interval Estimate of μ. If the value of σ is known, a level of confidence is specified, and the allowable error in estimating μ is given, a confidence interval of μ can be produced by selecting a sample of the correct size. For example, the average outstanding balance of signature loans issued by a bank varies from month to month. From experience, it is known that the amounts are normally distributed, with a standard deviation of $500. The bank wishes to compute an interval estimate of μ so that the probability is 0.95 that the point estimate will not differ from μ by more than \$60. The fact that the confidence interval is symmetrical simplifies calculations. The above conditions specify that the maximum deviation E of $\bar{x}$ from μ be

$$E = \bar{x} - \mu = \$60.$$

For a level of confidence of 95%

$$E = \$60 = 1.96\sigma_{\bar{x}}.$$

The sample size for this condition is computed by solving for n as follows:

$$\$60 = 1.96 \frac{\$500}{\sqrt{n}}$$

$$(\$60)^2 = \frac{3.84(\$500)^2}{n}$$

$$n = \frac{3.84(\$500)^2}{(\$60)^2}$$

$$n = 267.$$

If a sample of $n = 267$ accounts is selected, the probability is 0.95 that the mean of the sample will not deviate by more than \$60 from the universe mean, whatever its value. The formal expression for the general case is written:

$$n = \left[\frac{z \cdot \sigma}{E}\right]^2 \quad \dots\dots\dots\dots\dots\dots \quad \textbf{(9.19)}$$

➤ *Example.* A drug manufacturer wishes to control statistically the production of an antibiotic by taking samples periodically to compute an interval estimate of the process mean. It is especially important that accurate estimates of μ be made, for if there is a substantial shift in the process, the drugs may be hazardous for human consumption. It is known from production records that $\sigma = 10$ milligrams. The maximum allowable error is two milligrams and the level of confidence is specified as 99%. The desired sample size is computed

$$n = \left[\frac{(2.58)(10)}{2}\right]^2 = 166.$$

Sample Size for an Interval Estimate of π. A desired level of precision in estimating a universe proportion can be achieved by selecting an appropriate sample size. If no information is available concerning the universe proportion, a small pilot study can be made to obtain an estimate, or one can assume a value of π of 0.50, for which the standard error is a maximum for any fixed sample size. For example, for a sample size of 100, the standard error for selected values of π are as follows:

Value of π	σ_p
0.10	$\sqrt{\dfrac{(0.10)(0.90)}{100}} = 0.03$
0.25	$\sqrt{\dfrac{(0.25)(0.75)}{100}} = 0.04$
0.50	$\sqrt{\dfrac{(0.50)(0.50)}{100}} = 0.05$
0.75	$\sqrt{\dfrac{(0.75)(0.25)}{100}} = 0.04$
0.90	$\sqrt{\dfrac{(0.90)(0.10)}{100}} = 0.03.$

Given a value of E, the allowable error, and a level of confidence, the sample size for making an interval estimate of π is computed by solving

$$p - \pi = E = z_\alpha \sqrt{\frac{\pi(1 - \pi)}{n}}$$

for the value of n to obtain

$$n = \pi(1 - \pi)\left[\frac{z_\alpha}{E}\right]^2 \quad \text{...........................(9.20)}$$

➤ *Example.* A firm wishes to estimate with an error of no more than 0.03 and a level of confidence of 98 % the proportion of consumers that prefers its brand of household detergent. Sales reports indicate that about 0.20 of all consumers prefer the firm's brand. The required sample size is computed as

$$n = (0.20)(0.80)\left[\frac{2.33}{0.03}\right]^2$$

$$= 965.$$

➤ *Example.* A television station wishes to estimate, within 5%, the percent of viewers in an area that prefer a given program. The estimate is to be made with a level of confidence of 90%. The station has no information concerning the likely value of the percent of viewers preferring the program. The number of items that should be included in the sample is found by substituting percent for proportion in Formula 9.20 and solving

$$n = (50)(50) \left[\frac{1.64}{5} \right]^2$$

$$= 269$$

ESTIMATION OF FINITE UNIVERSE PARAMETERS

The statistical concepts developed in this chapter to this point are based on the assumption of an infinite universe. The selection of even a large sample from an infinite universe does not alter the value of the universe parameters. Suppose a universe is finite and consists of 300 items. If a sample of 125 is selected randomly without replacement from the universe, the size and variance of the universe will be steadily reduced as the sample is drawn. For this reason some modification is required in making estimates based on samples drawn from finite universes. As a rule of thumb, this type of modification is required if the sample size is 5% or more of the parent population.

The Finite Multiplier

Consider a firm which produces products on a job-shop basis; that is, all items are produced as ordered and as specified. An order is received for 150 identical engine mounting blocks. The blocks are manufactured and the quality inspector wishes to check the average thickness of the blocks. A sample of items is to be selected to estimate the universe mean. If a sample of 150 items is selected from the universe, it is clear that there can be no sampling error in estimating μ, since the entire universe is enumerated. The formula for the standard error of the mean for an infinite universe does not apply in this case since

$$\sigma_{\bar{x}} = \frac{\sigma}{\sqrt{n}}$$

implies that the standard error is something other than zero, even though the entire universe has been enumerated.

Where the sample size is a significant proportion of the universe (more than 5%), it is necessary to apply a *finite multiplier*, which is written

$$\frac{N - n}{N - 1} \quad \dots\dots\dots\dots\dots\dots\dots\dots\text{(9.21)}$$

where N is the population size and n is the sample size. The finite multiplier is approximately equal to the proportion of items in the finite universe that is not included in the sample. The fraction or proportion of universe items included in the sample is called the *sampling fraction* and is written

$$f = \frac{n}{N}.$$

The fraction of universe items not in the sample is

$$1 - f = 1 - \frac{n}{N} \quad \dots\dots\dots\dots\dots\dots\dots(9.22)$$

Rewriting the right-hand side of the preceding expression gives

$$1 - \frac{n}{N} = \frac{N}{N} - \frac{n}{N} = \frac{N - n}{N}.$$

Typically, the size of the universe is sufficiently large so that the difference between N and $N - 1$ is negligible. Consequently, the fraction of universe items not sampled is very nearly the same value as the finite multiplier. Written symbolically, this relationship is

$$\frac{N - n}{N} \cong \frac{N - n}{N - 1}.$$

Because these quantities are very nearly the same, the fraction of items not sampled is very often used as the finite multiplier. This fraction will be used in the remainder of this presentation when a finite correction is indicated. The finite correction is always appropriate in computing interval estimates, but the ratio approaches one for an infinite universe. If sample items are drawn from a finite universe, but sampling is done with replacement, the universe is, in effect, infinite.

Interval Estimate of the Mean of a Finite Universe

The foregoing discussion indicates that the formula for the standard error of the mean for samples drawn without replacement from a finite universe must be modified. This modification is accomplished by computing the variance of means by

$$\sigma_{\bar{x}}^2 = \frac{\sigma^2}{n}(1 - f) \quad \dots\dots\dots\dots\dots\dots(9.23)$$

The standard error of the mean for a finite universe is written

$$\sigma_{\bar{x}} = \frac{\sigma}{\sqrt{n}}\sqrt{1 - f}. \quad \dots\dots\dots\dots\dots(9.24)$$

The standard error of the mean computed by Formula 9.24 is used to make interval estimates in much the same manner described in the preceding discussion of interval estimation.

➤ *Example.* An auditor selects randomly, without replacement, a sample of 36 accounts from the total file of 100 accounts receivable to estimate the mean balance of all accounts. If the standard deviation of the balance of all accounts is $60 and the sample mean is $240, the 95% interval estimate of μ is

$$\bar{x} \pm z_{0.05} \frac{\sigma}{\sqrt{n}} \sqrt{1 - f} \qquad\qquad \$240 \pm (1.96) \frac{60}{\sqrt{36}} \sqrt{1 - \frac{36}{100}}$$

$$\$240 \pm (1.96)(10) \sqrt{0.64}$$

$$\$240 \pm \$15.68.$$

The confidence interval is

$$\$224.32 \text{ to } \$255.68.$$

The use of good estimators applies to finite populations. For example, if σ is unknown, the estimated standard error of the mean of a finite universe is computed

$$\hat{\sigma}_{\bar{x}} = \frac{s}{\sqrt{n - 1}} \sqrt{1 - f} \dots\dots\dots\dots\dots\dots(9.25)$$

➤ *Example.* A milling machine is used in a manufacturing plant to produce metal parts of different sizes. The machine is adjusted to produce a given number of parts of a specified size. Then the machine must be reset to produce parts of another size. Following a resetting, a sample of production is taken to determine if the parts are, on the average, of the desired size. In such a case the mean and the standard deviation are unknown prior to sampling. After one such adjustment of the machine, a bin of 200 parts is produced and a sample of 50 is selected without replacement. The sample mean is 4.200 inches and the standard deviation is 0.060 inches. The 95% confidence interval estimate of the average dimension of parts being produced is computed as

$$\bar{x} \pm z_{0.05} \frac{s}{\sqrt{n - 1}} \sqrt{1 - f} \qquad 4.200 \pm (1.96) \frac{0.060}{\sqrt{50 - 1}} \sqrt{1 - \frac{50}{200}}$$

$$4.200 \pm (1.96)(0.00857)(0.866)$$

$$4.200 \pm 0.0145.$$

The confidence interval is

$$4.1855 \text{ to } 4.2145 \text{ inches.}$$

Interval Estimate of the Universe Percent

The finite multiplier may be applied to the estimation of the universe percent in a manner analogous to the estimation of a universe mean. If a sufficiently large sample is drawn, without replacement, from a finite universe, the standard error of the percent should be corrected by application of the finite multiplier. The estimated standard error of the percent of a finite universe is written

$$\hat{\sigma}_p = \sqrt{1 - f}\,(100)\,\sqrt{\frac{p(1 - p)}{n - 1}} \quad \dots\dots\dots\dots\dots(9.26)$$

➤ *Example.* A salvage dealer purchases 300 used forced-air heaters and wishes to estimate the percent of heaters that are in working condition. A sample of 40 heaters is taken randomly and 32 of the heaters are found to be in working order. The 95% confidence interval estimate of the universe percent is computed

$$100p \pm 1.96\,\sqrt{1 - f}\,(100)\,\sqrt{\frac{p(1 - p)}{n - 1}}$$

$$80 \pm 1.96\,\sqrt{1 - \frac{40}{300}}\,(100)\,\sqrt{\frac{0.80(1 - 0.80)}{40 - 1}}$$

$$80 \pm (1.96)(0.931)(100)(0.0640)$$

$$80 \pm (1.96)(5.96)$$

$$80 \pm 11.68.$$

The confidence interval is 68.32 to 91.68.

STATISTICAL QUALITY CONTROL CHARTS

The term "mass production" calls to mind the concept of manufacturing large numbers of identical and interchangeable items. In reality, it is impossible to produce two items that are identical. If all dimensions are measured with sufficient precision, it can be determined that the objects differ in some degree. Manufacturing specifications or tolerance limits take into account the variability of "identical" items and allow a tolerance range within which measurements must fall. Manufactured items that fall within the tolerance limits are judged to be of acceptable quality and interchangeable. Items that do not meet specifications must be scrapped or reworked.

It is possible to insure that all manufactured items or parts meet specifications by inspecting each object for quality. This procedure requires that each produced object be gauged or measured for quality, but one hundred percent inspection of items is expensive. Worker fatigue and other factors also tend to make this type of inspection less than fully reliable. In the majority of instances, statistical quality control techniques can be applied to reduce the total cost of inspection. These techniques take into account the manufactured items and the distributions of sample statistics.

Classes of Variability

The variations in the characteristics of mass-produced items may be classified in terms of the sources of the variations. One class of variations encompasses those that are the result of factors that can be identified. The observed variation can be associated with the source. For example, marked variations in a product dimension may be observed as the result of the adjustment of a machine by an operator, a change in the character of input raw material, or mistakes made by workmen. These sources produce variations that tend not to be predictable statistically. Variations of this type are called *assignable variations*. Since the magnitude of these variations tends to be large, the sources of the variations can be assigned and eliminated.

A second class of variation includes variations that result from the interaction of a combination of many random variables that produce slight differences in product characteristics. Individually, these variables induce only slight changes in product dimensions, and it is impossible or uneconomical to identify or eliminate these causes. For example, slight changes in temperature, pressure, friction, metal hardness, and similar factors interact randomly to produce slight variations in product quality. Variations of this type are called *random variations*, and these are viewed as being characteristic of the production process.

Random variations tend to be predictable statistically. The range of variation is compared with set tolerance limits to determine if the process is capable of producing a sufficiently large percent of items that meet specifications. If not, the nature of the process or the tolerance limits must be changed. With a compatible relationship between process capability and tolerance limits obtained, the control of quality focuses on the identification and control of assignable sources of variation.

Control Charts for Variables

The identifying of assignable variations is facilitated by describing random variation in terms of probable limits of variation. These limits, called *control limits*, are based on the distributions of sample statistics. The control limits are presented graphically by *control charts* that depict the pattern of variation inherent in a process during a period of observation. Control charts indicate whether variations can be considered to be random or if assignable variations are also indicated. Control charts for variables are based on measured quantities. The most widely used are control charts for sample means and for ranges.

Control Charts for Sample Means. A *control chart for sample means*, or an $\bar{x}$ *chart*, is based on the distribution of sample means. It is used to determine if variations in a product dimension are random and to detect assignable variations. The control chart is based on a series of samples or *subgroups* of items drawn randomly from a process over a period of time. The arithmetic means of samples are computed and the dispersion of these means reflects the pattern of variation of the process. The mean of the sample means $\bar{\bar{x}}$ is computed as an unbiased estimate of the universe or process mean.

An unbiased estimate of the universe or process standard deviation can be obtained by computing the mean variance of samples and correcting for sample bias. Symbolically, this estimate is written

$$\hat{\sigma} = \sqrt{\bar{s}^2 \frac{n}{n-1}}.$$

The control limits for an $\bar{x}$ chart are the $3\hat{\sigma}_{\bar{x}}$ limits about the mean of a normally distributed universe. This interval is estimated by

$$\bar{\bar{x}} \pm 3 \frac{\hat{\sigma}}{\sqrt{n}}.$$

An extensive amount of computation is required to find $\bar{s}^2$ for a large number of samples. Computational effort can be reduced somewhat by estimating the universe dispersion by means of sample ranges, for ranges are easy to compute. The relationship between the range R of samples and the standard deviation σ of a normally distributed universe is the basis for finding the control limits for $\bar{x}$ charts.

The ranges of samples are summarized by the average range $\bar{R}$. The expected value of the ratio of the average range of samples of a given size to the standard deviation of the normal universe from which the samples are randomly drawn is written

$$d_2 = \frac{\bar{R}}{\sigma} \quad \dots\dots\dots\dots\dots\dots\dots\dots(9.27)$$

The values of d_2 for selected sample sizes have been computed and are listed in Table 9.4. An estimate of the universe standard deviation is obtained by writing Formula 9.27 in the form

$$\hat{\sigma} = \frac{\bar{R}}{d_2}.$$

The quantity $3\sigma_{\bar{x}}$ can be estimated by computing

$$3\hat{\sigma}_{\bar{x}} = \frac{3\bar{R}}{d_2 \sqrt{n}}.$$

From this expression the ratio

$$A_2 = \frac{3}{d_2 \sqrt{n}} \dots\dots\dots\dots\dots\dots\dots\text{(9.28)}$$

may be written. Values of A_2 for selected sample sizes are listed in Table 9.4.

Table 9.4

VALUES OF d_2 AND A_2 FOR COMPUTING
CONTROL LIMITS FOR $\bar{x}$ CHARTS

n	d_2	A_2
2	1.128	1.880
3	1.693	1.023
4	2.059	0.729
5	2.326	0.577
6	2.534	0.483
7	2.704	0.419
8	2.847	0.373
9	2.970	0.337
10	3.078	0.308

The estimated $3\sigma_{\bar{x}}$ limits about the universe mean are written

$$UCL_{\bar{x}} = \bar{\bar{x}} + A_2\bar{R} \dots\dots\dots\dots\dots\text{(9.29)}$$
$$LCL_{\bar{x}} = \bar{\bar{x}} - A_2\bar{R} \dots\dots\dots\dots\dots\text{(9.30)}$$

where $UCL_{\bar{x}}$ is called the *upper control limit* and $LCL_{\bar{x}}$ is the *lower control limit* for sample means. These limits reflect the range within which 99.73% of random variations of sample means are expected to occur. Sample means that fall outside these limits, while possibly reflecting random variation, tend to indicate assignable variation. It is expected that only 0.27% of sample means will occur outside the control limits as the result of random or chance variation.

➤ *Example.* Samples or subgroups of four items each are drawn randomly from the output of a machine that produces shafts. The machine is one of several identical machines that produce the shafts with a distribution of diameters summarized in Figure 9.13. The sample results are listed in Table 9.5. The mean diameter of all sampled parts is computed

$$\bar{\bar{x}} = \frac{443.00}{15}$$

$$= 29.53.$$

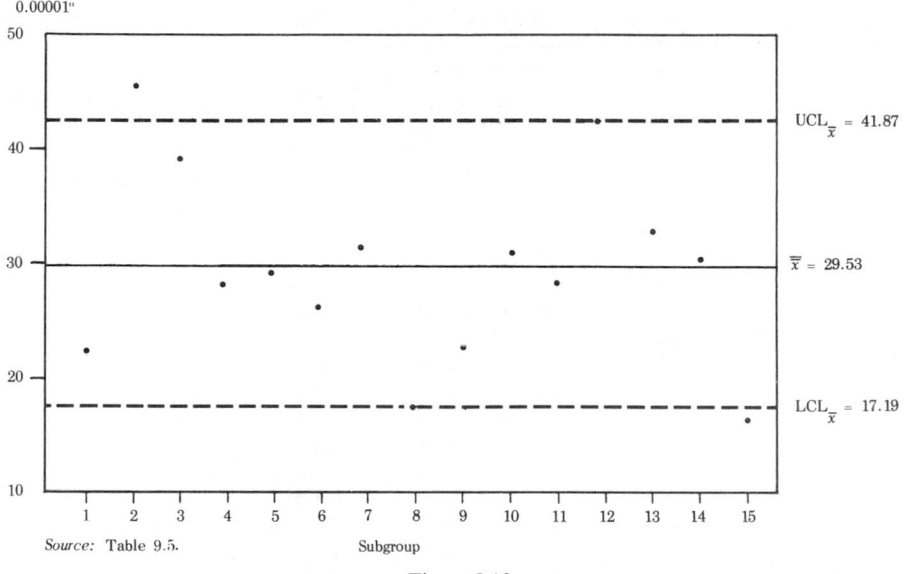

Figure 9.13

CONTROL CHART FOR THE MEANS OF SAMPLES OF FOUR SHAFTS
DRAWN FROM THE OUTPUT OF A MACHINE

The control limits for a control chart for means are computed on the basis of the mean range, which is computed

$$\bar{R} = \frac{254}{15}$$

$$= 16.93.$$

The control limits are found by use of the A_2 factor for $n = 4$ read from Table 9.4 as follows:

$$UCL_{\bar{x}} = \bar{\bar{x}} + A_2\bar{R}$$

$$= 29.53 + (0.729)(16.93)$$

$$= 41.87$$

and

$$LCL_{\bar{x}} = \bar{x} - A_2\bar{R}$$
$$= 29.53 - (0.729)(16.93)$$
$$= 17.19.$$

Table 9.5

RESULTS OF FIFTEEN SAMPLES OF FOUR SHAFTS DRAWN
FROM THE OUTPUT OF A MACHINE

(Values expressed in 0.00001″ deviations from a nominal dimension)

Subgroup	Observed values				Mean	Range
1	32	20	33	6	22.75	27
2	42	36	52	50	45.00	16
3	25	15	52	63	38.75	48
4	22	33	34	23	28.00	12
5	29	30	27	31	29.25	4
6	30	34	26	16	26.50	18
7	34	31	28	34	31.75	6
8	11	21	20	16	17.00	9
9	11	22	28	31	23.00	20
10	36	30	35	26	31.75	10
11	34	16	37	26	28.25	21
12	27	36	51	53	41.75	26
13	26	35	32	37	32.50	11
14	25	36	37	24	30.50	13
15	10	28	14	13	16.25	18
Totals					443.00	259

The sample means, plotted in Figure 9.13, reflect a significant lack of statistical stability. Samples 2, 8, and 15 have means that lie beyond the control limits. The inference is drawn that assignable causes of variation were present as these samples were drawn.

A process is judged to be stable statistically if all sample means are within the control limits, the tolerable range of random variation. If a variation, however, is judged to be the result of an assignable cause, it is important that this cause be identified and removed.

Control Charts for Ranges. The variations in sample dispersion can be presented graphically by a *control chart for ranges* or an *R chart*. The procedure for constructing this type of chart is similar to that for preparing $\bar{x}$ charts. The control limits for ranges are based on an estimate of $3\sigma_R$, or three times the standard deviation of ranges of samples of a given size.

The distribution of sample ranges is neither normal nor symmetric. Control limits for ranges, however, are assumed to be symmetric without undue loss of precision. The exception to this rule occurs for a lower control limit for small samples, which is negative in some cases. Since negative ranges cannot occur, the lower limit is taken to be zero rather than some negative value.

The control limits for an R chart are based on the factors written

$$D_3 = 1 - \frac{3\hat{\sigma}_{d_2}}{d_2}$$

and

$$D_4 = 1 + \frac{3\hat{\sigma}_{d_2}}{d_2}$$

where $\hat{\sigma}_{d_2}$ is the estimated standard deviation of the distribution of values of d_2 obtained by randomly drawing samples of a given size from a normal universe and computing R and $\frac{R}{\sigma}$ for each sample.

Values for the factors D_3 and D_4 for selected sample sizes are listed in Table 9.6. The upper and lower control limits for R charts are found by computing

$$UCL_R = D_4\bar{R} \quad \dots\dots\dots\dots\dots\dots\dots(9.31)$$

and

$$LCL_R = D_3\bar{R} \quad \dots\dots\dots\dots\dots\dots\dots(9.32)$$

The lower control limits of R charts for samples of six or fewer items are zero since D_3 is zero, as seen in Table 9.6.

Table 9.6

VALUES OF D_3 AND D_4 FOR COMPUTING
CONTROL LIMITS FOR R CHARTS

n	D_3	D_4
2	0	3.267
3	0	2.575
4	0	2.282
5	0	2.115
6	0	2.004
7	0.076	1.924
8	0.136	1.864
9	0.184	1.816
10	0.223	1.777

→ *Example.* Samples of four items each drawn from the output of a machine and the ranges of the samples are listed in Table 9.5. The mean range computed in the foregoing example is

$$\bar{R} = \frac{254}{15} = 16.93.$$

The control limits are found by use of the factors D_4 and D_3 corresponding to $n = 4$ read from Table 9.6. These limits are

$$UCL_R = D_4\bar{R}$$
$$= (2.282)(16.93)$$
$$= 38.634.$$
$$LCL_R = D_3\bar{R}$$
$$= (0)(16.93)$$
$$= 0.$$

Except for sample three, the sample ranges plotted in Figure 9.14 reflect statistical stability. It is inferred that this variation is the result of an assignable cause since it lies well beyond the upper control limit.

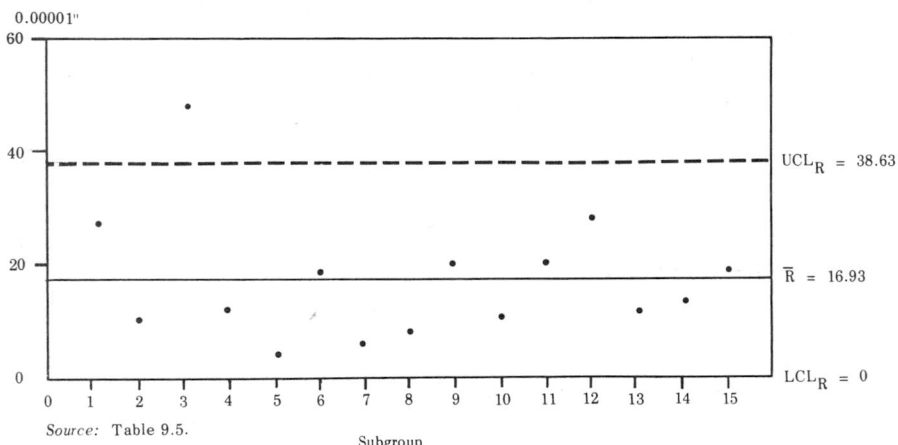

Source: Table 9.5.

Figure 9.14

CONTROL CHART FOR THE RANGES OF SAMPLES OF FOUR SHAFTS DRAWN FROM THE OUTPUT OF A MACHINE

Control Charts for Attributes

In contrast to a variable quantity that is a measured characteristic, the quality of a product may also be judged by whether a characteristic is of acceptable quality. For example, the quality of a shaft produced by a machine is dependent upon the diameter of the shaft being within specifications. If the shaft diameter is too large or too small, the shaft is judged defective and of unacceptable quality. Only two outcomes can occur in appraising the quality of a shaft diameter, since the diameter is either within or without the specifications. This quality characteristic is called an *attribute*.

Control charts for attributes may be constructed to reflect the pattern of variation and stability of a process in terms of the proportion or fraction of items produced that are defective. Charts may also be based on the number of defects per unit of output.

Control Charts for Fraction Defective. Much of the quality inspection of the output of processes consists of applying a gauge or a standard to an item to determine if it is acceptable or defective. For example, an inspector uses a gauge to test shafts produced by a machine. If the shaft fits within the gauge, it is accepted; otherwise, it is judged to be defective. Similarly, an accountant may examine accounts receivable to determine the fraction of accounts that is delinquent (defective).

Control charts may be constructed to reflect the pattern of random variation in the fraction of items that is defective in the output of a process. A *control chart for fraction defective*, or p chart, is based on the distribution of sample proportions. It is assumed that the items are produced by a Bernoulli process. This assumption implies that (1) there are only two possible outcomes (acceptable or defective), (2) the outcomes occur randomly, and (3) the probability of either outcome remains unchanged for each trial.

The control limits of this chart are the estimated $3\sigma_p$ limits about the estimated universe proportion. In the majority of cases, the universe proportion is less than 0.50 and the distribution of sample proportions is skewed. The use of symmetrical control limits is similar to utilizing a normal approximation of a binomial as a suitable approximation. Relatively large samples are used in constructing p charts, for small samples do not provide satisfactory results.

An estimate of the universe proportion denoted p' is found by dividing the total number of defective units in all samples by the total number of items sampled. The control limits are obtained by computing

$$3\hat{\sigma}_p = 3 \sqrt{\frac{p'(1 - p')}{n}}$$

and

$$UCL_p = p' + 3\hat{\sigma}_p \quad \text{......................(9.33)}$$
$$LCL_p = p' - 3\hat{\sigma}_p \quad \text{......................(9.34)}$$

These control limits denote the tolerable range of random variation. A proportion that falls beyond these limits is assumed to be the result of an assignable cause of variation.

➤ *Example.* Samples of 100 transistors are drawn randomly from the output of a process that produces several thousand units daily. Sampled items are inspected for quality, and faulty transistors are rejected. The results of a series of samples are shown in Table 9.7. The estimated process proportion of defective items and the estimated standard error of the proportion are computed as follows:

$$p' = \frac{220}{2,000}$$

$$= 0.11$$

and

$$\hat{\sigma}_p = \sqrt{\frac{(0.11)(0.89)}{100}}$$

$$= 0.0314.$$

Table 9.7

SAMPLE RESULTS OF 20 LOTS OF 100 TRANSISTORS
DRAWN FROM THE OUTPUT OF A PROCESS

Lot number	Number inspected	Number defective	Fraction defective
1	100	9	0.09
2	100	17	0.17
3	100	8	0.08
4	100	7	0.07
5	100	12	0.12
6	100	5	0.05
7	100	11	0.11
8	100	16	0.16
9	100	14	0.14
10	100	15	0.15
11	100	10	0.10
12	100	6	0.06
13	100	7	0.07
14	100	18	0.18
15	100	16	0.16
16	100	10	0.10
17	100	5	0.05
18	100	14	0.14
19	100	7	0.07
20	100	13	0.13
Totals	2,000	220	

The control limits of a p chart for the data are found as follows:

$$UCL_p = p' + 3\hat{\sigma}_p$$
$$= 0.11 + (3)(0.0314)$$
$$= 0.21$$

and

$$LCL_p = p' - 3\hat{\sigma}_p$$
$$= 0.11 - (3)(0.0314)$$
$$= 0.02.$$

None of the sample proportions lies outside the control limits, as shown in Figure 9.15. The process is apparently stable statistically, reflecting only random variations.

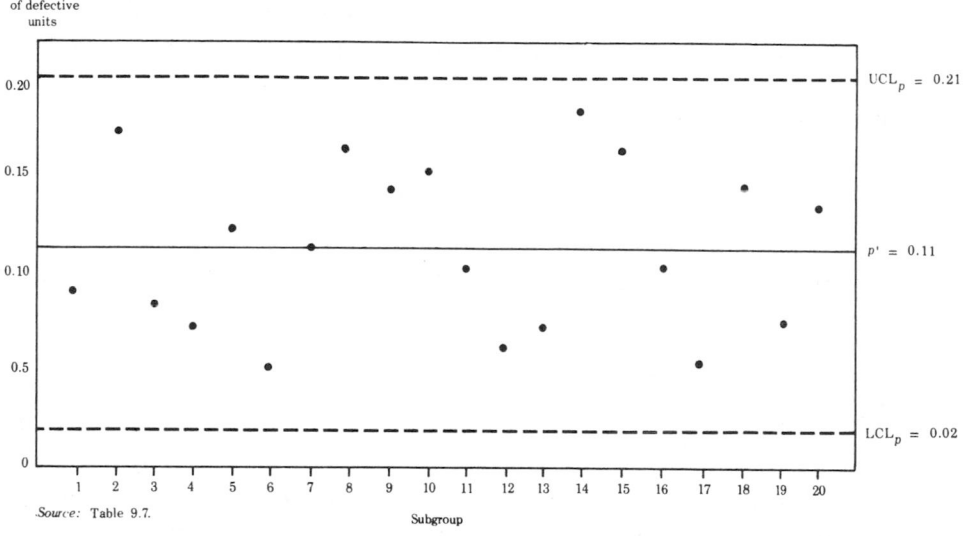

Figure 9.15

CONTROL CHART FOR FRACTION DEFECTIVE IN SAMPLES DRAWN FROM
THE OUTPUT OF A MACHINE

A control chart for fraction defective may also be constructed for lots of various sizes. The value of $\hat{\sigma}_p$ varies with the sample size; consequently, the control limits are shown as broken lines. These lines are symmetric about the center line p'. The method for computing p' is the same as described in the foregoing example. The control limits deviate from the center line so that the smaller the lot size, the greater the deviation. The amount of computation required for unequal lot sizes is increased somewhat, for a different value for $\hat{\sigma}_p$ must be computed for each lot size sampled.

Control Charts for Number of Defects. A control chart for fraction defective is useful for monitoring the quality of units produced by a Bernoulli process. There are applications, however, in which an item may fail to meet specifications in several respects. For example, a length of steel cable may be inspected for flaws and defects may be found in several different places. For this class of quality control problem, the Poisson rather than the binomial distribution is the appropriate theoretical basis. A control chart based on the Poisson distribution is called a *control chart for defects* or *c chart*.

A *defect* is defined as a success obtained in a trial from a Poisson process. It may also be viewed as the failure of a unit to meet specifications in any one of many possible locations. A single unit may contain any number of defects, and the unit may not necessarily be rejected even if one or more defects is present.

The expected number of defects per unit is denoted in the literature of statistical quality control by $\bar{c}$. This quantity corresponds to the value of λ, the mean of a Poisson process. The standard deviation of the process is denoted

$$\sigma_c = \sqrt{\bar{c}},$$

which is an alternative notation for the standard deviation of a Poisson distribution. The $3\sigma_c$ control limits of a *c* chart are obtained by computing

$$UCL_{\bar{c}} = \bar{c} + 3\sigma_c \quad\text{...........................(9.35)}$$

and

$$LCL_{\bar{c}} = \bar{c} - 3\sigma_c \quad\text{...........................(9.36)}$$

➤ *Example.* A final inspection is conducted to check for proper adjustment of card readers produced by a computer manufacturer. Inspection records indicate that defects in each of the adjustments of the card reader mechanism occur in a Poisson distributed manner. The total number of defects per card reader, the sum of several Poisson processes, is itself a Poisson process. The results of the inspection of 20 card readers are listed in Table 9.8. The average number of defects per unit is computed

$$\bar{c} = \frac{90}{20} = 4.5.$$

The standard deviation of the number of defects per unit is computed

$$\sigma_c = \sqrt{\bar{c}} = \sqrt{4.5} = 2.1.$$

Table 9.8

DEFECTS OBSERVED IN THE FINAL INSPECTION
OF CARD READERS

Card reader number	Number of observed defects
1	4
2	1
3	2
4	3
5	8
6	5
7	4
8	5
9	2
10	6
11	4
12	10
13	4
14	7
15	3
16	2
17	2
18	9
19	3
20	6
Total	90

The control limits for the number of defects per unit are computed

$$UCL_c = \bar{c} + 3\sigma_c$$
$$= 4.5 + (3)(2.1)$$
$$= 4.5 + 6.3$$
$$= 10.8$$

and

$$LCL_c = \bar{c} - 3\sigma_c$$
$$= 4.5 - 3(2.1)$$
$$= 4.5 - 6.3$$
$$= 0.$$

The lower control limit is zero, for a negative number of defects cannot occur. The observed number of defects in card readers inspected exhibit statistical stability, for none of the observed values lies beyond the control limits as shown by Figure 9.16.

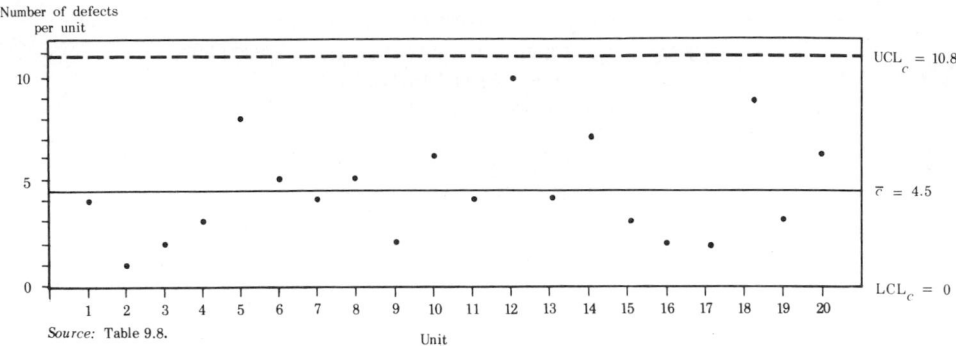

Source: Table 9.8.   Unit

Figure 9.16

CONTROL CHART FOR NUMBER OF DEFECTS PER UNIT FOR 20 SAMPLED
CARD READERS

The use of c charts is not limited to manufacturing problems, for the control chart may be applied to any phenomena that may be described as a Poisson process.

TECHNICAL NOTE NO. 1: *Verification of the Central Limit Theorem*

Consider the values of $x_1, x_2, \ldots, x_n$ as equiprobable elements of a random sample. For these values

$$E(x_i) = \mu,$$

and the mean is

$$\bar{x} = \frac{x_1 + x_2 + \ldots + x_n}{n}.$$

If the elements are independent and have a standard deviation σ, the expected value of a sample mean is

$$E(\bar{x}) = \sum_1^n \frac{1}{n} E(x_i).$$

Factoring out the constant term $\frac{1}{n}$ and substituting $E(x_i) = \mu$, then

$$E(\bar{x}) = \frac{1}{n} \sum_1^n \mu = \frac{n\mu}{n},$$

and

$$E(\bar{x}) = \mu.$$

The deviation of a sample mean from the universe mean is

$$\bar{x} - \mu = \frac{x_1 + x_2 + \ldots + x_n}{n} - \mu$$

$$= \frac{x_1 + x_2 + \ldots + x_n - n\mu}{n}$$

$$= \frac{1}{n} \sum_1^n (x_i - \mu).$$

The variance of sample means is derived by solving for the expected value of squared deviations of the sample means. This is written

$$\text{var}(\bar{x}) = \text{var}\left(\frac{x_1 + x_2 + \ldots + x_n}{n}\right)$$

$$= E\left[\left(\frac{x_1 + x_2 + \ldots + x_n - n\mu}{n}\right)^2\right]$$

$$= E\left[\frac{1}{n^2}(x_1 + x_2 + \ldots + x_n - n\mu)^2\right].$$

Factoring out the constant $\frac{1}{n^2}$ and summing the x values give

$$\text{var}(\bar{x}) = \frac{1}{n^2} E\left[\sum_1^n (x_i - \mu)^2\right],$$

which may also be written

$$\text{var}(\bar{x}) = \frac{1}{n^2} \sum_1^n E(x_i - \mu)^2$$

$$= \frac{1}{n^2} \cdot n\sigma^2$$

$$= \frac{\sigma^2}{n}.$$

TECHNICAL NOTE NO. 2: *Deriviation of a Maximum Likelihood Estimator*

If a sample of n items is drawn and it includes r successes, the likelihood function of θ may be written

$$L = \binom{n}{r} \theta^r (1 - \theta)^{n-r}.$$

The objective is the determination of the value of θ for which L, the "probability density of θ," is a maximum. If the likelihood function is expressed in terms of logarithms, the method of finding the maximum is simplified. Taking the logarithm of both sides of the equation gives

$$\log L = \log \binom{n}{r} + r\log\theta + (n - r) \log (1 - \theta).$$

The maximum value of L is found by noting the change in L with each change in θ. An example of this relationship is seen in Figure 9.16, in which the value of L is a maximum for a value of $\theta = \theta_1$.

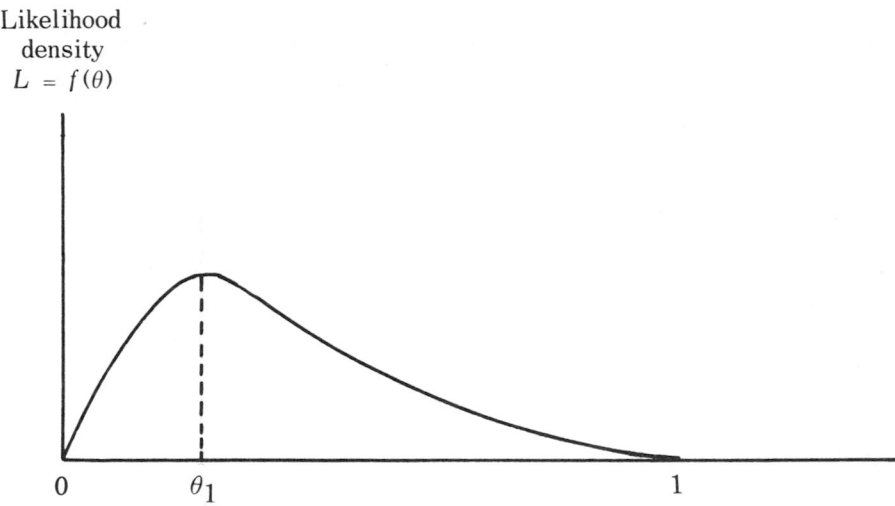

Likelihood
density
$L = f(\theta)$

0   θ_1 1

Value of the parameter θ

Figure 9.16
LIKELIHOOD (PROBABILITY) DENSITY OF THE PARAMETER θ

The mode of θ occurs at the value θ_1. If lines tangent to the curve $L = f(\theta)$ were drawn for all values of $0 < \theta < 1$, the line tangent to the curve at θ_1 would be horizontal and have a slope of zero. At this point the change in L with respect to θ is zero, and in this case indicates that L has reached a maximum. By means of calculus, an expression can be derived for determining the value of θ for which L achieves its greatest value. Maximizing L with respect to θ gives

$$\frac{d(\log L)}{d\theta} = \frac{r}{\theta} = \frac{n - r}{1 - \theta}.$$

This is an expression for the slope of $L = f(\theta)$. Since L is a maximum when the slope of a tangent to the curve is zero, the right-hand side of the equality above can be equated to zero. Setting the term equal to zero and solving for θ gives

$$\frac{r}{\theta} - \frac{n-r}{1-\theta} = 0$$

and

$$\frac{r}{n} = \theta.$$

The maximum likelihood estimator of θ is $\dfrac{r}{n}$. Since $\theta = p$ in this case,

the maximum likelihood estimator of π is the sample proportion $\dfrac{r}{n}$.

STUDY QUESTIONS

9-1. Explain briefly the meaning of each of the following terms:

a. simple random sample
b. random numbers
c. middle-square method
d. Lehmer's method
e. Monte Carlo method
f. Tchebycheff's inequality
g. central limit theorem
h. standard error of the mean
i. standard error of the median
j. standard error of the standard deviation
k. standard error of a sample proportion
l. point estimate
m. interval estimate
n. maximum likelihood estimator
o. confidence interval
p. level of confidence
q. allowable error
r. finite multiplier
s. sampling fraction
t. assignable variation
u. random variation
v. control limits
w. control chart
x. control chart for sample means ($\bar{x}$ chart)
y. control chart for ranges (R chart)
z. attribute
aa. control chart for fraction defective (p chart)
bb. control chart for defects (c chart)
cc. defect

9-2. Describe the use of random numbers in sampling and simulation.

9-3. What inference can be made on the basis of Tchebycheff's inequality?

9-4. What are the characteristics of the distribution of sample means that make it significant to statistical inference?

9-5. Compare the distributions of sample means, sample medians, and sample standard deviations.

9-6. Why is it important to correct for bias in making estimates based on sample statistics?

9-7. What are the properties of good estimators?

9-8. Outline the procedure for estimating a universe mean if:

  a. the universe standard deviation is known.

  b. the universe standard deviation is unknown.

9-9. Why would a confidence interval of 95% rather than 100% be used in estimating a universe mean?

9-10. What information and assumptions must be given to compute the sample size for an interval estimate of the universe mean?

9-11. In what circumstances should the finite multiplier be used?

9-12. What is meant by statistical stability?

9-13. What is the theoretical basis for control charts for sample means? for sample ranges?

9-14. Contrast the characteristics of p charts and c charts.

PROBLEMS

9-1. Compute a sequence of six four-digit random numbers by the middle-square method. Initialize the computations with the number 4,635 as the first of the six-number sequence.

9-2. Compute a sequence of 10 four-digit random numbers by the middle-square method. Initialize the computations with the number 3,281 as the first of the 10-number sequence.

9-3. Generate a series of five random numbers of four digits each by use of Lehmer's method. Use the number 90583264 as the initial value for the first iteration. Select the middle four digits of the difference as the random number computed in each iteration.

9-4. Generate a series of six random numbers of four digits each by use of Lehmer's method. Use the number 14295168 as the initial value for the first iteration. Select the middle four digits of the difference as the random number computed in each iteration.

9-5. The distribution of arrivals of ships at a loading dock is shown as follows:

Number of ships arriving per day	Frequency
0	0.30
1	0.40
2	0.18
3	0.09
4	0.03
	1.00

Select random numbers from Appendix N and use the Monte Carlo method to simulate the arrival of ships for 25 days and estimate the average number of ships arriving per day from the simulated results.

9-6. The service times required to load ships at a dock are summarized by the following distribution:

Service time (days)	Frequency
0.0 and under 0.5	0.63
0.5 and under 1.0	0.27
1.0 and under 1.5	0.08
1.5 and under 2.0	0.02
	1.00

Select random numbers from Appendix N and use the Monte Carlo method to simulate the times required to service 25 ships and estimate the average service time from the simulated results.

9-7. A customer is selected at random from those customers being checked out in a supermarket. The amount of the purchase being made by the customer is computed by the clerk. What is the probability that the computed purchase differs by more than 1.5 standard deviations from the average purchase of all customers?

9-8. The arrivals of automobiles at a municipal parking facility are Poisson distributed with a mean arrival rate of 30 vehicles per 15-minute period. A 15-minute period is selected at random and a count of the number of arriving automobiles is made. What is the probability that the number of automobiles arriving in the period is within 2.5 standard deviations of the mean arrival rate?

9-9. A freight train makes a regular run between two major cities. Records indicate that the average time required to complete the trip is nine hours, with a standard deviation of 0.30 hours. If a sample of 36 times required to complete the trip is selected at random, what is the probability that the sample mean will be in the range from 8.91 hours to 9.02 hours?

9-10. A worker in a shoe factory can attach heels to a type of shoe on an average of 30 per hour, with a standard deviation of 3 heels per hour. If a sample of the production for 16 randomly selected hour periods is taken, what is the probability that the sample mean will be greater than 28 heels per hour?

9-11. A sample of dry-cell batteries is selected at random from the production of a process and the useful life of each battery is recorded (in hours) as follows: 27, 31, 29, 33, 28, 32. Compute an unbiased estimate of the universe standard deviation and the estimated standard error of the mean.

9-12. The total amount of time (in hours) that a worker is idle because of machine failure or lack of input material during a day is recorded for a random sample of 10 days. The results are as follows: 0.6, 1.2, 0.8, 1.5, 1.0, 0.9, 1.8, 0.5, 0.8, and 0.9. Compute an unbiased estimate of the universe standard deviation and an estimate of the standard error of the mean.

9-13. A random sample of 50 vehicle records is drawn from the files of an automobile insurance company. The records indicate that nine of the sampled vehicles were involved in a collision within the past year.
  a. Compute a point estimate of the universe proportion of vehicles involved in a collision in the period of a year.
  b. Compute the exact 95% confidence interval estimate of π.
  c. Compute a symmetric approximation of the confidence interval in (b) above.

9-14. Solve Problem 9-13 in terms of a universe percent.

9-15. A new machine is installed in a manufacturing plant and is operated for the first time. A sample of 45 items of the initial output is taken randomly. The sample consists of observations of the diameter of cylindrical metal rods. The sample average is 1.020 inches, and the standard deviation is 0.030 inches.
  a. What is the point estimate of the universe mean diameter?
  b. Find the 98% confidence interval estimate of the universe mean.
  c. Compute the 95% one-sided interval estimate of the upper range of the universe diameter.

9-16. A new machine (see Problem 9-15) is operated for the first time and management wishes to obtain a 98% confidence interval estimate of the universe mean with upper and lower limits that differ by 0.010 inches. How large a sample should be selected?

9-17. A marketing research department wishes to estimate the useful life of automobile tires in terms of miles driven. It is estimated that 50% of the tires have a useful life that ranges from 18,000 to 20,000 miles. If useful life (miles) is distributed normally, how large a sample should be taken to estimate average useful life so that the probability is 95% that the universe mean does not differ from the sample mean by more than 500 miles?

9-18. A study is made to estimate the average length of calls made from a telephone booth in an airline terminal. The mean call length is to be estimated within 0.25 minutes with a level of confidence of 98%. Past studies show the standard deviation of call lengths to be approximately 0.80 minutes. If call lengths are distributed normally, what size sample should be taken?

9-19. An insurance firm estimates that 15% of passengers purchase flight insurance in a particular airline terminal. An estimate of the true proportion of passengers who purchase flight insurance is to be computed so that the estimated proportion will differ from the universe proportion by no more than 0.02 with a level of confidence of 95%. Compute the sample size required.

9-20. A meat packing firm wishes to determine the proportion of customers who purchase a new brand of dog food distributed by the firm. The estimate is to be computed so that the probability is 98% that the estimate will differ by no more than 0.05 from the universe proportion. What sample size should be used in making the estimate?

9-21. The average time in days required to process orders received by a metal fabrication company is to be estimated. A sample of 50 orders is selected randomly from a total of 375 orders processed over a period of six months. The sample mean is 5.4 days with a standard deviation of 1.4 days. Compute the 95% interval estimate of the average processing time.

9-22. The maintenance records of digital computers leased to customers by a manufacturer are analyzed to determine the frequency of service calls that involve failures in the input-output equipment. A random sample of 60 calls is drawn from a total of 420 calls recorded over a period of a month. Twenty-four of the sampled service calls involved failures in input-output equipment. Compute the 95% confidence interval estimate of the universe percent.

9-23. A machine fills boxes with dry cereal. Samples of four boxes are drawn randomly. The total weights of the sampled boxes are shown as follows:

Subgroup	Sample values			
1	11.02	10.81	10.94	11.07
2	10.98	11.21	11.04	11.26
3	11.04	10.79	10.92	11.01
4	10.97	11.31	11.27	11.25
5	11.15	10.97	10.89	10.91
6	11.34	11.18	11.36	11.40
7	10.87	11.17	10.93	11.03
8	10.82	10.76	11.01	10.85
9	11.60	11.48	11.56	11.52
10	11.43	11.15	11.14	11.56
11	10.54	10.81	10.91	10.78
12	11.59	11.74	11.68	11.95
13	11.23	11.19	11.02	11.04
14	11.67	11.54	11.63	11.60
15	11.72	11.41	11.61	11.46
16	10.81	11.17	11.02	11.08
17	11.24	11.19	11.27	11.34
18	11.23	11.14	11.15	11.12
19	11.45	11.71	11.58	11.82
20	11.47	11.32	11.33	11.60

Draw a control chart for sample means and determine whether the process exhibits statistical stability.

9-24. A chemical plant produces a plastic material in bulk. Periodically, samples of the plastic material are drawn to monitor the hardness of the material. The tolerance limits for mean hardness are 55 ± 6 hardness units. The results of samples drawn from the process are listed as follows:

Subgroup	Sample values				
1	60.5	55.4	51.2	59.8	56.7
2	71.2	57.3	64.7	50.3	54.4
3	58.1	50.4	55.4	52.7	60.9
4	48.2	54.1	46.2	56.8	58.9
5	47.3	59.7	55.0	48.4	49.6
6	53.7	46.3	57.5	52.0	55.7
7	57.8	56.4	59.6	61.2	54.5
8	62.3	57.2	58.8	50.4	59.7
9	45.8	56.1	52.3	52.2	51.1
10	54.1	42.6	50.1	47.6	43.3
11	63.4	52.1	54.9	49.7	64.9
12	58.7	57.2	53.6	54.3	56.7
13	55.0	48.6	57.4	54.6	55.4
14	53.6	48.2	50.2	50.3	57.2
15	51.2	54.9	57.4	55.3	56.2

Draw a control chart for sample means and determine if the process exhibits statistical stability.

9-25. Draw a control chart for sample ranges using the data of Problem 9-23 and determine if the process appears to be in control.

9-26. Draw a control chart for sample ranges using the data of Problem 9-24 and determine if the process appears to be in control.

9-27. Ten lots or samples of 200 items each were drawn from the output of a process. The number of defective units in each sample are listed as follows:

Lot number	Number of units inspected	Number of defective units
1	200	10
2	200	7
3	200	4
4	200	13
5	200	9
6	200	3
7	200	8
8	200	6
9	200	9
10	200	11

Draw a control chart for fraction defective and give an interpretation of the results.

9-28. A multiple-spindle milling machine is installed in a plant and lots or samples of 150 items each are drawn randomly to monitor the output. The number of items per sample that fail to meet specifications are listed as follows:

Lot number	Number of units inspected	Number of defective units
1	150	9
2	150	17
3	150	27
4	150	20
5	150	15
6	150	17
7	150	14
8	150	18
9	150	23
10	150	20

Draw a *p* chart for the data and give an interpretation of the results.

9-29. A plant produces paper for newsprint, and rolls of paper are inspected for defects. The results of the inspections for 20 rolls of paper are listed in the following table.

Roll number	Number of defects
1	12
2	6
3	18
4	4
5	5
6	9
7	4
8	1
9	12
10	14
11	10
12	8
13	11
14	14
15	21
16	12
17	9
18	13
19	10
20	7

Draw a control chart for defects and determine whether the inspection results indicate statistical stability.

9-30. Manual calculators are given a final inspection in a manufacturing plant. The number of defects observed during the inspection of 15 units are listed in the table on the next page.

Unit number	Number of defects
1	1
2	7
3	2
4	3
5	0
6	4
7	9
8	6
9	3
10	4
11	1
12	5
13	4
14	5
15	6

Draw a control chart for defects and determine whether the inspection results indicate statistical stability.

SELECTED READINGS

Bryant, Edward C. *Statistical Analysis.* 2d ed. New York: McGraw-Hill Book Company, Inc., 1966.

Sampling and estimation are related to probability and the normal distribution in Chapter 4.

Grant, Eugene L. *Statistical Quality Control.* 3d ed. New York: McGraw-Hill Book Company, Inc., 1964.

A thorough development of control charts is presented in Chapters 3 through 12.

McMillan, Claude, and Richard F. Gonzalez. *Systems Analysis.* Homewood, Illinois: Richard D. Irwin, Inc., 1965.

Techniques of generating random numbers for Monte Carlo simulation are presented in Chapter 8.

Chapter 10

Sample Design

INTRODUCTION

The previous chapter on sample distributions and estimation was concerned with the theory of what happens when simple random samples are drawn from either finite or infinite populations. It was assumed that the samples were large in every case. This chapter is devoted to some of the more practical problems involved in the application of sample theory to sample surveys, including the problems involved in using small samples.

Before discussing the problems involved in sample design, it is first appropriate to review a few basic sampling principles laid down in Chapter 9 and to define some additional terms that will be needed.

All sampling described previously has been simple random sampling in which each item in the universe has an equiprobable chance of being selected as a member of the sample. There are two distinct advantages to this type of sampling:

1. Probability theory can be used to measure the precision of sample results.
2. Bias which might otherwise result from the exercise of personal judgment in the selection of sample items may be avoided.

Precision and Accuracy

The term *precision* of sample results refers to the difference between a sample result and the result of a complete census taken under the same circumstances. This difference is called *sampling error*. In each case sampling error is measured by some type of standard error, i.e., standard error of the mean, standard error of a percent, or standard error of the median.

The difference between the sample result and the true state of the universe is called the *accuracy* of the sample result. This difference may include other types of error besides sampling error. For example, the difference may be caused by a clerical error, a computational error, or an incorrect answer to an unclear question used on a survey. Non-sampling error obviously can occur while completing a census as well as while taking a sample.

While it is the accuracy of the survey results with which the business-man is most concerned, it is the precision of the survey results that the statistician is able to measure. And he can measure the precision of the sample only if proper methods of random selection are used.

Definition of the Population

In Chapter 1 a population, or a universe, was defined as each and every member of some group. Once the population has been defined carefully, the sample must be drawn from that population and no other. Further, the sample statistic may be used to estimate a parameter of the population from which the sample was drawn and no other.

➤ *Example.* Suppose a state highway department establishes tourist information offices on its borders to give travel information to out-of-state visitors who stop to inquire for help. A sample of the visitors who stop at the offices are asked to estimate the number of nights they will stay in the state, and an average number of nights per tourist is computed from their answers. Can this sample statistic be used to estimate the average number of nights all tourists will stay in the state? The answer is, "no." The reason can be seen below:

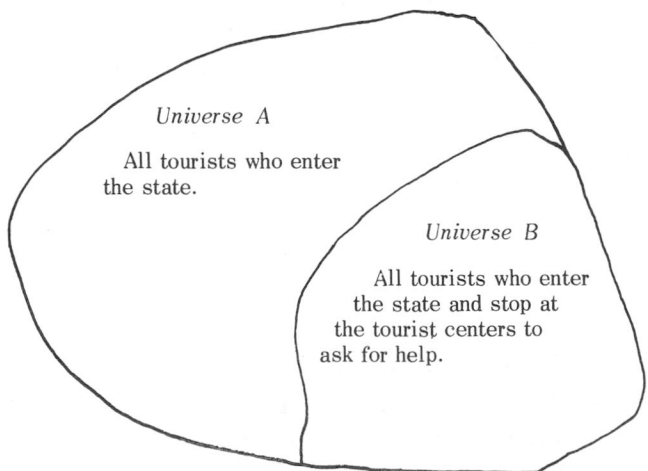

Since the sample was drawn from Universe *B*, the statistic can be used only to estimate the parameter of *B*, not *A*. It is quite possible that the characteristics of Universe *A* are different from those of Universe *B*. The tourists who stop to ask for help may not be typical of those who do not stop.

Arbitrary Sampling

As a practical matter, not all sampling is done on the basis of random selection. There are other types of samples variously called *judgment samples, representative samples, quota samples,* and *purposive samples.* These samples all involve *arbitrary selection.* For example, a survey firm interested in predicting how the electorate will vote in a state election might send out interviewers with instructions to interview a sample of voters with certain specified characteristics such as age, sex, income, and political registration. The purpose of the survey is to get a sample that is "representative" or "typical" of the universe. The design of the sample may be made with meticulous care, following the proportions of each characteristic in the universe as shown by a recent census. As a matter of fact, the sample results may be very accurate. The difficulty with this type of sample, however, lies in the fact that no measure of sampling error can be computed irrespective of the sampling technique used. Consequently, there is absolutely no way of evaluating the reliability of estimates based on samples that are arbitrarily selected.

Some Problems in Simple Random Sampling

While the concept of pure (or simple) random sampling is quite readily understood, its execution is often difficult or extremely expensive. A random sample of lottery tickets can be drawn easily from a drum which has been revolved to be sure that the tickets are thoroughly mixed, but it is not possible to treat housewives or personnel folders in this manner to get a random sample. A table of random numbers may be used to select a random sample if each item in the universe has, or can be assigned, a number; but this is not always possible.

In order to be sure that each item in the universe has an equal chance of selection, one needs a list or a *frame* from which to draw the sample. If a sample of households is being drawn from all of those in a large city, there may be no frame available. The universe may be defined as all the households within the city limits so that the survey team knows where the items in the universe are, but it does not know who they are. Any attempt to draw up a frame would be both difficult and very expensive. Families move in and out so rapidly that no list would ever be completely accurate. An approach to this problem will be discussed later in this chapter under the heading, "Cluster Sampling."

Quite frequently it is possible to overcome some of the difficulty and the cost of a pure random sample by using a systematic selection procedure by which every k^{th} item is selected from an ordered universe. This might be every 100th item on an assembly line, every 50th customer entering the main entrance of a department store, or every 250th card in a file of punched cards. If the first unit of the sample is selected at random, then theoretically every item has the same likelihood of selection even though all combinations of items are not possible of selection. Such samples are called *systematic random samples* and are generally considered to be quite acceptable as long as there is no cyclical or periodic pattern in the universe that might coincide with the size of k.

The amount of dispersion of the items in the universe has a great deal to do with the size of the sample required to provide a needed precision of the sample results. Populations of economic data are often highly heterogeneous, thus requiring a pure random sample of immense size and cost. Problems of this nature require special techniques that will be discussed in this chapter under the heading, "Stratified Sampling."

SMALL SAMPLES AND STUDENT'S t DISTRIBUTION

It was pointed out in Chapter 9 that if a universe has a mean, μ, and a standard deviation, σ, the distribution of sample means approaches a normal distribution with a mean, μ, and a standard deviation, $\dfrac{\sigma}{\sqrt{n}}$, as the sample size increases. This was called the central limit theorem. The distribution of sample means can be standardized by the transformation

$$z = \frac{\bar{x} - \mu}{\dfrac{\sigma}{\sqrt{n}}} \quad \dots\dots\dots\dots\dots\dots\dots\dots\dots(10.1)$$

The statistic, z, is normally distributed with a mean of 0 and a standard deviation of 1. The purpose of this transformation is to make it possible to determine areas of an infinite number of normal distributions using only one table of area under the normal curve (Appendix H or I).

Student's t Distribution

In order to compute the statistic, z, one must know the standard deviation of the universe. Usually σ is not known. In most sampling situations the investigator has only the sample mean and the sample standard deviation with which to work. In such an instance, the statistic that is used in place of z in problems involving both estimation and tests of significance is

$$t = \frac{\bar{x} - \mu}{\dfrac{s}{\sqrt{n-1}}} \quad \dots\dots\dots\dots\dots\dots\dots\text{(10.2)}$$

where $\dfrac{s}{\sqrt{n-1}} = \dfrac{\hat{\sigma}}{\sqrt{n}} = \hat{\sigma}_{\bar{x}}$ is the *estimated standard error of the mean.*

This distribution is called *Student's t distribution* after the pen name of "Student," used by W. S. Gosset, who published the pioneer work in this field in 1908.

The *t* distribution, shown in Figure 10.1, is a symmetrical distribution but slightly more scattered than the *z* or normal distribution. Unlike the normal distribution, the *t* distribution changes shape slightly with the size of the sample. More precisely, it changes shape with the number of *degrees of freedom.* In this case degrees of freedom will be defined as sample size minus one ($n - 1$). This definition will not hold in all instances, however, and will be redefined from time to time as the need arises. For an abbreviation for degrees of freedom, "*d.f.*" will be used.

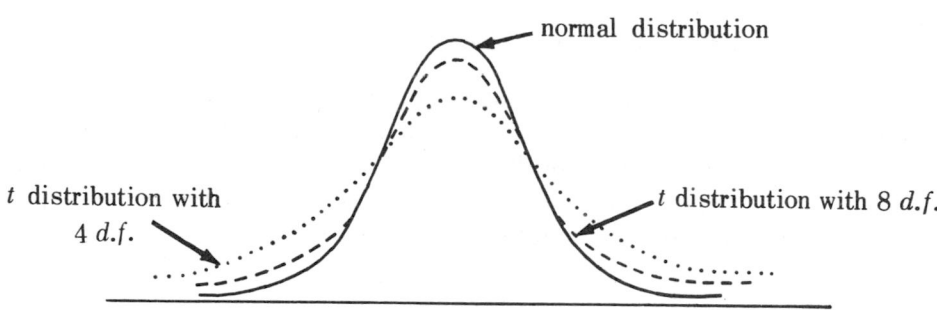

normal distribution

t distribution with 4 *d.f.*

t distribution with 8 *d.f.*

Figure 10.1

SHAPE OF STUDENT'S *t* DISTRIBUTION

As the number of degrees of freedom increases, the *t* distribution becomes asymptotic to normal. This explains why the normal distribution is used in sampling distributions when the sample size is large, even though the universe standard deviation is not known.

Because the *t* distribution has many different shapes, it is not practical to tabulate the entire distribution as is done for the normal distribution. This would require many tables of *t* values. Instead, only those values of *t* that give certain specified areas in the two tails are shown in the table in Appendix J.

➤ **Example.** Suppose one wishes to find the value of $\pm t$ which leaves 5% of the total area of the distribution in the two tails when the sample size is 21. Since $n = 21$, $d.f. = 20$, and the appropriate column in the t table in Appendix J is 0.05:

$$t_{0.05} \ (20 \ d.f.) = \pm 2.086.$$

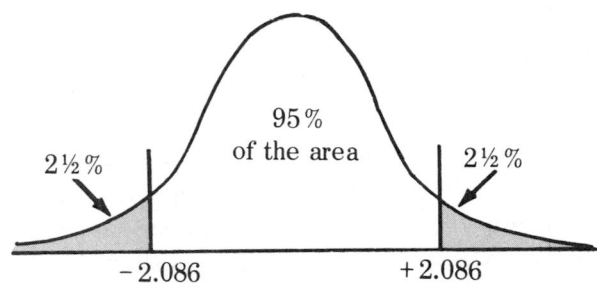

For more than 120 degrees of freedom, the table values of t are the same as the comparable value of z. For example,

$$z_{\alpha=0.05} = t_{\alpha=0.05}(\infty \ d.f.) = \pm 1.96.$$

Interval Estimates for Means, Small Samples

In the previous example it was shown that 5% of the area of the t distribution lies outside $\pm t_{0.05}$ and that 95% of the area lies between $\pm t_{0.05}$. This can be stated another way. There is a 95% probability that any t value computed from a random sample will fall between $\pm t_{0.05}$. This can be expressed as the following inequality:

$$-t_{0.05} \leq t \leq + t_{0.05}.$$

Substituting Formula 10.2 for t in the above,

$$-t_{0.05} \leq \frac{\bar{x} - \mu}{\hat{\sigma}_{\bar{x}}} \leq + t_{0.05} \quad \text{or}$$

$$\bar{x} - t_{0.05}\hat{\sigma}_{\bar{x}} \leq \mu \leq \bar{x} + t_{0.05}\hat{\sigma}_{\bar{x}}.$$

This may be written in a more general form to give an interval estimate of μ as

$$\bar{x} - t_{\alpha}\hat{\sigma}_{\bar{x}} \leq \mu \leq \bar{x} + t_{\alpha}\hat{\sigma}_{\bar{x}}. \quad \ldots\ldots\ldots\ldots\ldots(10.3)$$

where
   t is expressed in units of the estimated standard error of the mean, and α is the probability that μ will exceed the limits of the interval.

➤ *Example.* Suppose a quality control engineer wishes to estimate the average strength of a particular part being manufactured for an assembly operation. His measure is in terms of pounds per square inch (psi) that can be resisted before the part breaks. Because destructive sampling is costly, the engineer uses a small sample of eight parts. He also decides on an $\alpha = 0.01$. The results of the sample are:

$$\bar{x} = 254 \text{ psi} \qquad\qquad n = 8 \text{ parts}$$
$$s = 24 \text{ psi} \qquad\qquad t_{0.01}(7 \text{ d.f.}) = \pm 3.499.$$

Then $\qquad \hat{\sigma}_{\bar{x}} = \dfrac{s}{\sqrt{n-1}} = \dfrac{24}{\sqrt{7}} = 9.07 \quad$ and

$$254 - 3.499(9.07) \leq \mu \leq 254 + 3.499(9.07).$$

It may be stated that there is a 99% probability that μ is not less than 222.3 psi nor greater than 285.7 psi. This may give the engineer all the information he needs, in spite of the fact a very small sample was used.

Finite Populations

It has already been pointed out that in sampling problems dealing with finite populations, an additional refinement is necessary. This is particularly true if the sampling fraction, f, $\left(\text{which is } \dfrac{n}{N}\right)$ is equal to or greater than 5%. In those cases where the sampling fraction is large, the estimated standard error of the mean can be computed using Formula 9.25:

$$\hat{\sigma}_{\bar{x}} = \frac{s}{\sqrt{n-1}}\sqrt{1-f}$$

or it may be written

$$\hat{\sigma}_{\bar{x}} = \frac{\hat{\sigma}}{\sqrt{n}}\sqrt{1-f} \quad\dots\dots\dots\dots\dots\dots\dots\dots(10.4)$$

where $\hat{\sigma} = s\sqrt{\dfrac{n}{n-1}}$ is an unbiased estimate of σ.

➤ *Example.* If, in the previous example, the universe consists of only 50 parts of which eight have been tested for strength, then

$$\hat{\sigma}_{\bar{x}} = \frac{24}{\sqrt{7}}\sqrt{1-\frac{8}{50}} = 9.07(0.92) = 8.34.$$

There is a 99% probability that μ will not be less than 224.82 psi nor greater than 283.18 psi.

INCREASING THE EFFICIENCY OF SAMPLE DESIGN

A discussion of the problems involved in increasing the efficiency of sample design requires both a definition of what is meant by sample design and what is meant by increased efficiency. A *sample design* is a plan for securing a sample from a given universe. This planning takes place before any move is made to secure any sample data, and it involves such considerations as cost, sample size, precision requirements, and the way in which the sample is to be secured.

One sample design is said to be more *efficient* than another when it:

1. Produces a smaller standard error with the same size sample, or
2. Produces the same standard error with a smaller size sample.

Discussions on simple random sampling have shown that the magnitude of the standard error can be reduced in a given sampling distribution only by increasing the size of the sample. It can be demonstrated with an example that if the sample is drawn in a particular way from the universe, the resulting standard error can be reduced without using a larger sample. In other words, by drawing a sample in a particular way and under certain conditions, a more efficient sample can be drawn than is possible with a pure random sample. It should be carefully noted that while the number of possible samples of a given size that can be drawn is reduced by the new sample design, each sample which may be drawn is still a random sample and thus its standard error may be estimated.

➤ *Example.* Listed below is a hypothetical universe of seven items. The universe mean and the standard deviation have been computed and are also shown.

Item	Value	Parameters
A	5	
B	15	$\mu = 9$
C	4	$\sigma^2 = 28$
D	16	$\sigma \cong 5.29$
E	3	
F	6	
G	14	

If all possible simple random samples of $n = 4$ are drawn from this universe of $N = 7$, there are

$$_N C_n = {_7}C_4 = 35 \text{ possible samples.}$$

Table 10.1 shows the 35 samples, the 35 possible values of $\bar{x}$, and the standard error of the mean, which is a measure of how much, on the average, $\bar{x}$ varies from μ.

Table 10.1

ALL POSSIBLE SIMPLE RANDOM SAMPLES OF SIZE FOUR THAT
MIGHT BE DRAWN FROM A UNIVERSE OF SEVEN ITEMS

Samples	Values	Totals	$\bar{x}$ Means	$\bar{x} - \bar{\bar{x}}$	$(\bar{x} - \bar{\bar{x}})^2$
ABCD	5, 15, 4, 16	40	10.00	1.00	1.0000
ABCE	5, 15, 4, 3	27	6.75	−2.25	5.0625
ABCF	5, 15, 4, 6	30	7.50	−1.50	2.2500
ABCG	5, 15, 4, 14	38	9.50	0.50	0.2500
ABDE	5, 15, 16, 3	39	9.75	0.75	0.5625
ABDF	5, 15, 16, 6	42	10.50	1.50	2.2500
ABDG	5, 15, 16, 14	50	12.50	3.50	12.2500
ABEF	5, 15, 3, 6	29	7.25	−1.75	3.0625
ABEG	5, 15, 3, 14	37	9.25	0.25	0.0625
ABFG	5, 15, 6, 14	40	10.00	1.00	1.0000
ACDE	5, 4, 16, 3	28	7.00	−2.00	4.0000
ACDF	5, 4, 16, 6	31	7.75	−1.25	1.5625
ACDG	5, 4, 16, 14	39	9.75	0.75	0.5625
ACEF	5, 4, 3, 6	18	4.50	−4.50	20.2500
ACEG	5, 4, 3, 14	26	6.50	−2.50	6.2500
ACFG	5, 4, 6, 14	29	7.25	−1.75	3.0625
ADEF	5, 16, 3, 6	30	7.50	−1.50	2.2500
ADEG	5, 16, 3, 14	38	9.50	0.50	0.2500
ADFG	5, 16, 6, 14	41	10.25	1.25	1.5625
AEFG	5, 3, 6, 14	28	7.00	−2.00	4.0000
BCDE	15, 4, 16, 3	38	9.50	0.50	0.2500
BCDF	15, 4, 16, 6	41	10.25	1.25	1.5625
BCDG	15, 4, 16, 14	49	12.25	3.25	10.5625
BCEF	15, 4, 3, 6	28	7.00	−2.00	4.0000
BCEG	15, 4, 3, 14	36	9.00	0	0
BCFG	15, 4, 6, 14	39	9.75	0.75	0.5625
BDEF	15, 16, 3, 6	40	10.00	1.00	1.0000
BDEG	15, 16, 3, 14	48	12.00	3.00	9.0000
BDFG	15, 16, 6, 14	51	12.75	3.75	14.0625
BEFG	15, 3, 6, 14	38	9.50	0.50	0.2500
CDEF	4, 16, 3, 6	29	7.25	−1.75	3.0625
CDEG	4, 16, 3, 14	37	9.25	0.25	0.0625
CDFG	4, 16, 6, 14	40	10.00	1.00	1.0000
CEFG	4, 3, 6, 14	27	6.75	−2.25	5.0625
DEFG	16, 3, 6, 14	39	9.75	0.75	0.5625
	Totals		315.00	0	122.5000

$$\bar{\bar{x}} = \frac{315.00}{35} = 9 = \mu \qquad \sigma_{\bar{x}} = \sqrt{\frac{\Sigma(\bar{x} - \bar{\bar{x}})^2}{{}_N C_n}} = \sqrt{\frac{122.500}{35}}$$

$$= \sqrt{3.5} = 1.87.$$

The standard error of the mean may also be computed as

$$\sigma_{\bar{x}}^2 = \frac{\sigma^2}{n} \cdot \frac{N-n}{N-1} = \frac{28}{4} \cdot \frac{7-4}{7-1} = 3.5$$

$$\sigma_{\bar{x}} = \sqrt{3.5} = 1.87.$$

An examination of the size of the items in the universe shows two distinct groups:

Group	Individuals	Amounts	Totals
I	A, C, E, F	5, 4, 3, 6	18
II	B, D, G	15, 16, 14	45

If, again, all possible samples of $n = 4$ are drawn from this universe of $N = 7$, but with the additional restriction that two of the items in each sample must be drawn from each group, it is possible to have

$$(_4C_2)(_3C_2) = 6 \times 3 = 18 \text{ samples.}$$

Table 10.2 shows the 18 possible samples and the means of each. If the sample means are computed in the same way as those in Table 10.1 (an unweighted $\bar{x}$), the $\bar{\bar{x}} = 9.75 > \mu$. This makes $\bar{x}$ a biased estimate of μ. This is because the larger items in Group II are being given too much weight. This bias can be overcome by computing a weighted arithmetic mean

$$\bar{x} = \frac{\Sigma w_h x_h}{\Sigma w_h}$$

where

$$w_h = \frac{n_h}{N_h} = f_h, \text{ which is the sampling fraction from the } h^{\text{th}} \text{ group.}$$

When the sample means are computed as weighted arithmetic means, $\bar{\bar{x}} = \mu$, and $\bar{x}$ is again an unbiased estimate of μ.

Table 10.2 further shows the computation of the standard error of the mean, which is 0.42, as compared with 1.87 for simple random samples of size four drawn from this same universe. In other words, the standard error has been reduced without an increase in sample size but as a result of the way in which the sample was drawn.

The greater precision of the second sample design can be clearly shown in Table 10.3, which compares the precision of the two sampling methods used in the previous example.

Table 10.2

ALL POSSIBLE SAMPLES OF SIZE FOUR THAT MIGHT BE DRAWN
FROM A UNIVERSE OF SEVEN WHEN TWO SAMPLE ITEMS ARE
DRAWN FROM EACH OF TWO UNIVERSE GROUPS

Samples	Values	Unweighted means		Weighted means		$\bar{x} - \bar{\bar{x}}$	$(\bar{x} - \bar{\bar{x}})^2$
		Totals	Means $\bar{x}$	$\Sigma w_h x_h$	Means $\bar{x}$		
ACBD	5, 4, 15, 16	40	10.00	129	9.2	.2	.04
AEBD	5, 3, 15, 16	39	9.75	125	8.9	−.1	.01
AFBD	5, 6, 15, 16	42	10.50	137	9.8	.8	.64
CEBD	4, 3, 15, 16	38	9.50	121	8.6	−.4	.16
CFBD	4, 6, 15, 16	41	10.25	133	9.5	.5	.25
EFBD	3, 6, 15, 16	40	10.00	129	9.2	.2	.04
ACBG	5, 4, 15, 14	38	9.50	123	8.8	−.2	.04
AEBG	5, 3, 15, 14	37	9.25	119	8.5	−.5	.25
AFBG	5, 6, 15, 14	40	10.00	131	9.4	.4	.16
CEBG	4, 3, 15, 14	36	9.00	115	8.2	−.8	.64
CFBG	4, 6, 15, 14	39	9.75	127	9.1	.1	.01
EFBG	5, 4, 15, 14	38	9.50	123	8.8	−.2	.04
ACDG	5, 4, 16, 14	39	9.75	126	9.0	.0	.00
AEDG	5, 3, 16, 14	38	9.50	122	8.7	−.3	.09
AFDG	5, 6, 16, 14	41	10.25	134	9.6	.6	.36
CEDG	4, 3, 16, 14	37	9.25	118	8.4	−.6	.36
CFDG	4, 6, 16, 14	40	10.00	130	9.3	.3	.09
EFDG	3, 6, 16, 14	39	9.75	126	9.0	.0	.00
	Totals		175.50		162.00	0	3.18

Unweighted mean of the sample means:

$$\bar{\bar{x}} = \frac{175.50}{18} = 9.75 > \mu.$$

Mean of the weighted sample means:

$$\bar{\bar{x}} = \frac{162.0}{18} = 9 = \mu.$$

The standard error of the mean:

$$\sigma_{\bar{x}} = \sqrt{\frac{\Sigma(\bar{x} - \bar{\bar{x}})^2}{(_4C_2)(_3C_2)}} = \sqrt{\frac{3.18}{18}}$$
$$= \sqrt{0.1767} = 0.42.$$

Table 10.3

A COMPARISON OF THE PRECISION OF TWO SAMPLE DESIGNS

Error $\dfrac{\lvert \bar{x} - \mu \rvert}{\mu} \cdot 100$	Pure random samples		Random samples with two items from each group	
	Number of means	Percent of total	Number of means	Percent of total
Under 5%	3	8.6	12	66.7
5% but under 10%	8	22.9	6	33.3
10% but under 20%	13	37.1	0	0
20% and over	11	31.4	0	0
Totals	35	100.0	18	100.0

STRATIFIED SAMPLING

The stage was set for a discussion of stratified sampling in the previous section where it was shown that under certain circumstances one sample design may be more efficient than another. In fact, the example in which the universe was broken into two groups involved stratified sampling. *Stratification* represents an approach to sample design in which available information about the universe can be used to get greater precision from sample estimates.

The Nature of Stratified Sampling

Stratified sampling techniques are based upon the knowledge that a universe which is highly heterogeneous may be broken down into several groups or *strata* that are relatively homogeneous. A random sample of items is selected from each stratum, and these samples are then combined to form a single sample of the universe. The problem of determining the optimum number and type of stratum is one of the most difficult of all problems encountered in sampling and defies a unique solution.

➤ *Example.* If a researcher were interested in estimating the sales of manufacturers in Texas in 1967, he would be faced with a universe of some 10,500 firms making approximately 3,800 different classes of products. He would almost certainly need to make his estimate from a sample of these firms, and he could use as his frame the *Directory of Texas Manufacturers*, published by the Bureau of Business Research of The University of Texas. The listing in this book for each company gives no information on volume of sales, but it does show the employee-size group for each firm. It is logical to assume that a firm with a large number of employees will also have a large volume of sales, while a firm with few employees will have a smaller volume of sales. Thus, the universe of firms might be broken into strata on the basis of a known characteristic — employee-group size — in order to study another characteristic, sales. The second variable is assumed to be correlated with the first. If this correlation is very high, the job of stratification will be much better than if the correlation is poor.

The sampling illustration used in the discussion of efficiency of sample design showed that certain samples that were possible under simple random sampling were not possible with stratified sampling. The combinations that were eliminated under stratified sampling were those which contained the extreme samples. For example, the range of sample means in Table 10.1 ran from a low of 4.50 to a high of 12.75 for simple random samples. The range of weighted sample means was only 8.2 to 9.8 in Table 10.2 for the stratified samples.

In stratified sampling, the objective is to reduce the standard error for a given sample size. This can be done where it is possible to stratify the units so that the differences between units within each stratum are as small as possible. At the same time the differences between strata averages should be as large as possible.

Stratification can be most effective when there are extreme values in the universe that can be grouped into one separate stratum.

When the proportion of universe items in each stratum selected for the sample is the same for all strata, the result is called a *proportionate stratified random sample.* It is often more efficient, however, to select a smaller proportion of the items of one stratum than of another. When the sampling fractions are not the same for each stratum, the result is called a *disproportionate stratified random sample.* For example, in the illustration on Texas manufacturers, any manufacturer with 5,000 or more employees might, by virtue of his size, be so important to the study that the investigator would want to be sure to include each member of that stratum in his sample. It might be necessary to include only one firm out of every 100 of the small firms with fewer than eight employees.

If the universe is homogeneous, there is nothing to be gained by stratification. If, on the other hand, little is known about the universe, it may not be possible to arrange the data into strata.

Notation

All the special notation and formulas used in stratified sampling are shown in Table 10.4. The formulas needed for making optimum allocations are provided in a later section.

Table 10.4

STRATIFIED SAMPLING NOTATION AND FORMULAS

Universe	Sample	Definition	Formula	No.
N_h	n_h	L is the number of strata Number of listing units in the hth stratum		
N	n	Total number of listing units	$N = \sum\limits_{h=1}^{L} N_h$ $n = \sum\limits_{h=1}^{L} n_h$	
μ_h	$\bar{x}_h$	Mean of the hth stratum	$\bar{x}_h = \dfrac{\sum\limits_{i=1}^{n_h} x_{hi}}{n_h}$	10.5
X_{hi}	x_{hi}	The ith member of the sample from the hth stratum		
μ_{st}	$\bar{x}_{st}$	Mean of the stratified sample	$\bar{x}_{st} = \dfrac{\sum\limits_{h=1}^{L} N_h \bar{x}_h}{N}$	10.6
σ_h^2	$\hat{\sigma}_h^2$	Variance of the hth stratum ($\hat{\sigma}_h^2$ is an unbiased estimate of σ_h^2)	$\hat{\sigma}_h^2 = \dfrac{\sum\limits_{i=1}^{n_h} (x_{hi} - \bar{x}_h)^2}{n_h - 1}$	10.7
		Sampling fraction for the hth stratum	$f_h = \dfrac{n_h}{N_h}$	
		Finite population correction for h^{th} stratum	$1 - f_h$	
$\sigma_{\bar{x}_h}^2$	$\hat{\sigma}_{\bar{x}_h}^2$	Variance of the mean for the hth stratum	$\hat{\sigma}_{\bar{x}_h}^2 = \dfrac{\hat{\sigma}_h^2}{n_h}$	10.8
		If $f_h \geq 5\%$, then	$\hat{\sigma}_{\bar{x}_h}^2 = \dfrac{\hat{\sigma}_h^2}{n_h}(1 - f_h)$	10.9
$\sigma_{\bar{x}_{st}}$	$\hat{\sigma}_{\bar{x}_{st}}$	Standard error of the mean for a stratified sample	$\hat{\sigma}_{\bar{x}_{st}} = \dfrac{1}{N}\sqrt{\sum\limits_{h=1}^{L} N_h^2 \hat{\sigma}_{\bar{x}_h}^2}$	10.10
π_h	p_h	Percentage of a given characteristic in the hth stratum		
π_{st}	p_{st}	Percentage of a given characteristic of the stratified sample	$p_{st} = \dfrac{\sum\limits_{h=1}^{L} N_h p_h}{N}$	10.11
$\sigma_{p_h}^2$	$\hat{\sigma}_{p_h}^2$	Variance of the percentage for the hth stratum	$\hat{\sigma}_{p_h}^2 = \dfrac{p_h(1 - p_h)}{n_h - 1}$	10.12
		If $f_h \geq 5\%$, then	$\hat{\sigma}_{p_h}^2 = \dfrac{p_h(1 - p_h)}{n_{h=1}}(1 - f_h)$	10.13
$\sigma_{p_{st}}$	$\hat{\sigma}_{p_{st}}$	Standard error of the percent from a stratified sample	$\hat{\sigma}_{p_{st}} = \dfrac{1}{N}\sqrt{\sum\limits_{h=1}^{L} N_h^2 \hat{\sigma}_{p_h}^2}$	10.14
		Confidence interval for μ (large sample)	$\bar{x}_{st} - z_\alpha \hat{\sigma}_{\bar{x}_{st}} \leq \mu \leq$ $\bar{x}_{st} + z_\alpha \hat{\sigma}_{\bar{x}_{st}}$	10.15
		Confidence interval for μ (small sample)	$\bar{x}_{st} - t_\alpha \hat{\sigma}_{\bar{x}_{st}} \leq \mu \leq$ $\bar{x}_{st} + t_\alpha \hat{\sigma}_{\bar{x}_{st}}$	10.16
		Confidence interval for π	$p_{st} - z_\alpha \hat{\sigma}_{p_{st}} \leq \pi \leq$ $p_{st} + z_\alpha \hat{\sigma}_{p_{st}}$	10.17

Interval Estimates for Stratified Samples

Interval estimates for means, proportions, totals, and many other parameters may be made from stratified samples. In this book only the means of large samples will be considered, but the student who wishes to explore sampling theory in greater detail will find a list of selected readings in this field at the end of this chapter.

The problem of dividing the universe into strata is largely a matter of judgment based on the information available about the universe. The problem of how large a sample to draw from each stratum will be considered later. At this point it is assumed that these two problems have already been solved and that the statistician is concerned with analyzing the results of his sample study.

After the universe has been broken into strata and samples have been drawn from each, the means can be combined into an estimate of the universe mean, and the variances of each stratum may be combined to estimate the standard error of the mean. It is then possible to produce an interval estimate of μ using any desired level for α. If the sample is small, the α value will be a t rather than a z value. The computation of an interval estimate is illustrated in the following example using hypothetical data.

➤ *Example.* A universe of 10,000 items has been divided into four strata and a disproportionate stratified random sample of 139 items has been drawn, with the results shown in Table 10.5. The sampling fraction varies from a low of 0.005 for the first stratum to 0.010 for the fourth stratum.

Table 10.5

RESULTS OF A STRATIFIED SAMPLE

Stratum	N_h	n_h	f_h	$\bar{x}_h$	$\hat{\sigma}_h^2$
1	6,800	34	0.005	10	40
2	2,000	60	0.030	12	80
3	1,000	25	0.025	18	100
4	200	20	0.010	30	300
Totals	10,000	139			

Table 10.6 shows the computation of the mean of the stratified sample, and Table 10.7 shows the computation of the standard error of the mean.

Table 10.6

COMPUTATION OF THE MEAN
OF A STRATIFIED SAMPLE

Stratum	N_h	$\bar{x}_h$	$N_h\bar{x}_h$
1	6,800	10	68,000
2	2,000	12	24,000
3	1,000	18	18,000
4	200	30	6,000
Totals	10,000		116,000

$$\bar{x}_{st} = \frac{\sum\limits_{h=1}^{L} N_h\bar{x}_h}{N} = \frac{116,000}{10,000} = 11.6.$$

Table 10.7

COMPUTATION OF THE STANDARD ERROR OF THE MEAN OF A
STRATIFIED SAMPLE

Stratum	N_h	N_h^2	n_h	f_h	$\hat{\sigma}_{\bar{x}_h}^2 = \dfrac{\hat{\sigma}_h^2}{n_h}(1 - f_h)$	$N_h^2\hat{\sigma}_{\bar{x}_h}^2$
1	6,800	46,240,000	34	0.005	$\frac{40}{34}(1 - 0.005) = 1.171$	54,147,040
2	2,000	4,000,000	60	0.030	$\frac{80}{60}(1 - 0.030) = 1.293$	5,172,000
3	1,000	1,000,000	25	0.025	$\frac{100}{25}(1 - 0.025) = 3.900$	3,900,000
4	200	40,000	20	0.100	$\frac{300}{20}(1 - 0.100) = 13.50$	540,000
Totals	10,000		139			63,759,040

$$\hat{\sigma}_{\bar{x}_{st}} = \frac{1}{N}\sqrt{\sum_{h=1}^{L} N_h^2\hat{\sigma}_{\bar{x}_h}^2}$$

$$\hat{\sigma}_{\bar{x}_{st}} = \frac{1}{10,000}\sqrt{63,759.040}$$

$$= \frac{7,984.89}{10,000} \cong 0.80.$$

If one wishes to compute an interval estimate for μ with a confidence coefficient of 99.73%, this can be done using Formula 10.15:

$$\bar{x}_{st} - z_\alpha\hat{\sigma}_{\bar{x}_{st}} \leq \mu \leq \bar{x}_{st} + z_\alpha\hat{\sigma}_{\bar{x}_{st}}$$

$$11.6 - 3(0.80) \leq \mu \leq 11.6 + 3(0.80)$$

$$9.2 \leq \mu \leq 14.0.$$

Optimum Allocation

The problem of how to allocate the sample to the various strata in order to get the most precise results for the money available will be considered under two sets of conditions:

1. Optimum allocation with fixed costs, and
2. Optimum allocation with varying costs.

Optimum Allocation with Fixed Costs. If n has been determined as the total sample size to be used and if the cost per unit is the same for all strata, the size of the sample to be drawn from the hth stratum may be determined as follows:

$$n_h = n \cdot \frac{N_h \hat{\sigma}_h}{\sum\limits_{h=1}^{L} N_h \hat{\sigma}_h} \quad \dots\dots\dots\dots\dots\dots(10.18)$$

This formula is based on the assumption that something is known about the scatter of the items in each individual stratum and that there is more scatter in some strata than in others. If the standard deviation of each stratum were the same, the sample allocation could be made on the basis of the proportion of the universe total in each stratum. Formula 10.18 provides that the sample size in each stratum shall be proportionate to the product of the size of the stratum and the standard deviation of the stratum.

➤ *Example.* The figures in Table 10.8 show a universe of 10,000 items separated into four strata. Estimated standard deviations are available for each stratum. A total sample of 300 is allocated to the four strata on the assumption that it costs exactly the same to sample one unit from Stratum No. 1 as it does to sample one unit from each of the other three strata. The computation of the sample allocation for Stratum No. 1 is shown in detail at the top of the next page.

Table 10.8

OPTIMUM ALLOCATION OF A STRATIFIED SAMPLE
WITH FIXED COSTS

(Allocation for a sample of 300)

Stratum	N_h	$\hat{\sigma}_h$	$N_h \hat{\sigma}_h$	n_h
1	2,000	5	10,000	20
2	3,000	10	30,000	60
3	4,000	20	80,000	160
4	1,000	30	30,000	60
Totals	10,000		150,000	300

Allocation for the first stratum:

$$n_1 = n \frac{N_1 \hat{\sigma}_1}{\displaystyle\sum_{h=1}^{L} N_h \hat{\sigma}_h} = 300 \frac{10{,}000}{150{,}000} = 20.$$

Optimum Allocation with Varying Costs. Often it costs more to draw a sample item from one stratum than from another; thus, an additional factor must be considered in sample allocation. If the total cost of the survey is represented by C, then

$$C = C_1 n_1 + C_2 n_2 + \ldots + C_h n_h + \ldots + C_L n_L, \text{ or}$$

$$C = \sum_{h=1}^{L} C_h n_h \quad \text{..(10.19)}$$

where

C_h is the cost per sample unit for the hth stratum.

If the total cost, C, is determined first, the size of the sample, n, can be computed by the following formula:

$$n = \frac{C}{\displaystyle\sum_{h=1}^{L} N_h \hat{\sigma}_h \sqrt{C_h}} \sum_{h=1}^{L} \left(\frac{N_h \hat{\sigma}_h}{\sqrt{C_h}} \right) \quad \text{...............(10.20)}$$

Once the size of n has been determined, the total sample can be allocated to the various strata by the following formula:

$$n_h = \frac{\dfrac{N_h \hat{\sigma}_h}{\sqrt{C_h}}}{\displaystyle\sum_{h=1}^{L} \left(\dfrac{N_h \hat{\sigma}_h}{\sqrt{C_h}} \right)} n \quad \text{........................(10.21)}$$

➤ *Example.* The problem discussed in the previous example is shown again in Table 10.9. This time it is assumed that the cost per sample unit varies with the strata and that a total cost of $1,000 has been set for the survey. The size of the sample total is computed to be 369 using Formula 10.20, and this total is allocated to the four strata using Formula 10.21.

Table 10.9

OPTIMUM ALLOCATION OF A STRATIFIED SAMPLE
WITH VARIABLE COSTS

Stratum	N_h	$\hat{\sigma}_h$	$N_h\hat{\sigma}_h$	C_h	$\sqrt{C_h}$	$\dfrac{N_h\hat{\sigma}_h}{\sqrt{C_h}}$	$N_h\hat{\sigma}_h\sqrt{C_h}$	n_h
1	2,000	5	10,000	$0.50	0.707	14,144	7,070	53
2	3,000	10	30,000	1.00	1.000	30,000	30,000	114
3	4,000	20	80,000	4.00	2.000	40,000	160,000	151
4	1,000	30	30,000	5.00	2.237	13,411	67,110	51
	10,000		150,000			97,555	264,180	369

$$n = \frac{C}{\Sigma N_h\hat{\sigma}_h \sqrt{C_h}} \sum_{h=1}^{L} \left(\frac{N_h\hat{\sigma}_h}{\sqrt{C_h}}\right)$$

$$n = \frac{1,000}{264,180}(97,555) = 369.$$

With $n = 369$, then

$$n_1 = \frac{\dfrac{N_1\hat{\sigma}_1}{\sqrt{C_1}}}{\displaystyle\sum_{h=1}^{L}\left(\frac{N_h\hat{\sigma}_h}{\sqrt{C_h}}\right)} n = \frac{14,144}{97,555} 369 = 53.$$

CLUSTER SAMPLING

In the previous discussion of stratified sampling, the chief aim was to use a sample design that would provide maximum precision for a given size sample. There are two conditions under which this design will not provide the best approach to sampling:

1. There may not be available any frame or list of universe items from which the sample might be drawn. For example, if one wishes to interview a sample of farmers in a particular state, it might be impossible to find a list of them from which to draw the sample.

2. Even with a frame available, if the units in the universe are widely scattered, it may be cheaper to use a large sample of units that lie close to one another than it would be to use a small sample of widely scattered units. For example, it might be cheaper to interview 50 farmers in one county than 30 farmers in 30 different counties.

The Nature of Cluster Sampling

In designing a sample survey, the statistician is always interested in learning something about a universe of items that may be called *listing units* or *elementary units*. It is the characteristics of these elements that he is interested in counting or measuring. In the case of the farm survey, the individual farmer may be thought of as the listing unit.

Listing units may be selected individually, as in simple random sampling, or they may be selected in groups or clusters known as *primary units*. In the example of the farm survey, the counties might be considered as the primary units.

When a sample design calls for a random selection of primary units and when a random sample of listing units is selected from each of the sample of primary units, it is called a *cluster sample*. In this case it would be precise to say a *two-stage cluster sample*, since the sampling is done in two stages. A three-stage cluster sample would be one in which the sampling is done in three stages. For example, a city block might be the primary unit; a family, the secondary unit; and an individual person in the family, the listing unit.

In those instances where the population is broken into areas that constitute the primary sampling units, the sample is called an *area sample.* Another variation, in which listing units are taken in groups or chunks from the population, is called *chunk sampling*. This type of sampling is often most convenient in sampling internal records. For example, a chunk may be a box of punched cards taken from a file containing several such boxes. The contents of the sample box might be analyzed on a computer. In this case a very large sample may be inspected at a small cost.

The special advantages of the cluster sample are that it provides a way of selecting a random sample where there is no frame, and it often makes possible cost saving not obtainable with other sample designs.

Notation

All the special notation and formulas necessary to make interval estimates for means for two-stage cluster sampling are shown in Table 10.10. Interval estimates for percentage characteristics and for more than two stages in cluster sampling are not covered in this book. The formulas for optimum allocation in cluster sampling are covered in a later section of this chapter.

Figure 10.2 shows a hypothetical two-stage cluster (or area) sample drawn from a city map. The primary units are blocks, and the listing units are houses. This illustration is designed to make more understandable the notation to be used in this section.

Table 10.10

TWO-STAGE CLUSTER SAMPLING NOTATION AND FORMULAS

Universe	Sample	Definition	Formula	No.
M	m	Number of primary units		
N_i	n_i	Number of listing units in the ith primary unit		
N	n	Number of listing units	$N = \sum\limits_{i=1}^{M} N_i \quad \text{and}$ $n = \sum\limits_{i=1}^{m} n_i$	
$\bar{N}$	$\bar{n}$	Average number of listing units per primary unit	$\bar{N} = \dfrac{N}{M} \quad \text{and}$ $\bar{n} = \dfrac{n}{m}$	
		Sampling fraction:		
		1st stage	$f_1 = \dfrac{m}{M}$	
		2nd stage (uniform for all primary units)	$f_2 = \dfrac{n_i}{N_i} \text{ or } \dfrac{\bar{n}}{\bar{N}}$	
		Overall	$f = f_1 f_2$	
X_i	x_i	Cluster total of the listing units in the ith primary unit where x_{ij} is the observation of the jth listing unit of the ith primary unit in the sample	$x_i = \sum\limits_{j=1}^{n_i} x_{ij}$	
μ_i	$\bar{x}_i$	Sample mean of the ith primary unit	$\bar{x}_i = \dfrac{\sum\limits_{j=1}^{n_i} x_{ij}}{n_i}$	10.22
μ	$\bar{x}$	Overall sample mean	$\bar{x} = \dfrac{\sum\limits_{i=1}^{m} \bar{x}_i}{m}$	10.23
σ_b^2	$\hat{\sigma}_b^2$	Variance between primary units	$\hat{\sigma}_b^2 = \dfrac{\sum\limits_{i=1}^{m} n_i(\bar{x}_i - \bar{\bar{x}})^2}{m\bar{n}}$	10.24
		If n_i is a constant, then	$\hat{\sigma}_b^2 = \dfrac{\sum\limits_{i=1}^{m} (\bar{x}_i - \bar{\bar{x}})^2}{m - 1}$	10.25
σ_i^2	$\hat{\sigma}_i^2$	Variance of the sample of listing units within the ith primary unit	$\hat{\sigma}_i^2 = \dfrac{\sum\limits_{j=1}^{n_i} (x_{ij} - \bar{x}_i)^2}{n_i - 1}$	10.26
σ_w^2	$\hat{\sigma}_w^2$	Variance within primary units (a weighted mean of $\hat{\sigma}_i^2$)	$\hat{\sigma}_w^2 = \dfrac{\sum\limits_{i=1}^{m} n_i \hat{\sigma}_i^2}{n}$	10.27

(*continued*)

Table 10.10 (Continued)

TWO-STAGE CLUSTER SAMPLING NOTATION AND FORMULAS

Universe	Sample	Definition	Formula	No.
		If n_i is a constant, then	$\hat{\sigma}_w^2 = \dfrac{\sum_{i=1}^{m} \hat{\sigma}_i^2}{m}$	10.28
$\mathrm{Var}(\bar{x})$	$\hat{\sigma}_{\bar{x}}^2$	Variance of the sample mean of a two-stage sample	$\hat{\sigma}_{\bar{x}}^2 = \dfrac{\hat{\sigma}_b^2}{m} + \dfrac{\hat{\sigma}_w^2}{m\bar{n}}$	10.29
		If the sampling fractions are large (equal to or greater than 5%), then	$\hat{\sigma}_{\bar{x}}^2 = \dfrac{M-m}{M}\dfrac{\hat{\sigma}_b^2}{m} + \dfrac{\bar{N}-\bar{n}}{\bar{N}}\dfrac{\hat{\sigma}_w^2}{m\bar{n}}$	10.30
$\sigma_{\bar{x}}$	$\hat{\sigma}_{\bar{x}}$	Standard error of the mean of a two-stage sample	$\hat{\sigma}_{\bar{x}} = \sqrt{\hat{\sigma}_{\bar{x}}^2}$	10.31
		Confidence interval for μ, large sample	$\bar{x} - z_\alpha \hat{\sigma}_{\bar{x}} \le \mu \le$ $\bar{x} + z_\alpha \hat{\sigma}_{\bar{x}}$	10.32
		Confidence interval for μ, small sample	$\bar{x} - t_\alpha \hat{\sigma}_{\bar{x}} \le \mu \le$ $\bar{x} + t_\alpha \hat{\sigma}_{\bar{x}}$	10.33

Interval Estimates for Cluster Samples

Just as in stratified sampling, judgment must be exercised in determining how the sample will be designed. However, once the decision has been made as to the number of primary units to be drawn and the number of listing units to be sampled from each of them, the sampling process itself must be random. If each elementary unit has a known chance of selection, it is then possible to estimate the standard error of the mean and to compute a confidence interval based on a given confidence coefficient. The actual mechanics are best illustrated with an example.

➤ *Example.* A retailer has on hand 1,000 cartons of infrared heat lamps, each carton containing 24 lamps. The company wishes to estimate the average burning life of these lamps, which have been purchased from several suppliers and at different times. A sample of 200 lamps is drawn from the universe of 24,000 lamps as follows:

1. Twenty cartons are selected at random.
2. Ten lamps are selected at random from each of the 20 cartons.
3. The test lamps are burned until they burn out. The mean and the variance of each group of 10 lamps are shown in Table 10.11, page 364.

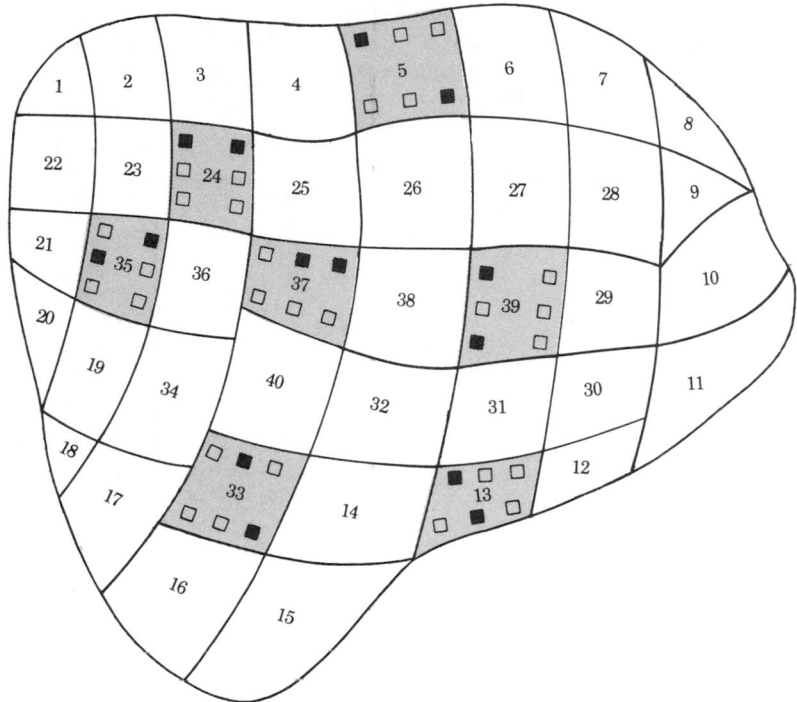

Definition	Notation	In this example
Number of primary units in the universe	M	40 blocks
Number of primary units in the sample	m	7 blocks (shaded)
Listing units in each primary unit	N_i or $\bar{N}$	6 houses in each block
Listing units sampled from each primary unit in the sample	n_i or $\bar{n}$	2 houses in each block (black)
Total listing units in universe	$\bar{N}M = N$	240 houses
Total listing units in sample	$\bar{n}m = n$	14 houses

Figure 10.2

HYPOTHETICAL TWO-STAGE CLUSTER SAMPLE DRAWN FROM A UNIVERSE OF 40 CITY BLOCKS WITH SIX HOUSES TO EACH BLOCK

The sample is a two-stage cluster sample with the following characteristics:

$M = 1,000$ cartons (primary units).

$m = 20$ cartons (number of primary units in the sample).

$N_i = \bar{N} = 24$ lamps (number of listing units per primary unit).

$n_i = \bar{n} = 10$ lamps (number of listing units sampled in each sample primary unit).

$N = M\bar{N} = 24,000$ lamps (total number of listing units in the population).

Table 10.11
RESULTS OF A TWO-STAGE CLUSTER SAMPLE OF HEAT LAMPS
(Burning life in 100's of hours)

Cluster number	$\bar{x}_i$	$\hat{\sigma}_i^2$	$\bar{x}_i - \bar{x}$	$(\bar{x}_i - \bar{x})^2$
1	20	2	−3	9
2	25	3	2	4
3	21	4	−2	4
4	26	5	3	9
5	20	3	−3	9
6	25	6	2	4
7	22	7	−1	1
8	26	2	3	9
9	21	6	−2	4
10	20	4	−3	9
11	19	5	−4	16
12	22	3	−1	1
13	27	6	4	16
14	24	4	1	1
15	26	2	3	9
16	22	2	−1	1
17	27	3	4	16
18	20	4	−3	9
19	26	5	3	9
20	21	2	−2	4
Totals	460	78	0	144

$n = \bar{n}m = 200$ lamps (total number of listing units in the sample).

$$f_1 = \frac{m}{M} = \frac{20}{1,000} \text{ (first-stage sampling fraction).}$$

$$f_2 = \frac{\bar{n}}{\bar{N}} = \frac{10}{24} \text{ (second-stage sampling fraction).}$$

$$f = f_1 f_2 = \frac{200}{24,000} \text{ (overall sampling fraction).}$$

The overall sample mean, which is the expected value of μ, is computed using Formula 10.23

$$\bar{\bar{x}} = \frac{\sum\limits_{i=1}^{m} \bar{x}_i}{m} = \frac{460}{20} = 23 \text{ (2,300 hours).}$$

Since n_i is constant for all clusters, the variance *within* clusters is computed using Formula 10.28

$$\hat{\sigma}_w^2 = \frac{\sum\limits_{i=1}^{m} \hat{\sigma}_i^2}{m} = \frac{78}{20} = 3.9.$$

The variance *between* clusters is computed using Formula 10.25.

$$\hat{\sigma}_b^2 = \frac{\sum\limits_{i=1}^{m} (\bar{x}_i - \bar{\bar{x}})^2}{m-1} = \frac{144}{19} = 7.58.$$

Using these two variances, it is now possible to compute the standard error of the mean using Formulas 10.30 and 10.31

$$\hat{\sigma}_{\bar{x}}^2 = \frac{M-m}{M} \cdot \frac{\hat{\sigma}_b^2}{m} + \frac{\bar{N}-\bar{n}}{\bar{N}} \cdot \frac{\hat{\sigma}_w^2}{m\bar{n}}$$

$$\hat{\sigma}_{\bar{x}}^2 = \frac{1,000-20}{1,000} \cdot \frac{7.58}{20} + \frac{24-10}{24} \cdot \frac{3.9}{(20)(10)} = 0.3828.$$

$$\hat{\sigma}_{\bar{x}} = \sqrt{\hat{\sigma}_{\bar{x}}^2} = \sqrt{0.3828} \cong 0.62.$$

The confidence interval for μ with a confidence coefficient of 99.73% can be computed using Formula 10.32

$$\bar{\bar{x}} - z_\alpha \hat{\sigma}_{\bar{x}} \le \mu \le \bar{\bar{x}} + z_\alpha \hat{\sigma}_{\bar{x}}$$
$$23 - 3(0.62) \le \mu \le 23 + 3(0.62)$$
$$21.14 \le \mu \le 24.86.$$

Optimum Allocation

The cluster sample with the lowest sampling error would naturally be one that has only one listing unit per primary unit. This, of course, turns out to be a simple random sample and may be much more expensive than one with more than one listing unit per cluster or primary unit. The question is, "How many primary units and how many listing units in each primary unit should be sampled to get the most precision for the money?"

The answer to this question depends on several factors. If the cluster means $(\bar{x}_i)$ are all alike, very few clusters would be needed, but the number of listing units per cluster should be high. On the other hand, if the variance between primary units $(\hat{\sigma}_b^2)$ is large, more primary units should be drawn and fewer listing units sampled per primary unit.

The key measure in this relationship is a value called delta (δ). Delta is the intraclass correlation between elementary units within primary units and can be expressed by the following formula:

$$\delta = \frac{\hat{\sigma}_b^2 - \dfrac{\hat{\sigma}^2}{\overline{N}}}{(\overline{N} - 1)\dfrac{\hat{\sigma}^2}{\overline{N}}} \quad \dots\dots\dots\dots\dots\dots(10.34)$$

where

$\hat{\sigma}^2 = \hat{\sigma}_b^2 + \hat{\sigma}_w^2$ is the estimate of total variance.

The determination of the optimum allocation of the sample must also take into account the total amount of money (exclusive of overhead costs) and the relative cost of drawing a primary unit as compared with that of drawing a listing unit. This cost function in its simplest form may be expressed as follows:

$$C = C_1 m + C_2 m\bar{n} \quad \dots\dots\dots\dots\dots(10.35)$$

where

C is the total cost of the survey, exclusive of overhead costs
C_1 is the cost per primary unit included in the survey
C_2 is the cost per listing unit included in the survey.

The cost of adding one primary unit to the survey, C_1, might include such items as transportation and communications costs that would be incurred in sampling from that cluster. The cost of adding one listing unit, C_2, might include the cost of interviewing and tabulating the data from one listing unit. It must be understood that these cost figures are estimates, and to a large extent the accuracy of the allocation depends on the accuracy of the cost estimates as well as the estimates of the two variances used to compute the value of δ.

In making the actual allocation, it is easiest to estimate first the optimum size of the sample of listing units to be drawn from each primary unit and then to solve for m in the cost function using the optimum $\bar{n}$. The optimum value of $\bar{n}$ may be computed using the following equation:

$$\text{Opt. } \bar{n} = \sqrt{\frac{C_1}{C_2} \frac{1 - \delta}{\delta}} \quad \dots\dots\dots\dots(10.36)$$

An illustration of optimum allocation is given in the following example.

➤ *Example.* Prior to making a sample survey using a two-stage cluster sample the following estimates are available:

C = $600 (total amount to be spent, exclusive of overhead)
C_1 = $10 (sampling cost per primary unit)
C_2 = $5 (sampling cost per listing unit)
M = 500 (number of primary units in the universe)

$\overline{N}$ = 10 (average number of listing units per primary unit, assumed in this case to be constant for all clusters)

N = $M\overline{N}$ = 5,000 (total number of listing units in the universe)

$\hat{\sigma}_w^2$ = 20 (estimate of variance of listing units within primary units)

$\hat{\sigma}_b^2$ = 5 (estimate of variance between primary units)

$\hat{\sigma}^2$ = $\hat{\sigma}_w^2 + \hat{\sigma}_b^2$ = 20 + 5 = 25 (estimate of total variance).

The problem is to estimate m and $\bar{n}$ so as to get maximum precision within the money allocated for the survey.

The first step is to compute δ using Formula 10.34

$$\delta = \frac{\hat{\sigma}_b^2 - \dfrac{\hat{\sigma}^2}{\overline{N}}}{(\overline{N} - 1)\dfrac{\hat{\sigma}^2}{\overline{N}}} = \frac{5 - \dfrac{25}{10}}{(10 - 1)\left(\dfrac{25}{10}\right)} = \frac{2.5}{22.5} \cong 0.11.$$

and $1 - 0.11 = 0.89$.

The optimum number of listing units to be drawn from each primary unit may be estimated using Formula 10.36

$$\text{Opt. } \bar{n} = \sqrt{\frac{C_1}{C_2} \frac{1 - \delta}{\delta}} = \sqrt{\frac{10}{5} \frac{0.89}{0.11}} = \sqrt{16.18} = 4.02$$

Opt. $\bar{n}$ = 4.

This value can now be substituted in the cost equation (Formula 10.35) to estimate the optimum size of m.

$$C = C_1 m + C_2 m\bar{n}$$
$$600 = 10m + 5m(4)$$
$$30m = 600$$
$$m = 20.$$

This would mean that the sample should consist of 20 primary units drawn at random from the universe of 500 primary units. From each primary unit in the sample, four listing units would be drawn at random making a total sample size of $n = m\bar{n}$, or 80 listing units.

SAMPLING AND COMPUTERS

Computers are useful in sampling only when the amount of computation is very large. It is helpful to think of any sample survey as taking place in three stages, with the computer playing a role in stages one and three.

Stage One — Planning the Survey

This stage involves the design of the survey; decisions as to precision and sample size; estimates of cost; and the computation of the optimum allocation of the sample. Figure 10.3 is a flow diagram showing the steps that might be followed in arriving at the optimum sample allocation for a two-stage cluster sample. If the survey is to be very large and complex, it would be worthwhile to depend on a computer solution to provide the optimum allocation of the sample.

Stage Two — Making the Survey

The sample survey should be undertaken using the plan developed in stage one. There is no computation necessary at this stage.

Stage Three — Evaluating the Results

Much computation may be involved in evaluating the results of the survey. This may be done by the computer in the interest of both accuracy and time. Figure 10.4 is a flow diagram showing the steps that might be followed to compute an interval estimate of μ from a two-stage cluster sample.

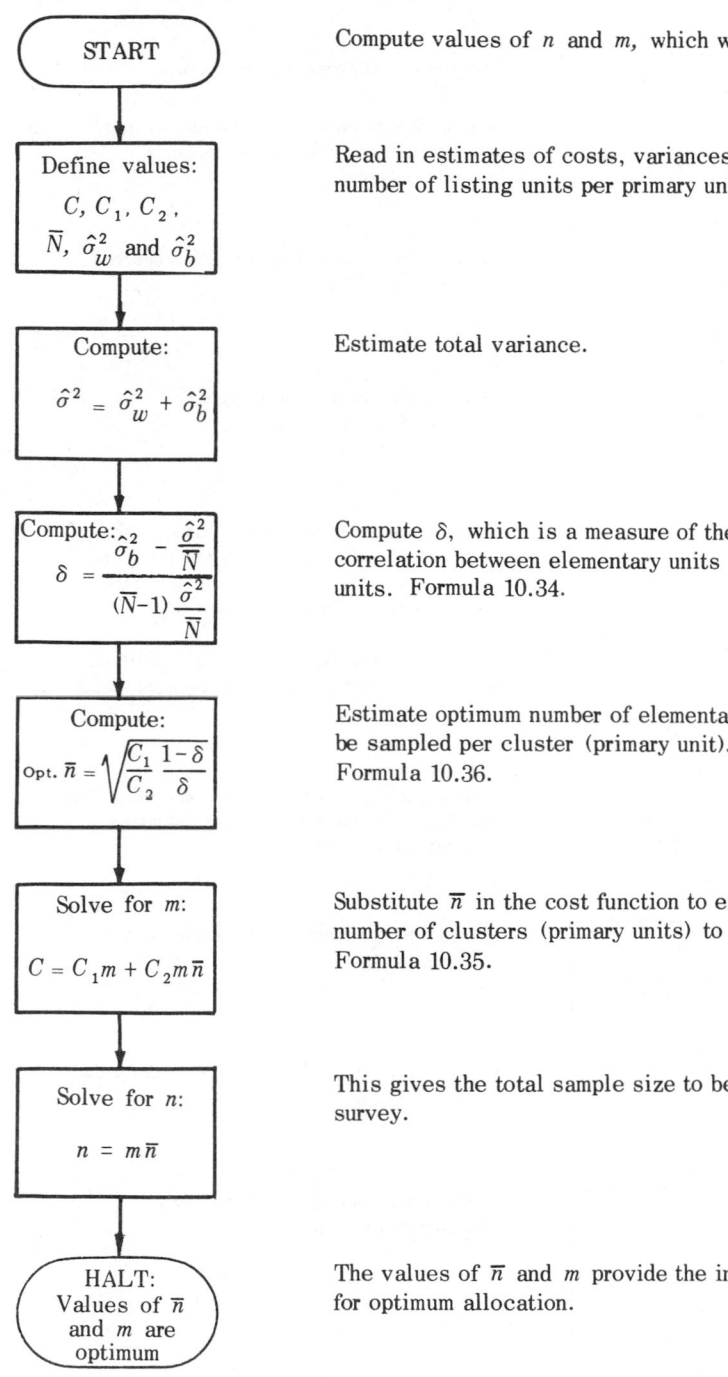

Compute values of n and m, which will be optimum.

Read in estimates of costs, variances, and average number of listing units per primary unit.

Estimate total variance.

Compute δ, which is a measure of the intraclass correlation between elementary units within primary units. Formula 10.34.

Estimate optimum number of elementary units to be sampled per cluster (primary unit). Formula 10.36.

Substitute $\bar{n}$ in the cost function to estimate the number of clusters (primary units) to sample. Formula 10.35.

This gives the total sample size to be used in the survey.

The values of $\bar{n}$ and m provide the information needed for optimum allocation.

Figure 10.3

A FLOW DIAGRAM FOR COMPUTING THE OPTIMUM SAMPLE
ALLOCATION FOR A TWO-STAGE CLUSTER SAMPLE

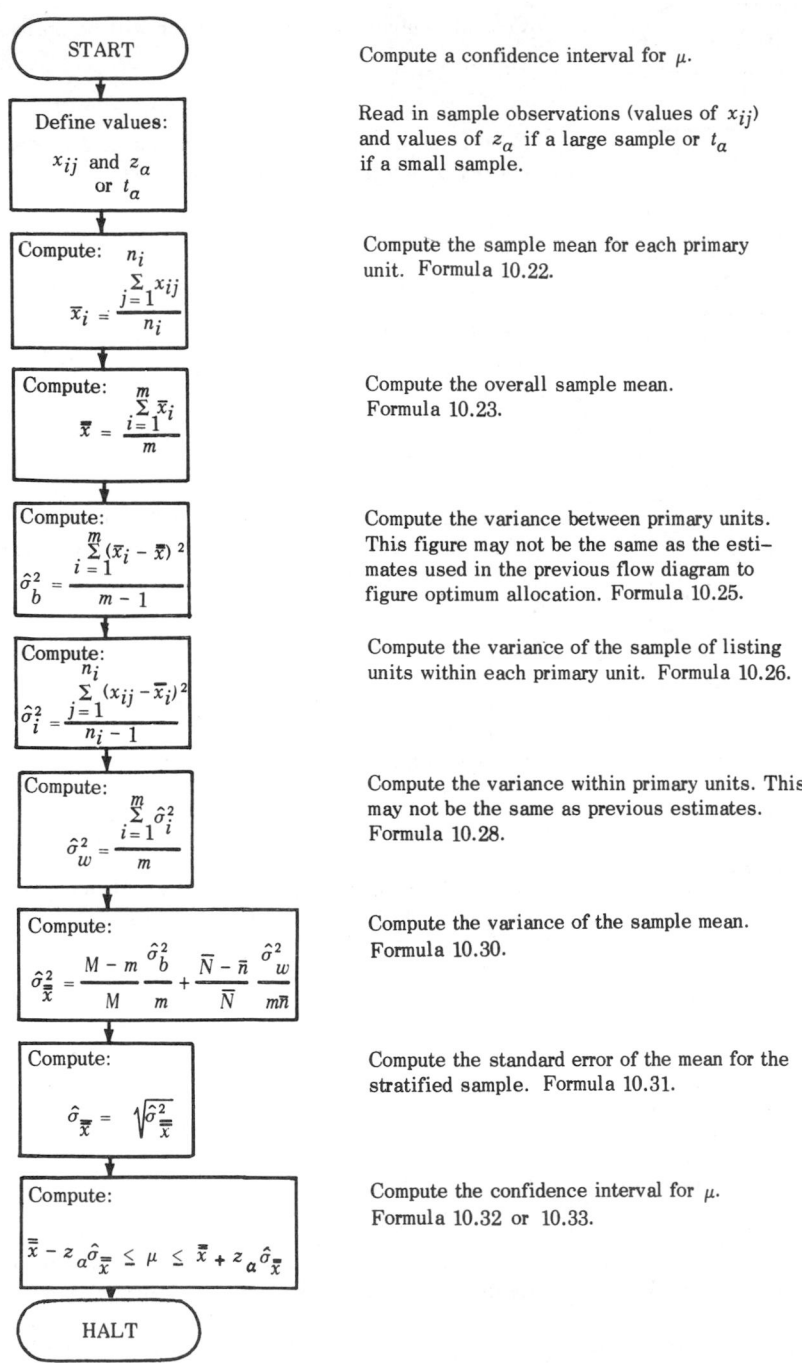

START	Compute a confidence interval for μ.
Define values: x_{ij} and z_a or t_a	Read in sample observations (values of x_{ij}) and values of z_a if a large sample or t_a if a small sample.
Compute: n_i $$\bar{x}_i = \frac{\sum\limits_{j=1} x_{ij}}{n_i}$$	Compute the sample mean for each primary unit. Formula 10.22.
Compute: $$\bar{x} = \frac{\sum\limits_{i=1}^{m} \bar{x}_i}{m}$$	Compute the overall sample mean. Formula 10.23.
Compute: $$\hat{\sigma}_b^2 = \frac{\sum\limits_{i=1}^{m}(\bar{x}_i - \bar{x})^2}{m-1}$$	Compute the variance between primary units. This figure may not be the same as the estimates used in the previous flow diagram to figure optimum allocation. Formula 10.25.
Compute: $$\hat{\sigma}_i^2 = \frac{\sum\limits_{j=1}^{n_i}(x_{ij} - \bar{x}_i)^2}{n_i - 1}$$	Compute the variance of the sample of listing units within each primary unit. Formula 10.26.
Compute: $$\hat{\sigma}_w^2 = \frac{\sum\limits_{i=1}^{m} \hat{\sigma}_i^2}{m}$$	Compute the variance within primary units. This may not be the same as previous estimates. Formula 10.28.
Compute: $$\hat{\sigma}_{\bar{x}}^2 = \frac{M-m}{M}\frac{\hat{\sigma}_b^2}{m} + \frac{\bar{N}-\bar{n}}{\bar{N}}\frac{\hat{\sigma}_w^2}{m\bar{n}}$$	Compute the variance of the sample mean. Formula 10.30.
Compute: $$\hat{\sigma}_{\bar{x}} = \sqrt{\hat{\sigma}_{\bar{x}}^2}$$	Compute the standard error of the mean for the stratified sample. Formula 10.31.
Compute: $$\bar{\bar{x}} - z_a\hat{\sigma}_{\bar{x}} \leq \mu \leq \bar{\bar{x}} + z_a\hat{\sigma}_{\bar{x}}$$	Compute the confidence interval for μ. Formula 10.32 or 10.33.
HALT	

Figure 10.4

A FLOW DIAGRAM FOR COMPUTING A CONFIDENCE INTERVAL FOR μ
FOR A TWO-STAGE CLUSTER SAMPLE

STUDY QUESTIONS

10-1. Explain briefly the meaning of each of the following terms:

a. precision of sample results
b. sampling error
c. accuracy of sampling results
d. arbitrary sampling
e. frame
f. systematic random sample
g. Student's *t* distribution
h. sample design
i. stratified sampling
j. strata

k. proportionate stratified random sample
l. disproportionate stratified random sample
m. listing unit
n. primary unit
o. cluster sample
p. two-stage cluster sample
q. area sample
r. chunk sampling

10-2. What are the advantages of using a simple random sample?

10-3. Why is the businessman more interested in the accuracy than in the precision of the sample results?

10-4. What is the one great weakness in all types of arbitrary sampling?

10-5. Describe how you would take a systematic random sample from the pages of a telephone book. Under what conditions might this be an appropriate sample to use?

10-6. When is it necessary to use the statistic *t* in place of *z* in computing an interval estimate of μ?

10-7. When is a stratified sample more efficient than a simple random sample?

10-8. Describe a situation in which it would be appropriate to use a stratified sample. Explain in your example the criterion you would use to break the universe into strata.

10-9. What factors play a part in the optimum allocation of a stratified sample?

10-10. Give an example of a four-stage cluster sample.

10-11. Under what conditions would you consider using a cluster sample?

10-12. What factors are involved in the optimum allocation of a cluster sample?

PROBLEMS

10-1. Compute the value of *t* for each of the following:

	$\bar{x}$	μ	s	n
a.	12	10	4	5
b.	27	28.9	5.8	61
c.	108	115	12	150
d.	4.2	4.8	0.5	26

10-2. Find the table value of t_α for each of the following:

	t_α	n
a.	0.05	7
b.	0.01	27
c.	0.10	41
d.	0.02	225

10-3. Compute a confidence interval for μ given the following:

$$\bar{x} = 27.5 \text{ inches}$$
$$s = 1.5 \text{ inches}$$
$$n = 29 \text{ observations}$$
$$\alpha = 0.05$$

10-4. A random sample of six castings drawn from a universe of 75 castings shows the following weight for each. Compute an interval estimate for μ using a value for α of 0.02.

Casting number	Weight (pounds)
1	82.9
2	83.5
3	84.1
4	83.6
5	82.5
6	84.4

10-5. Given the following universe:

$$A = 5 \qquad C = 4$$
$$B = 25 \qquad D = 3$$

a. Compute the standard error of the mean for all possible simple random samples of $n = 2$.

b. Assume the universe is divided into the following two strata.

Stratum	Individuals
I	$A, C,$ and D
II	B

Draw all possible samples of $n = 2$ with one sample unit being drawn from each stratum. Compute the standard error of the mean and compare this answer with that obtained in (a). Which method gives the smaller standard error and why?

10-6. Given the following universe:

$$A = 27 \qquad D = 122 \qquad G = 800$$
$$B = 117 \qquad E = 30$$
$$C = 125 \qquad F = 28$$

a. Into how many strata would you divide the universe for sampling purposes? Why?

b. If you had three strata, how many samples of five could you draw if each sample must contain two items from each of two strata and one item from the third?

c. Draw all possible samples called for in (b) and compute the sample means. Is the $\bar{x} = \mu$?

d. Compute the true standard error of the mean using all the means computed in (c).

10-7. Given the following results of a stratified sample, compute an interval estimate for μ with an $\alpha = 0.05$:

Stratum	N_h	n_h	$\bar{x}_h$	$\hat{\sigma}_h$
1	10,000	100	150	50
2	20,000	150	200	100
3	5,000	50	300	200

10-8. Given the following results of a very small stratified sample, compute a confidence interval for μ with $\alpha = 0.01$.

Stratum	N_h	n_h	Values of x_{hi}
1	100,000	6	18, 20, 19, 16, 21, 20
2	50,000	4	55, 61, 58, 62

10-9. If you plan to draw a stratified sample of 200 units from the following universe, what would you estimate to be the optimum size of n_h for each stratum?

Stratum	N_h	$\hat{\sigma}_h$
1	30,000	5
2	10,000	10
3	10,000	20

10-10. Given the information below, compute the total size of the sample and the optimum allocation of the sample to each stratum for a stratified sample to cost $2,000.

Stratum	N_h	$\hat{\sigma}_h$	C_h
1	1,000	5	$1.00
2	500	12	2.00
3	300	20	5.00
4	200	30	10.00

10-11. Suppose a universe has 500 primary sampling units with 40 listing units in each primary unit. A two-stage cluster sample is drawn with the following results:

$$\bar{x} = 120 \qquad m = 20$$
$$\hat{\sigma}_b^2 = 25 \qquad \bar{n} = 10$$
$$\hat{\sigma}_w^2 = 12$$

Compute an interval estimate for μ with $\alpha = 0.05$.

10-12. The table below shows the results of a two-stage cluster sample:

Cluster number	$\bar{x}_i$	$\hat{\sigma}_i^2$	
1	32	4	$N = 100,000$
2	31	5	$\bar{N} = 100$
3	30	3	$M = 1,000$
4	28	4	$m = 5$
5	29	6	$\bar{n} = 8$
			$n = 40$

Compute a confidence interval for μ if $\alpha = 0.01$.

10-13. Given the following estimates of the variances in a two-stage cluster sample and the average number of universe items per cluster, compute the value of δ:

$$\hat{\sigma}_b^2 = 50 \qquad \hat{\sigma}_w^2 = 10 \qquad \overline{N} = 20$$

10-14. Compute the value of δ for a two-stage cluster sample, given the following:

$$\hat{\sigma}^2 = 100 \qquad \hat{\sigma}_w^2 = 20 \qquad \overline{N} = 50$$

10-15. For a two-stage cluster sample with the values shown below, compute the optimum values of m and $\bar{n}$:

$$C = \$500.00; \quad C_1 = \$20.00; \quad C_2 = \$2.00; \quad \text{and} \quad \delta = 0.20$$

10-16. Given the following estimate for a two-stage cluster sample, how large should the sample be and how should it be allocated?

$$
\begin{aligned}
\sigma_b^2 &= 20 & C &= \$2,000 \\
\sigma_w^2 &= 15 & C_1 &= \$40.00 \\
\overline{N} &= 8 & C_2 &= \$10.00
\end{aligned}
$$

SELECTED READINGS

Cochran, William G. *Sampling Techniques.* New York: John Wiley & Sons, Inc., 1953.
>   A comprehensive account of sampling theory as it has been developed for use in sample surveys.

Deming, W. Edwards. *Sample Design in Business Research.* New York: John Wiley & Sons, Inc., 1960.
>   This book is written from the point of view of the theoretical statistician in industry who deals with surveys of consumers and business establishments as well as inspection and testing of physical materials.

Hansen, Morris H., William N. Hurwitz, and William G. Madow. *Sample Survey Methods and Theory.* New York: John Wiley & Sons, Inc., 1953.
>   This book is the most comprehensive presentation of both the theory of sampling and its application to practical problems available at this time. The book is in two volumes. Volume I is "Methods and Applications," and Volume II contains the derivations of the formulas and proofs of statements made in Volume I.

Yates, Frank. *Sampling Methods for Censuses and Surveys.* 3d ed. New York: Hafner Publishing Co., 1960.
>   A book written primarily for those who have little or no previous training in mathematical statistics but who have some training or experience in the presentation and handling of statistical data.

Chapter 11

Tests of Significance for Sample Means

INTRODUCTION

One of the most important areas of application of statistical theory is called *tests of significance* or *tests of hypotheses*. It is here that probability theory is playing an ever-increasing role in constructing the criteria on which business decisions are made. Tests of significance concerning sample means are covered in this chapter, and tests of significance concerning proportions are discussed in Chapter 12.

Because almost all business decisions must be made on the basis of incomplete information, there is always the risk of making an incorrect decision. Fortunately, there is now an extensive body of statistical methods available that makes possible the evaluation of these risks. These methods also lay down guidelines that minimize the probability of making wrong decisions.

In previous chapters the discussion of sampling distributions was aimed largely at statistical estimation. A statistic computed from a random sample drawn from a universe was used to estimate a confidence interval within which one could predict, with a given probability, the universe parameter would lie.

The type of problem viewed in this chapter is one in which a decision must be made to take one action or another based on the acceptance or the rejection of a given hypothesis. Hence, the term, "tests of hypotheses." The variety of hypotheses made by the businessman is endless: i.e., buy product A, invest in project B, accept shipment C, or adjust machine D.

The hypothesis is made about the value of some parameter, but the only facts available to estimate the true parameter are those provided by a sample. If the statistic differs from the hypothesis made about the parameter, a decision must be made as to whether or not this difference is significant. If it is, the hypothesis is rejected. If not, it must be accepted. Hence, the term, "tests of significance."

The problem of determining whether the observed difference is significant or not is one of determining whether the difference could be reasonably attributed to random causes or is so large as to make such a conclusion unlikely. It is here that probability and sampling theory play their part in decision making.

➤ *Example.* A machine is set to fill boxes of dry cereal with an average of eight ounces, net weight, per box. While it would be ideal if the operator could be absolutely sure each box would contain exactly the right amount of cereal, this is never possible. He must always contend with some slight random variation from box to box. He must always be alert to the possibility that the machine may get out of adjustment or something may go wrong to change the average amount being put into all the boxes.

As long as the machine is filling the boxes with a universe mean of eight ounces of cereal and as long as the variation in weight from box to box is random and within specifications, all is well and the process should be allowed to continue. If, however, the universe mean shifts to an amount that is either above or below eight ounces, the machine should be stopped and proper adjustments made.

While the decision to continue the process or stop the machine is simple in theory, it is made difficult in practice by the fact that the operator never knows what the universe mean really is. It would be far too slow and costly to check the exact weight of every box as it is filled. This means that he must rely on the information he gets from studying a random sample of boxes selected periodically from the production line. If he draws a sample of boxes and finds the sample mean, $\bar{x}$, to be 8.02 ounces, he is probably safe in assuming that the difference between that value and a universe mean, μ, of 8.00 ounces, is not significant and can be attributed to sampling variation. If, on the other hand, $\bar{x} = 6.5$ ounces, the difference of 1.5 ounces may be much too large to attribute to sampling variation alone, and he may conclude that the difference is significant. The machine is out of adjustment. If the difference lies somewhere between 0.02 and 1.5, the decision the operator should make is less clear. He needs a decision rule of some kind to tell him the value at which he should either stop the machine or continue the process.

While there are thousands of different kinds of decisions that may be made using tests of significance, the path followed is always much the same:

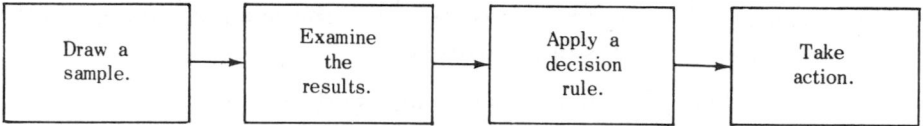

> **Example.** Suppose in the previous example the operator had been told to follow, once each hour, the procedure outlined below,

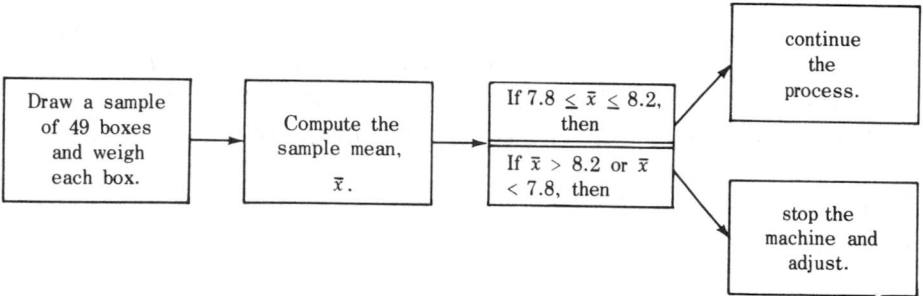

The operator might not know how the decision rule had been computed, but he would know how to act in controlling his machine. There would still be times in which he would stop the machine when it was still in adjustment or would continue operating when he should stop and adjust. These mistakes are inherent in the sampling process. The supervisor who computed the decision rule at least would know the frequency with which mistakes might be expected to occur.

THE STATISTICAL APPROACH TO DECISION MAKING

As with any new subject in statistics, it is first necessary to introduce and define the terminology that will be used. Because of the large variety of tests that may be used, a fairly rigid series of steps will be followed in the tests explained in this chapter. These same steps may be followed in later chapters with other tests of significance involving such techniques as analysis of variance and chi-square, to name only two.

The State of the World

In any test of significance there are always two possible states of the universe. These are often called *states of the world* or *states of nature*. These states are defined by the statistician in such a way as to be both *exhaustive* and *exclusive*. That is, for a given test, only these two and no other states are possible, and when one exists, the other cannot exist.

The first state of the world will be designated as W_1, and the second state of the world will be designated as W_2.

➤ *Example.* In the foregoing discussion of the machine filling boxes of cereal, the two states of the world are:

W_1: The machine is properly adjusted ($\mu = 8$ ounces)
W_2: The machine is not properly adjusted ($\mu \neq 8$ ounces).

Hypotheses about the State of the World

Unfortunately, the true state of the world is not known in most cases at the time a decision must be made and action taken. One may only set up hypotheses about the two possible states. These hypotheses can then be tested and accepted or rejected based on the outcome of the test.

➤ *Example.* Using the same illustration, it is possible to set up two hypotheses about the machine filling boxes with cereal:

H_1: $\mu = 8$ ounces (W_1 is the true state of the world)
H_2: $\mu \neq 8$ ounces (W_2 is the true state of the world).

The hypothesis H_1 is usually called the *null hypothesis*. The word "null" comes from the fact that this hypothesis assumes that there is "no significant difference" between the value of the universe parameter being tested and the value of the statistic computed from a sample drawn from that universe. Stated another way, the null hypothesis assumes that the difference between the parameter designated in the hypothesis and the statistic is a sampling difference.

Hypothesis H_2 is called the *alternate hypothesis*, and it is the hypothesis that will be accepted if statistical testing leads to a rejection of H_1.

The fact that H_1 is set up and tested first is largely a matter of convenience and does not necessarily mean that it is the belief of the experimenter that it is true. It is easier to assume that there is no significant difference and to accept or reject this hypothesis first before going on to the alternate hypothesis. If one begins by testing the hypothesis that there is a significant difference, he is confronted with the question, "How much difference?"

Decision Rules Determine Action

In spite of the fact that uncertainty always exists when decisions must be made on the basis of samples, action must be taken, nevertheless. *Action A_1* may be defined as that action which is taken if hypothesis H_1 is accepted on the assumption that W_1 is the true state of the world. *Action A_2* is that action which is taken if H_1 is rejected, and H_2 is accepted on the conclusion that W_2 is the true state of the world. The decision as to whether to take action A_1 or A_2 is made on the basis of a *decision rule*. The calculation of decision rules will be discussed later in this chapter. For the purposes of the present illustration, let the decision rule rest on two key values known as *critical values.* Suppose

$\bar{x}_{c_1}$ is the first critical value of the sample mean, and
$\bar{x}_{c_2}$ is the second critical value of the sample mean.

➤ *Example.* If the operator of the machine is told to continue the process as long as the mean of the weights of a sample of 49 boxes lies between $\bar{x}_{c_1}$ = 7.8 ounces and $\bar{x}_{c_2}$ = 8.2 ounces, inclusive, and to stop and adjust the machine if the sample mean falls outside these critical values, he has a decision rule.

Hypothesis	State of the world	Decision rule	Action
$H_1: \mu = 8$ ozs.	W_1: Machine is adjusted	$7.8 \leq \bar{x} \leq 8.2$	A_1: Continue
$H_2: \mu \neq 8$ ozs.	W_2: Machine is not adjusted	$\bar{x} < 7.8$ or $\bar{x} > 8.2$	A_2: Stop and adjust

Types of Error

Because a sample statistic is not always a reliable measure of a universe parameter, there will be times when it will lead to an incorrect decision. If the statistic causes one to reject H_1 (and accept H_2), thus taking action A_2 when the true state of the world is W_1, this is defined as a *Type I error*. This is also called an *alpha* (α) *error*.

If, on the other hand, a decision is made to accept H_1 and take action A_1 when the true state of the world is W_2, this is defined as a *Type II error*, or a *beta* (β) *error*.

➤ *Example.* This terminology applied to the problem of the machine operator may be shown as follows:

	States of the world	
Action	W_1 (H_1 is true)	W_2 (H_1 is false)
A_1: Continue	Correct decision	Type II (β) error
A_2: Stop and adjust	Type I (α) error	Correct decision

Probability of Making an Incorrect Decision

While it is recognized that some incorrect decisions are inevitable, it is the job of the statistician to estimate the probability of an incorrect decision so that the businessman can act with a knowledge of the magnitude of the risks he runs.

Probability of a Type I Error. By definition, a Type I or α error can be made only when the null hypothesis (H_1) is true and W_1 is the true state of the world. Given H_1 is true:

$$z = \frac{\bar{x}_c - \mu}{\sigma_{\bar{x}}} \dots\dots\dots\dots\dots\dots\dots\dots(11.1)$$

where,

$\bar{x}_c$ is the critical value of the sample mean
μ is the value designated in H_1
$\sigma_{\bar{x}}$ is the standard error of the mean.

➤ *Example.* Assume that the universe standard deviation of the weights of boxes of cereal filled by the machine under discussion has been determined from long experience to be 0.7 ounces. Further, assume that at the time the operator takes a particular sample of 49 boxes, the universe mean is $\mu = 8$ ounces.

The theoretical sampling distribution shown in Figure 11.1 represents a distribution of the means of all possible samples of 49 boxes that might be drawn by the operator at any one time. The distribution of $\bar{x}$'s is normally distributed with

$$\mu = 8 \text{ ounces,}$$

and the standard deviation of this distribution is the standard error of the mean

$$\sigma_{\bar{x}} = \frac{\sigma}{\sqrt{n}} = \frac{0.7}{\sqrt{49}} = \frac{0.7}{7} = 0.1 \text{ ounce.}$$

If the decision rule is to reject H_1 and take action A_2 when $\bar{x} < 7.8$ or $\bar{x} > 8.2$, the probability of a Type I error may be seen in the top distribution (Example A) in Figure 11.1 as the shaded area in each tail.

Since the theoretical sampling distribution is known to be normal, this probability may be computed as

$$z_1 = \frac{\bar{x}_{c_1} - \mu}{\dfrac{\sigma}{\sqrt{n}}} = \frac{7.8 - 8}{0.1} = \frac{-0.2}{0.1} = -2$$

$$z_2 = \frac{\bar{x}_{c_2} - \mu}{\dfrac{\sigma}{\sqrt{n}}} = \frac{8.2 - 8}{0.1} = \frac{0.2}{0.1} = 2.$$

GIVEN:

μ = 8 ounces

σ = 0.7 ounces

n = 49 boxes

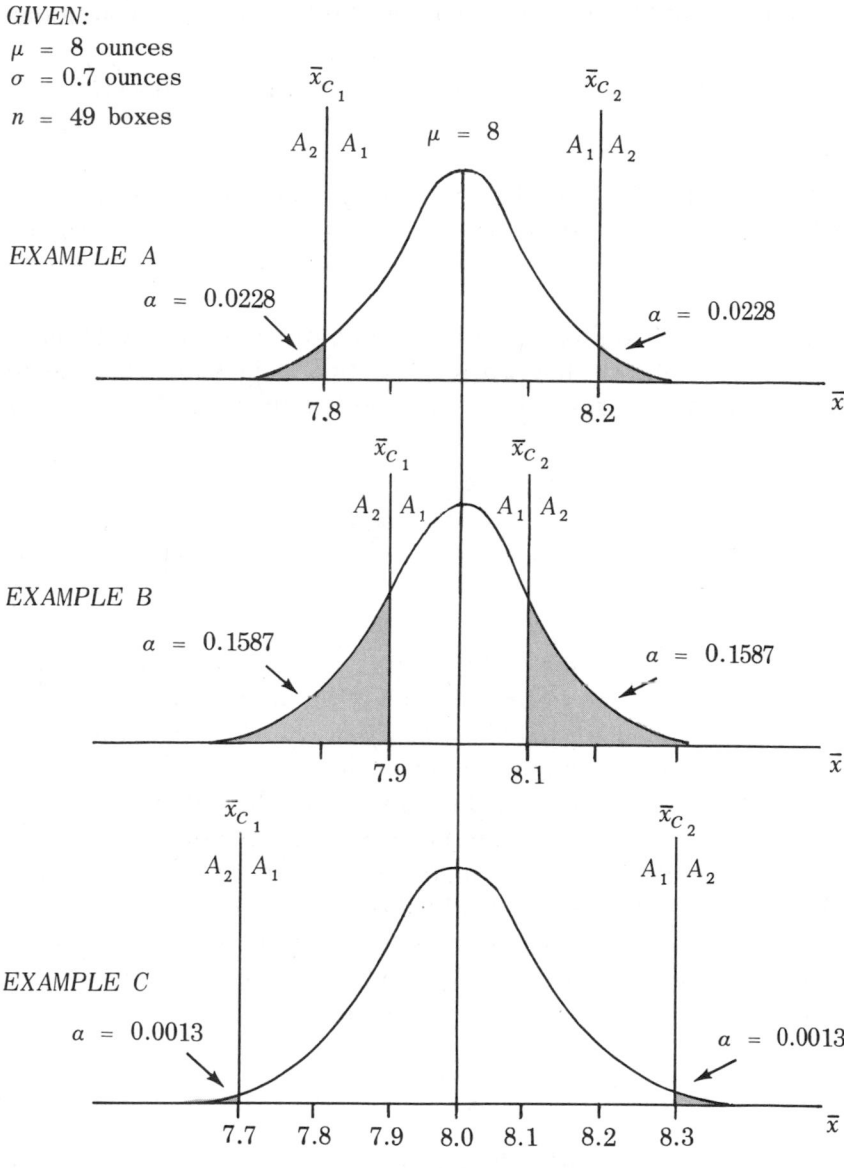

Figure 11.1

PROBABILITY OF MAKING A TYPE I ERROR
GIVEN H_1 IS TRUE

Using the table in Appendix I, the area in each tail is found to be 0.0228, or a combined area in both tails of 0.0456. This may be interpreted as

$$P(A_2 \mid W_1) = 0.0456 \text{ or } 4.56\%.$$

Also, the probability of a correct decision under these same conditions is

$$P(A_1 \mid W_1) = 1 - P(A_2 \mid W_1) = 1 - 0.0456 = 0.9544$$

or just over 95%.

The probability of a Type I error may be controlled by moving the critical values closer to or farther away from the parameter assumed in H_1.

➤ *Example.* An examination of the second distribution (Example B) in Figure 11.1 shows that when the critical values are changed to 7.9 and 8.1 ounces, respectively, the probability of a Type I error increases to

$$z_1 = \frac{7.9 - 8.0}{0.1} = \frac{-0.1}{0.1} = -1$$

$$z_2 = \frac{8.1 - 8.0}{0.1} = \frac{0.1}{0.1} = 1.$$

The area in each tail is now 0.1587, and $P(A_2 \mid W_1) = 0.1587 + 0.1587 = 0.3174$ or 31.74%. The probability of a correct decision is $1 - P(A_2 \mid W_1) = 1 - 0.3174 = 0.6826$ or 68.26%. This probability is represented by the white space under the curve.

If, as seen in Example C in this same figure, the critical values are changed to 7.7 and 8.3 ounces, respectively, the probability of a Type I error drops to 0.0013 in each tail, or 0.0026 for both tails.

If one wishes to set the critical values so that the probability of a Type I error is some given amount, say 5%, this may be done by finding the $\pm z$ value in the Table of Area in One Tail of the Normal Curve in Appendix I, which gives 2.5% in each tail.

$$\pm z = \frac{\bar{x}_c - \mu}{\sigma_{\bar{x}}}$$

$$-1.96 = \frac{\bar{x}_{c_1} - \mu}{\sigma_{\bar{x}}} = \frac{\bar{x}_{c_1} - 8}{0.1}$$

$$-0.196 = \bar{x}_{c_1} - 8$$

$$\bar{x}_{c_1} = 8 - 0.196 = 7.804, \text{ and}$$

$$1.96 = \frac{\bar{x}_{c_2} - \mu}{\sigma_{\bar{x}}} = \frac{\bar{x}_{c_2} - 8}{0.1}$$

$$0.196 = \bar{x}_{c_2} - 8$$

$$\bar{x}_{c_2} = 8 + 0.196 = 8.196.$$

Probability of a Type II Error. By definition, a Type II or β error can be made only when the null hypothesis (H_1) is false, and W_2 is the true state of the world. However, the computation of the probability of a Type II error is more difficult than that of a Type I error. The former can occur only when the parameter has changed, and the magnitude of the probability is dependent upon how much the parameter has changed.

➤ *Example.* Suppose in the previous example the universe mean, μ, is not 8 ounces but is some other value. The only kind of error the machine operator can now make is to fail to stop the machine and adjust. This is a Type II error. If $\mu = 7.7$ ounces,

$$z = \frac{\bar{x}_c - \mu}{\sigma_{\bar{x}}} = \frac{7.9 - 7.7}{0.1} = \frac{0.2}{0.1} = 2.$$

The probability of a β error lies in the tail of the distribution that falls between 7.9 and 8.1. This may be seen in Example A, Figure 11.2. The probability is

$$P(A_1 \mid W_2 = 7.7) = 0.0228 \text{ or } 2.28\%.$$

Also (Example B, Figure 11.2)

$$P(A_1 \mid W_2 = 7.9) = 0.4773 \text{ or } 47.73\%.$$

In Example C, Figure 11.2, H_1 is correct; so the only type of error that can be made is an α error.
But,

$$P(A_1 \mid W_2 = 8.1) = 0.4773, \text{ and}$$
$$P(A_1 \mid W_2 = 8.3) = 0.0028.$$

In general, it can be stated that if H_1 *is true*:

1. Probability of a correct decision is that area of the theoretical sampling distribution which lies between $\bar{x}_{c_1}$ and $\bar{x}_{c_2}$, and
2. Probability of a Type I error is that area of the distribution which lies outside $\bar{x}_{c_1}$ and $\bar{x}_{c_2}$.

But if H_1 *is false*:

1. Probability of a correct decision is that area of the theoretical sampling distribution which lies outside $\bar{x}_{c_1}$ and $\bar{x}_{c_2}$, and
2. Probability of a Type II error is that area of the distribution which lies between $\bar{x}_{c_1}$ and $\bar{x}_{c_2}$.

Another point which should be emphasized is that as the critical values are moved to decrease the probability of an α error, these changes automatically increase the probability of a β error if H_1 proves to be false.

GIVEN: σ = 0.7 ounces H_1: μ = 8 ounces
       n = 49 H_2: $\mu \neq$ 8 ounces
       $\bar{x}_{C_1}$ = 7.9 ounces
       $\bar{x}_{C_2}$ = 8.1 ounces

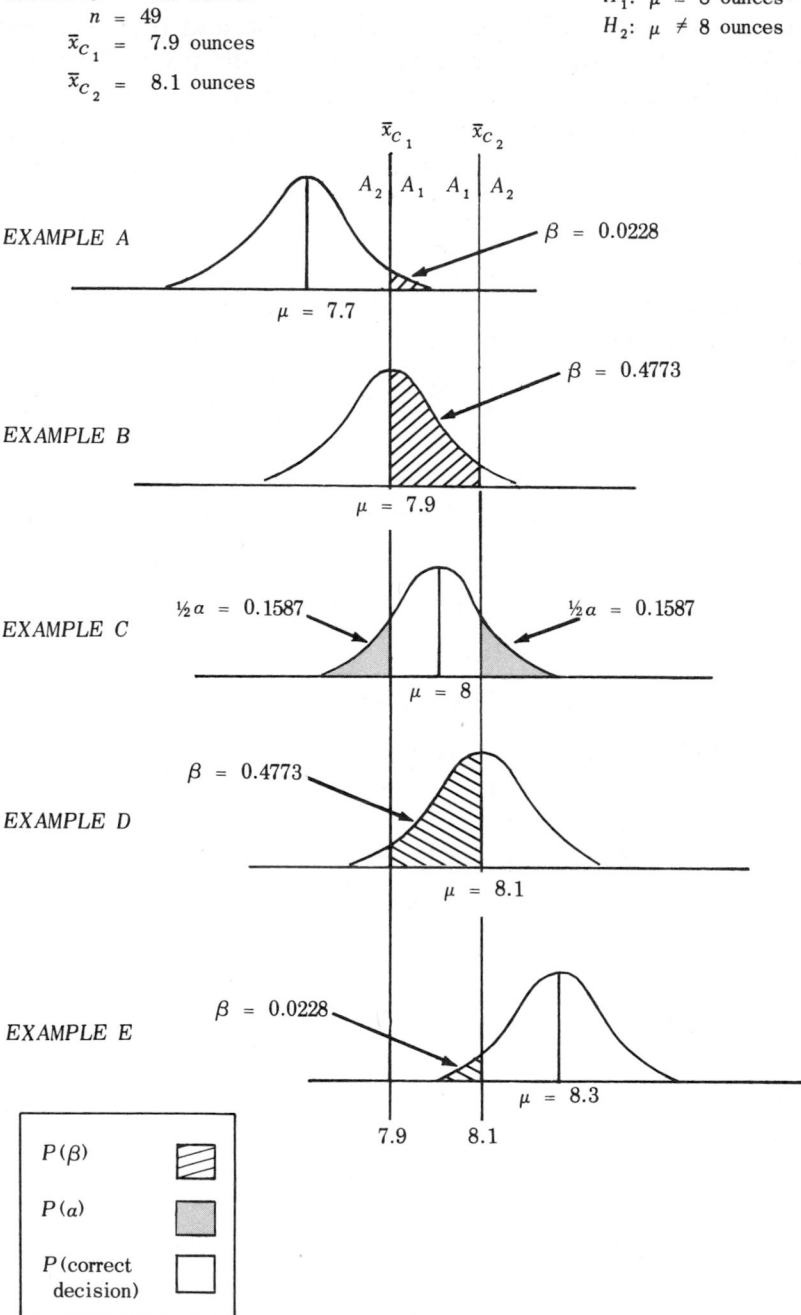

Figure 11.2

PROBABILITY OF MAKING AN ERROR FOR A GIVEN
VALUE OF THE PARAMETER

➤ *Example.* In Figure 11.3, Example A shows the probability of an α error when $\mu = 8$ and the critical values are 7.9 and 8.1. $P(A_2 \mid W_1) = 0.3174$. Example B shows the probability of a β error if $\mu = 8.2$ and the critical values are the same. $P(A_1 \mid W_2) = 0.1587$.

In Example C of the same figure, the critical values are moved to 7.8 and 8.2 to reduce the probability of an α error to 0.0456 when $\mu = 8$. These same critical values in Example D increase the probability of a β error to 0.5000 when $\mu = 8.2$.

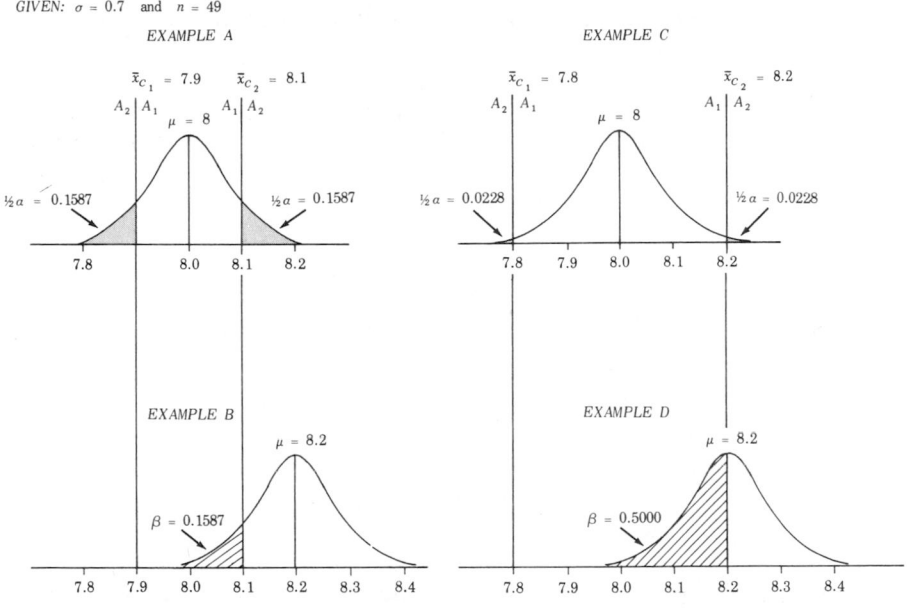

Figure 11.3

PROBABILITY OF MAKING AN ERROR FOR TWO VALUES
OF THE PARAMETER AND WITH TWO SETS OF
CRITICAL VALUES

One- and Two-Tail Tests

The test of significance examples discussed so far have been of the two-tail variety. Management was concerned with the problem of adjusting a machine whenever it was filling boxes with either too much or too little cereal. The region in which H_1 might be rejected lay in both tails of the sampling distribution. This is called a *two-tail test.*

In many other problems, one is concerned only with a rejection area in one tail of the sampling distribution. Tests of significance in such cases are called *one-tail tests.*

➤ *Example.* A service station operator has kept careful records of his sales for a two-year period and knows his average sale (μ) to be $4.00 with a standard deviation (σ) of $1.60. He starts giving double trading stamps with each fill-up of gasoline in the hope of improving the average size of sales. After trying the new promotional scheme for a few days, he draws a random sample of 100 sales slips and computes a sample mean.

If the operator had decided ahead of time that he was looking only for a significant increase in sales, he would set his critical value at some figure greater than $4.00, and he would conduct a one-tail test of significance. If he chose a critical value of $4.36, then

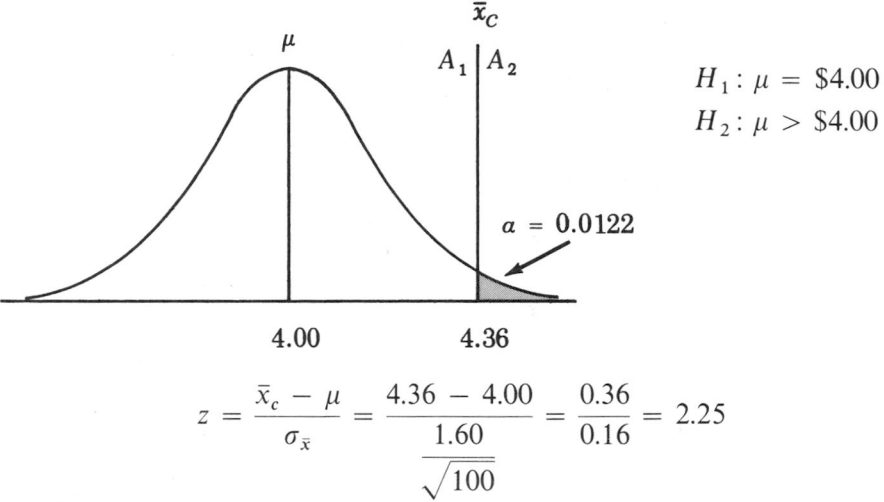

$$H_1: \mu = \$4.00$$
$$H_2: \mu > \$4.00$$

$$z = \frac{\bar{x}_c - \mu}{\sigma_{\bar{x}}} = \frac{4.36 - 4.00}{\dfrac{1.60}{\sqrt{100}}} = \frac{0.36}{0.16} = 2.25$$

and the $P(A_2 \mid W_1) = 0.0122$ if H_1 is true. $P(A_1 \mid W_2)$ if H_1 is false would depend on the new value of μ. The smaller the increase in μ, the greater $P(\beta)$; the greater the increase in μ, the smaller $P(\beta)$.

OPERATING CHARACTERISTIC AND POWER CURVES FOR MEANS

The following is a recapitulation of what has been discussed to this point:

1. The probability of a Type I error is $P(A_2 \mid W_1)$. This probability can be controlled for any given sample size when computing the critical values that determine when to accept and when to reject H_1.
2. The probability of a Type II error is $P(A_1 \mid W_2)$. The probability of this kind of error depends upon the value of W_2 when H_1 is false. While this probability cannot be computed when W_2 is unknown, it can be figured for assumed values of W_2.

➤ *Example.* The service station operator discussed in the previous example decides that if a random sample of 100 sales slips shows a significant increase in the amount of his average sale, he will continue giving double trading stamps with each fill-up. Otherwise, he will give up the new sales promotion. He decides on an α risk of 5%. His risks can be shown schematically as follows:

Action	$H_1: \mu = \$4.00$ W_1	$H_2: \mu > \$4.00$ W_2
A_1: Give up new sales promotion	$P(A_1 \mid W_1) = 0.95$	$\beta = P(A_1 \mid W_2)$ depends on the value of W_2.
A_2: Continue the new promotion	$\alpha = P(A_2 \mid W_1) = 0.05$	$P(A_2 \mid W_2)$ depends on the value of W_2.

The critical value may be determined by finding that z value in Appendix I which comes closest to giving an area of 0.0500 in the tail of the sampling distribution. A z value of 1.64 gives an area of 0.0505.

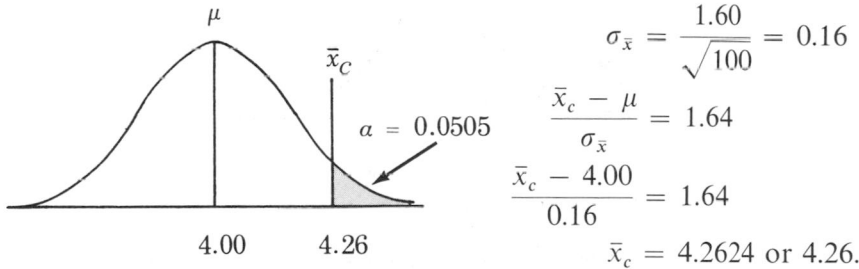

$$\sigma_{\bar{x}} = \frac{1.60}{\sqrt{100}} = 0.16$$

$$\frac{\bar{x}_c - \mu}{\sigma_{\bar{x}}} = 1.64$$

$$\frac{\bar{x}_c - 4.00}{0.16} = 1.64$$

$$\bar{x}_c = 4.2624 \text{ or } 4.26.$$

While the probability of a Type I error has been determined by the critical value, the probability of a Type II error varies with W_2 or μ when it is not $4.00. Table 11.1 shows the probability of both an incorrect and a correct decision for nine possible values of μ.

In Figure 11.4 the probability of an incorrect decision is shown as the shaded area of each distribution associated with a given value of μ. The white area in each sampling distribution represents the probability of a correct decision. As one might expect, the probability of correctly recognizing a change in μ increases rapidly as the change becomes greater.

The probability of a correct decision when H_1 is false is $1 - \beta = 1 - P(A_1 \mid W_2) = P(A_2 \mid W_2)$. The probability $1 - \beta$ is called the *power of the function*. If a series of values of $1 - \beta$ are computed and if these probabilities are shown as a line chart, the resulting graph is called a *power curve*. A graph of the β probabilities is called an *operating characteristic curve*. In most of the literature, this is shortened to *OC curve*.

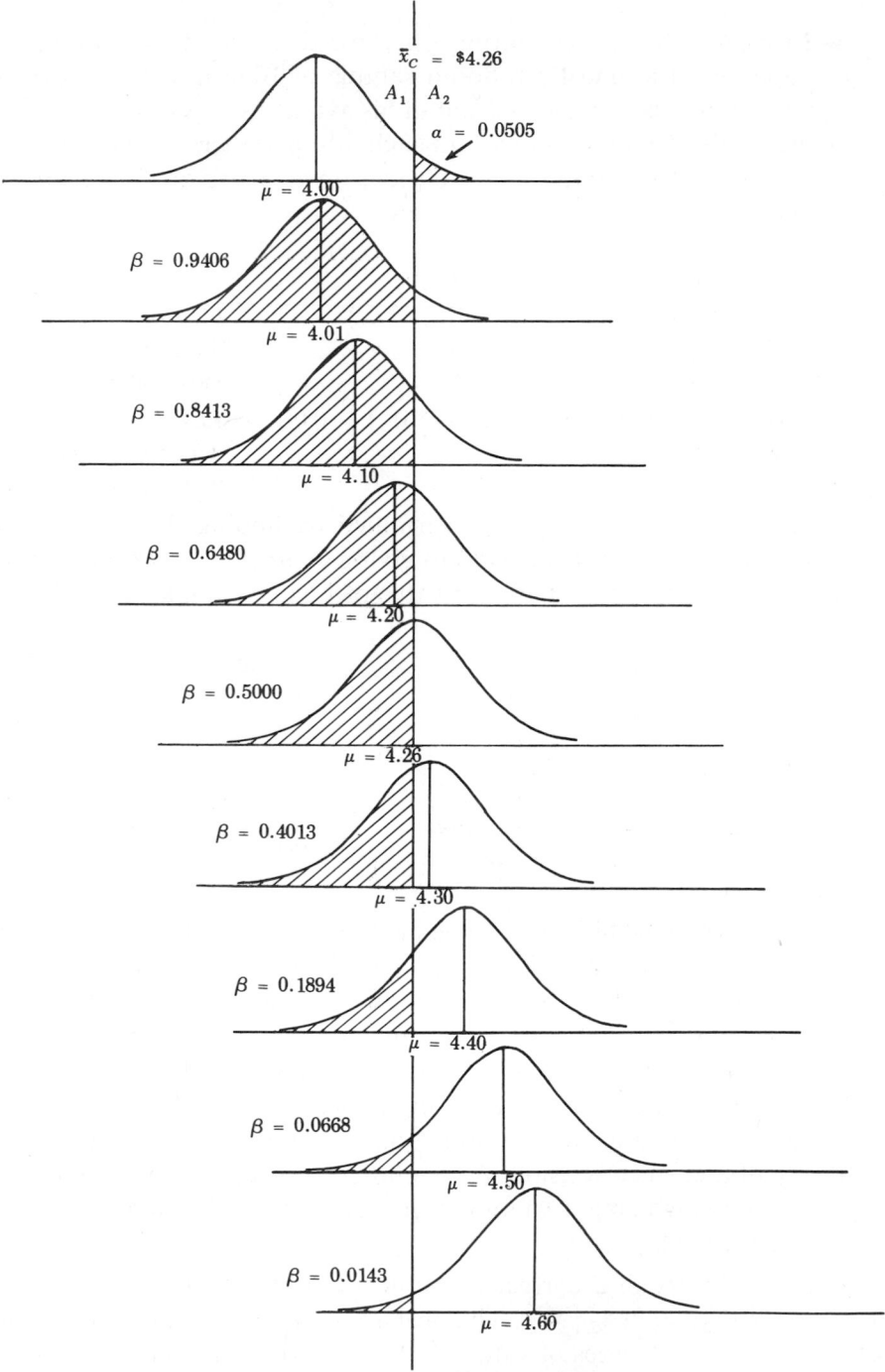

Figure 11.4

PROBABILITY OF AN INCORRECT DECISION FOR GIVEN
VALUES OF μ

Table 11.1

PROBABILITY OF MAKING A CORRECT DECISION WITH
GIVEN VALUES OF μ

Value of μ	$\dfrac{\bar{x}_c - \mu}{\sigma_{\bar{x}}}$	Area in tail	Probability of incorrect decision	Probability of correct decision
$4.00	1.64	0.0505	0.0505	0.9495
4.01	1.56	0.0594	0.9406	0.0594
4.10	1.00	0.1587	0.8413	0.1587
4.20	0.38	0.3520	0.6480	0.3520
4.26	0	0.5000	0.5000	0.5000
4.30	-0.25	0.4013	0.4013	0.5987
4.40	-0.88	0.1894	0.1894	0.8106
4.50	-1.50	0.0668	0.0668	0.9332
4.60	-2.19	0.0143	0.0143	0.9857

GIVEN: $\sigma = \$1.60$ $\bar{x}_c = 4.26$ $n = 100$.

➤ *Example.* Continuing with the service station example, Figure 11.5 shows the operating characteristic curve and the power curve that can be drawn using the probabilities given in Table 11.1. For any given value of μ, the probability of a Type II error can be read from the top graph in the figure, and the probability of a correct decision can be read from the bottom graph.

Effect of a Change in Sample Size

A change in the size of the sample used results both in a change in the critical value and a change in the power of the function or the effectiveness of the decision rule. If the size of the sample is increased, the critical value will be closer to the parameter assumed in H_1, and the probability of a β error will be reduced for a given value of W_2.

➤ *Example.* Suppose all the facts in the service station example are the same except the sample size is 400 rather than 100 sales slips.

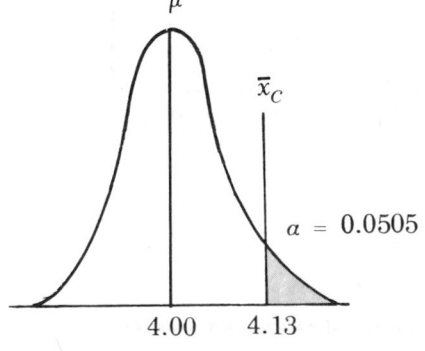

$$\sigma_{\bar{x}} = \frac{1.60}{\sqrt{400}} = 0.08$$

$$\frac{\bar{x}_c - \mu}{\sigma_{\bar{x}}} = 1.64$$

$$\frac{\bar{x}_c - 4.00}{0.08} = 1.64$$

$$\bar{x}_c = 4.1312 \text{ or } 4.13.$$

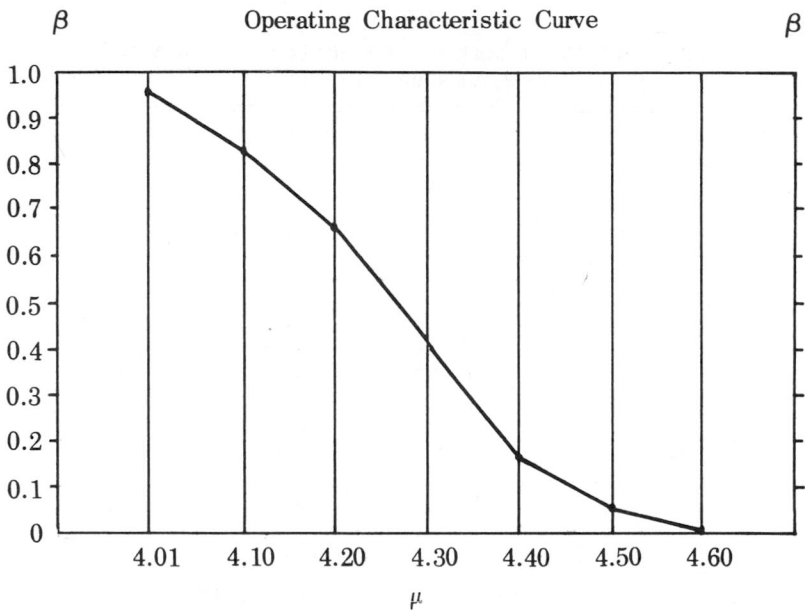

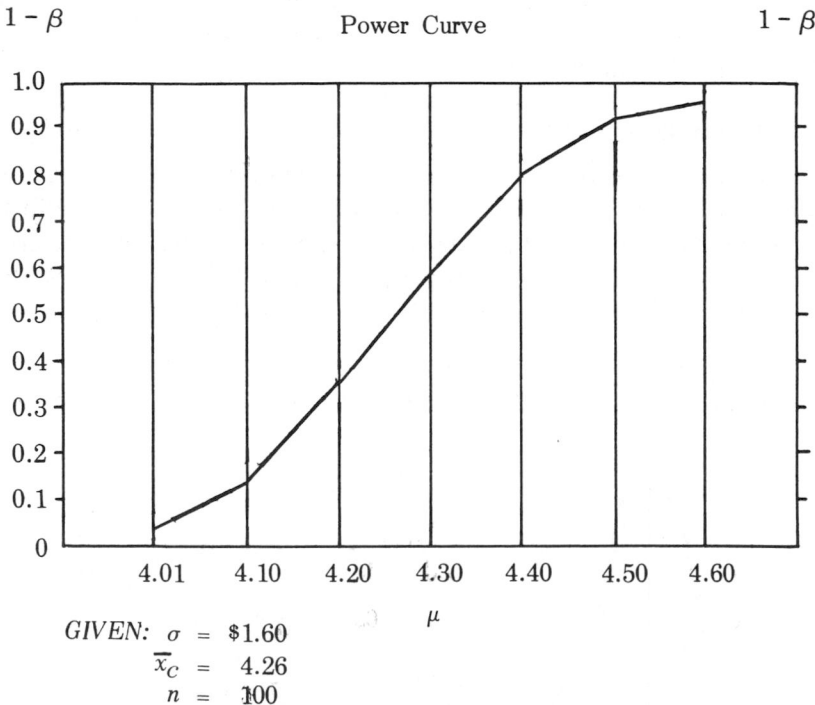

Figure 11.5

OPERATING CHARACTERISTIC AND POWER CURVES

The value of α is the same, 0.0505, but the values for β and $1 - \beta$ are substantially different, as may be seen in Figure 11.6. With a sample of 100, $P(A_1 \mid W_2 = 4.20) = 0.6480$. When the sample is increased to 400, $P(A_1 \mid W_2 = 4.20) = 0.1894$.

Two-Tail Test

Power curves and operating characteristic curves are possible for two-tail as well as for one-tail tests, and they are equally sensitive to changes in sample size.

➤ *Example.* The example used previously of the machine filling boxes with cereal involved a two-tail test. If management decided on an α level of 5% and a sample of 49 boxes, the critical values were computed on page 382 to be $\bar{x}_{c_1} = 7.804$, and $\bar{x}_{c_2} = 8.196$.

If the α level does not change but if the sample size is increased to 196 boxes, the critical values are $\bar{x}_{c_1} = 7.902$, and $\bar{x}_{c_2} = 8.098$.

Table 11.2 shows the β probabilities for 11 selected values of μ for each of the two sample sizes. Figure 11.7 shows two OC curves drawn from the data in Table 11.2. Again, it is possible to see the greater power of the decision rule using the larger of the two samples.

Table 11.2

PROBABILITY OF MAKING A TYPE II ERROR WITH GIVEN
VALUES OF μ AND TWO DIFFERENT SAMPLE SIZES

Value of μ	$n_1 = 49$		$n_2 = 196$	
	$\dfrac{\bar{x}_c - \mu}{\sigma_{\bar{x}}}$	β	$\dfrac{\bar{x}_c - \mu}{\sigma_{\bar{x}}}$	β
7.604	2.00	0.0228	5.96	0.0000
7.704	1.00	0.1587	3.96	0.0000
7.804	0	0.5000	−1.96	0.0250
7.902	−0.98	0.8365	0	0.5000
7.950	−1.46	0.9279	−0.96	0.8315
8.000	±1.96	...	±1.96	...
8.050	−1.46	0.9279	−0.96	0.8315
8.098	−0.98	0.8365	0	0.5000
8.196	0	0.5000	1.96	0.0250
8.296	1.00	0.1587	3.96	0.0000
8.396	2.00	0.0228	5.96	0.0000

GIVEN: $H_1 : \mu = 8.00$ ounces
$\qquad$ $H_2 : \mu \neq 8.00$ ounces
$\qquad$ $\sigma = 0.7$ ounces
$\qquad$ $\bar{x}_{c_1} = 7.804$ and $\bar{x}_{c_2} = 8.196$ when $n_1 = 49$
$\qquad$ $\bar{x}_{c_1} = 7.902$ and $\bar{x}_{c_2} = 8.098$ when $n_2 = 196$
$\qquad$ $\alpha = 0.05$.

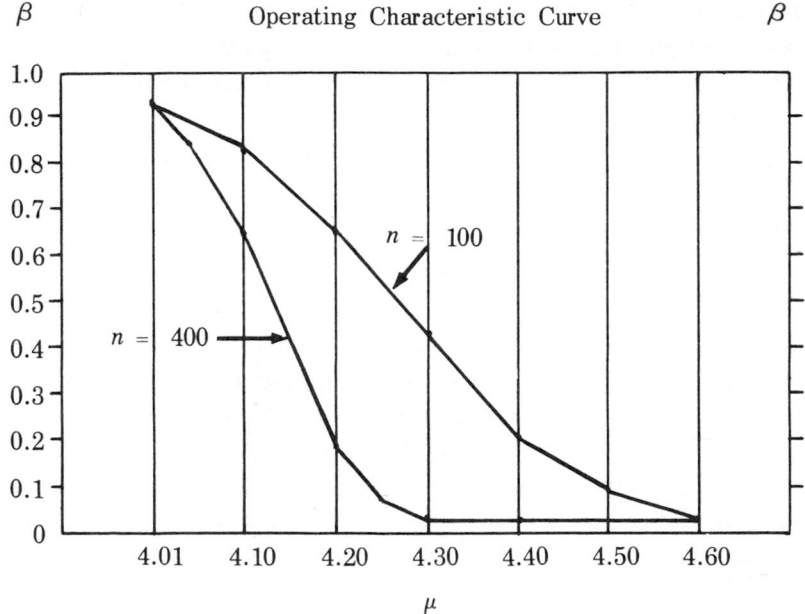

Operating Characteristic Curve

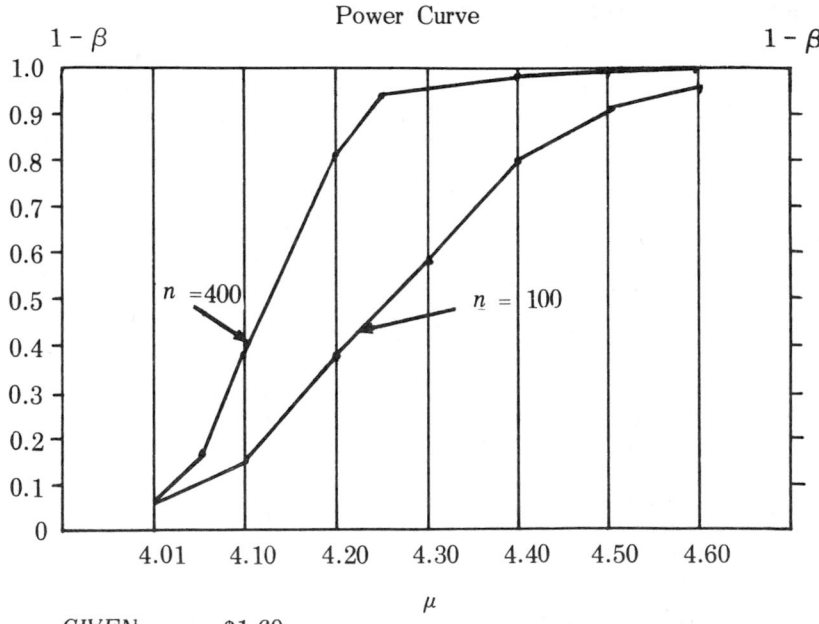

Power Curve

GIVEN: σ = \$1.60

$\bar{x}_C$ = 4.26 when n is 100

$\bar{x}_C$ = 4.13 when n is 400

Figure 11.6

OPERATING CHARACTERISTIC AND POWER CURVES
FOR TWO DIFFERENT SAMPLE SIZES

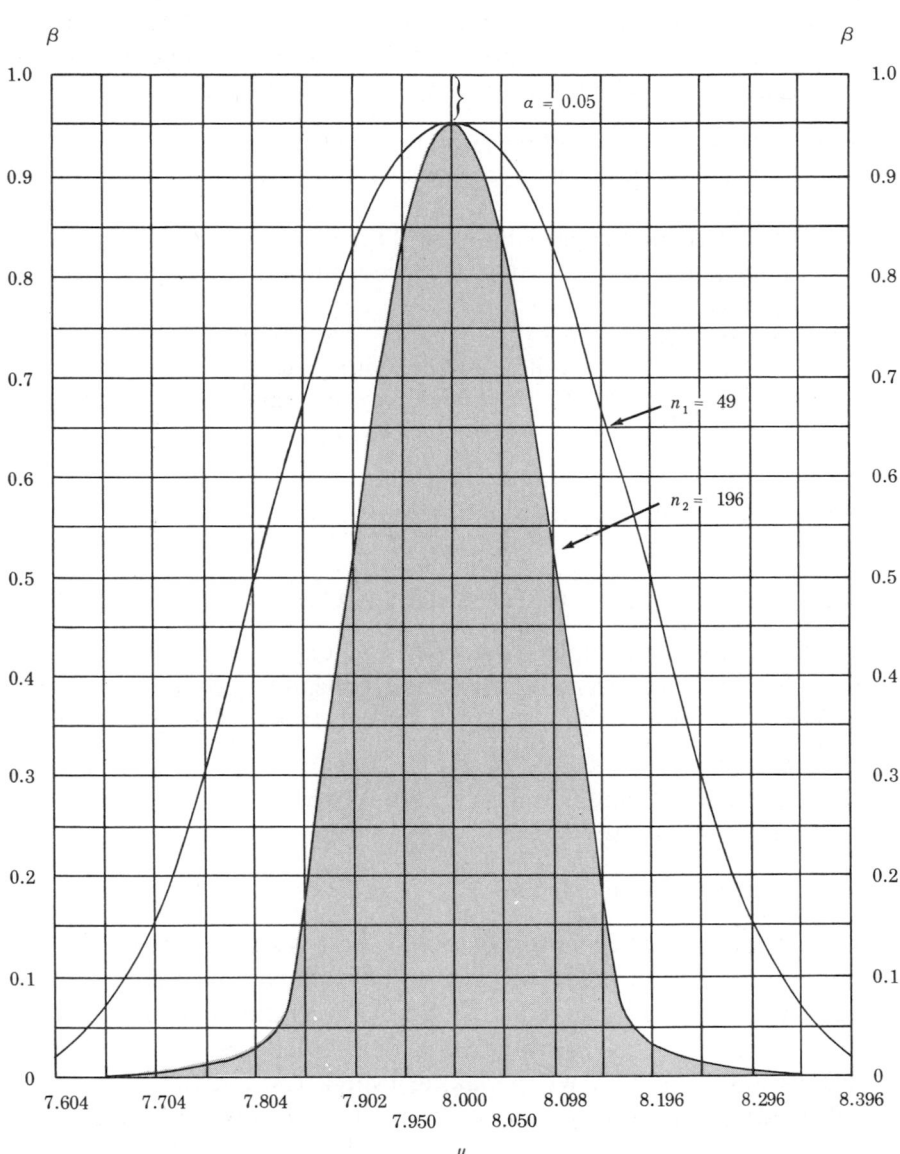

Source of data: Table 11.2.

Figure 11.7

OPERATING CHARACTERISTIC CURVE FOR TWO DIFFERENT SAMPLE SIZES

STEPS TO FOLLOW IN MAKING A TEST OF SIGNIFICANCE

At this point it is possible to revise somewhat the decision steps used in the tests of significance that were described in the introduction to this chapter. In this section the tests are stated in terms of the technical notation that has just been discussed. The five steps listed below may be used in conducting systematically any test of significance:

STEP 1. Set up a null hypothesis (H_1) to be tested.

STEP 2. Set up an alternate hypothesis (H_2) that can be accepted if H_1 is rejected.

STEP 3. Determine the probability of a Type I error that management is prepared to risk (α). Use this probability to determine a decision rule.

STEP 4. Use statistical theory to write a criterion stating the conditions under which H_1 will be accepted or rejected.

STEP 5. Apply the information provided by the sample to make a decision and to determine the action to be taken.

In the sections of this chapter that follow, these rules will be applied under a series of different test conditions.

TESTING THE MEAN OF A SINGLE SAMPLE

If a single random sample is drawn from a universe, and if one wishes to test a hypothesis concerning the universe mean based on the information from that sample, there are two basic types of problems to be considered:

1. The universe standard deviation is known, and
2. The universe standard deviation is not known.

Universe Standard Deviation Is Known

When the standard deviation of the universe is known, the theoretical sampling distribution of sample means from which a particular sample mean, $\bar{x}$, is drawn is a normal distribution with a mean, μ, and a standard deviation, $\sigma_{\bar{x}}$. For a given value of α, it is not necessary to compute critical values, $\bar{x}_{c_1}$ and $\bar{x}_{c_2}$, when making a single test since a table value of z will perform the same function. To distinguish this table value from another z value that will be computed using the sample data, the table value will be designated as z_α.

➤ *Example.* A manufacturer of television tubes produces a tube that has an average life (μ) of 580 hours and a standard deviation (σ) of 30 hours. He regularly draws random samples of 100 tubes from the production line to test for any significant change in μ. If a particular sample of 100 tubes shows a sample mean ($\bar{x}$) of 573 hours, test at an α level of 0.05 to determine if there has been a significant change.

STEPS:
 1. $H_1: \mu = 580$ hours
 2. $H_2: \mu \neq 580$ hours
 3. An α level of 0.05 (two-tail test) requires z_α values $= \pm 1.96$.

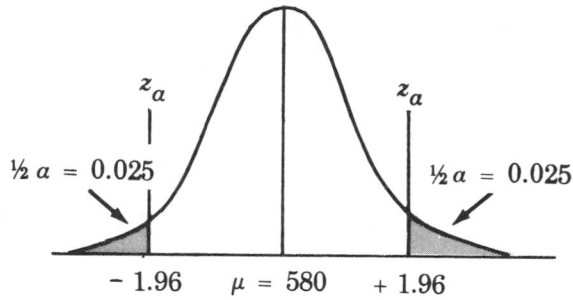

4. Criterion: Reject H_1 (accept H_2) if $z < -1.96$ or if $z > +1.96$; accept H_1 if $-1.96 \leq z \leq +1.96$, where,

$$z = \frac{\bar{x} - \mu}{\sigma_{\bar{x}}} \quad \dots\dots\dots\dots\dots\dots\dots\dots\dots\dots (11.2)$$

5. Using the sample data and the assumptions about the universe:

$$z = \frac{573 - 580}{3} = \frac{-7}{3} = -2.33$$

$$\text{where,} \sigma_{\bar{x}} = \frac{30}{\sqrt{100}} = 3.$$

Since $z(-2.33) < z_\alpha(-1.96)$, H_1 should be rejected and H_2 accepted. There has been a significant change in μ as indicated by this sample. When H_1 is rejected, the only type of error that can be made is Type I, and the probability of having made such an error is something less than 2.5 %. The probability of a correct decision in this case is 97.5 % or greater.

➤ *Example.* Suppose that in the previous example the sample mean had been 584 hours with a random sample of 225 tubes, and one wished to test for a significant change in μ at an α level of 0.01 with a one-tail test.

STEPS:
 1. $H_1: \mu = 580$ hours
 2. $H_2: \mu > 580$ hours

3. An α level of 0.01 (one-tail test) requires a z_α value of 2.33.

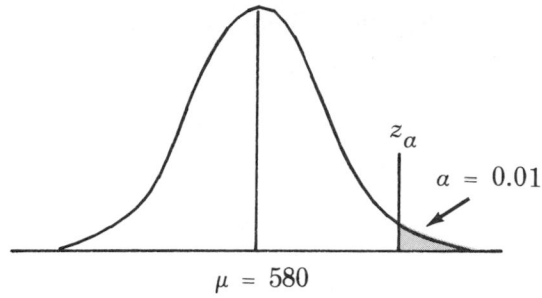

4. Criterion : Reject H_1 (accept H_2) if $z > 2.33$; accept H_1 if $z \leq 2.33$, where

$$z = \frac{\bar{x} - \mu}{\sigma_{\bar{x}}}.$$

5. Using the sample data

$$z = \frac{584 - 580}{\dfrac{30}{\sqrt{225}}} = \frac{4}{2} = 2.$$

Since $z(2) < z_\alpha(2.33)$, accept H_1. A significant change in μ cannot be shown from the sample. In making this decision, it is possible that a Type II error has been made, but there is no way to measure this probability.

Universe Standard Deviation Is Not Known

In many situations the universe standard deviation is not known, but it must be estimated from the sample. In such cases the distribution of sample means is not normal but is distributed as Student's t distribution with a mean, μ, and a standard deviation, $\hat{\sigma}_{\bar{x}}$.

➤ *Example.* If a manufacturer of television sets does not make his own tubes but buys them from another manufacturer, he may use tests of significance in determining whether to accept or to reject a particular shipment based on an inspection of a random sample of tubes drawn from the shipment. Suppose that the contract between the manufacturer of the tubes and the buyer calls for an average life of 550 hours. The firm receiving the shipment tests a sample of 25 tubes and finds $\bar{x} = 530$ hours, and $s = 37$ hours. If a one-tail test is made at an α level of 0.05, should the shipment be accepted or rejected?

STEPS:

1. $H_1 : \mu = 550$ hours
2. $H_2 : \mu < 550$ hours
3. An α level of 0.05 (one-tail test) requires a t_α value of -1.711. (Use $t_{0.10}$ with $n - 1$ or 24 degrees of freedom in the table in Appendix J to get t_α. The level of significance of 0.10 represents a total area of 10% in both tails or 5% in one tail.)

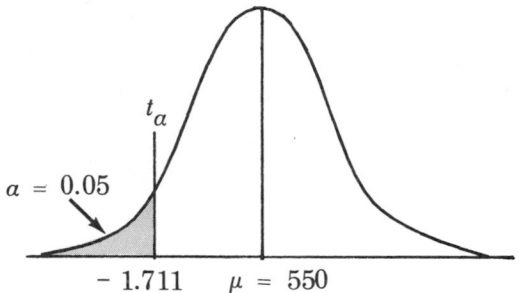

$\alpha = 0.05$

$-1.711 \qquad \mu = 550$

4. Criterion: Reject H_1 (accept H_2) if $t < -1.711$; accept H_1 if $t \geq -1.711$, where

$$ t = \frac{\bar{x} - \mu}{\hat{\sigma}_{\bar{x}}} \quad \dots\dots\dots\dots\dots\dots\dots (11.3) $$

$$ \text{and } \hat{\sigma}_{\bar{x}} = \frac{s}{\sqrt{n - 1}} $$

5. Using the sample data

$$ t = \frac{530 - 550}{7.55} = \frac{-20}{7.55} = -2.65 $$

$$ \text{where } \hat{\sigma}_{\bar{x}} = \frac{37}{\sqrt{24}} = 7.55. $$

Since $t(-2.65) < t_\alpha(-1.711)$, reject H_1 and accept H_2. The shipment would be rejected as not meeting the contract requirements for average length of life of the tubes.

➤ *Example.* An intercity bus company sets up a new bus schedule designed to make the trip between two towns in an average of five hours. After setting up the schedule, the company times a sample of 12 trips and finds the average time to be 5.2 hours, with a standard deviation of 0.5 hours. If a two-tail test is made at an α level of 0.05, is there a significant difference between the average planned time of the trip and the actual average time?

STEPS:

1. $H_1: \mu = 5$ hours
2. $H_2: \mu \neq 5$ hours
3. An α level of 0.05 (two-tail test) requires t_α values of ± 2.201 ($t_{0.05}$ with 11 degrees of freedom).
4. Criterion: Reject H_1 (accept H_2) if $t < -2.201$ or $t > +2.201$; accept H_1 if $-2.201 \leq t \leq +2.201$, where

$$t = \frac{\bar{x} - \mu}{\hat{\sigma}_{\bar{x}}}$$

5. Using the sample data

$$t = \frac{5.2 - 5.0}{0.15} = \frac{0.20}{0.15} = 1.33$$

$$\text{where } \hat{\sigma}_{\bar{x}} = \frac{0.5}{\sqrt{11}} = 0.15.$$

Since $t(1.33) < t_\alpha(2.201)$, accept H_1. The sample trips do not show a significant difference in the average time from that originally planned.

It may be noted that in cases where the sample is large enough, the sampling distribution approaches normal even though the universe standard deviation is not known.

TESTING THE DIFFERENCE BETWEEN THE MEANS OF TWO SAMPLES

A very common problem encountered in tests of significance is one in which it is necessary to determine if the means of two samples indicate that the samples were drawn from one universe or two.

If the two samples of sizes n_1 and n_2 have means $\bar{x}_1$ and $\bar{x}_2$, the null hypothesis may be stated as follows:

$$H_1: \mu_1 = \mu_2.$$

If this hypothesis is accepted, a decision has been made that the two samples were drawn from a single universe with a mean, μ, and that any difference in the sample means is a sampling difference and is not significant.

The alternate hypothesis may be stated as:

$$H_2: \mu_1 \neq \mu_2,$$
$$H_2: \mu_1 < \mu_2, \text{ or}$$
$$H_2: \mu_1 > \mu_2.$$

If H_1 is rejected, and H_2 is accepted, the conclusion reached is that the difference between $\bar{x}_1$ and $\bar{x}_2$ is too large to be explained as a sampling difference and, therefore, the samples were drawn from two universes with different means.

In approaching tests of this nature, two basic types of problems will be considered:

1. The universe standard deviations, σ_1 and σ_2, are known, and
2. The universe standard deviations are not known.

Universe Standard Deviations Are Known

Since the assumption in H_1 is that $\mu_1 = \mu_2$, then $\mu_1 - \mu_2 = 0$. When σ_1 and σ_2 are known, the theoretical sampling distribution of the statistics, $\bar{x}_1 - \bar{x}_2$, is assumed to be normal with a mean of zero and a standard deviation

$$\sigma_{\bar{x}_1 - \bar{x}_2} = \sqrt{\frac{\sigma_1^2}{n_1} + \frac{\sigma_2^2}{n_2}} \quad \ldots\ldots\ldots\ldots\ldots\ldots(11.4)$$

where,

$\sigma_{\bar{x}_1 - \bar{x}_2}$ is the standard error of the difference between the two sample means.

As with any theoretical sampling distribution that is normal, a z_α value can be established by use of a table of areas under the normal curve, and data supplied by the sample can be used to compute the z value to be compared with z_α. This value will always be

$$z = \frac{\text{statistic} - \text{parameter}}{\text{standard error}}.$$

The statistic is supplied by the sample data, in this case, $\bar{x}_1 - \bar{x}_2$. The parameter is that assumed in H_1, in this case, $\mu_1 - \mu_2$, which is zero. The standard error is the standard deviation of the theoretical sampling distribution, in this case, $\sigma_{\bar{x}_1 - \bar{x}_2}$. Thus, the formula to be used here for z is

$$z = \frac{(\bar{x}_1 - \bar{x}_2) - (\mu_1 - \mu_2)}{\sigma_{\bar{x}_1 - \bar{x}_2}} \quad \text{or} \quad \frac{\bar{x}_1 - \bar{x}_2}{\sigma_{\bar{x}_1 - \bar{x}_2}} \quad \ldots\ldots\ldots\ldots(11.5)$$

➤ *Example.* In a manufacturing plant there are two machines used to cut steel bars. While each machine can be adjusted to control the average length of the bars cut, there will always be some slight variation in the length of the individual bars. Over a period of time the variation in the production of each machine has been carefully measured and is shown in terms of standard deviations:

$$\text{Machine I:} \quad \sigma_1 = 0.10 \text{ inches}$$
$$\text{Machine II:} \quad \sigma_2 = 0.12 \text{ inches.}$$

A machinist is asked to set the two machines so that they will cut bars with equal average lengths. The workman sets the two machines to the best of his ability and then cuts a sample of 50 bars on each machine. The sample results are shown below:

Machine	Sample size	Sample mean
I	$n_1 = 50$	$\bar{x}_1 = 27.80$ inches
II	$n_2 = 50$	$\bar{x}_2 = 27.70$ inches.

The problem is to test at an α level of 0.01 with a one-tail test to see if the machines are set to cut bars of equal average lengths.

STEPS:
1. $H_1: \mu_1 = \mu_2$
2. $H_2: \mu_1 > \mu_2$
3. An α level of 0.01 (one-tail test) requires a z_α value of 2.33.

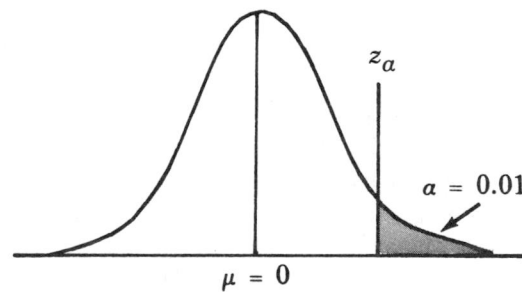

4. Criterion: Reject H_1 (accept H_2) if $z > 2.33$; accept H_1 if $z \leq 2.33$, where

$$z = \frac{\bar{x}_1 - \bar{x}_2}{\sigma_{\bar{x}_1 - \bar{x}_2}}$$

5. Using the sample data

$$z = \frac{27.80 - 27.70}{0.022} = \frac{0.10}{0.022} = 4.54$$

where

$$\sigma_{\bar{x}_1 - \bar{x}_2} = \sqrt{\frac{(0.10)^2}{50} + \frac{(0.12)^2}{50}} = 0.022.$$

Since $z(4.54) > z_\alpha(2.33)$, reject H_1 and accept H_2. The machines are not adjusted to cut bars of equal average lengths.

Universe Standard Deviations Are Not Known

Tests of significance involving two sample means are often made under conditions where the universe standard deviations are not known, and sample standard deviations must be used as estimates. In such cases, the theoretical sampling distribution of differences is assumed to be a t distribution with a mean equal to zero and a standard deviation that is the estimated standard error of the difference

$$\hat{\sigma}_{\bar{x}_1 - \bar{x}_2} = \sqrt{\frac{n_1 s_1^2 + n_2 s_2^2}{n_1 + n_2 - 2}} \sqrt{\frac{n_1 + n_2}{n_1 n_2}} \quad \ldots\ldots\ldots\ldots(11.6)$$

The t value can then be computed as

$$t = \frac{(\bar{x}_1 - \bar{x}_2) - (\mu_1 - \mu_2)}{\hat{\sigma}_{\bar{x}_1 - \bar{x}_2}} \quad \text{or} \quad \frac{\bar{x}_1 - \bar{x}_2}{\hat{\sigma}_{\bar{x}_1 - \bar{x}_2}} \quad \ldots\ldots\ldots\ldots(11.7)$$

➤ *Example.* Assume that two types of precast concrete beams are being considered for manufacture and sale. The only difference in the two beams is the type of coarse material used. A sample of each type is made and tested for strength, with the following results:

	Material A	Material B
Sample size	$n_1 = 12$	$n_2 = 10$
Sample mean	$\bar{x}_1 = 5{,}000$ psi	$\bar{x}_2 = 4{,}975$ psi
Sample standard deviation	$s_1 = 50$ psi	$s_2 = 60$ psi. ·

The problem is to test at an α level of 0.05 to determine if the beams made with Material A are stronger than the beams made with Material B.

STEPS:
1. $H_1 : \mu_1 = \mu_2$
2. $H_2 : \mu_1 > \mu_2$
3. An α level of 0.05 (one-tail test) requires a t_α value of 1.725 ($t_{0.10}$ with $n_1 + n_2 - 2$ degrees of freedom).

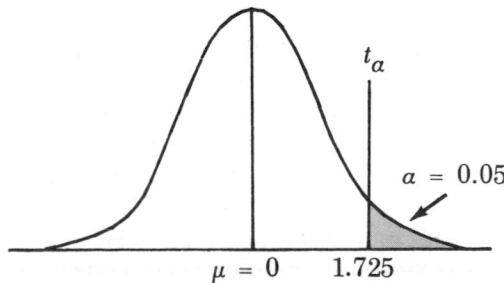

4. Criterion: Reject H_1 (accept H_2) if $t > 1.725$; accept H_1 if $t \leq 1.725$, where

$$t = \frac{\bar{x}_1 - \bar{x}_2}{\hat{\sigma}_{\bar{x}_1 - \bar{x}_2}}$$

5. Using the sample data

$$t = \frac{5{,}000 - 4{,}975}{24.59} = \frac{25}{24.59} = 1.02$$

where

$$\hat{\sigma}_{\bar{x}_1 - \bar{x}_2} = \sqrt{\frac{12(50)^2 + 10(60)^2}{20}} \sqrt{\frac{12 + 10}{(12)(10)}} = 24.59.$$

Since $t(1.02) < t_\alpha(1.725)$, accept H_1. It is not possible to show a significant difference in the strength of the two types of beams.

STUDY QUESTIONS

11-1. Explain briefly the meaning of each of the following terms:

a. test of significance
b. test of hypothesis
c. state of the world
d. state of nature
e. null hypothesis
f. alternate hypothesis
g. action
h. decision rule

i. critical value
j. Type I error
k. Type II error
l. two-tail test
m. one-tail test
n. power of the function
o. power curve
p. operating characteristic (OC) curve

11-2. Why is the null hypothesis the one normally set up to be tested?

11-3. Why is the criterion written to control the probability of a Type I error rather than the probability of a Type II error?

11-4. In what way can the probability of a Type I error be reduced?

11-5. If the decision maker is able to reduce the probability of making a Type I error, what effect does this action have on the probability of making a Type II error?

11-6. Explain the effect of an increase in sample size on the probability of making a Type II error.

11-7. What change would take place in the shape of a given OC curve if the sample size were reduced? What would be the effect on the power curve?

11-8. What are the steps to be followed in making a test of significance?

11-9. If a test of significance is made that involves a sample mean, what will be the shape of the theoretical sampling distribution of means in each of the following cases?

a. When the universe standard deviation is known.
b. When the universe standard deviation is not known.

11-10. In testing the difference between two sample means:
a. What is the value of the mean of the theoretical sampling distribution of differences assumed in H_1?
b. What is the shape of the sampling distribution? Explain the two cases.
c. What is the standard deviation of the theoretical sampling distribution called? What is its importance in the test of significance?

PROBLEMS

11-1. A manufacturer plans to purchase a franchise to make flashlight batteries if the process will produce batteries with an average life of 400 hours. If the life is less than 400 hours, he will not buy the franchise. If tests are made on a random sample of 100 batteries, find a decision rule for this company if $\alpha = 0.05$, and the universe standard deviation is known to be 20 hours. Also, draw an OC and a power curve in each of the following cases:
a. Assume that the error of not purchasing the franchise when the average length of life is 400 hours or more is more serious.
b. Assume that the error of purchasing the franchise when the average length of life is less than 400 hours is more serious.

11-2. An oil company will build a new service station on a given corner lot if an average of 2,000 cars per day passes the lot. The company will not build the station if the average is less than 2,000 cars. If it is assumed that the universe standard deviation is 100 cars, find a decision rule for the company using an α value of 0.05 and a random sample of 36 days. Assume that the error of building the station when the average number of cars is less than 2,000 is the more serious error. Also, draw an OC and a power curve to show the probabilities of a β error and of a correct decision.

11-3. An automatic machine is used to fill boxes of steel thumbtacks with an average of 104 tacks per box. The universe standard deviation is known to be 4 tacks per box. A sample of 25 boxes is checked each hour to determine if the machine is in adjustment. Using an α value of 0.05:
a. Compute the two critical values of the sample mean and write the instructions you would give the operator to tell him when he should stop and adjust his machine.
b. Draw an OC curve and a power curve.

11-4. The average time required for a worker to assemble an electric component is 20 minutes, with a universe standard deviation of four minutes. From time to time, the foreman takes a sample of the times required for a particular worker to assemble 16 of these units to see if his performance is above or below standard. Using an α level of 0.01:
a. Set up a decision rule that would allow you to decide when a worker is below and when he is above standard.
b. Draw an OC curve of the probability of making a Type II error.
c. Draw a power curve of the probability of making a correct decision.

11-5. If in Problem 11-1 a random sample of 300 batteries is drawn but all other facts remain the same, recompute the decision rules and redraw the OC and power curves to demonstrate the effect of the change in sample size.

11-6. Using all other facts as stated in Problem 11-4, determine the decision rule and redraw the OC and power curves for $n = 36$.

11-7. Given the following facts, test at an α level of 0.05 to determine which of the following samples have been drawn from a universe with a mean of 800 and a standard deviation of 50:

Sample	Sample size	Sample mean
A	100	805
B	900	805
C	400	805

11-8. Health statistics show that the average male high school senior in City A weighs 155 pounds, with a standard deviation of 20 pounds. If a random sample of 64 senior male students from a particular high school in the city has an average weight of 149 pounds, test at an α level of 0.01 the hypothesis that the test group is typical of all high school males in the city. Use a one-tail test.

11-9. A manufacturer of light bulbs promises an average life of 2,000 hours for his bulbs. Make a test of significance to determine whether or not to accept a large shipment of these bulbs if a random sample of 25 bulbs has a mean life of 1,950 hours and a standard deviation of 200 hours. Use an α of 0.05 and a one-tail test.

11-10. A manufacturer of automobile tires claims that his best grade of tire will last for 30,000 miles when used on a car of a given weight. A sample of 10 of his tires lasts for the distances shown below. Test his claim against the alternate that his claim is overstated, using an α of 0.025 and a one-tail test.

Tire	Miles of use
1	31,000
2	26,000
3	28,000
4	25,000
5	32,000
6	29,000
7	30,000
8	23,000
9	27,000
10	29,000

11-11. An automatic paint machine is designed to spray automobile fenders with an average of 2 ounces of paint each. There is a standard deviation of 0.1 ounce. Sample observations of the work of this machine taken on successive days show the following results:

	Monday	*Tuesday*
Sample size	$n_1 = 75$ fenders	$n_2 = 100$ fenders
Sample mean	$\bar{x}_1 = 1.99$ ounces	$\bar{x}_2 = 2.02$ ounces

Test at an α level of 0.05 the hypothesis that the machine was adjusted to spray the same average amount of paint on both days against the alternative hypothesis that the averages were different.

11-12. Given the following information, test, using an α level of 0.02, the hypothesis that the two universes have the same mean against the alternate hypothesis that the two universe means are different:

	Universe one	*Universe two*
Standard deviation	$\sigma_1 = 1.2$	$\sigma_2 = 1.6$
Sample size	$n_1 = 50$	$n_2 = 50$
Sample mean	$\bar{x}_1 = 22.3$	$\bar{x}_2 = 21.7$

11-13. Two randomly selected groups of 10 army recruits each are taught to shoot a pistol by two different instructors. After two weeks of training, each group shoots for the record with the following results:

	Group one	*Group two*
Standard deviation	$s_1 = 12$ points	$s_2 = 15$ points
Sample size	$n_1 = 10$	$n_2 = 10$
Average score	$\bar{x}_1 = 82$ points	$\bar{x}_2 = 76$ points

Test at an α level of 0.01 the hypothesis that the two instructors are equally capable teachers against the alternate hypothesis that the instructor who taught group one is better than the instructor who taught group two.

11-14. An identical typing test is given to a random sample of office employees from each of two large insurance companies. The results are shown below. Test at an α of 0.05 the hypothesis that office employees of both companies are equally good typists against the alternate hypothesis that those in one company are better than those in the other.

	Company one	*Company two*
Standard deviation	$s_1 = 6$ wpm	$s_2 = 10$ wpm
Sample size	$n_1 = 22$	$n_2 = 20$
Average score	$\bar{x}_1 = 48$ wpm	$\bar{x}_2 = 52$ wpm

SELECTED READINGS

Duncan, Acheson J. *Quality Control and Industrial Statistics.* 3d ed. Homewood, Illinois: Richard D. Irwin, Inc., 1965.

    Chapters 25 through 31 cover a wide variety of tests of hypothesis in considerable detail. These include tests of means, proportions, and variances.

Freund, John E. and Frank J. Williams. *Elementary Business Statistics: The Modern Approach.* Englewood Cliffs, New Jersey: Prentice-Hall, Inc., 1964.
Chapter 9, "Decision Making: Tests of Hypotheses," gives a simple, clear introduction to types of error and null hypotheses in significance tests, and discusses tests of means and proportions.

Greenwald, William I. *Statistics for Economics.* Columbus, Ohio: Charles E. Merrill Books, Inc., 1963.
Chapter 4 deals with statistical inference concerning means. It has a particularly good "how-to-do-it" type of approach.

Schlaifer, Robert. *Probability and Statistics for Business Decisions.* New York: McGraw-Hill Book Company, Inc., 1959.
Part Five discusses tests of significance and confidence intervals, including the classical theory of testing hypotheses.

Chapter 12

Tests of Significance for Sample Proportions

INTRODUCTION

The material in this chapter differs from that in Chapter 11 in that the numerical data being considered are qualitative rather than quantitative in nature. For example, if the investigator is concerned with whether housewives use his product or not, each observation results in a "yes" or "no" answer. If the number of yes answers is computed as a ratio to the total number of answers, the data are expressed as a sample percent.

OPERATING CHARACTERISTIC AND POWER CURVES FOR PERCENT OF A SINGLE LARGE SAMPLE

When decisions must be made using sample percents as estimates of universe percents, the problems involved are essentially the same as those inherent in dealing with means. The only difference lies in the fact that the statistician deals with theoretical sampling distributions of percents rather than means. He is still confronted with the need to measure the probability of Type I and Type II errors.

One-Tail Test

When a large random sample is drawn from a population and when a sample percent, p, is computed, it can be assumed that the distribution of p is normal with a mean, π, and a standard deviation, σ_p.

If a hypothesis is made concerning the value of the universe percent, the sample percent may be used as the basis for accepting or rejecting the hypothesis. The probability of a Type I error can be determined by management, and the probabilities of a Type II error may be shown by an OC curve; or, conversely, the probability of a correct decision may be shown by a power curve.

➤ *Example.* The management of a grocery chain is considering whether or not to build a new store in an existing shopping center. The manager of the shopping center claims that more than 55% of all the families living within a two-mile radius of the center shop there. If the grocery chain management accepts the "greater than 55%" estimate as fact, the store will be built. If it is concluded that the claim is too high, the store will not be built. The decision, of course, will have to be made on the basis of sample data, as it would be much too expensive to canvass all the families in the area to determine their shopping habits.

If the chain-store management is cautious about committing itself to build the new store without being reasonably sure of the shoppers it can attract, it will act only if it has a sample percent that clearly supports the 55% or more claim. The hypotheses and the risks involved may be shown schematically as follows:

	$H_1 : \pi \leq 0.55$	$H_2 : \pi > 0.55$
Action	W_1	W_2
A_1: Do not build	Correct decision	$\beta = P(A_1 \mid W_2)$
A_2: Build	$\alpha = P(A_2 \mid W_1)$	Correct decision

The null and alternate hypotheses are stated in such a way as to allow management to control the probability of a Type I error. This is the critical error of building a new store without sufficient shoppers. If management decides on a level of significance of 0.025 and plans to use a random sample of 225 families, the critical value may be computed using the following formula:

$$z = \frac{p_c - \pi}{\sigma_p} \qquad \dots\dots\dots\dots\dots\dots(12.1)$$

where,

p_c is the critical value of the sample percent

π is the value of the universe percent designated in H_1

σ_p is the standard error of the percent.

The z_α value in Appendix I that gives 0.025 in one tail of the normal distribution is 1.96. Also

$$\sigma_p = \sqrt{\frac{\pi(1 - \pi)}{n}} = \sqrt{\frac{(0.55)(0.45)}{225}} = 0.033$$

so that

$$1.96 = \frac{p_c - 0.55}{0.033} \quad \text{and} \quad p_c = 0.61468.$$

With this information, the company management can set up the following decision rule:

Hypothesis	State of the world	Decision rule	Action
$H_1: \pi \leq 0.55$	W_1: Not enough customers	$p \leq 0.61468$	A_1: Do not build
$H_2: \pi > 0.55$	W_2: Enough customers	$p > 0.61468$	A_2: Build

The probability that the company will build a new store when it should not do so is only 2.5%.

The probability that the company will not build the store when it should (a Type II error) depends upon the value of π, if it is greater than 55%. Values of β and $1 - \beta$ are shown in Table 12.1. The OC and power curves for this example are shown in Figure 12.1.

Table 12.1

PROBABILITY OF CORRECT DECISION WITH GIVEN
VALUES OF π

Value of π	$\dfrac{p_c - \pi}{\sigma_p}$	β	$1 - \beta$
0.55	1.96	...	...
0.56	1.66	0.9515	0.0485
0.58	1.05	0.8531	0.1469
0.60	0.44	0.6700	0.3300
0.61468	0	0.5000	0.5000
0.63	−0.46	0.3228	0.6772
0.65	−1.07	0.1423	0.8577
0.67	−1.68	0.0465	0.9535
0.69	−2.28	0.0113	0.9887

$$GIVEN: \quad \sigma_p = 0.033$$
$$p_c = 0.61468$$
$$n = 225$$

➤ *Example.* Suppose, in the previous example, the grocery chain management was most anxious to build the new store. If the management considered the most serious error they might make to be the decision not to build when in fact the universe percent of customers in the area was 55% or more, they might set up the problem somewhat differently.

Action	$H_1: \pi \geq 0.55$ W_1	$H_2: \pi < 0.55$ W_2
A_1: Build	Correct decision	$\beta = P(A_1 \mid W_2)$
A_2: Do not build	$\alpha = P(A_2 \mid W_1)$	Correct decision

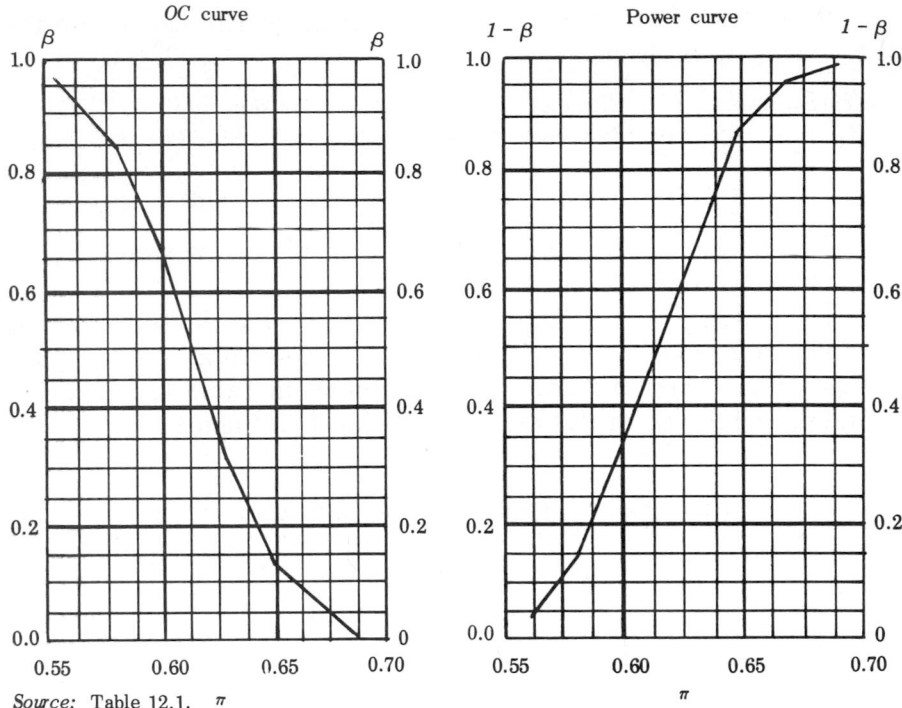

Source: Table 12.1.

Figure 12.1

OPERATING CHARACTERISTIC AND POWER CURVES

If, again, $\alpha = 0.025$ and $n = 225$, then

$$-1.96 = \frac{p_c - 0.55}{0.033}$$

$$p_c = 0.48532.$$

The decision rule has now become:

Hypothesis	State of the world	Decision rule·	Action
$H_1 : \pi \geq 0.55$	W_1 : Enough customers	$p \geq 0.48532$	A_1 : Build
$H_2 : \pi < 0.55$	W_2 : Not enough customers	$p < 0.48532$	A_2 : Do not build

The OC curve is shown in Figure 12.2.

Two-Tail Test

Some problems call for tests of significance that involve critical values in both tails of a theoretical sampling distribution of percents.

➤ *Example.* A food manufacturer sponsors a television program carried by one of the two TV stations serving an area. Past experience

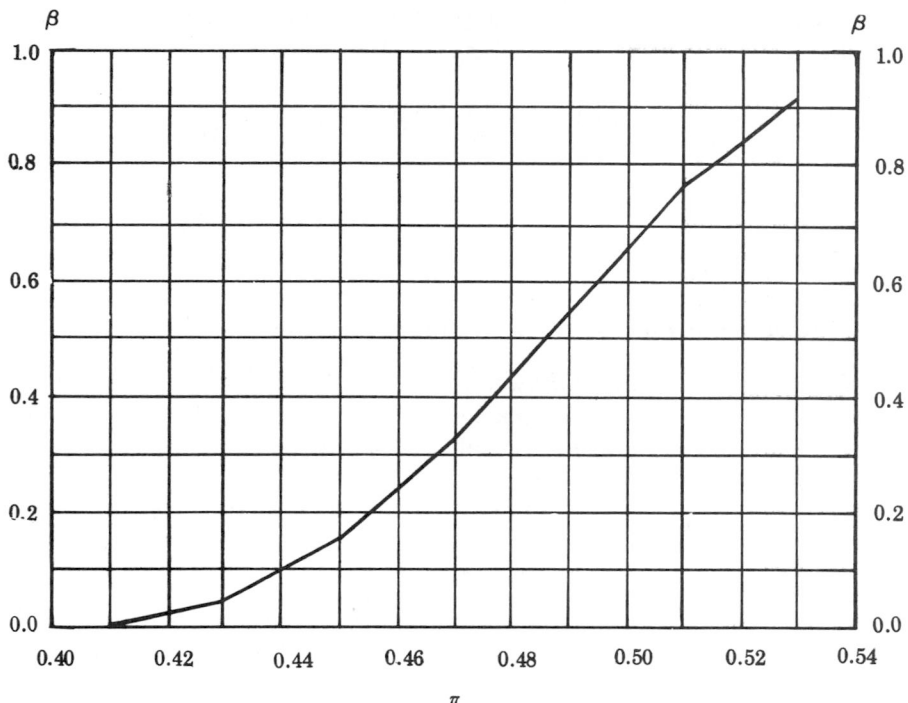

Figure 12.2

OPERATING CHARACTERISTIC CURVE

$$GIVEN: \quad \sigma_p = 0.033$$
$$p_c = 0.48532$$
$$n = 225$$

has shown that 40% of the viewers in the area watch the show. At regular intervals the manufacturer has his advertising agent draw a random sample of 250 viewers and check the proportion watching the program. As the sponsor of the show, the manufacturer is anxious to detect any significant change in the universe percent, either up or down. If he concludes that a significant change has taken place, he will want a further study in depth to determine the reasons for the change. To test for a significant change, he might use the following guide:

Action	$H_1: \pi = 0.40$ W_1	$H_2: \pi \neq 0.40$ W_2
A_1: Continue the program without further study	Correct decision	$\beta = P(A_1 \mid W_2)$
A_2: Conduct an intensive study of viewer re- action to the program	$\alpha = P(A_2 \mid W_1)$	Correct decision

The manufacturer can set the probability of making a Type I error. If he chooses an α level of 0.05, $z = \pm 1.96$, and

$$\sigma_p = \sqrt{\frac{\pi(1 - \pi)}{n}} = \sqrt{\frac{(0.40)(0.60)}{250}} = 0.031$$

so that $1.96 = \dfrac{p_{c_1} - 0.40}{0.031}$ and $p_{c_1} = 0.46076$. Also, $-1.96 = \dfrac{p_{c_2} - 0.40}{0.031}$ and $p_{c_2} = 0.33924$.

The decision rule can now be shown as follows:

Hypothesis	State of the world	Decision rule	Action
$H_1: \pi = 0.40$	W_1: No change in proportion of viewers	$0.33924 \leq p \leq 0.46076$	A_1: Continue
$H_2: \pi \neq 0.40$	W_2: Proportion of viewers has changed	$p < 0.33924$ or $p > 0.46076$	A_2: Make a study

If one wishes to know the probability that the sample percent will lead the manufacturer to make a β error, he may draw an OC curve of the values of β that will result from a series of possible values of π. For this example, values of β and $1 - \beta$ are shown in Table 12.2, and the OC curve is shown in Figure 12.3.

Table 12.2

VALUES OF β AND $1 - \beta$ FOR GIVEN VALUES OF π

Value of π	$\dfrac{p_c - \pi}{\sigma_p}$	β	$1 - \beta$
0.25	2.88	0.00199	0.99801
0.30	1.27	0.1020	0.8980
0.32	0.62	0.2676	0.7324
0.33924	0	0.5000	0.5000
0.35	-0.35	0.6368	0.3632
0.38	-1.31	0.9049	0.0951
0.40	± 1.96	...	...
0.42	1.31	0.9049	0.0951
0.45	0.35	0.6368	0.3632
0.46076	0	0.5000	0.5000
0.48	-0.62	0.2676	0.7324
0.50	-1.27	0.1020	0.8980
0.55	-2.88	0.00199	0.99801

GIVEN: $p_{c_1} = 0.33924$ $\sigma_p = 0.031$

              $p_{c_2} = 0.46076$ $n = 250$

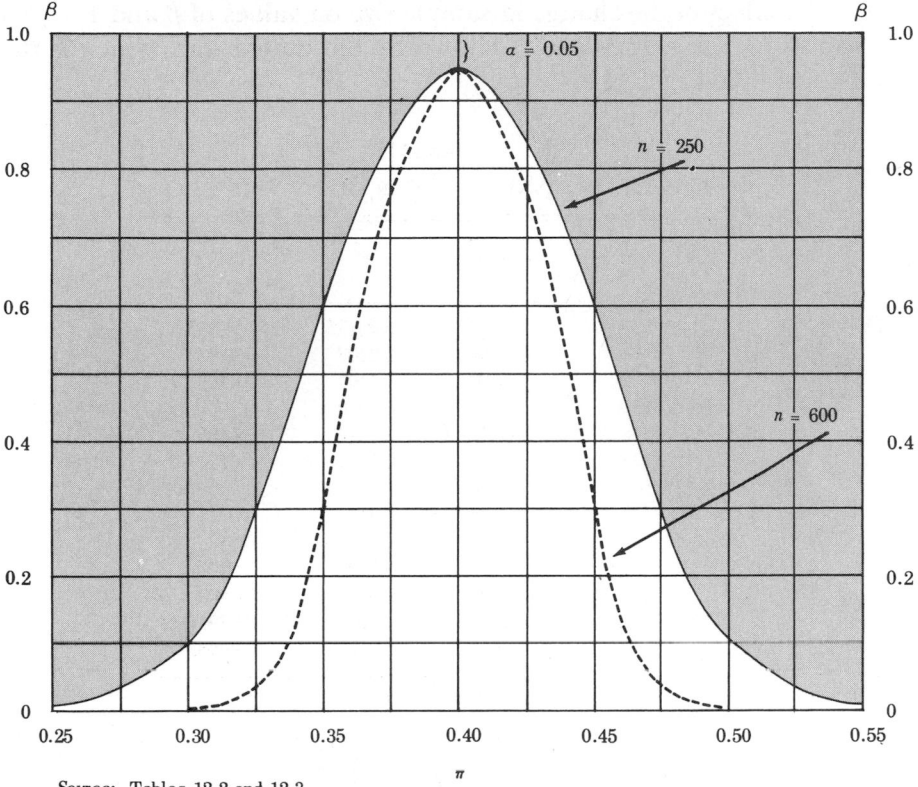

Source: Tables 12.2 and 12.3.

Figure 12.3

OPERATING CHARACTERISTIC CURVE

Effect of a Change in Sample Size

Just as with problems dealing with means, an increase in the size of the sample moves the critical values closer to the value of the parameter set up in H_1 and increases the power of the decision rule.

➤ *Example.* Suppose all the facts in the previous example about the television program are the same, with the exception of the sample size, which is increased from 250 to 600 viewers. At the same level of significance of 0.05, the critical values are:

$$p_{c_1} = 0.3608 \text{ or } 36.08 \text{ percent, and}$$
$$p_{c_2} = 0.4392 \text{ or } 43.92 \text{ percent}$$

where,

$$\sigma_p = \sqrt{\frac{\pi(1-\pi)}{n}} = \sqrt{\frac{(0.40)(0.60)}{600}} = 0.02.$$

The effect of the change in sample size on values of β and $1 - \beta$ is shown in Table 12.3, and is shown by the dotted line, which is the *OC* curve in Figure 12.3.

Table 12.3

VALUES OF β AND $1 - \beta$ FOR GIVEN VALUES OF π

π	$\dfrac{p_c - \pi}{\sigma_p}$	β	$1 - \beta$
0.30	3.04	0.00135	0.99865
0.32	2.04	0.0207	0.9793
0.34	1.04	0.1492	0.8508
0.3608	0	0.5000	0.5000
0.38	−0.96	0.8315	0.1685
0.39	−1.46	0.9279	0.0721
0.40	−1.96	...	...
0.41	1.46	0.9279	0.0721
0.42	0.96	0.8315	0.1685
0.4392	0	0.5000	0.5000
0.46	−1.04	0.1492	0.8508
0.48	−2.04	0.0207	0.9793
0.50	−3.04	0.00135	0.99865

$$GIVEN: \quad p_{c_1} = 0.3608$$
$$p_{c_2} = 0.4392$$
$$\sigma_p = 0.02$$
$$n = 600$$

TESTING THE PERCENT OF A SINGLE SAMPLE

In Chapter 7 it was noted that the binomial probability distribution is the appropriate model for a sampling distribution when the population is split into two qualitative categories. One group has a particular characteristic and the other group does not. For example, a shipment of parts can be divided into two groups, defective and nondefective. In one group the parts are all defective and in the other group no part has the characteristic of being defective.

When the percent occurrence of some characteristic of a sample is used to test a hypothesis concerning a universe percent of the same characteristic, there are two basic types of approaches to be considered:

1. The size of the sample is small.
2. The size of the sample is large.

The Sample Is Small

While the proper theoretical sampling distribution to use when dealing with a percent characteristic is always the binomial distribution, it can be used in practice only when the sample is small. In writing the criterion, it is usually not possible to set up an α value that is an exact 0.05 or 0.01 as normally used. It is possible, however, to choose from those values available one that satisfactorily controls the probability of a Type I error. This is demonstrated in the following example.

➤ *Example.* During World War II a recruiter for a large West Coast shipbuilder traveled about the country searching for qualified machinists, who were in short supply and in great demand. He interviewed a large number of applicants and tried to hire those who were qualified and to reject those who were not.

The interviewer, Mr. Jones, used as his basis of selection a multiple-choice quiz with 10 questions, each of which had four choices. If an applicant was an experienced machinist, he could usually pick the correct answer to a question. If he was not qualified and had to guess at an answer, his chances of selecting the correct one was only one out of four.

While interviewing in Central City, Mr. Jones gave his quiz to 10 applicants. Five made very low grades and were eliminated. The top five applicants made the grades shown below:

	Number of correct answers
Applicant	*out of 10 questions*
A	5
B	8
C	9
D	4
E	7

If Mr. Jones had to select those applicants who demonstrated through their answers to the questions a knowledge of the subject rather than just a series of lucky guesses, which ones should he hire? Assume that the company would be satisfied with an α level of no more than 0.05.

STEPS:
1. $H_1: \pi \leq 0.25$ (applicant is not qualified, reject)
2. $H_2: \pi > 0.25$ (applicant is qualified, hire)
3. To determine the critical value, it is necessary to look at the following table of binomial probabilities: (see Appendix C)

Number of correct answers r	Probability $P(r \mid n = 10, \pi = 0.25)$		
0	0.0563		
1	0.1877		
2	0.2816		
3	0.2503		
4	0.1460		
5	0.0584	0.0584	
6	0.0162	0.0162	0.0162
7	0.0031	0.0031	0.0031
8	0.0004	0.0004	0.0004
9	0.0000	0.0000	0.0000
10	0.0000	0.0000	0.0000
	1.0000	0.0781	0.0197

If Jones accepts an applicant who has 5 or more correct answers, the probability of accepting an unqualified applicant is $\alpha = P(A_2 \mid W_1)$ = 0.0781 or 7.81 %, which is too large a value for α. If Jones accepts an applicant who has 6 or more correct answers, the value of α is 0.0197. As this probability is well under the 0.05 required, 6 correct answers was taken as the critical value.

4. Criterion: If the applicant has 6 or more correct answers, reject H_1 and accept H_2. If the applicant has less than 6 correct answers, accept H_1.
5. Applying the criterion to the scores of the top five applicants, Mr. Jones would hire Applicants B, C, and E, and would reject Applicants A and D.

➤ **Example.** Assume that in the previous example Mr. Jones had used a true-false test with 20 questions to determine if an applicant was a qualified machinist. The probability of a correct answer based on a pure guess is 0.5. If his top five applicants made the scores listed below, which ones should he hire without exceeding an α of 0.05?

Applicant	Number of correct answers out of 20 questions
A	14
B	17
C	19
D	13
E	15

STEPS:
1. $H_1: \pi \leq 0.50$
2. $H_2: \pi > 0.50$

3. The following partial table shows the binomial probabilities needed to determine the critical value:

Number of correct answers r	Probability $P(r \mid n = 20, \pi = 0.50)$		
.	.		
.	.		
.	.		
13	0.0739		
14	0.0370	0.0370	
15	0.0148	0.0148	0.0148
16	0.0046	0.0046	0.0046
17	0.0011	0.0011	0.0011
18	0.0002	0.0002	0.0002
19	0.0000	0.0000	0.0000
20	0.0000	0.0000	0.0000
	1.0000	0.0577	0.0207

If the critical value is taken as 14 correct answers, $\alpha = 0.0577$, which is too large. If the critical value is taken as 15, $\alpha = 0.0207$, which meets the company requirements.

4. Applying this criterion to the scores of the top five applicants, Mr. Jones, again, would hire Applicants *B*, *C*, and *E*, and would reject Applicants *A* and *D*.

The Sample Is Large

When the sample becomes large, it is necessary to approximate the binomial distribution with the normal distribution because of the difficulties involved in solving the binomial formula for large values of *n*. Appendix C in this text gives the binomial values up to and including $n = 100$. Other tables seldom go beyond that number.

It is known that when $p = 0.5$ and *n* is large, the normal distribution is a good approximation of the binomial. As pointed out in Chapter 7, $E(r) = n\pi$ is the mean of the binomial distribution (Formula 7.5), and $\sigma_r = \sqrt{n\pi(1 - \pi)}$ is the standard deviation of the binomial distribution (Formula 7.7).

Since the binomial distribution is a discrete distribution and the normal distribution is continuous, the continuity correction discussed on page 246 of Chapter 8 is used in setting up the formula to compute the *z* value

$$z = \frac{r - \frac{1}{2} - E(r)}{\sigma_r} \quad \dots\dots\dots\dots\dots\dots(12.2)$$

where,

r is the number of successes in the experiment

$E(r)$ is n times the value of π in H_1

σ_r is the standard deviation of r.

➤ *Example.* Suppose in the last example Mr. Jones was trying to decide whether or not to hire Mr. *A*, who scored 14 correct answers out of 20 questions, and Mr. *E*, who scored 15 correct out of 20. Further, suppose he wished to use the normal curve approximation and an α of 0.05.

STEPS:

1. $H_1: \pi \leq 0.50$
2. $H_2: \pi > 0.50$
3. An α of 0.05 requires a z_α value of 1.64.
4. Criterion: Reject H_1 (accept H_2) if $z > 1.64$; accept H_1 if $z \leq 1.64$, when

$$z = \frac{r - \frac{1}{2} - E(r)}{\sigma_r}$$

5. In the case of Mr. *A*, $r = 14$, and

$$z = \frac{14 - \frac{1}{2} - 10}{2.24} = 1.56$$

when

$$E(r) = n\pi = 20(0.5) = 10, \text{ and}$$

$$\sigma_r = \sqrt{n\pi(1 - \pi)} = \sqrt{20(0.5)(0.5)} = 2.24.$$

Since $z\,(1.56) < z_\alpha\,(1.64)$, reject Mr. *A*.

In the case of Mr. *E*, $r = 15$, and

$$z = \frac{15 - \frac{1}{2} - 10}{2.24} = 2.01.$$

Since $z\,(2.01) > z_\alpha\,(1.64)$, hire Mr. *E*.

As the size of the sample continues to increase, the normal distribution can be used as an approximation of the binomial even in cases where $p \neq 0.5$. As a general rule of thumb, if $n\pi \geq 25$, the normal curve approximation is appropriate. Also, as n increases, the importance of the continuity correction becomes negligible, and the formula for z may be written

$$z = \frac{p - \pi}{\sigma_p} \quad \ldots\ldots\ldots\ldots\ldots\ldots\ldots\ldots\ldots(12.3)$$

where,

p is the sample percent

π is the universe percent in H_1

σ_p is the standard error of the percent.

➤ *Example.* A mail-order house that sells men's shirts has learned from long experience that 15% of all shirts sold are returned to the firm by customers who complain that the shirts do not fit properly. In an attempt to correct this situation, the firm redesigns the order blank that it sends its customers and finds that of the next 500 sales using the new blank, there are 60 returns. Test at an α level of 0.05 to see if there has been a significant change in the universe percent of returns.

STEPS:

1. $H_1 : \pi = 0.15$

2. $H_2 : \pi < 0.15$

3. An α level of 0.05 (one-tail test) requires a z_α value of -1.64.

4. Criterion: Reject H_1 (accept H_2) if $z < -1.64$; accept H_1 if $z \geq -1.64$, where

$$z = \frac{p - \pi}{\sigma_p}.$$

5. Using the sample data

$$z = \frac{0.12 - 0.15}{0.0160} = -1.875$$

where,

$$\sigma_p = \sqrt{\frac{\pi(1 - \pi)}{n}} = \sqrt{\frac{(0.15)(0.85)}{500}} = 0.0160, \text{ and}$$

$$p = \frac{60}{500} = 0.12.$$

Since $z(-1.875) < z_\alpha(-1.64)$, reject H_1 and accept H_2. There has been a significant change in the universe percent of returns as a result of the changes made in the order blank.

TESTING THE DIFFERENCE BETWEEN THE PERCENTS OF TWO LARGE SAMPLES

Testing the difference between percents of two samples is much the same as testing the difference between the means of two samples. The null hypothesis assumes that there is no difference in the parameters and that the difference observed between the sample percents is a sampling difference. The theoretical sampling distribution of differences is assumed to be normal, with a mean of zero ($\pi_1 - \pi_2 = 0$) and a standard deviation which is the standard error of the difference between the sample percents

$$\hat{\sigma}_{p_1 - p_2} = \sqrt{\frac{\hat{\pi}(1 - \hat{\pi})}{n_1} + \frac{\hat{\pi}(1 - \hat{\pi})}{n_2}} \quad \ldots\ldots\ldots\ldots(12.4)$$

where

$$\hat{\pi} = \frac{x_1 + x_2}{n_1 + n_2} \quad \ldots\ldots\ldots\ldots\ldots\ldots\ldots\ldots\ldots\ldots(12.5)$$

Since π is not known, it is estimated by combining the data from both samples to give $\hat{\pi}$.

Thus, the value of z can be computed as

$$z = \frac{(p_1 - p_2) - (\pi_1 - \pi_2)}{\hat{\sigma}_{p_1 - p_2}} \quad \ldots\ldots\ldots\ldots(12.6)$$

➤ *Example.* An importer of fine cheeses, who sells his product by direct-mail advertising, has developed an extensive mailing list to which he regularly sends brochures announcing new assortments of cheeses. In developing an announcement of his Christmas offerings, he has designed two radically different layouts and would like to know if one is better than the other. He decides to test them on samples of his customers drawn at random from the total mailing list before sending the final mailing to all the names on the list. He makes his test with the following results:

	Layout 1	Layout 2
Sample size:	$n_1 = 400$	$n_2 = 200$
Number of orders:	$x_1 = 100$	$x_2 = 44$
Sample percent:	$p_1 = \dfrac{x_1}{n_1} = \dfrac{100}{400} = 0.25$	$p_2 = \dfrac{x_2}{n_2} = \dfrac{44}{200} = 0.22.$

The problem is to test at an α level of 0.05 to see if Layout 1 is significantly better than Layout 2.

STEPS:

1. $H_1 : \pi_1 = \pi_2$
2. $H_2 : \pi_1 > \pi_2$
3. An α of 0.05 requires a z_α value of 1.64.
4. Criterion: Reject H_1 (accept H_2) if $z > 1.64$; accept H_1 if $z \leq 1.64$, when

$$z = \frac{(p_1 - p_2) - (\pi_1 - \pi_2)}{\hat{\sigma}_{p_1 - p_2}}.$$

5. Using the sample data

$$z = \frac{(0.25 - 0.22) - 0}{0.037} = \frac{0.03}{0.037} = 0.81$$

when

$$\hat{\pi} = \frac{100 + 44}{400 + 200} = 0.24, \text{ and}$$

$$\hat{\sigma}_{p_1 - p_2} = \sqrt{\frac{(0.24)(0.76)}{400} + \frac{(0.24)(0.76)}{200}} = 0.037.$$

Since $z(0.81) < z_\alpha(1.64)$, accept H_1. The test does not show that Layout 1 is significantly better than Layout 2.

STUDY QUESTIONS

12-1. In a test of significance involving the percent of a single sample:
   a. What is the theoretical sampling distribution involved?
   b. What are the mean and the standard deviation of this distribution?
   c. What effect does an increase in sample size have on the testing procedure?
12-2. In testing the difference between two sample percents:
   a. What kind of theoretical sampling distribution is involved?
   b. What are the mean and the standard deviation of this distribution?
12-3. Is it possible to make both a Type I and a Type II error on the same decision? Explain.
12-4. What is the relationship between tests of significance and the theory of sampling distributions discussed in Chapter 9?

PROBLEMS

12-1. A manufacturer of plastic water guns checks his production process every two hours. If there are more than 10% defective, he stops and adjusts the machine; otherwise, he continues the process. Given $\alpha = 0.05$ and $n = 100$, set up a decision rule and draw an *OC* curve in each of the following cases:

a. When the error of not stopping the machine when $\pi > 10\%$ is the more serious.

b. When the error of stopping the machine when $\pi \le 10\%$ is the more serious.

12-2. In a large university, experience has shown that it is normal for 40% of the students registered for the regular school term to return in the summer. The registrar, however, is alert to changes in student habits and makes a sample study each spring to determine student plans for the summer. If $\alpha = 0.05$ and it is important to detect either an increase or a decrease in the universe percent:

a. Compute a decision rule and draw an OC curve when $n = 225$.

b. Compute a decision rule and draw an OC curve when $n = 900$.

12-3. If you flip a coin 20 times, how many heads would you have to get to decide that the coin is unfair (balanced to favor heads)? The value of α should be ≤ 0.05.

a. Use the binomial distribution.

b. Use the normal curve approximation with a continuity correction.

12-4. If a multiple-choice quiz has eight questions with five choices for each question, how many correct answers would a student have to get to convince you that he knew something about the subject and was not guessing at the answers? The value of α should be ≤ 0.05.

a. Use the binomial distribution.

b. Use the normal curve approximation with a continuity correction.

12-5. An automobile dealer claims that 60% of his 1966 cars were sold with rear seat belts installed. Test this claim at an α of 0.01 if 172 of a random sample of 320 such cars showed that they had been bought with seat belts.

12-6. Credit records in a large retail store show that 85% of all charge accounts are paid by the 10th of the month. An additional service charge is announced as a penalty for overdue accounts in the hope of improving payments. After a trial period, a sample of 500 credit accounts shows that 435 were paid before the 10th. Test at an $\alpha = 0.01$ the hypothesis that the new service charge has not influenced the percent of accounts paid on time against the alternate hypothesis that it has influenced payment on time.

12-7. Two manufacturing processes produce 15 and 24 defective pieces in samples of 300 and 400 respectively. Use an $\alpha = 0.05$ to test the hypothesis that the proportion of defective pieces is the same for both processes against the alternate hypothesis that the proportions are not the same.

12-8. A random sample of 150 shoppers taken during daytime hours at a shopping center shows that 70% are women. A sample of similar size taken at night shows that 62% are women. Is there a significant difference in the proportion of women shoppers at the two times? Test at an α of 0.01.

SELECTED READINGS

See the list of selected readings given at the end of Chapter 11, pages 405 and 406.

Chapter 13

Chi-square and Other Nonparametric Methods

THE NATURE OF NONPARAMETRIC METHODS

In Chapters 11 and 12 the tests of significance were made on the assumption that the form or type of population distribution was known. For example, a test of significance might be based on the assumption that the sample values were drawn from a normally distributed universe, or that two samples were drawn from universes having the same variance. The testing procedures also assumed that the unknown values of the parameters, about which statistical inferences were to be made, could be estimated from statistics obtained from random samples. This approach to inferential statistics may be called *parametric methods*, since the concern is with the value of a parameter.

There are many situations in which it is not possible for the statistician to make rigid assumptions about the shape of the population from which samples are being drawn. This limitation has led to the development of a group of alternate techniques known as nonparametric or distribution-free methods. A *nonparametric method* may be defined as a statistical test in which no hypothesis is made about specific values of parameters. *Distribution-free tests* may be defined as methods for testing a hypothesis that do not depend on assumptions concerning the form of the underlying distribution.

As a practical matter, the terms "nonparametric" and "distribution free" are used almost synonymously, and the entire group of tests is called nonparametric methods.

Not only do the nonparametric methods make it possible to overcome some of the difficulties associated with many parametric methods, but they also have certain other advantages:

1. Many nonparametric methods provide easy, "short-cut" tests that have much less mathematical detail and are simpler to understand.

2. Many nonparametric methods may be used to test data that are not exact in any numerical sense, but which, in effect, are simply rankings.
3. Many nonparametric methods make it possible to work with very small samples. This is particularly helpful to the researcher collecting pilot study data or to the medical researcher working with a rare disease.

If all the assumptions of the parametric statistical model can be met in the data, the classical methods are generally preferred to the non-parametric methods as they are more precise, and for that reason they are more efficient.

THE CHI-SQUARE DISTRIBUTION

The most important of all distribution-free tests is the chi-square (χ^2) test introduced in 1900 by Karl Pearson. While the test is distribution free, as it makes no assumptions about the population from which the sample is drawn, there is a rigidly defined chi-square distribution with a mathematically expressed frequency function. The *chi-square distribution* may be defined as the sum of the squares of independent, normally distributed variables with zero means and unit variances.

If $Y_1, Y_2, \ldots, Y_n$ are normally distributed variables with mean, μ, and variance, σ^2, these variables may be standardized by the transformation

$$X_i = \frac{Y_i - \mu}{\sigma}.$$

The variable X_i will also be normally distributed with a mean of zero and a variance of one. The statistic, μ, which is the $\sum\limits_{i=1}^{n} X_i^2$ is the chi-square distribution.

Even though chi-square is a statistic, it is denoted by a Greek letter as it has no parameter. The chi-square distribution can be best applied to the solution of practical problems when expressed in the following form

$$\chi^2 = \sum \frac{(f_o - f_e)^2}{f_e} \quad \ldots\ldots\ldots\ldots\ldots\ldots\ldots\ldots\ldots(13.1)$$

where,
f_o is an observed frequency, and
f_e is an expected or theoretical frequency.

The characteristics of this distribution are completely defined by the number of degrees of freedom:

$$E(\chi^2) = d.f.$$
$$\text{Var}(\chi^2) = 2 \, d.f.$$
$$\text{Mode} = d.f. - 2.$$

The number of degrees of freedom may be described as the number of observations that are free to vary after certain restrictions have been placed on the data. These restrictions are inherent in the organization of the data. For example, if a sample of 50 items is classified as "effective" or "defective," the determination that 40 are effective automatically means that the remaining group of 10 is defective. For this example, $d.f. = 2 - 1 = 1$. Since the number of parts is known, when the total in one category is ascertained, the total in the other category is determined.

The use of the chi-square table (see Appendix K) is illustrated in Figure 13.1.

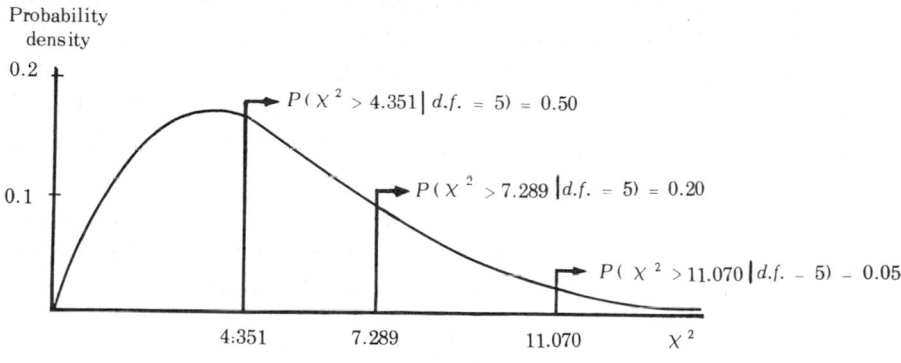

Probability
density

$P(\chi^2 > 4.351 \,|\, d.f. = 5) = 0.50$

$P(\chi^2 > 7.289 \,|\, d.f. = 5) = 0.20$

$P(\chi^2 > 11.070 \,|\, d.f. = 5) = 0.05$

Figure 13.1

DISTRIBUTION OF CHI-SQUARE FOR FIVE DEGREES OF FREEDOM

As with Student's t distribution, the chi-square distribution is a different distribution with each change in the number of degrees of freedom. It is badly skewed (to the right) for a few degrees of freedom and approaches the shape of the normal distribution when the number of degrees of freedom is approximately 30. The table of chi-square values in Appendix K lists the values of chi-square that give a specified area in the right-hand tail of the distribution. For example, in Figure 13.1 with five degrees of freedom, the area in the tail to the right of $\chi^2 = 11.070$ is 0.05 or 5%. The area to the right of $\chi^2 = 7.289$ is 0.20 or 20%.

There are several ways in which chi-square tests may be classified, for they may be used for many different purposes. In this chapter two main types or categories of tests are considered — tests on "goodness of fit" and tests on "independence of classification." Several tests of each type will be considered in detail.

Tests of "Goodness of Fit"

An observed sample distribution of any type may be compared with a theoretical distribution assumed to be the population distribution from which the sample was drawn. If there is a high degree of conformity between the two distributions, any slight difference may be assumed to be the result of sampling variation. On the other hand, any large discrepancy between the two distributions may lead to the conclusion that the sample was drawn from some theoretical distribution other than the one proposed.

The null hypothesis usually states that the sample is drawn from the theoretical population distribution, and the alternate hypothesis usually states that it is not.

Uniform Distribution. One of the simplest tests is one in which the observed sample distribution is assumed to come from a population with a uniform distribution. In this instance the expected values (f_e) for each class are the total number of observations divided by the total number of classes. The number of degrees of freedom are the number of groups (or classes) minus one degree of freedom for the requirement of the total for the distribution.

➤ *Example.* A personnel director is interested in trying to determine if the season of the year has any effect on the number of employees who resign. His records give the following information:

Season	Number of resignations
Winter	10
Spring	22
Summer	19
Fall	9
Total	60

The problem is to test at an α level of 0.05 to determine if there is a significant deviation between the observed distribution and a uniform distribution.

STEPS:

1. H_1: The observed distribution is drawn from a population that is a uniform distribution. (This is to say that the proportion of resignations is independent of the season of the year.)
2. H_2: The observed distribution is drawn from a population that is not uniformly distributed.
3. An α of 0.05 (one-tail test) requires a χ^2 value of 7.815 (column in the chi-square table headed 0.05 with three degrees of freedom).

4. Criterion: Reject H_1 (accept H_2) if $\chi^2 > 7.815$; accept H_1 if $\chi^2 \le 7.815$, where

$$\chi^2 = \sum \frac{(f_o - f_e)^2}{f_e}.$$

5. Using the sample data, chi-square is computed in the following table.

Table 13.1

COMPUTATION OF CHI-SQUARE FOR A GOODNESS OF FIT
TO A UNIFORM DISTRIBUTION

Season	f_o	f_e	$(f_o - f_e)$	$(f_o - f_e)^2$	$\dfrac{(f_o - f_e)^2}{f_e}$
Winter	10	15	−5	25	1.67
Spring	22	15	7	49	3.27
Summer	19	15	4	16	1.07
Fall	9	15	−6	36	2.40
Total	60	60	0		$\chi^2 = 8.41$

Since $\chi^2(8.41) > \chi_\alpha^2(7.815)$, reject H_1 and accept H_2. The number of resignations does vary significantly from a uniform distribution. The season of the year has a significant effect upon the number of employees who resign.

There are two rules of thumb normally applied to the use of a chi-square test:

1. The total number of observations (frequencies) should not be too small, usually not less than 50.
2. There should be at least a frequency of five in each expected frequency class.

The foregoing example meets both of these rules as the total frequency is 60, and the expected frequency in each class is 15.

Poisson Distribution. In Chapter 7 it was pointed out that the Poisson distribution applies to many situations in which one is concerned with the analysis of the formation of waiting lines at service facilities. When an observed sample distribution is thought to come from a parent population that is Poisson distributed, this can be tested using chi-square.

➤ ***Example.*** A study is conducted of the volume of calls received on the switchboard of an insurance firm. A count is made of the number of incoming calls per minute for a sample of 100 minutes. The results of the study are shown at the top of the next page.

Number of calls per minute r	Number of minutes f_o
none	40
1	35
2	14
3	8
4	2
5	1
Total	100

The statistician making the study believes that the incoming calls are distributed according to the Poisson distribution, and he uses a chi-square test to check his hypothesis at an α of 0.05.

STEPS:

1. H_1: The universe distribution of incoming calls is Poisson distributed.
2. H_2: The universe distribution of incoming calls is not Poisson distributed.
3. Before the α value can be translated into a table value for chi-square, it is necessary to determine the number of degrees of freedom. This will be the number of classes being compared minus one degree of freedom for each restriction placed on the expected distribution. Since a Poisson distribution can be completely determined by λ (which is the mean of the distribution) and the total frequency, there will be two restrictions. The theoretical Poisson distribution is computed in Table 13.2.

Table 13.2

COMPUTATION OF A POISSON DISTRIBUTION WITH
THE SAME MEAN AND TOTAL FREQUENCY
AS AN OBSERVED DISTRIBUTION

Observed distribution			Poisson distribution		
r	f_o	$f_o r$	r	$P(r \mid \lambda = 1)$	f_e
0	40	0	0	0.3679	36.79
1	35	35	1	0.3679	36.79
2	14	28	2	0.1839	18.39
3	8	24	3	0.0613	6.13
4	2	8	4	0.0153	1.53
5	1	5	5	0.0031	0.31
			6	0.0005	0.05
	100	100	7	0.0001	0.01
Mean $= \dfrac{\Sigma f_o r}{\Sigma f_o} = \dfrac{100}{100} = 1 = \lambda$				1.0000	100.00

Because of the general rule which states that there should be at least five items in each theoretical frequency class, it is necessary to group the last several classes of both the observed and the expected distributions into a class of "3 or more." This leaves a total of four classes minus two degrees of freedom for the requirements (mean and total) of the Poisson distribution, or two degrees of freedom for chi-square. The table value for $\chi^2_{\alpha=0.05}(2\ d.f.) = 5.991$.

4. Criterion: Reject H_1 (accept H_2) if $\chi^2 > 5.991$; accept H_1 if $\chi^2 \leq 5.991$, when χ^2 is computed using Formula 13.1.

5. Using the sample data, the value of chi-square is computed in the following table.

Table 13.3

COMPUTATION OF CHI-SQUARE FOR A TEST OF GOODNESS OF FIT
TO A POISSON DISTRIBUTION

Number of calls per minute (r)	f_o	f_e	$(f_o - f_e)$	$(f_o - f_e)^2$	$\dfrac{(f_o - f_e)^2}{f_e}$
0	40	36.79	3.21	10.3041	0.28
1	35	36.79	−1.79	3.2041	0.09
2	14	18.39	−4.39	19.2721	1.05
3 or more	11	8.03	2.97	8.8209	1.10
Totals	100	100.00	0		$\chi^2 = 2.52$

Since $\chi^2(2.52) < \chi^2_\alpha(5.991)$, accept H_1. The observed distribution is drawn from a parent population that is Poisson distributed.

Normal Distribution. Since the normal distribution is one of the most useful distributions in statistics, it is often helpful to be able to use a chi-square test to see whether it is likely that an observed distribution is drawn from a population that is normally distributed. This is done in the following example.

➤ *Example.* The foreman of an assembly department that hires several hundred women is anxious to know if the distribution of times required to perform a particular assembly operation is normal. He times a sample of 100 workers doing this job and records the results in the distribution shown below.

Time required to make one assembly (in minutes)	Number of workers f_o
20 and under 25	7
25 and under 30	25
30 and under 35	33
35 and under 40	27
40 and under 45	8
Total	100

The mean of the observed distribution is 32.7 minutes, and the standard deviation is 5.3 minutes.

The problem is to use chi-square to test, at an $\alpha = 0.05$, the hypothesis that the distributions of worker times comes from a population that is normally distributed.

STEPS:

1. H_1: The population distribution of worker times is normal.
2. H_2: The population distribution of worker times is not normal.
3. In Chapter 8 it is shown that if the mean, standard deviation, and total frequency are known, a normal distribution can be constructed to fit any given frequency distribution. Using a mean of 32.7, a standard deviation of 5.3, and a total frequency of 100, the following normal distribution has been constructed using the ordinates method shown in Table 8.3, page 238.

Time required *(minutes)*	*Expected normal* *curve frequencies*
Under 20 minutes	0.8
20 and under 25	6.3
25 and under 30	23.4
30 and under 35	36.5
35 and under 40	24.8
40 and under 45	7.3
45 and over	0.9
Total	100.0

Because the first and the last classes are too small, they are combined in each case with the adjoining class to give a theoretical frequency in each class of at least five. After combining the first two and the last two classes, the number of degrees of freedom for chi-square is the number of classes (five) minus one degree of freedom for each of the three parameters (μ, σ, and Σf_o) of the expected distribution. Therefore, the table value of $\chi^2_{\alpha=0.05}(2 \ d.f.) = 5.991$.

4. Criterion: Reject H_1 (accept H_2) if $\chi^2 > 5.991$; accept H_1 if $\chi^2 \leq 5.991$, when chi-square is computed using Formula 13.1.
5. Using the sample data, the value of chi-square is computed in Table 13-4.

Since $\chi^2(0.646) < \chi^2_x(5.991)$, accept H_1. The population from which the sample of worker times was drawn is normal.

Tests of "Independence of Classification"

In tests of *independence of classification,* the sample data are classified according to several attributes. Chi-square is used to determine if the principles or criteria used for cross classification are meaningful. As a

Table 13.4

COMPUTATION OF CHI-SQUARE FOR A TEST OF GOODNESS OF FIT
TO A NORMAL DISTRIBUTION

Time required (minutes)	f_o	f_e	$(f_o - f_e)$	$(f_o - f_e)^2$	$\dfrac{(f_o - f_e)^2}{f_e}$
Under 25 minutes	7	7.1	−0.1	0.01	0.001
25 and under 30	25	23.4	1.6	2.56	0.109
30 and under 35	33	36.5	−3.5	12.25	0.336
35 and under 40	27	24.8	2.2	4.84	0.195
40 and over	8	8.2	−0.2	0.04	0.005
Totals	100	100.0	0		$\chi^2 = 0.646$

test of independence of classification, chi-square is not a measure of the degree or form of relationship but only a help in determining if the relationship is significant. The tables of values that result from the cross classification of data are often called *contingency tables*. These may vary in size from a 2 × 2 table to the general form with r rows and c columns, known as an r × c table.

This type of test gets its name from the fact that the hypothesis to be tested is the hypothesis that the principles of classification are independent.

The number of degrees of freedom in a test of independence of classification is always the product of the number of rows minus one times the number of columns minus one, i.e., $d.f. = (r - 1)(c - 1)$.

2 × 2 Contingency Table. The simplest type of contingency table to test with chi-square is one with only two rows and two columns.

➤ *Example.* The manager of a chamber of commerce in a small town in the Lower Rio Grande Valley in Texas is interested in learning more about the tourists who spend part of each winter in the Valley. He secures from the local hotel and motel association a list of the tourists from the past season. The manager plans to send questionnaires to the people on the list to find out why they came to the Valley, how much they spent, how long they stayed, and what their future plans are. He speculates that if he offers to send each respondent a free can of grapefruit juice, he will increase the percentage of questionnaires that is returned. To test this theory, he sends questionnaires to a random sample of 30 persons on the list with the offer of the premium. He sends another sample of 30 with no premium offer. The results of his experiment are shown in Table 13.5.

Table 13.5

RESULTS OF A RANDOM SAMPLE OF 60 QUESTIONNAIRES
IN WHICH HALF RECEIVED THE OFFER OF A PREMIUM
TO ENCOURAGE RESPONSE

	Questionnaire		
Premium	Returned	Not returned	Totals
Offered	22	8	30
Not offered	14	16	30
Totals	36	24	60

The problem is to test at $\alpha = 0.05$ to see if there is a significant difference in the proportion of returns when the premium is offered.

STEPS:
1. H_1: The universe proportion of returns is independent of the promise of a premium.
2. H_2: The universe proportion is affected by the promise of a premium.
3. An α of 0.05 requires a chi-square value of 3.841 (column 0.05 with $(r-1)(c-1)$ or one degree of freedom).
4. Criterion: Reject H_1 (accept H_2) if $\chi^2 > 3.841$; accept H_1 if $\chi^2 \leq 3.841$, where chi-square is computed using Formula 13.1.
5. Using the sample data, the chi-square value is computed in the following table. Since 36 out of 60 of the questionnaires were returned, the expected value for cells one and three is 60% of 30, or 18. For cells two and four, it is 40% of 30, or 12.

Table 13.6

COMPUTATION OF CHI-SQUARE FOR A TEST OF INDEPENDENCE OF
CLASSIFICATION FOR A 2 × 2 CONTINGENCY TABLE

Cell	f_o	f_e	$(f_o - f_e)$	$(f_o - f_e)^2$	$\dfrac{(f_o - f_e)^2}{f_e}$
1. Premium, returned	22	18	4	16	0.89
2. Premium, not returned	8	12	−4	16	1.33
3. No premium, returned	14	18	−4	16	0.89
4. No premium, not returned	16	12	4	16	1.33
Totals	60	60	0		$\chi^2 = 4.44$

Since $\chi^2(4.44) > \chi_\alpha^2(3.841)$, reject H_1 and accept H_2. The universe proportion of returns is influenced by the premium offer.

Yates' Correction for Continuity. Tables of chi-square values are derived from a smooth distribution function, and the distribution shown in Figure 13.1 is a continuous curve. However, since the number of possible combinations of frequencies in the observed matrix is finite, the probability distribution of chi-square may also be thought of as being discrete under certain conditions. When using tables of area under the normal curve to approximate binomial probabilities in Chapter 8, a continuity correction was used to give a better approximation of a discrete distribution while using a continuous one. *Yates' correction for continuity* makes the same type of correction in a chi-square test when chi-square has *only one degree of freedom.* Yates' correction for continuity is shown in the following formula, which reduces the computed value of chi-square:

$$\chi^2 = \sum \frac{(|f_o - f_e| - \frac{1}{2})^2}{f_e} \qquad \ldots\ldots\ldots\ldots\ldots\ldots\ldots(13.2)$$

where,
$|f_o - f_e|$ is the absolute difference between f_o and f_e.

➤ *Example.* In the previous example a chi-square test is made for only one degree of freedom, so Yates' correction for continuity should have been used. All the steps in the test are the same, with the exception of Step 5 in which chi-square is computed and the decision is made as to which hypothesis is to be accepted.

Table 13.7

COMPUTATION OF CHI-SQUARE USING YATES' CORRECTION FOR CONTINUITY FOR A 2 × 2 CONTINGENCY TABLE

Cell	f_o	f_e	$\lvert f_o - f_e \rvert - \frac{1}{2}$	$(\lvert f_o - f_e \rvert - \frac{1}{2})^2$	$\dfrac{(\lvert f_o - f_e \rvert - \frac{1}{2})^2}{f_e}$
1. Premium, returned	22	18	3.5	12.25	0.68
2. Premium, not returned	8	12	3.5	12.25	1.02
3. No premium, returned	14	18	3.5	12.25	0.68
4. No premium, not returned	16	12	3.5	12.25	1.02
Totals	60	60			$\chi^2 = 3.40$

Since $\chi^2(3.40) < \chi_\alpha^2(3.841)$, it is now appropriate to accept rather than to reject H_1. The sample returns do not show a difference that is large enough to reject H_1.

An r × c *Contingency Table.* Another useful characteristic of the chi-square distribution is that it can be used to test any number of cross classifications. Tables of chi-square values are normally given for 30 degrees of freedom. If the number of degrees of freedom exceeds 30, the quantity $\sqrt{2\chi^2}$ is approximately normally distributed with a mean of $\sqrt{2(d.f.) - 1}$, and a standard deviation of one. This may be expressed as

$$z = \frac{\sqrt{2\chi^2} - \sqrt{2(d.f.) - 1}}{1} \quad \text{or}$$

$$z = \sqrt{2\chi^2} - \sqrt{2(d.f.) - 1} \dots\dots\dots\dots(13.3)$$

➤ *Example.* If, in a chi-square test involving 60 degrees of freedom, the computed value of $\chi^2 = 98$, then, using Formula 13.3,

$$z = \sqrt{2(98)} - \sqrt{(2)(60) - 1}$$

$$z = \sqrt{196} - \sqrt{119} = 14 - 10.9 = 3.1$$

The probability of a deviation of more than three standard deviations from the mean of a normal distribution is so remote as to cause one to reject the null hypothesis.

An example of an $r \times c$ table with three rows and three columns is shown below.

➤ *Example.* The board of directors of a labor union wishes to sample the opinion of its members before submitting a change in its constitution at a forthcoming annual meeting. Questionnaires are sent to a random sample of 100 members in three union locals. The results of the survey are shown in Table 13.8.

Table 13.8

REACTIONS OF A SAMPLE OF UNION MEMBERS TO A PROPOSED CHANGE IN THE UNION CONSTITUTION

Reaction	Union local			Totals
	A	B	C	
Favor change	18	22	10	50
Against change	7	14	9	30
No response	5	4	11	20
Totals	30	40	30	100

The problem here is not to try to determine whether or not the union members are in favor of the change. The problem is to test at an $\alpha = 0.05$ to see if there is a significant difference in the proportions of opinion of the members of the three locals to the proposed change.

STEPS:

1. H_1: The true universe proportions of reactions of the members of the three locals are the same.
2. H_2: The true universe proportions of reactions of the members of the three locals are not the same.
3. An α of 0.05 requires a chi-square value of 9.488 (column 0.05 with $(r - 1)(c - 1)$ or four degrees of freedom).
4. Criterion: Reject H_1 (accept H_2) if $\chi^2 > 9.488$; accept H_1 if $\chi^2 \leq 9.488$, where chi-square is computed using Formula 13.1.
5. Using the sample data, the chi-square value is computed in Table 13.9. The expected values are computed based on the assumptions in the null hypothesis. For example, for row one, column one, the value of $f_e = 15$. This value is the product of 50% times 30 (the total percent that favor the change times the sample size for local A).

Table 13.9

COMPUTATION OF CHI-SQUARE FOR A TEST OF INDEPENDENCE OF CLASSIFICATION FOR AN $r \times c$ CONTINGENCY TABLE

		Cell						$\dfrac{(f_o - f_e)^2}{f_e}$
r	c	Reaction	Local	f_o	f_e	$f_o - f_e$	$(f_o - f_e)^2$	
1	1	In favor	A	18	15	3	9	0.60
1	2	of	B	22	20	2	4	0.20
1	3	change	C	10	15	-5	25	1.67
2	1	Against	A	7	9	-2	4	0.44
2	2	the	B	14	12	2	4	0.33
2	3	change	C	9	9	0	0	0
3	1	No	A	5	6	-1	1	0.17
3	2	response	B	4	8	-4	16	2.00
3	3		C	11	6	5	25	4.17
		Totals		100	100	0		$\chi^2 = 9.58$

Since $\chi^2(9.58) > \chi_\alpha^2(9.488)$, reject H_1 and accept H_2. There is a significant difference in the reactions of the memberships of the three locals to the proposed change.

THE KOLMOGOROV-SMIRNOV ONE-SAMPLE TEST

The Kolmogorov-Smirnov one-sample test may be used as an alternative to a chi-square test for goodness of fit when one is concerned with the hypothesis that an observed sample distribution is drawn from a population with a given theoretical distribution. It has two advantages over chi-square:

1. The Kolmogorov-Smirnov test treats individual observations separately. Thus, it is not necessary to lose information by combining categories as is often required in chi-square. This makes it a more powerful test than chi-square.
2. When samples are very small, it may be possible to use the Kolmogorov-Smirnov test when chi-square would be impractical because of the requirement that each expected frequency be at least five.

The Kolmogorov-Smirnov test involves working with two cumulative frequency distributions. One is an observed cumulative frequency distribution secured from the sample, and the other is a theoretical cumulative frequency distribution assumed in the null hypothesis. The point at which these two distributions show the greatest divergence is determined, and a decision is made to accept or reject the null hypothesis depending on the probability that the observed difference would occur if the observations were really a random sample from the theoretical distribution.

If F_o represents the cumulative values of f_o (the same observed distribution used in chi-square) expressed as a proportion of the total, and if F_e represents the cumulative values of f_e (the expected distribution) shown as a proportion of the total, then D can be defined as the maximum absolute difference between F_o and F_e.

$$D = \text{maximum} \,|\, F_o - F_e |\dots\dots\dots\dots\dots(13.4)$$

This maximum difference, D, can be compared with a known theoretical sampling distribution of D that is determined by the assumptions in H_1. Certain critical values of this known distribution are shown in Table 13.10. The table gives values of D for five different levels of significance for samples as large as 35. For samples larger than 35, the value of D can be computed using the fractions shown in the bottom row of the table. For example, if the sample size, n, is 49, $D = \dfrac{1.36}{\sqrt{49}} = 0.19$ for $\alpha = 0.05$ (two-tail test).

➤ *Example.* A baker who plans to add fruitcake to his line of baked goods wishes to test a statement made by one of his competitors to the effect that, "If you want a popular fruitcake that will sell, put in lots of nuts."

Table 13.10

TABLE OF CRITICAL VALUES OF *D* IN THE KOLMOGOROV-SMIRNOV ONE-SAMPLE TEST*

Sample size (*n*)	Level of significance for $D = $ maximum $\lvert F_o - F_e \rvert$				
	.20	.15	.10	.05	.01
1	.900	.925	.950	.975	.995
2	.684	.726	.776	.842	.929
3	.565	.597	.642	.708	.828
4	.494	.525	.564	.624	.733
5	.446	.474	.510	.565	.669
6	.410	.436	.470	.521	.618
7	.381	.405	.438	.486	.577
8	.358	.381	.411	.457	.543
9	.339	.360	.388	.432	.514
10	.322	.342	.368	.410	.490
11	.307	.326	.352	.391	.468
12	.295	.313	.338	.375	.450
13	.284	.302	.325	.361	.433
14	.274	.292	.314	.349	.418
15	.266	.283	.304	.338	.404
16	.258	.274	.295	.328	.392
17	.250	.266	.286	.318	.381
18	.244	.259	.278	.309	.371
19	.237	.252	.272	.301	.363
20	.231	.246	.264	.294	.356
25	.21	.22	.24	.27	.32
30	.19	.20	.22	.24	.29
35	.18	.19	.21	.23	.27
Over 35	$\dfrac{1.07}{\sqrt{n}}$	$\dfrac{1.14}{\sqrt{n}}$	$\dfrac{1.22}{\sqrt{n}}$	$\dfrac{1.36}{\sqrt{n}}$	$\dfrac{1.63}{\sqrt{n}}$

*Adapted from Massey, F. J., Jr., 1951. The Kolmogorov-Smirnov test for goodness of fit. *Journal of the American Statistical Association*, pp. 46, 70, with the kind permission of the author and publisher.

The baker makes a dozen fruitcakes from each of six different recipes — a total of 72 cakes in all. The recipes differ only in the proportion of nuts used. Cake *A* has the smallest proportion of nuts and Cake *F* has the largest proportion of nuts. The baker gives one of each of the six cakes to each of 12 housewives. The women agree to try the cakes and to designate the one that each likes best and would be most likely to buy. The results of the test are shown at the top of the next page.

Fruitcake ranked by the proportion of nuts (A has the fewest nuts)	Number of housewives selecting each cake
A	0
B	1
C	1
D	1
E	5
F	4
Total	12

The problem is to test at $\alpha = 0.05$ the hypothesis that the proportion of nuts is not important to the popularity of the fruitcake.

STEPS:

1. H_1: The observed distribution comes from a population that has a uniform distribution (*i.e.*, the proportion of nuts is not important).
2. H_2: The observed distribution comes from a population that does not have a uniform distribution (*i.e.*, the proportion of nuts is important).
3. An $\alpha = 0.05$ requires a value of $D = 0.375$ $(D_{\alpha = 0.05}$ for $n = 12)$.
4. Criterion: Reject H_1 (accept H_2) if $D > 0.375$; accept H_1 if $D \leq 0.375$, when $D = \text{maximum} \mid F_o - F_e \mid$.
5. Using the sample results, the value of D is computed in Table 13.11. The assumption underlying the expected distribution is that if the proportion of nuts is not important, each recipe for fruitcake should be chosen by two housewives.

Table 13.11

COMPUTATION OF D FOR A KOLMOGOROV-SMIRNOV ONE-SAMPLE TEST

Fruitcake ranked by proportion of nuts (A has fewest nuts)	Number chosen		F_o	F_e	$\mid F_o - F_e \mid$
	f_o	f_e			
A	0	2	$\frac{0}{12}$	$\frac{2}{12}$	$\frac{2}{12}$
B	1	2	$\frac{1}{12}$	$\frac{4}{12}$	$\frac{3}{12}$
C	1	2	$\frac{2}{12}$	$\frac{6}{12}$	$\frac{4}{12}$
D	1	2	$\frac{3}{12}$	$\frac{8}{12}$	$\frac{5}{12} = D$
E	5	2	$\frac{8}{12}$	$\frac{10}{12}$	$\frac{2}{12}$
F	4	2	$\frac{12}{12}$	$\frac{12}{12}$	0
Totals	12	12			

Since D $(\frac{5}{12} = 0.417) > D_{\alpha}(0.375)$, reject H_1 and accept H_2. The proportion of nuts in the fruitcake does make a difference in its acceptance.

The power[1] of the Kolmogorov-Smirnov test, when compared with a chi-square test, is demonstrated in the following example.

➤ *Example.* The foreman of a shop making castings is of the opinion that more faulty castings are made during the latter part of the day when employees are tired than earlier in the day when they are fresh. For a period of one month, he keeps records on faulty castings and notes the shift hour when each faulty unit is cast. The results of his sample of observations are shown below.

Shift hour	*Number of faulty castings*
1	3
2	4
3	3
4	3
5	2
6	7
7	8
8	10
Total	40

The foreman uses a chi-square test of goodness of fit to determine if the sample is drawn from a population with a uniform distribution. The $\chi^2_{\alpha=0.05}$(with 7 *d.f.*) = 14.067, and the computed value of chi-square using the sample results is 12.000. The foreman would be led to conclude from this test that the time of day is not a significant factor in the occurrence of a faulty product. He would, therefore, accept the null hypothesis.

The problem here is to determine whether or not the Kolmogorov-Smirnov test will support a rejection of the null hypothesis at $\alpha = 0.05$ when the chi-square test will not.

STEPS:

    1. H_1: The observed distribution comes from a population with a uniform distribution.

    2. H_2: The observed distribution does not come from a population with a uniform distribution.

    3. An $\alpha = 0.05$ and a sample of 40 requires a $D = \dfrac{1.36}{\sqrt{40}} = 0.215$.

    4. Criterion: Reject H_1 (accept H_2) if $D > 0.215$; accept H_1 if $D \leq 0.215$, when $D = \text{maximum}\,|F_o - F_e|$.

---

[1]The *power of a test* is defined as the probability of making a correct decision when H_1 is false. Power $= 1 - \beta$.

5. Using the sample data, the value of D is computed in Table 13.12.

Table 13.12

COMPUTATION OF D FOR A KOLMOGOROV-SMIRNOV ONE-SAMPLE TEST

Shift hour	f_o	f_e	F_o	F_e	$\lvert F_o - F_e \rvert$
1	3	5	$\frac{3}{40}$	$\frac{5}{40}$	$\frac{2}{40}$
2	4	5	$\frac{7}{40}$	$\frac{10}{40}$	$\frac{3}{40}$
3	3	5	$\frac{10}{40}$	$\frac{15}{40}$	$\frac{5}{40}$
4	3	5	$\frac{13}{40}$	$\frac{20}{40}$	$\frac{7}{40}$
5	2	5	$\frac{15}{40}$	$\frac{25}{40}$	$\frac{10}{40} = D = 0.250$
6	7	5	$\frac{22}{40}$	$\frac{30}{40}$	$\frac{8}{40}$
7	8	5	$\frac{30}{40}$	$\frac{35}{40}$	$\frac{5}{40}$
8	10	5	$\frac{40}{40}$	$\frac{40}{40}$	0
Totals	40	40			

Since $D(0.250) > D_\alpha(0.215)$, reject H_1 and accept H_2. There is a significant difference in the volume of faulty work due to the time of day.

In the example on page 429, a chi-square test of goodness of fit was made to determine if it was probable that an observed distribution of assembly times of 100 workers was drawn from a universe that was normally distributed. The Kolmogorov-Smirnov test could also be used for this purpose.

➤ *Example.* The observed and expected distributions of workers' times are shown below:

Time (minutes)	f_o	f_e
Under 20	0	0.8
20 and under 25	7	6.3
25 and under 30	25	23.4
30 and under 35	33	36.5
35 and under 40	27	24.8
40 and under 45	8	7.3
45 and over	0	0.9
Totals	100	100.0

Each distribution can be shown as a "less than" percentage distribution to permit the computation of $D = $ maximum $\lvert F_o - F_e \rvert$.

	Percent of total		
Time (minutes)	F_o	F_e	$|F_o - F_e|$
Less than 20	0.000	0.008	0.008
Less than 25	0.070	0.071	0.001
Less than 30	0.320	0.305	0.015
Less than 35	0.650	0.670	0.020 = D
Less than 40	0.920	0.919	0.002
Less than 45	1.000	0.991	0.009

For $\alpha = 0.05$, the critical value of D found in Table 13.10 is $D = \dfrac{1.36}{\sqrt{100}} = 0.136$. Since the value of $D(0.020) < D_\alpha(0.136)$, it is still appropriate to accept the null hypothesis and to decide that the sample distribution is drawn from a population which is normally distributed. In this particular example, the null hypothesis has been accepted when using both the chi-square and the Kolmogorov-Smirnov tests; thus, the outcome is rather conclusive.

TESTS USING SIGNS AND RANKS

There are a number of very useful nonparametric tests based on the signs of differences and on ranks of data. Often experimental data are easier to collect in this form; the methods are quick and easy to apply; and the tests do not require that the underlying distribution be specified. In market research it is possible to rank products according to consumer preference when no quantitative measurement of preference is possible.

Three of the most common tests of this type are discussed in this section — (1) the sign test, (2) the Wilcoxon matched-pairs signed-ranks test, and (3) the Mann-Whitney U test. Chapter 16 has a discussion on rank correlation techniques. In each case the size of the sample used is sufficiently large to obviate the need for special tables of critical values. The selected readings at the end of this chapter provide sources of additional information on small sample techniques requiring special tables and on additional tests using signs and ranks of data.

The Sign Test

The *sign test* is so called because it uses plus and minus signs as its data rather than quantitative measures. The test is based on the signs of the differences between pairs of observations, and it does not take into consideration the magnitudes of the differences. Magnitudes will be considered in a later test. The sign test has particular application when dealing with two samples that are not independent.

If the first observation in each pair is designated x_i and the second observation is designated y_i, the value of the term $x_i - y_i$ will be $+$, $-$, or 0. All cases in which $x_i - y_i = 0$ will be ignored, and the total of the remaining pairs of observations will constitute the sample, n. The null hypothesis assumes that

$$P(x_i > y_i) = P(x_i < y_i) = \tfrac{1}{2} = \pi.$$

Since there are only two possible outcomes, $+$ or $-$, the probability of a given number of $+$'s or $-$'s can be determined as $P(r \mid n; p = \tfrac{1}{2})$, which is the binomial probability distribution. It is also known that in a binomial distribution

$$E(r) = n\pi \quad \text{(Formula 7.5)}$$

and $\sigma_r = \sqrt{n\pi(1 - \pi)}$ (Formula 7.7).

For samples of more than 25, it can be assumed that the theoretical sampling distribution of r is normally distributed and

$$z = \frac{r - \tfrac{1}{2} - E(r)}{\sigma_r} \quad \text{(Formula 12.2)}$$

where,

> r is the number of $+$'s (or, if there are more of them, the number of $-$'s).

➤ **Example.** The general manager of a chain of 30 food stores is interested in determining whether packages of paper cartons to be used for storing food in home freezers will sell best when located in the store next to the frozen foods or located with the paper goods. He asks each of his local managers to try a display of the cartons in his store for one week in the first location and then for one week in the second location. The results of the study are shown in Table 13.13.

The problem is to use the sign test and an $\alpha = 0.05$ to determine if there are significantly more $-$'s than $+$'s. If there are, this would mean that the best location for the cartons is with the paper goods.

STEPS:

1. H_1: $P(x_i > y_i) = P(x_i < y_i)$. The universe proportions of $+$'s and $-$'s are the same. It makes no difference in which place the cartons are located.
2. H_2: $P(x_i > y_i) < P(x_i < y_i)$. There are significantly more $-$'s than $+$'s. The paper goods location is the better.
3. An $\alpha = 0.05$ requires a $z = 1.64$ if r represents the number of $-$'s.
4. Criterion: Reject H_1 (accept H_2) if $z > 1.64$; accept H_1 if $z \le 1.64$ when z is computed using Formulas 7.5, 7.7, and 12.2.
5. The sample data in Table 13.13 show $10 +$'s, $18 -$'s, and two 0's. When the observations for stores 10 and 21 are eliminated from the study, the following measures are available:

$$n = 28 \text{ (number of pairs of observations)}$$
$$r = 18 \text{ (number of } - \text{'s)}.$$
$$E(r) = n\pi = 28(0.5) = 14$$

$$\sigma_r = \sqrt{n\pi(1 - \pi)} = \sqrt{28(0.5)(0.5)} = 2.65$$
$$z = \frac{17.5 - 14}{2.65} = 1.32.$$

Since $z(1.32) < z_\alpha(1.64)$, the decision would be to accept H_1. The sign test does not show a significant difference.

Table 13.13

SALES OF FROZEN FOOD CARTONS AT TWO DIFFERENT LOCATIONS
IN EACH OF 30 DIFFERENT STORES

	Number of cartons sold				Number of cartons sold		
Store	Frozen foods	Paper goods	Sign	Store	Frozen foods	Paper goods	Sign
1	40	65	−	16	20	29	−
2	75	60	+	17	49	60	−
3	24	36	−	18	32	22	+
4	21	15	+	19	15	32	−
5	8	12	−	20	80	120	−
6	10	15	−	21	30	30	0
7	15	12	+	22	16	32	−
8	30	48	−	23	41	20	+
9	22	21	+	24	35	11	+
10	16	16	0	25	24	50	−
11	15	8	+	26	18	49	−
12	56	85	−	27	16	58	−
13	12	20	−	28	10	8	+
14	4	18	−	29	37	18	+
15	32	45	−	30	50	70	−

Wilcoxon Matched-Pairs Signed-Ranks Test

The *Wilcoxon test* is a more powerful test than the sign test as it gives more weight to a large difference than to a small one. It considers both the sign of the difference within pairs of observations and the magnitude of that difference.

If d_i represents the absolute difference between x_i and y_i, then each pair of observations will have a value for d_i. If $d_i = 0$, that pair of observations is again dropped from the study. After the values of d_i are computed, they are ranked in order of magnitude from the smallest to the largest without regard to sign. If there are ties in ranks, all the tied values of d_i are given the same rank. For example, if $+4$ and -4 are tied for rank two, both would be listed as 2.5.

After the values of d_i are ranked, each rank is then given the sign of the original difference between x_i and y_i. The value T is either the sum of the positive ranks or of the negative ranks, whichever sum is smaller. The null hypothesis assumes that for the universe the sum of the liked-sign ranks is equal. For samples of more than 25 observations, the theoretical sampling distribution of T is approximately normal and

$$\mu_T = \frac{n(n+1)}{4} \dots\dots\dots\dots\dots\dots\dots\dots(13.5)$$

$$\sigma_T = \sqrt{\frac{n(n+1)(2n+1)}{24}} \dots\dots\dots\dots(13.6)$$

$$\text{and } z = \frac{T - \mu_T}{\sigma_T} \dots\dots\dots\dots\dots\dots\dots(13.7)$$

➤ **Example.** To show the greater discriminatory power of this test over the sign test, the example of the frozen food cartons is repeated, but the test is made using the Wilcoxon matched-pairs signed-ranks test.

STEPS:
1. H_1: For the universe the sum of the positive-sign ranks is the same as the sum of the negative-sign ranks. The two locations are equally good.
2. H_2: For the universe the sum of the positive-sign ranks is less than the sum of the negative-sign ranks. The paper goods location is the better.
3. An $\alpha = 0.05$ requires a $z = -1.64$.
4. Criterion: Reject H_1 (accept H_2) if $z < -1.64$; accept H_1 if $z \geq -1.64$, when z is computed using Formulas 13.5, 13.6, and 13.7.
5. The computation of T is shown in Table 13.14. The figures shown in the column headed d_i are the absolute differences between the values of x_i and y_i in Table 13.13. After the rank of each value of d_i is determined, it is given the sign of the original difference. The sum of the negative ranks is -300, and the sum of the positive ranks is 106. Since the absolute value of 106 is less than the absolute value of -300, T is taken as 106. Stores 10 and 21 are eliminated as they have values of $d_i = 0$. The value of n is 28.

$$\mu_T = \frac{n(n+1)}{4} = \frac{(28)(29)}{4} = 203$$

$$\sigma_T = \sqrt{\frac{n(n+1)(2n+1)}{24}} = \sqrt{\frac{(28)(29)(57)}{24}} = 43.9$$

$$z = \frac{T - \mu_T}{\sigma_T} = \frac{106 - 203}{43.9} = -2.21.$$

Since $z(-2.21) < z_\alpha(-1.64)$, reject H_1 and accept H_2. The location of the frozen food cartons with the paper goods will lead to greater sales than in a location near the frozen foods.

Table 13.14

COMPUTATION OF T FOR A WILCOXON MATCHED-PAIRS
SIGNED-RANKS TEST

Store	d_i	Rank of d_i	Rank with less frequent sign (+)
1	25	-23	
2	15	$+15$	15
3	12	-12	
4	6	$+6$	6
5	4	-4	
6	5	-5	
7	3	$+3$	3
8	18	-18	
9	1	$+1$	1
10	0	(This store was eliminated)	
11	7	$+7$	7
12	29	-25	
13	8	-8	
14	14	-14	
15	13	-13	
16	9	-9	
17	11	-11	
18	10	$+10$	10
19	17	-17	
20	40	-27	
21	0	(This store was eliminated)	
22	16	-16	
23	21	$+21$	21
24	24	$+22$	22
25	26	-24	
26	31	-26	
27	42	-28	
28	2	$+2$	2
29	19	$+19$	19
30	20	-20	

$$T = 106$$

Mann-Whitney U Test

The *Mann-Whitney U test* may be used to test whether two independent samples are drawn from the same universe or from two universes having the same mean. This test is a good substitute for the parametric tests of the difference between two sample means discussed in Chapter 11. The U test can be used by the statistician who wishes to avoid the assumptions that must be made in a parametric test or who wishes a short-cut method.

Suppose that n_1 represents the number of items in the first sample, and n_2 represents the number of items in the second sample. The first step in the U test is to combine the two samples into one group and to rank the values from smallest to largest, keeping track of the sample to which each value belongs. The value R_1 represents the total of the ranks assigned to values of the first sample. The statistic U is defined as

$$U = n_1 n_2 + \frac{n_1(n_2 + 1)}{2} - R_1 \dots\dots\dots\dots(13.8)$$

If n_1 and n_2 are each ≥ 10, the theoretical sampling distribution of U is approximately normal and

$$\mu_U = \frac{n_1 n_2}{2} \dots\dots\dots\dots\dots\dots\dots\dots\dots\dots\dots(13.9)$$

$$\sigma_U = \sqrt{\frac{n_1 n_2(n_1 + n_2 + 1)}{12}} \dots\dots\dots\dots(13.10)$$

$$z = \frac{U - \mu_U}{\sigma_U} \dots\dots\dots\dots\dots\dots\dots\dots\dots(13.11)$$

➤ **Example.** Two mixes, A and B, are used to make concrete beams. A sample of 12 beams made from Mix A is tested and found to have an average strength of 5,094 psi (pounds per square inch). A sample of 10 beams made from Mix B is tested and found to have an average strength of 5,745 psi. The problem is to determine at an $\alpha = 0.05$ whether Mix B produces stronger beams than Mix A. The sample results are shown below:

Strength of concrete beams (in psi)

	Mix A	Mix B
	5,050	4,280
	6,120	5,920
	5,000	5,500
	4,650	4,988
	5,100	6,700
	4,800	6,000
	5,120	4,320
	4,900	7,100
	5,210	6,040
	5,020	6,602
	5,041	
	5,117	
Totals	61,128	57,450
Means	5,094	5,745

STEPS:

  1. $H_1: \mu_A = \mu_B.$
  2. $H_2: \mu_A \neq \mu_B.$
  3. An $\alpha = 0.05$ requires a z value of ± 1.96.
  4. Criterion: Reject H_1 (accept H_2) if $z < -1.96$ or if $z > 1.96$; accept H_1 if $-1.96 \leq z \leq 1.96$, when z is computed using Formulas 13.8, 13.9, 13.10, and 13.11.

5. The computation of R_1 using the sample values is shown in Table 13.15.

Table 13.15

COMPUTATION OF R_1 FOR A MANN-WHITNEY U TEST

(Sample values given in psi)

Array of the sample values	Mix	Rank	Ranks assigned to values of Mix *A*
4,280	B	1	
4,320	B	2	
4,650	A	3	3
4,800	A	4	4
4,900	A	5	5
4,988	B	6	
5,000	A	7	7
5,020	A	8	8
5,041	A	9	9
5,050	A	10	10
5,100	A	11	11
5,117	A	12	12
5,120	A	13	13
5,210	A	14	14
5,500	B	15	
5,920	B	16	
6,000	B	17	
6,040	B	18	
6,120	A	19	19
6,602	B	20	
6,700	B	21	
7,100	B	22	
			$R_1 = 115$

$n_1 = 12$ (number with Mix A) $n_2 = 10$ (number with Mix B)

$$U = n_1 n_2 + \frac{n_1(n_2 + 1)}{2} - R_1 = 120 + \frac{132}{2} - 115 = 71$$

$$\mu_U = \frac{n_1 n_2}{2} = \frac{120}{2} = 60$$

$$\sigma_U = \sqrt{\frac{n_1 n_2 (n_1 + n_2 + 1)}{12}} = \sqrt{\frac{(120)(23)}{12}} = 15.17$$

$$z = \frac{U - \mu_U}{\sigma_U} = \frac{71 - 60}{15.17} = 0.73.$$

Since $z(0.73)$ is $< z_\alpha(1.96)$, accept H_1 and reject H_2. This is always a two-tail test. Since the sample mean for Mix B is greater than that for Mix A, the conclusion would be that B is the better mix.

TEST OF RANDOMNESS

Any time a researcher uses a sample statistic to make an estimate about a universe parameter, he can make probability statements about the accuracy of his estimate only if he is dealing with a random sample. While the concept of a random sample is simple, the execution of the concept is often difficult.

For example, suppose a merchant wishes to take a random sample of shoppers leaving his store in order to learn what customers think about the store's pricing policies. The merchant instructs an interviewer to stand outside the store and to stop every tenth person who leaves to ask his opinion. If the interviewer's records show the following sequence of the sex of the person interviewed, it is clear he talked only to women: *F F F F F F F F F F F F F F F F*. If the sequence is *F F F F F F F F M M M M M M M*, he talked first only to women and then only to men. The sequence *M F M F M F M F M F M F M F* is also obviously not random. The question is, "How can one test a sequence to see if it is random?" The test presented here is called a *one-sample runs test*. Such a test is based on the order in which the individual sample observations were obtained. A *run* is defined as a series of identical occurrences that are preceded and followed by different occurrences or by none at all. For example, suppose a coin is tossed 12 times and lands with heads (*H*) or tails (*T*) in the following sequence:

$$\underset{1}{\underline{H\ H}}\ \underset{2}{\underline{T}}\ \underset{3}{\underline{H}}\ \underset{4}{\underline{T\ T}}\ \underset{5}{\underline{H\ H\ H\ H}}\ \underset{6}{\underline{T\ T}}.$$

If R represents the number of runs, $R = 6$ in this example. Also, if n_1 represents the number of heads, $n_1 = 7$; and if n_2 represents the number of tails, $n_2 = 5$.

If either n_1 or n_2 is greater than 20, the theoretical sampling distribution of R is approximately normal with

$$\mu_R = \frac{2n_1 n_2}{n_1 + n_2} + 1 \quad \dots\dots\dots\dots\dots\dots\dots\dots\dots\text{(13.12)}$$

$$\sigma_R = \sqrt{\frac{2n_1 n_2 (2n_1 n_2 - n_1 - n_2)}{(n_1 + n_2)^2 (n_1 + n_2 - 1)}} \quad \dots\dots\dots\dots\text{(13.13)}$$

and $z = \dfrac{R - \mu_R}{\sigma_R}$ $\quad \dots\dots\dots\dots\dots\dots\dots\dots\dots\dots\dots\text{(13.14)}$

The test will always be two tail.

➤ *Example.* Assume that in the example of the persons being interviewed as they left the department store, the interviewer recorded the sex of 64 persons interviewed in the order in which they were stopped. His records are presented in Table 13.16. The problem is to determine at $\alpha = 0.05$ whether his sample was random with respect to male and female.

Table 13.16

ORDER AND SEX OF 64 PERSONS INTERVIEWED
WHILE LEAVING A DEPARTMENT STORE

Row	Sex of person interviewed*
1	*F M F F M F F F*
2	*M M F M F F M M*
3	*F M F F F M M M*
4	*F F M F M F F M*
5	*F M M F F M F F*
6	*M F F F F M M M*
7	*F M F M F F M F*
8	*M F F F M F M M*

*M represents male and F represents female.
Note: Order is from left to right by row.
Runs have been underlined for emphasis.

STEPS:
1. H_1: The order of males and females is random.
2. H_2: The order of males and females is not random.
3. An $\alpha = 0.05$ requires a $z = \pm 1.96$.
4. Criterion: Reject H_1 (accept H_2) if $z < -1.96$ or if $z > 1.96$; accept H_1 if $-1.96 \leq z \leq 1.96$, when z is computed using Formulas 13.12, 13.13, and 13.14.
5. If n_1 represents the number of females, $n_1 = 36$. If n_2 represents the number of males, $n_2 = 28$. Since there is a total of 40 runs, $R = 40$.

$$\mu_R = \frac{2n_1 n_2}{n_1 + n_2} + 1 = \frac{2(36)(28)}{36 + 28} + 1 = 32.5$$

$$\sigma_R = \sqrt{\frac{2n_1 n_2 (2n_1 n_2 - n_1 - n_2)}{(n_1 + n_2)^2 (n_1 + n_2 - 1)}} = \sqrt{\frac{2(36)(28)(2{,}016 - 36 - 28)}{64^2(63)}}$$

$$= 3.91$$

$$z = \frac{R - \mu_R}{\sigma_R} = \frac{40 - 32.5}{3.91} = 1.92$$

Since $z(1.92) < z_\alpha(1.96)$, accept H_1. The order of the males and females in the sample is random.

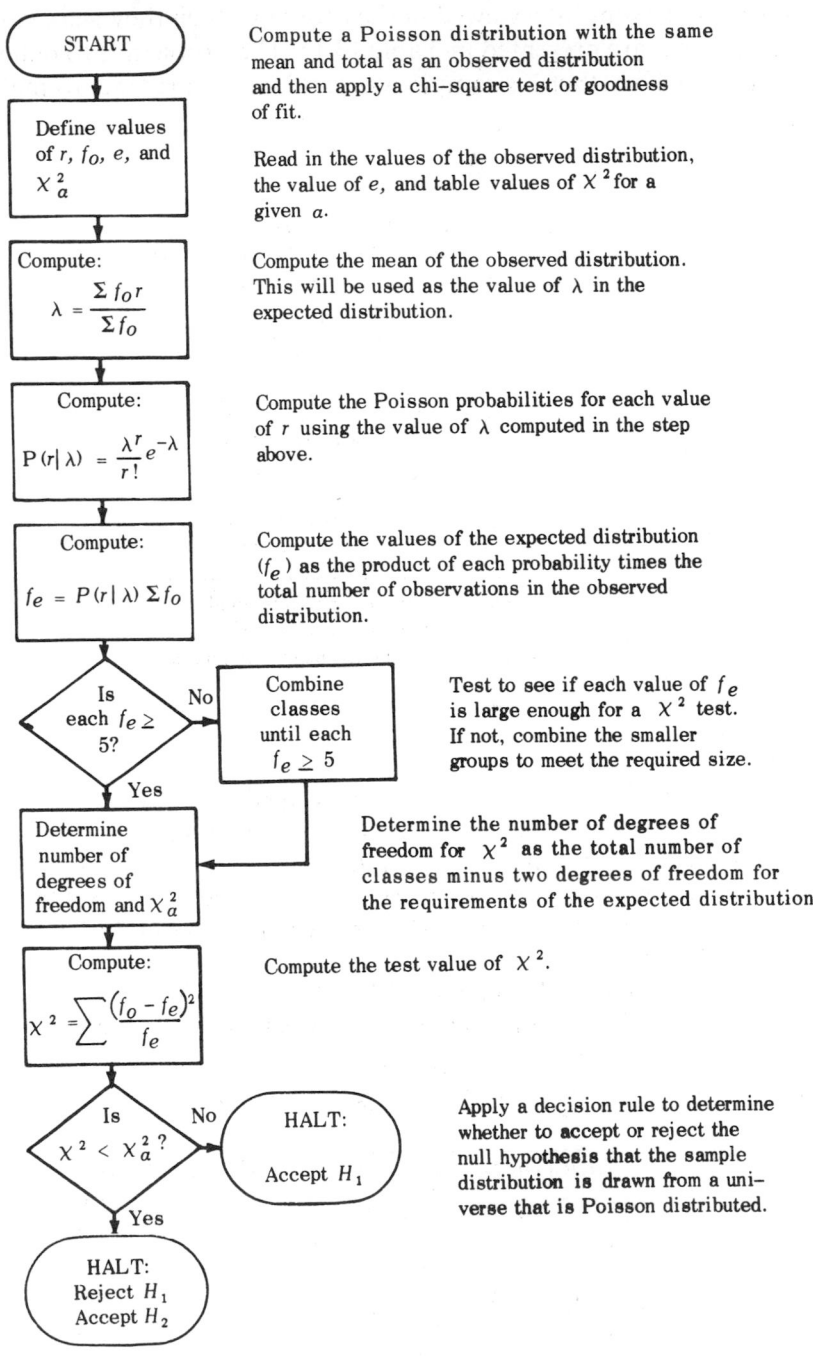

Compute a Poisson distribution with the same mean and total as an observed distribution and then apply a chi-square test of goodness of fit.

Read in the values of the observed distribution, the value of e, and table values of X^2 for a given a.

Compute the mean of the observed distribution. This will be used as the value of λ in the expected distribution.

Compute the Poisson probabilities for each value of r using the value of λ computed in the step above.

Compute the values of the expected distribution (f_e) as the product of each probability times the total number of observations in the observed distribution.

Test to see if each value of f_e is large enough for a X^2 test. If not, combine the smaller groups to meet the required size.

Determine the number of degrees of freedom for X^2 as the total number of classes minus two degrees of freedom for the requirements of the expected distribution.

Compute the test value of X^2.

Apply a decision rule to determine whether to accept or reject the null hypothesis that the sample distribution is drawn from a universe that is Poisson distributed.

Figure 13.2

FLOW DIAGRAM FOR MAKING A CHI-SQUARE TEST OF GOODNESS OF
FIT FOR A POISSON DISTRIBUTION

NONPARAMETRIC METHODS AND COMPUTERS

Computers are useful in any test of significance if the amount of data to be handled is very large or if a test is used with great frequency as might be true in an industrial situation.

Figure 13.2 is a flow diagram showing the steps to be followed to make a chi-square test of goodness of fit for a Poisson distribution.

STUDY QUESTIONS

13-1. Explain briefly the meaning of each of the following terms:

a. parametric method
b. nonparametric method
c. distribution-free test
d. chi-square distribution
e. test of goodness of fit
f. test of independence of classification

g. contingency table
h. Yates, correction for continuity
i. sign test
j. Wilcoxon test
k. Mann-Whitney *U* test
l. one-sample runs rest
m. run

13-2. What advantages do nonparametric or distribution-free tests have over parametric tests?

13-3. Discuss the shape of the chi-square distribution. What are its mean and standard deviation?

13-4. How would you describe the number of degrees of freedom of a chi-square distribution? Give an example.

13-5. What type of null hypothesis is made in chi-square tests of goodness of fit? What type of alternate hypothesis is made?

13-6. In a test of goodness of fit to a normal distribution, what are the requirements of the expected distribution?

13-7. What type of null hypothesis is made in chi-square tests of independence of classification? What type of alternate hypothesis is made?

13-8. Under what conditions is it appropriate to use Yates' correction for continuity in a chi-square test? Does it increase or decrease the computed value of chi-square?

13-9. In what ways is the Kolmogorov-Smirnov one-sample test superior to the chi-square test?

13-10. When is it possible to use tests of signs and ranks when parametric tests cannot be used? Give an example.

13-11. What probability distribution is basic to the development of the sign test? What other probability distribution is used to approximate it and why?

13-12. What makes the Wilcoxon test a more powerful test than the sign test?

13-13. What kind of test is the Mann-Whitney U test? What type of parametric test may it be used to replace?

13-14. What kind of test is the one-sample runs test? Why is this kind of test important?

PROBLEMS

13-1. A manufacturer of lawn furniture plans to introduce and sell his product for the first time in a large city. He divides the city on the map into what he considers to be four equal sales territories. During the first week of advertising, the following number of inquiries is received from each territory:

Sales territory	Number of inquiries
Northwest	23
Southwest	12
Southeast	25
Northeast	16

Use a chi-square test of goodness of fit to test at $\alpha = 0.05$ the hypothesis that the four territories are equally good.

13-2. Six plots of land of equal size are all planted in corn. The number of bushels of corn produced on each plot is shown below:

Plot	Number of bushels of corn
A	52
B	41
C	60
D	57
E	63
F	45

Use a chi-square test of goodness of fit to test at $\alpha = 0.01$ the hypothesis that the six plots are equally good for growing corn.

13-3. The number of customers in a supermarket who arrive at the check-out stations each minute on a Saturday are shown below. Use a chi-square test of goodness of fit and an $\alpha = 0.01$ to test the observed sample distribution to see if it is drawn from a universe that is Poisson distributed. Note: Use the table value for λ that comes closest to the mean of the observed distribution.

Number of customers per minute r	Number of minutes f_o
0	153
1	203
2	117
3	49
4	8
5	4
6	1
7	0
Total	535

13-4. Fit a Poisson distribution to the observed distribution shown below and test for goodness of fit using chi-square and $\alpha = 0.05$.

Number of trucks arriving at a loading dock per 15-minute period r	Number of 15-minute periods f_o
0	31
1	60
2	72
3	60
4	42
5	21
6	9
7	3
8	1
9	1
Total number of 15-minute periods	300

13-5. The table at the top of the next page shows an observed distribution of 200 long-distance telephone calls and a normal distribution with the same mean, standard deviation, and total frequency.

   a. Use a chi-square test of goodness of fit and an $\alpha = 0.01$ to test the hypothesis that the observed distribution is drawn from a normally distributed population.

   b. Use a Kolmogorov-Smirnov test and an $\alpha = 0.05$.

Time (in minutes)	Observed distribution f_o	Normal distribution f_e
Under 1	0	4
1 and under 2	12	14
2 and under 3	50	38
3 and under 4	64	64
4 and under 5	46	46
5 and under 6	14	24
6 and under 7	10	8
7 and over	4	2
Totals	200	200

Distribution of the length of 200 long-distance calls

13-6. The following distribution shows expenses as a percent of earnings for 300 mortgage loan companies. The mean of this distribution is 65.4% and the standard deviation is 8.8%.

  a. Use a chi-square test of goodness of fit and an $\alpha = 0.05$ to test the hypothesis that the observed distribution is drawn from a normally distributed universe.

  b. Use a Kolmogorov-Smirnov test and an $\alpha = 0.05$.

Expenses as a percent of earnings	Number of mortgage loan companies
40 and under 45	3
45 and under 50	9
50 and under 55	24
55 and under 60	45
60 and under 65	60
65 and under 70	66
70 and under 75	51
75 and under 80	30
80 and under 85	9
85 and under 90	3
Total	300

13-7. The personnel director of a large company is interested in determining whether marriage is a factor in the frequency of absence from work of female employees. A random sample of the absence records of 400 women reveals the following:

Married	Often absent	Seldom absent	Totals
yes	84	96	180
no	62	158	220
Totals	146	254	400

Use a chi-square test and an $\alpha = 0.05$ to determine if the universe proportion of the "often absent" group is independent of marriage. *Note:* Use Yates' correction for continuity.

13-8. A book company that normally sends announcements of new books to a large number of professional people is interested to learn if an announcement in color is more effective than one in black and white. It sends 100 black and white announcements to a random sample of names on its mailing list and 100 announcements, identical to the first except that they are in color, to another random sample of 100. The results are shown below:

Announcement	Sale	No sale	Totals
Black and white	20	80	100
Color	30	70	100
Totals	50	150	200

Use a chi-square test and $\alpha = 0.01$ to determine if the universe proportion of sales is independent of the color of the announcement. *Note:* Use Yates' correction for continuity.

13-9. A random sample of 120 college professors was asked their opinion on whether more or less emphasis should be placed on a teacher's research as a basis for his promotion. The survey produced the following results.

Emphasis on research	Teaching field			Totals
	Liberal Arts	Sciences	Professional	
More	20	20	10	50
Less	15	5	20	40
Same	15	5	10	30
Totals	50	30	40	120

Use a chi-square test with $\alpha = 0.05$ to test the hypothesis that the universe distribution of proportions of opinion is the same for all faculty groups.

13-10. A morale survey of a random sample of employees from four employee groups of a large organization produced the following results:

Feelings about employee morale	Employee group			
	Office	Sales	Shop	Management
Better than average	15	20	5	10
Average	10	10	10	3
Below average	5	5	25	2

Use a chi-square test with $\alpha = 0.01$ to test the hypothesis that the universe distribution of proportions of opinion is the same for all employee groups.

13-11. Use a Kolmogorov-Smirnov one-sample test and $\alpha = 0.05$ to test the hypothesis that the following sample distribution comes from a universe that is a uniform distribution:

Category	f_o	f_e
A	6	3
B	8	3
C	2	3
D	1	3
E	0	3
F	1	3
Totals	18	18

13-12. Four coins are placed in a cup, shaken well, and then tossed onto a hard surface so that the number of heads can be counted. This experiment is conducted 20 times with the following results:

Number of heads on one trial	Number of trials
0	1
1	3
2	10
3	4
4	2
Total	20

Use a Kolmogorov-Smirnov one-sample test and $\alpha = 0.05$ to test the hypothesis that the sample distribution comes from a universe that is a binomial distribution with value of $\pi = \frac{1}{2}$.

13-13. Given the following observations in which the differences between pairs of values are shown as $+$'s and $-$'s, use the sign test and $\alpha = 0.01$ to test the hypothesis that the universe proportion of $+$'s and $-$'s is the same.

Observation number	Sign	Observation number	Sign
1	+	16	+
2	−	17	+
3	−	18	+
4	+	19	−
5	−	20	+
6	+	21	+
7	+	22	−
8	−	23	−
9	+	24	+
10	−	25	+
11	−	26	+
12	+	27	+
13	+	28	−
14	+	29	+
15	+	30	−

13-14. The weights of 26 children are checked at the beginning and again at the end of summer camp to determine if each child gained or lost weight during the season. The recorded weights are shown below:

Camper number	Weight (pounds) Beginning X	Weight (pounds) Ending Y	Sign $X - Y$
1	96	119	−
2	60	64	−
3	80	75	+
4	72	89	−
5	105	119	−
6	140	114	+
7	93	102	−
8	95	102	−
9	82	81	+
10	102	81	+
11	100	118	−
12	75	63	+
13	115	113	+
14	111	130	−
15	85	100	−
16	130	154	−
17	97	110	−
18	110	88	+
19	96	90	+
20	95	98	−
21	115	135	−
22	65	76	−
23	160	135	+
24	72	80	--
25	105	121	.−
26	88	78	+

Use a sign test and $\alpha = 0.05$ to test the hypothesis that the universe proportion of +'s and −'s is the same.

13-15. Use a Wilcoxon matched-pairs signed-ranks test and an $\alpha = 0.05$ to test the hypothesis that in **Problem 13-14** the universe sum of positive signed ranks is the same as the universe sum of negative signed ranks.

13-16. Use a Wilcoxon matched-pairs signed-ranks test and an $\alpha = 0.05$ to test the hypothesis that the universe sum of positive signed ranks is the same as the universe sum of negative signed ranks. Use the sample of 25 observations shown at the top of the next page.

Observation number	Value of X	Value of Y
1	50	49
2	65	61
3	72	59
4	61	78
5	74	68
6	52	76
7	84	92
8	72	58
9	59	58
10	82	63
11	90	70
12	51	58
13	90	95
14	58	73
15	80	62
16	88	87
17	62	41
18	66	55
19	56	78
20	69	59
21	86	63
22	70	79
23	68	52
24	75	63
25	54	29

13-17. A random sample of 12 clerical employees from each of two departments in a company is given clerical aptitude tests. The test scores are shown below. Use a Mann-Whitney U test and an $\alpha = 0.05$ to test the hypothesis that $\mu_A = \mu_B$.

Scores on a clerical aptitude test	
Department A	Department B
70	74
63	112
76	68
91	96
65	115
60	90
75	105
100	120
85	61
93	82
65	110
78	95

13-18. A firm with several hundred salesmen on the road uses two brands of automobiles. A random sample of 10 repair bills for Brand I cars and a random sample of 15 repair bills for Brand II cars are shown below. Use a Mann-Whitney U test and an $\alpha = 0.05$ to test the hypothesis that the universe average cost of maintaining Brand I cars is the same as the universe average cost of maintaining Brand II cars.

Size of repair bills				
Brand I		Brand II		
$26.00	$5.20	$17.82	$72.27	$26.50
63.00	527.00	6.80	28.25	10.25
14.80	30.57	25.10	3.40	29.97
32.00	105.05	45.00	26.50	2.67
225.00	20.10	22.00	314.00	23.50

13-19. Test the sequence of 0's and 1's shown below with a one-sample runs test to see if the sequence is random. Use $\alpha = 0.05$.

1 1 0 1 1 1 0 0 1 0 0 0 1 1 1 1 0 1 0 1 0 0 1 1 0 0 0 1
0 0 0 0 1 1 1 0 1 0 0 1 1 0 0 0 1 0 1 1 0 0 0 0 1 1 0 1

13-20. A professor making up a true-false test is interested in arranging the questions so that the sequence of true and false answers is random. If the key to the test follows the pattern shown below, has he achieved his objective? Use $\alpha = 0.05$.

T F T F T F T T F F T F T F T T F T T F T
T T F T F F T F T F T F T T F T F T F F T

13-21. Draw a flow diagram of the steps to be followed in making a chi-square test of goodness of fit to a binomial distribution.

13-22. Draw a flow diagram of the steps to be followed in making a Mann-Whitney U test.

SELECTED READINGS

Chou, Ya-lun. *Applied Business and Economic Statistics.* New York: Holt, Rinehart and Winston, Inc., 1963.
  Appendix C has a very clear, concise description of the chi-square distribution and its uses.

Handbook of Tables for Probability and Statistics. Cleveland: The Chemical Rubber Company, 1965.

>   Part X of this handbook gives complete tables of critical values to be used in nonparametric tests such as the sign test, Mann-Whitney U test, Kolmogorov-Smirnov one-sample test, Spearman's Rank Correlation Coefficient, and the matched-pairs signed-ranks test. These tables make it possible to apply these tests to very small samples.

Siegel, Sidney. *Nonparametric Statistics for Behavioral Sciences.* New York: McGraw-Hill Book Company, Inc., 1956.

>   This book pulls together into one source a wide variety of nonparametric tests. It is particularly useful to the researcher who is in need of non-parametric tests in the analysis of his research data but who lacks an extensive background in mathematics and classical statistics.

Chapter 14

The *F* Distribution

The foregoing discussions of inference present the rationale for apply-ing tests of significance in a variety of situations. The normal distribution is utilized in making tests concerning a significant difference in a sample mean and a universe mean, a sample proportion and a universe pro-portion, the means of two samples, etc., where the universe mean and the variance are known or hypothesized and presumably based on a very large number of observations. The *t* distribution is utilized in the types of significance tests for which the normal curve is used, except the universe variance is estimated from a sample statistic computed from a finite number of observations (usually less than 30). The chi-square distribution is applied in nonparametric tests in which several observed and expected frequencies or several observed and expected proportions are compared.

While these distributions provide bases for making inferences in a variety of problem situations, there is another class of inferential problems for which none of the distributions discussed previously is appropriate. This class of problems concerns a test of significance of two or more sample estimates of the universe variance. Tests of significance for this class of problems require the use of the *F* distribution (the *F* is in honor of the statistical theorist, R. A. Fisher). Before considering the *F* distribution in detail, it is well to consider the nature of the distribution of sample variances.

SIGNIFICANCE TEST AND CONFIDENCE LIMITS OF A SAMPLE VARIANCE

The means of samples drawn randomly from a normal universe are distributed normally. However, the variances of random samples drawn from a normal universe have a distribution that is skewed positively. The sample variance distribution is a function of the sample size and the universe variance as is the distribution of sample means. Because the variance distribution is neither normal nor symmetric, a separate table of areas would have to be derived for each combination of n and σ^2 in order to determine if a significant difference exists between sample and universe variances.

A significance test involving a sample variance and the corresponding universe variance is simplified because of a fortuitous relationship. This relationship is expressed by

$$\chi^2 = \frac{(n-1)\hat{\sigma}^2}{\sigma^2} \quad \dots\dots\dots\dots\dots\dots\dots\dots(14.1)$$

where the ratio of the unbiased estimator times the number of degrees of freedom (based on the sample size) to the universe variance has a chi-square distribution for $d.f. = n - 1$. Since the unbiased estimator of the universe variance has the relationship

$$\hat{\sigma}^2 = \frac{n}{n-1}s^2$$

by Formula 9.9, Formula 14.1 may be written alternatively as

$$\chi^2 = \frac{(n-1)\dfrac{n}{n-1}s^2}{\sigma^2}$$

or

$$\chi^2 = \frac{ns^2}{\sigma^2} \quad \dots\dots\dots\dots\dots\dots\dots\dots\dots(14.2)$$

Significance Test for a Sample Variance

A sample variance may be tested for significance by use of the chi-square distribution.

➤ *Example.* A tire manufacturing process is designed to produce tires with a standard deviation of 0.30 ounces. A sample of 10 tires is taken and the sample standard deviation is 0.35 ounces. A significance test is made to test the null hypothesis, which states that the sample variance does not differ significantly from that of the universe. The test of significance is made by using Formula 14.2 and computing

$$\chi^2 = \frac{ns^2}{\sigma^2}$$

$$= \frac{(10)(0.35)^2}{(0.30)^2}$$

$$= \frac{10(0.1225)}{0.09}$$

$$= 13.611$$

for $d.f. = n - 1 = 9$. The value of $\chi^2_{0.20} = 12.242$ and $\chi^2_{0.10} = 14.684$ for $d.f. = 9$. Since $12.242 < 13.611 < 14.684$, the null hypothesis is not rejected.

Confidence Interval of a Universe Variance

The confidence interval for estimating the universe variance can be computed by use of Formula 14.2 and the appropriate values read from Appendix K. The 96% confidence limits for σ^2 are found by reading the $\chi^2_{0.02}$ and $\chi^2_{0.98}$ values from Appendix K, substituting these values into Formula 14.2, and solving for the value of σ^2 at the upper and lower limits.

➤ *Example.* A random sample of 25 observations is drawn from a normal universe. The sample standard deviation is six. The values of σ^2 at the 96% confidence limits are computed by reading $\chi^2_{0.02} = 40.270$ and $\chi^2_{0.98} = 11.992$ from Appendix K and solving

$$\chi^2_{0.02} = \frac{ns^2}{\sigma^2}$$

$$40.270 = \frac{25(6)^2}{\sigma^2}$$

$$40.270\sigma^2 = 900$$

$$\sigma^2 = 22.3$$

and

$$\chi^2_{0.98} = \frac{ns^2}{\sigma^2}$$

$$11.992 = \frac{25(6)^2}{\sigma^2}$$

$$11.992\,\sigma^2 = 900$$

$$\sigma^2 = 75.1$$

The lower and upper 96% confidence limits of σ^2 are, respectively, 22.3 and 75.1.

CHARACTERISTICS OF THE *F* DISTRIBUTION

A test of significance concerning two sample variances is based on the ratio rather than on the difference between these variances. The *statistic F* is the ratio of unbiased estimates of the universe variance. The distribution of *F* describes the frequency of the ratio of two unbiased estimates of the universe variance that can be obtained by chance in drawing two samples randomly from a normal universe.

The Density Function of the Statistic *F*

Formula 14.2 shows that the ratio of ns^2 to σ^2 has a chi-square distribution for $n - 1$ degrees of freedom. Consider two samples drawn randomly from a normally distributed universe with sample sizes n_1 and n_2 and sample variances s_1^2 and s_2^2, respectively. For each sample, the ratio given by Formula 14.2 is computed

$$\chi_1^2 = \frac{n_1 s_1^2}{\sigma^2}, \qquad \text{for } d.f._1 = n_1 - 1$$

and

$$\chi_2^2 = \frac{n_2 s_2^2}{\sigma^2}, \qquad \text{for } d.f._2 = n_2 - 1$$

The statistic *F* is the ratio

$$F = \frac{\dfrac{n_1 s_1^2}{(n_1 - 1)}}{\dfrac{n_2 s_2^2}{(n_2 - 1)}} \quad \dots\dots\dots\dots\dots\dots\dots(14.3)$$

and is called the *variance ratio*. Since

$$\hat{\sigma}^2 = \frac{n}{n - 1} s^2$$

Formula 14.3 may be written

$$F = \frac{\hat{\sigma}_1^2}{\hat{\sigma}_2^2} \quad \dots\dots\dots\dots\dots\dots\dots\dots(14.4)$$

The density function of the statistic *F* is based on the value of F, $d.f._1$, and $d.f._2$. This function is the formidable expression

$$g(F) = \frac{\left(\dfrac{d.f._1 + d.f._2 - 2}{2}\right)!}{\left(\dfrac{d.f._1 - 2}{2}\right)! \cdot \left(\dfrac{d.f._2 - 2}{2}\right)!} \left(\frac{d.f._1}{d.f._2}\right)^{\frac{d.f._1}{2}} \frac{F^{\frac{d.f._1 - 2}{2}}}{\left(1 + \dfrac{d.f._1 F}{d.f._2}\right)^{\frac{d.f._1 + d.f._2}{2}}} \quad (14.5)$$

where $d.f._1 = n_1 - 1$ and $d.f._2 = n_2 - 1$. The value of $g(F)$ varies with the values of $d.f._1$ and $d.f._2$.

The *F* distribution is skewed positively for small values of $d.f._1$ and $d.f._2$, but as $d.f._1$ and $d.f._2$ increase, the *F* distribution approaches a normal distribution. The range of values of *F* is from zero to positive infinity. The *F* distribution for relatively small values of $d.f._1$ and $d.f._2$ is shown in Figure 14.1.

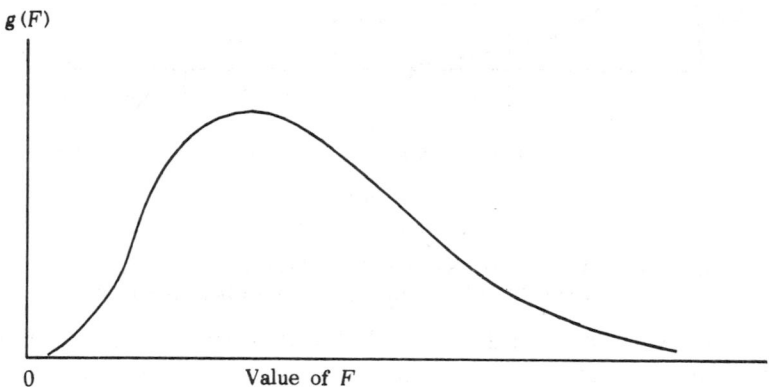

Figure 14.1

DISTRIBUTION OF THE STATISTIC *F*

Values of the Likelihood of *F*

In making a significance test concerning the ratio of two unbiased estimates of the universe variance, it is necessary to know the likelihood of obtaining various values of *F* as the result of chance. Values of *F* have been computed and are given in Appendix L. This appendix shows values of *F* that correspond to various areas in the right tail of the *F* distribution.

➤ *Example.* The *F* distribution for $d.f._1 = 5$ and $d.f._2 = 5$ is shown in Figure 14.2. The values of *F* for selected likelihoods (areas in the right tail) are obtained from Appendix L by reading the values corresponding to the intersection of column $d.f._1 = 5$ and row $d.f._2 = 5$. Note that the probability is 0.500 that a value of *F* of 1.00 or more will be obtained due to chance. The probability is 0.025 of obtaining a value of *F* of 7.15 or larger due to chance, etc.

A Significance Test for Two Sample Variances

In some business problems it is desirable to determine if the variances of two samples can be considered to be homogeneous. In other words, suppose sample 1 is drawn randomly from a normal universe *A* with a

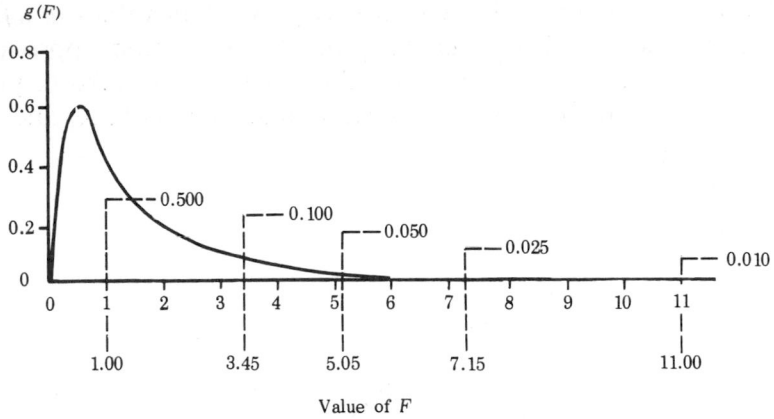

Value of F

Figure 14.2

DISTRIBUTION OF THE STATISTIC F FOR $d.f._1 = 5$ AND $d.f._2 = 5$
AND VALUES OF F FOR SELECTED LIKELIHOODS

standard deviation σ_A and sample 2 is drawn from a normal universe B with a standard deviation σ_B. The question is whether the assumption $\sigma_A = \sigma_B$ is valid. This assumption (the null hypothesis) can be tested by computing F for the sample variances and determining the probability of obtaining the computed value of F as the result of chance.

➤ *Example.* The purchasing agent of a firm wishes to choose between two brands of plastic bags for packaging food products. A sample of each brand is taken and the mean and the standard deviation of the bursting strength are computed for each sample. The results are as follows:

Sample 1	*Sample* 2
(*Brand A*)	(*Brand B*)
$n_1 = 21$	$n_2 = 16$
$s = 2.5$ psi	$s = 1.5$ psi

A significance test is made to determine if it can be assumed that the variance of the bursting strength of the two brands of plastic bags is the same. In other words, can it be assumed that $\sigma_A = \sigma_B$, where the former is the standard deviation of the process for Brand A and the latter term is the standard deviation for the production process for Brand B? The F ratio is computed

$$F = \frac{\hat{\sigma}_1^2}{\hat{\sigma}_2^2} = \frac{\dfrac{n_1 s_1^2}{(n_1 - 1)}}{\dfrac{n_2 s_2^2}{(n_2 - 1)}} = \frac{\dfrac{(21)(2.5)^2}{(21 - 1)}}{\dfrac{(16)(1.5)^2}{(16 - 1)}} = \frac{6.562}{2.400} = 2.73$$

for $d.f._1 = 20$ and $d.f._2 = 15$. The corresponding values in Appendix L compared with the computed value of F are

$$F_{0.100} < F < F_{0.050}$$
$$2.33 < 2.73 < 2.76.$$

The sample variances differ significantly at the 0.100 level.

In some situations it may happen that an F ratio of less than one is obtained. For instance, in the foregoing example if the designation of the samples had been reversed, the computed F ratio would have been less than one. In that case, the reciprocal of the F ratio should be used and the degrees of freedom should be reversed. Alternatively, since the designation of the samples is arbitrary, the sample with the largest variance could be designated sample 1 to insure that a value of F of not less than one is obtained.

THE RELATIONSHIP OF THE NORMAL, *t*, CHI-SQUARE, AND *F* DISTRIBUTIONS

It can be demonstrated that over the range of probability values used most commonly for making significance tests, the F distribution is equivalent to the normal, t, and chi-square distributions. A comparison of the assumptions implicit in the use of each of the distributions is summarized in Table 14.1. Note that the F distribution is appropriate for every combination of assumptions. The relationship of the values of F with the corresponding characteristics of each of the other three distributions is summarized in Table 14.2.

Table 14.1

ASSUMPTIONS IN THE USE OF SELECTED DISTRIBUTIONS

| Distribution | Basis of inference | | Source of the value of the variance used in the test |
	Number of observations	Number of parameters or estimates	
Normal	Infinite	Two	Known
t	Finite	Two	Estimated
Chi-square	Infinite	Two or more	Known
F	Finite or infinite	Two or more	Known or estimated

Table 14.2

THE RELATIONSHIP OF THE F DISTRIBUTION WITH TAIL VALUES
OF THE NORMAL, t, AND CHI-SQUARE DISTRIBUTIONS FOR A
PROBABILITY OF 0.10 OR LESS

Distribution	Equivalent F value	Corresponding degrees of freedom
Normal	$F = z^2$	$d.f._1 = 1$, $d.f._2 = \infty$
t	$F = t^2$	$d.f._1 = 1$, $d.f._2 =$ Any finite integer greater than zero
Chi-square	$F = \dfrac{\chi^2}{d.f._1}$	$d.f._1 =$ Any finite integer greater than zero
		$d.f._2 = \infty$

A Comparison of Values of z and F

The tail values of normal deviates can be obtained from the F table by taking the square root of the F values for $d.f._1 = 1$ and $d.f._2 = \infty$.

➤ *Example.* The F values for $d.f._1 = 1$ and $d.f._2 = \infty$ read from Appendix L and the corresponding normal curve deviates read from Appendix I are as follows:

Probability	Normal deviate z	F Value* $F = z^2$
0.100	1.65	$2.71 = (1.65)^2$
0.050	1.96	$3.84 = (1.96)^2$
0.025	2.24	$5.02 = (2.24)^2$
0.010	2.58	$6.63 = (2.58)^2$
0.005	2.81	$7.88 = (2.81)^2$
0.001	3.29	$10.83 = (3.29)^2$

*Some precision is lost in comparing F and z^2 due to rounding error.

The equivalence of z^2 and F holds for the right tails of the respective distributions, but not for the entire distributions. For example, the value of z for a probability of 0.500 is zero, but the F value for $d.f._1 = 1$ and $d.f._2 = \infty$ is 0.455.

The Relationship of the t and F Distributions

Values of the t distribution for relatively small probabilities can be obtained from the F table by taking the square root of the value of F for $d.f._1 = 1$ and $d.f._2$ equal to the degrees of freedom used in selecting a value of t.

➤ *Example.* The values of t for selected degrees of freedom and probabilities read from Appendix J and the corresponding F values for

$d.f._1 = 1$ in the F table for selected values of $d.f._2$, which correspond to the degrees of freedom in the t table.

Probability	Value of t d.f. = 5	Value of F $F = t^2$ $d.f._1 = 1, d.f._2 = 5$
0.100	2.02	$4.06 = (2.02)^2$
0.050	2.57	$6.61 = (2.57)^2$
0.010	4.03	$16.3 = (4.03)^2$
0.001	6.86	$47.0 = (6.86)^2$
	d.f. = 15	$d.f._1 = 1, d.f._2 = 15$
0.100	1.75	$3.07 = (1.75)^2$
0.050	2.13	$4.54 = (2.13)^2$
0.010	2.95	$8.68 = (2.95)^2$
0.001	4.07	$16.6 = (4.07)^2$
	d.f. = ∞	$d.f._1 = 1, d.f._2 = ∞$
0.100	1.65	$2.71 = (1.65)^2$
0.050	1.96	$3.84 = (1.96)^2$
0.010	2.58	$6.63 = (2.58)^2$
0.001	3.29	$10.83 = (3.29)^2$

Note that for $d.f._1 = 1$ and $d.f._2 = ∞$, the values of t and z are equal and $F = t^2 = z^2$. The values of t^2 are found in the column denoted $d.f._1 = 1$ in the F table for selected values of $d.f._2$, which correspond to the degrees of freedom in the t table.

The Relationship of Values of Chi-Square and F

The tail values of χ^2 for selected probabilities can be obtained from the F table for selected values of $d.f._1$ and for $d.f._2 = ∞$. The relationship between χ^2 and F is obtained from the relationship

$$F = \frac{\chi^2}{d.f.} = \frac{\hat{\sigma}^2}{\sigma^2},$$

where $d.f.$ corresponds to the degrees of freedom in applying the chi-square distribution and $d.f._1$ of the F distribution.

➤ *Example.* The equivalence of the values of F (Appendix L) and the values of chi-square (Appendix K) for selected degrees of freedom and selected tail probabilities is shown as follows:

		Value of F
Probability	Value of chi-square	$F = \dfrac{\chi^2}{d.f.}$
	$d.f. = 1$	$d.f._1 = 1, d.f._2 = \infty$
0.100	2.71	$2.71 = \dfrac{2.71}{1}$
0.050	3.84	$3.84 = \dfrac{3.84}{1}$
0.010	6.63	$6.63 = \dfrac{6.63}{1}$
	$d.f. = 5$	$d.f._1 = 5, d.f._2 = \infty$
0.100	9.24	$1.85 = \dfrac{9.24}{5}$
0.050	11.07	$2.21 = \dfrac{11.07}{5}$
0.010	15.09	$3.02 = \dfrac{15.09}{5}$
	$d.f. = 15$	$d.f._1 = 15, d.f._2 = \infty$
0.100	22.31	$1.49 = \dfrac{22.31}{15}$
0.050	25.00	$1.67 = \dfrac{25.00}{15}$
0.010	30.58	$2.04 = \dfrac{30.58}{15}$

Note that for $d.f._1 = 1$ and $d.f._2 = \infty$, the value of F corresponds to

$$F = z^2 = t^2 = \chi^2.$$

This relationship between the F distribution and values of t^2, z^2, and χ^2 is shown in Table 14.3. This table demonstrates that the F distribution may be viewed as the general case, while the normal, t, and chi-square distributions may be viewed as special cases of F.

ANALYSIS OF VARIANCE

The technique of analysis of variance is one of the most powerful of statistical methods. This method provides the basis for determining whether several sample means differ significantly. A test of significance for two sample means, presented in Chapter 11, is the simplest case of analysis of variance.

Table 14.3

AN ILLUSTRATION OF THE RELATIONSHIP BETWEEN VALUES OF
z, t, χ^2, AND F

$d.f._2$	P	$d.f._1 = 1$	2	3	...	∞
	0.500	1.00	1.50	1.71		2.20
	0.100	39.9	49.5	53.6		63.3
	0.050	161	200	216		254
1	0.025	648	800	864	...	1,020
	0.010	4,050	5,000	5,400		3,370
	0.005	16,200	20,000	21,600		25,500
	0.001	405,284	500,000	540,379		636,619
	0.500	0.667	1.00	1.13		1.44
	0.100	8.53	9.00	9.16		9.49
	0.050	18.5	19.0	19.2		19.5
2	0.025	38.5	39.0	39.2	...	39.5
	0.010	98.5	99.0	99.2		99.5
	0.005	199	199	199		200
	0.001	998.5	999.0	999.2		999.5
	0.500	0.585	0.881	1.00		1.27
	0.100	5.54	5.46	5.39		5.13
	0.050	10.1	9.55	9.28		8.53
3	0.025	17.4	16.0	15.4	...	13.9
	0.010	34.1	30.8	29.5		26.1
	0.005	55.6	49.8	47.5		41.8
	0.001	167.5	148.5	141.1		123.5
⋮	⋮	⋮	⋮	⋮		⋮
	0.500	0.455	0.693	0.789		1.00
	0.100	2.71	2.30	2.08		1.00
	0.050	3.84	3.00	2.60		1.00
∞	0.025	5.02	3.69	3.12	...	1.00
	0.010	6.63	4.61	3.78		1.00
	0.005	7.88	5.30	4.28		1.00
	0.001	10.8	6.91	5.42		1.00

$\dfrac{\chi^2}{d.f._1}$

z^2 t^2

In the discussion that follows, methods for analyzing the dispersion of
several sample means are presented.

➤ *Example.* Ten service stations are rated in terms of overall quality
and effectiveness. More than 20 factors are considered in computing
the rating score. A sample of five ratings is made for each station and
the results are shown in Table 14.4. The distributor of petroleum

products to these service stations wishes to determine if the stations differ significantly in their average rating score or whether the variation in the average scores can be attributed to sampling error.

Table 14.4

QUALITY RATINGS OF 10 SERVICE STATIONS

					Service Station						Total
	1	2	3	4	5	6	7	8	9	10	
	99	70	90	99	65	85	75	70	85	92	830
	96	65	80	95	70	88	70	51	84	91	790
	95	60	48	87	48	75	71	93	80	93	750
	98	65	70	95	67	82	73	94	86	90	820
	97	65	62	99	60	80	76	92	90	89	810
Totals	485	325	350	475	310	410	365	400	425	455	4,000
Means	97	65	70	95	62	82	73	80	85	91	800

The analysis of the ratings of the service stations, as an example of the application of analysis of variance to empirical data, is chosen on several assumptions concerning data and the types of conclusions reached.

Assumptions in Analysis of Variance

A test of significance involving two or more sample means is based on the following assumptions:

1. Each sample is drawn randomly from a normal universe and the sample statistics tend to reflect the characteristics of the universe. In the example, each set of possible ratings for a given service station represents a normal universe.
2. The universes from which the samples are drawn have identical means and variances. In the example, the 10 universes have assumed characteristics so that

$$\mu_1 = \mu_2 = \mu_3 = \ldots = \mu_{10}$$

and

$$\sigma_1 = \sigma_2 = \sigma_3 = \ldots = \sigma_{10}.$$

3. The null hypothesis is tested in that it is assumed that the dispersion of sample observations is the result of random sampling error. The null hypothesis may be written

$$x_{ij} = \mu + \varepsilon$$

where x_{ij} is a random variable distributed normally about μ; the subscripts i and j denote rows and columns, respectively; μ is the universe mean; and

ε, which denotes the effect of sampling error, is a normally distributed random variable with a mean of zero and a variance σ_ε^2. In the example, it is assumed that sample observations differ only because of the effects of random sampling since the universe means are assumed to be equal.

4. A significant difference in sample means implies the existence of *bias* in one or more of the universe means. The effect of bias in the random variable being analyzed may be written

$$x_{ij} = \mu + \theta_j + \varepsilon$$

where θ_j denotes the extent to which the value of the random variable x_{ij} reflects bias or consistent deviation from the hypothesized value of the universe mean. The null hypothesis assumes that θ_j is zero. If bias is present, θ_j may be assumed to be either a fixed or a random variable. In the example, if the 10 stations comprise a finite universe of stations, θ_j is assumed to be a fixed relative bias for each classification. If the 10 stations are a random sample drawn from many stations, then θ_j (the relative bias) of the stations is considered to be a random variable, and the θ_j values are a random sample of biases of stations.

An Estimate of Universe Variance Based on the Dispersion of Sample Means

The standard error of the mean, as described in Chapter 9, is the standard deviation of the means of samples of a given size, drawn from a universe of values. The estimated standard error of the mean is computed by Formula 9.12 to be

$$\hat{\sigma}_{\bar{x}} = \frac{\hat{\sigma}}{\sqrt{n}}.$$

An expression of the estimated universe variance may be obtained by writing

$$\hat{\sigma}^2 = n\hat{\sigma}_{\bar{x}}^2 \quad \text{.............................(14.6)}$$

The standard error of the mean may be estimated by computing the standard deviation of the sample means and correcting for small sample bias. This unbiased estimator (free of bias due to smallness in sample size) expressed as a variance is written

$$\hat{\sigma}_{\bar{x}}^2 = \frac{\sum\limits_{j}(\bar{x}_j - \bar{\bar{x}})^2}{c - 1} \quad \text{.........................(14.7)}$$

where j designates columns, $\bar{x}_j$ denotes a sample mean, $\bar{\bar{x}}$ is the mean of the observed values in all samples taken together, c (for columns) is the number of samples, and $c - 1$ is the number of degrees of freedom.

➤ *Example.* An unbiased estimator of the variance of sample means for samples of five ratings for each of 10 service stations is computed by using the data in Table 14.4 as follows:

$$c = 10 \qquad\qquad \bar{\bar{x}} = \frac{\sum\limits_{j} \bar{x}_j}{c} = \frac{800}{10} = 80$$

$$\hat{\sigma}_{\bar{x}}^2 = \frac{\sum\limits_{j} (\bar{x}_j - \bar{\bar{x}})^2}{c - 1}$$

$$= \frac{\begin{array}{c}(97 - 80)^2 + (65 - 80)^2 + (70 - 80)^2 + (95 - 80)^2 + \\ + (62 - 80)^2 + (82 - 80)^2 + (73 - 80)^2 + \\ + (80 - 80)^2 + (85 - 80)^2 + (91 - 80)^2\end{array}}{10 - 1}$$

$$= \frac{1{,}362}{9} = 151.33.$$

An estimate of the universe variance based on the estimate of the variance of sample means is found by writing Formula 14.6 in terms of estimated values to give

$$\hat{\sigma}^2 = r\hat{\sigma}_{\bar{x}}^2$$

where r is the number of rows in the table of observed data and $r = n$, the sample size. The estimated variance of sample means is substituted into the expression for the estimated universe variance by writing

$$\hat{\sigma}_c^2 = \frac{r\sum\limits_{j} (\bar{x}_j - \bar{\bar{x}})^2}{c - 1} \dots\dots\dots\dots\dots\dots\dots(14.8)$$

The value obtained from Formula 14.8 is the estimated variance based on the variation between sample (column) means, as denoted by the subscript c. This variance is abbreviated MSC (Mean Square Column).

➤ *Example.* The estimate of the variance of rating scores of service stations based on the variation *between* sample means is computed by using Formula 14.8, the results of the preceding example, and the data in Table 14.4 to give

$$\hat{\sigma}_c^2 = \frac{r\sum\limits_{j} (\bar{x}_j - \bar{\bar{x}})^2}{c - 1} = MSC$$

$$= \frac{5\begin{array}{c}[(97 - 80)^2 + (65 - 80)^2 + (70 - 80)^2 + (95 - 80)^2 + \\ + (62 - 80)^2 + (82 - 80)^2 + (73 - 80)^2 + \\ + (80 - 80)^2 + (85 - 80)^2 + (91 - 80)^2]\end{array}}{10 - 1}$$

$$= \frac{5(1{,}362)}{9} = \frac{6{,}810}{9}$$

$$MSC = 756.67.$$

If bias is present in one or more sample means, this bias will tend to be reflected in the relative magnitude of $\hat{\sigma}_c^2$. Should the dispersion of sample means be greater than that expected as the result of random sampling error (chance), $\hat{\sigma}_c^2$ will be too large and will overstate the value of σ^2 significantly.

Whether $\hat{\sigma}_c^2$ is significantly greater than σ^2 can be tested by use of Formula 14.4, where $\hat{\sigma}_c^2$ is the numerator of the F ratio. The value of F can be obtained if a second estimator of σ^2 can be computed as the denominator of the F ratio. The denominator must be another estimate of the universe variance that is inherently free of any bias (θ_j) which may be present in sample values of the random variable x_{ij}. The method for computing a second estimate of the universe variance is described in the discussion that follows.

An Estimate of Universe Variance Based on the Dispersion of Sample Observations

The standard deviation of a sample tends to reflect the dispersion of the universe from which the sample is drawn. An estimate of the universe variance can be obtained from the dispersion of sample data about the sample mean. Sample data, expressed as deviations, are free from bias (θ_j), for any consistent bias that may be present in the data is eliminated by subtracting $x_{ij} - \bar{x}_j$. In other words, since the extent of this consistent bias is reflected in the value of the sample mean $\bar{x}_j$, and since $\bar{x}_j$ is subtracted from each observation of that sample, the bias is eliminated from the sample observations.

By subtracting the sample mean from the respective sample observations, a residual ε is obtained. The distribution of ε is assumed to be normal. This residual results from random sampling error and therefore is unbiased. The estimate of the universe variance computed from the sum of the squared error values is the required term for the denominator of the F ratio.

An unbiased (free from small sample bias) estimate of the universe variance is obtained by combining the squared deviations of all samples. An unbiased estimate of the universe variance based on a single sample may be written

$$\hat{\sigma}^2 = \frac{\sum_i (x_{ij} - \bar{x}_j)^2}{(r - 1)}$$

where r is the number of rows (sample size). An unbiased estimate of the universe variance is obtained by summing the deviations of all samples and averaging accordingly. The sum of the squared deviations of the observations in all samples is written

$$\left[\frac{\sum\limits_{i}(x_{i1} - \bar{x}_1)^2}{r - 1} + \frac{\sum\limits_{i}(x_{i2} - \bar{x}_2)^2}{r - 1} + \cdots + \frac{\sum\limits_{i}(x_{ic} - \bar{x}_c)^2}{r - 1}\right] = \frac{\sum\limits_{i}\sum\limits_{j}(x_{ij} - \bar{x}_j)^2}{r - 1}.$$

The desired variance estimate is the mean sum of squared deviations, written

$$\hat{\sigma}_\varepsilon^2 = \frac{\sum\limits_{i}\sum\limits_{j}(x_{ij} - \bar{x}_j)^2}{c(r - 1)} \quad\quad\quad\quad\quad\quad (14.9)$$

This estimate is called the variance estimate based on variation *within* the samples or the residual *error* values; hence. the subscript ε. This variance is abbreviated *MSE* (Mean Square Error).

➤ *Example.* The estimated universe variance based on variations *within* samples is computed for the service station rating data in Table 14.4 by use of Formula 14.9 as follows:

$$\hat{\sigma}_\varepsilon^2 = \frac{\sum\limits_{i}\sum\limits_{j}(x_{ij} - \bar{x}_j)^2}{c(r - 1)} = MSE$$

$$= \frac{1}{(10)(5 - 1)}[(99 - 97)^2 + (96 - 97)^2 + (95 - 97)^2 +$$
$$+ (98 - 97)^2 + (97 - 97)^2 + (70 - 65)^2 +$$
$$+ (65 - 65)^2 + (60 - 65)^2 + (65 - 65)^2 +$$
$$+ (65 - 65)^2 + (90 - 70)^2 + (80 - 70)^2 +$$
$$+ (48 - 70)^2 + (70 - 70)^2 + (62 - 70)^2 +$$
$$+ (99 - 95)^2 + (95 - 95)^2 + (87 - 95)^2 +$$
$$+ (95 - 95)^2 + (99 - 95)^2 + (65 - 62)^2 +$$
$$+ (70 - 62)^2 + (48 - 62)^2 + (67 - 62)^2 +$$
$$+ (60 - 62)^2 + (85 - 82)^2 + (88 - 82)^2 +$$
$$+ (75 - 82)^2 + (82 - 82)^2 + (80 - 82)^2 +$$
$$+ (75 - 73)^2 + (70 - 73)^2 + (71 - 73)^2 +$$
$$+ (73 - 73)^2 + (76 - 73)^2 + (70 - 80)^2 +$$
$$+ (51 - 80)^2 + (93 - 80)^2 + (94 - 80)^2 +$$
$$+ (92 - 80)^2 + (85 - 85)^2 + (84 - 85)^2 +$$
$$+ (80 - 85)^2 + (86 - 85)^2 + (90 - 85)^2 +$$
$$+ (92 - 91)^2 + (91 - 91)^2 + (93 - 91)^2 +$$
$$+ (90 - 91)^2 + (89 - 91)^2]$$

$$= \frac{3,138}{40}$$

$$MSE = 78.450$$

Test of Significance for a One-Way Classification Analysis of Variance Model

The rating scores in Table 14.4 are an example of a *one-way classification* of data. The data are classified by service stations and each of the samples is shown as a column of five values. If the data were classified further so that each of the rows of values would comprise a sample of data in terms of a second classification criterion, the data would be described as a *two-way classification* arrangement. This type of problem is discussed in Chapter 15.

Analysis of variance is applied to the one-way classification model by computing the F ratio of the two estimates of the universe variance. This ratio is expressed by

$$F = \frac{\hat{\sigma}_c^2}{\hat{\sigma}_\varepsilon^2} \quad\ldots\ldots\ldots\ldots\ldots\ldots\ldots\ldots\text{(14.10)}$$

where $d.f._1 = c - 1$ and $d.f._2 = c(r - 1)$. The value of $d.f._1 = c - 1$ results from the fact that only $c - 1$ of the column (sample) means $\bar{x}_j$ can be chosen arbitrarily without affecting the value of the mean of all items $\bar{\bar{x}}$. Similarly, $d.f._2 = c(r - 1)$ since $r - 1$ sample values may be chosen without affecting a column (sample) mean, and there is a total of c samples.

The required data for analysis of variance for a one-way classification are summarized in Table 14.5. Note that the total sum of the squared deviations (SST) is written

$$SST = \sum_i \sum_j (x_{ij} - \bar{\bar{x}})^2,$$

and the components of SST are SSC (Sum of Squared Deviations Column) and SSE (Sum of Squared Deviations Error).

Table 14.5

TABLE FOR ANALYSIS OF VARIANCE FOR A ONE-WAY CLASSIFICATION

Source of variation	Sum of squares	d.f.	Mean square	Variance ratio
Between samples (Column means)	$SSC = r\sum_j (\bar{x}_j - \bar{\bar{x}})^2$	$d.f._1 = c - 1$	$MSC = \hat{\sigma}_c^2$	$F = \dfrac{\hat{\sigma}_c^2}{\hat{\sigma}_\varepsilon^2}$
Within samples (Residual error)	$SSE = \sum_i \sum_j (x_{ij} - \bar{x}_j)^2$	$d.f._2 = c(r - 1)$	$MSE = \hat{\sigma}_\varepsilon^2$	
Total	$SST = \sum_i \sum_j (x_{ij} - \bar{\bar{x}})^2$	$(c - 1) + c(r - 1)$	...	...

The relationship between the sums of squares is such that

$$\text{Total} = \text{Between} + \text{Within}$$
$$SST = SSC + SSE$$

or
$$\sum_i\sum_j(x_{ij} - \bar{\bar{x}})^2 = r\sum_j(\bar{x}_j - \bar{\bar{x}})^2 + \sum_i\sum_j(x_{ij} - \bar{x}_j)^2.$$

➤ **Example.** Analysis of variance is applied to the rating scores data in Table 14.4 by use of Formula 14.10 and is summarized as follows:

Table 14.6

TABLE FOR ANALYSIS OF VARIANCE FOR A ONE-WAY CLASSIFICATION

Source of variation	Sum of squares	d.f.	Mean square	Variance ratio
Between service stations (Column means)	$SSC = 6{,}810$	$d.f._1 = 9$	$MSC = 756.67$	$\dfrac{MSC}{MSE} = 9.65$
Within samples (Residual error)	$SSE = 3{,}138$	$d.f._2 = 40$	$MSE = 78.45$	
Total	$SST = 9{,}948$	49		

The value of $F_{0.001}$ for $d.f._1 = 9$ and $d.f._2 = 40$ interpolated from Appendix L is 3.30. Since the computed value of $F = 9.65$ is larger than the table value, the null hypothesis is rejected at the 0.001 level.

The rejection of the null hypothesis in the foregoing example implies that the service stations are not alike in terms of rating score. In other words, one or more of the average rating scores reflects bias, or $\theta_j \neq 0$ for one or more columns.

Alternative Computational Methods

The values of $\hat{\sigma}_c^2$ and $\hat{\sigma}_\varepsilon^2$ may be computed by alternative methods that are equivalent algebraically to the methods presented previously. The following alternative methods offer some advantages for computation in that deviations need not be computed.

Total Variation. The total variation (sum of squared deviations)

$$SST = \sum_i\sum_j(x_{ij} - \bar{\bar{x}})^2$$

may be written in an alternative form by completing the square in the preceding expression, summing, and collecting terms to give

$$SST = \Sigma\Sigma x_{ij}^2 - \frac{\left(\underset{i\,j}{\Sigma\Sigma}x_{ij}\right)^2}{(c)(r)} \quad \ldots\ldots\ldots\ldots(14.11)$$

The term
$$C = \frac{\left(\underset{i\,j}{\Sigma\Sigma}x_{ij}\right)^2}{(c)(r)}$$

is sometimes called the *correction factor*. The total variation is found by (1) squaring and summing all sample values, and (2) subtracting the square of the sum of all sample values divided by the total number of items.

Between Variation. The variation between sample means (sum of squares)
$$SSC = r\underset{j}{\Sigma}(\bar{x}_j - \bar{x})^2$$

may be written in alternative form by completing the square in the preceding expression, summing, and collecting terms to give
$$SSC = \frac{\underset{j}{\Sigma}\left(\underset{i}{\Sigma}x_{ij}\right)^2}{r} - C \quad \ldots\ldots\ldots\ldots\ldots(14.12)$$

The between variation is found by (1) squaring each column total, summing the squared totals, and dividing the sum by the sample size, and (2) subtracting the square of the sum of all sample values divided by the total number of items.

Within Variation. The within variation (residual sum of squares) can be computed by using the relationship
$$SSE = SST - SSC$$
$$= \text{Total} - \text{Between} \quad \ldots\ldots\ldots\ldots(14.13)$$

The values for the variation between and within samples may be substituted into Formulas 14.8 and 14.9 to obtain $\hat{\sigma}_c^2$ and $\hat{\sigma}_\varepsilon^2$, respectively.

➤ *Example.* The alternative computational methods are applied to the data of Table 14.4 to compute $\hat{\sigma}_c^2$ and $\hat{\sigma}_\varepsilon^2$ as follows:

$$SST = \underset{i\,j}{\Sigma\Sigma} x_{ij}^2 - C$$
$$= (99)^2 + (96)^2 + (95)^2 + (98)^2 + (97)^2 + (70)^2 + \ldots +$$
$$+ (90)^2 + (92)^2 + (91)^2 + (93)^2 + (90)^2 + (89)^2 -$$
$$- \frac{(4,000)^2}{(10)(5)}$$
$$= 329,948 - \frac{16,000,000}{50} = 9,948.$$

$$SSC = \frac{\sum_j (\sum_i x_{ij})^2}{r} - C$$

$$= \tfrac{1}{5}\left[(485)^2 + (325)^2 + (350)^2 + \dots + (425)^2 + (455)^2\right] -$$
$$- \frac{(4,000)^2}{(10)(5)}$$

$$= \frac{1,634,050}{5} - \frac{16,000,000}{50}$$

$$= 326,810 - 320,000$$

$$= 6,810.$$

$$SSE = SST - SSC$$
$$= \text{Total} - \text{Between}$$
$$= 9,948 - 6,810$$
$$= 3,138.$$

The required variance estimates are computed

$$MSC = \frac{SSC}{d.f._1}$$
$$= \frac{6,810}{9}$$
$$= 756.67.$$

$$MSE = \frac{SSE}{d.f._2}$$
$$= \frac{3,138}{40}$$
$$= 78.45.$$

An algorithm for computing the F ratio for a one-way classification problem by use of the alternative expressions given in Formulas 14.11, 14.12, and 14.13 is shown in Figures 14.3 and 14.4.

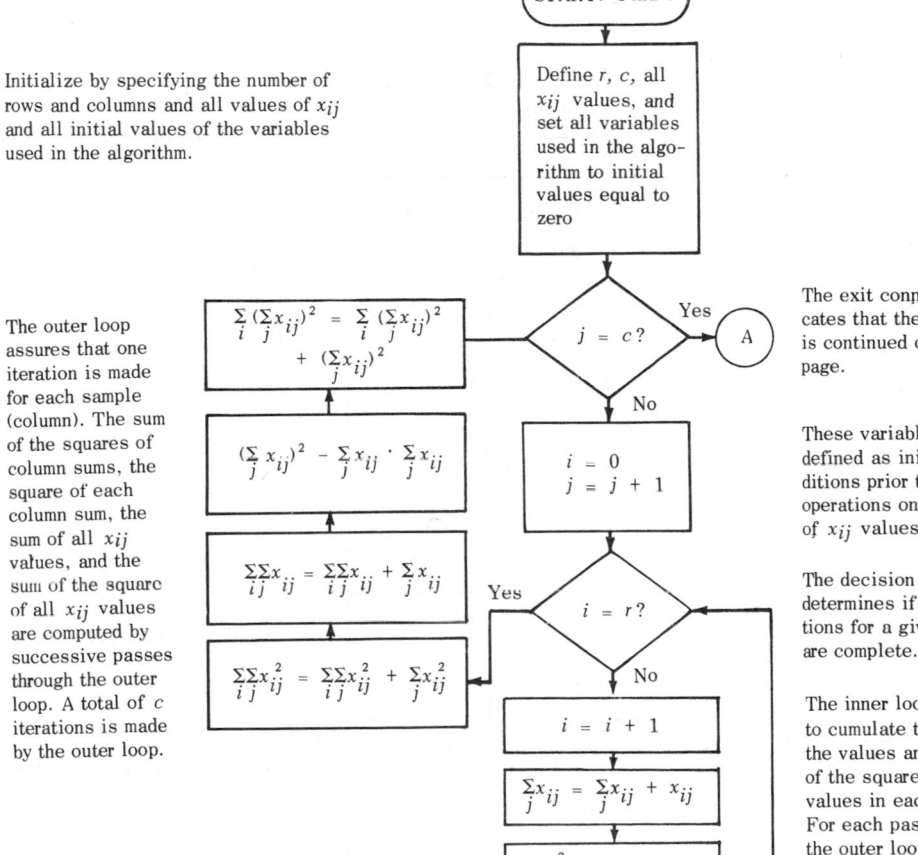

The outer loop assures that one iteration is made for each sample (column). The sum of the squares of column sums, the square of each column sum, the sum of all x_{ij} values, and the sum of the square of all x_{ij} values are computed by successive passes through the outer loop. A total of c iterations is made by the outer loop.

Initialize by specifying the number of rows and columns and all values of x_{ij} and all initial values of the variables used in the algorithm.

The exit connector indicates that the algorithm is continued on another page.

These variables are redefined as initial conditions prior to arithmetic operations on each column of x_{ij} values.

The decision statement determines if the iterations for a given column are complete.

The inner loop is used to cumulate the sum of the values and the sum of the squares of the values in each column. For each pass through the outer loop, a total of r passes is made through the inner loop. Thus, a total of c times r iterations is made by the inner loop.

Figure 14.3

A PARTIAL ALGORITHM FOR COMPUTING THE *F* RATIO FOR A ONE-WAY
CLASSIFICATION ANALYSIS OF VARIANCE PROBLEM

Entry connector that continues
the algorithm from Figure 14.3.

Compute the correction factor.   From Formulas 14.11 and 14.12

Compute the total variation
of x_{ij}.   Formula 14.11

Compute the variation between
column means.   Formula 14.12

Compute the variation within
samples.   Formula 14.13

Compute the variance estimate
based on variation between   An equivalent form of Formula 14.8
column means.

Compute the variance estimate
based on variation within   An equivalent form of Formula 14.9
columns.

Compute the F ratio.   Formula 14.10

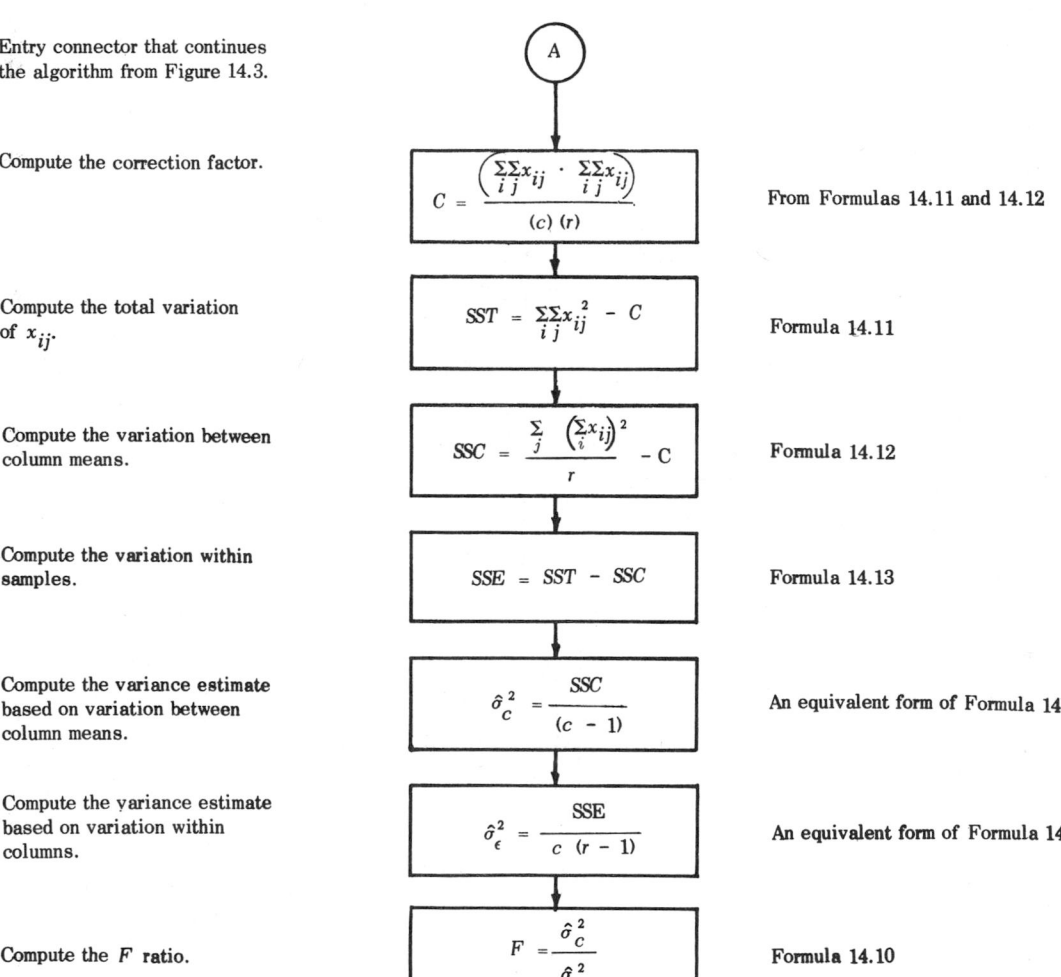

$$A$$

$$C = \frac{\left(\sum_i \sum_j x_{ij} \cdot \sum_i \sum_j x_{ij} \right)}{(c)\,(r)}$$

$$SST = \sum_i \sum_j x_{ij}^2 - C$$

$$SSC = \frac{\sum_j \left(\sum_i x_{ij} \right)^2}{r} - C$$

$$SSE = SST - SSC$$

$$\hat{\sigma}_c^2 = \frac{SSC}{(c - 1)}$$

$$\hat{\sigma}_\epsilon^2 = \frac{SSE}{c\,(r - 1)}$$

$$F = \frac{\hat{\sigma}_c^2}{\hat{\sigma}_\epsilon^2}$$

HALT: F for $d.f._1 = (c - 1)$
and $d.f._2 = (c)\,(r - 1)$ is the
answer

Figure 14.4

**A PARTIAL ALGORITHM FOR COMPUTING THE F RATIO FOR A ONE-WAY
CLASSIFICATION ANALYSIS OF VARIANCE PROBLEM**

STUDY QUESTIONS

14-1. Explain briefly the meaning of each of the following terms:
   a. the statistic F
   b. variance ratio
   c. analysis of variance
   d. between variation
   e. within variation
   f. one-way classification
   g. correction factor

14-2. Distinguish between the types of problems for which the normal, t, and chi-square distributions are appropriate.

14-3. Of what value is a significance test for a sample variance?

14-4. What are the characteristics of the F distribution?

14-5. What assumptions are implicit in a test of significance of two sample means?

14-6. Summarize briefly the relationship between the normal, t, chi-square, and F distributions.

14-7. What assumptions are implicit in the analysis of variance for a one-way classification problem?

14-8. What is the theoretical basis for the two-variance estimates utilized in the analysis of variance for a one-way classification problem?

14-9. Of what value is a test of significance in a one-way classification analysis of variance problem?

PROBLEMS

14-1. An automatic grinding machine is designed to produce metal parts with a standard deviation of 0.0010 inch, provided the machine is adjusted properly. A sample of 25 parts is taken randomly and the standard deviation is 0.0013. Is the machine adjusted properly?

14-2. An electronics manufacturer purchases copper plates from a vendor. The purchase agreement specifies that the thickness of the plates shall be in the range 10 ± 0.20 millimeters. A sample of 16 plates, taken from a shipment received by the manufacturer, has a standard deviation of 0.01 millimeters. If the manufacturing process is assumed to produce plates that are distributed normally in thickness, is it likely that at least 99% of all plates produced conform to specifications?

14-3. Compute the 96% confidence limits of the universe variance for Problem 14-1.

14-4. Compute the 98% confidence limits of the process variance for Problem 14-2.

14-5. The dispersion in value of purchases in two department stores is to be tested for homogeneity. A sample of 16 purchases taken from store X has a standard deviation of $12. Twenty-five purchases sampled from store Y have a standard deviation of $10. Can the dispersion of the purchases of the two stores be considered consistent?

14-6. A sample of nine accounts is drawn randomly from a normal universe of accounts receivable. The sample standard deviation is $30. If a second sample of six accounts is drawn randomly, the probability is 0.01 that the standard deviation of the second sample will be larger than what value?

14-7. The weekly earnings of five salesmen for a sample of three weeks are as follows:

Roberts	Edmonds	Shultz	Hebert	Gonzales
167	151	147	171	114
177	179	134	166	120
199	156	121	143	150

Determine if the average earnings of the salesmen differ significantly or whether the difference could be considered the result of sampling error.

14-8. A plastics manufacturer tests the tensile strength of different types of polyethylene material. A sample of three measurements is taken for each material type. The data in pounds per square inch are as follows:

Type I	Type II	Type III
380	350	350
390	320	370
390	330	360

Determine if the mean tensile strength of the types of materials differs significantly.

14-9. The number of automobiles arriving at four toll stations were recorded for a four-hour time period (8:00 a.m.–12:00 p.m.) for each of six different days. The data are as follows:

Gate 1	Gate 2	Gate 3	Gate 4
490	525	475	527
450	506	460	507
510	473	525	492
478	526	420	505
504	502	499	530
482	505	472	555

Determine whether the rate of arrivals is essentially the same at each toll station.

14-10. A manufacturer has four identical machines that are used in a production process. Each machine is operated by a different operator. A sample of the production (expressed as deviations in thousandths of an inch from a given dimension) is taken from each machine. The results are as follows:

	MACIIINES		
A	*B*	*C*	*D*
7	8	11	12
3	10	10	10
11	6	11	9
10	5	10	10

Test the hypothesis that the average dimension of parts produced by each machine is identical.

14-11. Draw a flow diagram to summarize the steps in making a test of significance of two sample variances.

14-12. Draw a flow diagram of an algorithm for computing an estimate of the universe variance based on variations within samples.

SELECTED READINGS

Freund, John E., Paul E. Livermore, and Irwin Miller. *Manual of Experimental Statistics.* Englewood Cliffs, New Jersey: Prentice-Hall, Inc., 1960.
> An excellent manual on the most frequently used statistical techniques, including complete examples. It is not complete enough to be used as a text.

Hicks, Charles R. *Fundamental Concepts in the Design of Experiments.* New York: Holt, Rinehart, and Winston, Inc., 1964.
> A text presenting the fundamental concepts in the design of experiments. It uses simple numerical problems, many from actual research work.

Kempthorne, Oscar. *The Design and Analysis of Experiments.* New York: John Wiley & Sons, Inc., 1952
> A book that combines the extensive literature on the design of experiments into a systematic account of the subject from the point of view of the user and of the consultant.

Winer, B. J. *Statistical Principles in Experimental Design.* New York: McGraw-Hill Book Company, Inc., 1962.
> A comprehensive reference source on the statistical principles underlying experimental design for research workers in the area of behavioral sciences.

Chapter 15

Experimental Design

INTRODUCTION

An experimental design is a plan for the orderly collection and analysis of data. The chief objective of a good design is to obtain more information for less cost than normally can be obtained by traditional sampling methods.

The Problem of Design

Many investigators proceed to gather data under the assumption that statistical problems must be faced only when the task of analysis begins. The need for careful planning well in advance of a statistical study is as important as the detailed blueprints and specifications that must precede the construction of a house. In a statistical study, bad planning or no planning at all can lead to poor results or exorbitant costs, or both.

Some of the considerations of sample design in problems of estimation were discussed in Chapters 9 and 10, in the section on sampling. Chapters 11, 12, and 13 have examined some of the problems involved in the design of certain kinds of tests of significance. In Chapter 14, the nature of the F distribution was discussed, and one-way analysis of variance was introduced for those situations in which all the samples were the same size.

This chapter is basically an extension of the material presented in Chapter 14. All the experimental designs discussed here involve the use of F ratios in tests of significance. Emphasis is placed on the way in which data are gathered and organized so as to make the most efficient use of the information available. This chapter is only a brief introduction to a highly specialized field of statistics that is usually treated in books which are limited to this one technical area alone.

Method of Presentation

In order to provide an orderly approach to the complex problems involved in looking at a whole series of experimental designs, the following plan of presentation has been adopted for this chapter:

1. The organization of the data to be analyzed will be shown and the notation to be used will be defined.
2. The model to be used and the hypotheses to be tested will be established.
3. An analysis of variance table will be shown to make it possible to see at a glance the type of variation being studied, the degrees of freedom involved, the mean square variation, and the F ratios to be computed.
4. Computational formulas, which may be used for solution either on a computer or with the help of an electric calculator, will be shown.
5. An example will be shown to illustrate the application of the particular design to a practical problem.

ONE-WAY ANALYSIS OF VARIANCE, SAMPLE SIZES UNEQUAL

In Chapter 14, quality ratings of 10 service stations were tested to determine if there were significant differences in the average ratings. The sample of ratings for each station consisted of five observations.

Often it is desired to test the hypothesis that the means of c normal populations are equal when the sample size n_j is not the same for all samples.

Organization of the Data

	Sample 1	Sample 2		Sample j		Sample c	
	x_{11}	x_{12}	$\cdots$	x_{1j}	$\cdots$	x_{1c}	
	x_{21}	x_{22}	$\cdots$	x_{2j}	$\cdots$	x_{2c}	
	$\vdots$	$\vdots$		$\vdots$		$\vdots$	
	x_{i1}	x_{i2}	$\cdots$	x_{ij}	$\cdots$	x_{ic}	
	$\vdots$	$\vdots$		$\vdots$		$\vdots$	
	x_{r1}	x_{r2}	$\cdots$	x_{rj}	$\cdots$	x_{rc}	
Totals	$T_{.1}$	$T_{.2}$		$T_{.j}$		$T_{.c}$	$\sum\limits_{j=1}^{c} T_{.j} = T$

Observation x_{ij} is the ith observation of the jth sample where the samples are arranged in columns. The samples are assumed to be random and independent but need not be all the same size. The total $T_{.j}$ is the total of the n_j observations of the jth sample, and T is the grand total of all c samples.

The Model

The model may be expressed as

$$x_{ij} = \mu + \theta_j + \varepsilon_{ij} \qquad (j = 1, 2, \ldots, c)$$

where,

μ is the universe mean

θ_j is the effect of the jth sample, with the restriction that $\sum\limits_{j=1}^{c} \theta_j = 0$

ε_{ij} is the effect of sampling error on the ith observation of the jth sample.

The Hypotheses

The hypotheses may be expressed in either of two ways:

H_1: $\mu_1 = \mu_2 = \ldots = \mu_j = \ldots = \mu_c$
H_2: At least two of the universe means are unequal, or
H_1: $\theta_j = 0$ for all j samples
H_2: θ_j are not all $= 0$.

Analysis of Variance Table

Table 15.1 is comparable to Table 14.5, except that Table 15.1 can be used when the samples are not all the same size. Abbreviations are for "sum of squares" and "mean square." These abbreviations are defined in the following section on computational formulas.

Table 15.1

TABLE FOR ANALYSIS OF VARIANCE FOR A ONE-WAY CLASSIFICATION

(Sample sizes unequal)

Source of variation	Sum of squares	d.f.	Mean square	Variance ratio
Between samples (Column means)	SSC	$d.f._1 = c - 1$	$MSC = \dfrac{SSC}{c - 1}$	$F = \dfrac{MSC}{MSE}$
Within samples (Error)	SSE	$d.f._2 = N - c$	$MSE = \dfrac{SSE}{N - c}$	
Total	SST	$N - 1$		

Computational Formulas

In the latter part of Chapter 14 short-cut formulas for computing variation were discussed under the heading, "Alternative Computational

Methods." These formulas were shown to give the same results as the more conventional ones, but with simpler computations. In this chapter, short-cut computational formulas will be used throughout, as they are particularly well-adapted to computer solution.

Correction Factor.

$$C = \frac{T^2}{N} \dotfill (15.1)$$

where,

$N = n_1 + n_2 + \ldots + n_j + \ldots + n_c$ is the total number of observations in all the samples.

Between Columns (Samples) Sum of Squares.

$$SSC = \sum_{j=1}^{c} \frac{T_{.j}^2}{n_j} - C \dotfill (15.2)$$

Total Sum of Squares.

$$SST = \sum_{i=1}^{r} \sum_{j=1}^{c} x_{ij}^2 - C \dotfill (15.3)$$

Error Sum of Squares.

$$SSE = SST - SSC \dotfill (15.4)$$

➤ *Example.* Table 15.2 shows quality ratings of five service stations, with the number of observations in each sample varying from a minimum of two to a maximum of five. There is a total of 18 observations.

Table 15.2

QUALITY RATINGS OF FIVE SERVICE STATIONS

Ratings	Service station					Total
	1	2	3	4	5	
1	72	82	86	70	80	
2	80	80	83	73	80	
3	78	84	82	70	...	
4	70	...	80	75	...	
5	...	...	79	...	...	
Totals	300	246	410	288	160	1,404
Means	75	82	82	72	80	

The problem is to test at an α level of 0.05 to determine if there is a significant difference in the average ratings of the five service stations.

STEPS:

1. H_1: $\mu_1 = \mu_2 = \mu_3 = \mu_4 = \mu_5$
2. H_2: At least two of the μ's are not equal.
3. An $\alpha = 0.05$ requires an F value of 3.18, which is interpolated from the table in Appendix L, using the following degrees of freedom:

$$d.f._1 = c - 1 = 4$$
$$d.f._2 = N - c = 18 - 5 = 13.$$

4. Criterion: Reject H_1 (accept H_2) if $F > 3.18$; accept H_1 if $F \leq 3.18$, where,

$$F = \frac{MSC}{MSE}.$$

5. The sample data are now used to compute F using Formulas 15.1, 15.2, 15.3, and 15.4.

$$C = \frac{T^2}{N} = \frac{(1,404)^2}{18} = \frac{1,971,216}{18}$$

$$C = 109,512.$$

$$SSC = \sum_{j=1}^{c} \frac{T_j^2}{n_j} - C$$

$$SSC = \frac{300^2}{4} + \frac{246^2}{3} + \frac{410^2}{5} + \frac{288^2}{4} + \frac{160^2}{2} - 109,512$$

$$SSC = 22,500 + 20,172 + 33,620 + 20,736 + 12,800 - 109,512$$

$$SSC = 316.$$

$$SST = \sum_{i=1}^{r} \sum_{j=1}^{c} x_{ij}^2 - C$$

$$SST = (72)^2 + (80)^2 + (78)^2 + \ldots + (80)^2 - C$$

$$SST = 5,184 + 6,400 + 6,084 + 4,900 + 6,724 + 6,400 + 7,056 + 7,396 + 6,889 + 6,724 + 6,400 + 6,241 + 4,900 + 5,329 + 4,900 + 5,625 + 6,400 + 6,400 - C$$

$$SST = 109,952 - 109,512 = 440.$$

$$SSE = SST - SSC = 440 - 316 = 124.$$

$$MSC = \frac{SSC}{c - 1} = \frac{316}{4} = 79.$$

$$MSE = \frac{SSE}{N - c} = \frac{124}{18 - 5} = 9.54.$$

$$F = \frac{MSC}{MSE} = \frac{79}{9.54} = 8.28.$$

Since $F(8.28) > F_\alpha(3.18)$, reject H_1 and accept H_2. There is a significant difference in the average ratings.

TWO-WAY ANALYSIS OF VARIANCE, ONE OBSERVATION PER CELL

Often it is desirable to test hypotheses concerning two variables. These two variables may be referred to as *row effects* and *column effects*.

In the previous example on the rating of service stations, the question was whether or not there were significant differences between stations. As the samples were arranged by columns, the concern was with column effects. To carry this example a step further, assume there were five raters who rated each of the service stations. The investigator might be interested also in testing to see if there was a significant difference in the average scores of the raters. If the ratings of each rater were arranged in rows, the concern would be with row effects.

Organization of the Data

	c_1	c_2		c_j		c_c	Totals
r_1	x_{11}	x_{12}	...	x_{1j}	...	x_{1c}	$T_{1.}$
r_2	x_{21}	x_{22}	...	x_{2j}	...	x_{2c}	$T_{2.}$
	.	.		.		.	.
	.	.		.		.	.
r_i	x_{i1}	x_{i2}	...	x_{ij}	...	x_{ic}	$T_{i.}$
	.	.		.		.	.
	.	.		.		.	.
r_r	x_{r1}	x_{r2}	...	x_{rj}	...	x_{rc}	$T_{r.}$
Totals	$T_{.1}$	$T_{.2}$		$T_{.j}$		$T_{.c}$	$T_{..}$

The observation x_{ij} is the value for the ith row and the jth column. The value $T_{i.}$ is the total of the ith row, and the value $T_{.j}$ is the total of the jth column. The value $T_{..}$ is the grand total of all observations.

The Model

The model may be expressed as

$$x_{ij} = \mu + \tau_i + \theta_j + \varepsilon_{ij} \quad \begin{cases} i = 1, 2, \ldots, r \\ j = 1, 2, \ldots, c \end{cases}$$

where,

τ_i is the effect of the ith row

θ_j is the effect of the jth column, with the restrictions

$$\sum_{i=1}^{r} \tau_i = 0 \text{ and } \sum_{j=1}^{c} \theta_j = 0.$$

The Hypotheses

In two-way analysis of variance with one observation per cell, there are two sets of hypotheses to be tested.

For row means:

H_1: $\tau_i = 0$ for all i

H_2: τ_i are not all equal to zero.

The null hypothesis has the effect of saying that there is no significant difference in the row means.

For column means:

H_1: $\theta_j = 0$ for all j

H_2: θ_j are not all equal to zero.

Here the null hypothesis is saying that there is no significant difference in the column means. This is the same hypothesis that was tested in the one-way analysis of variance case.

Analysis of Variance Table

Table 15.3 is the analysis of variance table for two-way analysis with one observation per cell. Total variation is now defined as that which results from column differences, from row differences, and from residual random (error) differences. Two F ratios are computed. The first, F_C, is used to test for significant differences between column means; the second, F_R, is used to test for significant differences between row means.

Table 15.3

TABLE FOR ANALYSIS OF VARIANCE FOR A TWO-WAY CLASSIFICATION

(One observation per cell)

Source of variation	Sum of squares	d.f.	Mean square	Variance ratio
Between columns	SSC	$d.f._1 = c - 1$	$MSC = \dfrac{SSC}{c - 1}$	$F_C = \dfrac{MSC}{MSE}$
Between rows	SSR	$d.f._1 = r - 1$	$MSR = \dfrac{SSR}{r - 1}$	$F_R = \dfrac{MSR}{MSE}$
Error	SSE	$d.f._2 = (c - 1)(r - 1)$	$MSE = \dfrac{SSE}{(r - 1)(c - 1)}$	
Total	SST	$cr - 1$		

Computational Formulas

Correction Factor.

$$C = \frac{T_{..}^2}{r \cdot c} \dots\dots\dots\dots\dots\dots\dots\dots\dots\dots\dots\dots\dots\dots\dots\dots\dots\dots\dots (15.5)$$

where,

r is the number of rows, and c is the number of columns.

Between Rows Sum of Squares.

$$SSR = \frac{\sum\limits_{i=1}^{r} T_{i.}^2}{c} - C \dots\dots\dots\dots\dots\dots\dots\dots\dots\dots\dots\dots\dots\dots (15.6)$$

Between Columns Sum of Squares.

$$SSC = \frac{\sum\limits_{j=1}^{c} T_{.j}^2}{r} - C \dots\dots\dots\dots\dots\dots\dots\dots\dots\dots\dots\dots\dots (15.7)$$

Total Sum of Squares.

$$SST = \sum\limits_{i=1}^{r} \sum\limits_{j=1}^{c} x_{ij}^2 - C \dots\dots\dots\dots\dots\dots\dots\dots\dots\dots\dots\dots\dots (15.3)$$

Error Sum of Squares.

$$SSE = SST - SSR - SSC \dots\dots\dots\dots\dots\dots\dots\dots\dots\dots\dots\dots (15.8)$$

➤ *Example.* Table 15.4 shows the same information presented in Table 14.4, except the row values have been identified as the ratings made by five raters.

Table 15.4

QUALITY RATINGS OF 10 SERVICE STATIONS BY FIVE
PROFESSIONAL RATERS

					Service Station							
Rater	1	2	3	4	5	6	7	8	9	10	Totals	Means
A	99	70	90	99	65	85	75	70	85	92	830	83
B	96	65	80	95	70	88	70	51	84	91	790	79
C	95	60	48	87	48	75	71	93	80	93	750	75
D	98	65	70	95	67	82	73	94	86	90	820	82
E	97	65	62	99	60	80	76	92	90	89	810	81
Totals	485	325	350	475	310	410	365	400	425	455	4,000	400
Means	97	65	70	95	62	82	73	80	85	91	800	80

The problem is to test at an α level of 0.05 to determine if there is a significant difference in the average ratings of the 10 service stations or in the average ratings given by the five professional raters. A significant difference in the row means would show that some raters tend to be more lenient or stricter than others in their ratings.

STEPS:

For row means	For column means
1. H_1: $\tau_i = 0$ for all i	H_1: $\theta_j = 0$ for all j
2. H_2: τ_i are not all equal to zero	H_2: θ_j are not all equal to zero
3. $\alpha = 0.05$ gives a table value for	$\alpha = 0.05$ gives a table value for

$F = 2.63$ with $d.f._1 = r - 1 = 4$ and $d.f._2 = (r-1)(c-1) = 36$.

$F = 2.15$ with $d.f._1 = c - 1 = 9$ and $d.f._2 = (r-1)(c-1) = 36$.

4. Criterion: Reject H_1 (accept H_2) if $F_R > 2.63$; accept H_1 if $F_R \leq 2.63$, when

Reject H_1 (accept H_2) if $F_C > 2.15$; accept H_1 if $F_C \leq 2.15$, when

$$F_R = \frac{MSR}{MSE}$$

$$F_C = \frac{MSC}{MSE}$$

5. The sample data are now used to compute F_R and F_C using Formulas 15.4 through 15.8:

$$C = \frac{T_{..}^2}{r \cdot c} = \frac{(4,000)^2}{(5)(10)} = 320,000.$$

$$SSR = \frac{\sum_{i=1}^{r} T_{i.}^2}{c} - C$$

$$SSR = \frac{830^2 + 790^2 + 750^2 + 820^2 + 810^2}{10} - C$$

$$SSR = 320,400 - 320,000 = 400.$$

$$SSC = \frac{\sum_{j=1}^{c} T_{.j}^2}{r} - C$$

$$SSC = \frac{(485)^2 + \ldots + (455)^2}{5} - C$$

$$SSC = 326,810 - 320,000 = 6,810.$$

$$SST = \sum_{i=1}^{c} \sum_{j=1}^{r} x_{ij}^2 - C$$

$$SST = 99^2 + 96^2 + 95^2 + \ldots + 89^2 - C$$

$$SST = 329,948 - 320,000 = 9,948.$$

$$SSE = 9,948 - 400 - 6,810 = 2,738.$$

$$MSC = \frac{SSC}{c-1} = \frac{6{,}810}{9} = 756.67$$

$$MSR = \frac{SSR}{r-1} = \frac{400}{4} = 100.00.$$

$$MSE = \frac{SSE}{(r-1)(c-1)} = \frac{2{,}738}{(4)(9)} = \frac{2{,}738}{36} = 76.06.$$

$$F_R = \frac{MSR}{MSE} = \frac{100.00}{76.06} = 1.31$$

$$F_C = \frac{MSC}{MSE} = \frac{756.67}{76.06} = 9.95.$$

Since $F_R(1.31) < F_\alpha(2.63)$, accept H_1 and decide that there is no significant difference (bias) between raters.

Since $F_C(9.95) > F_\alpha(2.15)$, reject H_1 and accept H_2. There are significant differences between stations.

TWO-WAY ANALYSIS OF VARIANCE, n OBSERVATIONS PER CELL

In testing hypotheses concerning two variables, it is possible to have more than one observation per cell. For example, in the rating of service stations by professional raters, each rater might rate each station several times. The arrangement of the observations might take the form shown at the top of the next page.

Organization of the Data

The observation x_{ijk} is the kth observation of the ith row and the jth column. The value $T_{i..}$ is the total of all observations in the ith row, and $T_{.j.}$ is the total of all the observations in the jth column. The value $T_{...}$ is the grand total of all the observations. The value of n is the number of observations per cell and must be the same for all cells.

The Model

The model may be expressed as

$$x_{ijk} = \mu + \tau_i + \theta_j + \gamma_{ij} + \varepsilon_{ijk} \qquad \begin{cases} i = 1, 2, \ldots, r \\ j = 1, 2, \ldots, c \\ k = 1, 2, \ldots, n \end{cases}$$

	c_1	c_2		c_j		c_c	
	x_{111}	x_{121}	$\cdots$	x_{1j1}	$\cdots$	x_{1c1}	
	x_{112}	x_{122}	$\cdots$	x_{1j2}	$\cdots$	x_{1c2}	
r_1	$\vdots$	$\vdots$		$\vdots$		$\vdots$	$T_{1..}$
	x_{11n}	x_{12n}	$\cdots$	x_{1jn}	$\cdots$	x_{1cn}	
	x_{211}	x_{221}	$\cdots$	x_{2j1}	$\cdots$	x_{2c1}	
	x_{212}	x_{222}	$\cdots$	x_{2j2}	$\cdots$	x_{2c2}	
r_2	$\vdots$	$\vdots$		$\vdots$		$\vdots$	$T_{2..}$
	x_{21n}	x_{22n}	$\cdots$	x_{2jn}	$\cdots$	x_{2cn}	
	x_{i11}	x_{i21}	$\cdots$	x_{ij1}	$\cdots$	x_{ic1}	
	x_{i12}	x_{i22}	$\cdots$	x_{ij2}	$\cdots$	x_{ic2}	
r_i	$\vdots$	$\vdots$		$\vdots$		$\vdots$	$T_{i..}$
	x_{i1n}	x_{i2n}	$\cdots$	x_{ijn}	$\cdots$	x_{icn}	
	x_{r11}	x_{r21}	$\cdots$	x_{rj1}	$\cdots$	x_{rc1}	
	x_{r12}	x_{r22}	$\cdots$	x_{rj2}	$\cdots$	x_{rc2}	
r_r	$\vdots$	$\vdots$		$\vdots$		$\vdots$	$T_{r..}$
	x_{r1n}	x_{r2n}	$\cdots$	x_{rjn}	$\cdots$	x_{rcn}	
	$T_{.1.}$	$T_{.2.}$		$T_{.j.}$		$T_{.c.}$	$T_{...}$

where,

τ_i is the effect of the ith row

θ_j is the effect of the jth column

γ_{ij} is the interaction of the ith row with the jth column, with the restrictions

$$\sum_{i=1}^{r} \tau_i = 0, \ \sum_{j=1}^{c} \theta_j = 0, \text{ and } \sum_{i=1}^{r} \sum_{j=1}^{c} \gamma_{ij} = 0.$$

The Hypotheses

When the two-way classification has more than one observation per cell, there are three sets of hypotheses to be tested.

For row means:
H_1: $\tau_i = 0$ for all i
H_2: τ_i are not all equal to zero.
For column means:
H_1: $\theta_j = 0$ for all j
H_2: θ_j are not all equal to zero.
For interaction between rows and columns:
H_1: $\gamma_{ij} = 0$ for all i and j
H_2: γ_{ij} are not all equal to zero.

Analysis of Variance Table

Table 15.5 is the analysis of variance table for two-way analysis with n observations per cell. The total variation is defined as the sum of that which results from row differences, from column differences, from interaction between rows and columns, and from residual random (error) differences. Three F ratios are used to test the three sets of hypotheses described above.

Table 15.5

TABLE FOR ANALYSIS OF VARIANCE FOR A TWO-WAY CLASSIFICATION

(n observations per cell)

Source of variation	Sum of squares	d.f.	Mean square	Variance ratio
Between columns	SSC	$d.f._1 = c - 1$	$MSC = \dfrac{SSC}{c-1}$	$F_C = \dfrac{MSC}{MSE}$
Between rows	SSR	$d.f._1 = r - 1$	$MSR = \dfrac{SSR}{r-1}$	$F_R = \dfrac{MSR}{MSE}$
Interaction	SSI	$d.f._1 = (c-1)(r-1)$	$MSI = \dfrac{SSI}{(c-1)(r-1)}$	$F_I = \dfrac{MSI}{MSE}$
Error	SSE	$d.f._2 = rc(n-1)$	$MSE = \dfrac{SSE}{rc(n-1)}$	
Total	SST	$rcn - 1$		

Computational Formulas

Correction Factor.

$$C = \frac{T^2_{...}}{r \cdot c \cdot n} \quad \dots\dots\dots\dots\dots\dots\dots\dots\dots\dots\dots\dots\dots\dots(15.9)$$

where,

    r is the number of rows

    c is the number of columns

    n is the number of observations per cell and is the same for all cells.

Between Rows Sum of Squares.

$$SSR = \frac{\sum_{i=1}^{r} T_{i..}^2}{c \cdot n} - C \dots\dots\dots\dots\dots(15.10)$$

Between Columns Sum of Squares.

$$SSC = \frac{\sum_{j=1}^{c} T_{.j.}^2}{r \cdot n} - C \dots\dots\dots\dots\dots(15.11)$$

Between Means Sum of Squares.

$$SSM = \frac{\sum_{i=1}^{r} \sum_{j=1}^{c} T_{ij}^2}{n} - C \dots\dots\dots\dots\dots(15.12)$$

where T_{ij} is the total for the cell in the ith row and j^{th} column.

Interaction Sum of Squares.

$$SSI = SSM - SSR - SSC \dots\dots\dots\dots\dots(15.13)$$

Total Sum of Squares.

$$SST = \sum_{i=1}^{r} \sum_{j=1}^{c} \sum_{k=1}^{n} x_{ijk}^2 - C \dots\dots\dots\dots\dots(15.14)$$

Error Sum of Squares.

$$SSE = SST - SSM \dots\dots\dots\dots\dots(15.15)$$

➤ *Example.* In the ratings of the service stations, imagine that each of four raters rated each of three stations twice. The results of the ratings are shown in Table 15.6.

    The problem is to test at an α level of 0.05 to determine if there is a significant difference between the average ratings of the three stations; between the average ratings of the four raters; and if there is a significant interaction between raters and stations. An interaction might be the bias of one rater (either favorable or unfavorable) for a particular oil company or a particular station because of some previous experience that will unknowingly influence his ratings.

Table 15.6

QUALITY RATINGS OF THREE SERVICE STATIONS BY FOUR·RATERS WITH
EACH RATER RATING EACH STATION TWICE

Raters	Stations			Total	Means
	c_1	c_2	c_3		
r_1	72	66	80		
	76	72	84	450	75
r_2	71	69	97		
	75	73	95	480	80
r_3	81	75	100		
	83	75	96	510	85
r_4	70	64	95		
	72	66	89	456	76
Totals	600	560	736	1,896	
Means	75	70	92		

STEPS:

	Row means	Column means	Interaction
1. H_1:	$\tau_i = 0$ for all i	$\theta_j = 0$ for all j	$\gamma_{ij} = 0$ for all i and j
2. H_2:	τ_i not all $= 0$	θ_j not all $= 0$	γ_{ij} not all $= 0$

3. $d.f._1$: $r - 1 = 3$ $c - 1 = 2$ $(c-1)(r-1) = 6$
$d.f._2$: $rc(n-1) = 12$ $= 12$ $= 12$
Table value for F: $F_{\alpha=0.05} = 3.49$ $= 3.89$ $= 3.00$

4. Criterion:
Reject H_1 If $F_R > 3.49$ If $F_C > 3.89$ If $F_I > 3.00$
(Accept H_2)
Accept H_1 If $F_R \leq 3.49$ If $F_C \leq 3.89$ If $F_I \leq 3.00$

5. The sample data are now used to compute F_R, F_C, and F_I using Formulas 15.9 through 15.15.

$$C = \frac{T_{...}^2}{r \cdot c \cdot n} = \frac{1,896^2}{(4)(3)(2)} = \frac{3,594,816}{24} = 149,784.$$

$$SSR = \frac{\sum\limits_{i=1}^{r} T_{i..}^2}{c \cdot n} - C$$

$$SSR = \frac{450^2 + 480^2 + 510^2 + 456^2}{(3)(2)} - C$$

$$SSR = 150,156 - 149,784 = 372.$$

$$SSC = \frac{\sum\limits_{j=1}^{c} T_{.j.}^2}{r \cdot n} - C$$

$$SSC = \frac{600^2 + 560^2 + 736^2}{(4)(2)} - C = 151{,}912 - 149{,}784 = 2{,}128.$$

$$SSM = \frac{\sum\limits_{i=1}^{r} \sum\limits_{j=1}^{c} T_{ij}^2}{n} - C$$

Table 15.7 shows the totals for each cell (T_{ij}).

Table 15.7

TABLE OF CELL TOTALS (T_{ij})

Raters	Service Stations		
	c_1	c_2	c_3
r_1	148	138	164
r_2	146	142	192
r_3	164	150	196
r_4	142	130	184

$$SSM = \frac{148^2 + 146^2 + \ldots + 184^2}{2} - C$$

$$SSM = 152{,}460 - 149{,}784 = 2{,}676.$$

$$SSI = SSM - SSR - SSC$$

$$SSI = 2{,}676 - 372 - 2{,}128 = 176.$$

$$SST = \sum\limits_{i=1}^{r} \sum\limits_{j=1}^{c} \sum\limits_{k=1}^{n} x_{ijk}^2 - C$$

$$SST = 72^2 + 76^2 + \ldots + 89^2 - C$$

$$SST = 152{,}562 - 149{,}784 = 2{,}778.$$

$$SSE = SST - SSM$$

$$SSE = 2{,}778 - 2{,}676 = 102.$$

$$MSC = \frac{SSC}{c - 1} = \frac{2{,}128}{2} = 1{,}064.$$

$$MSR = \frac{SSR}{r - 1} = \frac{372}{3} = 124.$$

$$MSI = \frac{SSI}{(c - 1)(r - 1)} = \frac{176}{6} = 29.33.$$

$$MSE = \frac{SSE}{rc(n - 1)} = \frac{102}{12} = 8.5.$$

$$F_R = \frac{MSR}{MSE} = \frac{124}{8.5} = 14.59.$$

$$F_C = \frac{MSC}{MSE} = \frac{1,064}{8.5} = 125.18.$$

$$F_I = \frac{MSI}{MSE} = \frac{29.33}{8.5} = 3.45.$$

The null hypotheses would be rejected in all three cases. There are significant differences between stations and between raters, and there is significant interaction between raters and stations. It should be noted, however, that at an $\alpha = 0.01$ it would not be possible to show significant interaction.

LATIN SQUARES

When the experimenter wishes to study the effects of three variables on the basis of relatively few observations, he may turn to the use of a Latin-square design. The experiment is performed by arranging the levels of one factor which are denoted by the letters A, B, C, etc., into an array so that every letter appears once and only once in every row and column. One Latin square with four levels for one variable is shown below:

B	A	C	D
D	B	A	C
C	D	B	A
A	C	D	B

For example, the study group engaged in rating service stations might be concerned with another variable, the time of day when the rating was made. They may feel that during very busy times of the day the service station operator is not able to give as good service as at other times and that this factor might influence the rating of the station. The letters A, B, C, and D might be used to refer to four different times with different levels of business activity. These different levels are commonly called *treatments*.

Organization of the Data

The size of the Latin square is determined by the number of treatments. The observations $x_{ij(k)}$ are r^2 in number in a Latin square of r rows and r columns. The subscript i refers to the row; the subscript j refers to the column; and the subscript k refers to the treatment. The number of rows and columns will always be the same as the number of treatments. The totals are denoted as

$T_{i.}$ is the total for the ith row
$T_{.j}$ is the total for the jth column
T_k is the total of the observations for the kth treatment
$T_{..}$ is the grand total of all the observations.

The Model

The model may be expressed as

$$x_{ij(k)} = \mu + \tau_i + \theta_j + \gamma_k + \varepsilon_{ij(k)} \qquad \begin{cases} i = 1, 2, \ldots, r \\ j = 1, 2, \ldots, r \\ k = 1, 2, \ldots, r \end{cases}$$

where,
τ_i is the effect of the ith row
θ_j is the effect of the jth column
γ_k is the effect of the kth treatment, with the restrictions

$$\sum_{i=1}^{r} \tau_i = 0, \; \sum_{j=1}^{r} \theta_j = 0, \text{ and } \sum_{k=1}^{r} \gamma_k = 0.$$

The Hypotheses

There are three sets of hypotheses to be tested in a Latin square, regardless of the number of treatments.
For row means:
   H_1: $\tau_i = 0$ for all i
   H_2: τ_i are not all equal to zero.
For column means:
   H_1: $\theta_j = 0$ for all j
   H_2: θ_j are not all equal to zero.
For treatments:
   H_1: $\gamma_k = 0$ for all k
   H_2: γ_k are not all equal to zero.

Analysis of Variance Table

Table 15.8 is the analysis of variance table for a Latin square. The total variation is the sum of the row variation, the column variation, the treatment variation, and the error variation. Three F ratios are used to test the three sets of hypotheses described above.

Table 15.8

TABLE FOR ANALYSIS OF VARIANCE FOR A LATIN SQUARE

Source of variation	Sum of squares	d.f.	Mean square	Variance ratio
Rows	SSR	$d.f._1 = r - 1$	$MSR = \dfrac{SSR}{r-1}$	$F_R = \dfrac{MSR}{MSE}$
Columns	SSC	$d.f._1 = r - 1$	$MSC = \dfrac{SSC}{r-1}$	$F_C = \dfrac{MSC}{MSE}$
Treatments	SS(Tr)	$d.f._1 = r - 1$	$MS(Tr) = \dfrac{SS(Tr)}{r-1}$	$F_{Tr} = \dfrac{MS(Tr)}{MSE}$
Error	SSE	$d.f._2 = (r-1)(r-2)$	$MSE = \dfrac{SSE}{(r-1)(r-2)}$	
Total	SST	$r^2 - 1$		

Computational Formulas

Correction Factor.

$$C = \frac{T_{..}^2}{r^2} \quad \dotfill \quad (15.16)$$

where r is the number of rows.

Between Rows Sum of Squares.

$$SSR = \frac{\sum\limits_{i=1}^{r} T_{i.}^2}{r} - C \dotfill (15.17)$$

Between Columns Sum of Squares.

$$SSC = \frac{\sum\limits_{j=1}^{r} T_{.j}^2}{r} - C \dotfill (15.18)$$

Between Treatments Sum of Squares.

$$SS(Tr) = \frac{\sum\limits_{k=1}^{r} T_{k}^2}{r} - C \dotfill (15.19)$$

Total Sum of Squares.

$$SST = \sum_{i=1}^{r} \sum_{j=1}^{r} x_{ij(k)}^2 - C \dotfill (15.20)$$

Error Sum of Squares.

$$SSE = SST - SSR - SSC - SS(Tr) \dotfill (15.21)$$

➤ *Example.* Suppose that four raters rate the same four service stations, following carefully the time pattern shown below as treatments:

Treatment	Time of rating	Latin Square
A	7:45 a.m.	B A C D
B	12:00 noon	D B A C
C	5:15 p.m.	C D B A
D	9:00 p.m.	A C D B

The results of the ratings are shown in Table 15.9.

Table 15.9

QUALITY RATINGS OF SERVICE STATIONS
WITH FOUR RATERS RATING EACH OF FOUR
STATIONS AT FOUR DIFFERENT TIMES

(A four-by-four Latin Square)

Raters	Stations				Totals
	c_1	c_2	c_3	c_4	
r_1	85	79	76	78	318
r_2	73	81	84	75	313
r_3	75	78	92	83	328
r_4	82	70	79	90	321
Totals	315	308	331	326	1,280

The problem is to test at an α of 0.05 to determine if there is a significant difference in raters, stations, and treatments (time of day the rating is made).

STEPS:

	Row means	Column means	Treatments
1. H_1:	$\tau_i = 0$ for all i	$\theta_j = 0$ for all j	$\gamma_k = 0$ for all k
2. H_2:	τ_i not all $= 0$	θ_j not all $= 0$	γ_k not all $= 0$
3. $d.f._1$:	$r - 1 = 3$	$r - 1 = 3$	$r - 1 = 3$
$d.f._2$:	$(r - 1)(r - 2) = 6$	$(r - 1)(r - 2) = 6$	$(r - 1)(r - 2) = 6$
Table value for F	$F_{\alpha=0.05} = 4.76$	$F_{\alpha=0.05} = 4.76$	$F_{\alpha=0.05} = 4.76$

4. Criterion:

Reject H_1 (Accept H_2)	If $F_R > 4.76$	If $F_C > 4.76$	If $F_{Tr} > 4.76$
Accept H_1	If $F_R \leq 4.76$	If $F_C \leq 4.76$	If $F_{Tr} \leq 4.76$

5. The sample data are now used to compute F_R, F_C, and F_{Tr} using Formulas 15.16 through 15.21.

Table 15.10 shows the treatment totals, T_k.

Table 15.10

TABLE OF TREATMENT TOTALS, T_k

Treatment	Service station ratings				Totals
A: 7:45 a.m.	79	84	83	82	328
B: 12:00 noon	92	90	85	81	348
C: 5:15 p.m.	76	70	75	75	296
D: 9:00 p.m.	79	78	73	78	308
					1,280

Source: Table 15.9.

$$C = \frac{T_{..}^2}{r^2} = \frac{1,280^2}{4^2} = \frac{1,638,400}{16} = 102,400.$$

$$SSR = \frac{\sum\limits_{i=1}^{r} T_{i.}^2}{r} - C$$

$$SSR = \frac{318^2 + \ldots + 321^2}{4} - C$$

$$SSR = 102,430 - 102,400 = 30.$$

$$SSC = \frac{\sum\limits_{j=1}^{r} T_{.j}^2}{r} - C$$

$$SSC = \frac{315^2 + \ldots + 326^2}{4} - C$$

$$SSC = 102,482 - 102,400 = 82.$$

$$SS(Tr) = \frac{\sum\limits_{k=1}^{r} T_{k}^2}{r} - C$$

$$SS(Tr) = \frac{328^2 + \ldots + 308^2}{4} - C$$

$$SS(Tr) = 102,792 - 102,400 = 392.$$

$$SST = \sum_{i=1}^{r} \sum_{j=1}^{r} x_{ij(k)}^2 - C$$

$$SST = 85^2 + 73^2 + \ldots + 90^2 - C$$

$$SST = 102,924 - 102,400 = 524.$$

$$SSE = SST - SSR - SSC - SS(Tr)$$

$$SSE = 524 - 30 - 82 - 392 = 20.$$

$$MSR = \frac{SSR}{r-1} = \frac{30}{3} = 10.$$

$$MSC = \frac{SSC}{r-1} = \frac{82}{3} = 27.33.$$

$$MS(Tr) = \frac{SS(Tr)}{r-1} = \frac{392}{3} = 130.67.$$

$$MSE = \frac{SSE}{(r-1)(r-2)} = \frac{20}{6} = 3.33.$$

$$F_R = \frac{MSR}{MSE} = \frac{10}{3.33} = 3.00.$$

$$F_C = \frac{MSC}{MSE} = \frac{27.33}{3.33} = 8.21.$$

$$F_{Tr} = \frac{MS(Tr)}{MSE} = \frac{130.67}{3.33} = 39.24.$$

The null hypothesis on rater (row) differences would be accepted. There is no rater bias. The other two null hypotheses would be rejected; there are significant differences in stations and in treatments.

FACTORIAL EXPERIMENTS

Factorial designs permit the experimenter to evaluate the effect of two or more experimental variables when they are used simultaneously. The information obtained in this fashion is more complete than that obtained from a series of single-factor experiments such as the Latin square, where one treatment was observed at several levels. In factorial experiments, an effect attributable to the combination of variables can be measured when this would not be possible if the variables were considered singly.

For example, suppose that the researchers rating service stations would like to know if there were significant differences in ratings when the rater was a man or a woman, when the rater drove a small car or a large one, and whether the inspection was made in good weather or bad. The experimenters might also wish to know if any combinations of these factors were important.

In an experiment of this kind, the term *factor* is used interchangeably with the terms treatment and variable. A factor may have two or more *levels*. For example, the factor of weather may have the two levels, "good" and "bad," or a factor of temperature might have several levels, such as 30°, 50°, 70°, and 90°. The design discussed here will be limited to three factors, A, B, and C, each at two levels, 0 and 1. This gives a total of 2^3, or eight observations, in a complete *replication*, or set of observations. Each observation represents a different combination of levels of the factors.

➤ *Example.* Using the sex of rater, size of car, and weather as factors, the levels and variable combinations are shown in Tables 15.11 and 15.12.

Table 15.11

LEVELS USED FOR THREE FACTORS BEING
CONSIDERED IN A 2^3 FACTORIAL EXPERIMENT

Factors	Level 0	Level 1
A: Rater	Man	Woman
B: Car	Small	Large
C: Weather	Bad	Good

Table 15.12

FACTOR COMBINATIONS FOR A 2^3 FACTORIAL EXPERIMENT

Factor combinations	Level of factor A	B	C
1	Man driving a small car in bad	weather.	
a	Woman driving a small car in bad	weather.	
b	Man driving a large car in bad	weather.	
c	Man driving a small car in good weather.		
ab	Woman driving a large car in bad	weather.	
ac	Woman driving a small car in good weather.		
bc	Man driving a large car in good weather.		
abc	Woman driving a large car in good weather.		

Source: Table 15.11.

Organization of the Data

For a 2^3 factorial experiment with rp replications, the data may be organized in the form shown below:

Factor combination	Level of factor A	B	C	First replicate	...	rp^{th} replicate
1	0	0	0	x_{0001}	...	x_{000rp}
a	1	0	0	x_{1001}	...	x_{100rp}
b	0	1	0	x_{0101}	...	x_{010rp}
c	0	0	1	x_{0011}	...	x_{001rp}
ab	1	1	0	x_{1101}	...	x_{110rp}
ac	1	0	1	x_{1011}	...	x_{101rp}
bc	0	1	1	x_{0111}	...	x_{011rp}
abc	1	1	1	x_{1111}	...	x_{111rp}

Each treatment combination is shown as one or more lowercase letters. If a letter is present, the corresponding factor has the level of 1. If a letter is not present, the level is 0. For example, the factor combination *ac* denotes A at level 1, B at level 0, and C at level 1. The combination 1 is traditionally used when all factors are at level 0.

The observation x_{ijkl} is taken from the ith level of A, the jth level of B, the kth level of C, and the lth replicate. The subscripts i, j, and k can have only two values, 0 and 1. The values of l are $1, 2, \ldots, rp$.

Table 15.13 shows the notation for effect totals and the way in which they are computed.

Table 15.13

TABLE FOR COMPUTATION OF EFFECT TOTALS

Factor combination								Effect totals
1	a	b	c	ab	ac	bc	abc	
+	+	+	+	+	+	+	+	T_I = Grand total
−	+	−	−	+	+	−	+	T_a
−	−	+	−	+	−	+	+	T_b
−	−	−	+	−	+	+	+	T_c
+	−	−	+	+	−	−	+	T_{ab}
+	−	+	−	−	+	−	+	T_{ac}
+	+	−	−	−	−	+	+	T_{bc}
−	+	+	+	−	−	−	+	T_{abc}

The total T_a is obtained by adding all factor combinations in which the factor A is at level 1 and subtracting all combinations in which factor A is at level 0. This same general technique is used to get the other effect totals following the pattern in the table. All factor combinations are added to get the effects grand total.

The sums of the observations within each replicate are denoted T_1, $T_2, \ldots, T_{rp}$.

The Model

The model may be expressed as

$$x_{ijkl} = \mu + \alpha_i + \beta_j + \gamma_k + (\alpha\beta)_{ij} + (\alpha\gamma)_{ik} + (\beta\gamma)_{jk} + (\alpha\beta\gamma)_{ijk} +$$
$$+ \rho_l + \varepsilon_{ijkl} \quad \begin{cases} i, j, k = 0, 1 \\ l = 1, 2, \ldots, rp \end{cases}$$

where,

α_i is the effect of the ith level of A

β_j is the effect of the jth level of B

γ_k is the effect of the kth level of C

$(\alpha\beta)_{ij}$ is the interaction of the ith level of A with the jth level of B

$(\alpha\gamma)_{ik}$ is the interaction of the ith level of A with the kth level of C

$(\beta\gamma)_{jk}$ is the interaction of the jth level of B with the kth level of C

$(\alpha\beta\gamma)_{ijk}$ is the interaction of the ith level of A with the jth level of B with the kth level of C

ρ_l is the effect of the lth replicate, with the restrictions that the sums of α_i, β_j, γ_k, and ρ_l are all equal to zero.

The Hypotheses

There are eight sets of hypotheses to be tested in a 2^3 factorial experiment.

For main effects:

Factor A:

H_1: $\alpha_0 = \alpha_1$

H_2: $\alpha_0 \neq \alpha_1$

Factor B:

H_1: $\beta_0 = \beta_1$

H_2: $\beta_0 \neq \beta_1$

Factor C:

H_1: $\gamma_0 = \gamma_1$

H_2: $\gamma_0 \neq \gamma_1$

For two-factor interactions:

Factors A and B:

H_1: $(\alpha\beta)_{11} + (\alpha\beta)_{00} = (\alpha\beta)_{10} + (\alpha\beta)_{01}$

H_2: $(\alpha\beta)_{11} + (\alpha\beta)_{00} \neq (\alpha\beta)_{10} + (\alpha\beta)_{01}$

Factors A and C:

H_1: $(\alpha\gamma)_{11} + (\alpha\gamma)_{00} = (\alpha\gamma)_{10} + (\alpha\gamma)_{01}$

H_2: $(\alpha\gamma)_{11} + (\alpha\gamma)_{00} \neq (\alpha\gamma)_{10} + (\alpha\gamma)_{01}$

Factors B and C:

H_1: $(\beta\gamma)_{11} + (\beta\gamma)_{00} = (\beta\gamma)_{10} + (\beta\gamma)_{01}$

H_2: $(\beta\gamma)_{11} + (\beta\gamma)_{00} \neq (\beta\gamma)_{10} + (\beta\gamma)_{01}$

For three-factor interactions:

H_1: $(\alpha\beta\gamma)_{111} + (\alpha\beta\gamma)_{100} + (\alpha\beta\gamma)_{010} + (\alpha\beta\gamma)_{001} = (\alpha\beta\gamma)_{110} + (\alpha\beta\gamma)_{101} + (\alpha\beta\gamma)_{011} + (\alpha\beta\gamma)_{000}$

H_2: $(\alpha\beta\gamma)_{111} + (\alpha\beta\gamma)_{100} + (\alpha\beta\gamma)_{010} + (\alpha\beta\gamma)_{001} \neq (\alpha\beta\gamma)_{110} + (\alpha\beta\gamma)_{101} + (\alpha\beta\gamma)_{001} + (\alpha\beta\gamma)_{000}$

For replicates:

H_1: $\rho_1 = \rho_2 = \ldots = \rho_{rp}$

H_2: All values of ρ are not equal.

Analysis of Variance Table

Table 15.14 is the analysis of variance table for a 2^3 factorial experiment. Eight F ratios are used to test the eight sets of hypotheses described on the preceding page.

Table 15.14

TABLE FOR ANALYSIS OF VARIANCE FOR 2^3 FACTORIAL EXPERIMENTS

Source of variation	Sum of squares	d.f.	Mean square	Variance ratio
Replications	$SS(Rp)$	$d.f._1 = rp - 1$	$MS(Rp) = \dfrac{SS(Rp)}{rp - 1}$	$F_{Rp} = \dfrac{MS(Rp)}{MSE}$
Main effects				
A	SSA	1	$MSA = SSA$	$F_A = \dfrac{MSA}{MSE}$
B	SSB	$d.f._1$ 1	$MSB = SSB$	$F_B = \dfrac{MSB}{MSE}$
C	SSC	1	$MSC = SSC$	$F_C = \dfrac{MSC}{MSE}$
Two-factor interactions				
AB	$SS(AB)$	1	$MS(AB) = SS(AB)$	$F_{AB} = \dfrac{MS(AB)}{MSE}$
AC	$SS(AC)$	$d.f._1$ 1	$MS(AC) = SS(AC)$	$F_{AC} = \dfrac{MS(AC)}{MSE}$
BC	$SS(BC)$	1	$MS(BC) = SS(BC)$	$F_{BC} = \dfrac{MS(BC)}{MSE}$
Three-factor interactions				
ABC	$SS(ABC)$	$d.f._1 = 1$	$MS(ABC) = SS(ABC)$	$F_{ABC} = \dfrac{MS(ABC)}{MSE}$
Error	SSE	$d.f._2 = 2^3(rp - 1) - 1$	$MSE = \dfrac{SSE}{2^3(rp - 1) - 1}$	$\cdots$
Total	SST	$rp \cdot 2^3 - 1$		

Computational Formulas

Correction Factor.

$$C = \frac{T_I^2}{rp \cdot 2^3} \quad \dots\dots\dots\dots\dots\dots\dots\dots\dots\dots\dots\dots\dots\dots\dots\dots\dots\dots (15.22)$$

Main Effect Sum of Squares.

$$SSA = \frac{T_a^2}{rp \cdot 2^3} \quad \dots\dots\dots\dots\dots\dots\dots\dots\dots\dots\dots\dots\dots\dots\dots\dots(15.23)$$

$$SSB = \frac{T_b^2}{rp \cdot 2^3} \quad \dots\dots\dots\dots\dots\dots\dots\dots\dots\dots\dots\dots\dots\dots\dots\dots(15.24)$$

$$SSC = \frac{T_c^2}{rp \cdot 2^3} \quad \dots\dots\dots\dots\dots\dots\dots\dots\dots\dots\dots\dots\dots\dots\dots\dots(15.25)$$

Interactions Sum of Squares.

$$SS(AB) = \frac{T_{ab}^2}{rp \cdot 2^3} \quad \dots\dots\dots\dots\dots\dots\dots\dots\dots\dots\dots\dots\dots\dots(15.26)$$

$$SS(AC) = \frac{T_{ac}^2}{rp \cdot 2^3} \quad \dots\dots\dots\dots\dots\dots\dots\dots\dots\dots\dots\dots\dots\dots(15.27)$$

$$SS(BC) = \frac{T_{bc}^2}{rp \cdot 2^3} \quad \dots\dots\dots\dots\dots\dots\dots\dots\dots\dots\dots\dots\dots\dots(15.28)$$

$$SS(ABC) = \frac{T_{abc}^2}{rp \cdot 2^3} \quad \dots\dots\dots\dots\dots\dots\dots\dots\dots\dots\dots\dots\dots(15.29)$$

Replication Sum of Squares.

$$SS(Rp) = \frac{\sum\limits_{l=1}^{rp} T_l^2}{2^3} - C \dots\dots\dots\dots\dots\dots\dots\dots\dots\dots\dots\dots\dots(15.30)$$

Total Sum of Squares.

$$SST = \sum_{i=0}^{1} \sum_{j=0}^{1} \sum_{k=0}^{1} \sum_{l=1}^{rp} x_{ijkl}^2 - C \dots\dots\dots\dots\dots\dots\dots\dots(15.31)$$

Error Sum of Squares.

$$SSE = SST - SSA - SSB - SSC - SS(AB) - SS(AC) - $$
$$- SS(BC) - SS(ABC) - SS(Rp) \dots\dots\dots\dots(15.32)$$

➤ *Example.* The previous example involving the three factors of sex of the rater (A), size of car (B), and weather (C) is continued here. The factors were explained in Tables 15.11 and 15.12. Table 15.15 shows the results of two complete sets (replications) of observations, one for each of two service stations.

Table 15.15

RESULTS OF RATING TWO SERVICE STATIONS
WITH THREE FACTORS AND TWO LEVELS

| Factor combination | Stations (replications) | | Totals |
	1	2	
1	69	74	143
a	72	81	153
b	71	80	151
c	75	82	157
ab	73	80	153
ac	77	87	164
bc	79	94	173
abc	82	95	177
Totals	$T_1 = 598$	$T_2 = 673$	$T_1 = 1,271$

The problem is to test at an α of 0.05 to determine if there is a significant difference in ratings that results from the levels of the three factors, from combinations of these factors at different levels, or from the stations themselves.

STEPS:
1. The null hypotheses are those stated on page 510.
2. The alternate hypotheses are those stated on page 510.
3. An $\alpha = 0.05$ requires a table value of $F = 5.59$, with $d.f._1 = 1$ and $d.f._2 = 2^3(rp - 1) - 1 = 7$.
4. Criterion: Reject any H_1 (accept H_2) if $F > 5.59$; accept any H_1 if $F \le 5.59$.
5. The sample data are now used to compute the eight F ratios using Formulas 15.22 through 15.32. Table 15.16 shows the computation of effects totals needed.

Table 15.16

COMPUTATION OF EFFECT TOTALS

| Factor combination | | | | | | | | Effects total |
1	*a*	*b*	*c*	*ab*	*ac*	*bc*	*abc*	
+ 143	+ 153	+ 151	+ 157	+ 153	+ 164	+ 173	+ 177	T_1 = 1,271
− 143	+ 153	− 151	− 157	+ 153	+ 164	− 173	+ 177	T_a = 23
− 143	− 153	+ 151	− 157	+ 153	− 164	+ 173	+ 177	T_b = 37
− 143	− 153	− 151	+ 157	− 153	+ 164	+ 173	+ 177	T_c = 71
+ 143	− 153	− 151	+ 157	+ 153	− 164	− 173	+ 177	T_{ab} = −11
+ 143	− 153	+ 151	− 157	− 153	+ 164	− 173	+ 177	T_{ac} = −1
+ 143	+ 153	− 151	− 157	− 153	− 164	+ 173	+ 177	T_{bc} = 21
− 143	+ 153	+ 151	+ 157	− 153	− 164	− 173	+ 177	T_{abc} = 5

Source: Table 15.15.

$$C = \frac{T_I^2}{rp \cdot 2^3} = \frac{(1{,}271)^2}{(2)(8)} = \frac{1{,}615{,}441}{16} = 100{,}965.06.$$

$$SSA = \frac{T_a^2}{rp \cdot 2^3} = \frac{23^2}{16} = \frac{529}{16} = 33.06.$$

$$SSB = \frac{T_b^2}{rp \cdot 2^3} = \frac{37^2}{16} = \frac{1{,}369}{16} = 85.56.$$

$$SSC = \frac{T_c^2}{rp \cdot 2^3} = \frac{71^2}{16} = \frac{5{,}041}{16} = 315.06.$$

$$SS(AB) = \frac{T_{ab}^2}{rp \cdot 2^3} = \frac{(-11)^2}{16} = \frac{121}{16} = 7.56.$$

$$SS(AC) = \frac{T_{ac}^2}{rp \cdot 2^3} = \frac{(-1)^2}{16} = \frac{1}{16} = 0.06.$$

$$SS(BC) = \frac{T_{bc}^2}{rp \cdot 2^3} = \frac{21^2}{16} = \frac{441}{16} = 27.56.$$

$$SS(ABC) = \frac{T_{abc}^2}{rp \cdot 2^3} = \frac{5^2}{16} = \frac{25}{16} = 1.56.$$

$$SS(Rp) = \frac{\sum\limits_{l=1}^{rp} T_l^2}{2^3} - C$$

$$SS(Rp) = \frac{598^2 + 673^2}{8} - C = 101{,}316.62 - 100{,}965.06$$

$$SS(Rp) = 351.56.$$

$$SST = \sum_{i=0}^{1} \sum_{j=0}^{1} \sum_{k=0}^{1} \sum_{l=1}^{2} x_{ijkl}^2 - C$$

$$SST = 69^2 + 72^2 + \ldots + 95^2 - C$$

$$SST = 101{,}825.00 - 100{,}965.06 = 859.94.$$

$$SSE = SST - SSA - SSB - SSC - SS(AB) - SS(AC) - SS(BC) \\ - SS(ABC) - SS(Rp)$$

$$SSE = 859.94 - 33.06 - 85.56 - 315.06 - 7.56 - 0.06 - 27.56 \\ - 1.56 - 351.56$$

$$SSE = 37.96.$$

Since the number of degrees of freedom is one for replications, main effects, and all the interactions, the mean square values are the same as the sum of squares values computed above.

$$MSE = \frac{SSE}{2^3(rp-1)-1} = \frac{37.96}{7} = 5.42.$$

The F ratios are

$$F_{Rp} = \frac{MS(Rp)}{MSE} = \frac{351.56}{5.42} = 64.86.$$

$$F_A = \frac{MSA}{MSE} = \frac{33.06}{5.42} = 6.1.$$

$$F_B = \frac{MSB}{MSE} = \frac{85.56}{5.42} = 15.79.$$

$$F_C = \frac{MSC}{MSE} = \frac{315.06}{5.42} = 58.13.$$

$$F_{AB} = \frac{MS(AB)}{MSE} = \frac{7.56}{5.42} = 1.39.$$

$$F_{AC} = \frac{MS(AC)}{MSE} = \frac{0.06}{5.42} = 0.01.$$

$$F_{BC} = \frac{MS(BC)}{MSE} = \frac{27.56}{5.42} = 5.08.$$

$$F_{ABC} = \frac{MS(ABC)}{MSE} = \frac{1.56}{5.42} = 0.29.$$

Since $F_{\alpha=0.05}(d.f._1 = 1$ and $d.f._2 = 7) = 5.59$, H_1 is rejected in the first four tests and is accepted in the last four tests. The stations are significantly different, the main effects are significant, but none of the interactions is significant. The interaction of factors B and C (size of car and weather), while not significant at the 0.05 level, would be significant at the 0.10 level.

COMPUTERS AND EXPERIMENTAL DESIGN

The use of a computer can be most helpful in solving problems of the type discussed in this chapter. The short-cut formulas that have been shown are especially well adapted to computer solution. The computer provides answers with a speed and an accuracy which are far beyond anything that can be achieved by any other method.

➤ *Example.* Figure 15.1 shows a flow diagram for the use of a Latin-square test of significance.

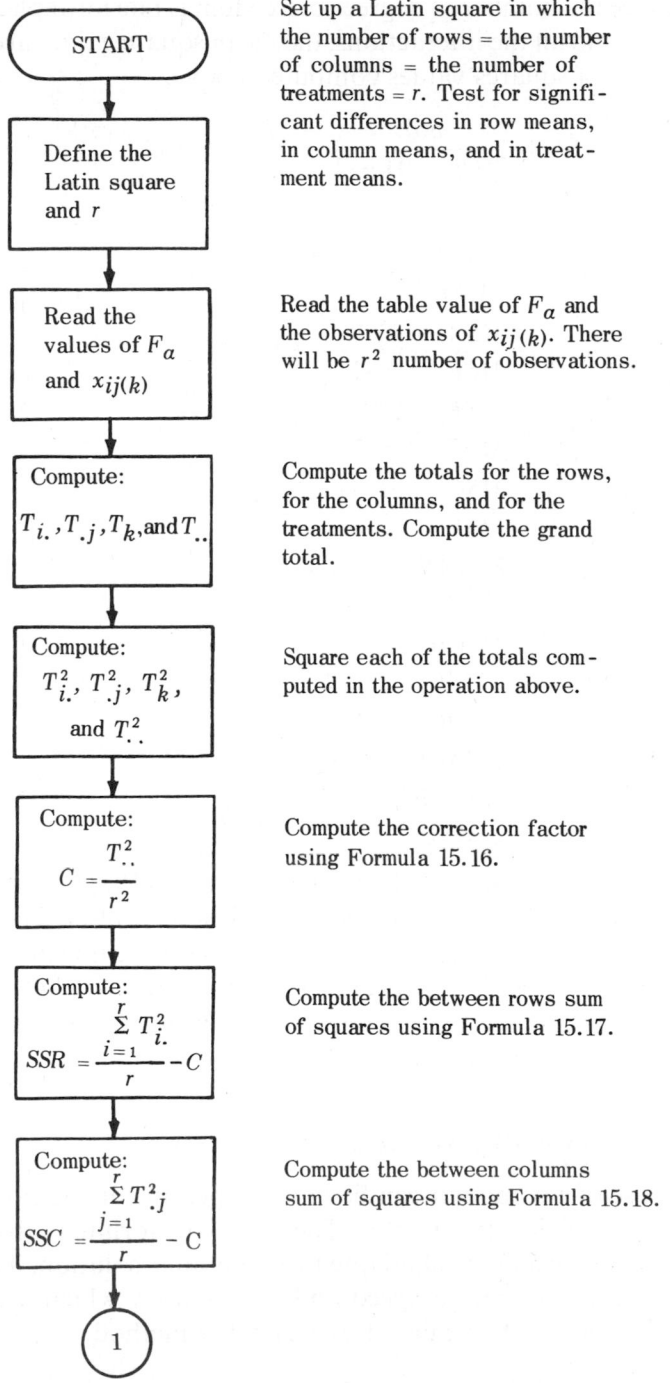

Set up a Latin square in which
the number of rows = the number
of columns = the number of
treatments = r. Test for significant differences in row means,
in column means, and in treatment means.

Read the table value of F_α and
the observations of $x_{ij(k)}$. There
will be r^2 number of observations.

Compute the totals for the rows,
for the columns, and for the
treatments. Compute the grand
total.

Square each of the totals computed in the operation above.

Compute the correction factor
using Formula 15.16.

Compute the between rows sum
of squares using Formula 15.17.

Compute the between columns
sum of squares using Formula 15.18.

Figure 15.1

FLOW DIAGRAM FOR LATIN-SQUARE TEST OF SIGNIFICANCE

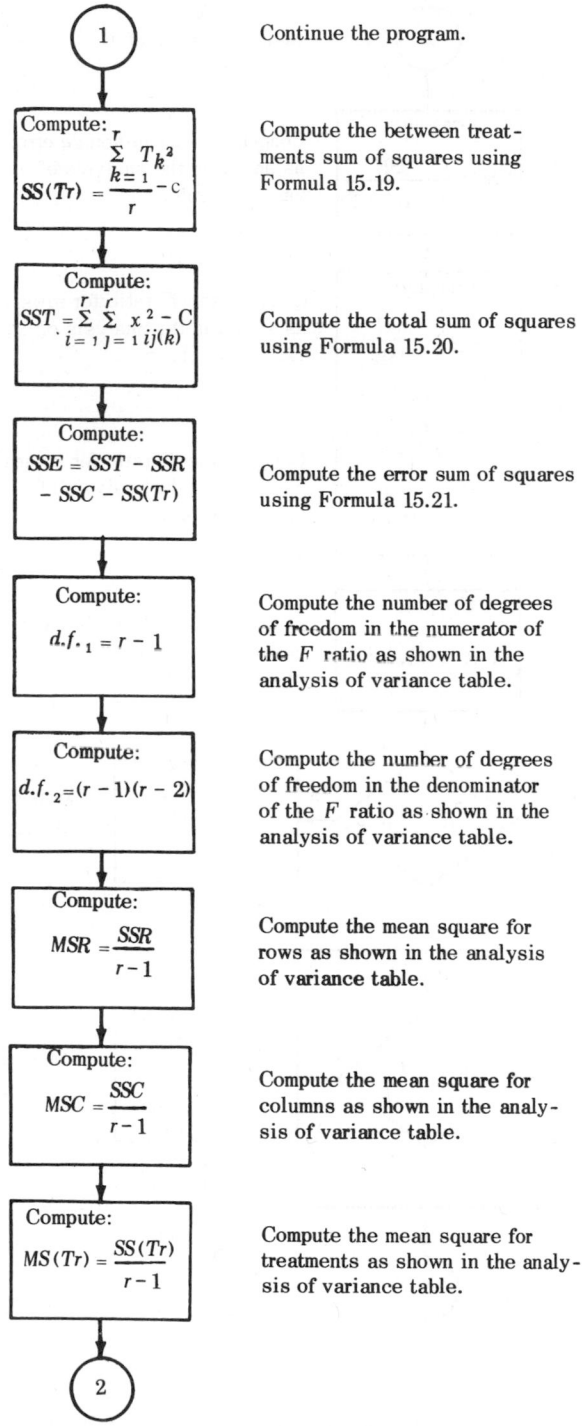

Continue the program.

Compute the between treatments sum of squares using Formula 15.19.

Compute the total sum of squares using Formula 15.20.

Compute the error sum of squares using Formula 15.21.

Compute the number of degrees of freedom in the numerator of the F ratio as shown in the analysis of variance table.

Compute the number of degrees of freedom in the denominator of the F ratio as shown in the analysis of variance table.

Compute the mean square for rows as shown in the analysis of variance table.

Compute the mean square for columns as shown in the analysis of variance table.

Compute the mean square for treatments as shown in the analysis of variance table.

Figure 15.1 (Continued)

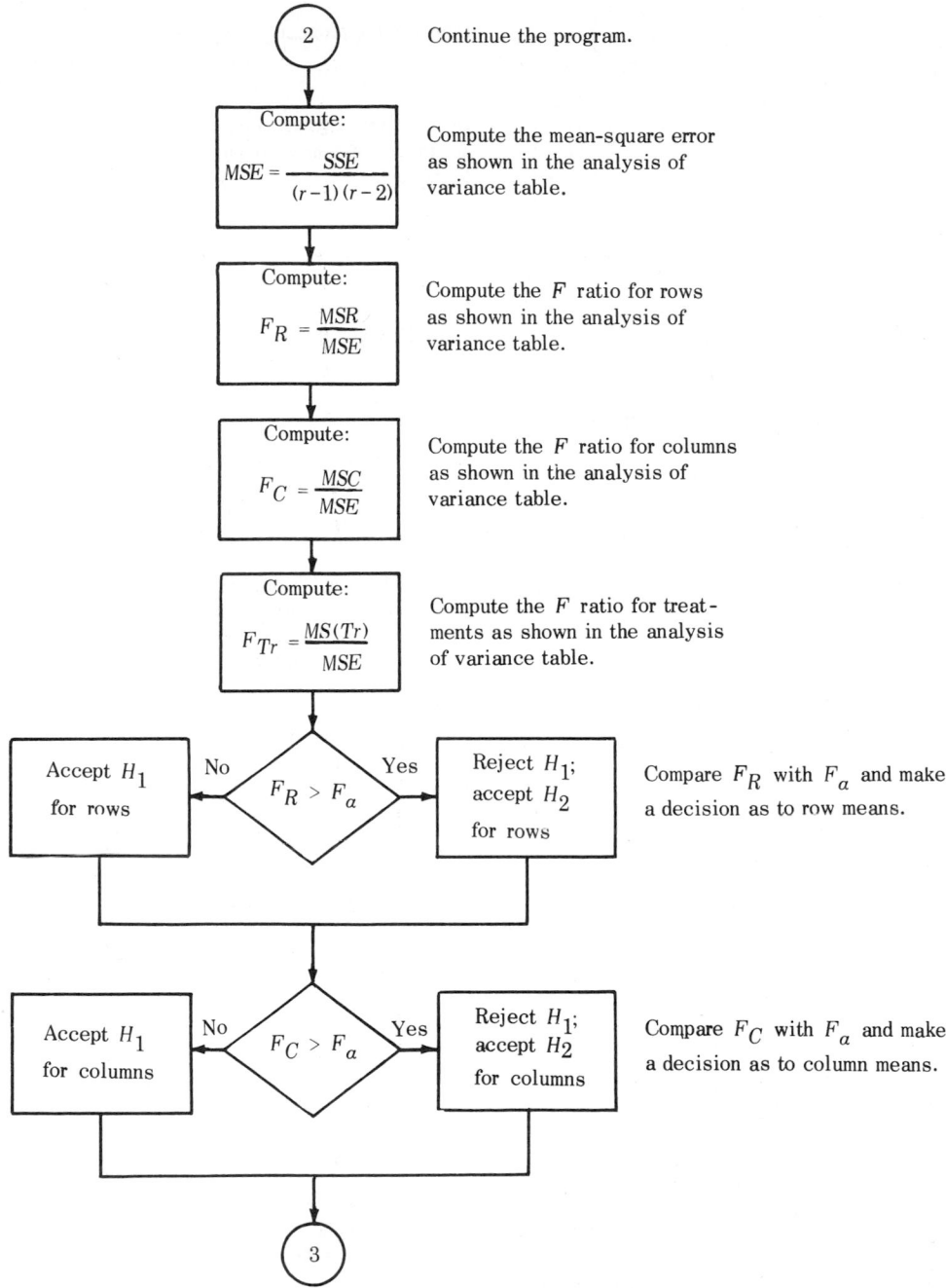

Figure 15.1 (Continued)

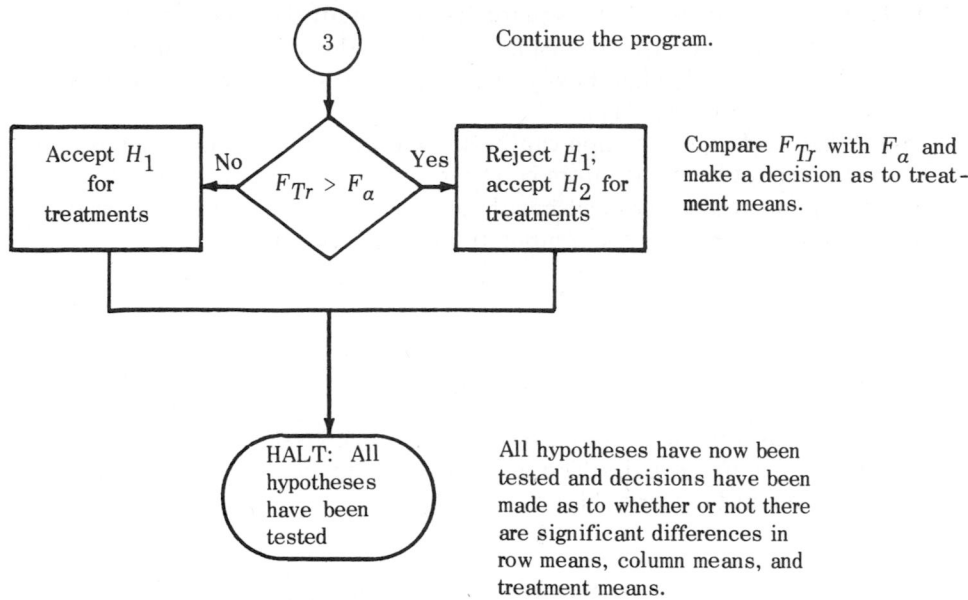

Figure 15 1 (Concluded)

STUDY QUESTIONS

15-1. Explain briefly the meaning of each of the following terms:

a. experimental design   f. treatment

b. row effects   g. factor

c. column effects   h. level of a factor

d. interaction   i. replication

e. Latin square

15-2. Why is a good experimental design important to the success of a research project?

15-3. In a one-way analysis of variance problem, is it always necessary to have all samples the same size?

15-4. What are the sources of variation in one-way analysis of variance?

15-5. What are the sources of variation in a two-way analysis of variance problem:

a. When there is only one observation per cell?

b. When there are "n" observations per cell?

15-6. Why are there more null hypotheses to be tested in a two-way analysis of variance when there are more than one observation per cell?

15-7. Explain the meaning of the following notation for totals:

a. $T_{i.}$ e. $T_{..}$

b. $T_{i..}$ f. T_k

c. $T_{.j}$ g. $T_{...}$

d. $T_{.j.}$ h. T_{abc}

15-8. If you wish to use a Latin-square design to study the effect on sales of the amount of shelf space used to display a food product in a supermarket, how could this be done? Explain how you would set up such an experiment using five different sizes of shelf space.

15-9. What kind of information can be secured from a factorial design experiment that cannot be learned from considering each variable separately?

15-10. If a factorial experiment has three variables and each is considered at three levels, how many factor combinations would there be?

PROBLEMS

15-1. The following table shows the average weekly salary paid typists in a sample of different size cities. Test at an $\alpha = 0.05$ to see if there is a significant difference in typists' salaries based on city size.

AVERAGE WEEKLY SALARIES OF TYPISTS

(in dollars)

City	City size		
	Under 25,000	25,000 and under 500,000	500,000 and over
1	60	68	73
2	65	72	75
3	61	65	
4		67	

15-2. Records are kept on the sales of four salesmen for one week. Not all men work all days in the week, but sales for the days they did work are shown below. Test at an $\alpha = 0.01$ to see if there is a significant difference in their average sales.

SALES FOR FOUR SALESMEN FOR ONE WEEK

(in dollars)

Day of week	Salesman			
	Jones	Smith	Walters	Brown
Monday	750	890	780	500
Tuesday	...	950	720	1,000
Wednesday	850	...	500	...
Thursday	800	...	420	750
Friday	820	200	705	...

15-3. The table below shows the average weekly wage for a sample of employers of key-punch operators classified by type of business and city size. Test at an $\alpha = 0.05$ to see if there are significant differences based on type of employer and by size of city.

SAMPLE OF WEEKLY WAGES PAID KEY-PUNCH OPERATORS
(in dollars)

Type of employer	City size		
	Under 25,000	25,000 and under 500,000	500,000 and over
Retail	70	75	83
Manufacturing	75	82	85
Banking	71	78	88
Government	85	87	90

15-4. The table below shows the sales for four salesmen in a week in which they all worked on each of five days. Test at an $\alpha = 0.01$ to see if there are significant differences in average sales by days and by salesman.

SALES FOR FOUR SALESMEN FOR FIVE DAYS
(in dollars)

Day of week	Salesman			
	Jones	Smith	Walters	Brown
Monday	1,200	890	780	500
Tuesday	750	950	720	1,000
Wednesday	800	400	500	610
Thursday	820	150	420	760
Friday	850	200	700	315

15-5. The following table shows the times required by four operators to mill a part using each of three machines twice. Test at an $\alpha = 0.05$ to see if there are significant differences in machines, in operators, and in interactions between operators and machines.

TIMES REQUIRED TO MILL A MACHINE PART
(in minutes)

Machine	Operator			
	Chaney	Lonsdale	Kennedy	Anderson
1	4.2	6.0	3.5	6.2
	5.6	7.1	4.3	5.8
2	5.1	5.3	3.2	6.7
	6.2	3.3	4.2	6.6
3	3.8	4.7	4.4	7.2
	4.1	5.2	5.0	4.8

15-6. The table below shows the life of a mold, in units produced, based on type of metal poured and heat. There are two observations in each cell. Test at an $\alpha = 0.05$ to see if there are significant differences in metals, in heats, and in interactions between metals and heats.

LIFE OF A MOLD BY TYPE AND HEAT OF METAL USED
(in units produced)

Metal	Heat	
	High	Very high
A	14	12
	16	13
B	21	18
	22	16
C	19	15
	18	16

15-7. The table below gives all the information needed for a simple Latin-square design in which $r = 3$. Test at an $\alpha = 0.05$ for significant differences in rows, in columns, and in treatments. The three treatments are designated as A, B, and C.

LATIN SQUARE EXPERIMENT

Row	Column		
	I	II	III
1	$A = 17$	$B = 24$	$C = 29$
2	$C = 25$	$A = 16$	$B = 17$
3	$B = 17$	$C = 25$	$A = 12$

15-8. The table below shows a Latin-square design with $r = 4$. Four operators work for 30 minutes, each making parts on four different machines. The four treatments represent four different grades of raw materials. Test at $\alpha = 0.05$ to see if there are significant differences in machines, in operators, and in raw materials.

NUMBER OF EFFECTIVE PARTS PRODUCED

Machine	Operator			
	I	II	III	IV
1	20	26	27	19
2	22	23	21	24
3	22	30	18	17
4	27	21	24	23

LATIN SQUARE

Machine	Operator			
	I	II	III	IV
1	B	C	D	A
2	A	B	C	D
3	C	D	A	B
4	D	A	B	C

15-9. The two tables below give the information needed for a 2^3 factorial problem. Output in terms of units produced per hour is shown for two complete replications. The factors to be considered are the experience of the operator, the shift time, and the method of payment. Test at an $\alpha = 0.05$ to see if there are significant differences in output that result from the levels of the three factors, from combination of these factors at different levels, and from replications.

FACTORIAL EXPERIMENT

Factor	Level	
	0	1
A – Operator	inexperienced	experienced
B – Shift	night	day
C – Pay	straight time	incentive

Treatment combination	Replication (in units per hour)	
	1	2
1	15	16
a	18	17
b	17	19
c	21	23
ab	19	18
ac	24	23
bc	25	23
abc	27	30

15-10. The results of a 2^3 factorial experiment with three replications are shown in the tables below. A specimen of standard dimensions is made from clay and baked in an oven before being tested to determine its breaking point in terms of pounds per square inch (psi). The treatments (being tested at two levels each) are baking temperature, humidity, and baking time. Test at an $\alpha = 0.01$ to see if there are significant differences in strength that result from the levels of the three factors, from combinations of the factors at different levels, and from replications.

FACTORIAL EXPERIMENT

Factor	Levels	
	0	1
A – Temperature	400°	650°
B – Humidity	low	high
C – Baking time	20 minutes	35 minutes

Treatment combination	Replication (in breaking strength of psi)		
	1	2	3
1	27	31	29
a	26	30	27
b	32	30	34
c	35	38	32
ab	25	20	26
ac	24	23	19
bc	28	32	26
abc	15	19	16

SELECTED READINGS

Freund, John E., Paul E. Livermore, and Irwin Miller. *Manual of Experimental Statistics.* Englewood Cliffs, New Jersey: Prentice-Hall, Inc., 1960.
    An excellent manual on the most frequently used statistical techniques, including complete examples. It is not complete enough to be used as a text.

Hicks, Charles R., *Fundamental Concepts in the Design of Experiments.* New York: Holt, Rinehart, and Winston, 1964.
    A text presenting the fundamental concepts in the design of experiments. It uses simple numerical problems, many from actual research work.

Kempthorne, Oscar, *The Design and Analysis of Experiments.* New York: John Wiley & Sons, Inc., 1952.
    A book that combines the extensive literature on the design of experiments into a systematic account of the subject from the point of view of the user and of the consultant.

Winer, B. J., *Statistical Principles in Experimental Design.* New York: McGraw-Hill Book Company, Inc., 1962.
    A comprehensive reference source on the statistical principles underlying experimental design for research workers in the area of behavioral sciences.

Chapter 16

Regression and Correlation: Linear Bivariate Analysis

Much of the effort expended in scientific research is devoted to the search for a cause-and-effect relationship that may exist between phenomena. The process of discovery in this deterministic (cause-and-effect) mode of inquiry involves learning by association. Events are observed and related, and, on the basis of this analysis, a decision is made whether the events are related causally. The events analyzed include a set of observed variations of a dependent variable and a set of corresponding variations for each of one or more independent (and hypothetically causal) variables.

Regression and correlation are powerful statistical tools that provide quantitative expressions or models of the manner or extent to which events are related mathematically. The application of these statistical methods cannot offer proof of the existence of a causal relationship between selected variables. Statistical analysis with these methods can, however, provide valuable information that the analyst can employ to support a judgment concerning the existence of a cause-and-effect relationship between the variables selected for analysis.

This chapter is concerned principally with the simplest case, *linear bivariate analysis* — the application of regression and correlation methods to two variables, one dependent and one independent. Chapters 17 and 18 take up more complex cases in which a nonlinear bivariate relation exists and in which the variations of a dependent variable are related to those of two or more independent variables.

ANALYSIS BY ASSOCIATION

An associative method that makes use of the statistical features of variations of selected variables can be illustrated by a realistic example adapted from an industrial situation.

A petrochemical manufacturer operates an experimental pilot plant with which to study the effects of varying manufacturing conditions, such as temperature and pressure, on the hardness of a type of plastic material. The principal component of the pilot plant is a steel pressure vessel, called a reactor. A hydrocarbon gas is pumped into the reactor, and during its passage through the reactor, the molecular structure of the entering gas is changed. This transformation results in the formation of a plastic material. The quality of the plastic produced in the reactor is measured in terms of the hardness of the material. The relationship between plastic hardness (presumably the dependent variable) and the corresponding temperature and pressure in the reactor (assumed to be independent variables) is the focus of the statistical analysis.

The analysis is begun by observing sets of events—the hardness of the plastic material and the pressure and temperature of the reactor as the plastic is produced. The plastic is produced in a batch of several hundred pounds of material. The temperature and pressure of the reactor are recorded as each batch is produced, and an equal number of batches for each degree of hardness are selected for analysis. The plastic hardness of the selected batches ranges from 30 to 80, measured in hardness units based on the scaling of laboratory test equipment. This range is presented in Table 16.1 and Figure 16.1.

The mean hardness of all batches selected is 55 units and the standard deviation is 10 units. The expected value of a batch chosen randomly is 55 units, but the degree of error associated with the expectation or estimate of hardness of the batch is expressed by the standard deviation of 10 units. Tchebycheff's inequality suggests that the likely error in estimating the hardness of the batch is relatively large. How can the degree of error associated with estimating the hardness of a batch be reduced? Perhaps if the variations in one of the independent variables such as temperature can be associated with variations in hardness of batches, the reliability of estimation can be improved. An analysis of the variations in hardness associated with temperature can be approached by classifying batches in terms of temperature.

Association Analysis by Single Classification

Reactor temperature is a continuous variable, and for the sake of simplicity in presenting the associative method, the range of recorded temperatures is divided. The lower half of temperatures corresponds to the event denoted T_I, and the upper half, the event T_{II}. This simple classification provides an insight into the general way in which hardness

Table 16.1

HARDNESS CHARACTERISTICS OF SELECTED SUBSETS OF BATCHES OF PLASTIC MATERIAL

Characteristics of hardness of groups	Set of all batches produced	Designation of batch groupings							
		Subset of batches produced with temperature I (T_I)	Subset of batches produced with temperature II (T_{II})	Subset of batches produced with temperature I and pressure A (T_I, P_A)	Subset of batches produced with temperature I and pressure B (T_I, P_B)	Subset of batches produced with temperature II and pressure A (T_{II}, P_A)	Subset of batches produced with temperature II and pressure B (T_{II}, P_B)	Subset of batches produced with pressure A (P_A)	Subset of batches produced with pressure B (P_B)
Range	30–80	30–70	40–80	30–50	50–70	40–60	60–80	30–60	50–80
Expected value $E(H)$	55	50	60	40	60	50	70	45	65
Standard deviation σ_H	10	8	8	4	4	4	4	6	6

Source: Company records of the firm.

Designation of groups of batches

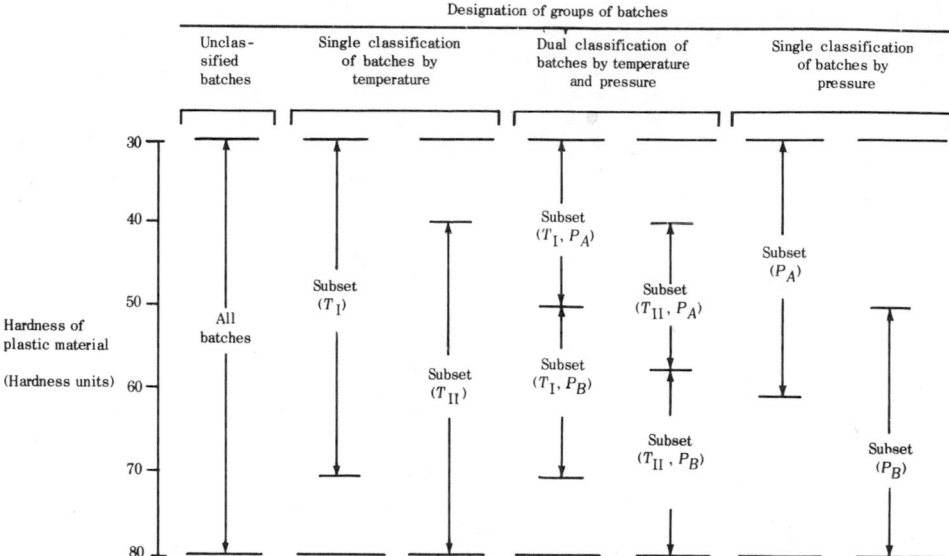

Figure 16.1

RANGE OF HARDNESS OF SELECTED GROUPS OF BATCHES
OF PLASTIC MATERIAL PRODUCED BY A REACTOR

and temperature are related. An examination of Figure 16.1 indicates that low hardness is associated with low temperatures (T_I) and the converse is true for high temperatures (T_{II}).

More precisely, the subset of batches produced with condition T_I has a mean of 50 and a standard deviation of 8. The corresponding statistical measures for the subset of batches produced with condition T_{II} are 60 and 8, respectively. The information derived from classifying or structuring the batches by temperature permits a relative reduction in the error of estimating batch hardness (in terms of the respective standard deviations) of one fifth, which is computed

$$\frac{10 - 8}{10} = 0.20.$$

This ratio can be viewed as a measure of the degree of association that exists between hardness and temperature. The larger the absolute value of the ratio, the greater the degree of association.

The estimate of batch hardness is more precise if temperature is known, because the smaller standard deviation of the subset can be associated with the mean of the subset. For example, if a batch is selected randomly from the subset produced with T_I, the expected value of hardness denoted (H) is the conditional value

$$E(H \mid T_I) = 50,$$

which is read "the expected value of hardness, given T_I, is equal to 50."
Similarly, the standard deviation for this subset is written

$$\sigma(H \mid T_I) = 8.$$

The range of hardness for this subset of batches is

$$\text{Range } (H \mid T_I) = 30 \text{ to } 70.$$

The corresponding values for the subset of batches produced with T_{II}
are:

$$E(H \mid T_{II}) = 60$$
$$\sigma(H \mid T_{II}) = 8$$
$$\text{Range } (H \mid T_{II}) = 40 \text{ to } 80.$$

The classification of batches by temperature setting in this example is
valuable in providing information for estimating plastic hardness. Why
not structure batches further by a more complex classification scheme
and observe whether additional information (reduction of estimation or
random error) can be obtained? Suppose batches are classified by temperature setting *and* reactor pressure. Continuing the simplicity of
classification, let the lower half of reactor pressure settings be denoted
P_A and the upper half be P_B. If pressure is not related to hardness, the
added dimension in classification of batches would not reduce further
the error of estimating the hardness of a batch selected at random from
the dually classified subset. Expressed another way, if hardness and
pressure are not related variables, a batch selected randomly from the
subset produced with a given temperature setting is as likely to have one
hardness value as another over the hardness range of the subset.

In this example, hardness and pressure appear to be related, for small
values of hardness are associated with low pressure, as seen in the right-
hand columns of Table 16.1 and Figure 16.1. The conditional values for
the single classification by pressure are:

$$E(H \mid P_A) = 45$$
$$\sigma(H \mid P_A) = 6$$
$$\text{Range } (H \mid P_A) = 30 - 60$$

and

$$E(H \mid P_B) = 65$$
$$\sigma(H \mid P_B) = 6$$
$$\text{Range } (H \mid P_B) = 50 - 80.$$

The classification of batch hardness by pressure is more effective in
reducing hardness estimation error than single grouping by temperature, for the standard deviation of hardness given pressure is 6, compared

with the standard deviation of hardness given temperature of 8. Since both temperature and pressure are related statistically (and may be causally) with hardness, a dual classification of batch hardness by temperature and pressure should provide more reliable estimates of hardness.

Association Analysis by Dual Classification

The expected value, standard deviation, and range of the subset of batches produced with T_I and P_A are read from Table 16.1 as follows:

$$E(H \mid T_I, P_A) = 40$$
$$\sigma(H \mid T_I, P_A) = 4$$
$$\text{Range } (H \mid T_I, P_A) = 30 - 50.$$

The corresponding characteristics of the three other subsets of dually classified batches are presented in Table 16.1. The standard deviations of these subsets are the smallest of any subset identified in this example. It follows that since one has more information about variations in batch hardness as the result of the dual classification, a more reliable estimate of hardness can be made. The relative reduction in the error of estimation, which can be achieved by the second classification over that obtained from the single classification, is one half and is computed

$$\frac{8 - 4}{8} = 0.50.$$

This ratio may be viewed as the relative reduction in the estimation error resulting from the classification by pressure, given that temperature is known. The variation in hardness is in part associated with temperature and also partially associated with pressure. The degree of partial association of variations in hardness with pressure, given that temperature is constant (i.e., variations associated with temperature are excluded), is expressed by the value 0.50.

The degree of total association of hardness with temperature and pressure is

$$\frac{10 - 4}{10} = 0.60,$$

which reflects the total relative reduction in the estimation error arising from the dual classification. The sequence of classification can be reversed in that batches can be classified first by pressure and then classified dually by pressure and temperature. The degree of association between hardness and pressure is

$$\frac{10 - 6}{10} = 0.40,$$

which is somewhat larger than the 0.20 reduction in the estimation error obtained from a single classification by temperature. If pressure is held constant (variations in hardness associated with pressure are excluded), the degree of association between hardness and temperature is

$$\frac{6 - 4}{6} = 0.33.$$

This relative reduction in expected error of estimating is an expression of the degree of partial association of variations in hardness with temperature fluctuations, given that the effects of pressure are excluded. This type of stepwise analysis is considered in more detail in Chapter 17 in the discussion of partial correlation methods.

The Relationship of Association and Causation

In the analysis of business problems, there is a strong motivation to identify cause-and-effect relationships that may exist between variables. On the basis of the results obtained in the foregoing example, one might be inclined toward the opinion that plastic hardness is at least partially determined by temperature and pressure settings. However, these results only indicate that the hardness of selected batches tends to vary directly with temperature and pressure.

The choice of hardness as the dependent variable involves a judgment on the part of the analyst, and this choice cannot be determined strictly by associative analysis. For example, one could associate temperature (as being dependent) with pressure and hardness (assumed to be independent variables). If this seems illogical, it is because one makes a judgment concerning the most appropriate designation of the variables as being dependent or independent. Measures of the degree of association of temperature variations with those of pressure and hardness can be computed in a way similar to that illustrated previously. But if variations in temperature are associated with those in hardness, should one conclude that plastic hardness is a causal factor which determines reactor temperature? Common sense suggests that the reverse is true in this example. This conclusion concerning which is the causal variable and which is the dependent variable is based on judgment rather than the result of statistical outcomes.

On the other hand, if variations in hardness were related to those of temperature and the degree of association were minute, this statistical result would suggest that there is no causal relationship between the variables or that the variables are only slightly related. The appraisal of this type of statistical result is discussed more fully in the presentation of tests of significance of regression and correlation coefficients in the sections that follow.

The Line of Average Relationship

Analysis by association may be extended to provide information about the functional relationship that exists between variables. This extension is illustrated by means of the temperature-hardness relationship in the plastic material example. Temperature condition T_I in Table 16.1 corresponds to the range of temperatures from 400°F to 450°F. Similarly, condition T_{II} corresponds to the temperature range from 450°F to 500°F. The hardness characteristics for these conditions are read from Table 16.1 and written as follows:

Batch hardness characteristic	Subset	
	T_I (400°F–450°F)	T_{II} (450°F–500°F)
Range	30–70	40–80
Expected value $E(H)$	50	60
Standard deviation σ_H	8	8

These data provide the basis for an approximation of the functional relationship between hardness and temperature. Suppose a batch of material is selected at random from the subset of batches T_I. The expected hardness of the batch is $E(H) = 50$, and the expected temperature at which the material was produced is 425°F, the midpoint or mean of the temperature range. Continuing in this manner, the mean hardness and mean temperature of subset T_{II} are 60 and 475°F, respectively. These average data are plotted in Figure 16.2. The line drawn through the points is called the *line of average relationship* and is an approximation of the functional relationship between the variables. The dotted lines above and below the line of average relationship correspond to the limits of the range of batch hardness for each temperature. A prediction of batch hardness can be made from this crude approximation of the functional relationship. Reading vertically upward from a temperature of 450°F to the line of average relationship and then across horizontally to the scale of hardness on the left, it is seen that a hardness of 55 is the expected value corresponding to this temperature.

The value of hardness of 55 may be viewed as a conditional mean written

$$E(\text{Hardness} \mid \text{Temperature} = 450) = 55.$$

Conditional means can be determined for other values of temperature, and, thus, the line of average relationship may be called the *line of con-*

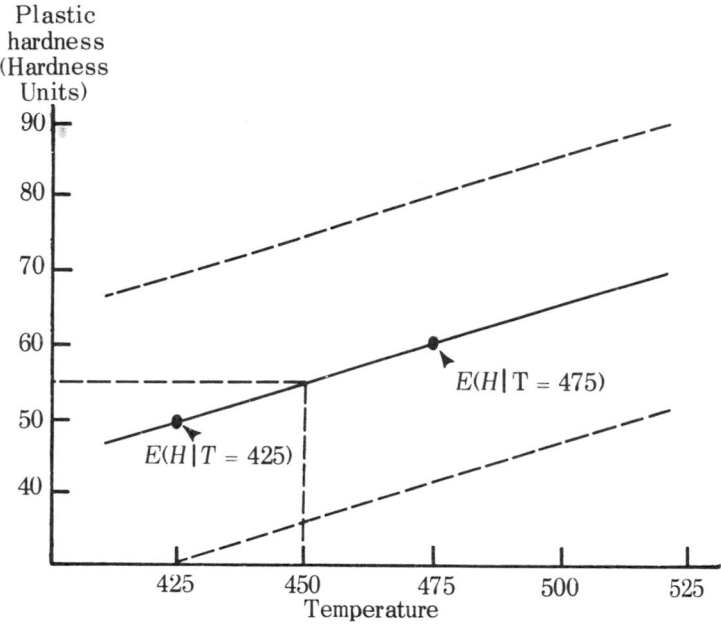

Figure 16.2

LINE OF AVERAGE RELATIONSHIP BETWEEN HARDNESS
AND TEMPERATURE

ditional means. In this sense, the mean of the subset of values of hardness that corresponds to a given temperature lies on the line of conditional means.

In order to make more precise estimates, the approximation of the functional relationship must be refined. This modification is accomplished by use of an analytical technique called the *method of least squares.* This method is described in the following discussion of regression and in Technical Note No. 1 at the end of this chapter.

REGRESSION ANALYSIS

In many business problems it is highly desirable to make predictions or estimates of the value of a dependent variable from given values of an independent variable. In experimentation or in the operation of a process, it may be especially beneficial to know to what extent the value of a dependent variable can be expected to be altered by a change in the independent variables of one unit. In the plastic hardness example, one may wish to determine by how much the hardness can be expected to change with a shift of one degree of temperature. This and related questions are considered in the following discussion.

Notation for Functional Relationships

The problem of making a prediction or an estimate of the value of a dependent variable corresponding to a given value of an independent variable requires that a mathematical expression in equation form be derived to express the relationship between the relevant variables. This equation is an expression of the functional relationship between the assumed dependent variable and one or more independent variables. In the discussions that follow, the dependent variable is denoted X_1, and the independent variables are designated by higher subscripts such as X_2, $X_3, X_4, \ldots$.

The relationship in which a dependent variable can be determined exactly from a selected value of an independent variable X_2 is described by the functional expression

$$X_1 = f(X_2),$$

which is read "X_1 is a function of X_2." The dependent variable involved in many business problems is a function of more than one independent variable, and this case is considered in detail in Chapter 18. In most business problems the dependent variable cannot be determined exactly from a set of specified values of the independent variable(s), even if these values are determined without error. Consequently, the best relationship that can be derived is an average value of X_1 associated with a specified value of the independent variable(s).

➤ *Example.* The output X_1 in units of a plant is related to the number of man-hours of labor X_2 used in production. Because of variations in the actual productivity of each hour of labor used, the exact number of units that will be produced with a specified number of man-hours of labor cannot be stated by a functional expression. However, an expression can be written that relates the average output with the labor hours used.

The average value of X_1 associated with a value of an independent variable is denoted X_{1c}. The relationship between the variables is written

$$X_{1c} = f(X_2; \theta_1, \ldots, \theta_r) \quad \ldots\ldots\ldots\ldots\ldots\ldots(16.1)$$

where $\theta_1, \ldots, \theta_r$ are the parameters of the functional expression. This expression is read "The average value of X_1 is a function of a specified value of X_2 and the values of the parameters $\theta_1, \ldots, \theta_r$ and is denoted as X_{1c}." The parameters of the functional expression relate values of the independent variable to corresponding values of the dependent variable.

➤ **Example.** Consider the case in which the average value of the dependent variable X_1 has a linear relationship with an independent variable X_2. The general form of this relationship is written

$$X_{1c} = \alpha + \beta X_2,$$

where X_{1c} is the average value of X_1, α and β are parameters or constants, and X_2 is the independent variable. This expression states that for any specified value of X_2, there exists a corresponding value of X_{1c}. The value of X_{1c} is equal to the transformed value of X_2. The transformation is accomplished by adding the value of the parameter α to the product of the parameter β times a specified value of X_2. The functional relationship between X_{1c} and X_2 can be written in the form of Formula 16.1 as

$$X_{1c} = f(X_2; \theta_1, \theta_2),$$

where $\theta_1 = \alpha$ and $\theta_2 = \beta$. This expression, while useful for purposes of notation, is less valuable in regression analysis than the former expression, which states the precise manner in which the parameters and variables are related.

➤ **Example.** In a study of the annual income of the salaried personnel of an electronics firm, the personnel director analyzed the relationship between annual income and age for employees between 25 and 65 years of age. The analysis revealed that the average annual income of employees varies directly with age in a straight-line or linear manner. A functional expression of the relationship is written

$$X_{1c} = f(X_2; \theta_1, \theta_2)$$

where X_{1c} is the average annual income, X_2 is age of years, and θ_1 and θ_2 are constants. This functional expression describes the relationship between average income and age since the income of one employee may differ from that of another employee of the same age. The exact income of a randomly selected employee cannot ordinarily be computed by use of the equation derived in this example. The values of the constants of the functional expression are found to be $\theta_1 = \$2,000$ and $\theta_2 = \$300$. In order to compute the average annual income for a given age, the functional expression is stated alternatively by substituting $\theta_1 = \alpha$ and $\theta_2 = \beta$ and writing

$$X_{1c} = \alpha + \beta X_2$$

and

$$X_{1c} = \$2,000 + \$300 X_2.$$

The average annual income for a male employee 30 years of age is computed

$$X_{1c} = \$2,000 + (\$300)(30)$$
$$= \$11,000.$$

Similarly, the average annual income of a male employee 60 years of age is computed

$$X_{1c} = \$2,000 + (\$300)(60)$$
$$= \$20,000.$$

Bivariate Distributions

Graphic Presentation Methods. Regression analysis is concerned primarily with the derivation of an equation that describes mathematically the manner in which selected variables vary jointly or covary. The choice of the most appropriate form of descriptive equation, whether linear or curvilinear, may be facilitated by plotting the observed values of the variables. An example of this technique is illustrated in Figure 16.3, which shows the plot of hardness versus temperature condition for batches of plastic material. The ordinate of each point is an observed value of the plastic hardness (X_1) of a batch. The corresponding abcissa is the temperature (X_2) present as the batch of material was manufactured.

The distribution of points in a scatter diagram provides a clue to the functional relationship that exists between two variables, especially if limited information is available concerning this relationship. The line drawn through the points in Figure 16.3 is a geometric representation of the best estimate of a linear equation of the general form $X_{1c} = \alpha + \beta X_2$ fitted by visual inspection. This is the line of average relationship between hardness and temperature, because all points do not lie on the line. While the information provided by the scatter diagram may be quite useful for discovering whether the general form of an appropriate equation is linear or curvilinear, it is of limited value for calculating expected values of hardness on the basis of temperature. The calculation of expected values of the dependent variable requires an explicit statement of the parameters of the equation of average relationship. Before considering the methods for deriving an explicit statement of the relationship, it is well to consider some of the theoretical assumptions implicit in the bivariate analysis.

If the variables to be analyzed are continuous, the range of the variables to be considered may be divided into discrete intervals or class limits. This division is applied to the hardness and temperature observa-

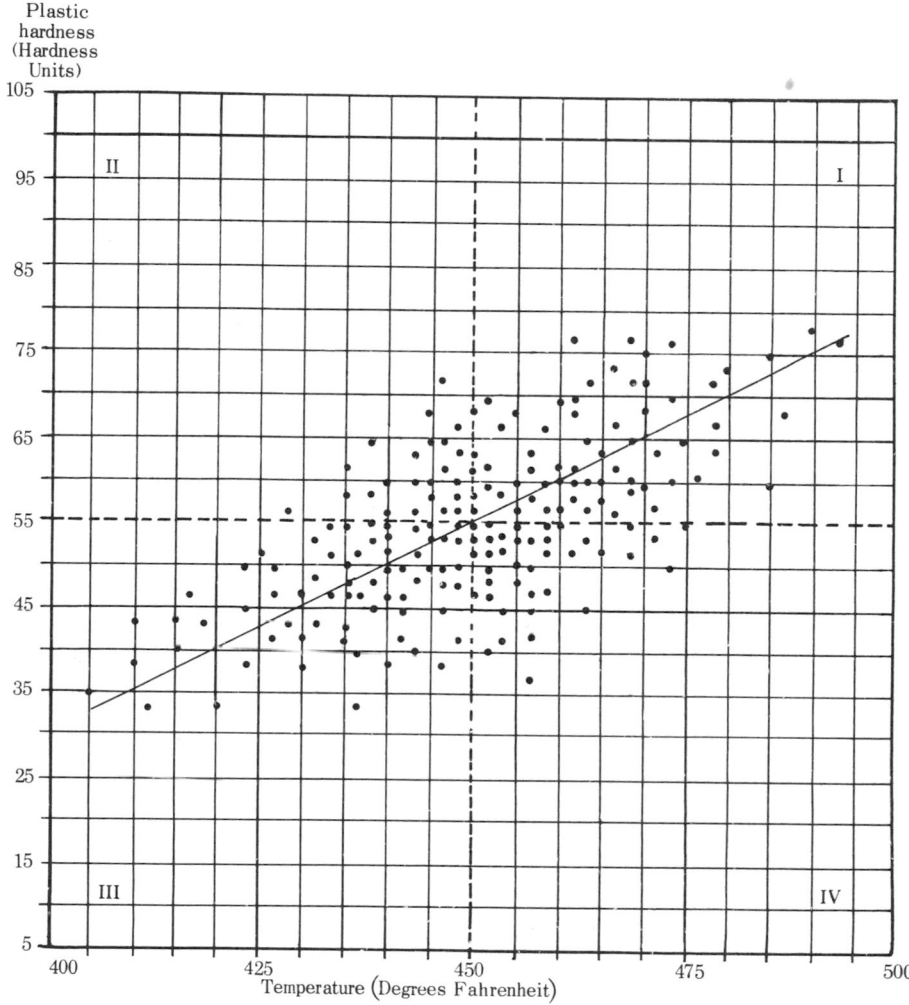

Figure 16.3

SCATTER DIAGRAM OF THE JOINT DISTRIBUTION OF OBSERVATIONS
OF PLASTIC HARDNESS AND REACTOR TEMPERATURE FOR A
UNIVERSE OF 194 BATCHES OF MATERIAL

tions shown in Figure 16.3. A count of the points occurring in each of the
intersections of class limits or cells produces the *bivariate frequency
distribution* shown in Figure 16.4. The density of points or paired
observations is reflected by the number of items in the respective cells. A
vertical column of cells is called a *vector*. The density of points in each
vector represents the variation of a subset of observed values of the
dependent variable that corresponds to a given range of the independent
variable.

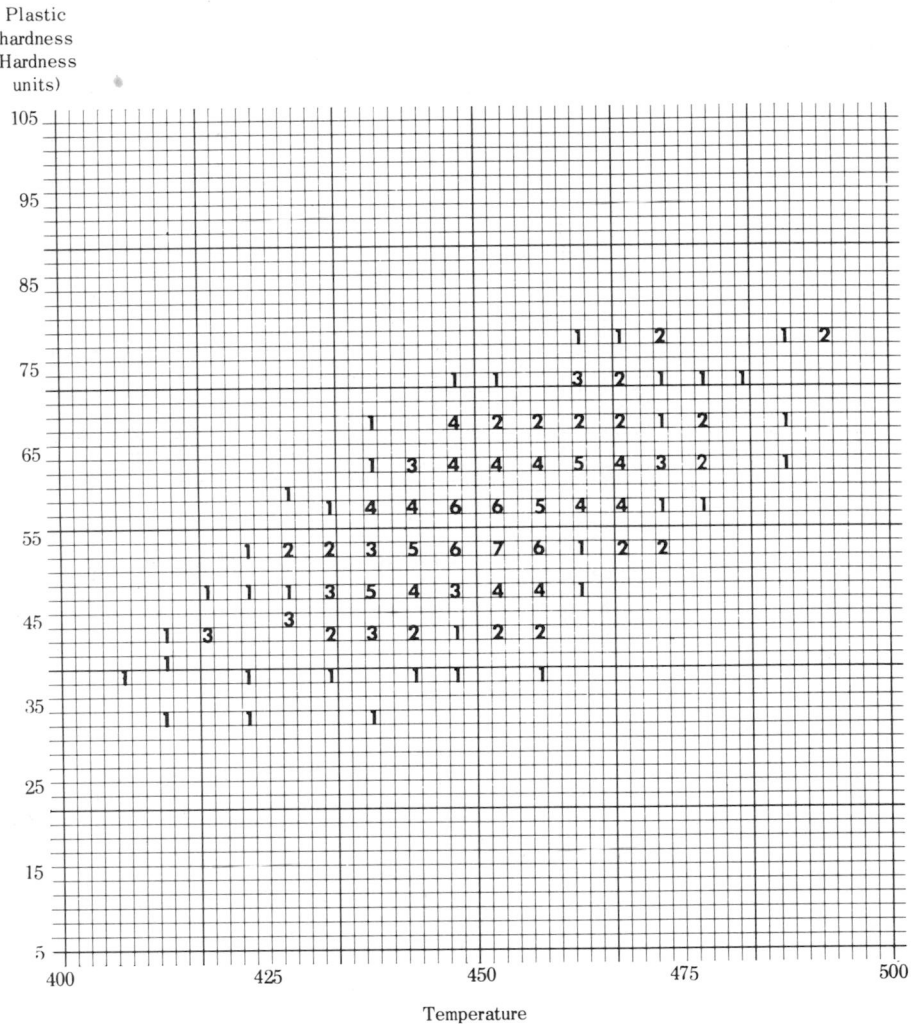

Plastic
hardness
(Hardness
units)

Temperature
(Degrees Fahrenheit)

Figure 16.4

BIVARIATE FREQUENCY DISTRIBUTION OF OBSERVATIONS OF
PLASTIC HARDNESS AND TEMPERATURE FOR A UNIVERSE
OF 194 BATCHES OF MATERIAL

If the number of paired observations is very large, the class interval of
the bivariate frequency distribution can be reduced to approach zero
width. The density of points in a given cell can be expressed as a likelihood or probability equal to the ratio of points in the cell to the total
number of points. Since the number of cells is also very large, the density
of points can be represented as a continuous surface called a *bivariate
regression surface*. A surface of this type is shown in Figure 16.5.

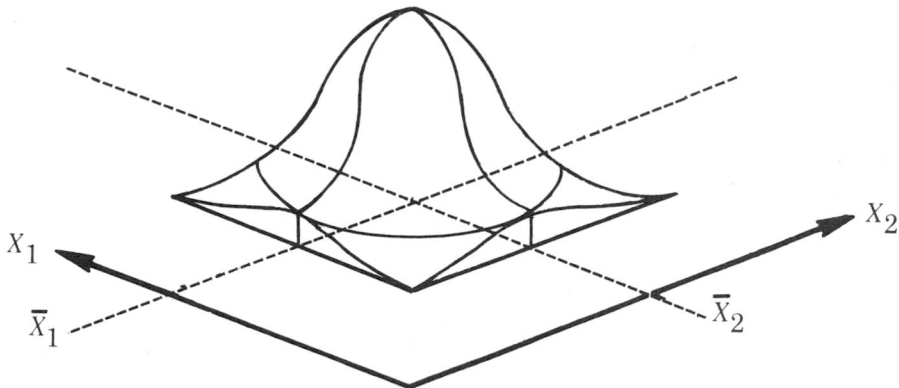

Figure 16.5
BIVARIATE REGRESSION SURFACE

The maximum height of the surface lies above the intersection of $\overline{X}_1$ and $\overline{X}_2$, the expected values of the respective variables. The volume under the surface corresponds to probability. The probability that a point selected at random occurs in a selected area or cell in the X_1, X_2 plane is represented by the portion of the volume under the regression surface that lies above the chosen area.

Regression analysis is always applied to a finite number of observations of the variables. The technique of regression analysis, however, is based on the assumption that the variables are continuous and that the regression surface is an appropriate model of the values of the variables.

Point Scatter and the Relationship Between Variables. The locus of points in the scatter diagram provides an insight into the functional relationship that exists between the variables. An examination of the points in each of the quadrants in Figure 16.3 reveals that the pattern of scatter is shaped like an oval and the majority of points lies in quadrants I and III. This pattern suggests that there is a positive relationship between hardness and temperature, for if there were no degree of association between the variables, the pattern of scatter would be circular. The proportion of points in each quadrant would be equal if the scatter of points is circular. If the majority of points occurs in quadrants II and IV, an inverse or negative relationship is implied between the dependent and independent variables.

A first approximation of the type of relationship or degree of association between the variables could be obtained by counting the points in each quadrant or adding the numbers in the cells in each quadrant. A more precise measure of the nature of the relationship or association is obtained by taking into account the position of each point in its respective quadrant. The value of a scatter diagram lies in the representation of the correspondence between variables in terms of the position of points. Similarly, a quantitative expression of this correspondence between variables is achieved by computing an aggregate expression of the relative values of the observations.

The farther a point lies from the expected values $\overline{X}_1$ and $\overline{X}_2$, the greater its significance for indicating the manner in which the variables are related. The position of a point can be designated by expressing its coordinates as deviations from the expected values of each of the variables X_1 and X_2. In this manner, the ordinate of a point is written $(X_1 - \overline{X}_1)$ and the abcissa is written $(X_2 - \overline{X}_2)$. A point in quadrant I would have coordinates that are positive values if the coordinates are expressed as deviations. Similarly, a point in quadrant II has a positive ordinate $(X_1 - \overline{X}_1)$ and a negative abcissa $(X_2 - \overline{X}_2)$. In quadrant III, the coordinates of each point are both negative with respect to the expected values of the variables.

An expression of the position of a point in its respective quadrant is achieved by computing the product of its coordinates expressed as deviations. The result of the multiplication of $(X_1 - \overline{X}_1)(X_2 - \overline{X}_2)$ is called a *cross product*. The cross products of points in quadrants I and III are all positive, since both coordinates (deviations) are positive in quadrant I and the coordinates of points in quadrant III are negative. The cross products of points in quadrants II and IV are negative since one of the coordinates is positive and the other is negative.

➤ *Example.* The hardness and temperature for a batch of material are 68 and 490, respectively. The cross product of the point in quadrant I in Figure 16.3 is computed

$$(X_1 - \overline{X}_1)(X_2 - \overline{X}_2) = (68 - 55)(490 - 450)$$
$$= (13)(40)$$
$$= 520.$$

A point in quadrant IV that corresponds to a batch of plastic material with hardness of 48 and a recorded temperature of 465 has a cross product of

$$(X_1 - \overline{X}_1)(X_2 - \overline{X}_2) = (48 - 55)(465 - 450)$$
$$= (-7)(15)$$
$$= -105.$$

The arithmetic mean or expected value of the cross products is called the *covariance*, which is denoted $cov(X_1, X_2)$. The value of the covariance is influenced by the units in which the deviations are expressed and the number of points involved. For example, a deviation in degrees Fahrenheit in Figure 16.3 has a larger numeric value than the same temperature expressed in degrees centigrade, although the condition is qualitatively the same in each case. The covariance would be smaller if temperature were measured in degrees centigrade as the result of the unit of measurement. The influence of unit of measurement can be eliminated by standardizing the covariance. This is accomplished by expressing the covariance in standard deviation units, which is written

$$\frac{E(X_1 - \bar{X}_1)(X_2 - \bar{X}_2)}{\sigma_{X_1}\sigma_{X_2}} = \frac{\frac{1}{N}\Sigma(X_1 - \bar{X}_1)(X_2 - \bar{X}_2)}{\sigma_{X_1}\sigma_{X_2}} \quad \ldots(16.2)$$

This measure is an expression of the degree to which the variables are related linearly.

The covariance of points in a circular pattern of scatter is zero, since the proportion of points in each quadrant is equal. A positive standardized covariance reflects a positive relationship between the variables. The larger the positive value of the standardized covariance, the greater the positive relationship. Conversely, the more negative the standardized covariance, the greater the inverse relationship between the variables.

➤ *Example.* The amount of impurity in water (X_1) (in parts per million) and percent acid concentration (X_2) in the cooling system of five identical pieces of equipment are recorded as follows:

System	Amount of impurity	Acid concentration
A	25	5
B	20	7
C	30	3
D	15	8
E	35	2

The standardized covariance is computed:

$$\frac{E(X_1 - \bar{X}_1)(X_2 - \bar{X}_2)}{\sigma_{X_1}\sigma_{X_2}}$$

$$= \frac{\frac{1}{5}[(25 - 25)(5 - 5) + (20 - 25)(7 - 5) + (30 - 25)(3 - 5) + (15 - 25)(8 - 5) + (35 - 25)(2 - 5)]}{(7.1)(2.3)}$$

$$= \frac{\frac{1}{5}[(0) - (10) - (10) - (30) - (30)]}{16.33}$$

$$= \frac{\frac{1}{5}(-80)}{16.33} = \frac{-16}{16.33} = -0.96.$$

The standardized covariance is negative, indicating a definite inverse relationship between the amount of impurity and acid concentration. This relationship is reflected by the scatter of points in Figure 16.6 and the negative slope of the line of average relationship, which is fitted visually.

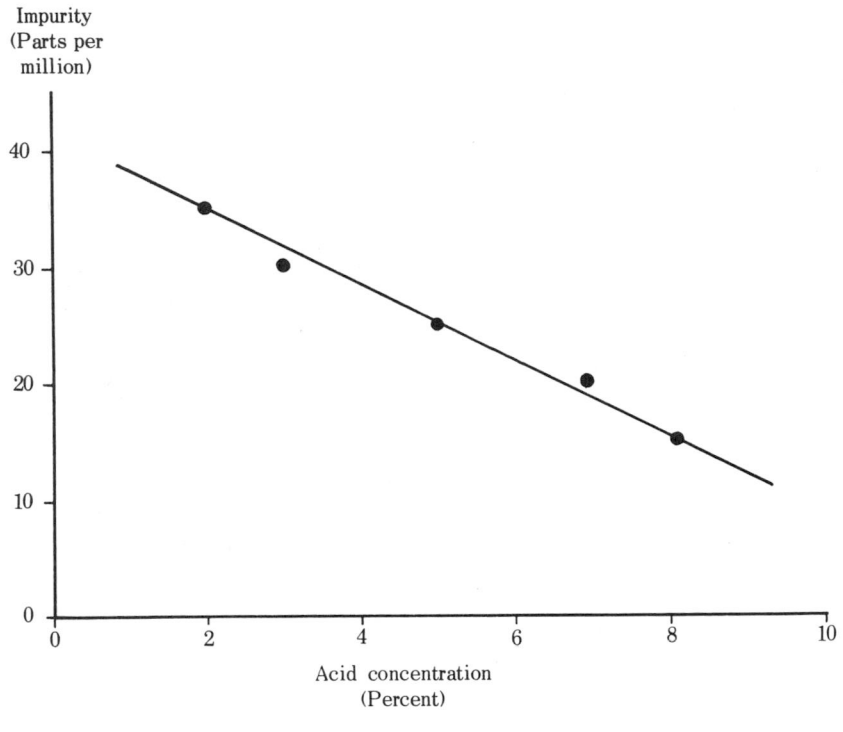

Figure 16.6

SCATTER DIAGRAM OF IMPURITY AND ACID CONCENTRATION

The locus of points in a scatter diagram may also suggest the nature of a line of average relationship with which to relate the variables. For example, the locus of points in each of the diagrams in Figure 16.7 suggests the presence or absence of functional relationships. Diagram (a) suggests a positive linear relationship; the relationship in (b) is negative linear; distinct curvilinearity is reflected by (c); and in (d) a causal relationship between the variables is not indicated because of the circular pattern.

If the relationship between the variables can be represented properly with a linear function, the slope of the line can be derived by making use of the cross products of the data. This method is considered in the discussion that follows.

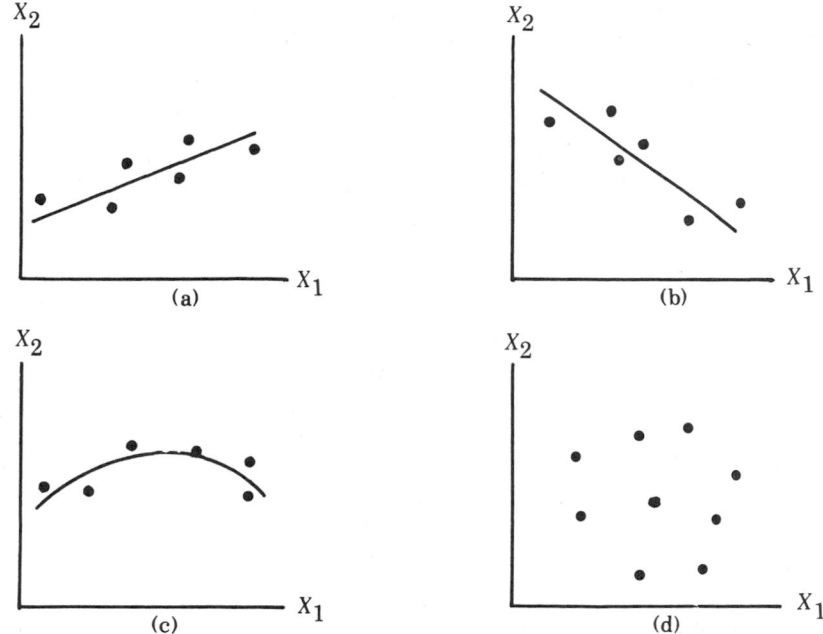

Figure 16.7

SCATTER DIAGRAMS SHOWING VARIOUS TYPES OF RELATIONSHIPS
BETWEEN VARIABLES

Line of Regression

In fitting visually a line of average relationship to a series of points, the objective is to position the line so that it lies at the center of the range of points. This type of approach can be stated explicitly by specifying the conditions that define the line which best fits the data. Since the equation of a line of averages is to be derived, the properties of the arithmetic mean are used to specify the desired conditions. One of these properties states that the sum of the deviations of a random variable about its mean is zero and is written

$$\Sigma(X - \bar{X}) = 0.$$

A second property of the arithmetic mean is that the sum of the squared deviations about the mean is a minimum and is written

$$\text{Minimum Sum of Squares} = \Sigma(X - \bar{X})^2.$$

If the deviations are squared and summed about any value of the random variable other than the mean, the sum of the squared deviations about that value of the random variable will exceed the least squares sum obtained about the mean.

Each point on the line of conditional means represents the mean of a vector or a subset of values of the dependent variable that corresponds to a specified range of the independent variable. Each of these mean values is a least squares value. The composite of these averages is the *least squares regression line*. The functional expression of the mean value of a vector of a bivariate universe with a linear relationship is denoted

$$X_{1c} = f(X_2; \theta_1, \theta_2)$$

where X_{1c} is the mean of a subset of values corresponding to X_2, a specified value of the independent variable, and the parameters θ_1 and θ_2. In general form, the linear equation is written

$$X_{1c} = \alpha_{1.2} + \beta_{12}X_2 \dots\dots\dots\dots\dots\dots(16.3)$$

where $\alpha_{1.2} = \theta_1$, and $\beta_{12} = \theta_2$. The coefficient $\alpha_{1.2}$ represents the intercept of the regression line at the origin ($X_2 = 0$). The subscript 1.2 refers to the regression of X_1 on X_2. The coefficient β_{12} is the rate of change of X_1 with respect to X_2. The subscript 12 connotes the relationship of X_1 with X_2, but if X_1 were regressed with a third variable X_3, the corresponding subscript would be 13. Formula 16.3 is also referred to as the true regression of X_1 on X_2, since it is based on a bivariate universe of values.

The regression model expressed by Formula 16.3 is based on the following assumptions:

1. A linear functional expression is an appropriate model of the relationship that exists between variables X_1 and X_2.
2. The subset of X_1 values that corresponds to a given X_2 is distributed normally.
3. The standard deviation of the X_1 values that corresponds to a given X_2 is the same for all X_2 values. A bivariate distribution with this property is said to be *homoscedastic*. The converse of this property is termed *heteroscedastic*.
4. The X_2 values do not have a distribution and are considered to be fixed. This implies that X_2 is a mathematical variable and not a random variable.

Given a line of regression defined by Formula 16.3, a value of X_1 is expressed in general form by

$$X_1 = \alpha_{1.2} + \beta_{12}X_2 + \varepsilon \dots\dots\dots\dots\dots.(16.4)$$

where ε is the error of estimating X_1 with X_{1c}. Since X_{1c} is the expected value of X_1 given a value of X_2, Formula 16.4 may be written

$$X_1 = E(X_1 \mid X_2) + \varepsilon \dots\dots\dots\dots\dots.(16.5)$$

The error term for a single observation of X_1 is written

$$\varepsilon = X_1 - X_{1c}.$$

The values of ε are assumed to be distributed normally about the line of regression so that

$$E(\varepsilon) = 0.$$

The variance of ε is written

$$\text{Var } (\varepsilon) = E[X_1 - E(X_1 \mid X_2)]^2$$
$$= \sigma_{1.2}^2$$

where $\sigma_{1.2}^2$ is the variance of the deviations of X_1 from X_{1c}.

Parameter Estimates from Sample Data. In many business problems it is impossible or impractical to obtain all the observations of a bivariate universe and, consequently, the analysis must be based on a sample of paired observations. The use of sample data in regression analysis presents the problems of sampling error similar to those considered in the discussions of inference. The sample observations are used to estimate the relationship between the variables. For a bivariate distribution, the estimate of the functional relationship is written

$$x_{1c} = f(x_2; \hat{\theta}_1, \hat{\theta}_2),$$

where x_{1c} is a function of a specific sample value of x_2 and the parameter estimates $\hat{\theta}_1$ and $\hat{\theta}_2$. The linear equation associated with this function is written

$$x_{1c} = a_{1.2} + b_{12}x_2 \quad\dots\dots\dots\dots\dots\dots(16.6)$$

where $a_{1.2} = \hat{\theta}_1$ and $b_{12} = \hat{\theta}_2$. Formula 16.6 is called the *estimated regression of X_1 on X_2* and is used to make a point estimate of the dependent variable, given a specified value of the independent variable. Given an estimated line of regression defined by Formula 16.6, the error of predicting x_1 with x_{1c} is

$$\varepsilon = x_1 - x_{1c}$$

and

$$\varepsilon = x_1 - E(x_1 \mid x_2).$$

An individual sample value of the dependent variable is written

$$x_1 = a_{1.2} + b_{12}x_2 + \varepsilon \quad\dots\dots\dots\dots\dots(16.7)$$

and

$$x_1 = E(x_1 \mid x_2) + \varepsilon \quad\dots\dots\dots\dots\dots(16.8)$$

As in the case of the true line of regression derived from population data

$$E(\varepsilon) = E[x_1 - E(x_1 \mid x_2)]$$
$$= 0.$$

The method of least squares provides estimates of θ_1 and θ_2 that are both efficient and unbiased. A subset of observations of the dependent variable is assumed to correspond to each value of the independent variable. If the values of each vector are normally distributed, it can be demonstrated that the parameter estimates $\hat{\theta}_1$ and $\hat{\theta}_2$ are maximum likelihood estimators. The method of least squares therefore is a technique for deriving the estimators of the parameters θ_1 and θ_2 which minimize the sum of squared deviations.

The sum of squared deviations, $\Sigma(x_1 - x_{1c})^2$, is a function of the estimators $a_{1.2} = \hat{\theta}_1$ and $b_{12} = \hat{\theta}_2$. This sum is a minimum about a line defined by the estimators

$$b_{12} = \frac{n\Sigma x_1 x_2 - (\Sigma x_1)(\Sigma x_2)}{n\Sigma x_2^2 - (\Sigma x_2)^2} \qquad \ldots\ldots\ldots\ldots\ldots(16.9)$$

and

$$a_{1.2} = \bar{x}_1 - b_{12}\bar{x}_2 \qquad \ldots\ldots\ldots\ldots\ldots\ldots\ldots(16.10)$$

These relationships for computing the values of estimators $a_{1.2}$ and b_{12} are derived by the method of least squares in Technical Note No. 1.

The relationship of b_{12} and the sum of squared deviations of the values of x_1 and x_2 about the respective means is shown as follows. If the origin is taken at $\bar{x}_1, \bar{x}_2$ rather than at 0, 0, the normal equations in Technical Note No. 1 may be written

$$(x_1 - \bar{x}_1) = na_{1.2} + b_{12}\Sigma(x_2 - \bar{x}_2)$$
$$(x_1 - \bar{x}_1)(x_2 - \bar{x}_2) = a_{1.2}\Sigma(x_2 - \bar{x}_2) + b_{12}\Sigma(x_2 - \bar{x}_2)^2.$$

But $\Sigma(x_1 - \bar{x}_1) = 0$ and $\Sigma(x_2 - \bar{x}_2) = 0$. Consequently,

$$b_{12} = \frac{\Sigma(x_1 - \bar{x}_1)(x_2 - \bar{x}_2)}{\Sigma(x_2 - \bar{x}_2)^2}.$$

The numerator of this expression is the sum of cross products of the observed values of x_1 and x_2. The denominator is the sum of squared deviations of the independent variable x_2. The coefficient b_{12} reflects the change in x_1 that corresponds to a unit change in x_2. Formula 16.9 is preferred for computing b_{12} because the values of the observed data can be used and the tedious process of computing deviations is avoided. The coefficient $a_{1.2}$ is the intercept of the estimated regression line at the origin ($x_2 = 0$), and is computed from the observed data by means of Formula 16.10.

➤ *Example.* A sample of five paired observations of processing time in hours (x_1) and the number of surfaces cut by a milling machine (x_2) on metal parts produced in a machine shop are given at the top of the next page.

x_1	x_2	$x_1 x_2$	x_1^2	x_2^2
5	3	15	25	9
8	4	32	64	16
7	5	35	49	25
6	2	12	36	4
4	1	4	16	1
30	15	98	190	55

The least squares estimators b_{12} and $a_{1.2}$ are computed as follows:

$$b_{12} = \frac{n\Sigma x_1 x_2 - (\Sigma x_1)(\Sigma x_2)}{n\Sigma x_2^2 - (\Sigma x_2)^2}$$

$$= \frac{5(98) - (30)(15)}{5(55) - (15)^2}$$

$$= \frac{490 - 450}{275 - 225}$$

$$= \frac{40}{50}$$

$$= 0.80.$$

$$a_{1.2} = \bar{x}_1 - b_{12}\bar{x}_2$$

$$= 6 - 0.8(3)$$

$$= 6 - 2.4$$

$$= 3.6.$$

The estimated regression of processing time on number of surfaces cut is expressed by

$$x_{1c} = 3.6 + 0.8x_2,$$

where,

$$a_{1.2} = \hat{\theta}_1 = 3.6, \quad b_{12} = \hat{\theta}_2 = 0.8.$$

The estimated processing time for three cuts is computed

$$x_{1c} = E(x_1 \mid x_2 = 3)$$
$$= 3.6 + 0.8(3)$$
$$= 6.0.$$

The value of five hours observed for three cuts deviates from the estimate by

$$\varepsilon = x_1 - E(x_1 \mid x_2 = 4) = 5.0 - 6.0 = -1.0.$$

The error of estimating x_1, given $x_2 = 3$, is shown in Figure 16.8.

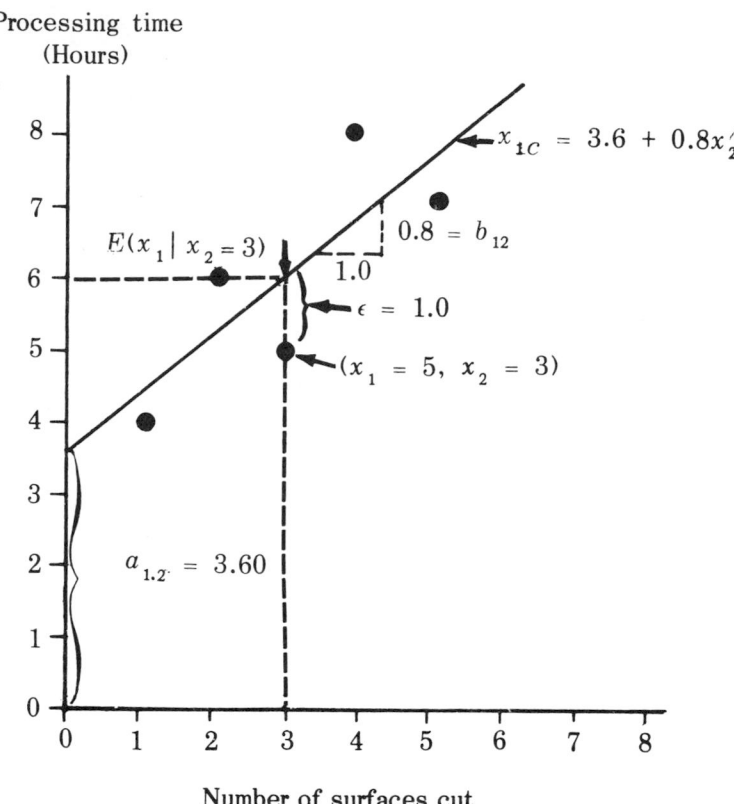

Figure 16.8

ESTIMATED REGRESSION OF PROCESSING TIME ON NUMBER OF
SURFACES CUT BY A MILLING MACHINE

The error of estimation for each of the observed values of the dependent variable is shown in the following table.

x_1	$a_{1.2}$	b_{12}	x_2	$a_{1.2} + b_{12}x_2$	$\varepsilon = x_1 - (a_{1.2} + b_{12}x_2)$
5	3.6	0.8	3	6.0	-1.0
8	3.6	0.8	4	6.8	1.2
7	3.6	0.8	5	7.6	-0.6
6	3.6	0.8	2	5.2	0.8
4	3.6	0.8	1	4.4	-0.4

$$\Sigma\varepsilon = 0.0$$

The sum of the error terms is zero, which reflects the fact that the estimated line of regression is a line of average relationship obtained by use of unbiased estimators $a_{1.2}$ and b_{12}.

The Standard Error of Estimate. The deviation of the paired observations of x_1 and x_2 from the estimated line of regression shown in Figure 16.8 reflects the degree of goodness of fit of the line with the data. If it is assumed that the deviations or prediction errors are independent and distributed normally about the line of regression, a numeric measure of these variations can be computed. This measure is the standard deviation of the errors of estimating x_1 from x_2, and is called the *standard error of the estimate.* For a universe of values, this measure is written

$$\sigma_{1.2} = \sqrt{\frac{\Sigma(X_1 - X_{1c})^2}{N}} \quad\ldots\ldots\ldots\ldots\ldots\ldots(16.11)$$

Formula 16.11 is based on the assumption that the error values are distributed normally and homoscedastically about the line of regression. This type of distribution is illustrated in Figure 16.9, which shows the relationship between plastic hardness and temperature. Normal curve properties are used in making an interval estimate of X_1.

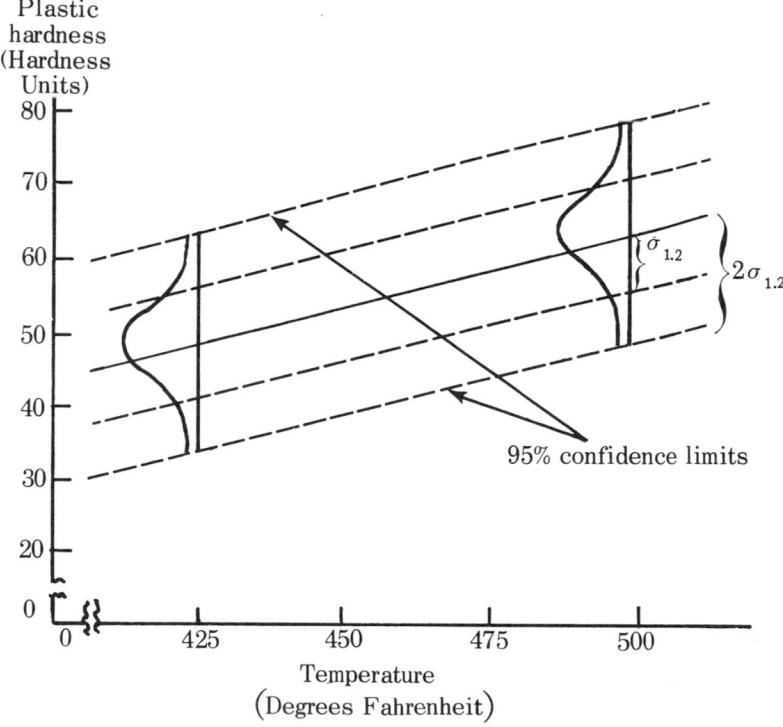

Figure 16.9

CONFIDENCE LIMITS ABOUT A LINE OF REGRESSION

➤ *Example.* The relationship between the universe of plastic hardness and temperature values shown in Figure 16.9 is described by the true line of regression

$$X_{1c} = -35.0 + 0.2X_2$$

and the normal distribution of estimation errors with the standard error of estimate

$$\sigma_{1.2} = 7.0.$$

A point estimate of plastic hardness for a temperature setting of 425°F is computed

$$
\begin{aligned}
X_{1c} &= \alpha_{1 \cdot 2} + \beta_{12} X_2 \\
&= -35.0 + 0.2(425) \\
&= -35.0 + 85.0 \\
&= 50.0.
\end{aligned}
$$

The 95.4% interval estimate of plastic hardness, given $X_2 = 425°F$, is computed

$$
\begin{aligned}
E(X_1 \mid X_2) &\pm z_{0.046}\sigma_{1.2} \\
E(X_1 \mid X_2 = 425) &\pm 2(7) \\
50 &\pm 14 \\
36 \text{ to } 64.
\end{aligned}
$$

An Unbiased Estimate of the Standard Error of Estimate. If regression analysis is based on sample data, the standard error of estimate must be approximated from the sample observations. Recalling that the variance of a sample is a biased estimator of the universe variance, it follows that a sample estimate of the standard error of estimate must also be corrected for bias. An unbiased estimator of the universe standard deviation of x_1 is written

$$\hat{\sigma}_{x_1} = \sqrt{\frac{n}{n-1}}\, S_{x_1}.$$

The loss of one degree of freedom results from the use of $\bar{x}_1$ as an estimate of μ_{x_1} in the computation.

An unbiased estimator of $\sigma_{1.2}$ obtained by the method of maximum likelihood is

$$\hat{\sigma}_{1.2} = \sqrt{\frac{\Sigma(x_1 - x_{1c})^2}{n-2}} \quad \dots\dots\dots\dots\dots\dots(16.12)$$

The loss of two degrees of freedom in this expression reflects the use of $a_{1.2}$ and b_{12} as estimates of $\alpha_{1.2}$ and β_{12} in computing the standard error of estimate.

Manual computation of $\hat{\sigma}_{1.2}$ is facilitated by using an alternate expression obtained by writing Formula 16.12 as

$$\hat{\sigma}_{1.2} = \sqrt{\frac{\Sigma(x_1 - a_{1.2} - b_{12}x_2)^2}{n - 2}}.$$

Squaring and substituting terms in the numerator gives the alternate expression

$$\hat{\sigma}_{1.2} = \sqrt{\frac{\Sigma x_1^2 - a_{1.2}\Sigma x_1 - b_{12}\Sigma x_1 x_2}{n - 2}} \quad\quad\ldots\ldots\ldots(16.13)$$

Formula 16.13 permits one to avoid the tedious task of computing the error terms required by Formula 16.12.

➤ *Example.* The estimated standard error obtained from the data in the table on page 547 is computed as follows:

$$\hat{\sigma}_{1.2} = \sqrt{\frac{\Sigma x_1^2 - a_{1.2}\Sigma x_1 - b_{12}\Sigma x_1 x_2}{n - 2}}$$

$$= \sqrt{\frac{190 - 3.6(30) - 0.8(98)}{5 - 2}}$$

$$= \sqrt{\frac{3.6}{3}}$$

$$= 1.10.$$

This result is verified by computing the standard deviation of the estimation errors in the table on page 548 by means of Formula 16.12.

$$\hat{\sigma}_{1.2} = \sqrt{\frac{\Sigma(x_1 - x_{1c})^2}{n - 2}}$$

$$= \sqrt{\frac{(-1.0)^2 + (1.2)^2 + (0.8)^2 + (-0.4)^2 + (-0.6)^2}{5 - 2}}$$

$$= \sqrt{\frac{3.60}{3}}$$

$$= 1.10.$$

Sampling Error Associated with the Estimated Line of Regression

An estimate of the true line of regression is computed from sample data in order to predict the value of a dependent variable for a given value of an independent variable. The statistics $a_{1.2}$ and b_{12} are unbiased estimators of the parameters $\alpha_{1.2}$ (θ_1) and β_{12} (θ_2), but the values of these statistics are subject to sampling error. It follows that predictions made by use of an estimated line of regression are subject to sampling error. Sampling error may arise in the estimate of $\alpha_{1.2}$, the intercept of the regression line at the origin, and of β_{12}, the slope of the line of regression.

The Sampling Error of b_{12}. The slope of the line of regression b_{12} is a random variable with a mean

$$E(b_{12}) = \beta_{12}.$$

The sampling distribution of the statistic b_{12} is distributed normally about β_{12}. An example of this distribution is shown in Figure 16.10.

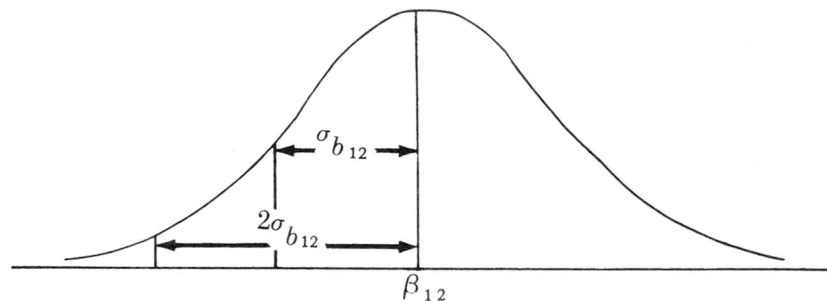

Values of the statistic b_{12}

Figure 16.10

NORMAL DISTRIBUTION OF THE STATISTIC b_{12}
ABOUT THE PARAMETER β_{12}

The standard deviation of the distribution of b_{12} is called the *standard error of b_{12}.* This parameter is written

$$\sigma_{b_{12}} = \frac{\sigma_{1.2}}{\sqrt{\Sigma(x_2 - \bar{x}_2)^2}} \quad \dots\dots\dots\dots\dots\text{(16.14)}$$

The magnitude of $\sigma_{b_{12}}$ varies directly with the standard error of the estimate but inversely with the number of sample observations and the variability of the independent variable. An unbiased estimator of $\sigma_{b_{12}}$ is written

$$\hat{\sigma}_{b_{12}} = \frac{\hat{\sigma}_{1.2}}{\sqrt{\Sigma(x_2 - \bar{x}_2)^2}} \quad \dots\dots\dots\dots\dots\text{(16.15)}$$

An equivalent algebraic form is written

$$\hat{\sigma}_{b_{12}} = \frac{\hat{\sigma}_{1.2}}{\sqrt{\Sigma x_2^2 - \frac{(\Sigma x_2)^2}{n}}} \quad \ldots\ldots\ldots\ldots\ldots\ldots(16.16)$$

A value of b_{12} obtained from a sample of observations does not necessarily lead to the conclusion that the slope of the universe line of regression has a value other than zero. It is possible to obtain a nonzero value of b_{12} even if $\beta_{12} = 0$. This type of result arises from sampling error and creates the need for a test of significance of the value of b_{12}.

A sample value of b_{12} can be tested for significance by testing the hypothesis that $\beta_{12} = 0$, which implies that the dependent and the independent variables are not related. A sample value of b_{12} must differ significantly from zero before it supports the conclusion that a functional relationship does exist between the variables. A test of significance is made by computing the statistic

$$t = \frac{b_{12} - \beta_{12}}{\hat{\sigma}_{b_{12}}} \quad \ldots\ldots\ldots\ldots\ldots\ldots\ldots(16.17)$$

and comparing the result with the value of t for $n - 2$ degrees of freedom. The t distribution is used because $\hat{\sigma}_{1.2}$ is used in the calculation.

➤ *Example.* The slope of the estimated line of regression for the data in the table on page 547 is tested for significance in the following steps. The results computed from these data in preceding examples are:

$$n = 5$$
$$b_{12} = 0.8$$

and

$$\hat{\sigma}_{1.2} = 1.10.$$

The statistic t for these data is obtained by computing

$$t = \frac{b_{12} - \beta_{12}}{\hat{\sigma}_{b_{12}}} = \frac{\dfrac{0.8 - 0.0}{1.1}}{\sqrt{55 - \dfrac{(15)^2}{5}}}$$

$$= \frac{0.727}{\sqrt{10}}$$

$$= 0.23.$$

This result is compared with the values of t for $n - 2 = 5 - 2 = 3$ degrees of freedom. Since

$$t_{0.90} < t < t_{0.80}$$

or

$$0.137 < 0.23 < 0.277$$

for a two-tailed test of significance, the value of b_{12} is not significant at the 0.80 level.

The Standard Error of an Estimated Mean. An estimated line of regression is subject to sampling error in estimating $\alpha_{1.2}$ and β_{12}. As a consequence, an estimate of the mean of the X_1 values that correspond to a given X_2, denoted $E(X_1 \mid X_2) = \bar{X}_1$, is also subject to sampling error. The sample estimate of $\bar{X}_1$ is the estimated regression value

$$\bar{x}_1 = a_{1.2} + b_{12}x_2.$$

An unbiased estimator of the *standard error of an estimated mean*, also called the estimated *standard error of a regression line*, is written

$$\hat{\sigma}_{(\bar{X}_1 \mid X_2)} = \hat{\sigma}_{1.2} \sqrt{\frac{1}{n} + \frac{(x_2' - \bar{x}_2)^2}{\Sigma x_2^2 - \frac{(\Sigma x_2)^2}{n}}} \quad \ldots\ldots\ldots\ldots(16.18)$$

where x_2' is a specified value of the variable X_2.

This statistic is a measure of the error of the estimate of the mean value of X_1 for a specified value of X_2. The term $\dfrac{1}{n}$ reflects the error of the estimator $a_{1.2}$, and the second term under the radical corresponds to the error of the estimator b_{12} of the estimated regression equation. The value of $\hat{\sigma}_{(\bar{X}_1 \mid X_2)}$ is a minimum for $x_2' = \bar{x}_2$, for which the second term under the radical is equal to zero. This value increases as the selected value of x_2' deviates from $\bar{x}_2$.

➤ *Example.* The estimated standard error of the regression line in the example of processing time and number of cuts by a milling machine is computed by Formula 16.18. Substituting the results

$$\hat{\sigma}_{1.2} = 1.10$$

$$\Sigma x_2^2 - \frac{(\Sigma x)^2}{n} = 10.0$$

computed previously, the estimated standard error in estimating the mean value of processing time x_1, given that four surfaces are cut, $X_2 = 4$ is computed

$$\hat{\sigma}_{(\bar{X}_1 \mid X_2)} = \hat{\sigma}_{1.2} \sqrt{\frac{1}{n} + \frac{(X_2 - \bar{x}_2)^2}{\Sigma x_2^2 - \frac{(\Sigma x_2)^2}{n}}}$$

$$\hat{\sigma}_{(\bar{X}_1 \mid X_2 = 4)} = 1.10 \sqrt{\frac{1}{5} + \frac{(4 - 3)^2}{10}}$$

$$= 1.10 \sqrt{0.3}$$

$$= 0.6 \text{ for } X_2 = 4.$$

This result is interpreted to mean that if many regression lines were computed from random samples of five paired observations, the estimates of the average processing time for machining four surfaces would have a standard deviation of 0.6 hours. The standard deviations for other numbers of surfaces machined are:

Number of surfaces X_2	$\hat{\sigma}_{(\bar{X}_1 \mid X_2)}$
1	0.8
2	0.6
3	0.5
4	0.6
5	0.8

The minimum value of $\hat{\sigma}_{(\bar{X}_1 \mid X_2)}$ corresponds to $x_2' = \bar{x}_2 = 3$ and increases as the selected value of x_2' deviates from $\bar{x}_2$. The estimated standard error $\hat{\sigma}_{(\bar{X}_1 \mid X_2)}$ can be decreased by enlarging the sample size.

The 95% confidence interval estimate of the mean value of X_1, given $X_2 = 4$, is found by computing the confidence interval about the point estimate

$$E(x_{1c} \mid X_2 = 4) = a_{1.2} + b_{12}(4)$$
$$= 3.6 + 0.8(4)$$
$$= 6.8$$

Lower limit	Upper limit
$\bar{X}_1 - t_{0.05}\hat{\sigma}_{(\bar{X}_1 \mid X_2)}$	$\bar{X}_1 + t_{0.05}\hat{\sigma}_{(\bar{X}_1 \mid X_2)}$
$6.8 - 3.18(0.60)$	$6.8 + 3.18(0.60)$
$6.8 - 1.9$	$6.8 + 1.9$
4.9	8.7

These confidence limits are shown in Figure 16.11.

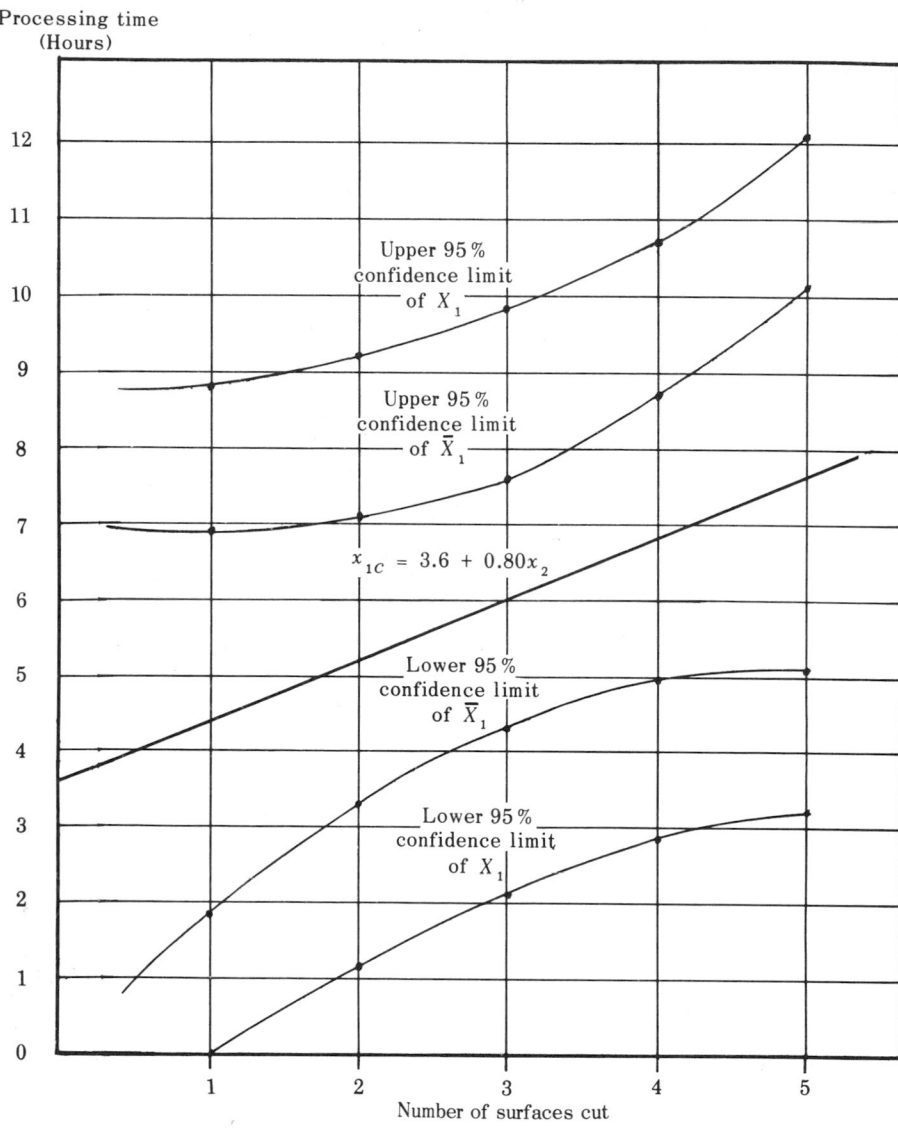

Processing time
(Hours)

Upper 95%
confidence limit
of X_1

Upper 95%
confidence limit
of $\bar{X}_1$

$x_{1C} = 3.6 + 0.80x_2$

Lower 95%
confidence limit
of $\bar{X}_1$

Lower 95%
confidence limit
of X_1

Number of surfaces cut

Figure 16.11

95% CONFIDENCE LIMITS FOR ESTIMATING $\bar{X}_1$ AND X_1

The Standard Error of an Estimated Value of X_1. The principal objective of most regression analysis applications is the derivation of an expression with which to predict values of X_1 for specified values of X_2. The prediction of values of X_1 is subject to two types of error. The first occurs if a less than perfect relationship exists between the variables. In this case, even if all the universe data were known, some degree of error would occur in predicting X_1.

The second source of prediction error is sampling, for the estimators $a_{1.2}$ and b_{12} are subject to sampling error. An estimate of an individual value of X_1 is $x_{1c} = X_1$. An estimator of the standard error of an estimated value of X_1 is written

$$\hat{\sigma}_{(X_1 \mid X_2)} = \hat{\sigma}_{1.2} \sqrt{1 + \frac{1}{n} + \frac{(X_2 - \bar{x}_2)^2}{\Sigma x_2^2 - \dfrac{(\Sigma x_2)^2}{n}}} \quad \dots\dots(16.19)$$

The statistic $\hat{\sigma}_{(X_1 \mid X_2)}$ approaches $\hat{\sigma}_{1.2}$ as a limit for $X_2 = \bar{x}_2$ as the sample size n becomes very large.

➤ *Example.* The value of $\hat{\sigma}_{(X_1 \mid X_2)}$ is computed from the data in the foregoing example. Given

$$n = 5$$
$$\hat{\sigma}_{1.2} = 1.10$$
$$X_2 = 4$$
$$\Sigma x_2^2 - \frac{(\Sigma x)^2}{n} = 10.0,$$

the value of $\hat{\sigma}_{(X_1 \mid X_2)}$ is computed

$$\hat{\sigma}_{(X_1 \mid X_2)} = \hat{\sigma}_{1.2} \sqrt{1 + \frac{1}{n} + \frac{(X_2 - \bar{x}_2)^2}{\Sigma x_2^2 - \dfrac{(\Sigma x_2)^2}{n}}}$$

$$\hat{\sigma}_{(X_1 \mid X_2 = 4)} = 1.10 \sqrt{1 + \frac{1}{5} + \frac{(4 - 3)^2}{10}}$$

$$= 1.10 \sqrt{1.3}$$
$$= 1.10(1.14)$$
$$= 1.26 \text{ for } X_2 = 4.$$

The point estimate of X_1 is $E(X_1 \mid X_2 = 4)$ and is computed

$$X_1 = x_{1c} = a_{1.2} + b_{12}x_2$$
$$= 3.6 + 0.8(4)$$
$$= 6.8.$$

The 95 % interval estimate of $X_1 = x_{1c} = E(X_1 \mid X_2 = 4)$ is computed as follows:

Lower limit	Upper limit
$x_{1c} - t_{0.05}\hat{\sigma}_{(X_1 \mid X_2)}$	$x_{1c} + t_{0.05}\hat{\sigma}_{(X_1 \mid X_2)}$
$6.8 - 3.182(1.26)$	$6.8 + 3.182(1.26)$
$6.8 - 4.0$	$6.8 + 4.0$
2.8	10.8

The estimated standard error of the individual X_1 value estimates in the table on page 548 is shown as follows:

X_2	x_{1c}	$\hat{\sigma}_{(X_1 \mid X_2)}$	95% confidence limits
1	4.4	1.40	0.0 − 8.8
2	5.2	1.26	1.2 − 9.2
3	6.0	1.21	2.2 − 9.8
4	6.8	1.26	2.8 − 10.8
5	7.6	1.40	3.2 − 12.0

The value of $\hat{\sigma}_{(X_1 \mid X_2)}$ is a minimum for $X_2 = \bar{x}_2$ and increases as X_2 deviates from $\bar{x}_2$. The 95% confidence limits of predicted values of X_1 are shown in Figure 16.11.

A summary of the methods for computing the required statistics for applying regression analysis to sample data is shown in Figure 16.12.

CORRELATION ANALYSIS

Regression analysis is concerned with the derivation of an appropriate mathematical expression of the functional relationship between variables. This expression is derived for the express purpose of predicting values of a dependent variable on the basis of independent variables. Situations occur in the analysis of business problems in which an expression of the degree of association between variables is desired, and the ability to predict values of the dependent variable may or may not be of particular value. It is in this type of situation that *correlation analysis* is applicable. Regression analysis and correlation analysis of two variables as presented in this discussion are contrasted as follows:

Regression analysis model	*Correlation analysis model*
X_1 is a random variable and X_2 is a mathematical or fixed variable.	X_1 and X_2 are random variables.
A functional relationship $X_1 = f(X_2)$ is known or assumed and the variables are identified as dependent and independent.	The analysis is appropriate for either $X_1 = f(X_2)$ or $X_2 = f(X_1)$.
An analysis of one variable as being dependent upon another.	An analysis of interrelationship and mutual variation.
A model for estimating and predicting X_1 on the basis of X_2.	A model for testing and verifying the degree of association between variables.
The extent of relationship is indicated principally by the regression coefficient β_{12}.	The degree of association is reflected by the correlation coefficient ρ_{12}.
The results obtained from sample data are subject to sampling error.	The result obtained from sample data is subject to sampling error.

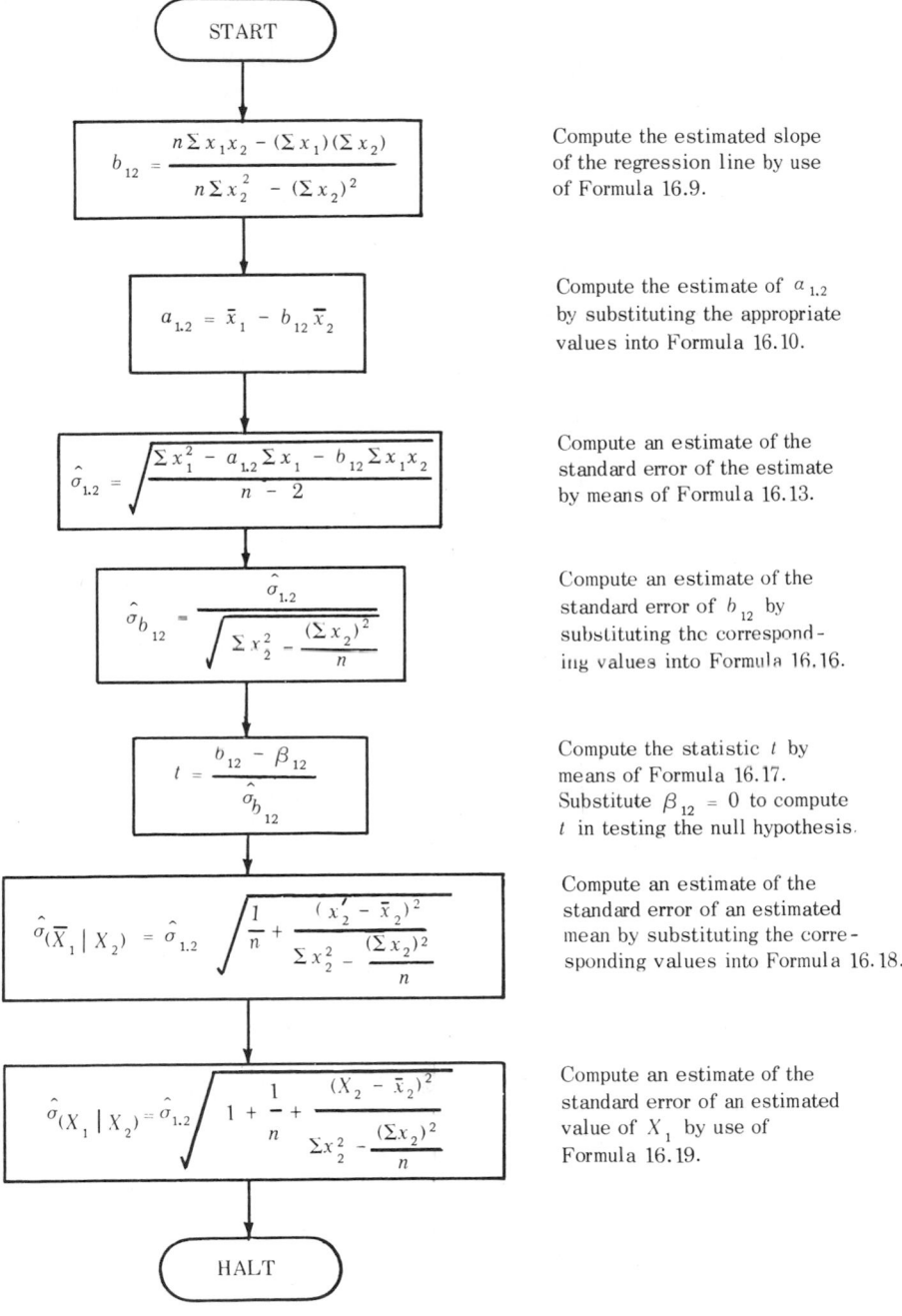

Compute the estimated slope of the regression line by use of Formula 16.9.

Compute the estimate of $a_{1.2}$ by substituting the appropriate values into Formula 16.10.

Compute an estimate of the standard error of the estimate by means of Formula 16.13.

Compute an estimate of the standard error of b_{12} by substituting the corresponding values into Formula 16.16.

Compute the statistic t by means of Formula 16.17. Substitute $\beta_{12} = 0$ to compute t in testing the null hypothesis.

Compute an estimate of the standard error of an estimated mean by substituting the corresponding values into Formula 16.18.

Compute an estimate of the standard error of an estimated value of X_1 by use of Formula 16.19.

Figure 16.12

A FLOW DIAGRAM FOR COMPUTING THE STATISTICS FOR APPLYING
REGRESSION ANALYSIS TO A SAMPLE OF PAIRED OBSERVATIONS

Variation and Correlation

An indicator of the degree of association between two variables can be obtained by computing the relative reduction in the error of estimating the dependent variable (in terms of the standard deviation). This approach is considered in the first portions of this chapter. A more explicit measure is obtained by computing the standardized covariance by use of Formula 16.2.

Universe Coefficient of Correlation

The expression stated by Formula 16.2 is called the *universe coefficient of correlation*, which may be written

$$\rho_{12} = \frac{cov(X_1, X_2)}{\sigma_{X_1}\sigma_{X_2}} \quad \dots\dots\dots\dots\dots\dots(16.20)$$

This coefficient is a measure of the extent to which two variables are related linearly. It is an abstract measure since it is divorced from the units of X_1 and X_2. The range of this measure is $(-1 \leq \rho_{12} \leq +1)$. The algebraic sign denotes an inverse (negative) or direct (positive) relationship between the variables. A value of $\rho_{12} = 0$ is interpreted to mean that the variables covary in absolute independence of one another and are not related linearly. A value of ρ_{12} that approaches (-1) reflects a very close inverse linear relationship. As ρ_{12} approaches $(+1)$, the indication is that a linear regression line with a positive slope is a very good expression of the relationship between the variables. This indication is seen more clearly by considering an alternative approach to the meaning of correlation.

The concept of correlation can be illuminated by examining further the variations in the dependent variable that are associated with those of the independent variable. The regression equation reflects the functional relationship between the variables, and ρ_{12}^2 indicates the percent of dispersion of the dependent variable that is associated with the independent variable. The *total variation* of the dependent variable is the sum of the squared deviations, written

$$\text{total sum of squares} = \Sigma(X_1 - \bar{X}_1)^2.$$

If there is a perfect linear relationship between X_1 and X_2, then $(X_1 \mid X_2) = E(X_1 \mid X_2)$ for all X_2, and all the X_1 values lie on the regression line. It follows that

$$\text{associated sum of squares} = \Sigma(X_{1c} - \bar{X}_1)^2$$

is equal to the total sum of squares and

$$\text{unassociated sum of squares} = \Sigma(X_1 - X_{1c})^2$$

is equal to zero in this case.

If the regression of X_1 on X_2 is not perfect, some values of $(X_1 \mid X_2)$ differ from $E(X_1 \mid X_2)$ for some values of X_2, and the unassociated sum of squares is greater than zero. The sum of squares has the relationship

$$\text{total} = \text{associated} + \text{unassociated}.$$

A measure of the degree to which X_1 and X_2 are related linearly is written

$$\rho_{12}^2 = \frac{\text{associated sum of squares}}{\text{total sum of squares}}$$

and

$$\rho_{12}^2 = \frac{\Sigma(X_{1c} - \overline{X}_1)^2}{\Sigma(X_1 - \overline{X}_1)^2} \quad \dots\dots\dots\dots\dots\dots\dots\text{(16.21)}$$

The term ρ_{12}^2 is called the *universe coefficient of determination* and is the ratio of the variation of X_1 associated with the variation of X_2. The range of this ratio is $(0 \le \rho_{12}^2 \le 1)$ since the numerator of Formula 16.21 cannot exceed the denominator.

The square root of ρ_{12}^2 is the universe coefficient of correlation. The relationship between Formulas 16.20 and 16.21 is shown by algebraic manipulation. The line of regression may be written in the form

$$X_{1c} = \overline{X}_1 + \beta_{12}(X_2 - \overline{X}_2).$$

Subtracting $\overline{X}_1$ from both sides of the expression gives

$$X_{1c} - \overline{X}_1 = \beta_{12}(X_2 - \overline{X}_2).$$

This expression is substituted into Formula 16.21 so that

$$\rho_{12}^2 = \frac{\beta_{12}^2 \Sigma(X_2 - \overline{X}_2)^2}{\Sigma(X_1 - \overline{X}_1)^2}.$$

Substituting the expression

$$\beta_{12} = \frac{\Sigma(X_1 - \overline{X}_1)(X_2 - \overline{X}_2)}{\Sigma(X_2 - \overline{X}_2)^2}$$

into the preceding equation and simplifying gives

$$\rho_{12}^2 = \left[\frac{\Sigma(X_1 - \overline{X}_1)(X_2 - \overline{X}_2)}{\Sigma(X_2 - \overline{X}_2)} \right]^2 \left[\frac{\Sigma(X_2 - \overline{X}_2)^2}{\Sigma(X_1 - \overline{X}_1)^2} \right]$$

$$\rho_{12}^2 = \frac{[\Sigma(X_1 - \bar{X}_1)(X_2 - \bar{X}_2)]^2}{\Sigma(X_2 - \bar{X}_2)^2 \, \Sigma(X_1 - \bar{X}_1)^2}$$

$$= \frac{\left[\dfrac{1}{N}\Sigma(X_1 - \bar{X}_1)(X_2 - \bar{X}_2)\right]^2}{\dfrac{1}{N}\Sigma(X_1 - \bar{X}_1)^2 \, \dfrac{1}{N}\Sigma(X_2 - \bar{X}_2)^2}$$

$$= \left[\frac{cov(X_1, X_2)}{\sigma_{X_1}\sigma_{X_2}}\right]^2 .$$

This demonstrates equivalence of the use of the analysis of variation of X_1 and the use of covariance in deriving ρ_{12}.

A related measure denoted

$$1 - \rho_{12}^2 = \frac{\text{unassociated sum of squares}}{\text{total sum of squares}}, \text{ or}$$

$$1 - \rho_{12}^2 = \frac{\Sigma(X_1 - X_{1c})^2}{\Sigma(X_1 - \bar{X}_1)^2} \quad \dots\dots\dots\dots\dots\dots\text{(16.22)}$$

is called the *universe coefficient of nondetermination*. The square root of this term is called the *coefficient of alienation*.

➤ *Example.* A member of the staff of the personnel department of a firm recorded the performance ratings (X_1) and corresponding scores made on an aptitude test (X_2) for a universe of five employees in a specialized section of the firm. The observed data and related computations are shown in the following table. The regression coefficients for these data are computed

$$\beta_{12} = \frac{N\Sigma X_1 X_2 - (\Sigma X_1)(\Sigma X_2)}{N\Sigma X_2^2 - (\Sigma X_2)^2}$$

$$= \frac{5(26{,}650) - (440)(300)}{5(18{,}250) - (300)^2}$$

Employee	(1) X_1	(2) X_2	(3) X_1^2	(4) X_2^2	(5) $X_1 X_2$	(6) $(X_{1c} \mid X_2)$	(7) $(X_1 - \bar{X}_1)$
A	75	50	5,625	2,500	3,750	78	−13
B	100	70	10,000	4,900	7,000	98	12
C	85	55	7,225	3,025	4,675	83	−3
D	95	60	9,025	3,600	5,700	88	7
E	85	65	7,225	4,225	5,525	93	−3
Totals	440	300	39,100	18,250	26,650	440	0

$$= \frac{133,250 - 132,000}{91,250 - 90,000}$$

$$= \frac{1,250}{1,250}$$

$$= 1,$$

and

$$\alpha_{1.2} = \bar{X}_1 - \beta_{12}\bar{X}_2$$
$$= 88 - (1)(60)$$
$$= 28.$$

The value of the regression line for a selected value of X_2 is computed

$$(X_{1c} \mid X_2 = 70) = \alpha_{1.2} + \beta_{12}(70)$$
$$= 28 + (1)(70)$$
$$= 98.$$

This value is shown in column (6) in the table below. The total deviations, associated deviations, and unassociated deviations for $X_2 = 70$ are found in columns (7), (9), and (11), respectively. Examples of these deviations are identified by the braces in Figure 16.13. The total squared deviations, associated squared deviations, and unassociated squared deviations are shown in columns (8), (10), and (12), respectively. The totals of these columns demonstrate that the relationship between total and component sums of squares is

$$\text{total} = \text{associated} + \text{unassociated}$$
$$380 = 250 + 130.$$

The coefficient of determination is computed

$$\rho_{12}^2 = \frac{\Sigma(X_{1c} - \bar{X}_1)^2}{\Sigma(X_1 - \bar{X}_1)^2}$$

$$= \frac{250}{380} = 0.658.$$

(8) $(X_1 - \bar{X}_1)^2$	(9) $(X_{1c} - \bar{X}_1)$	(10) $(X_{1c} - \bar{X}_1)^2$	(11) $(X_1 - X_{1c})$	(12) $(X_1 - X_{1c})^2$
169	−10	100	−3	9
144	10	100	2	4
9	−5	25	2	4
49	0	0	7	49
9	5	25	−8	64
380	0	250	0	130

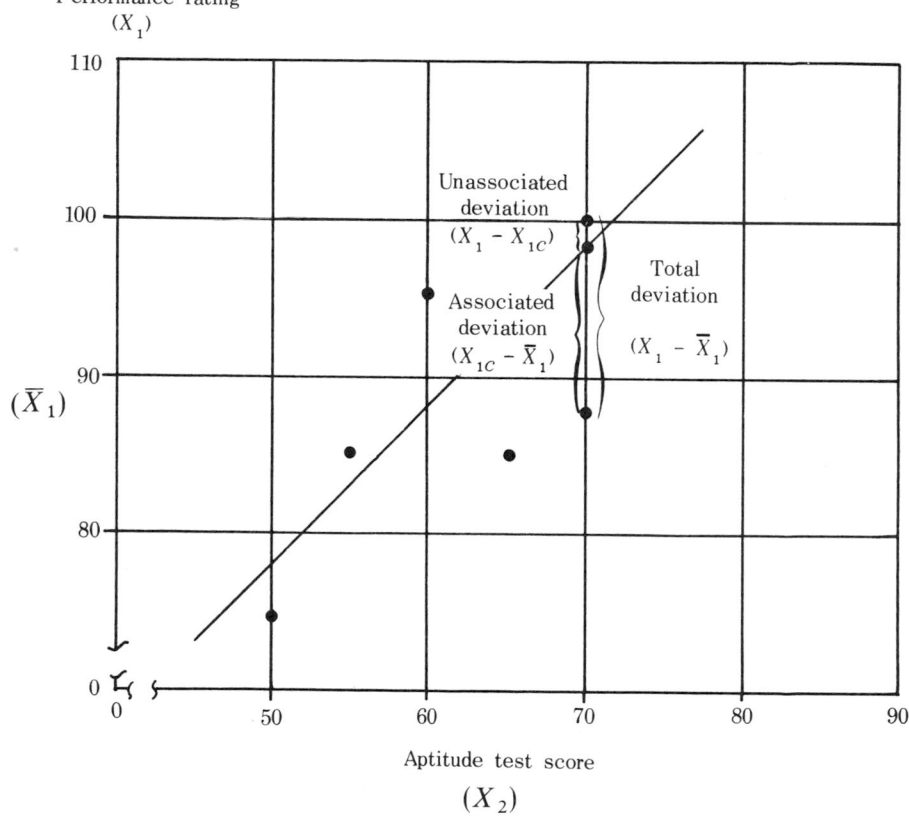

Figure 16.13

A SCATTER DIAGRAM ILLUSTRATING TOTAL DEVIATIONS.
ASSOCIATED DEVIATIONS. AND UNASSOCIATED DEVIATIONS

The coefficient of correlation is computed

$$\rho_{12} = \sqrt{\rho_{12}^2}$$

$$= \sqrt{0.658}$$

$$= 0.811.$$

This result indicates that a linear regression line is a rather good representation of the relationship between the variables X_1 and X_2. The coefficient of nondetermination is

$$1 - \rho_{12}^2 = \frac{\Sigma(X_1 - X_{1c})^2}{\Sigma(X_1 - \bar{X}_1)^2}$$

$$= \frac{130}{380} = 0.342,$$

and the coefficient of alienation is

$$\sqrt{1 - \rho_{12}^2} = \sqrt{1 - 0.658}$$
$$= \sqrt{0.342}$$
$$= 0.585.$$

CORRELATION AND SAMPLING THEORY

A Point Estimate of ρ_{12}

A point estimate of the universe coefficient of determination can be obtained by computing the value of the maximum likelihood estimator r_{12}^2 from sample data. This estimator is written

$$r_{12}^2 = \frac{\Sigma(x_{1c} - \bar{x}_1)^2}{\Sigma(x_1 - \bar{x}_1)^2},$$

where $r_{12}^2 = \hat{\rho}_{12}^2$, the ratio of the associated to the total sum of squares of the sample. Computing r_{12}^2 by means of this expression is tedious, for one must express the values of $E(x_1 \mid x_2)$ and x_1 as deviations about $\bar{x}_1$ and calculate the ratio of the corresponding sums of squares.

The computation of a point estimate of ρ_{12} can be facilitated by use of a formula derived from the expression for r_{12}^2 given above. An equivalent form of r_{12}^2 is written

$$r_{12}^2 = \frac{b_{12}^2 \Sigma(x_2 - \bar{x}_2)^2}{\Sigma(x_1 - \bar{x}_1)^2}.$$

This expression is analogous to that obtained in the demonstration of the equivalence of Formulas 16.20 and 16.21. Substituting the algebraic form of b_{12} into the alternative formula for r_{12}^2 and simplifying yields

$$r_{12}^2 = \left[\frac{\Sigma(x_1 - \bar{x}_1)(x_2 - \bar{x}_2)}{\Sigma(x_2 - \bar{x}_2)} \right]^2 \left[\frac{\Sigma(x_2 - \bar{x}_2)^2}{\Sigma(x_1 - \bar{x}_1)^2} \right]$$
$$= \frac{[\Sigma(x_1 - \bar{x}_1)(x_2 - \bar{x}_2)]^2}{\Sigma(x_1 - \bar{x}_1)^2 \, \Sigma(x_2 - \bar{x}_2)^2}.$$

The second of the above expressions is a point estimate of ρ_{12}^2. A point estimate of ρ_{12} is found by taking the square root of this expression, which is written

$$r_{12} = \frac{\Sigma(x_1 - \bar{x}_1)(x_2 - \bar{x}_2)}{\sqrt{\Sigma(x_1 - \bar{x}_1)^2 \, \Sigma(x_2 - \bar{x}_2)^2}}.$$

This expression is simplified for computation purposes by multiplying and collecting terms to yield

$$r_{12} = \frac{n\Sigma x_1 x_2 - (\Sigma x_1)(\Sigma x_2)}{\sqrt{[n\Sigma x_1^2 - (\Sigma x_1)^2][n\Sigma x_2^2 - (\Sigma x_2)^2]}} \qquad \text{.........(16.23)}$$

where $r_{12} = \hat{\rho}_{12}$ is the maximum likelihood estimator of ρ_{12} and is called the *sample coefficient of correlation*. Formula 16.23 is called the *product-moment* formula for the correlation coefficient.

➤ *Example.* The sample coefficient of correlation is computed for five paired observations of processing time in hours, x_1, and the number of required surfaces machined, x_2, on metal parts. The data are given as follows:

x_1	x_2	$x_1 x_2$	x_1^2	x_2^2
5	3	15	25	9
8	4	32	64	16
7	5	35	49	25
6	2	12	36	4
4	1	4	16	1
—	—	—	—	—
30	15	98	190	55

The point estimate of ρ_{12} is computed

$$
\begin{aligned}
r_{12} &= \frac{n\Sigma x_1 x_2 - (\Sigma x_1)(\Sigma x_2)}{\sqrt{[n\Sigma x_1^2 - (\Sigma x_1)^2][n\Sigma x_2^2 - (\Sigma x_2)^2]}} \\
&= \frac{5(98) - (30)(15)}{\sqrt{[5(190) - (30)^2][5(55) - (15)^2]}} \\
&= \frac{490 - 450}{\sqrt{(950 - 900)(275 - 225)}} \\
&= \frac{40}{\sqrt{(50)^2}} = 0.80.
\end{aligned}
$$

In this example r_{12} and b_{12} are equal, but this results from the fact that $\hat{\sigma}_{x_1}$ and $\hat{\sigma}_{x_2}$ are equal. In many other problems $\hat{\sigma}_{x_1}$ and $\hat{\sigma}_{x_2}$ will not necessarily be equal.

The Relationship Between r_{12} and b_{12}

The sample coefficient of correlation is the geometric mean of the slopes of the lines of regression of X_1 on X_2 and X_2 on X_1. For a random sample, these lines of regression are

$$x_{1c} = a_{1.2} + b_{12}x_2$$
$$x_{2c} = a_{2.1} + b_{21}x_1.$$

The regression coefficients are expressed by

$$b_{12} = \frac{\Sigma(x_1 - \bar{x}_1)(x_2 - \bar{x}_2)}{\Sigma(x_2 - \bar{x}_2)^2}$$

$$b_{21} = \frac{\Sigma(x_1 - \bar{x}_1)(x_2 - \bar{x}_2)}{\Sigma(x_1 - \bar{x}_1)^2}.$$

Multiplying b_{12} and b_{21} gives

$$b_{12} \cdot b_{21} = \frac{[\Sigma(x_1 - \bar{x}_1)(x_2 - \bar{x}_2)]^2}{\Sigma(x_1 - \bar{x}_1)^2 \, \Sigma(x_2 - \bar{x}_2)^2}.$$

This expression is the same as that obtained for r_{12}^2 in the derivation of Formula 16.23 and therefore

$$r_{12}^2 = b_{12} \cdot b_{21}$$

and

$$r_{12} = \sqrt{b_{12} \cdot b_{21}}.$$

This relationship assumes that regression analysis is applied to a bivariate distribution in which the regressions of X_1 on X_2 and X_2 on X_1 are computed. In a causal relationship, both regressions may not have operational meaning. The value of r_{12} does not indicate which variable is dependent and which is independent.

The relationship between r_{12} and b_{12} is also shown by the expression

$$r_{12} = b_{12} \div \frac{\hat{\sigma}_{X_1}}{\hat{\sigma}_{X_2}}.$$

Stated in this manner, r_{12} is the standardized slope of the regression line where the values of X_1 and X_2 are expressed in standard deviation units.

➤ *Example.* The relationship between r_{12} and b_{12} is demonstrated by using the data for five paired observations of performance rating, x_1, and aptitude test score, x_2, as sample observations.

$$\begin{aligned}
b_{12} &= \frac{n\Sigma x_1 x_2 - (\Sigma x_1)(\Sigma x_2)}{n\Sigma x_2^2 - (\Sigma x_2)^2} \\
&= \frac{5(26,650) - (440)(300)}{5(18,250) - (300)^2} \\
&= \frac{133,250 - 132,000}{91,250 - 90,000} = \frac{1,250}{1,250} = 1.
\end{aligned}$$

$$b_{21} = \frac{n\Sigma x_1 x_2 - (\Sigma x_1)(\Sigma x_2)}{n\Sigma x_1^2 - (\Sigma x_1)^2}$$

$$= \frac{5(26,650) - (440)(300)}{5(39,100) - (440)^2}$$

$$= \frac{133,250 - 132,000}{195,500 - 193,600}$$

$$= \frac{1,250}{1,900}$$

$$= 0.659.$$

$$r_{12} = \sqrt{b_{12} \cdot b_{21}}$$

$$= \sqrt{(1)(0.659)}$$

$$= 0.811.$$

This is the correlation coefficient obtained previously. The relationship between r_{12} and b_{12} is also demonstrated by

$$r_{12} = b_{12} \div \frac{\hat{\sigma}_{x_1}}{\hat{\sigma}_{x_2}}$$

$$= b_{12} \div \frac{\sqrt{\dfrac{n}{n-1}} \sqrt{\dfrac{\Sigma x_1^2}{n} - \left[\dfrac{\Sigma x_1}{n}\right]^2}}{\sqrt{\dfrac{n}{n-1}} \sqrt{\dfrac{\Sigma x_2^2}{n} - \left[\dfrac{\Sigma x_2}{n}\right]^2}}$$

$$= (1) \div \frac{\sqrt{\dfrac{5}{4}} \sqrt{\dfrac{39,100}{5} - (88)^2}}{\sqrt{\dfrac{5}{4}} \sqrt{\dfrac{18,250}{5} - (60)^2}}$$

$$= (1) \div \frac{\sqrt{1.25}\sqrt{76}}{\sqrt{1.25}\sqrt{50}}$$

$$= (1) \div \frac{\sqrt{95}}{\sqrt{62.5}}$$

$$= \frac{7.906}{9.747}$$

$$= 0.811.$$

Test of Significance for r_{12}

A value of the statistic r_{12} is subject to sampling error. If ρ_{12} is actually zero and X_1 and X_2 vary independently, a value of r_{12} other than zero can be obtained due to sampling error. Before the judgment is made whether there is correlation between variables, a test of significance should be made to determine the likelihood that the sample result could have been obtained by chance. This is accomplished by testing the hypothesis that $\rho_{12} = 0$, for unless the value of r_{12} is significantly different from zero, there is little support for the judgment that X_1 and X_2 are correlated.

A significance test of r_{12} can be performed by computing the statistic

$$t = \frac{r_{12} - \rho_{12}}{\sigma_{r_{12}}}.$$

The distribution of r_{12} is symmetric about $\rho_{12} = 0$, but the distribution becomes increasingly skewed as ρ_{12} approaches plus or minus one. The standard error of r_{12} for the null hypothesis $\rho_{12} = 0$ is written

$$\sigma_{r_{12}} = \sqrt{\frac{1 - r_{12}^2}{n - 2}}.$$

The ratio for testing the null hypothesis is

$$t = \frac{r_{12} - 0}{\sigma_{r_{12}}}$$

$$= \frac{r_{12}}{\sqrt{\dfrac{1 - r_{12}^2}{n - 2}}},$$

which may be written

$$t = r_{12} \sqrt{\frac{n - 2}{1 - r_{12}^2}} \quad\dots\dots\dots\dots\dots\dots\text{(16.24)}$$

This statistic has a t distribution with $n - 2$ degrees of freedom.

➤ *Example.* The sample correlation coefficient for five paired observations of performance rating (x_1) and aptitude test score (x_2) shown in the foregoing example is tested for significance. Assuming the null hypothesis,

$$t = r_{12} \sqrt{\frac{n - 2}{1 - r_{12}^2}}$$

$$= 0.811 \sqrt{\frac{5 - 2}{1 - 0.659}}$$

$$= 0.811 \sqrt{\frac{3}{0.341}}$$

$$= 0.811 \sqrt{8.80} = 2.41.$$

From Appendix J it is seen that for $d.f. = 5 - 2 = 3$

$$t_{0.10} < t < t_{0.05}$$
$$2.353 < 2.41 < 3.182,$$

and the value of r_{12} is significant at the 0.10 level of significance.

Appendix M is constructed especially for facilitating a test of significance of r_{12} assuming the null hypothesis. In the foregoing example, the value of $r_{12} = 0.811$ is compared with the values in Appendix M for $d.f. = 3$. This comparison shows

$$r_{12} < r_{12\,0.05}$$
$$0.811 < 0.8783$$

and the sample coefficient is not significant at the 0.05 level of significance.

The methods for significance tests for r_{12} are equivalent to performing an analysis of variance on the sources of variation. This technique will be presented in Chapter 18 in the discussion of multiple regression and correlation.

RANK CORRELATION

A nonparametric statistical method may be applied to the analysis of the degree of association between series of data that are ranked rather than measured in terms of exact quantitative value. The ranking of collegiate football teams by wire services is familiar to sports fans, and there is considerable interest in the consistency of the ratings. As another example, a marketing analyst may wish to determine if the brand preferences of two groups of consumers are consistent.

A measure of the correlation between ranked series is expressed by

$$r_{\text{rank}} = 1 - \frac{6\Sigma d^2}{n(n^2 - 1)} \quad \dots\dots\dots\dots\dots(16.25)$$

where d is the difference in rank between paired items in the series and n is the number of ranked items in a series.

➤ *Example.* Two groups of consumers, each in a different marketing area, were asked to rank brands of coffee in order of preference. The results are as follows:

Brand of coffee	Ranking		Difference	
	Group I	Group II	d	d^2
A	2	1	1	1
B	1	3	-2	4
C	3	2	1	1
D	4	4	0	0
E	5	5	0	0
F	6	7	-1	1
G	7	6	1	1
			$\Sigma d = 0$	$\Sigma d^2 = 8$

$$r_{rank} = 1 - \frac{6\Sigma d^2}{n(n^2 - 1)}$$

$$= 1 - \frac{6(8)}{7(49 - 1)} = 1 - \frac{48}{336} = 0.857.$$

The sampling distribution of r_{rank} is symmetrical about $\rho_{rank} = 0$ and approaches normality as n becomes large. A test of significance for r_{rank} is made by computing

$$z = \frac{r_{rank} - \rho_{rank}}{\sigma_{r_{rank}}}$$

where the standard error of r_{rank} is

$$\sigma_{r_{rank}} = \frac{1}{\sqrt{n - 1}}$$

The value of r_{rank} obtained for the ranking of brands of coffee is tested for significance, assuming the null hypothesis as follows:

$$z = \frac{r_{rank}}{\dfrac{1}{\sqrt{n - 1}}} \quad \dotfill \quad (16.26)$$

$$= \frac{0.857}{\dfrac{1}{\sqrt{7 - 1}}} = \frac{0.857}{0.406} = 2.11.$$

The value of r_{rank} is significant at the 0.05 level of significance, but not at the 0.01 level.

TECHNICAL NOTE NO. 1: The Method of Least Squares

The *method of least squares* is a method for deriving a linear expression that best fits a series of paired observations. The coefficients $a_{1.2}$ and b_{12} derived by this method are maximum likelihood estimators of θ_1 and θ_2, the parameters of the true linear expression. The line that best fits the data is the one for which the sum of squared estimation error between the observed values of the dependent variable and the corresponding values of the linear equation is a minimum.

Let S denote the sum of squared estimation error for all values of x_1 so that

$$S = \Sigma \varepsilon^2$$

where $\varepsilon^2 = (x_1 - x_{1c})^2$. The estimated value of x_{1c} is written

$$x_{1c} = a_{1.2} + b_{12}x_2$$

and values of $a_{1.2}$ and b_{12} are to be derived so that

$$S = \Sigma \varepsilon^2 = \Sigma(x_1 - x_{1c})^2$$
$$= \Sigma(x_1 - a_{1.2} - b_{12}x_2)^2$$

is a minimum. Assume that $a_{1.2}$ and b_{12} are variables and that S is a function of these variables, or $S = f(a_{1.2}, b_{12})$. Values of $a_{1.2}$ and b_{12} are to be found which jointly make S a minimum, if it exists. These values are found by minimizing S with respect to $a_{1.2}$ and b_{12}, setting the partial derivatives equal to zero, and solving the equations simultaneously. The expression of S can be written

$$S = \Sigma(x_1 - a_{1.2} - b_{12}x_2)^2$$
$$= \Sigma(x_1^2 - 2x_1a_{1.2} - 2b_{12}x_1x_2 + a_{1.2}^2 + 2a_{1.2}b_{12}x_2 + b_{12}^2x_2^2).$$

Maximizing S with respect to $a_{1.2}$ and b_{12} gives

$$\frac{\partial S}{\partial a_{1.2}} = -2\Sigma(x_1 - a - b_{12}x_2)$$

and

$$\frac{\partial S}{\partial b_{12}} = -2\Sigma(x_1x_2 - a_{1.2}x_2 - b_{12}x_2^2),$$

respectively.

Equating these partials to zero and rearranging terms, the expressions give the *normal equations* for estimating $\alpha_{1.2}$ and β_{12}. These equations are

$$\Sigma x_1 = na_{1.2} + b_{12}\Sigma x_2$$

and

$$\Sigma x_1x_2 = a_{1.2}\Sigma x_2 + b_{12}\Sigma x_2^2.$$

If x_1 and x_2 are expressed as deviations from the respective means $\bar{x}_1$ and $\bar{x}_2$, $\Sigma x_1 = 0$ and $\Sigma x_2 = 0$. Solving the second normal equation for b_{12} gives

$$b_{12} = \frac{\Sigma(x_1 - \bar{x}_1)(x_2 - \bar{x}_2)}{\Sigma(x_2 - \bar{x}_2)^2}.$$

Performing the multiplications and collecting terms, b_{12} is expressed by

$$b_{12} = \frac{n\Sigma x_1 x_2 - (\Sigma x_1)(\Sigma x_2)}{n\Sigma x_2^2 - (\Sigma x_2)^2}.$$

Having found an explicit expression for b_{12}, the first normal equation is solved for $a_{1.2}$ to give

$$a_{1.2} = \frac{\Sigma x_1}{n} - b_{12}\frac{\Sigma x_2}{n}$$

$$= \bar{x}_1 - b_{12}\bar{x}_2.$$

➤ *Example.* The estimators $a_{1.2}$ and b_{12} are derived by the least squares method for five paired observations.

x_1	x_2	$(x_1 - a_{1.2} - b_{12}x_2)$	$S = (x_1 - a_{1.2} - b_{12}x_2)^2$
1	2	$1 - a_{1.2} - 2b_{12}$	$1 - 2a_{1.2} - 4b_{12} + a_{1.2}^2 + 4a_{1.2}b_{12} + 4b_{12}^2$
2	4	$2 - a_{1.2} - 4b_{12}$	$4 - 4a_{1.2} - 16b_{12} + a_{1.2}^2 + 8a_{1.2}b_{12} + 16b_{12}^2$
3	5	$3 - a_{1.2} - 5b_{12}$	$9 - 6a_{1.2} - 30b_{12} + a_{1.2}^2 + 10a_{1.2}b_{12} + 25b_{12}^2$
4	6	$4 - a_{1.2} - 6b_{12}$	$16 - 8a_{1.2} - 48b_{12} + a_{1.2}^2 + 12a_{1.2}b_{12} + 36b_{12}^2$
5	8	$5 - a_{1.2} - 8b_{12}$	$25 - 10a_{1.2} - 80b_{12} + a_{1.2}^2 + 16a_{1.2}b_{12} + 64b_{12}^2$
15	25	$15 - 5a_{1.2} - 25b_{12}$	$55 - 30a_{1.2} - 178b_{12} + 5a_{1.2}^2 + 50a_{1.2}b_{12} + 145b_{12}^2$

$$\frac{\partial S}{\partial a_{1.2}} = -2\Sigma(x_1 - a_{1.2} - b_{12}x_2) = 0$$

$$= -2(\Sigma x_1 - na_{1.2} - b_{12}\Sigma x_2) = 0$$
$$= -30 + 10a_{1.2} + 50b_{12} = 0$$
$$= 15 - 5a_{1.2} - 25b_{12} = 0$$

$$\frac{\partial S}{\partial b_{12}} = -2\Sigma(x_1 x_2 - a_{1.2}x_2 - b_{12}x_2^2) = 0$$

$$= -2(\Sigma x_1 x_2 - a_{1.2}\Sigma x_2 - b_{12}\Sigma x_2^2) = 0$$
$$= -178 + 50a_{1.2} + 290b_{12} = 0$$
$$= 89 - 25a_{1.2} - 145b_{12} = 0.$$

Solving the last expressions of the partials (the normal equations) simultaneously yields

$$b_{12} = 0.7$$
$$a_{1.2} = -0.5.$$

These results can be obtained with the formulas for b_{12} and $a_{1.2}$ given in a foregoing portion of this note.

$$b_{12} = \frac{n\Sigma x_1 x_2 - (\Sigma x_1)(\Sigma x_2)}{n\Sigma x_2^2 - (\Sigma x_2)^2}$$

$$= \frac{(5)(89) - (15)(25)}{(5)(145) - (25)^2}$$

$$= \frac{(445) - (375)}{(725) - (625)}$$

$$= \frac{70}{100}$$

$$= 0.7.$$

$$a_{1.2} = \bar{x}_1 - b_{12}\bar{x}_2$$

$$= 3 - 0.7(5)$$

$$= 3 - 3.5$$

$$= -0.5.$$

STUDY QUESTIONS

16-1. Explain briefly the meaning of each of the following terms:

a. causal relationship
b. linear bivariate analysis
c. line of average relationship
d. line of conditional means
e. bivariate frequency distribution
f. vector
g. bivariate regression surface
h. cross product
i. covariance
j. least squares regression line
k. homoscedastic

l. heteroscedasticity
m. estimated regression of X_1 on X_2
n. standard error of the estimate
o. correlation analysis
p. universe coefficient of correlation
q. universe coefficient of determination
r. universe coefficient of nondetermination
s. coefficient of alienation
t. sample coefficient of correlation
u. rank correlation

16-2. What is meant by analysis by association?

16-3. How can statistics be used in deciding whether a causal relationship exists between two variables?

16-4. Why is a line of regression called a line of conditional means?

16-5. What is the purpose of a scatter diagram?

16-6. Describe what is meant by the method of least squares.

16-7. Upon what assumptions is the linear regression model based?

16-8. Describe the sampling problems in regression analysis.

16-9. Why should a test of significance be used in interpreting sample regression results?

16-10. Contrast regression analysis and correlation analysis.

16-11. What is the relationship between the correlation coefficient r_{12} and the regression coefficient b_{12}?

16-12. Describe the problem of sampling in correlation analysis.

16-13. Why is rank correlation called a nonparametric method?

PROBLEMS

16-1. A department store chain collected data on sales wages and sales volume for each of its stores. These data for the past month are:

Store	Sales wages (thousands of dollars) X_1	Sales volume (100,000 dollars) X_2
A	51.3	4.7
B	30.1	3.6
C	41.5	4.4
D	61.9	5.4
E	24.8	2.9
F	45.9	4.6
G	43.6	3.9
H	38.2	3.4

a. Plot a scatter diagram of the data.
b. Compute the least squares line of regression for the data.
c. Compute a point estimate of sales wages if sales volume is $4.2 hundred thousand.
d. What is the 95% interval estimate of sales wages if sales volume is $6.4 hundred thousand?

16-2. A record of maintenance cost is kept on each of several nearly identical automatic machines. These data are to be compared with machine age to determine if a suitable functional relationship can be derived for estimating maintenance cost.

Maintenance cost (Dollars)	Age (Years)	Maintenance cost (Dollars)	Age (Years)
126	6	68	2
49	2	82	4
181	7	64	1
63	5	105	8
110	3	117	5
23	1	141	9
92	6	40	3

a. Plot a scatter diagram of the data.

b. Fit a least squares line of regression to the data.

c. Compute a point estimate of maintenance cost for a machine five years of age.

d. Find the 95% interval estimate of maintenance cost for a machine three years of age.

16-3. Compute the coefficient of correlation for the data given in Problem 16-1.

16-4. Compute the coefficient of correlation for the data given in Problem 16-2.

16-5. A time-study analyst observes a packaging operation and collects data of time required for the operation and package volume. A sample of observations recorded during the packing operation is as follows:

Time (Seconds) (x_1)	Volume (Cubic feet) (x_2)
10.8	0.72
14.4	0.88
19.6	1.23
18.0	1.12
8.4	0.48
15.2	1.09
11.0	0.63
13.3	0.82
23.1	1.40

a. Plot a scatter diagram of the data.

b. Estimate the regression of operation time on package volume.

c. Compute the estimated standard error of the estimate.

d. Use a 0.05 level of significance to test the significance of b_{12}.

e. Compute the 95% interval estimate of the mean value of operation time for a package volume of 1.15 cubic feet.

f. What is the 95% interval estimate of operation time for a package volume of 0.80 cubic feet?

16-6. A member of the personnel department staff records the wage rate of a sample of key jobs in a plant and the corresponding evaluation of the key jobs on the basis of a point system. These data are given as follows:

Rate (Dollars) (x_1)	Points (x_2)	Rate (Dollars) (x_1)	Points (x_2)
1.85	105	2.58	200
1.80	125	2.95	222
1.90	135	3.30	248
2.25	150	3.18	272
2.52	162	3.35	275
2.40	170	3.60	295

a. Plot a scatter diagram of the data.

b. Estimate the regression of wage rate on point evaluation.

c. Compute the estimated standard error of the estimate.

d. Use a 0.05 level of significance to test the significance of b_{12}.

e. Compute the 95% interval estimate of the mean wage rate for a job evaluation of 180 points.

f. What is the 95% interval estimate of a wage rate for a job evaluation of 250 points?

16-7. Use the data in Problem 16-5 to:

a. Estimate the coefficient of correlation.

b. Test the estimate of the coefficient of correlation for significance at the 0.05 level.

16-8. Use the data in Problem 16-6 to:

a. Estimate the coefficient of correlation.

b. Test the estimate of the coefficient of correlation for significance at the 0.05 level.

16-9. A statistician interested in the population growth of Texas cities of 10,000 or more population collected data on population and total employment for a sample of cities. The data, taken from the *U.S. Census of Population,* 1960, are as follows:

City	Population (Thousands)	Employment (Thousands)
Abilene	90.4	30.5
Austin	186.5	69.8
Beaumont	119.2	44.1
Corpus Christi	167.7	55.7
Dallas	679.7	287.4
El Paso	276.7	81.9
Fort Worth	356.3	138.0
Galveston	67.2	25.4
Harlingen	41.2	11.6
Houston	938.2	363.6
Lubbock	128.7	48.7
Odessa	80.3	29.8
Palestine	14.0	4.9
Pasadena	58.7	20.8
San Antonio	587.7	185.6
Tyler	51.2	20.3
Waco	97.8	35.8
Wichita Falls	101.7	32.8

a. Determine if the regression of population on total employment is significant.

b. Is there a significant degree of correlation between the variables?

c. Are the regression and correlation models appropriate representations of the relationship between the variables? (Consider the assumptions of each of the models.)

16-10. The marketing department of a firm wishes to determine if there is a relationship between sales and the number of television commercials broadcast in a sample of cities. The data are given as follows:

City	Sales (Thousands of units per year)	TV commercials (Broadcasts per day)
A	8	11
B	5	6
C	7	8
D	10	9
E	13	12
F	11	16
G	14	15
H	10	10
I	7	12
J	8	8
K	12	11
L	15	9

    a. Is the regression of sales on television broadcasts significant?
    b. Determine if the hypothesis $\rho_{12} = 0$ is supported by the data.
    c. Interpret the regression and correlation results in terms of the effectiveness of current television advertising.

16-11. Two managers are asked to rank a group of employees in order of potential for eventually becoming top managers. The rankings are as follows:

Employee	Ranking by Manager I	Ranking by Manager II
Rogers	1	3
Black	2	4
Jones	3	6
Green	4	2
Smith	5	1
Edwards	6	5
White	7	9
Evans	8	8
Roberts	9	7
Adams	10	13
Brown	11	10
Thomas	12	19
Gray	13	17
Clark	14	16
James	15	15
Martin	16	14
Johnson	17	11
Richards	18	18
West	19	12
Short	20	20

a. Compute the coefficient of rank correlation.

b. Determine if the correlation is significant.

16-12. The rankings of collegiate football teams by two panels of judges are given as follows:

College	Panel I	Panel II
Arkansas	1	3
Nebraska	2	2
Michigan State	3	1
Notre Dame	4	4
Texas	5	5
Louisiana State	6	6
Purdue	7	8
Florida	8	10
U.C.L.A.	9	7
Alabama	10	9

a. Compute the coefficient of rank correlation.

b. Assuming that the distribution of sample values of r_{rank} is distributed normally, determine if the coefficient computed previously is significant.

16-13. Draw a flow diagram of an algorithm for computing b_{12} and $a_{1.2}$ for a sample of n paired observations of x_1 and x_2.

16-14. Draw a flow diagram of an algorithm for computing r_{12} and the statistic t for testing the null hypothesis $\rho_{12} = 0$.

SELECTED READINGS

Richmond, Samuel B. *Statistical Analysis*. 2d ed. New York: The Ronald Press Company, 1964.

A readable treatment of regression and correlation is found in Chapter 19.

Stockton, John R. *Introduction to Business and Economic Statistics*. 3d ed. Cincinnati: South-Western Publishing Company, 1966.

Chapter 21 presents a condensed discussion of bivariate regression and correlation.

Yamane, Taro. *Statistics, An Introductory Analysis*. New York: Harper and Row Publishers, 1964.

A somewhat rigorous presentation of linear bivariate regression and correlation is found in Chapters 14 and 15.

Chapter 17

Regression and Correlation:
Curvilinear Analysis

The bivariate relationship of variables can be approximated by a line drawn on a scatter diagram that represents the average relationship of paired observations. In many instances, the average relationship may be represented appropriately by a straight line. In other cases, the scatter of paired observations suggests a curvilinear (nonlinear) average relationship that is not well represented by a straight line. The greater the degree to which a bivariate relationship differs from linearity, the more inappropriate are linear regression and correlation models for representing the relationship. If the average relationship of two variables is distinctly curvilinear, the application of linear regression and correlation models will yield poor results.

Regression and correlation models for analyzing nonlinear bivariate relationships are derived by means of the method of least squares. The rationale used in the derivation of the linear models in the foregoing chapter is utilized in this chapter in the derivation of curvilinear regression and correlation models.

CURVILINEAR BIVARIATE REGRESSION

An expression that has the functional form such as that of a linear bivariate regression equation is called a *first-order polynomial* equation. The term, first-order, refers to a linear expression such as

$$x_{1c} = a + b_{12}x_2,$$

where x_2 is of the first order or degree. A curvilinear (nonlinear) expression may take the form of a higher order polynomial such as

$$x_{1c} = a + b_{12}x_2 + c_{12}x_2^2,$$

where x_2^2 is of the second order or degree. This equation expresses the nonlinear relationship between the variables x_1 and x_2.

Nonlinear relationships may also be expressed by equations involving transformations with logarithms or reciprocals. These transformations are used to convert data into a form in which the relationship between two series of data may be considered linear. The techniques for using polynomials and transformations in nonlinear regression analysis are considered in the discussions that follow.

Polynomial Regression

In many applications of regression analysis, the relationship between two variables is curvilinear and is assumed to be a polynomial function. The general form of a polynomial expression of the estimated nonlinear regression of x_1 on x_2 obtained from sample data is written

$$x_{1c.x_2x_2^2 \ldots x_2^q} = a_{1.2} + b_{12}x_2 + c_{12}x_2^2 + \ldots + r_{12}x_2^q$$

where q indicates the order or degree of the polynomial. The coefficients in this expression are maximum likelihood estimators of the respective parameters. The values of these estimators are obtained by the method of least squares.

Second-Order Polynomial Regression

A scatter diagram of paired sample observations of two variables may indicate that a parabola is a more appropriate expression of the relationship between the variables than a straight line.

➤ *Example.* A sample of observations of the volume of production and the size of work force in a small manufacturing firm is taken. The data are shown in Table 17.1 and are plotted in Figure 17.1. The linear regression of production volume (x_1) of number of men in the work force (x_2) is computed as follows:

$$b_{12} = \frac{n\Sigma x_1 x_2 - (\Sigma x_1)(\Sigma x_2)}{n\Sigma x_2^2 - (\Sigma x_2)^2}$$

$$= \frac{(24)(1,007) - (188)(125)}{(24)(815) - (125)^2}$$

$$= \frac{668}{3,935} = 0.17.$$

$$a_{1.2} = \bar{x}_1 - b_{12}\bar{x}_2$$
$$= 7.83 - 0.17(5.21)$$
$$= 6.95.$$

$$\hat{\sigma}_{1.2} = \sqrt{\frac{\Sigma x_1^2 - a_{1.2}\Sigma x_1 - b_{12}\Sigma x_1 x_2}{n - 2}}$$

$$= \sqrt{\frac{1,508 - (6.95)(188) - (0.17)(1,007)}{24 - 2}} = \sqrt{\frac{29}{22}} = 1.15.$$

$$r_{12} = \frac{n\Sigma x_1 x_2 - (\Sigma x_1)(\Sigma x_2)}{\sqrt{[n\Sigma x_1^2 - (\Sigma x_1)^2][n\Sigma x_2^2 - (\Sigma x_2)^2]}}$$

$$= \frac{24(1,007) - (188)(125)}{\sqrt{[(24)(1,508) - (188)^2][(24)(815) - (125)^2]}}$$

$$= \frac{24,168 - 23,500}{\sqrt{(36,192 - 35,344)(19,560 - 15,625)}}$$

$$= 0.37.$$

Table 17.1

DATA FOR CURVILINEAR REGRESSION OF PRODUCTION VOLUME (x_1)
ON SIZE OF WORK FORCE (x_2)

x_1	x_2	x_1^2	x_2^2	$x_1 x_2$	$x_1 x_2^2$	x_2^3	x_2^4
5	1	25	1	5	5	1	1
6	1	36	1	6	6	1	1
6	2	36	4	12	24	8	16
7	2	49	4	14	28	8	16
8	2	64	4	16	32	8	16
7	3	49	9	21	63	27	81
8	3	64	9	24	72	27	81
7	4	49	16	28	112	64	256
8	4	64	16	32	128	64	256
9	4	81	16	36	144	64	256
8	5	64	25	40	200	125	625
9	5	81	25	45	225	125	625
10	5	100	25	50	250	125	625
8	6	64	36	48	288	216	1,296
9	6	81	36	54	324	216	1,296
10	6	100	36	60	360	216	1,296
8	7	64	49	56	392	343	2,401
9	7	81	49	63	441	343	2,401
7	8	49	64	56	448	512	4,096
8	8	64	64	64	512	512	4,096
9	8	81	64	72	576	512	4,096
7	9	49	81	63	567	729	6,561
8	9	64	81	72	648	729	6,561
7	10	49	100	70	700	1,000	10,000
188	125	1,508	815	1,007	6,545	5,975	46,955

The estimated line of regression is plotted in Figure 17.1. The fit of the linear regression line to the data is poor. A second-order polynomial fitted to the data provides a more appropriate model.

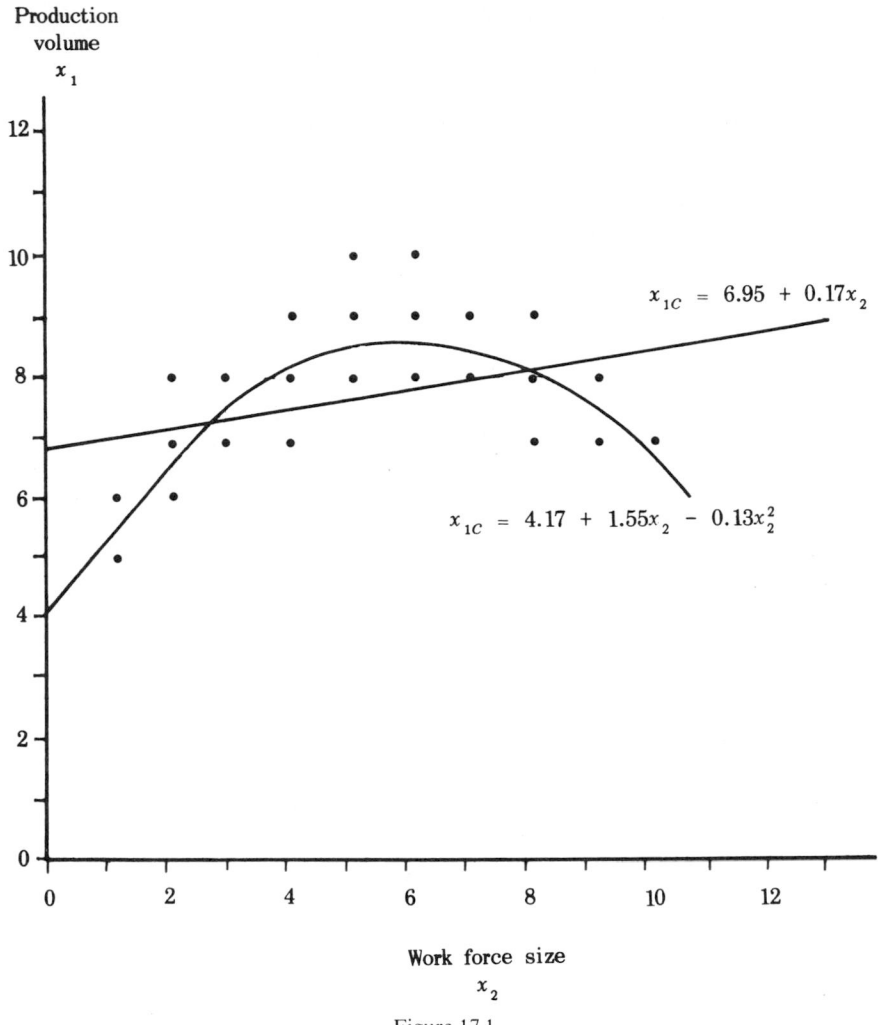

Figure 17.1

FIRST- AND SECOND-ORDER POLYNOMIAL REGRESSION EQUATIONS FITTED
TO DATA OF PRODUCTION VOLUME (x_1) AND WORK FORCE SIZE (x_2)

The Method of Least Squares and Polynomial Regression. The simplest
parabola is a second-order polynomial regression equation, which is
written

$$x_{1c.x_2x_2^2} = a_{1.2} + b_{12}x_2 + c_{12}x_2^2 \quad \text{..............}(17.1)$$

The coefficients of this expression are maximum likelihood estimators
which are found by solving a set of simultaneous equations. These
equations are obtained by the method of least squares in a manner
similar to that presented in Technical Note No. 1 of Chapter 16. The

simultaneous or normal equations are derived by expressing the sum of squared deviations of the dependent variable about a regression line as a function of the coefficients $a_{1.2}$, b_{12}, and c_{12}. First-order partial derivatives of the function (sum of squared deviations) with respect to $a_{1.2}$, b_{12}, and c_{12} are taken and set equal to zero. The three resulting expressions are the normal equations for the second-order polynomial case, which are written

$$\text{I. } \Sigma x_1 = na_{1.2} + b_{12}\Sigma x_2 + c_{12}\Sigma x_2^2$$
$$\text{II. } \Sigma x_1 x_2 = a_{1.2}\Sigma x_2 + b_{12}\Sigma x_2^2 + c_{12}\Sigma x_2^3$$
$$\text{III. } \Sigma x_1 x_2^2 = a_{1.2}\Sigma x_2^2 + b_{12}\Sigma x_2^3 + c_{12}\Sigma x_2^4.$$

Note that these equations are related in form, and differ only by powers of x_2 in the summations.

The estimators $a_{1.2}$, b_{12}, and c_{12} are found by solving the normal equations simultaneously. The simultaneous solution of these equations can be accomplished by the method of elimination.

➤ *Example.* A second-order polynomial or parabola can be fitted to the sample data plotted in Figure 17.1 by solving the normal equations simultaneously for the estimators $a_{1.2}$, b_{12}, and c_{12}. The appropriate totals from Table 17.1 are substituted into the normal equations to give:

$$\text{I. } 188 = 24a_{1.2} + 125b_{12} + 815c_{12}$$
$$\text{II. } 1{,}007 = 125a_{1.2} + 815b_{12} + 5{,}975c_{12}$$
$$\text{III. } 6{,}545 = 815a_{1.2} + 5{,}975b_{12} + 46{,}955c_{12}.$$

Equations I and II are solved simultaneously by eliminating the $a_{1.2}$ terms as follows:

$\left(-\dfrac{125}{24} \text{ times Equation I}\right)$ $-979 = -125a_{1.2} - 651b_{12} - 4{,}245c_{12}$

(Equation II) $1{,}007 = 125a_{1.2} + 815b_{12} + 5{,}975c_{12}$

(Equation II + I) $28 = \qquad\qquad 164b_{12} + 1{,}730c_{12}$

Similarly, Equations II and III are solved simultaneously as follows:

$\left(-\dfrac{815}{125} \text{ times Equation II}\right) -6{,}566 = -815a_{1.2} - 5{,}314b_{12} - 38{,}957c_{12}$

(Equation III) $6{,}545 = 815a_{1.2} + 5{,}975b_{12} + 46{,}955c_{12}$

(Equation III + II) $-21 = \qquad\qquad 661b_{12} + 7{,}998c_{12}$

The two equations that result from the elimination of the $a_{1.2}$ terms are solved for the value of b_{12} as follows:

(Equations III + II) $-21 = 661b_{12} + 7,998c_{12}$

$\left(-\dfrac{7,998}{1,730} \text{ times Equations II + I}\right)$ $\dfrac{-129 = -758b_{12} - 7,998c_{12}}{-150 = -97b_{12}}$

$$b_{12} = 1.54.$$

The value of b_{12} is substituted into Equation (II + I), which is written

$$28 = (164)(1.55) + 1,730c_{12},$$

and solving for c_{12} gives

$$c_{12} = \frac{28 - (164)(1.55)}{1,730}$$

$$= \frac{-226}{1,730}$$

$$= -0.13.$$

Finally, the value of $a_{1.2}$ is found by substituting b_{12} and c_{12} into Equation I, which is written

$$188 = 24a_{1.2} + (125)(1.54) + (815)(-0.13),$$

and solving for $a_{1.2}$ gives

$$a_{1.2} = \frac{188 - (125)(1.54) - (815)(-0.13)}{24}$$

$$= \frac{101}{24}$$

$$= 4.21.$$

The second-order polynomial regression equation is written

$$x_{1c \cdot x_2x_2^2} = 4.17 + 1.55x_2 - 0.13x_2^2.$$

This equation is plotted in Figure 17.1, and visual inspection suggests that the second-order polynomial regression equation is a more appropriate model than the linear model.

Estimated Standard Error of the Estimate. The universe standard error of estimate for the second-order polynomial regression equation can be estimated from sample data. An unbiased estimator of the universe standard error of the estimate, $\sigma_{x_1 \cdot x_2x_2^2}$, is written

$$\hat{\sigma}_{x_1 \cdot x_2x_2^2} = \sqrt{\frac{\Sigma(x_{1c \cdot x_2x_2^2} - x_1)^2}{n - 3}} \quad \dots\dots\dots\dots(17.2)$$

where $n - 3$ represents the number of degrees of freedom. The loss of three degrees of freedom results from the use of $a_{1.2}$, b_{12}, and c_{12} as estimators of the respective universe parameters. An alternative form of Formula 17.2, which is better suited to manual computation, is written

$$\hat{\sigma}_{x_1.x_2x_2^2} = \sqrt{\frac{\Sigma x_1^2 - a_{1.2}\Sigma x_1 - b_{12}\Sigma x_1 x_2 - c_{12}\Sigma x_1 x_2^2}{n - 3}} \quad ...(17.3)$$

➤ **Example.** The estimated standard error of the estimate for the data in Table 17.1 is computed as follows:

$$\hat{\sigma}_{x_1.x_2x_2^2} = \sqrt{\frac{\Sigma x_1^2 - a_{1.2}\Sigma x_1 - b_{12}\Sigma x_1 x_2 - c_{12}\Sigma x_1 x_2^2}{n - 3}}$$

$$= \sqrt{\frac{1,508 - (4.21)(188) - (1.54)(1,007) - (-0.13)(6,545)}{24 - 3}}$$

$$= \sqrt{\frac{16}{21}} = 0.87.$$

This value, when compared with $\hat{\sigma}_{1.2} = 1.15$ for the linear regression model, indicates that the second-order regression model provides more reliable estimates of the dependent variable.

Computers and Polynomial Regression

The selection of the polynomial expression that provides the most suitable representation of the regression between two variables can be obtained by: (1) computing successively higher order polynomial regression equations (first order, second order, third order, etc.) for the data, (2) obtaining the standard error of the estimate for each regression equation, and (3) selecting the equation for which the standard error is a minimum. If approached manually, the calculations required for applying this technique can be prohibitive. The computational capability of a computer, however, makes this technique feasible for most problems.

Normal Equations for Higher Order Polynomials. The normal equations for a second-order polynomial regression equation can be obtained from the normal equations of the first-order (linear) polynomial. The normal equations for the second-order polynomial are:

$$\text{I. } \Sigma x_1 = na_{1.2} + b_{12}\Sigma x_2 + c_{12}\Sigma x_2^2$$
$$\text{II. } \Sigma x_1 x_2 = a_{1.2}\Sigma x_2 + b_{12}\Sigma x_2^2 + c_{12}\Sigma x_2^3$$
$$\text{III. } \Sigma x_1 x_2^2 = a_{1.2}\Sigma x_2^2 + b_{12}\Sigma x_2^3 + c_{12}\Sigma x_2^4.$$

The terms within the rectangle are the normal equations for the first-order polynomial. The normal equations for the second-degree polynomial are obtained in the following manner. Add the $c_{12}\Sigma x_2^2$ term to the first normal equation for the linear case to obtain Equation I. Increase by one degree the power of x_2 in each summation in Equation I to give Equation II. Similarly, increase the power of x_2 in each summation in Equation I by two degrees to obtain Equation III.

The normal equations for the third-order polynomial are derived from those of the second-order case as follows. Add the terms $d_{12}\Sigma x_2^3$ to Equation I, $d_{12}\Sigma x_2^4$ to Equation II, and $d_{12}\Sigma x_2^5$ to Equation III. Since these equations involve four unknowns, a fourth normal equation is required to obtain the solution. This equation is obtained by increasing the power of x_2 in each of the summations in Equation III. The equations that result from these modifications are written:

$$\text{I. } \Sigma x_1 = na_{1.2} + b_{12}\Sigma x_2 + c_{12}\Sigma x_2^2 + d_{12}\Sigma x_2^3$$
$$\text{II. } \Sigma x_1 x_2 = a_{1.2}\Sigma x_2 + b_{12}\Sigma x_2^2 + c_{12}\Sigma x_2^3 + d_{12}\Sigma x_2^4$$
$$\text{III. } \Sigma x_1 x_2^2 = a_{1.2}\Sigma x_2^2 + b_{12}\Sigma x_2^3 + c_{12}\Sigma x_2^4 + d_{12}\Sigma x_2^5$$
$$\text{IV. } \Sigma x_1 x_2^3 = a_{1.2}\Sigma x_2^3 + b_{12}\Sigma x_2^4 + c_{12}\Sigma x_2^5 + d_{12}\Sigma x_2^6.$$

The second-order normal equations are shown within the rectangle. The four equations can be solved simultaneously to obtain the third-order polynomial regression coefficients. The normal equations for higher order polynomials can be obtained in a similar manner.

➤ *Example.* The normal equations for a seventh-order polynomial expression are written in general form as follows:

$$\text{I. } \Sigma x_1 = na_{1.2} + b_{12}\Sigma x_2 + \ldots + h_{12}\Sigma x_2^7$$
$$\text{II. } \Sigma x_1 x_2 = a_{1.2}\Sigma x_2 + b_{12}\Sigma x_2^2 + \ldots + h_{12}\Sigma x_2^8$$
$$\text{III. } \Sigma x_1 x_2^2 = a_{1.2}\Sigma x_2^2 + b_{12}\Sigma x_2^3 + \ldots + h_{12}\Sigma x_2^9$$
$$\vdots \qquad \vdots \qquad \vdots \qquad \vdots \qquad \vdots$$
$$\text{VIII. } \Sigma x_1 x_2^7 = a_{1.2}\Sigma x_2^7 + b_{12}\Sigma x_2^8 + \ldots + h_{12}\Sigma x_2^{14}.$$

The seventh-order polynomial expression involves eight coefficients and, therefore, eight equations are required. The exponent of x_2 in the hth term of Equation I is equal to the order of the polynomial. The exponent of x_2 in the hth term of Equation VIII is equal to twice the order of the polynomial.

Stated generally, the rth order polynomial expression involves $r + 1$ coefficients, and $r + 1$ normal equations are required to solve for the value of these coefficients. The amount of computation increases rapidly with the order of the polynomial, and manual simultaneous solution of a large number of equations is all but prohibitive. Solving the normal equations for the coefficients is facilitated by the use of a computer, but the method of elimination, illustrated in a foregoing section of this chapter, is not well suited for computer solution. An equivalent method that is more efficient for computer solution is presented in the following discussion.

An Algorithm for Solving Simultaneous Equations. A series of normal equations can be solved for the maximum likelihood estimators of the polynomial regression coefficients by use of matrix algebra. The basic concepts implicit in the use of matrix algebra are presented in Technical Note No. 1 at the end of this chapter. The algorithm presented in this discussion is an extension of the procedure described in the technical note.

The normal equations for the second-order polynomial regression case may be written in matrix notation as

$$\begin{bmatrix} \Sigma x_1 \\ \Sigma x_1 x_2 \\ \Sigma x_1 x_2^2 \end{bmatrix} = \begin{bmatrix} n & \Sigma x_2 & \Sigma x_2^2 \\ \Sigma x_2 & \Sigma x_2^2 & \Sigma x_2^3 \\ \Sigma x_2^2 & \Sigma x_2^3 & \Sigma x_2^4 \end{bmatrix} \begin{bmatrix} a_{1.2} \\ b_{12} \\ c_{12} \end{bmatrix}$$

or

$$\mathbf{b} \quad = \quad \mathbf{A} \quad \quad \mathbf{y}$$

The equations are solved by computing $\mathbf{A}^{-1}$, the inverse of the matrix $\mathbf{A}$, and solving

$$\mathbf{y} = \mathbf{A}^{-1}\mathbf{b}.$$

The inverse of the matrix $\mathbf{A}$ is found by performing successive transformations on the rows of an augmented matrix

$$[\mathbf{A} \mid \mathbf{I} \mid \mathbf{b}],$$

so that the matrix is transformed to

$$[\mathbf{I} \mid \mathbf{A}^{-1} \mid \mathbf{y}].$$

The general form of an augmented matrix for three normal equations is written

$$[\mathbf{A} \mid \mathbf{I} \mid \mathbf{b}] = \begin{bmatrix} a_{11} & a_{12} & a_{13} & 1 & 0 & 0 & b_1 \\ a_{21} & a_{22} & a_{23} & 0 & 1 & 0 & b_2 \\ a_{31} & a_{32} & a_{33} & 0 & 0 & 1 & b_3 \end{bmatrix},$$

where $a_{11} = n$, the first component of the first row of matrix $\mathbf{A}$, etc., and $b_1 = \Sigma x_1$, etc. The inverse of matrix $\mathbf{A}$ is computed by transforming the rows of the augmented matrix.

The transformations are performed by the following steps:

1. Transform the first component (a_{11}) of the first row (R_1) to one by dividing each component of R_1 by a_{11} and defining R_1 equal to its transformed value.

2. Transform the components of the first column, except a_{11}, to zero by subtracting $R_2 - a_{21}R_1$ and $R_3 - a_{31}R_1$ and defining R_2 and R_3 equal to the respective transformed values.

3. Transform the second component (a_{22}) of the second row (R_2) to one by dividing R_2 by a_{22} and defining R_2 equal to its transformed value.

4. Transform the components of the second column, except a_{22}, to zero by subtracting $R_1 - a_{12}R_2$ and $R_3 - a_{32}R_2$ and defining R_1 and R_3 equal to the respective transformed values.

5. Transform the third component (a_{33}) of the third row (R_3) to one by dividing R_3 by a_{33} and defining R_3 equal to its transformed value.

6. Transform the components of the third column, except a_{33}, to zero by subtracting $R_1 - a_{13}R_3$ and $R_2 - a_{23}R_3$ and defining R_1 and R_2 equal to the respective transformed values.

These steps are illustrated in the following example.

➤ **Example.** The steps for finding the inverse of a matrix **A** and solving for the coefficients of a second-order polynomial expression are applied to the data of Table 17.1 substituted into the three normal equations. The augmented matrix obtained from these equations is written

$$[\mathbf{A} \,|\, \mathbf{I} \,|\, \mathbf{b}] = \begin{bmatrix} a_{11} & a_{12} & a_{13} & 1 & 0 & 0 & b_1 \\ a_{21} & a_{22} & a_{23} & 0 & 1 & 0 & b_2 \\ a_{31} & a_{32} & a_{33} & 0 & 0 & 1 & b_3 \end{bmatrix}$$

$$\begin{bmatrix} n & \Sigma x_2 & \Sigma x_2^2 & 1 & 0 & 0 & \Sigma x_1 \\ \Sigma x_2 & \Sigma x_2^2 & \Sigma x_2^3 & 0 & 1 & 0 & \Sigma x_1 x_2 \\ \Sigma x_2^2 & \Sigma x_2^3 & \Sigma x_2^4 & 0 & 0 & 1 & \Sigma x_1 x_2^2 \end{bmatrix} = \begin{bmatrix} 24 & 125 & 815 & 1 & 0 & 0 & 188 \\ 125 & 815 & 5{,}975 & 0 & 1 & 0 & 1{,}007 \\ 815 & 5{,}975 & 46{,}955 & 0 & 0 & 1 & 6{,}545 \end{bmatrix}.$$

The inverse of the matrix **A** and the solution values of the coefficients of the regression equation are found by applying the transformations indicated by the following steps:

Steps 1 *and* 2. The transformations performed by these steps give

$$\begin{array}{l} R_1 = \dfrac{R_1}{a_{11}} \\[4pt] R_2 = R_2 - a_{21}R_1 \\ R_3 = R_3 - a_{31}R_1 \end{array} \begin{bmatrix} 1 & 5.2083333 & 33.9583333 & 0.0416666 & 0 & 0 & 7.8333333 \\ 0 & 163.9583333 & 1{,}730.2083333 & -5.2083333 & 1 & 0 & 27.8333333 \\ 0 & 1{,}730.2083333 & 19{,}278.9583333 & -33.9583333 & 0 & 1 & 160.8333333 \end{bmatrix}$$

Steps 3 and 4. These transformations give

$$
\begin{aligned}
R_1 &= R_1 - a_{12}R_2 \\
R_2 &= \dfrac{R_2}{a_{22}} \\
R_3 &= R_3 - a_{32}R_2
\end{aligned}
\left[
\begin{array}{ccc|ccc|c}
1 & 0 & -21.0038171 & 0.2071156 & -0.0317662 & 0 & 6.9491741 \\
0 & 1 & 10.5527319 & -0.0317662 & 0.0060991 & 0 & 0.1697586 \\
0 & 0 & 1{,}020.5336841 & 21.0038171 & -10.5527319 & 1 & -132.8843709
\end{array}
\right]
$$

Steps 5 and 6. The transformations indicated by these steps give

$$
\begin{aligned}
R_1 &= R_1 - a_{13}R_3 \\
R_2 &= R_2 - a_{23}R_3 \\
R_3 &= \dfrac{R_3}{a_{33}}
\end{aligned}
\left[
\begin{array}{ccc|ccc|c}
1 & 0 & 0 & 0.6393996 & -0.2489542 & 0.0205812 & 4.2142531 \\
0 & 1 & 0 & -0.2489542 & 0.1152191 & -0.0103404 & 1.5438368 \\
0 & 0 & 1 & 0.0205812 & -0.0103404 & 0.0009799 & -0.1302107
\end{array}
\right].
$$

The rather large number of decimal places is necessary to obtain sufficiently precise values for the regression coefficients.

The solution vector $\mathbf{y}$ is written

$$
\mathbf{y} =
\begin{bmatrix} y_1 \\ y_2 \\ y_3 \end{bmatrix}
=
\begin{bmatrix} a_{1.2} \\ b_{12} \\ c_{12} \end{bmatrix}
=
\begin{bmatrix} 4.21 \\ 1.54 \\ -0.13 \end{bmatrix}.
$$

The identical values for the estimated regression coefficients were obtained by the simultaneous solution of the normal equations.

Manual solution of a large number of simultaneous equations can be cumbersome and tedious, especially if a rather large number of significant digits must be maintained to avoid significant loss of precision in the values of the matrix components and the regression coefficients. The procedure for solving simultaneous equations by matrix operations can be generalized to provide an algorithm for solving any finite number of equations. This algorithm can be translated into a suitable language for the solution of simultaneous equations with the use of a computer.

A flow diagram for solving simultaneous equations is shown in Figure 17.2. The portion of the flow diagram shown on page 592 summarizes the procedure for transforming the components of each row so that a value of one is obtained for each component on the principal diagonal of the matrix $\mathbf{A}$. This portion of the algorithm corresponds to the type of transformation performed by Steps 1, 3, and 5, described previously.

The flow diagram on page 593 summarizes the procedure for transforming the rows so that a value of zero is obtained for the components of the matrix $\mathbf{A}$ that do not lie on the principal diagonal. This portion of the algorithm corresponds to the type of transformations performed by Steps 2, 4, and 6, described previously.

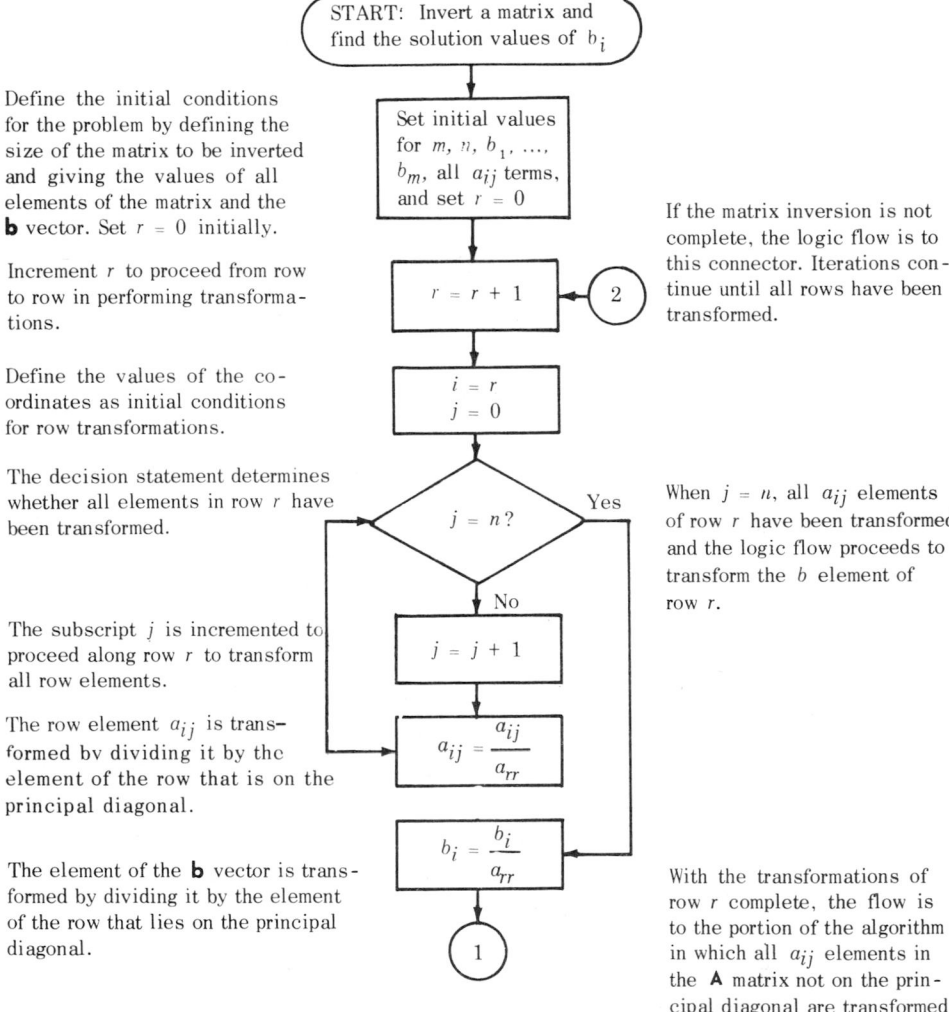

Define the initial conditions for the problem by defining the size of the matrix to be inverted and giving the values of all elements of the matrix and the **b** vector. Set $r = 0$ initially.

Increment r to proceed from row to row in performing transformations.

Define the values of the coordinates as initial conditions for row transformations.

The decision statement determines whether all elements in row r have been transformed.

The subscript j is incremented to proceed along row r to transform all row elements.

The row element a_{ij} is transformed by dividing it by the element of the row that is on the principal diagonal.

The element of the **b** vector is transformed by dividing it by the element of the row that lies on the principal diagonal.

START: Invert a matrix and find the solution values of b_i

Set initial values for m, n, b_1, ..., b_m, all a_{ij} terms, and set $r = 0$

$r = r + 1$ ②

$i = r$
$j = 0$

$j = n$?   Yes

No

$j = j + 1$

$a_{ij} = \dfrac{a_{ij}}{a_{rr}}$

$b_i = \dfrac{b_i}{a_{rr}}$

①

If the matrix inversion is not complete, the logic flow is to this connector. Iterations continue until all rows have been transformed.

When $j = n$, all a_{ij} elements of row r have been transformed and the logic flow proceeds to transform the b element of row r.

With the transformations of row r complete, the flow is to the portion of the algorithm in which all a_{ij} elements in the **A** matrix not on the principal diagonal are transformed to zero.

Figure 17.2

A PARTIAL ALGORITHM FOR INVERTING A MATRIX AND FINDING THE
SOLUTION VALUES OF A SET OF SIMULTANEOUS LINEAR EQUATIONS

The algorithm is continued and in this portion all a_{ij} elements in the **A** matrix, except those on the principal diagonal, are transformed to zero.

The subscript i is set to one so that the first row is consid- ered initially.

The subscript j is set equal to zero as an initial condition.

The decision statement tests to avoid transforming the a_{ij} ele- ment on the principal diagonal from one to zero.

The decision statement tests whether the required zeros have been obtained in the **A** matrix. If the answer is "Yes," the computations are complete.

The subscript i is incremented to proceed to the next row.

The transformation coefficient corresponding to row i is defined.

The subscript j is incremented to permit the transformation of the succeeding a_{ij} element in row i.

Transform the element with coordinates i and j to zero.

The outer loop controls the iterations so that the required transformations are performed on all rows except the row for which $i = r$.

The inner loop controls the iterations so that the required transformations are performed for all a_{ij} elements in a given row.

Transform the b_i element corre- sponding to row i.

Increment the subscript i to permit transformations to be performed on the succeeding row.

The logic flow proceeds and the succeeding row is transformed to obtain a value of one for the a_{ij} element on the principal diagonal.

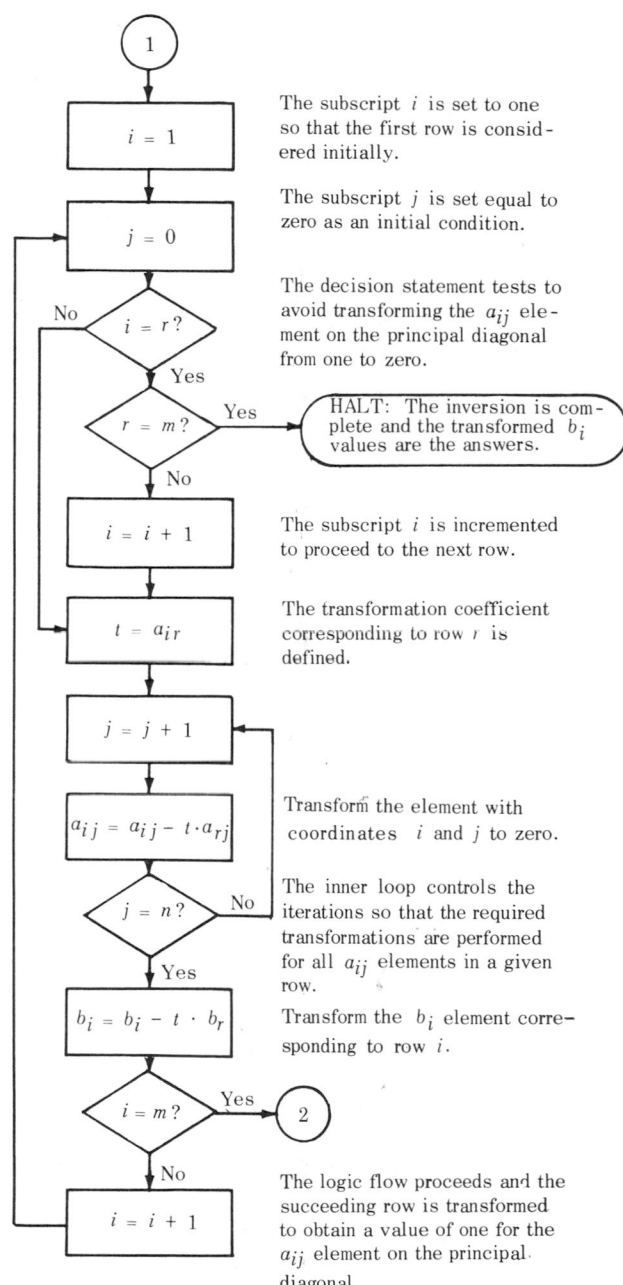

Figure 17.2 (Continued)

A PARTIAL ALGORITHM FOR INVERTING A MATRIX AND FINDING THE
SOLUTION VALUES OF A SET OF SIMULTANEOUS LINEAR EQUATIONS

➤ *Example.* The algorithm in Figure 17.2 is used to find the inverse of the augmented matrix

$$[A \mid I \mid b] = \begin{bmatrix} a_{11} \; a_{12} & 1 \; 0 & b_1 \\ a_{21} \; a_{22} & 0 \; 1 & b_2 \end{bmatrix} = \begin{bmatrix} 2 \; 1 & 1 \; 0 & 10 \\ 3 \; 4 & 0 \; 1 & 30 \end{bmatrix}.$$

In this example $m = 2$ and $n = 4$, since the $[A \mid I]$ matrix consists of two rows and four columns. The components of this portion of the augmented matrix are denoted a_{ij}. The components of the **b** vector are denoted b_i. The variable r is set equal to zero as an initial condition. The initial conditions for transforming the first row are fixed by setting $r = 0 + 1 = 1$ (which indicates the first row), $i = r = 0 + 1 = 1$ (the first component), and $j = 0$. Next, a test is made to determine if all the components of the first row have been transformed by testing whether "$j = n$?" The answer is "No," and the flow proceeds to set $j = 0 + 1$ (where $j = 1$ indicates the first column). The component $a_{ij} = a_{11}$ is transformed to one by computing

$$a_{ij} = \frac{a_{ij}}{a_{rr}} = \frac{a_{11}}{a_{11}} = \frac{2}{2} = 1,$$

where $a_{rr} = a_{11}$ since $r = 1$ and $j = 1$ at this stage. The flow continues through the loop to test "$j = n$?" Since $j = 1$, the answer is "No," and j is incremented so that $j = 1 + 1 = 2$. With $j = 2$, the component $a_{ij} = a_{12}$ is transformed by computing

$$a_{ij} = \frac{a_{ij}}{a_{rr}} = \frac{a_{12}}{a_{11}} = \frac{1}{2},$$

where $a_{rr} = a_{11}$ for the first row. The flow continues in this manner to compute all the transformed values of the first row so that when "$j = 4$?" is "Yes," the flow moves to transform the component b_i to give

$$b_i = \frac{b_i}{a_{rr}} = \frac{b_1}{a_{11}} = \frac{10}{2} = 5.$$

With this operation, the initial transformation of the first row is completed and the flow is to connector ①.

The row transformations to obtain a zero for every component in the first column, except a_{11}, are begun by setting the initial condition $i = 1$. Next, $j = 0$ is defined to initialize the iterative loop. Then, a test is made to determine if "$i = r$?" (a test if the a_{ij} element of row i, which is on the principal diagonal, has been transformed to one). Since $i = r = 1$, the answer is "Yes." The first component of the first row should not be transformed to zero. Consequently, the flow continues to test if the last row ($r = m$) has been considered. The answer is "No" and the flow continues to increment i to $i = i + 1 = 1 + 1 = 2$. The transformation coefficient t for the second row is then computed so that $t = a_{ir} = a_{21} = 3$. The flow proceeds to increment $j = j + 1 = 0 + 1 = 1$ and transforms the first component of the second row to zero by subtracting t times row one from row two, or

$$a_{ij} = a_{ij} - ta_{rj} = a_{21} - ta_{11} = 3 - (3)(1) = 0,$$

where $a_{rj} = 1$ is the transformed value of a_{11} computed previously.

The flow continues to test if all components of the second row have been transformed, and since $j = 1$, the answer to "$j = n$?" is "No." The second iteration is begun by computing $j = j + 1 = 1 + 1 = 2$. The second component of the second row is then transformed by computing

$$a_{ij} = a_{ij} - ta_{rj} = a_{22} - ta_{12} = 4 - (3)(\tfrac{1}{2}) = \tfrac{5}{2},$$

where $a_{rj} = \tfrac{1}{2}$ is the transformed value of a_{12} computed previously by use of Figure 17.2. The iterations for transforming the second row continue until the answer to "$j = n$?" is "Yes," and the transformation of the a_{ij} components of the second row is complete. The next operation consists of transforming b_2 to give

$$b_i = b_i - tb_r = b_2 - a_{21}b_1 = 30 - 3(5) = 15,$$

where $b_r = 5$ is the transformed value of b_1 obtained in the initial transformation of the first row. Next, the flow is to connector ② since $i = m = 2$ at this stage.

The value $r = r + 1 = 1 + 1 = 2$ is computed to indicate that the second component of the second row is to be transformed to one. The value $i = r = 2$ is defined and j is set equal to zero to set initial values for the iterations. Since the answer to the test "$j = n$?" is "No," the iterations begin by incrementing $j = j + 1 = 0 + 1 = 1$. The first component of the second row is transformed by computing

$$a_{ij} = \frac{a_{ij}}{a_{rr}} = \frac{a_{21}}{a_{22}} = \frac{0}{(\tfrac{5}{2})} = 0,$$

where $a_{rr} = a_{22} = \tfrac{5}{2}$ is the transformed value of a_{22} computed previously by use of Figure 17.2. The flow proceeds to test "$j = n$?" and the answer is "No," since $j = 2$ at this stage and $n = 4$. The iterations continue by incrementing $j = j + 1 = 1 + 1 = 2$ and computing

$$a_{ij} = \frac{a_{ij}}{a_{rr}} = \frac{a_{22}}{a_{22}} = \frac{(\tfrac{5}{2})}{(\tfrac{5}{2})} = 1.$$

The iterations continue so that all the remaining components are transformed, at which time $j = 4$. The answer to "$j = n$?" then is "Yes" and the flow is to transform the component b_2. Then, the flow is to connector ①.

All components of the second column, except a_{22}, are to be transformed to zero. The initial condition $i = 1$ is defined so that transformations begin with row one. The initial condition $j = 0$ is set to begin the iterations. The test "$i = r$?" is negative and t is set equal to $t = a_{ir} = a_{12}$, since $i = 1$ and $r = 2$ at this stage. The flow proceeds to increment $j = j + 1 = 0 + 1 = 1$ and transforms the first component of the first row by computing

$$a_{ij} = a_{ij} - ta_{rj} = a_{11} - a_{21}a_{11} = 1 - 0(1) = 1,$$

where $a_{11} = 1$ and $a_{21} = 0$ are transformed values computed previously. The flow continues to test whether all components of the first row have been transformed. Since $j = 1$, the answer to "$j = n$?" is "No." The second iteration is begun by computing $j = j + 1 = 1 + 1 = 2$. The second component of the first row is then transformed by computing

$$a_{ij} = a_{ij} - ta_{rj} = a_{12} - a_{22}a_{12} = \tfrac{1}{2} - 1(\tfrac{1}{2}) = 0.$$

The flow continues to perform the iterations until all a_{ij} components of the first row are transformed. At this point the answer to "$j = n$?" is "Yes," and $b_i = b_1$ is transformed. Since i is less than m at this stage, i is set equal to $i = i + 1 = 1 + 1 = 2$. The flow proceeds to set the initial condition $j = 0$ and then test "$i = r$?" The answer is "Yes," since $i = r = 2$ at this stage. Next, a test is made to determine if zeros have been obtained in the desired column components. Since "$r = m$?" is positive and $r = m = 2$ at this stage, the transformations are complete. The complete transformations of this example matrix are found in Technical Note No. 1 at the end of this chapter.

The foregoing example demonstrates a systematic procedure for solving simultaneous equations that may be written as a computer program. More efficient algorithms have been devised for computational purposes and are available generally in program libraries.

An Approach to the Selection of a Polynomial Regression Equation. One approach to the selection of the most suitable polynomial regression equation for observations of two variables consists of computing the regression equation and standard error of the estimate for several polynomial cases. The most appropriate regression equation is that for which the standard error is a minimum.

An algorithm can be written fairly easily to compute a specified number of polynomial regression equations by extending the procedures described in Figure 17.2. This extension consists of a definition of the matrix (normal equations) for the highest order polynomial equation to be computed, an iterative procedure for computing successively higher order polynomial equations, and a procedure for computing the respective standard error values.

This type of algorithm is sometimes called a polynomial curve fit program. Programs of this type are commonly available in program libraries.

Transformations in Bivariate Regression

If the regression of one variable upon another is curvilinear, the values of one or both of the variables may be changed to a form that is linear. This change is accomplished by transforming the data. The most commonly used transformations are logarithms in exponential regression and reciprocals in hyperbolic regression. The transformation converts the data into such form that the relationship between a converted series and an original series may be considered linear.

➤ *Example.* A sample of observations of the total cost of production and number of units produced in a manufacturing firm is taken. The data are shown in Table 17.2 and are plotted in Figure 17.3. The plot of the original data in Figure 17.3 reflects the curvilinear relationship of the variables. The total cost data are transformed by use of logarithms, and the plot of this converted series with the original output data is shown in Figure 17.4. The scatter of the points is approximately linear.

Table 17.2

SEVEN OBSERVATIONS OF TOTAL COST AND
TOTAL OUTPUT OF A MANUFACTURING FIRM

Observation number	Total cost (thousands)	Total output (units)
1	$ 62	27
2	68	58
3	102	106
4	127	124
5	184	153
6	217	172
7	264	194

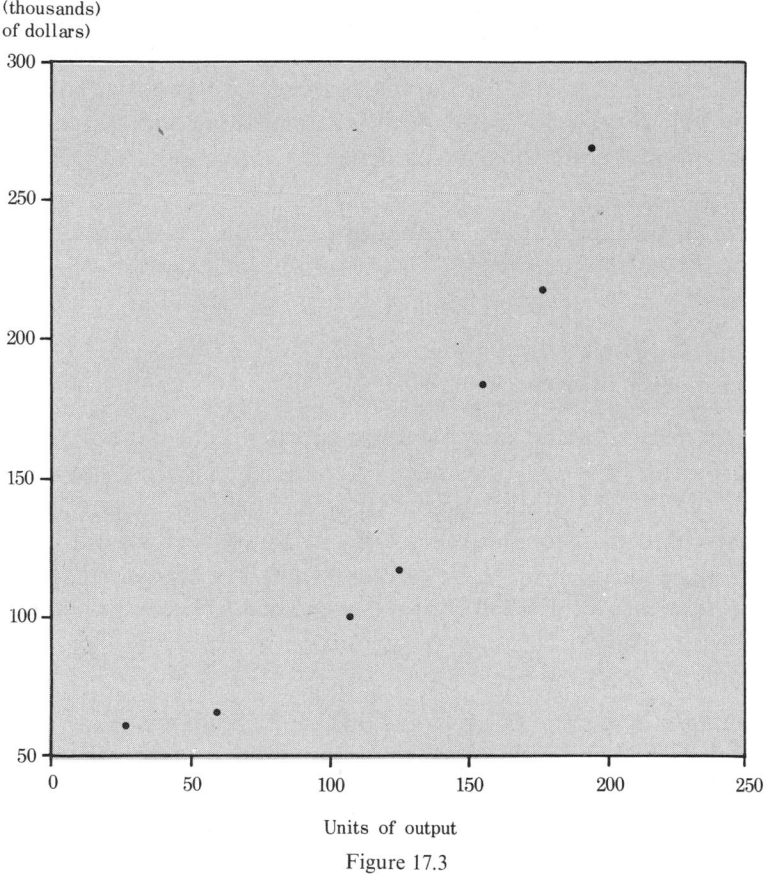

Figure 17.3

A SAMPLE OF OBSERVATIONS OF VOLUME OF OUTPUT AND
CORRESPONDING TOTAL COST OF PRODUCTION

The transformation of the total cost (x_1) values in the foregoing example yields the data required for the use of the normal equations. The relationship of the logarithms of the x_1 values to the original values of x_2 is approximately linear, as shown in Figure 17.4. These series of data provide the data for substitution into the linear normal equation to solve for the coefficients of the estimated regression equation.

Exponential Regression. The simplest case, *first-degree exponential regression*, involves two series of data, one of which is transformed by use of logarithms. For example, the dependent variable, transformed by logarithms, may be regressed on the untransformed independent variable to give a regression equation with the functional form

$$x_{1c} = a_{1.2}(b_{12})^{x_2}.$$

The linear form of the regression equation is written

$$(\log x_1)_c = \log a_{1.2} + x_2 \log b_{12} \quad \ldots\ldots\ldots\ldots(17.4)$$

The estimators of the regression coefficients are found by solving simultaneously the normal equations

$$\text{I. } \Sigma(\log x_1) \quad = n \log a_{1.2} \quad + \log b_{12} \, \Sigma x_2$$
$$\text{II. } \Sigma(x_2 \log x_1) = \log a_{1.2} \, \Sigma x_2 + \log b_{12} \, \Sigma x_2^2.$$

An unbiased estimator of the standard error of the estimate is obtained by solving the expression

$$\hat{\sigma}_{\log x_1 . x_2} = \sqrt{\frac{\Sigma[\log x_1 - (\log x_1)_c]^2}{n - 2}} \quad \ldots\ldots\ldots\ldots(17.5)$$

➤ *Example.* An exponential regression equation is fitted to the data in Table 17.2 by transforming the observed values of total cost (x_1) by use of logarithms and by solving the normal equations. The data substituted into these equations are shown in Table 17.3. The equations are solved as follows:

$$\text{I.} \quad 14.76018 = \quad 7 \log a_{1.2} + \quad 834 \log b_{12}$$
$$\text{II. } 1{,}846.64189 = 834 \log a_{1.2} + 121{,}334 \log b_{12}$$

$$\left(-\frac{834}{7} \text{ times I}\right) -1{,}758.57002 = - \; 834 \log a_{1.2} - \quad 99{,}365 \log b_{12}$$

$$\text{(II)} \quad \frac{1{,}846.64189 = \quad 834 \log a_{1.2} + 121{,}334 \log b_{12}}{88.07187 = \qquad\qquad\qquad\qquad 21{,}969 \log b_{12}}$$

$$\log b_{12} = \frac{88.07187}{21{,}969} = 0.0040089$$

$$\log a_{1.2} = \frac{14.76018 - 834(0.0040089)}{7} = 1.63097.$$

The estimated standard error of the estimate is computed

$$\hat{\sigma}_{\log x_1 . x_2} = \sqrt{\frac{0.007456}{7 - 2}} = 0.03862.$$

The regression equation

$$(\log x_1)_c = \log a_{1.2} + x_2 \log b_{12}$$
$$= 1.63097 + 0.0040089 x_2$$

is plotted in Figure 17.4. The exponential regression equation provides a very good representation of the relationship between x_1 and x_2.

Table 17.3

CALCULATIONS FOR THE EXPONENTIAL REGRESSION OF TOTAL COST ON TOTAL OUTPUT

Total cost (x_1)	Total output (x_2)	$\log x_1$	$x_2 \log x_1$	x_2^2	$(\log x_1)_c$ $= \log a_{1.2}$ $+ x_2 \log b_{12}$	$\left[\log x_1 - (\log x_1)_c \right]^2$
62	27	1.79239	48.39453	729	1.73921	0.002828
68	58	1.83251	106.28558	3,364	1.86349	0.000960
102	106	2.00860	212.91160	11,236	2.05591	0.002238
127	124	2.10380	260.87120	15,376	2.12807	0.000589
184	153	2.26482	346.51746	23,409	2.24433	0.000420
217	172	2.33646	401.87112	29,584	2.32050	0.000255
264	194	2.42160	469.79040	37,636	2.40870	0.000166
1,024	834	14.76018	1,846.64189	121,334	...	0.007456

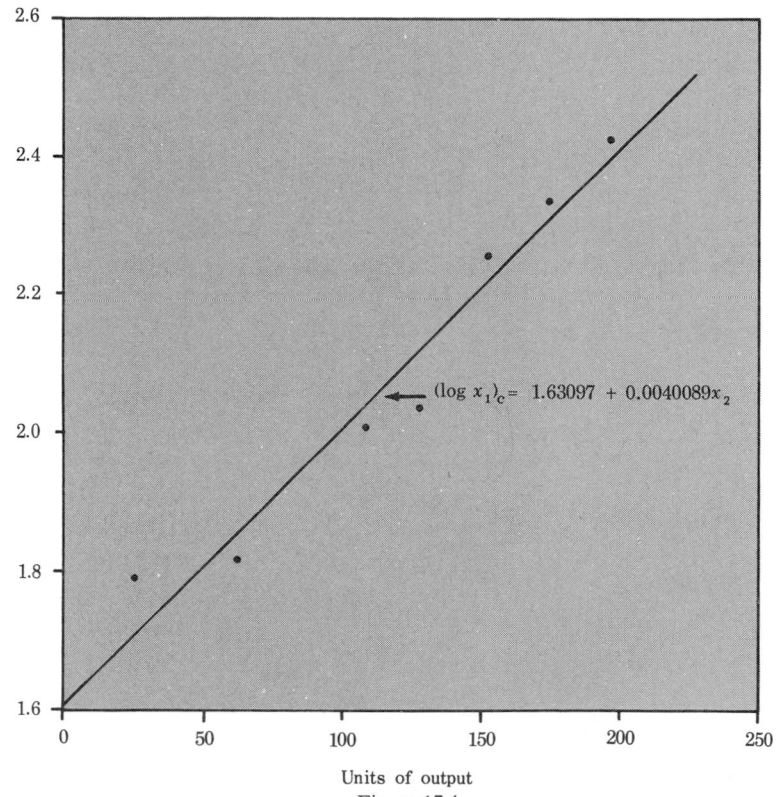

Logarithm of total cost $(\log x_1)$

$(\log x_1)_c = 1.63097 + 0.0040089x_2$

Units of output

Figure 17.4

A PLOT OF THE LOGARITHMS OF TOTAL COST AND VOLUME OF OUTPUT

It is important to note that the minimum sum of squared deviations obtained by use of the normal equations relates to the deviations of the *logarithms* of total cost (x_1) about the regression line and not to the minimum sum of squared deviations of the actual data (x_1) about the regression line. Expected values of x_1 are obtained by computing $(\log x_1)_c$ for given values of x_2 and taking the antilog of the result. The expected value of x_1, given $x_2 = 150$, in the foregoing example, is computed

$$E(\log x_1 \mid x_2 = 150) = 1.63097 + (.0040089)(150)$$
$$= 2.23230$$
$$E(x_1 \mid x_2 = 150) = \text{antilog } 2.23230$$
$$= 177.4.$$

Exponential regression may also involve the regression of the logarithmic transformation of both variables. This regression equation has the functional form

$$x_{1c} = a_{1.2}(x_2)^{b_{12}}.$$

The linear form of the regression equation is written

$$(\log x_1)_c = \log a_{1.2} + b_{12} \log x_2 \quad \ldots\ldots\ldots\ldots (17.6)$$

The estimators of the regression coefficients are found by solving simultaneously the normal equations

I. $\Sigma(\log x_1) \qquad = n \log a_{1.2} \qquad\qquad + b_{12} \Sigma(\log x_2)$

II. $\Sigma(\log x_1 \log x_2) = \log a_{1.2} \, \Sigma(\log x_1) + b_{12} \Sigma(\log x_2)^2.$

An unbiased estimator of the standard error of the estimate is found by substituting the appropriate values into the expression

$$\hat{\sigma}_{\log x_1 . \log x_2} = \sqrt{\frac{\Sigma[\log x_1 - (\log x_1)_c]^2}{n - 2}} \quad \ldots\ldots\ldots\ldots (17.7)$$

Hyperbolic Regression. Regression involving the reciprocal transformation of the dependent variable on the independent variable is an example of the simplest case of *hyperbolic regression*. The equation for this regression is written

$$\left(\frac{1}{x_1}\right)_c = a_{1.2} + b_{12}x_2 \ldots\ldots\ldots\ldots\ldots (17.8)$$

The estimators of the regression coefficients are found by solving simultaneously the normal equations

$$\text{I. } \Sigma\left(\frac{1}{x_1}\right) = na_{1.2} + b_{12}\Sigma x_2$$

$$\text{II. } \Sigma\left(\frac{1}{x_1}\right)x_2 = a_{1.2}\Sigma x_2 + b_{12}\Sigma x_2^2.$$

An unbiased estimator of the standard error of the estimate is obtained by use of the expression

$$\hat{\sigma}_{\frac{1}{x_1}\cdot x_2} = \sqrt{\frac{\Sigma\left[\left(\frac{1}{x_1}\right) - \left(\frac{1}{x_1}\right)_c\right]^2}{n-2}} \quad\ldots\ldots\ldots\ldots(17.9)$$

➤ *Example.* A hyperbolic regression equation is fitted to the data in Table 17.2 by transforming the observed values of total cost (x_1) by use of reciprocals and solving the normal equations. The data substituted into these equations are shown in Table 17.4. The equations are solved as follows:

$$\text{I. } 0.062344 = 7a_{1.2} + 834b_{12}$$

$$\text{II. } 5.66304 = 834a_{1.2} + 121{,}334b_{12}$$

$$\left(-\frac{834}{7}\text{ times I}\right) - 7.42784 = -834a_{1.2} - 99{,}365b_{12}$$

$$\underline{\text{(II)}\quad 5.66304 = 834a_{1.2} + 121{,}334b_{12}}$$

$$-1.76480 = 21{,}969b_{12}$$

$$b_{12} = \frac{-1.76480}{21{,}969} = -0.000080331$$

$$a_{1.2} = \frac{0.062344 - 834(0.000080331)}{7} = 0.018477.$$

The estimated standard error of the estimate is computed:

$$\hat{\sigma}_{\frac{1}{x_1}\cdot x_2} = \sqrt{\frac{0.000262543}{7-2}} = 0.007245.$$

The regression equation written

$$\left(\frac{1}{x_1}\right)_c = a_{1.2} + b_{12}x_2$$

$$= 0.018477 - 0.000080331x_2$$

is plotted in Figure 17.5. The hyperbolic regression equation provides an excellent representation of the relationship between x_1 and x_2.

Table 17.4

CALCULATIONS FOR THE HYPERBOLIC REGRESSION
OF TOTAL COST ON TOTAL OUTPUT

Total cost (x_1)	Total output (x_2)	$\left(\dfrac{1}{x_1}\right)$	$\left(\dfrac{1}{x_1}\right)x_2$	$\left(\dfrac{1}{x_1}\right)^2$	x_2^2	$\left(\dfrac{1}{x_1}\right)_c = a_{1.2} + b_{12}x_2$	$\left[\left(\dfrac{1}{x_1}\right) - \left(\dfrac{1}{x_1}\right)_c\right]^2$
62	27	0.016129	0.43548	0.00026014	729	0.016308	0.000003204
68	58	0.014706	0.85295	0.00021626	3,364	0.013817	0.000079032
102	106	0.009804	1.03922	0.00009612	11,236	0.009962	0.000002496
127	124	0.007874	0.97638	0.00006200	15,376	0.008516	0.000041216
184	153	0.005435	0.83156	0.00002954	23,409	0.006186	0.000056400
217	172	0.004608	0.79258	0.00002123	29,584	0.004660	0.000000003
264	194	0.003788	0.73487	0.00001434	37,636	0.002893	0.000080102
1,024	834	0.062344	5.66304	0.00069963	121,334	...	0.000262543

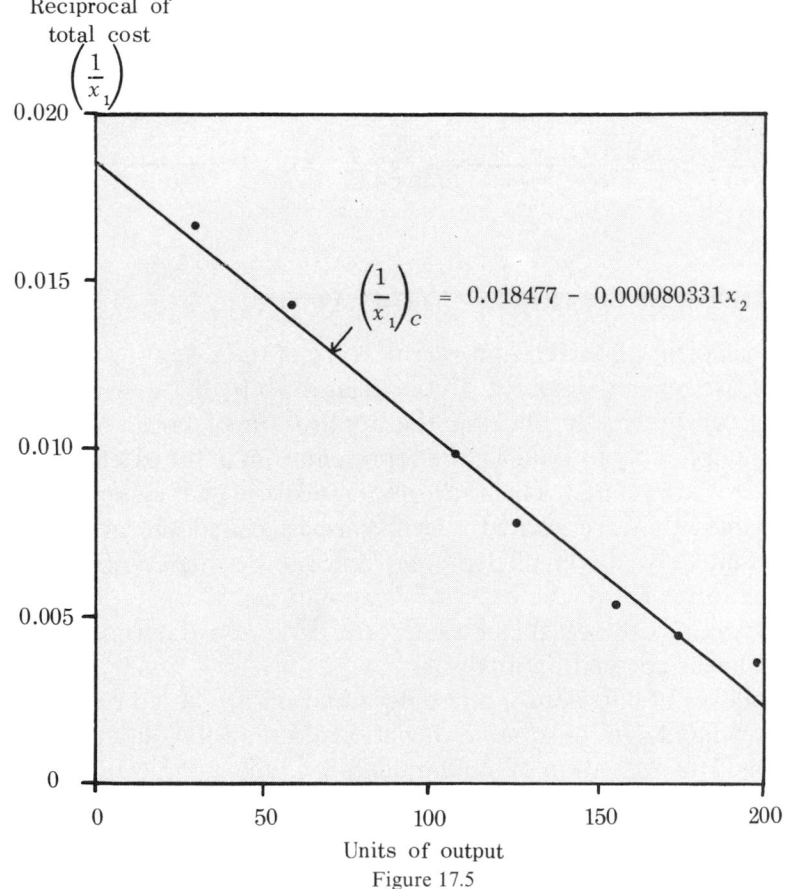

Figure 17.5

A PLOT OF THE RECIPROCALS OF TOTAL COST
AND VOLUME OF OUTPUT

The minimum sum of squared deviations computed in the foregoing example is that of deviations of the *reciprocals* of the original data about the regression line and not the deviations of the original data. Expected values of x_1 are obtained by computing $\left(\dfrac{1}{x_1}\right)_c$ for given values of x_2 and finding the value for which $\left(\dfrac{1}{x_1}\right)_c$ is the reciprocal. For example, the expected value of x_1 for $x_2 = 150$ in the foregoing example is computed

$$E\left[\left(\frac{1}{x_1}\right)_c \mid x_2 = 150\right] = 0.018477 - (0.000080331)(150)$$

$$= 0.018477 - 0.012030$$

$$= 0.006427$$

$$E(x_1 \mid x_2 = 150) = \frac{1}{\left(\dfrac{1}{x_1}\right)_c}$$

$$= \frac{1}{0.006427}$$

$$= 155.59.$$

CURVILINEAR BIVARIATE CORRELATION

The coefficient of correlation is a measure of the extent to which two variables are related linearly. If the relationship of two variables is distinctly curvilinear (nonlinear), the application of linear correlation methods is not likely to yield a good representation of the extent to which the variables are related. The appropriate measure of the correlation of two variables that are related curvilinearly is called the *index of correlation*. Similarly, the coefficient that reflects the degree of nonlinear determination is called the *index of determination*. These two measures are analogous to the coefficients of correlation and determination for bivariate linear correlation analysis.

The indexes of correlation and determination are based on the ratio of the associated sum of squared deviations to the total sum of squared deviations. The derivation of these indexes is similar to that presented in Chapter 16, which describes the derivation of the correlation and determination coefficients for the linear case. Indexes of correlation and determination for bivariate curvilinear relationships including polynomial, exponential, and hyperbolic functions are presented in this chapter.

Polynomial Correlation

Second-Order Polynomial Correlation. The index of determination for the second-order polynomial case is the ratio

$$I^2_{x_1 \cdot x_2 x_2^2} = \frac{\text{associated sum of squares}}{\text{total sum of squares}}$$

$$= \frac{\text{total sum of squares} - \text{unassociated sum of squares}}{\text{total sum of squares}}$$

$$= \frac{\Sigma(x_1 - \bar{x})^2 - \Sigma(x_1 - x_{1c \cdot x_2 x_2^2})^2}{\Sigma(x_1 - \bar{x})^2}.$$

Squaring and collecting terms gives

$$I^2_{x_1 \cdot x_2 x_2^2} = \frac{[\Sigma x_1^2 - 2\bar{x}_1 \Sigma x_1 + n\bar{x}_1^2] - [\Sigma x_1^2 - a_{1.2}\Sigma x_1 - b_{12}\Sigma x_1 x_2 - c_{12}\Sigma x_1 x_2^2]}{\Sigma x_1^2 - 2\bar{x}_1 \Sigma x_1 + n\bar{x}_1^2}.$$

This expression is simplified by multiplying the term $(-2\bar{x}_1 \Sigma x_1)$ in the numerator and denominator by $\dfrac{n}{n}$ to give

$$\frac{n}{n}(-2\bar{x}_1 \Sigma x_1) = -2n\bar{x}_1 \frac{\Sigma x_1}{n} = -2n\bar{x}_1^2.$$

Substituting this result into the expression for the index of determination gives

$$I^2_{x_1 \cdot x_2 x_2^2} = \frac{\Sigma x_1^2 - 2n\bar{x}_1^2 + n\bar{x}_1^2 - \Sigma x_1^2 + a_{1.2}\Sigma x_1 + b_{12}\Sigma x_1 x_2 + c_{12}\Sigma x_1 x_2^2}{\Sigma x_1^2 - 2n\bar{x}_1^2 + n\bar{x}_1^2}.$$

Collecting the terms yields the expression

$$I^2_{x_1 \cdot x_2 x_2^2} = \frac{a_{1.2}\Sigma x_1 + b_{12}\Sigma x_1 x_2 + c_{12}\Sigma x_1 x_2^2 - n\bar{x}_1^2}{\Sigma x_1^2 - n\bar{x}_1^2} \quad \text{...(17.10)}$$

The index of correlation is the square root of the index of determination.

➤ ***Example.*** The index of determination for the data in Table 17.1 is obtained by substituting the appropriate values into Formula 17.10 and solving

$$I^2_{x_1 \cdot x_2 x_2^2} = \frac{a_{1.2}\Sigma x_1 + b_{12}\Sigma x_1 x_2 + c_{12}\Sigma x_1 x_2^2 - n\bar{x}_1^2}{\Sigma x_1^2 - n\bar{x}_1^2}$$

$$= \frac{4.214(188) + 1.544(1{,}007) - 0.130(6{,}545) - 24(7.833)^2}{1{,}508 - 24(7.8333)^2}$$

$$= \frac{792.2 + 1{,}555.0 - 851.0 - 1{,}473.0}{1{,}508.0 - 1{,}473.0} = \frac{23.2}{35.0} = 0.663.$$

The index of correlation is found by solving

$$I_{x_1 . x_2 x_2^2} = \sqrt{I^2_{x_1 . x_2 x_2^2}}$$

$$= \sqrt{0.66}$$

$$= 0.81.$$

The value of this index is somewhat larger than the value $r_{12} = 0.37$ obtained in the linear correlation analysis of the data in Table 17.1. This result indicates that the second-degree polynomial regression equation is a significantly better representation of the bivariate relationship than is the linear regression model.

Higher Order Polynomial Correlation. The index of determination for polynomials of an order greater than two can be obtained by means of the general expression

$$I^2_{x_1 . x_2 \ldots x_2^k} = \frac{a_{1.2}\Sigma x_1 + b_{12}\Sigma x_1 x_2 + \ldots + k\Sigma x_1 x_2^k - n\bar{x}_1^2}{\Sigma x_1^2 - n\bar{x}_1^2} \quad \ldots\ldots(17.11)$$

where k indicates the order of the polynomial.

➤ ***Example.*** The index of determination for the fifth-order polynomial case is written

$$I^2_{x_1 . x_2 \ldots x_2^5} = \frac{\begin{aligned}a_{1.2}\Sigma x_1 + b_{12}\Sigma x_1 x_2 + c_{12}\Sigma x_1 x_2^2 + d_{12}\Sigma x_1 x_2^3 + \\ + e_{12}\Sigma x_1 x_2^4 + f_{12}\Sigma x_1 x_2^5 - n\bar{x}_1^2\end{aligned}}{\Sigma x_1^2 - n\bar{x}_1^2}.$$

The coefficient of correlation for the fifth-order polynomial case is found by taking the square root of the index of determination.

Significance Test for an Index of Determination. The selection of a polynomial regression equation may be approached by making a test of significance to determine if an index of determination is significantly greater than that obtained for a polynomial of the next lower order. For example, suppose one wishes to determine if the associated sum of squares for a second-order polynomial is significantly greater than the associated sum of squares for the first-order polynomial. One would test to see if the addition of the x_2^2 term in the regression increases the associated sum of squares by a greater amount than that which is expected to be obtained by chance.

This test is made by computing the proportion of unassociated sum of squares for the first-order polynomial regression that is associated with the addition of x_2^2 in the second-order regression and determining whether the proportion is significantly greater than that which could be obtained by chance. The proportionate increase in associated sum of squares is written

$$
\begin{bmatrix} \text{proportion of total sum of squares} \\ \text{not associated with linear regression} \\ \text{which is associated with the} \\ \text{addition of } x_2^2 \end{bmatrix} = \frac{\begin{bmatrix} \text{second-order associated} \\ \text{sum of squares} \end{bmatrix} - \begin{bmatrix} \text{first-order associated} \\ \text{sum of squares} \end{bmatrix}}{\begin{bmatrix} \text{total sum of} \\ \text{squares} \end{bmatrix} - \begin{bmatrix} \text{first-order associated} \\ \text{sum of squares} \end{bmatrix}}.
$$

The sum of squares may be expressed as a ratio to the total sum of squares by writing

$$
r_{x_1 x_2^2 . x_2}^2 = \frac{I_{x_1 . x_2 x_2^2}^2 - r_{12}^2}{1 - r_{12}^2} \quad \dots\dots\dots\dots\dots (17.12)
$$

where $r_{x_1 x_2^2 . x_2}^2$ is the proportion of the unassociated sum of squares for the first-order polynomial that is associated with the addition of x_2^2 as an independent variable. This proportion is called the *index of partial determination.*

The index of partial determination can be tested for significance by computing the statistic

$$
t = \sqrt{\frac{r_{x_1 x_2 . x_2}^2 (n - 3)}{1 - r_{x_1 x_2 . x_2}^2}} \quad \dots\dots\dots\dots\dots (17.13)
$$

This statistic has a t distribution with $n - 3$ degrees of freedom and is analogous to the statistic expressed by Formula 16.24.

➤ **Example.** The data in Table 17.1 are used to compute the coefficient of correlation for the linear regression (Figure 17.1). This value is used in conjunction with the index of determination computed previously to test the coefficient of partial determination for significance. The coefficient r_{12}^2 is computed by use of Formula 16.23 to be

$$
r_{12} = \frac{24(1{,}007) - (188)(125)}{\sqrt{[24(1{,}508) - (188)^2][24(815) - (125)^2]}}
$$

$$
= 0.366, \text{ and squaring the result to give}
$$

$$
r_{12}^2 = 0.133.
$$

The index of partial determination is computed by Formula 17.12 to be

$$
r_{x_1 x_2^2 . x_2}^2 = \frac{0.663 - 0.133}{1 - 0.133}
$$

$$
= \frac{0.530}{0.867} = 0.611.
$$

The statistic t is computed by Formula 17.13 to yield

$$t = \sqrt{\frac{0.611(24 - 3)}{1 - 0.611}}$$

$$= \sqrt{\frac{12.83}{0.389}}$$

$$= 5.74.$$

The computed value of $t = 5.74$ for 21 degrees of freedom exceeds the value of 3.819 at the 0.001 level, as seen in Appendix J. The conclusion is that x_2^2 has a significant relationship with x_1.

The test of significance of an index of partial determination can be computed by substituting the appropriate values into Formula 17.12 to compute the desired partial determination index and computing the necessary value of t by the corresponding substitution into Formula 17.13.

An Alternative Method for Selecting a Polynomial Regression Equation. The significance test provides an alternative approach to the selection of a polynomial regression equation to express the relationship between two variables. The statistic t for the index of partial determination associated with each successive higher order polynomial regression equation can be computed. A test can be made to determine if the additional term in the next higher order polynomial reduces significantly the residual unassociated sum of squares related to the next lower polynomial regression. Successively higher polynomials can be computed until additional terms are not significant in reducing the unassociated sum of squares.

Correlation Involving Transformations

Exponential Correlation. The index of correlation for the first-degree exponential case involving the logarithms of the dependent variable is found readily by use of the product-moment formulation. The product-moment formulation for the linear case is given by Formula 16.23. The corresponding expression for the first-degree exponential case is obtained by substituting $\log x_1$ for x_1 in Formula 16.23 and writing

$$I_{\log x_1 \cdot x_2} = \frac{n\Sigma(x_2 \log x_1) - (\Sigma\log x_1)(\Sigma x_2)}{\sqrt{[n\Sigma(\log x_1)^2 - (\Sigma\log x_1)^2][n\Sigma x_2^2 - (\Sigma x_2)^2]}} \quad \ldots\ldots(17.14)$$

The coefficient of determination is obtained by finding the square of the index of correlation.

➤ *Example.* The index of correlation for the exponential relationship of total cost and total output data shown in Table 17.3 is computed by use of Formula 17.14 as follows:

$$I_{\log x_1 . x_2} = \frac{(7)(1{,}012.64189) - (7.76018)(834)}{\sqrt{[(7)(8.96344) - (7.76018)^2][(7)(121{,}334) - (834)^2]}}$$

$$= \frac{7{,}088.49 - 6{,}471.99}{\sqrt{(62.74408 - 60.22039)(849{,}338 - 695{,}556)}}$$

$$= \frac{617.50}{\sqrt{388{,}098}}$$

$$= \frac{617.50}{622.97}$$

$$= 0.99.$$

The index of correlation is very close to unity, indicating that the exponential correlation model is an excellent representation of the relationship between the variables.

The index of correlation for the first-degree exponential case involving the logarithms of both variables is found by use of the product-moment formula

$$I_{\log x_1 . \log x_2} = \frac{n\Sigma(\log x_1 \, \log x_2) - (\Sigma\log x_1)(\Sigma\log x_2)}{\sqrt{[n\Sigma(\log x_1)^2 - (\Sigma\log x_1)^2][n\Sigma(\log x_2)^2 - (\Sigma\log x_2)^2]}}$$

$$\dots\dots\dots(17.15)$$

Hyperbolic Correlation. The product-moment formula also provides a convenient means for finding the index of correlation for the hyperbolic case where the dependent variable is transformed by use of reciprocals. This formula is written

$$I_{\left(\frac{1}{x_1}\right) . x_2} = \frac{n\Sigma\left(\frac{1}{x_1}\right)x_2 - \left(\Sigma\frac{1}{x_1}\right)(\Sigma x_2)}{\sqrt{\left[n\Sigma\left(\frac{1}{x_1}\right)^2 - \left(\Sigma\frac{1}{x_1}\right)^2\right][n\Sigma x_2^2 - (\Sigma x_2)^2]}} \dots\dots\dots(17.16)$$

➤ *Example.* The index of correlation for the hyperbolic relationship of total cost and total output data shown in Table 17.4 is computed by use of Formula 17.14 as follows:

$$I_{\left(\frac{1}{x_1}\right)\cdot x_2} = \frac{(7)(5.66304) - (0.062344)(834)}{\sqrt{[(7)(.00069963) - (.062344)^2][(7)(121,334) - (834)^2]}}$$

$$= \frac{39.64 - 51.99}{\sqrt{(0.0048974 - 0.0038868)(849,338 - 695,556)}}$$

$$= \frac{-12.35}{\sqrt{155.41}} = \frac{-12.35}{12.46} = -0.99.$$

The index of correlation is very close to negative unity, indicating that the hyberbolic correlation model is an excellent representation of the relationship between the variables. In this particular example, the data of total cost and total output are equally well represented by either exponential or hyberbolic correlation. In other instances, the results obtained by each of the nonlinear correlation models will differ, depending upon which of the models is the more appropriate representation. The negative sign that appears before the index of correlation for the hyperbolic case indicates that the reciprocals of the total cost data are correlated inversely with the total output data. This is a consistent result, for the largest observed values have the smallest reciprocals. The inverse relationship is indicative of the degree of correlation, for the index of correlation reflects the correlation of the reciprocals of total cost with the actual values of total output.

TECHNICAL NOTE NO. 1: Elements of Matrix Algebra

The concepts discussed in this note are selected topics from matrix algebra that are useful in solving simultaneous linear equations for the values of regression coefficients.

Vectors

A *row vector* is an ordered set or collection of numbers. Some examples of row vectors are

$$[1 \quad 3], \quad [2 \quad 1 \quad -3], \quad [1.631 \quad -2.310 \quad 0.003].$$

The elements or individual numbers of a vector are called *components*. The number of components designates the order or size of a vector. A *column vector* is an ordered set or collection of numbers. For example:

$$\begin{bmatrix} 2 \\ 6 \end{bmatrix}, \quad \begin{bmatrix} -1 \\ 6 \\ 0 \end{bmatrix}, \quad \begin{bmatrix} 0.3 \\ -0.9 \\ 1.2 \\ 2.4 \end{bmatrix}$$

Interpreted geometrically, a vector represents a point in space. For example, a two-component vector [2 3] denotes a point in two-dimensional space. Two-dimensional space may be represented by Cartesian coordinates. The vector [2 3] denotes a point defined by the intersection of the coordinate 2 on one axis and the coordinate 3 on the other axis. The row vector [2 3] may be written in transposed form as the *column vector*

$$\begin{bmatrix} 2 \\ 3 \end{bmatrix}.$$

The column vector designates the same point as the row vector, since in *transposing* the components of the row vector, the Cartesian coordinates are also interchanged.

Matrices

A *matrix* is a rectangular array of numbers. Some examples of matrices are

$$\begin{bmatrix} 2 & 5 \\ 4 & 1 \end{bmatrix}, \quad \begin{bmatrix} 2 & 6 & 1 \\ 3 & 0 & -2 \end{bmatrix}, \quad \begin{bmatrix} 3 & 1 \\ 0 & 2 \\ -1 & 6 \\ 4 & 5 \end{bmatrix}, \quad [3 \quad 0 \quad 1 \quad 6 \quad 4].$$

These matrices may be viewed as being composites of vectors, where each row and each column of the matrix is a vector. The first of the example matrices is a 2 × 2 matrix; the second, a 2 × 3; the third, a 4 × 2; and the fourth, a 1 × 5. A vector is a matrix with one row or one column.

Two matrices are said to be *conformable* if the number of columns of one matrix is equal to the number of rows of another matrix. For example, the first and the second matrices shown above are conformable, since the first matrix has two columns and the second matrix has two rows. The third and the fourth matrices are not conformable with either the first or the second matrix.

Operations with Vectors and Matrices

Addition. The sum of two vectors or matrices is accomplished by adding the corresponding components of the expressions. For example,

$$[2 \quad 1] + [3 \quad 6] = [2+3 \quad 1+6] = [5 \quad 7]$$

$$\begin{bmatrix} 3 \\ 1 \\ 4 \end{bmatrix} + \begin{bmatrix} 5 \\ 0 \\ -2 \end{bmatrix} = \begin{bmatrix} 3+5 \\ 1+0 \\ 4-2 \end{bmatrix} = \begin{bmatrix} 8 \\ 1 \\ 2 \end{bmatrix}$$

$$\begin{bmatrix} 1 & 0 & 4 \\ 3 & 1 & 5 \\ -4 & 2 & 3 \end{bmatrix} + \begin{bmatrix} 6 & 3 & 1 \\ 4 & -1 & 2 \\ 1 & 3 & 4 \end{bmatrix} = \begin{bmatrix} 1+6 & 0+3 & 4+1 \\ 3+4 & 1-1 & 5+2 \\ -4+1 & 2+3 & 3+4 \end{bmatrix} = \begin{bmatrix} 7 & 3 & 5 \\ 7 & 0 & 7 \\ -3 & 5 & 7 \end{bmatrix}.$$

Subtraction. The difference between two vectors or matrices is found by subtracting the corresponding components of the expressions. Some examples are:

$$[3 \quad 2] - [1 \quad 4] = [3 - 1 \quad 2 - 4] = [1 \quad -2]$$

$$\begin{bmatrix} 4 \\ 2 \end{bmatrix} - \begin{bmatrix} 0 \\ 2 \end{bmatrix} = \begin{bmatrix} 4 - 0 \\ 2 - 2 \end{bmatrix} = \begin{bmatrix} 4 \\ 0 \end{bmatrix}$$

$$\begin{bmatrix} 0 & 4 \\ 1 & 5 \\ 2 & 3 \end{bmatrix} - \begin{bmatrix} 3 & 1 \\ -1 & 2 \\ 3 & 4 \end{bmatrix} = \begin{bmatrix} 0 - 3 & 4 - 1 \\ 1 + 1 & 5 - 2 \\ 2 - 3 & 3 - 4 \end{bmatrix} = \begin{bmatrix} -3 & 3 \\ 2 & 3 \\ -1 & -1 \end{bmatrix}.$$

Multiplication. The multiplication of vectors and matrices is defined only for expressions that are conformable. Matrix multiplication involves some special rules and these are demonstrated in the following examples. The result of the multiplication of conformable vectors is called the *inner product.* For example, the inner product of the vectors

$$[2 \quad 3 \quad 1] \quad \text{and} \quad \begin{bmatrix} 1 \\ 2 \\ 4 \end{bmatrix}$$

is found by multiplying corresponding row and column components and summing the products. This procedure is illustrated as follows:

$$[2 \quad 3 \quad 1] \begin{bmatrix} 1 \\ 2 \\ 4 \end{bmatrix} = [(2)(1) + (3)(2) + (1)(4)] = 12.$$

The inner product is always a number, and in this example the inner product is 12.

The multiplication of matrices is more complex because of the greater number of components involved. The multiplication of matrices is accomplished by multiplying corresponding row and column components and summing the products. For example, consider the matrices

$$\mathbf{A} = \begin{bmatrix} 3 & 1 \\ 4 & 2 \end{bmatrix} \text{and } \mathbf{B} = \begin{bmatrix} 1 & 2 \\ 0 & -1 \end{bmatrix}.$$

The product of these matrices, $\mathbf{A} \cdot \mathbf{B}$, is perhaps more easily found by use of a slightly modified placement of the vectors, which is shown as follows:

$$\mathbf{B} = \begin{bmatrix} 1 & 2 \\ 0 & -1 \end{bmatrix}$$

$$\mathbf{A} = \begin{bmatrix} 3 & 1 \\ 4 & 2 \end{bmatrix} \quad \begin{bmatrix} \mathbf{A} \cdot \mathbf{B} \end{bmatrix}.$$

The first component of the **A·B** matrix is an inner product found by multiplying the corresponding elements in the first row of **A** by the first column of **B** and summing the products. This procedure is illustrated by

$$\mathbf{B} = \begin{bmatrix} 1 & 2 \\ 0 & -1 \end{bmatrix}$$

$$\mathbf{A} = \begin{bmatrix} 3 & 1 \\ 4 & 2 \end{bmatrix} \begin{bmatrix} 3 + 0 & \\ & \end{bmatrix}$$

The remaining components of the **A·B** matrix are found by computing the inner product of each of the respective combinations of row vectors of matrix **A** and the column vectors of matrix **B**. The matrix **A·B** is the product of the **A** and **B** matrices, which is written

$$\mathbf{B} = \begin{bmatrix} 1 & 2 \\ 0 & -1 \end{bmatrix}$$

$$\mathbf{A} = \begin{bmatrix} 3 & 1 \\ 4 & 2 \end{bmatrix} \begin{bmatrix} 3 & 5 \\ 4 & 6 \end{bmatrix} = \mathbf{A} \cdot \mathbf{B}.$$

The matrix **B·A** is found by multiplying the matrix **A** on the left by matrix **B**. This multiplication is written

$$\mathbf{A} = \begin{bmatrix} 3 & 1 \\ 4 & 2 \end{bmatrix}$$

$$\mathbf{B} = \begin{bmatrix} 1 & 2 \\ 0 & -1 \end{bmatrix} \begin{bmatrix} 11 & 5 \\ -4 & -2 \end{bmatrix} = \mathbf{B} \cdot \mathbf{A}.$$

The result of this multiplication shows that $\mathbf{A} \cdot \mathbf{B} \neq \mathbf{B} \cdot \mathbf{A}$. Therefore, the commutative law does not apply to matrix multiplication.

A vector or a matrix may be multiplied by a number, called a *scalar*. Some examples are:

$$(3)\begin{bmatrix} 2 & 1 & 4 \end{bmatrix} = \begin{bmatrix} (3)(2) & (3)(1) & (3)(4) \end{bmatrix} = \begin{bmatrix} 6 & 3 & 12 \end{bmatrix}$$

$$(\tfrac{1}{4})\begin{bmatrix} 3 & 4 \end{bmatrix} = \begin{bmatrix} (\tfrac{1}{4})(3) & (\tfrac{1}{4})(4) \end{bmatrix} = \begin{bmatrix} \tfrac{3}{4} & 1 \end{bmatrix}$$

$$(4)\begin{bmatrix} 3 & 1 \\ 2 & 5 \end{bmatrix} = \begin{bmatrix} (4)(3) & (4)(1) \\ (4)(2) & (4)(5) \end{bmatrix} = \begin{bmatrix} 12 & 4 \\ 8 & 20 \end{bmatrix}.$$

The Inverse of a Matrix

The reciprocal of a number p is denoted $\dfrac{1}{p}$ or p^{-1}. The product

$$p \cdot p^{-1} = 1$$

reflects the relationship in which the product of a number and its reciprocal is unity. A similar relationship exists for certain square matrices. In matrix notation, a matrix that is analogous to unity is denoted $\mathbf{I}$ and is called an *identity* or a *unit* matrix. In this type of matrix, each component on the principal diagonal is a one and every other component is zero. For example, a 3×3 identity matrix is written

$$\mathbf{I} = \begin{bmatrix} 1 & 0 & 0 \\ 0 & 1 & 0 \\ 0 & 0 & 1 \end{bmatrix}.$$

Any matrix $\mathbf{A}$, when multiplied by an identity matrix $\mathbf{I}$, has the product $\mathbf{AI} = \mathbf{IA} = \mathbf{A}$. Examples of this relationship are obtained by solving

$$\begin{bmatrix} 2 & 1 \\ 3 & 4 \end{bmatrix} \begin{bmatrix} a_{11} \\ a_{21} \end{bmatrix} = \begin{bmatrix} 1 \\ 0 \end{bmatrix}.$$

Similarly, the second column vector of $\mathbf{A}^{-1}$ is found by solving

$$\begin{bmatrix} 2 & 1 \\ 3 & 4 \end{bmatrix} \begin{bmatrix} a_{12} \\ a_{22} \end{bmatrix} = \begin{bmatrix} 0 \\ 1 \end{bmatrix}.$$

The two expressions are equations that can be solved simultaneously by the following procedure:

1. Write the matrix $\mathbf{A}$ and augment it or add to it an identity matrix $\mathbf{I}$ as follows:

(a) $\mathbf{A} \mid \mathbf{I} = \begin{bmatrix} 2 & 1 & | & 1 & 0 \\ 3 & 4 & | & 0 & 1 \end{bmatrix}$

2. Let R_1 denote the first row of the augmented matrix, and R_2, the second row.

3. Transform or modify the rows of the augmented matrix by appropriate steps so that $\mathbf{A}$ is transformed into an identity matrix. Transform the components of the complete augmented matrix.

4. Transform the first row so that the first component of R_1 is one by dividing R_1 by its first component and copying the second row R_2 to give

(b) $\begin{bmatrix} \frac{1}{2}R_1 \\ R_2 \end{bmatrix} = \begin{bmatrix} \frac{2}{2} & \frac{1}{2} & | & \frac{1}{2} & 0 \\ 3 & 4 & | & 0 & 1 \end{bmatrix} = \begin{bmatrix} 1 & \frac{1}{2} & | & \frac{1}{2} & 0 \\ 3 & 4 & | & 0 & 1 \end{bmatrix}$

5. Transform R_2 so that the first component of R_2 is zero by subtracting three times R_1 from R_2 and copying the first row R_1 (result of previous transformation) to give

(c) $\begin{bmatrix} R_1 \\ R_2 - 3R_1 \end{bmatrix} = \begin{bmatrix} 1 & \frac{1}{2} & | & \frac{1}{2} & 0 \\ 3-3 & 4-3(\frac{1}{2}) & | & 0-3(\frac{1}{2}) & 1-3(0) \end{bmatrix} = \begin{bmatrix} 1 & \frac{1}{2} & | & \frac{1}{2} & 0 \\ 0 & \frac{5}{2} & | & -\frac{3}{2} & 1 \end{bmatrix}$

6. Transform the second row so that the second component of R_2 is one by multiplying R_2 by $\frac{2}{5}$ and copying R_1 to yield

(d) $\begin{bmatrix} R_1 \\ \frac{2}{5}R_2 \end{bmatrix} = \begin{bmatrix} 1 & \frac{1}{2} & \frac{1}{2} & 0 \\ \frac{2}{5}(0) & \frac{2}{5}(\frac{5}{2}) & \frac{2}{5}(-\frac{3}{2}) & \frac{2}{5}(1) \end{bmatrix} = \begin{bmatrix} 1 & \frac{1}{2} & \frac{1}{2} & 0 \\ 0 & 1 & -\frac{3}{5} & \frac{2}{5} \end{bmatrix}$

7. Transform the first row so that its second component is zero by subtracting $\frac{1}{2}$ times R_2 from R_1 and copying R_2 to give

(e) $\begin{bmatrix} R_1 - \frac{1}{2}R_2 \\ R_2 \end{bmatrix} = \begin{bmatrix} 1-\frac{1}{2}(0) & \frac{1}{2}-\frac{1}{2}(1) & \frac{1}{2}-\frac{1}{2}(-\frac{3}{5}) & 0-\frac{1}{2}(\frac{2}{5}) \\ 0 & 1 & -\frac{3}{5} & \frac{2}{5} \end{bmatrix} =$

$= \begin{bmatrix} 1 & 0 & \frac{4}{5} & -\frac{1}{5} \\ 0 & 1 & -\frac{3}{5} & \frac{2}{5} \end{bmatrix} = \mathbf{I} \mid \mathbf{A}^{-1}.$

Since the matrix $\mathbf{A}$ has been transformed into an identity matrix, the calculations are complete. The inverse $\mathbf{A}^{-1}$ is the transformed identity matrix that was augmented. The product $\mathbf{A}^{-1}\mathbf{A} = \mathbf{I}$ is demonstrated by multiplying

$$\begin{bmatrix} \frac{4}{5} & -\frac{1}{5} \\ -\frac{3}{5} & \frac{2}{5} \end{bmatrix} \begin{bmatrix} 2 & 1 \\ 3 & 4 \end{bmatrix} = \begin{bmatrix} 1 & 0 \\ 0 & 1 \end{bmatrix}.$$

The above procedure for finding the inverse of a square matrix is equivalent to the method for solving simultaneous equations by elimination.

Solution of Simultaneous Equations by Computing the Inverse of a Matrix

The procedure for finding the inverse of a matrix may appear to be an unduly complicated method for solving simultaneous equations. This is true if few equations are involved. For large systems of equations, the method of elimination is cumbersome, but the matrix inversion method provides a computationally efficient procedure for solving these equations. Simple examples will be used, however, to aid in following the solution procedure.

Consider the simultaneous equations

$$2y_1 + y_2 = 10$$
$$3y_1 + 4y_2 = 30.$$

In general matrix form, these equations may be written

$$\mathbf{Ay} = \mathbf{b},$$

where,

$$\mathbf{A} = \begin{bmatrix} 2 & 1 \\ 3 & 4 \end{bmatrix} \quad \mathbf{y} = \begin{bmatrix} y_1 \\ y_2 \end{bmatrix}, \text{ and } \mathbf{b} = \begin{bmatrix} 10 \\ 30 \end{bmatrix}.$$

These equations are solved simultaneously by transforming the rows of the augmented matrix

$$\mathbf{A}\,|\,\mathbf{I}\,|\,\mathbf{b} = \begin{bmatrix} 2 & 1 & 1 & 0 & 10 \\ 3 & 4 & 0 & 1 & 30 \end{bmatrix}$$

to replace $\mathbf{A}$ with $\mathbf{I}$, $\mathbf{I}$ with $\mathbf{A}^{-1}$, and $\mathbf{b}$ with the solution values of $\begin{bmatrix} y_1 \\ y_2 \end{bmatrix}$.

The components of the vector $\mathbf{b}$ are transformed with the components of the remainder of each row.

The transformations are similar to those obtained in the presentation of the procedure for finding $\mathbf{A}^{-1}$ described in the previous discussion. These transformations are:

(a)
$$\begin{bmatrix} R_1 \\ R_2 \end{bmatrix} = \begin{bmatrix} 2 & 1 & 1 & 0 & 10 \\ 3 & 4 & 0 & 1 & 30 \end{bmatrix}$$

(b)
$$\begin{bmatrix} \frac{1}{2}R_1 \\ R_2 \end{bmatrix} = \begin{bmatrix} 1 & \frac{1}{2} & \frac{1}{2} & 0 & 5 \\ 3 & 4 & 0 & 1 & 30 \end{bmatrix}$$

(c)
$$\begin{bmatrix} R_1 \\ R_2 - 3R_1 \end{bmatrix} = \begin{bmatrix} 1 & \frac{1}{2} & \frac{1}{2} & 0 & 5 \\ 0 & \frac{5}{2} & 0 & 1 & 15 \end{bmatrix}$$

(d)
$$\begin{bmatrix} R_1 \\ \frac{2}{5}R_2 \end{bmatrix} = \begin{bmatrix} 1 & \frac{1}{2} & \frac{1}{2} & 0 & 5 \\ 0 & 1 & -\frac{3}{5} & \frac{2}{5} & 6 \end{bmatrix}$$

(e)
$$\begin{bmatrix} R_1 - \frac{1}{2}R_2 \\ R_2 \end{bmatrix} = \begin{bmatrix} 1 & 0 & \frac{4}{5} & -\frac{1}{5} & 2 \\ 0 & 1 & -\frac{3}{5} & \frac{2}{5} & 6 \end{bmatrix} = [\,\mathbf{I}\,|\,\mathbf{A}^{-1}\,|\,\mathbf{y}\,].$$

The successive operations on the components of the augmented matrix transform the matrix $\mathbf{A}$ into an identity matrix. This procedure is equivalent to multiplying $\mathbf{A}^{-1}\mathbf{A} = \mathbf{I}$. Since the same sequence of operations is applied to all the components of the augmented matrix, these transformations are equivalent to multiplying each submatrix in the augmented matrix by $\mathbf{A}^{-1}$. The general matrix form of the problem is written

$$\mathbf{A}\mathbf{y} = \mathbf{b}.$$

Multiplying each side of the equality by $\mathbf{A}^{-1}$ gives

$$\mathbf{A}^{-1}\mathbf{A}\mathbf{y} = \mathbf{A}^{-1}\mathbf{b}$$
$$\mathbf{I}\mathbf{y} = \mathbf{A}^{-1}\mathbf{b}$$
$$\mathbf{y} = \mathbf{A}^{-1}\mathbf{b}.$$

If each submatrix of the augmented matrix is multiplied by $\mathbf{A}^{-1}$, the result is

$$[\mathbf{A}^{-1}\mathbf{A}\,|\,\mathbf{A}^{-1}\mathbf{I}\,|\,\mathbf{A}^{-1}\mathbf{b}] = [\mathbf{I}\,|\,\mathbf{A}^{-1}\,|\,\mathbf{y}].$$

This is the result obtained in matrix (e) above. The components of the vector **y** are the solution values

$$\mathbf{y} = \mathbf{A}^{-1}\mathbf{b}$$

$$\begin{bmatrix} y_1 \\ y_2 \end{bmatrix} = \begin{bmatrix} \frac{4}{5} & -\frac{1}{5} \\ -\frac{3}{5} & \frac{2}{5} \end{bmatrix} \begin{bmatrix} 10 \\ 30 \end{bmatrix} = \begin{bmatrix} 2 \\ 6 \end{bmatrix}.$$

The solution of a large number of simultaneous linear equations can be obtained efficiently by computing the inverse of a matrix **A** by the method described in this discussion. Alternative or modified methods have been devised to offer more efficient computer algorithms for solving these equations.

STUDY QUESTIONS

17-1. Explain briefly the meaning of each of the following terms:
a. first-order polynomial equation
b. polynomial regression
c. exponential regression
d. hyperbolic regression
e. index of correlation
f. index of determination
g. index of partial determination

17-2. What techniques may be used to determine if a nonlinear regression equation is a more suitable bivariate model than a linear regression equation?

17-3. Describe the relationship between the normal equations for first-order polynomial and higher order polynomial regression.

17-4. What is the advantage of using matrix algebra in solving normal equations in regression analysis?

17-5. Outline the steps for solving simultaneous equations by matrix methods.

17-6. When should a significance test be applied to the index of determination computed in regression analysis?

17-7. How can the most appropriate polynomial regression for a bivariate relationship be selected?

PROBLEMS

17-1. The sales volume of a product and the corresponding prices are recorded as follows:

Sales volume (thousands of units)	Price (dollars)
56.0	1.52
85.1	1.20
65.9	1.38
64.2	1.32
45.0	1.61
51.0	1.75
55.0	1.45
51.9	1.63
46.2	1.84

a. Plot a scatter diagram of the data.

b. Compute a second-order polynomial regression of sales volume on price and plot the result.

c. Compute a point estimate of sales volume for a price of $1.48.

d. Compute an estimate of the standard error of estimate.

17-2. The total monthly sales of a brand of candy and the amount of advertising expense for the month are shown as follows:

Sales volume (thousands of units)	Advertising expense (hundreds of dollars)
206	1.68
158	1.38
251	2.19
192	1.60
182	1.50
254	2.50
230	1.90
130	1.32
223	1.78

a. Plot a scatter diagram of the data.

b. Compute a second-order polynomial regression equation and plot the result.

c. Compute a point estimate of sales volume if advertising expense is $1.92 (hundred dollars).

d. Compute an estimate of the standard error of the estimate.

17-3. The times required to check out customers in a supermarket and the corresponding value of purchases are shown as follows:

Time required for checkout (minutes)	Value of purchase (dollars)
3.8	30.6
4.2	30.5
0.9	2.4
5.6	42.2
3.1	21.8
1.7	6.2
4.4	40.1
0.2	2.0
2.6	15.5
1.2	6.5

a. Plot a scatter diagram of the data.

b. Compute a second-order polynomial regression equation and plot the result.

c. What is the expected time to be required to check out a customer with a purchase of $29?

d. Compute the estimated standard error of the estimate.

17-4. A market analyst is interested in the possibility of a relationship between the average length of time between purchases of a given type of product and the consistency with which a particular brand of product is chosen. A sample of data is taken with the following results:

Frequency of purchase of a given brand (percent)	Average length of time between purchases (days)
18	143
46	30
14	182
70	10
41	50
35	60
55	15
81	7
9	350
13	264

a. Plot a scatter diagram of the data.
b. Compute a second-order polynomial regression equation and plot the result.
c. What is the expected percent of repeat purchases for an average length of time between purchases of 45 days?
d. Compute the estimated standard error of the estimate.

17-5. Use the data in Problem 17-1 to:
a. Compute the index of correlation.
b. Test the index of determination for significance.

17-6. Use the data in Problem 17-2 to:
a. Compute the index of correlation.
b. Test the index of determination for significance.

17-7. Use the data in Problem 17-3 to:
a. Compute the index of correlation.
b. Test the index of determination for significance.

17-8. Use the data in Problem 17-4 to:
a. Compute the index of correlation.
b. Test the index of determination for significance.

17-9. Obtain a computer library program and use it to compute the third-order polynomial regression equation and corresponding standard error of the estimate for the data in Problem 17-1. Determine if the third-order polynomial regression provides a more precise prediction model than the second-order regression equation.

17-10. Obtain a computer library program to compute the third-order polynomial regression equation and corresponding standard error of the estimate for the data in Problem 17-2. Determine if the third-order polynomial regression provides a more precise prediction model than the second-order regression equation.

17-11. A sample of observations of price and per capita consumption of natural gas in selected Texas cities is summarized as follows:

City	Average price (dollars per thousand cubic feet)	Consumption per customer (thousand cubic feet)
1 Amarillo	0.30	134
2 Borger	0.31	112
3 Brownsville	0.89	39
4 Corpus Christi	0.50	56
5 Dalhart	0.37	136
6 Granger	0.73	55
7 Iowa Park	0.57	35
8 Karnes City	0.97	46
9 La Pryor	1.02	42
10 Llano	0.88	49
11 Marshall	0.54	77
12 Mathis	1.00	40
13 Memphis	0.60	58
14 Mercedes	0.92	36
15 Millsap	0.58	56
16 Palestine	0.54	43
17 Palo Pinto	0.58	65
18 Royalty	0.43	105
19 Shamrock	0.42	109
20 Texarkana	0.45	87

Source: Sixty-first Annual Report of the Railroad Commission of Texas—Gas Utilities Division·

a. Plot a scatter diagram of the data using an arithmetic chart.
b. Plot a scatter diagram of the data using a semilogarithmic chart.
c. Compute the first-degree exponential regression equation and the corresponding standard error of the estimate.
d. What is the point estimate of per capita consumption, given a price of $0.48?

17-12. Use the data in Problem 17-11 to:
a. Compute the hyperbolic regression equation and the corresponding standard error of estimate.
b. Find the point estimate of per capita consumption, given a price of $0.48.

17-13. Compute the index of correlation for the first-degree exponential case applied to the data of Problem 17-11.

17-14. Compute the index of correlation for the hyperbolic case applied to the data of Problem 17-11.

SELECTED READINGS

Croxton, Frederick E., and Dudley J. Cowden. *Applied General Statistics.* 2d ed. Englewood Cliffs, New Jersey: Prentice-Hall, Inc., 1955.
    Concepts of curvilinear regression are presented in Chapter 20.
Ezekial, Mordecai, and Karl A. Fox. *Methods of Correlation and Regression Analysis.* 3d ed. New York: John Wiley & Sons, Inc., 1959.
    A standard reference in regression and correlation analysis.

Chapter 18

Regression and Correlation: Multivariate Analysis

The regression and correlation methods presented in Chapters 16 and 17 are used to derive mathematical models of the relationship between two variables. If there is a high degree of association between the variations of the dependent variable and one independent variable, a bivariate regression or correlation model provides a good approximation of this relationship. The variation of a dependent variable, in most instances, however, results from the interaction of two or more independent variables.

For example, the relationship of plastic hardness, temperature, and pressure, described in the first portion of Chapter 15, is *multivariate* (several variables) rather than bivariate (two variables). The variation in plastic hardness is related to the two independent variables that are observed (and perhaps more that were not observed). The degree of association of the variation of the dependent variable with either of the independent variables taken individually is significant. A much higher portion of the variation is associated (explained), however, if the variations of the dependent variable and the two independent variables are analyzed jointly.

The multivariate analysis of variations in plastic hardness, temperature, and pressure is presented in an example in this chapter. The regression and correlation methods for multivariate analysis are extensions of the bivariate methods and are derived by the method of least squares. The derivation of these methods and related techniques of application are described in the discussions in this chapter.

MULTIVARIATE ANALYSIS BY ASSOCIATION

Regression analysis is concerned with the derivation of a mathematical model with which to relate quantitatively the variation of a dependent variable with the variations of one or more independent variables. The degree to which the dependent and the independent variables covary is reflected by the proportion of the total variation of the dependent variable that is associated with the variations of the independent variables. The regression and correlation coefficients derived in the analysis reflect the extent of covariation of the variables.

Multivariate analysis by association may be viewed as a stepwise procedure in which the dependent variable is regressed or correlated successively on the independent variables. The dependent variable is regressed on an independent variable and the degree of covariation is computed. Next, the variation of the dependent variable not associated with this independent variable is related by regression to the variation of a second independent variable. The extent to which this residual variation is related to the second independent variable is computed. The process is continued in this manner until the variation of the last of the independent variables is related to the residual variation from the previous step. This process for a universe of data is illustrated in Figure 18.1.

The variation of X_1 is shown as the bar at the top of Figure 18.1 and the corresponding variance of X_1 is shown in the right-hand column. The variation of X_1 associated with the variation of X_2 as the result of the regression of X_1 on X_2 is represented by the unshaded portion of the second bar and is denoted A_{12}. The corresponding portion of the variation of X_1 not associated with the variation of X_2 is the residual or unassociated variation denoted U_{12}. The variance of estimating X_1 is $\sigma_{1.2}^2 = 0.55\sigma_1^2$ since 55 % of the variation of X_1 is not associated with the variation of X_2, where σ_1^2 and σ_2^2 are measures of average variation.

Only a portion of the variation of X_1 is associated with that of X_2 and, in a sense, accounted for or explained. Therefore, only the unassociated variation U_{12} is related to the variation of a third (second independent) variable X_3 to determine if this residual variation can be reduced. The portion of the unassociated variation (U_{12}) that is associated with the variation of X_3 is the portion of the third bar denoted $A_{13.2}$. The subscript 13.2 denotes the relationship derived from the regression of X_1 on X_3 with the variation of X_1 associated with that of X_2 excluded. The variance of estimating X_1 that results from the multiple regression of X_1 on X_2 and X_3 is $\sigma_{1.23}^2 = 0.18\sigma_1^2$, since 18 % of the variation of X_1 is not associated with that of X_2 or X_3.

The final step in this example consists of relating the variation of X_1 not associated with X_2 or X_3, denoted $U_{13.2}$, with the variation of a fourth (third independent) variable X_4. The portion of the residual variation $U_{13.2}$ associated with the variation of X_4 is denoted $A_{14.23}$. The subscript indicates the regression of X_1 on X_4 with the variation of X_1

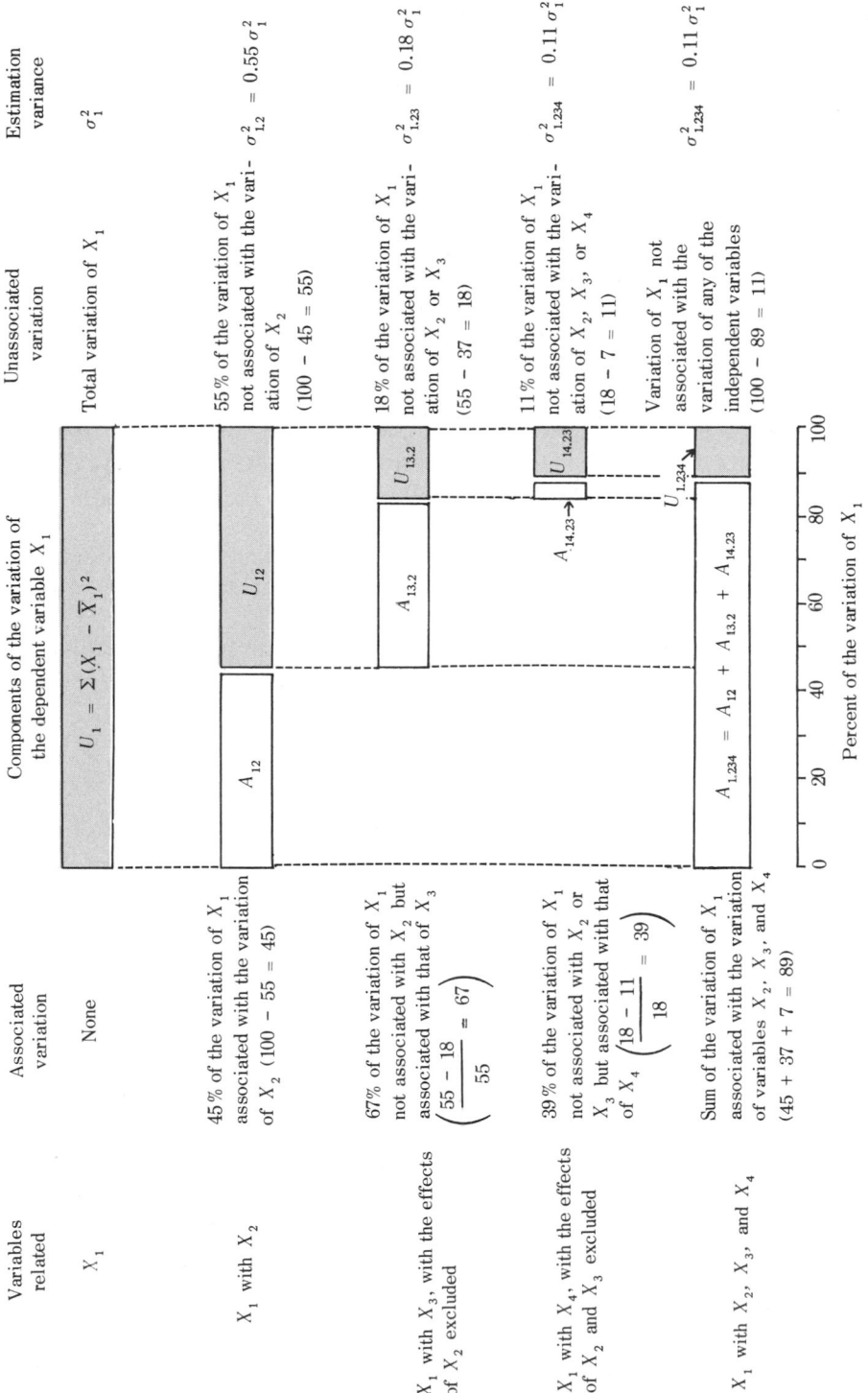

Figure 18.1

AN ILLUSTRATION OF THE STEPWISE MULTIVARIATE ANALYSIS OF A
DEPENDENT VARIABLE WITH THREE INDEPENDENT VARIABLES

associated with X_2 and X_3 excluded. The variance of estimating X_1 based on the regression of X_1 on X_2, X_3, and X_4 is $\sigma_{1.234}^2 = 0.11\sigma_1^2$, for 11% of the variation of X_1 is not associated with that of X_2, X_3, or X_4.

The portion of the variation of X_1 associated with that of the independent variables X_2, X_3, and X_4 is $A_{1.234} = 0.89 \left[\Sigma(X_1 - \bar{X}_1)^2\right]$. Or, 89% of the variation of X_1 is associated with the variation of X_2, X_3, or X_4. This result indicates that a rather precise estimate of X_1 can be obtained by use of a regression equation derived from the regression of the four variables. The multiple regression equation is of the general form

$$X_1 = f(X_2, X_3, \ldots, X_r \mid \theta_1, \theta_2, \theta_3, \ldots, \theta_r),$$

where X_1, X_2, X_3, ..., X_r are the respective variables, and $\theta_1, \theta_2, \theta_3, \ldots,$ θ_r are the parameters. The procedure for deriving the coefficients of a multiple regression equation is described in the following discussion.

TRIVARIATE REGRESSION

The linear regression of a dependent variable X_1 on two independent variables X_2 and X_3 produces an estimating equation written in the form

$$X_{1c.23} = \alpha_{1.23} + \beta_{12.3}X_2 + \beta_{13.2}X_3.$$

The parameter $\theta_1 = \alpha_{1.23}$ is the intercept of the plane of regression (in three dimensions) with the X_1 axis. The term $\theta_2 = \beta_{12.3}$ is called the *coefficient of partial regression* and is the expected increase (decrease) in X_1 for a change of one unit in X_2. $\theta_3 = \beta_{13.2}$ is a coefficient of partial regression that indicates the expected change in X_1 for a unit change in X_3. For example, a value of $\beta_{12.3} = 1.2$ indicates an expected change of 1.2 in X_1 for a change of one unit (1.0) in X_2. An unbiased estimate of the trivariate regression equation obtained from sample data is denoted

$$x_{1c.23} = a_{1.23} + b_{12.3}x_2 + b_{13.2}x_3 \quad \ldots\ldots\ldots\ldots\ldots(18.1)$$

For purposes of this discussion, multiple regression is based on the following assumptions:

1. The dependent variable is a normally distributed random variable.
2. The independent variables are mathematical or fixed (not random) variables.
3. The variance of the estimation of the dependent variable is homoscedastic.

4. The coefficients $a_{1.23...r}$, $b_{12.3...r}$, $b_{13.2...r}$, $b_{1r.2...r-1}$, are maximum likelihood estimators of the respective parameters $\theta_1, \theta_2, \theta_3, \ldots, \theta_r$.
5. The error term ε is distributed normally and

$$E(\varepsilon) = E[\Sigma(x_1 - E(x_1 \mid x_2, x_3, \ldots, x_r))] = 0.$$

Trivariate Regression Equation

The estimators of the regression coefficients can be obtained by use of normal equations derived by the method of least squares. The equations are derived in a manner similar to that demonstrated in Technical Note 1 of Chapter 16. The normal equations for trivariate regression (for which $\Sigma\varepsilon^2$ is a minimum) are based on the following expressions derived by the method of least squares:

$$\Sigma(x_1 - a_{1.23} - b_{12.3}x_2 - b_{13.2}x_3) = 0$$
$$\Sigma x_2(x_1 - a_{1.23} - b_{12.3}x_2 - b_{13.2}x_3) = 0$$
$$\Sigma x_3(x_1 - a_{1.23} - b_{12.3}x_2 - b_{13.2}x_3) = 0.$$

Performing the indicated multiplications and summations and re-arranging terms gives

$$\text{I. } na_{1.23} + b_{12.3}\Sigma x_2 + b_{13.2}\Sigma x_3 = \Sigma x_1$$
$$\text{II. } a_{1.23}\Sigma x_2 + b_{12.3}\Sigma x_2^2 + b_{13.2}\Sigma x_2 x_3 = \Sigma x_1 x_2$$
$$\text{III. } a_{1.23}\Sigma x_3 + b_{12.3}\Sigma x_2 x_3 + b_{13.2}\Sigma x_3^2 = \Sigma x_1 x_3.$$

The number of normal equations to be solved can be reduced by expressing the observed values of the three variables as deviations about the respective means. Written in this manner, the terms $\Sigma(x_1 - \bar{x}_1)$, $\Sigma(x_2 - \bar{x}_2)$, and $\Sigma(x_3 - \bar{x}_3)$ are all zero and, consequently, $a_{1.23}$ is also zero. The three equations reduce to the two equations

$$\text{II. } b_{12.3}\Sigma(x_2 - \bar{x}_2)^2 + b_{13.2}\Sigma(x_2 - \bar{x}_2)(x_3 - \bar{x}_3)$$
$$= \Sigma(x_1 - \bar{x}_1)(x_2 - \bar{x}_2)$$
$$\text{III. } b_{12.3}\Sigma(x_2 - \bar{x}_2)(x_3 - \bar{x}_3) + b_{13.2}\Sigma(x_3 - \bar{x}_3)^2$$
$$= \Sigma(x_1 - \bar{x}_1)(x_3 - \bar{x}_3).$$

These equations are solved simultaneously for the partial regression coefficients. The sums of squares and cross-products of the deviations to be substituted into the normal equations are obtained by the relationships

$$\Sigma d_1^2 = \Sigma(x_1 - \bar{x}_1)^2 = \Sigma x_1^2 - n\bar{x}_1^2$$
$$\Sigma d_2^2 = \Sigma(x_2 - \bar{x}_2)^2 = \Sigma x_2^2 - n\bar{x}_2^2$$
$$\Sigma d_3^2 = \Sigma(x_3 - \bar{x}_3)^2 = \Sigma x_3^2 - n\bar{x}_3^2$$

$$\Sigma d_{12} = \Sigma(x_1 - \bar{x}_1)(x_2 - \bar{x}_2) = \Sigma x_1 x_2 - n\bar{x}_1 \bar{x}_2$$
$$\Sigma d_{13} = \Sigma(x_1 - \bar{x}_1)(x_3 - \bar{x}_3) = \Sigma x_1 x_3 - n\bar{x}_1 \bar{x}_3$$
$$\Sigma d_{23} = \Sigma(x_2 - \bar{x}_2)(x_3 - \bar{x}_3) = \Sigma x_2 x_3 - n\bar{x}_2 \bar{x}_3$$

The d terms provide simpler notation for the respective sums of squares and cross-products of the deviations. The matrix of d values is called the *moment matrix*. Using this simplified notation, the normal equations are written

$$\left. \begin{array}{l} \text{II. } b_{12.3}\Sigma d_2^2 + b_{13.2}\Sigma d_{23} = \Sigma d_{12} \\ \text{III. } b_{12.3}\Sigma d_{23} + b_{13.2}\Sigma d_3^2 = \Sigma d_{13} \end{array} \right\} \quad \dots\dots\dots(18.2)$$

In matrix form, these equations are written

$$\begin{bmatrix} \Sigma d_2^2 & \Sigma d_{23} \\ \Sigma d_{23} & \Sigma d_3^2 \end{bmatrix} \begin{bmatrix} b_{12.3} \\ b_{13.2} \end{bmatrix} = \begin{bmatrix} \Sigma d_{12} \\ \Sigma d_{13} \end{bmatrix}.$$

The value of $a_{1.23}$ is obtained by solving the expression

$$a_{1.23} = \bar{x}_1 - b_{12.3}\bar{x}_2 - b_{13.2}\bar{x}_3 \quad \dots\dots\dots\dots(18.3)$$

The variation of x_1 not associated with x_2 or x_3 is computed by the expression

$$\Sigma u_{1.23}^2 = \Sigma(x_1 - \bar{x}_1)^2 - b_{12.3}\Sigma(x_1 - \bar{x}_1)(x_2 - \bar{x}_2) - $$
$$- b_{13.2}\Sigma(x_1 - \bar{x}_1)(x_3 - \bar{x}_3).$$

An unbiased estimate of the variance of the estimate of x_1 is computed by $\dfrac{\Sigma u_{1.23}^2}{n-3}$, which is written alternatively by the formula

$$\hat{\sigma}_{1.23}^2 = \frac{\Sigma d_1^2 - b_{12.3}\Sigma d_{12} - b_{13.2}\Sigma d_{13}}{n-3} \quad \dots\dots\dots(18.4)$$

where the loss of three degrees of freedom results from the estimation of three parameters in the regression equation.

➤ *Example.* A sample of 25 observations of plastic hardness (x_1), temperature (x_2), and reactor pressure (x_3) is taken from a chemical process. Multiple regression analysis is to be applied to derive an expression for predicting plastic hardness on the basis of the observed operating conditions. The sample data, shown in Table 18.1, are taken from a process similar to that discussed in Chapter 16. The observations of the variable percent additive (x_4) are used in the next portion of the chapter, which presents the regression of four variables. The required means and sums of squares and cross-products are given at the top of page 628.

Table 18.1

SAMPLE DATA OF 25 OBSERVATIONS OF PLASTIC HARDNESS (x_1), TEMPERATURE (x_2), REACTOR PRESSURE (x_3), AND PERCENT ADDITIVE (x_4)

x_1	x_2	x_3	x_4	x_1^2	x_2^2	x_3^2	x_4^2	x_1x_2	x_1x_3	x_1x_4	x_2x_3	x_2x_4	x_3x_4
44	410	22.1	4.9	1,936	168,100	488.41	24.01	18,040	972.4	215.6	9,061.0	2,009.0	108.29
47	419	22.5	3.0	2,209	175,561	506.25	9.00	19,693	1,057.5	141.0	9,427.5	1,257.0	67.50
60	427	23.1	1.5	3,600	182,329	533.61	2.25	25,620	1,386.0	90.0	9,863.7	640.5	34.65
71	431	24.0	0.6	5,041	185,761	576.00	0.36	30,601	1,704.0	42.6	10,344.0	258.6	14.40
61	464	22.6	1.8	3,721	215,296	510.76	3.24	28,304	1,378.6	109.8	10,486.4	835.2	40.68
60	481	21.7	3.3	3,600	231,361	470.89	10.89	28,860	1,302.0	198.0	10,437.7	1,587.3	71.61
56	467	22.0	2.1	3,136	218,089	484.00	4.41	26,152	1,232.0	117.6	10,274.0	980.7	46.20
66	482	24.6	0.2	4,356	232,324	605.16	0.04	31,812	1,623.6	13.2	11,857.2	96.4	4.92
51	457	21.1	3.8	2,601	208,849	445.21	14.44	23,307	1,076.1	193.8	9,642.7	1,736.6	80.18
53	448	22.2	4.5	2,809	200,704	492.84	20.25	23,744	1,176.6	238.5	9,945.6	2,016.0	99.90
74	496	24.8	0.1	5,476	246,016	615.04	0.01	36,704	1,835.2	7.4	12,300.8	49.6	2.48
33	412	20.5	4.8	1,089	169,744	420.25	23.04	13,596	676.5	158.4	8,446.0	1,977.6	98.40
54	447	21.9	2.3	2,916	199,809	479.61	5.29	24,138	1,182.6	124.2	9,789.3	1,028.1	50.37
52	473	20.8	0.3	2,704	223,729	432.64	0.09	24,596	1,081.6	15.6	9,838.4	141.9	6.24
30	404	20.0	2.7	900	163,216	400.00	7.29	12,120	600.0	81.0	8,080.0	1,090.8	54.00
58	409	23.3	4.4	3,364	167,281	542.89	19.36	23,722	1,351.4	255.2	9,529.7	1,799.6	102.52
59	498	21.3	3.9	3,481	248,004	453.69	15.21	29,382	1,256.7	230.1	10,607.4	1,942.2	83.07
52	427	22.9	1.4	2,704	183,329	524.41	1.96	22,204	1,190.8	72.8	9,778.3	597.8	32.06
56	459	22.3	2.7	3,136	210,681	497.29	7.29	25,704	1,248.8	151.2	10,235.7	1,239.3	60.21
49	423	22.6	2.7	2,401	178,929	510.76	7.29	20,727	1,107.4	132.3	9,559.8	1,142.1	61.02
63	490	22.4	2.2	3,969	240,100	501.76	4.84	30,870	1,411.2	138.6	10,976.0	1,078.0	49.28
61	434	23.8	0.7	3,721	188,356	566.44	0.49	26,474	1,451.8	42.7	10,329.2	303.8	16.66
39	416	20.6	3.1	1,521	173,056	424.36	9.61	16,224	803.4	120.9	8,569.6	1,289.6	63.86
62	432	24.4	0.6	3,844	186,624	595.36	0.36	26,784	1,512.8	37.2	10,540.8	259.2	14.64
78	494	25.0	4.6	6,084	244,036	625.00	21.16	38,532	1,950.0	358.8	12,350.0	2,272.4	115.00
1,389	11,200	562.5	62.2	80,319	5,040,284	12,702.63	212.18	627,910	31,569.0	3,286.5	252,270.8	27,629.3	1,378.14

Source: Company records of the firm.

$$\bar{x}_1 = \frac{1,389}{25} = 55.56 \qquad\qquad \bar{x}_3 = \frac{562.5}{25} = 22.50$$

$$\bar{x}_2 = \frac{11,200}{25} = 448.00$$

$$\Sigma d_1^2 = \Sigma(x_1 - \bar{x}_1)^2 = \Sigma x_1^2 - n\bar{x}_1^2 = 80,319 - 25(55.56)^2$$
$$= 80,319 - 77,172.84 = 3,146.16$$

$$\Sigma d_2^2 = \Sigma(x_2 - \bar{x}_2)^2 = \Sigma x_2^2 - n\bar{x}_2^2 = 5,040.284 - 25(448.00)^2$$
$$= 5,040,284 - 5,017,600 = 22,684$$

$$\Sigma d_3^2 = \Sigma(x_3 - \bar{x}_3)^2 = \Sigma x_3^2 - n\bar{x}_3^2 = 12,702.63 - 25(22.5)^2$$
$$= 12,702.63 - 12,656.25 = 46.38$$

$$\Sigma d_{12} = \Sigma(x_1 - \bar{x}_1)(x_2 - \bar{x}_2) = \Sigma x_1 x_2 - n\bar{x}_1\bar{x}_2$$
$$= 627,910 - 25(55.56)(448.00) = 627,910 - 622,272$$
$$= 5,638$$

$$\Sigma d_{13} = \Sigma(x_1 - \bar{x}_1)(x_3 - \bar{x}_3) = \Sigma x_1 x_3 - n\bar{x}_1\bar{x}_3$$
$$= 31,569.0 - 25(55.56)(22.50) = 31,569.0 - 31,252.5$$
$$= 316.5$$

$$\Sigma d_{23} = \Sigma(x_2 - \bar{x}_2)(x_3 - \bar{x}_3) = \Sigma x_2 x_3 - n\bar{x}_2\bar{x}_3$$
$$= 252,270.8 - 25(448.00)(22.50) = 252,270.8 - 252,000.0$$
$$= 270.8.$$

The normal equations are

$$\text{II. } 22,684b_{12.3} + 270.8b_{13.2} = 5,638$$
$$\text{III. } 270.8b_{12.3} + 46.38b_{13.2} = 316.5.$$

These equations are solved by the method of elimination as follows:

(Equation II) $\qquad\qquad\qquad 22,684b_{12.3} + 270.8b_{13.2} = 5,638.0$

$\left(-\dfrac{22,684}{270.8}\text{ times Equation II}\right)$ $-22,684b_{12.3} - 3,885.1b_{13.2} = -26,512.1$

(Equation II–III) $\qquad\qquad\qquad\qquad -3,614.3b_{13.2} = 20,874$
$$b_{13.2} = 5.7754.$$

The value of $b_{13.2}$ is substituted into Equation II, and solving for $b_{12.3}$ gives

$$\text{(Equation II) } 22,684b_{12.3} + 270.8(5.7754) = 5,638.0$$
$$22,684b_{12.3} + 1,564.0 = 5,638.0$$
$$22,684b_{12.3} = 4,074$$
$$b_{12.3} = 0.179598.$$

Alternatively, the normal equations may be written in matrix notation in the form

$$\begin{bmatrix} 22{,}684 & 270.8 \\ 270.8 & 46.38 \end{bmatrix} \begin{bmatrix} b_{12.3} \\ b_{13.2} \end{bmatrix} = \begin{bmatrix} 5{,}638 \\ 316.5 \end{bmatrix}.$$

The equations are solved by matrix inversion in the following steps:

(a)

$$\begin{bmatrix} \Sigma d_2^2 & \Sigma d_{23} & | & 1 & 0 & | & \Sigma d_{12} \\ \Sigma d_{23} & \Sigma d_3^2 & | & 0 & 1 & | & \Sigma d_{13} \end{bmatrix} = \begin{bmatrix} a_{22} & a_{23} & | & 1 & 0 & | & b_1 \\ a_{32} & a_{33} & | & 0 & 1 & | & b_2 \end{bmatrix}$$

$$= \begin{matrix} R_2 \\ R_3 \end{matrix} \begin{bmatrix} 22{,}684 & 270.8 & | & 1 & 0 & | & 5{,}638 \\ 270.8 & 46.38 & | & 0 & 1 & | & 316.5 \end{bmatrix}$$

(b)

$$\begin{matrix} \dfrac{R_2}{a_{22}} \\[2mm] R_3 - a_{32}R_2 \end{matrix} \begin{bmatrix} 1 & 0.0119379 & | & 0.0000440839 & 0 & | & 0.248545 \\ 0 & 43.147217 & | & -0.01193792 & 1 & | & 249.194014 \end{bmatrix}$$

(c)

$$\begin{matrix} R_2 - a_{23}R_3 \\[2mm] \dfrac{R_3}{a_{33}} \end{matrix} \begin{bmatrix} 1 & 0 & | & 0.0000473869 & -0.000276679 & | & 0.179598 \\ 0 & 1 & | & -0.000276679 & 0.0231764 & | & 5.775436 \end{bmatrix}.$$

This solution gives

$$b_{12.3} = 0.179598$$
$$b_{13.2} = 5.775436.$$

Substituting the partial regression coefficients into Formula 18.3 gives

$$\begin{aligned} a_{1.23} &= \bar{x}_1 - b_{12.3}\bar{x}_2 - b_{13.2}\bar{x}_3 \\ &= 55.56 - 0.179598(448.00) - 5.775436(22.50) \\ &= 55.56 - 80.4599 - 129.94731 \\ &= -154.84721. \end{aligned}$$

The variation of x_1 not associated with that of x_2 or x_3 is found by solving

$$\begin{aligned} \Sigma u_{1.23}^2 &= \Sigma d_1^2 - b_{12.3}\Sigma d_{12} - b_{13.2}\Sigma d_{13} \\ &= 3{,}146.16 - 0.179598(5{,}638) - 5.775436(316.5) \\ &= 3{,}146.16 - 1{,}012.57 - 1{,}827.92 \\ &= 305.67. \end{aligned}$$

An unbiased estimate of the variance of the error of estimating x_1 is obtained by solving Formula 18.4 to yield

$$\hat{\sigma}^2_{1.23} = \frac{\Sigma u^2_{1.23}}{n - 3}$$

$$= \frac{305.67}{25 - 3}$$

$$= 13.894.$$

The estimated standard error of the estimate of x_1 is computed by

$$\hat{\sigma}_{1.23} = \sqrt{\frac{\Sigma u^2_{1.23}}{n - 3}}$$

$$= \sqrt{13.894}$$

$$= 3.727.$$

A Comparison of Bivariate and Trivariate Regression Results

The reduction in the expected variance in estimating x_1 by the addition of a third variable x_3 is demonstrated by comparing the results of the foregoing example with the bivariate regression of x_1 on x_2 and x_1 on x_3. Formula 16.9 may be written in terms of deviations in the form

$$b_{12} = \frac{n\Sigma x_1 x_2 - (\Sigma x_1)(\Sigma x_2)}{n\Sigma x^2_2 - (\Sigma x_2)^2}$$

$$= \frac{\Sigma(x_1 - \bar{x}_1)(x_2 - \bar{x}_2)}{\Sigma(x_2 - \bar{x}_2)^2}$$

$$= \frac{\Sigma d_{12}}{\Sigma d^2_2}.$$

The regression coefficient is found by substituting the appropriate data from Table 18.1 and computing

$$b_{12} = \frac{\Sigma d_{12}}{\Sigma d^2_2} = \frac{5,638}{22,684} = 0.2485.$$

The estimated variance of the error of estimating x_1 is found by writing Formula 16.13 in terms of deviations in the form

$$\hat{\sigma}^2_{1.2} = \frac{\Sigma x^2_1 - a_{1.2}\Sigma x_1 - b_{12}\Sigma x_1 x_2}{n - 2}$$

$$= \frac{\Sigma(x_1 - \bar{x}_1)^2 - b_{12}\Sigma(x_1 - \bar{x}_1)(x_2 - \bar{x}_2)}{n - 2}$$

$$= \frac{\Sigma d^2_1 - b_{12}\Sigma d_{12}}{n - 2}.$$

The term $a_{1.2}\Sigma(x_1 - \bar{x}_1)$ is zero since the sum of the deviations of x_1 is zero. The estimated variance of the error of estimating x_1 is computed by

$$\hat{\sigma}^2_{1.2} = \frac{3,146.16 - 0.2485(5,638)}{25 - 2}$$

$$= \frac{1,745.12}{23}$$

$$= 75.87.$$

Similarly, the values of b_{13} and $\hat{\sigma}^2_{1.3}$ for the bivariate regression of x_1 on x_3 are computed

$$b_{13} = \frac{\Sigma d_{13}}{\Sigma d_3^2}$$

$$= \frac{316.5}{46.38}$$

$$= 6.8240,$$

and

$$\hat{\sigma}^2_{1.3} = \frac{\Sigma d_1^2 - b_{13}\Sigma d_{13}}{n - 2}$$

$$= \frac{3,146.16 - 6.824(316.5)}{25 - 2}$$

$$= \frac{986.36}{23}$$

$$= 42.89.$$

The variance of the estimate of x_1 based on the trivariate regression is compared with the bivariate results by writing

$$\hat{\sigma}^2_{1.23} = 13.89$$

$$\hat{\sigma}^2_{1.2} = 75.87$$

$$\hat{\sigma}^2_{1.3} = 42.89.$$

The variance based on the trivariate regression is less than either of the two bivariate regression results. The addition of the third variable aids in reducing the variance of estimating x_1 since x_2 and x_3 are not correlated perfectly. If x_2 and x_3 were correlated perfectly, the addition of x_3 in the trivariate regression would not reduce the variance of the estimate since the variations of x_2 and x_3 would be, in effect, identical. The bivariate regressions indicate that x_3 is more highly related with x_1 than x_2, for $\hat{\sigma}^2_{1.3}$ is less than $\hat{\sigma}^2_{1.2}$. In general, the addition of an independent variable in multiple regression will reduce the unassociated variation of the dependent variable and thereby produce more precise estimates of x_1. The exception to this general statement arises when the addition of an independent variable does not reduce the residual variation sufficiently to offset the loss of an additional degree of freedom. In such a case, the variance of the estimate of x_1 may increase, but this would be interpreted to mean that the additional independent variable does not aid in making more precise estimates of x_1.

The regression coefficients may be compared by writing

$$b_{12} = 0.2485 \qquad b_{12.3} = 0.1796$$
$$b_{13} = 6.8240 \qquad b_{13.2} = 5.7754.$$

The partial regression coefficient $b_{12.3}$, which relates x_1 and x_2 with the effects of x_3 held constant, is less than the corresponding value of the gross regression relationship b_{12}, which does not take x_3 into account. A similar relationship exists between $b_{13.2}$ and b_{13}. An estimate of x_1 made by use of the trivariate regression equation is based on particular values of x_2 and x_3. Since the values of two independent variables are used in the estimate, the trivariate regression coefficients would be expected to be smaller than the corresponding bivariate partial regression coefficients.

Sampling Error in Trivariate Regression

The multiple regression coefficients $a_{1.23}$, $b_{12.3}$, and $b_{13.2}$ are maximum likelihood estimators of the parameters $\theta_1 = \alpha_{1.23}, \theta_2 = \beta_{12.3}$, and $\theta_3 = \beta_{13.2}$. Sample estimates of the parameters are distributed normally about the respective parameters. An unbiased estimate of the standard error of the sample estimate of $\alpha_{1.23}$ is written

$$\hat{\sigma}_{a_{1.23}} = \frac{\hat{\sigma}_{1.23}}{\sqrt{n}}.$$

An unbiased estimate of the standard error of the estimate of $\beta_{12.3}$ is expressed by

$$\hat{\sigma}_{b_{12.3}} = \frac{\hat{\sigma}_{1.23}}{\sqrt{\Sigma d_2^2 - \dfrac{(\Sigma d_{23})^2}{\Sigma d_3^2}}} \qquad \ldots\ldots\ldots\ldots\ldots(18.5)$$

A test of significance can be applied to $b_{12.3}$ as the basis for judging whether the coefficient is significantly different from zero. The value of $\beta_{12.3} = 0$ if the variables are not related. The same type of test can be applied to $b_{13.2}$ by computing

$$\hat{\sigma}_{b_{13.2}} = \frac{\hat{\sigma}_{1.23}}{\sqrt{\Sigma d_3^2 - \frac{(\Sigma d_{23})^2}{\Sigma d_2^2}}} \qquad \ldots\ldots\ldots\ldots\ldots(18.6)$$

and utilizing the result in a test of significance.

Formulas 18.5 and 18.6 may be written in alternate form to include the values of terms computed in obtaining the inverse of the moment matrix (normal equations). A general expression for the estimated standard error of a partial regression coefficient is written

$$\hat{\sigma}_{b_{1i.j}} = \hat{\sigma}_{1.23} \sqrt{c_{ii}} \qquad \ldots\ldots\ldots\ldots\ldots\ldots(18.7)$$

where i denotes the independent variable regressed, j denotes the independent variable held constant, and c_{ii} is the element in the ith row and the ith column (i.e., on the principal diagonal) of the inverse of the moment matrix. A c_{ii} element is called the *Gaussian multiplier*. The ith row and the ith column correspond to the moment matrix defined in terms of the observed values rather than these values expressed as deviations. For example, the value $c_{22} = 0.0000473869$ is read from the inverse of the moment matrix obtained in the trivariate regression of plastic hardness with temperature and pressure. The inverse of the moment matrix in that example is written

$$\begin{bmatrix} a_{22} & a_{23} \\ a_{32} & a_{33} \end{bmatrix}^{-1} = \begin{bmatrix} c_{22} & c_{23} \\ c_{32} & c_{33} \end{bmatrix} = \begin{bmatrix} 0.0000473869 & -0.000276678 \\ -0.000276678 & 0.0231764 \end{bmatrix}.$$

➤ *Example.* The partial regression coefficients obtained in the trivariate regression of plastic hardness (x_1), temperature (x_2), and pressure (x_3) are tested for significance by computing the required standard errors and the ratio needed for the significance test. The standard errors are computed

$$\hat{\sigma}_{b_{12.3}} = \frac{\hat{\sigma}_{1.23}}{\sqrt{\Sigma d_2^2 - \frac{(\Sigma d_{23})^2}{\Sigma d_3^2}}}$$

$$= \frac{3.727}{\sqrt{22,684 - \frac{(270.8)^2}{46.38}}}$$

$$= \frac{3.727}{\sqrt{21,102.87}}$$

$$= \frac{3.727}{145.28} = 0.02565,$$

and

$$\hat{\sigma}_{b_{13.2}} = \frac{\hat{\sigma}_{1.23}}{\sqrt{\Sigma d_3^2 - \frac{(\Sigma d_{23})^2}{\Sigma d_2^2}}}$$

$$= \frac{3.727}{\sqrt{46.38 - \frac{(170.8)^2}{22,684}}}$$

$$= \frac{3.727}{\sqrt{43.15}} = \frac{3.727}{6.569} = 0.5674.$$

The values of $\hat{\sigma}_{b_{12.3}}$ and $\hat{\sigma}_{b_{13.2}}$ are obtained alternatively by Formula 18.7 by solving

$$\hat{\sigma}_{b_{12.3}} = \hat{\sigma}_{1.23} \sqrt{c_{22}}$$

$$= 3.727 \sqrt{0.0000473869}$$
$$= (3.727)(0.0068838)$$
$$= 0.02566$$

$$\hat{\sigma}_{b_{13.2}} = \hat{\sigma}_{1.23} \sqrt{c_{33}}$$

$$= 3.727 \sqrt{0.0231764}$$
$$= (3.727)(0.15223)$$
$$= 0.5674.$$

The value $\hat{\sigma}_{b_{12.3}} = 0.02566$ is slightly larger than the result obtained previously because of rounding error. Note that

$$\frac{1}{\sqrt{\Sigma d_2^2 - \frac{(\Sigma d_{23})^2}{\Sigma d_3^2}}} = \sqrt{c_{22}}$$

$$\frac{1}{\sqrt{21,102.87}} = 0.068838,$$

and

$$\frac{1}{\sqrt{\Sigma d_3^2 - \frac{(\Sigma d_{23})^2}{\Sigma d_2^2}}} = \sqrt{c_{33}}$$

$$\frac{1}{\sqrt{43.15}} = 0.15223.$$

The ratios for the significance tests are computed

$$t = \frac{b_{12.3} - 0}{\hat{\sigma}_{b_{12.3}}}$$

$$= \frac{0.1796}{0.02565} = 7.002,$$

and

$$t = \frac{b_{13.2} - 0}{\hat{\sigma}_{b_{13.2}}}$$

$$= \frac{5.775}{0.5674} = 10.18.$$

The value of $t = 7.002$ for $25 - 3 = 22$ degrees of freedom exceeds $t_{0.001} = 3.792$, as read from Appendix J. The difference $b_{12.3} - 0$ is judged to be significant. Similarly, the value $t = 10.18$ exceeds $t_{0.001} = 3.792$ for a significance test of $b_{13.2}$. The regression of x_1 on x_3, with the effects of x_2 held constant, is judged to be significant.

TRIVARIATE CORRELATION

The degree of association between the variables in a trivariate regression can be determined by *multiple correlation* analysis.

Coefficient of Multiple Determination

The extent to which a linear multiple regression equation fits the observed data can be indicated by the ratio of the associated variation to the total variation of the dependent variable. A maximum likelihood estimator of the universe *coefficient of determination* for the trivariate case is written

$$R^2_{1.23} = \frac{\text{associated sum of squares}}{\text{total sum of squares}}$$

and

$$R^2_{1.23} = \frac{\Sigma(x_{1c} - \bar{x}_1)^2}{\Sigma(x_1 - \bar{x}_1)^2} \quad \dots\dots\dots\dots\dots\dots\dots\dots(18.8)$$

where $R^2_{1.23}$ is an estimator of the universe determination coefficient. Formula 18.8 may be expressed in more convenient computational form by writing

$$R^2_{1.23} = \frac{b_{12.3}\Sigma d_{12} + b_{13.2}\Sigma d_{13}}{\Sigma d_1^2} \quad \dots\dots\dots\dots\dots(18.9)$$

The *coefficient of multiple correlation* is simply the square root of the multiple determination coefficient.

➤ *Example.* The coefficients of multiple determination and correlation are computed for the data on plastic hardness, temperature, and pressure given in the trivariate regression example. The multiple determination coefficient is computed

$$R^2_{1.23} = \frac{b_{12.3}\Sigma d_{12} + b_{13.2}\Sigma d_{13}}{\Sigma d_1^2}$$

$$= \frac{0.1796(5{,}638) + 5.775(316.5)}{3{,}146.16}$$

$$= \frac{2{,}840.37}{3{,}146.16} = 0.9028.$$

The coefficient of multiple correlation is

$$R_{1.23} = \sqrt{R^2_{1.23}} = \sqrt{0.9028} = 0.9501.$$

The value of $R^2_{1.23} = 0.9028$ obtained in the foregoing example may be interpreted by stating that 90.28% of the total variation of the dependent variable is associated with or explained by the regression of x_1 on x_2 and x_3.

Significance Test for a Multiple Determination Coefficient

Multiple correlation results obtained from sample data are subject to sampling error. A test of significance can be applied to the multiple determination coefficient by application of analysis of variance. This test is equivalent to testing whether the joint regression of the dependent variable on the independent variables is significant. This test is applied by computing the ratio of the mean associated sum of squares to the mean unassociated sum of squares. This ratio has an F distribution for degrees of freedom $d.f._1 = r - 1$ and $d.f._2 = n - r$. The components of this ratio for the trivariate case are summarized in Table 18.2. This ratio is expressed in terms of the multiple determination coefficient by the general expression

$$F = \frac{\dfrac{(R^2_{1.23\ldots r})}{(r - 1)}}{\dfrac{(1 - R^2_{1.23\ldots r})}{(n - r)}} \quad \ldots\ldots\ldots\ldots\ldots\ldots(18.10)$$

where r denotes the total number of variables in the correlation.

Table 18.2

ANALYSIS OF VARIANCE FOR TRIVARIATE LINEAR REGRESSION

Source of variation	Sum of squares	Degrees of freedom	Mean sum of squares
Regression of x_1 on x_2 and x_3	associated	$d.f._1 = r - 1$	$\dfrac{\text{associated}}{r - 1}$
Residual	unassociated	$d.f._2 = n - r$	$\dfrac{\text{unassociated}}{n - r}$
Total	associated + unassociated	$d.f. = n - 1$	...

→ *Example.* A test of significance is applied to the trivariate regression of plastic hardness on temperature and pressure and the resulting multiple determination coefficient. The necessary data are summarized as follows:

Source of variation	Sum of squares	Degrees of freedom	Mean sum of squares
Regression of x_1 on x_2 and x_3	2,840.37	$d.f._1 = 3 - 1 = 2$	1,420.18
Residual	305.79	$d.f._2 = 25 - 3 = 22$	13.90
Total	3,146.16	$d.f. = 25 - 1 = 24$	...

The F ratio is computed

$$F = \frac{\text{mean associated sum of squares}}{\text{mean unassociated sum of squares}}$$

$$= \frac{1,420.18}{13.90} = 102.17.$$

An alternative derivation of the F ratio is found by use of Formula 18.10 and computing

$$F = \frac{\dfrac{(R^2_{1.23})}{(r - 1)}}{\dfrac{(1 - R^2_{1.23})}{(n - r)}}$$

$$= \frac{\dfrac{(0.9028)}{(3 - 1)}}{\dfrac{(1 - 0.9028)}{(25 - 3)}} = \frac{0.4514}{0.004418} = 102.17.$$

Since $F_{0.001}$ for $d.f._1 = 2$ and $d.f._2 = 22$ interpolated from Appendix L is 9.64, and $F = 102.17$ in this example, the multiple determination coefficient is highly significant. The hypothesis that the universe determination coefficient is zero is rejected. The same conclusion applies to the multiple correlation coefficient.

PARTIAL CORRELATION

The degree to which the residual variation of a dependent variable is correlated with the variation of an independent variable can be expressed by the *cofficient of partial determination*. This coefficient may be interpreted as the percent of residual variation associated with or explained by an independent variable.

Zero- and First-Order Partial Coefficients

The order of a partial determination coefficient corresponds to the number of independent variables regressed as a particular residual was obtained. Zero- and first-order partial determination coefficients can be computed from trivariate regression results. These are summarized in Table 18.3.

➤ *Example.* The zero- and first-order partial determination coefficients for the regression of plastic hardness (x_1) on temperature (x_2) and pressure (x_3) are computed from the trivariate regression and correlation results. The zero-order coefficients are computed as follows:

$$r_{12}^2 = \frac{b_{12}\Sigma d_{12}}{\Sigma d_1^2} \qquad\qquad r_{13}^2 = \frac{b_{13}\Sigma d_{13}}{\Sigma d_1^2}$$

$$= \frac{0.2485(5,638)}{3,146.16} \qquad\qquad = \frac{6.8140(316.5)}{3,146.16}$$

$$= \frac{1,401.04}{3,146.16} = 0.4453 \qquad\qquad = \frac{2,159.80}{3,146.16} = 0.6865.$$

The first-order partial determination coefficients are computed as follows:

$$r_{12.3}^2 = \frac{b_{12.3}\Sigma d_{12} + b_{13.2}\Sigma d_{13} - b_{13}\Sigma d_{13}}{\Sigma d_1^2 - b_{13}\Sigma d_{13}} \quad\ldots\ldots\ldots\ldots(18.11)$$

$$= \frac{0.1796(5,638) + 5.7754(316.5) - 6.8240(316.5)}{3,146.16 - 6.8240(316.5)}$$

$$= \frac{1,012.23 + 1,827.91 - 2,159.80}{3,146.16 - 2,159.80} = \frac{680.34}{986.36} = 0.6897.$$

Table 18.3

CHARACTERISTICS OF ZERO- AND FIRST-ORDER PARTIAL DETERMINATION COEFFICIENTS FOR TRIVARIATE REGRESSION

Order	Regression	Description	Computation formula (in terms of variation)	Computation formula (in terms of determination coefficients)	Partial determination coefficient
Zero	x_1 on x_2	Percent of variation of x_1 associated with the variation of x_2	$\dfrac{b_{12}\Sigma d_{12}}{\Sigma d_1^2}$ (Alternative form of Formula 16.9)	r_{12}^2 (16.9)	r_{12}^2
	x_1 on x_3	Percent of variation of x_1 associated with the variation of x_3	$\dfrac{b_{13}\Sigma d_{13}}{\Sigma d_1^2}$ (Alternative form of Formula 16.9)	r_{13}^2 (16.9)	r_{13}^2
First	x_1 on x_2 with x_3 held constant	Percent of the residual variation of the regression of x_1 on x_3 associated with the variation of x_2	$\dfrac{b_{12.3}\Sigma d_{12} + b_{13.2}\Sigma d_{13} - b_{13}\Sigma d_{13}}{\Sigma d_1^2 - b_{13}\Sigma d_{13}}$ (18.11)	$\dfrac{R_{1.23}^2 - r_{13}^2}{1 - r_{13}^2}$ (18.13)	$r_{12.3}^2$
	x_1 on x_3 with x_2 held constant	Percent of the residual variation of the regression of x_1 on x_2 associated with the variation of x_3	$\dfrac{b_{12.3}\Sigma d_{12} + b_{13.2}\Sigma d_{13} - b_{12}\Sigma d_{12}}{\Sigma d_1^2 - b_{12}\Sigma d_{12}}$ (18.12)	$\dfrac{R_{1.23}^2 - r_{12}^2}{1 - r_{12}^2}$ (18.14)	$r_{13.2}^2$

$$r_{13.2}^2 = \frac{b_{12.3}\Sigma d_{12} + b_{13.2}\Sigma d_{13} - b_{12}\Sigma d_{12}}{\Sigma d_1^2 - b_{12}\Sigma d_{12}} \quad\ldots\ldots\ldots(18.12)$$

$$= \frac{0.1796(5,638) + 5.7754(316.5) - 0.2485(5,638)}{3,146.16 - 0.2485(5,638)}$$

$$= \frac{1,012.23 + 1,827.91 - 1,401.04}{3,146.16 - 1,401.04}$$

$$= \frac{1,439.10}{1,745.12} = 0.8246.$$

Alternatively, the first-order coefficients are computed

$$r_{12.3}^2 = \frac{R_{1.23}^2 - r_{13}^2}{1 - r_{13}^2} \quad\ldots\ldots\ldots\ldots(18.13)$$

$$= \frac{0.9028 - 0.6865}{1 - 0.6865}$$

$$= \frac{0.2163}{0.3135} = 0.6899.$$

$$r_{13.2}^2 = \frac{R_{1.23}^2 - r_{12}^2}{1 - r_{12}^2} \quad\ldots\ldots\ldots\ldots(18.14)$$

$$= \frac{0.9028 - 0.4453}{1 - 0.4453}$$

$$= \frac{0.4575}{0.5547} = 0.8248.$$

The slight differences in the two methods for computing the first-order coefficients result from rounding error.

Comparison of Partial and Multiple Determination Coefficients

The partial determination coefficients computed in the foregoing example may be interpreted as follows:

Coefficient	*Interpolation*
$r_{12}^2 = 0.4453$	About 45% of the variation of plastic hardness is explained by variations in temperature, with pressure not considered.
$r_{13}^2 = 0.6865$	Approximately 69% of the variation of plastic hardness is explained by variations in pressure, with temperature not considered.

Coefficient	*Interpolation*
$r_{12.3}^2 = 0.6897$	Almost 69% of the variation in plastic hardness not explained by variations in pressure is explained by variations in temperature.
$r_{13.2}^2 = 0.8246$	More than 82% of the variation in plastic hardness not explained by variations in temperature is explained by variations in pressure.

The relationship of partial determination coefficients to the multiple determination coefficient is illustrated by use of the plastic hardness example as follows:

Percent of the variation of x_1 associated with the variation of x_2 and x_3		Percent of the variation of x_1 associated with the variation of x_2		Percent of the variation of x_1 not associated with the variation of x_2		Percent of the variation of x_1 not associated with x_2 that is associated with the variation of x_3
$R_{1.23}^2$	$=$	r_{12}^2	$+$	$(1 - r_{12}^2)$	$\cdot$	$(r_{13.2}^2)$

Substituting the values for the coefficients gives

$$R_{1.23}^2 = r_{12}^2 + (1 - r_{12}^2)(r_{13.2}^2)$$
$$= 0.4453 + (1 - 0.4453)(0.8246)$$
$$= 0.4453 + (0.5547)(0.8246)$$
$$= 0.4453 + 0.4574 = 0.9027.$$

This value of $R_{1.23}^2$ is the same, except for very slight rounding error, as that obtained previously. This illustration is analogous to the example shown graphically in Figure 18.1. The corresponding values in the two examples are, respectively,

$$R_{1.23}^2 = r_{12}^2 + (1 - r_{12}^2)(r_{13.2}^2) \qquad \text{and}$$

$$A_{1.23} = A_{12} + (U_1 - A_{12})\frac{A_{13.2}}{U_{12}}$$

$$= A_{12} + (U_{12})\frac{A_{13.2}}{U_{12}} = A_{12} + A_{13.2}.$$

The multiple determination coefficient is also related to partial determination coefficients based on x_3. The relationship is written

$$R_{1.23}^2 = r_{13}^2 + (1 - r_{13}^2)(r_{12.3}^2)$$
$$= 0.6865 + (1 - 0.6865)(0.6897)$$
$$= 0.6865 + (0.3135)(0.6897)$$
$$= 0.6865 + 0.2162 = 0.9027.$$

This result is precisely that obtained in the foregoing illustration.

It should be noted that the value of $R_{1.23}^2$ is obtained from the joint regression of x_1, x_2, and x_3. The partial determination coefficients, in contrast, reflect what might be viewed as the order or sequence in which the variables are regressed. But, as seen in the foregoing illustrations, the same value of $R_{1.23}^2$ is obtained *regardless of the order used* in regressing the variables.

REGRESSION AND CORRELATION OF MORE THAN THREE VARIABLES

Multiple regression or correlation problems may involve more than three variables. The following discussion concerning the regression and correlation of four variables is designed to provide insight into the analysis of complex multivariate relationships. The regression and correlation of four variables is an extension of the basic concepts introduced in the discussion of trivariate analysis.

Regression of Four Variables

The regression equation that expresses the linear relationship of a dependent variable with three independent variables can be written in the functional form

$$x_1 = f(x_2, x_3, x_4 \,|\, \hat{\theta}_1, \hat{\theta}_2, \hat{\theta}_3, \hat{\theta}_4)$$

where x_1, x_2, x_3, x_4 are the respective variables and $\hat{\theta}_1 = a_{1.234}$, $\hat{\theta}_2 = b_{12.34}$, $\hat{\theta}_3 = b_{13.24}$, and $\hat{\theta}_4 = b_{14.23}$. The regression equation is written

$$x_{1c.234} = a_{1.234} + b_{12.34}x_2 + b_{13.24}x_3 + b_{14.23}x_4.$$

The assumptions implicit in Formula 18.1 also apply to the four-variable regression case. The parameter estimators are obtained by solving the normal equations

$$\text{II. } b_{12.34}\Sigma d_2^2 + b_{13.24}\Sigma d_{23} + b_{14.23}\Sigma d_{24} = \Sigma d_{12}$$
$$\text{III. } b_{12.34}\Sigma d_{23} + b_{13.24}\Sigma d_3^2 + b_{14.23}\Sigma d_{34} = \Sigma d_{13}$$
$$\text{IV. } b_{12.34}\Sigma d_{24} + b_{13.24}\Sigma d_{34} + b_{14.23}\Sigma d_4^2 = \Sigma d_{14}$$

for the partial regression coefficients and by solving

$$a_{1.234} = \bar{x}_1 - b_{12.34}\bar{x}_2 - b_{13.24}\bar{x}_3 - b_{14.23}\bar{x}_4 \quad\ldots\ldots(18.15)$$

for the constant term. The estimated variance of the error of estimating x_1 is obtained by solving

$$\hat{\sigma}_{1.234}^2 = \frac{\Sigma d_1^2 - b_{12.34}\Sigma d_{12} - b_{13.24}\Sigma d_{13} - b_{14.23}\Sigma d_{14}}{n - 4} \quad\ldots\ldots(18.16)$$

where the loss of four degrees of freedom results from the estimation of four parameters in the regression equation.

➤ *Example.* A sample of 25 observations of plastic hardness (x_1), temperature (x_2), pressure (x_3), and percent additive (x_4) is taken from a chemical process. The four variables are regressed to derive an expression for predicting plastic hardness on the basis of the observed operating conditions. The sample data are shown in Table 18.1, a portion of which was used in the trivariate regression example. The required means and sums of squares and cross-products are as follows:

$$\bar{x}_1 = \frac{1,389}{25} = 55.56$$

$$\bar{x}_2 = \frac{11,200}{25} = 448.00$$

$$\bar{x}_3 = \frac{562.5}{25} = 22.50$$

$$\bar{x}_4 = \frac{62.2}{25} = 2.488.$$

$\Sigma d_1^2 = \Sigma(x_1 - \bar{x}_1)^2 \quad = \Sigma x_1^2 - n\bar{x}_1^2 \quad = 80,319 - 25(55.56)^2 \quad = 80,319 - 77,172.84 \quad = 3,146.16$

$\Sigma d_2^2 = \Sigma(x_2 - \bar{x}_2)^2 \quad = \Sigma x_2^2 - n\bar{x}_2^2 \quad = 5,040,284 - 25(448.00)^2 \quad = 5,040,284 - 5,017,600 = 22,684$

$\Sigma d_3^2 = \Sigma(x_3 - \bar{x}_3)^2 \quad = \Sigma x_3^2 - n\bar{x}_3^2 \quad = 12,702.63 - 25(22.5)^2 \quad = 12,702.63 - 12,656.25 = 46.38$

$\Sigma d_4^2 = \Sigma(x_4 - \bar{x}_4)^2 \quad = \Sigma x_4^2 - n\bar{x}_4^2 \quad = 212.18 - 25(2.488)^2 \quad = 212.18 - 154.75 \quad = 57.42$

$\Sigma d_{12} = \Sigma(x_1 - \bar{x}_1)(x_2 - \bar{x}_2) = \Sigma x_1 x_2 - n\bar{x}_1\bar{x}_2 = 627,910 - 25(55.56)(448.00) = 627,910 - 622,272 \quad = 5,638$

$\Sigma d_{13} = \Sigma(x_1 - \bar{x}_1)(x_3 - \bar{x}_3) = \Sigma x_1 x_3 - nx_1\bar{x}_3 = 31,569.0 - 25(55.56)(22.50) \quad = 31,569.0 - 31,252.5 \quad = 316.5$

$\Sigma d_{14} = \Sigma(x_1 - \bar{x}_1)(x_4 - \bar{x}_4) = \Sigma x_1 x_4 - n\bar{x}_1\bar{x}_4 = 3,286.5 - 25(55.56)(2.488) \quad = 3,286.5 - 3,455.8 \quad = -169.3$

$\Sigma d_{23} = \Sigma(x_2 - \bar{x}_2)(x_3 - \bar{x}_3) = \Sigma x_2 x_3 - n\bar{x}_2\bar{x}_3 = 252,270.8 - 25(448.00)(22.50) = 252,270.8 - 252,000.0 = 270.8$

$\Sigma d_{24} = \Sigma(x_2 - \bar{x}_2)(x_4 - \bar{x}_4) = \Sigma x_2 x_4 - n\bar{x}_2\bar{x}_4 = 27,629.3 - 25(448.00)(2.488) \quad = 27,629.3 - 27,865.6 \quad = -236.3$

$\Sigma d_{34} = \Sigma(x_3 - \bar{x}_3)(x_4 - \bar{x}_4) = \Sigma x_3 x_4 - n\bar{x}_3\bar{x}_4 = 1,378.14 - 25(22.50)(2.488) \quad = 1,378.14 - 1,399.5 \quad = -21.36$

The normal equations are

II. $\quad 22,684 b_{12.34} + 270.8 b_{13.24} - 236.3 b_{14.23} = 5,638$

III. $\quad 270.8 b_{12.34} + 46.38 b_{13.24} - 21.36 b_{14.23} = 316.5$

IV. $\quad -236.3 b_{12.34} - 21.36 b_{13.24} + 57.42 b_{14.23} = -169.3.$

The normal equations are written in matrix form to give

$$\begin{bmatrix} 22,684 & 270.8 & -236.3 \\ 270.8 & 46.38 & -21.36 \\ -236.3 & -21.36 & 57.42 \end{bmatrix} \begin{bmatrix} b_{12.34} \\ b_{13.24} \\ b_{14.23} \end{bmatrix} = \begin{bmatrix} 5,638 \\ 316.5 \\ -169.3 \end{bmatrix}$$

The simultaneous equations are solved by matrix inversion in the following steps:

(a)

$$
\begin{bmatrix}
\Sigma d_2^2 & \Sigma d_{23} & \Sigma d_{24} & 1 & 0 & 0 & \Sigma d_{12} \\
\Sigma d_{23} & \Sigma d_3^2 & \Sigma d_{34} & 0 & 1 & 0 & \Sigma d_{13} \\
\Sigma d_{24} & \Sigma d_{34} & \Sigma d_4^2 & 0 & 0 & 1 & \Sigma d_{14}
\end{bmatrix}
=
\begin{bmatrix}
a_{22} & a_{23} & a_{24} & 1 & 0 & 0 & b_1 \\
a_{32} & a_{33} & a_{34} & 0 & 1 & 0 & b_2 \\
a_{42} & a_{43} & a_{44} & 0 & 0 & 1 & b_3
\end{bmatrix}
$$

$$
=
\begin{matrix}
R_2 \\
R_3 \\
R_4
\end{matrix}
\begin{bmatrix}
22.684 & 270.8 & -236.3 & 1 & 0 & 0 & 5.638 \\
270.8 & 46.38 & -21.36 & 0 & 1 & 0 & 316.5 \\
-236.3 & -21.36 & 57.42 & 0 & 0 & 1 & -169.3
\end{bmatrix}
$$

(b)

$$
\begin{matrix}
\dfrac{R_2}{a_{22}} \\[2mm]
R_3 - a_{32}R_2 \\[1mm]
R_4 - a_{42}R_2
\end{matrix}
\begin{bmatrix}
1 & 0.0119379296 & -0.0104170338 & 0.000044083935 & 0 & 0 & 0.248545225 \\
0 & 43.14720866 & -18.53906725 & -0.0119379201 & 1 & 0 & 249.1939531 \\
0 & -18.53906725 & 54.9584549 & 0.1041703384 & 0 & 1 & -110.5694663
\end{bmatrix}
$$

(c)

$$
\begin{matrix}
R_2 - a_{23}R_3 \\[1mm]
\dfrac{R_3}{a_{33}} \\[1mm]
R_4 - a_{43}R_3
\end{matrix}
\begin{bmatrix}
1 & 0 & -0.0052876619 & 0.0000473869076 & -0.000276678847 & 0 & 0.179598475 \\
0 & 1 & -0.42967014 & -0.000276678847 & 0.023176470 & 0 & 5.7754361782 \\
0 & 0 & 46.99277128 & 0.0052876619 & 0.42967014 & 1 & -3.49826660
\end{bmatrix}
$$

(d)

$$
\begin{matrix}
R_2 - a_{24}R_4 \\[1mm]
R_3 - a_{34}R_4 \\[1mm]
\dfrac{R_4}{a_{44}}
\end{matrix}
\begin{bmatrix}
1 & 0 & 0 & 0.0000479818 & -0.0002283320 & 0.0001125075 & 0.17920487 \\
0 & 1 & 0 & -0.0002283320 & 0.0272750234 & 0.0091433239 & 5.74345040 \\
0 & 0 & 1 & 0.0001125075 & 0.0091433239 & 0.0212798680 & -0.07444265
\end{bmatrix}.
$$

This solution gives the results

$$
b_{12.34} = 0.179205
$$
$$
b_{13.24} = 5.743450
$$
$$
b_{14.23} = -0.074443.
$$

Substituting the partial regression coefficients into Formula 18.15 gives

$$
\begin{aligned}
a_{1.234} &= 55.56 - 0.179205(448.00) - 5.743450(22.50) \\
&\quad + 0.074443(2.488) \\
&= 55.56 - 80.28 - 129.23 + 0.19 \\
&= -153.76.
\end{aligned}
$$

The multiple regression equation is

$$
x_{1c.234} = -153.76 + 0.179205 b_{12.34} + 5.743450 b_{13.24} \\
- 0.074443 b_{14.23}.
$$

An unbiased estimate of the variance of the error of estimating x_1 is computed by Formula 18.16 to give

$$\hat{\sigma}^2_{1.234} = \frac{3{,}146.16 - 0.179205(5{,}638) - 5.743450(316.5)}{25 - 4}$$
$$\qquad\qquad\quad\; - 0.074443(169.3)$$

$$= \frac{3{,}146.16 - 1{,}010.36 - 1{,}817.80 - 12.60}{21}$$

$$= \frac{305.40}{21} = 14.543.$$

$$\hat{\sigma}_{1.234} = \sqrt{\hat{\sigma}^2_{1.234}} = \sqrt{14.543} = 3.813.$$

Significance Tests for the Regression Coefficients

The residual variation for the regression of four variables in the fore-going example is 305.40, obtained in the computation of $\hat{\sigma}_{1.234}$. This unassociated variation is slightly less than the value 305.67, the residual variation from the trivariate regression. The addition of the fourth variable, percent additive, increases the associated variation. Since the decrease in the unassociated variation is so slight, it is questionable whether the decrease is significant statistically. A comparison of $\hat{\sigma}_{1.23} = 3.727$ and $\hat{\sigma}_{1.234} = 3.813$ shows that the latter is the larger. This results from the fact that the reduction in unassociated variation is more than offset by the loss of a degree of freedom.

A test of significance can be applied to each regression coefficient to determine if each of the independent variables is related significantly to the dependent variable in the joint regression of four variables.

➤ *Example.* The partial regression coefficients obtained in the regression of the four variables, plastic hardness, temperature, pressure, and percent additive are tested for significance by use of an extension of Formula 18.7. The estimated standard error of a partial regression coefficient is computed by use of the expression

$$\hat{\sigma}_{b_{1i.jk}} = \hat{\sigma}_{1.234} \sqrt{c_{ii}}.$$

The inverse of the moment matrix is

$$\begin{bmatrix} a_{22} & a_{23} & a_{24} \\ a_{32} & a_{33} & a_{34} \\ a_{42} & a_{43} & a_{44} \end{bmatrix}^{-1} = \begin{bmatrix} c_{22} & c_{23} & c_{24} \\ c_{32} & c_{33} & c_{34} \\ c_{42} & c_{43} & c_{44} \end{bmatrix} =$$

$$\begin{bmatrix} 0.0000479818 & -0.0002283320 & 0.0001125075 \\ -0.0002283320 & 0.0272750234 & 0.0091433239 \\ 0.0001125075 & 0.0091433239 & 0.0212798680 \end{bmatrix}.$$

The values of the required estimates are, respectively,

$$\hat{\sigma}_{b_{12.34}} = \hat{\sigma}_{1.234} \sqrt{c_{22}} = 3.813 \sqrt{0.0000479818} = 0.02641$$

$$\hat{\sigma}_{b_{13.24}} = \hat{\sigma}_{1.234} \sqrt{c_{33}} = 3.813 \sqrt{0.0272750234} = 0.6295$$

$$\hat{\sigma}_{b_{14.23}} = \hat{\sigma}_{1.234} \sqrt{c_{44}} = 3.813 \sqrt{0.0212798680} = 0.5563.$$

The t values for the significance tests are, respectively,

$$t = \frac{b_{12.34} - 0}{\hat{\sigma}_{b_{12.34}}} = \frac{0.179205}{0.02641} = 6.785$$

$$t = \frac{b_{13.24} - 0}{\hat{\sigma}_{b_{13.24}}} = \frac{5.743450}{0.6295} = 9.123$$

$$t = \frac{b_{14.23} - 0}{\hat{\sigma}_{b_{14.23}}} = \frac{-0.074443}{0.5563} = -0.1338.$$

The value $t_{0.001} = 3.819$ for $25 - 4 = 21$ degrees of freedom is read from Appendix J. The coefficients $b_{12.34}$ and $b_{13.24}$ differ significantly from zero. The coefficient $b_{14.23}$ is not significant since $t = -0.1338$ is greater than $t_{0.80} = -0.257$ for $25 - 4 = 21$ degrees of freedom, as read from Appendix J.

Multiple Correlation of More Than Three Variables

Determination Coefficient. The multiple determination coefficient for the correlation of more than three variables is computed by the general expression

$$R_{1.23\ldots r}^2 = \frac{b_{12.3\ldots r}\Sigma d_{12} + b_{13.2\ldots r}\Sigma d_{13} + \ldots + b_{1r.2\ldots r-1}\Sigma d_{1r}}{\Sigma d_1^2}$$

$$\ldots\ldots(18.17)$$

where r denotes the number of variables regressed.

➤ *Example.* The multiple determination coefficient for the four-variable regression example presented previously is computed

$$R_{1.234}^2 = \frac{b_{12.34}\Sigma d_{12} + b_{13.24}\Sigma d_{13} + b_{14.23}\Sigma d_{14}}{\Sigma d_1^2}$$

$$= \frac{0.179205(5,638) + 5.743450(316.5) - (-0.074443)(-169.3)}{3,146.16}$$

$$= \frac{2,840.76}{3,146.16}$$

$$= 0.9029.$$

The coefficient of multiple correlation is computed

$$R_{1.234} = \sqrt{R_{1.234}^2}$$

$$= \sqrt{0.9029}$$

$$= 0.9502.$$

The difference between $R_{1.234}^2 = 0.9029$ and $R_{1.23}^2 = 0.9028$ indicates that the addition of variable x_4 increases the associated variation by an insignificant amount.

Significance Test for the Coefficient of Multiple Determination. A test of significance for the coefficient of multiple determination is made by the application of analysis of variance.

➤ ***Example.*** Analysis of variance is applied to the regression of plastic hardness on temperature, pressure, and percent additive by use of the following data:

Source of variation	Sum of squares	Degrees of freedom	Mean sum of squares
Regression of x_1 on x_2, x_3, and x_4	2,840.76	$d.f._1 = 4 - 1 = 3$	946.92
Residual	305.40	$d.f._2 = 25 - 4 = 21$	14.54
Total	3,146.16	$d.f. = 25 - 1 = 24$	...

The F ratio is computed

$$F = \frac{\text{mean associated sum of squares}}{\text{mean unassociated sum of squares}}$$

$$= \frac{946.92}{14.54}$$

$$= 65.13.$$

The value $F_{0.001} = 7.96$ for $d.f._1 = 3$ and $d.f._2 = 21$ is interpolated from Appendix L. Since $F = 65.13$, the coefficient is highly significant. The significance of this coefficient reflects the joint correlation of the four variables rather than the significance of any one variable.

Partial Correlation

The effect of the regression of the fourth variable (third independent) can be measured by second-order partial determination and correlation coefficients. The second-order partial determination coefficient for the fourth variable is computed by

$$r^2_{14.23} = \frac{R^2_{1.234} - R^2_{1.23}}{1 - R^2_{1.23}} \quad \ldots \ldots \ldots \ldots \text{(18.18)}$$

where $r^2_{14.23}$ is the percent of the variation of x_1 unassociated with x_2 and x_3 but associated with x_4.

→ **Example.** The second-order partial determination coefficient for the correlation of plastic hardness and percent additive with the effects of temperature and pressure held constant is computed

$$r^2_{14.23} = \frac{R^2_{1.234} - R^2_{1.23}}{1 - R^2_{1.23}}$$

$$= \frac{0.9029 - 0.9028}{1 - 0.9028}$$

$$= \frac{0.0001}{0.0972}$$

$$= 0.00103.$$

The corresponding second-order correlation coefficient is

$$r_{14.23} = \sqrt{r^2_{14.23}}$$

$$= \sqrt{0.00103}$$

$$= 0.0321.$$

The second-order partial determination and correlation coefficients are very small. These results confirm that x_4 is not correlated significantly with x_1. The same conclusion was obtained in the significance test of $b_{14.23}$.

USING COMPUTERS IN MULTIPLE REGRESSION AND CORRELATION ANALYSIS

The application of multiple regression and correlation analysis requires extensive, highly precise computations. Consequently, it is no surprise that computers are used widely in the application of these techniques. A large number of computer installations have one or more multiple regression and correlation programs in the program library that are available to users.

The availability of these programs enables many an analyst to obtain the desired regression and correlation results without the analyst having to spend time writing a computer program. The suitability of a given

library program for use in a particular problem depends upon the input
requirements, operating procedure, and results computed by the program. Many library programs are sufficiently general and comprehensive
to fulfill the requirements of a wide variety of users.

The flexibility of some general-purpose multiple regression and correlation programs is such as to give the user the matrix of sums of squares,
the inverse of the matrix of sums of squares, constant term, partial regression coefficients, determination and correlation coefficients, t or F
ratios for significance tests, and a variety of other results that the analyst
may desire. With the benefit of this type of versatile program, one can
concentrate on the analysis of results and avoid the time-consuming task
of computing the results manually.

➤ **Example.** The multiple regression and correlation of plastic hardness with temperature, pressure, and percent additive is computed by
use of a library program. The output of the program is shown in Table
18.4. This program includes a deletion feature which provides that the
total number of variables is regressed initially. Then, the variable with
the smallest F or t^2 ratio for the corresponding partial regression
coefficient is deleted, and the remaining variables are regressed. The
deletion operation is repeated, a second independent variable is
deleted, and the remaining variables are regressed. The process
continues until the dependent variable is regressed on a single independent variable. This deletion feature provides excellent diagnostic
information in the selection of variables that are related significantly
with the dependent variable. The values in Table 18.4 differ slightly
from those in the examples in this chapter because of rounding error.
The computer program carries computations to eight significant
digits.

Table 18.4

COMPUTER OUTPUT OF A MULTIPLE REGRESSION PROGRAM
WITH DELETION FEATURES

Variable	Average	Variance
x_1	55.559999	131.090080
x_2	447.999990	945.174990
x_3	22.499999	1.932541
x_4	2.487999	2.392767

Variables		Correlation
x_1	x_1	1.000000
x_1	x_2	0.667381
x_1	x_3	0.828544
x_1	x_4	−0.398375
x_2	x_2	1.000000
x_2	x_3	0.264017
x_2	x_4	−0.207035
x_3	x_3	1.000000
x_3	x_4	−0.413878
x_4	x_4	1.000000

Independent variables	Regression coefficient	F or t^2 ratio	
x_2	0.179199	46.016362	
x_3	5.743030	83.669138	Delete variable x_4
x_4	−0.07169	0.018259	

Error variance	Constant term	Multiple F	$d.f._1$	$d.f._2$	R_2
14.544052	−153.752330	65.106497	3	21	0.902921

Independent variables	Regression coefficient	F or t^2 ratio	
x_2	0.179596	48.986952	Delete variable x_2
x_3	5.775327	103.574860	

Error variance	Constant term	Multiple F	$d.f._1$	$d.f._2$	R^2
13.895029	−154.844090	102.211770	2	22	0.902836

Independent variables	Regression coefficient	F or t^2 ratio
x_2	6.823957	50.361954

Error variance	Constant term	Multiple F	$d.f._1$	$d.f._2$	R^2
42.885468	−97.979040	50.361959	1	23	0.686486

Source: Adapted from a library program by O. Dykstra, Jr., entitled "Multiple Regression Package for the Card 1620," program number 6.0.043, IBM 1620 Users Group.

STUDY QUESTIONS

18-1. Explain briefly the meaning of each of the following terms:

a. multiple regression

b. coefficient of partial regression

c. moment matrix

d. multiple correlation

e. coefficient of partial determination

f. zero-order partial correlation

g. first-order partial correlation

18-2. Describe the rationale of multiple regression.

18-3. Give a brief description of each of the terms in the trivariate regression equation in Formula 18.1.

18-4. When should a significance test be applied to the partial regression coefficients in multiple regression?

18-5. What is the significance of the following matrices?

$$\begin{bmatrix} c_{22} & c_{23} \\ c_{32} & c_{33} \end{bmatrix}, \quad \begin{bmatrix} c_{22} & c_{23} & c_{24} \\ c_{32} & c_{33} & c_{34} \\ c_{42} & c_{43} & c_{44} \end{bmatrix}$$

18-6. Why is an F test required for a significance test for a multiple determination coefficient?

18-7. Distinguish between multiple determination coefficients and partial determination coefficients.

18-8. Write the transpose of the moment matrix for the four variable regression case and compare it with the original moment matrix.

18-9. Describe the value of computers in multiple regression and correlation analysis.

PROBLEMS

18-1. Observations of strength of fiberboard (x_1), length of fibers in raw material (x_2), and processing temperature (x_3) of a process are taken. The results are listed as follows:

Fiberboard strength (psi) x_1	Fiber length (mm.) x_2	Processing temperature (°F) x_3
114.2	3.07	303
175.0	3.21	300
125.0	3.13	287
106.1	3.12	272
119.5	3.10	294
65.3	2.56	282
80.3	2.67	291
115.0	3.05	307

a. Compute the equation for the linear regression of fiberboard strength on fiber length and processing temperature.
b. Compute the 95% confidence limits of the expected value of fiberboard strength for a fiber length of 3.30 mm. and a processing temperature of 270 F.
c. Test the partial regression coefficients for significance.

18-2. Sales volume of a product (x_1), price per unit (x_2), and advertising expense (x_3) are recorded as follows:

Sales volume (thousands of units) x_1	Price per unit (dollars) x_2	Advertising expense (hundreds of dollars) x_3
10.1	1.3	8.8
6.5	1.9	7.1
5.1	1.7	5.5
11.8	1.5	13.8
9.9	1.6	18.5
14.7	1.2	9.8
4.8	1.6	6.4
12.2	1.4	10.2

a. Compute the equation for the linear regression of sales volume on price per unit and advertising expense.
b. Compute the 95% confidence limits of sales volume for a price of $1.6 per unit and an advertising expense of $10.5 hundred dollars.
c. Test the partial regression coefficients for significance.

18-3. Representative data for output (x_1), labor input (x_2), variable cost (x_3), and fixed expenses (x_4) are listed as follows:

Output (units) x_1	Labor input (hours) x_2	Variable cost (dollars) x_3	Fixed expense (dollars) x_4
6	7	23	3
4	5	22	6
10	9	19	6
9	10	24	3
7	8	22	8
5	7	25	4
2	4	22	1
8	8	19	6
4	2	24	3
10	9	21	7

   a. Compute the equation for the linear regression of output on labor input and variable cost.

   b. Compute the 95% confidence limits of the expected value of output for a labor input of six hours and a variable cost of $20.

   c. Test the partial regression coefficients for significance.

18-4. Use the data in Problem 18-3 to:

   a. Compute the equation for the linear regression of output on labor input, variable cost, and fixed-expense.

   b. Compute the 95% confidence limits of the expected value of output for a labor input of eight hours, a variable cost of $22, and a fixed expense of $6.

   c. Test the partial regression coefficients for significance.

18-5. Correlate the change in fiberboard strength with fiber length and processing temperature (see Problem 18-1) and

   a. Compute the multiple determination coefficient.

   b. Test the multiple correlation for significance.

18-6. Correlate the change in sales volume with price per unit and advertising expense (see Problem 18-2) and

   a. Compute the multiple determination coefficient.

   b. Test the multiple correlation for significance.

18-7. Correlate the change in output with labor input and variable cost (see Problem 18-3) and

   a. Compute the multiple determination coefficient.

   b. Test the multiple correlation for significance.

18-8. Correlate the change in output with labor input and variable cost (see Problem 18-4) and

   a. Compute the multiple determination coefficient.

   b. Test the multiple correlation for significance.

   c. Compute $r^2_{14.23}$.

18-9. An analyst wishes to determine if there is a relationship between various census statistics and the 1950–1960 increase in population of selected cities. Observations of several variables are summarized in Table 18.A, page 654.

   a. Compute the linear equation for the regression of population change on employment per household and change in employment.

   b. What are the 95% confidence limits of the expected change in population for an employment per household ratio of 1.37 and a change of 55.8% in employment?

   c. Test the partial regression coefficients for significance.

18-10. Use the data in Table 18.A to:

   a. Compute the regression of change in population on change in employment and median age.

   b. Find the 95% confidence interval of change in population for 17.7% change in employment and a median age of 28.9 years.

   c. Test the partial regression coefficients for significance.

Table 18.A

SELECTED POPULATION AND ECONOMIC STATISTICS FOR SELECTED CITIES

City	Change in population 1950–1960 (percent)	Employment per house-hold, 1950	Change in employment 1950–1960 (percent)	Median age of the population (years)	Median income 1950 (dollars)	Change in median income 1950–1960 (percent)
1	98.30	1.36	63.50	27.20	2473.00	120.80
2	26.80	1.20	23.30	23.20	2367.00	74.90
3	40.80	1.38	41.90	27.20	2126.00	140.80
4	22.50	1.28	15.70	28.20	4045.00	71.50
5	95.30	1.26	103.20	28.20	5128.00	60.60
6	80.70	1.32	48.90	27.30	3098.00	83.40
7	33.20	1.19	29.00	23.30	1846.00	63.70
8	− 15.90	1.09	− 9.10	30.50	1932.00	111.30
9	19.20	1.10	22.80	33.40	2592.00	95.70
10	54.90	1.30	40.40	26.30	2880.00	81.30
11	56.40	1.48	43.70	30.90	3042.00	96.40
12	31.00	1.12	19.30	23.90	1746.00	98.70
13	25.60	1.42	36.20	23.60	885.00	464.30
14	51.10	1.23	59.90	23.30	1816.00	66.70
15	27.80	1.38	17.20	30.10	2830.00	93.80
16	16.30	1.14	16.20	32.70	2232.00	112.90
17	264.20	1.41	245.40	26.10	3398.00	99.90
18	108.20	1.30	110.30	26.70	3307.00	74.30
19	77.40	1.29	41.10	24.30	2225.00	87.30
20	− 8.70	1.26	− 12.40	41.50	5144.00	166.50
21	49.70	1.28	27.10	23.90	2207.00	97.80
22	16.20	1.30	15.40	24.90	2642.00	88.20
23	63.50	1.33	51.40	28.90	2491.00	115.00
24	79.40	1.39	70.00	25.70	2646.00	111.00
25	63.10	1.26	67.50	24.70	2095.00	80.90
26	30.30	1.22	25.90	31.90	2209.00	96.20
27	8.60	1.16	12.70	21.80	1208.00	98.30
28	188.40	1.34	175.60	26.70	3842.00	84.60
29	2.80	1.24	5.50	27.20	1599.00	128.60
30	28.00	1.24	26.30	27.90	2371.00	94.20
31	20.90	1.20	12.50	25.50	2913.00	89.20
32	11.80	1.13	3.80	33.30	2325.00	96.50
33	− 3.10	1.07	0.20	31.80	1725.00	108.90
34	161.30	1.27	157.70	25.20	3990.00	79.80
35	15.90	1.30	4.30	29.00	3386.00	67.10
36	12.90	1.21	11.10	27.80	2530.00	83.80
37	23.70	1.15	28.40	22.60	1598.00	84.30
38	24.00	1.21	15.50	31.50	2494.00	90.60
39	2.20	1.30	− 4.20	28.00	2819.00	72.20
40	19.40	1.25	18.20	30.10	2440.00	84.80
41	22.10	1.22	13.10	30.90	2069.00	110.40
42	92.90	1.24	85.50	26.10	3502.00	74.20
43	− 4.40	1.33	2.30	35.50	4578.00	125.10
44	− 4.00	1.21	− 2.40	29.90	2443.00	82.50
45	104.90	1.37	79.10	28.70	2638.00	100.10
46	15.50	1.28	12.90	29.20	2274.00	113.70
47	13.80	1.22	22.20	29.40	1972.00	127.10
48	− 14.30	1.29	3.30	33.90	5760.00	48.10
49	6.30	1.15	10.30	22.70	3233.00	68.70
50	49.50	1.29	42.60	25.00	1764.00	209.00

Source: 1960 United States Census.

18-11. Use the data in Table 18.A to:
  a. Compute the regression of the change in population on employment per household, change in employment, and median age.
  b. Find the 95% confidence interval estimate of change in population for an employment per household ratio of 1.28, a change in employment of 14.8%, and a median age of 25.2 years.
  c. Test the partial regression coefficients for significance.

18-12. Use the data in Table 18.A to:
  a. Compute the regression of the change in population on change in employment, median age, and change in median income.
  b. Find the 95% confidence interval estimate of change in population for change in employment of 46.8%, a median age of 27.9 years, and a change in median income of 92.2%.
  c. Test the partial regression coefficients for significance.

18-13. Correlate the change in population with employment per household and change in population (see Problem 18-9) and
  a. Compute the multiple determination coefficient.
  b. Test the multiple correlation for significance.
  c. Compute $r_{13.2}^2$.

18-14. Correlate the change in population with change in employment and median age (see Problem 18-10) and
  a. Compute the multiple determination coefficient.
  b. Test the multiple correlation for significance.
  c. Compute $r_{13.2}^2$.

18-15. Correlate the change in population with employment per household, change in employment, and median age (see Problem 18-11) and
  a. Compute the multiple determination coefficient.
  b. Test the correlation for significance.
  c. Compute $r_{14.23}^2$ and interpret the result.

18-16. Correlate the change in population with change in employment, median age, and change in median income (see Problem 18-12) and
  a. Determine if the multiple correlation is significant.
  b. Compute $r_{14.23}^2$ and interpret the result.

18-17. Obtain a computer library program and use it and the data in Table 18.A to compare the regression and correlation of change in population with employment per household, change in employment, median age, and median income, and interpret the results.

18-18. Obtain a computer library program and use it to compute the regression and correlation of change in population with all the independent variables shown in Table 18.A and interpret the results.

SELECTED READINGS

Croxton, Frederick E., and Dudley J. Cowden. *Applied General Statistics.* 2d ed. Englewood Cliffs, New Jersey: Prentice-Hall, Inc., 1955.

Various topics in regression and correlation analysis are presented in Chapters 19 through 22.

Duncan, Acheson J. *Quality Control and Industrial Statistics.* 3d ed. Homewood, Illinois: Richard D. Irwin, 1965.

A thorough discussion of multiple regression and correlation is presented in Chapter 33.

Ezekial, Mordecai, and Karl A. Fox. *Methods of Correlation and Regression Analysis.* 3d ed. New York: John Wiley & Sons, Inc., 1959.

A standard reference in regression and correlation analysis that includes a discussion of the graphic method of regression analysis.

Chapter 19

Time Series: Trend Analysis

INTRODUCTION

A set of ordered observations of a quantitative variable taken at successive points in time is called a *time series*. Time, in terms of years, months, days, or hours is simply a device that enables one to relate all phenomena to a set of common, stable reference points.

Importance of Time-Series Analysis to the Businessman

The statistical analysis of time-series data is of particular interest to the businessman because a large proportion of the basic statistical data with which he must deal are time-series data. The quantitative measurement of inventories, sales, costs, prices, and many other business and economic variables is classified on the basis of intervals of time. Since one of the chief responsibilities of management is to forecast the future, the careful, detailed study of time series data is a prerequisite of survival. The chief aim in analyzing statistical information about the past is the desire to gain an understanding of the forces at work and to use that understanding to predict the future. Every businessman must forecast, and his success or failure may well depend upon the accuracy of his predictions.

Problems of Analysis

The analysis of time-series data presents its own unique set of problems and pitfalls. The very fact that economic data exist in such vast quantities and in such complex surroundings is enough to discourage all but the most determined investigator. Further, the application of many conventional statistical methods is difficult because it cannot be assumed that successive observations are statistically independent. A sample of data ordered in time is not the same as a random sample of observations drawn from a population, and it cannot be treated in the same fashion in analysis. For example, the cost of operating a factory in one month is not independent of the cost of operating the factory the month before. It is true that costs may change from one time period to another, but these changes are not entirely random. They are part of a changing pattern over time.

Another complexity of time-series analysis comes from the fact that the individual observations in the time series are a composite of several forces which may be pulling together or in opposite directions at any one point in time. An attempt to break the time-series model down into its component parts will assist in an understanding of the historical past and may give some insight into the future. This process of breaking the series into its component parts is called the *decomposition* of time series.

THE CLASSICAL APPROACH

The classical approach to time-series analysis holds that any given observation is made up of trend, seasonal, cyclical, and erratic components. The fact is that this is probably an oversimplification of the true state of affairs, for the art of time-series analysis is not so well developed as some other branches of statistics. Not all economists agree as to the classification of the components used here or as to the manner in which they are related. Some argue that there are more than four components, and some think that trend and cyclical movements are produced by the same set of forces.

During the past two or three decades the attempt to make forecasting more scientific has led to the development of alternate approaches such as econometrics. *Econometrics* attempts to express economic theories in mathematical models that can be tested and verified by statistical methods. It tries to measure the impact of one economic variable upon another in the hope of being able to predict future events.

The approach in this chapter is to present the classical statistical approach to time-series analysis, but at the same time to point out that many other possible models exist which are based on different assumptions and which may lead to different results.

Time-Series Components

A typical time series may be thought of as being made up of four types of fluctuations:

1. A *trend* component, which may be defined as long-term growth or decay.
2. A *seasonal* component, which may be defined as a regularly recurring periodic fluctuation.

3. A *cyclical* component, which may be defined as a wavelike fluctuation about trend. The length and the amplitude of the cycle are not constant, as in the seasonal component, but may vary from one cycle to the next.
4. An *erratic* or random component, which is completely unsystematic.

The Time-Series Model

If the letters T, S, C, and E are used to represent the four components of trend, seasonal, cyclical, and erratic fluctuations, respectively, the time series, y, may be written as

$$y = T \times S \times C \times E \dots\dots\dots\dots\dots\text{(19.1)}$$

This normally is called the *multiplicative model* and is the most commonly used model in the decomposition of time series.

Many econometricians and others prefer the *additive model*, in which

$$y = T + S + C + E \dots\dots\dots\dots\dots\text{(19.2)}$$

To prevent confusion between the two models, it should be pointed out that in the multiplicative model (Formula 19.1) S, C, and E are indexes expressed as decimal percents. In the additive model (Formula 19.2) S, C, and E are quantitative deviations about trend that can be expressed as seasonal, cyclical, and erratic in nature.

➤ **Example.** If in the multiplicative model, $T = 500$, $S = 1.20$, $C = 1.05$, and $E = 0.90$, then

$$y = (500)(1.20)(1.05)(0.90) = 567.$$

If in the additive model, $T = 500$, $S = +100$, $C = +25$, and $E = -45$, then

$$y = 500 + 100 + 25 - 45 = 580.$$

The additive model assumes that all the components of the time series are independent of one another. For example, it assumes that trend has no effect on the seasonal component no matter how high or how low this value may become. Further, it assumes that the business cycle has no effect on the seasonal component. If the index for December is typically 1.50 or 150%, this percent will not be affected by either prosperity or recession. While the additive model may work well within limits, it is doubtful if one always can rely on the independence of components that it assumes.

In the multiplicative model, it is assumed that the four components are due to different causes but they are not necessarily independent and they can affect one another. This model is also much easier to use and makes possible the isolation of the components.

The manipulation of these models will be considered after first examining in more detail the four basic types of fluctuations.

TREND

The trend in a times series may be represented graphically by a straight line or by one of many types of smooth curves. It can be represented algebraically by an equation. If the vertical axis of the graph is taken as the Y axis and if the horizontal axis is taken as the X axis, then Y, which is the variable being measured, may be shown as a function of X, which represents time. The general form of this equation is

$$Y = f(X).$$

If the functional relationship is that of a straight line, the equation may be written

$$y_c = a + bx \dots\dots\dots\dots\dots\dots\dots\text{(19.3)}$$

where,

a is the Y intercept

b is the slope of the line

y_c values are the computed values of Y on the trend line.

A Runs Test for Trend

Before facing the problem of the type of trend equation that is the most appropriate to a given set of observations, it is well to test the hypothesis that the time-series data constitute a random sequence. Unless this hypothesis can be rejected, no trend equation will have meaning.

A simple, distribution-free test for trend can be made using the one-sample runs test discussed in Chapter 13. The only difference lies in the fact that the attributes considered as runs are time-series values above and below the median. The values below the median for the series are designated by b and those above the median by a. Any values that are the same as the median are ignored. If, in fact, there is an upward trend in the series, there will be a concentration of b values in the early part of the series and a predominance of a values in the latter part. The number of runs will be significantly smaller than would be expected in a random sequence.

➤ *Example.* Table 19.1 shows the number of tornadoes recorded in Texas from 1920 through 1963, a total of 44 observations. The median number of tornadoes is 17.5, and there are 12 runs. A test for trend may be made as follows:

STEPS:

1. H_1:   The order of a's and b's is random and there is no trend.
2. H_2:   There is a significant trend.

3. An $\alpha = 0.05$ requires a $z = \pm 1.96$.
4. Criterion: Reject H_1 (accept H_2) if $z > 1.96$ or $z < -1.96$; accept H_1 if $-1.96 \le z \le 1.96$, when z is computed using Formulas 13.12, 13.13, and 13.14.
5. If n_1 represents the number of b's, $n_1 = 22$.
   If n_2 represents the number of a's, $n_2 = 22$.
   There are 12 runs, so $R = 12$.

$$\mu_R = \frac{2n_1 n_2}{n_1 + n_2} + 1 = \frac{2(22)(22)}{22 + 22} + 1 = \frac{968}{44} + 1 = 23.$$

$$\sigma_R = \sqrt{\frac{2n_1 n_2 (2n_1 n_2 - n_1 - n_2)}{(n_1 + n_2)^2 (n_1 + n_2 - 1)}} = \sqrt{\frac{(968)(968 - 44)}{(44)^2 (43)}} = 3.28.$$

$$z = \frac{R - \mu_R}{\sigma_R} = \frac{12 - 23}{3.28} = -3.36.$$

Since $z(-3.36) < z_\alpha (-1.96)$, reject H_1 and accept H_2. There is a significant trend in the number of tornadoes recorded in Texas between 1920 and 1963.

Table 19.1

NUMBER OF TORNADOES RECORDED IN TEXAS, 1920–1963

Year	Number	Relation to median	Runs	Year	Number	Relation to median	Runs
1920	4	below		1942	11	below	
1921	17	below		1943	17	below	
1922	14	below		1944	4	below	7
1923	8	below		1945	18	above	8
1924	7	below		1946	15	below	
1925	6	below		1947	14	below	
1926	11	below	1	1948	15	below	9
1927	25	above		1949	21	above	
1928	19	above		1950	21	above	10
1929	25	above		1951	15	below	
1930	20	above	2	1952	13	below	11
1931	8	below		1953	32	above	
1932	10	below		1954	77	above	
1933	13	below	3	1955	105	above	
1934	21	above		1956	57	above	
1935	28	above	4	1957	145	above	
1936	12	below		1958	74	above	
1937	7	below		1959	83	above	
1938	16	below	5	1960	77	above	
1939	22	above		1961	122	above	
1940	18	above	6	1962	143	above	
1941	12	below		1963	80	above	12

Source: United States Weather Bureau.

Moving Average

The most flexible device for describing the growth or decline in a time series is a moving average. It is particularly effective if the trend of a series is very irregular. Averages are normally computed for an odd number of time periods and are plotted in the center of the time span each represents. By averaging out the unusual highs and lows, a smoothing of the data results. The larger the number of time periods in the average, the greater the smoothing.

➤ *Example.* Data on the number of tornadoes recorded in Texas from 1920 through 1940 are shown in Table 19.2 and are plotted in Figure 19.1. Because this time series is so irregular for the years shown, it would be very difficult to find an equation for a line that would describe adequately the series. A three-year moving average smooths out many of the highs and lows, and a five-year moving average does an even better smoothing job.

Table 19.2

NUMBER OF TORNADOES RECORDED IN TEXAS, 1920–1940

Year	Number recorded	Three-year Total	Three-year Average	Five-year Total	Five-year Average
1920	4	...	...	...	...
1921	17	35	11.7	...	...
1922	14	39	13.0	50	10.0
1923	8	29	9.7	52	10.4
1924	7	21	7.0	46	9.2
1925	6	24	8.0	57	11.4
1926	11	42	14.0	68	13.6
1927	25	55	18.3	86	17.2
1928	19	69	23.0	100	20.0
1929	25	64	21.3	97	19.4
1930	20	53	17.7	82	16.4
1931	8	38	12.7	76	15.2
1932	10	31	10.3	72	14.4
1933	13	44	14.7	80	16.0
1934	21	62	20.7	84	16.8
1935	28	61	20.3	81	16.2
1936	12	47	15.7	84	16.8
1937	7	35	11.7	85	17.0
1938	16	45	15.0	75	15.0
1939	22	56	18.7	...	...
1940	18	...	...	...	...

Source: Table 19.1.

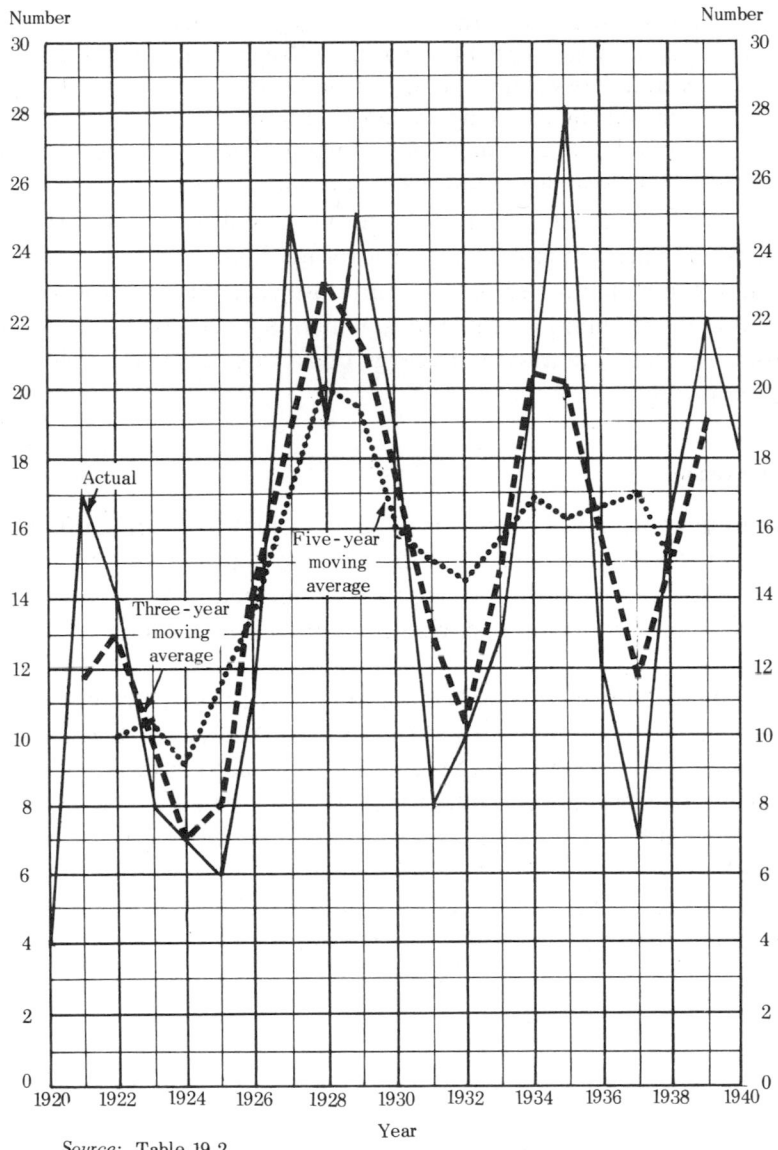

Number

Source: Table 19.2.

Figure 19.1

NUMBER OF TORNADOES RECORDED IN TEXAS, 1920–1940

There are a number of difficulties involved in using a moving average as a measure of trend:

1. Depending on the number of time periods used in the average, a moving average may obliterate periodic fluctuations in the data or it may, in unusual circumstances, create false ones not present in the original data.

2. It is not possible to extrapolate a moving average into the future as is possible with other types of trend lines. When a moving average is used to forecast, it always tends to lag behind trend.

3. A moving average is cumbersome to compute if the number of time periods used is large. Even when a computer is used, the memory requirements of the data may be excessive in some instances.

In spite of its shortcomings, the moving average has important uses. It does provide a method for smoothing data; a 12-month moving average is particularly useful in eliminating seasonal variation; and the technique of exponential smoothing, which is discussed in the following chapter, is based on a moving average but is designed to overcome most of its shortcomings.

Linear Trend

When the amount of increase (or decrease) is fairly constant from one time period to another, a straight line may be appropriate as a trend line. While such a line might be drawn by inspection, a more objective method of computing the equation for such a line is generally preferred.

Method of Semiaverages. This method produces a straight line that passes through two points. The first point is the arithmetic mean of the Y values for the first half of the series and is located in the middle of that time period. The second point is the arithmetic mean of the Y values for the second half of the series and is located in the middle of that time period. Since the data must be divided into two equal parts, an even number of years should be used in computing the trend equation. The constants in the trend equation can be found as

$$a = \frac{2S_1}{n} \quad \dots\dots\dots\dots\dots\dots\dots\dots\dots\dots(19.4)$$

$$b = \frac{4(S_2 - S_1)}{n^2} \quad \dots\dots\dots\dots\dots\dots(19.5)$$

where,
   S_1 is the sum of the Y values for the first half of the series
   S_2 is the sum of the Y values for the second half of the series
   n is the number of time periods (X units).

➤ *Example.* Per capita income in Texas from 1955 through 1964 is shown in Table 19.3. The trend equation for a straight line fitted to these data by the method of semiaverages is computed as follows, using Formulas 19.3, 19.4, and 19.5:

$$a = \frac{2S_1}{n} = \frac{2(8,953)}{10} = \$1,790.60, \text{ and}$$

$$b = \frac{4(S_2 - S_1)}{n^2} = \frac{4(10,172 - 8,953)}{10^2} = \$48.76.$$

$$y_c = 1,790.60 + 48.76x$$

origin : July 1, 1957
X unit: one year
Y unit : per capita income in dollars.

The original data and the trend line are shown in Figure 19.2.

In the previous example there was an odd number of years in each half so that the origin was taken as the middle of the middle year in the first half of the series, and the X unit was conveniently one year. Where there

Table 19.3

PER CAPITA INCOME IN TEXAS, 1955–1964
Computation of trend by method of semiaverages

Year	Per capita income y	Subperiod totals	x	Trend values y_c
1955	$1,645 ⎫		−2	$1,693.08
1956	1,732 ⎪		−1	1,741.84
1957	1,815 ⎬	$S_1 = \$8,953$	0	1,790.60 = a
1958	1,843 ⎪		1	1,839.36
1959	1,918 ⎭		2	1,888.12
1960	1,917 ⎫		3	1,936.88
1961	1,973 ⎪		4	1,985.64
1962	2,019 ⎬	$S_2 = \$10,172$	5	2,034.40
1963	2,088 ⎪		6	2,083.16
1964	2,175 ⎭		7	2,131.92

Source: Office of Business Economics, U.S. Department of Commerce, *Survey of Current Business.*

is an even number of years in each half, the origin will be the first of a year, and the X unit should be taken as six months. The value of n will then be two times the number of years in the series.

Method of Least Squares. Technical Note No. 1 at the end of Chapter 16 develops the method of least squares as a method of deriving a linear expression that best fits a series of paired observations. In Chapter 16 the least squares line was used as a regression equation to describe the relationship between two variables, x_1 and x_2. In time-series analysis

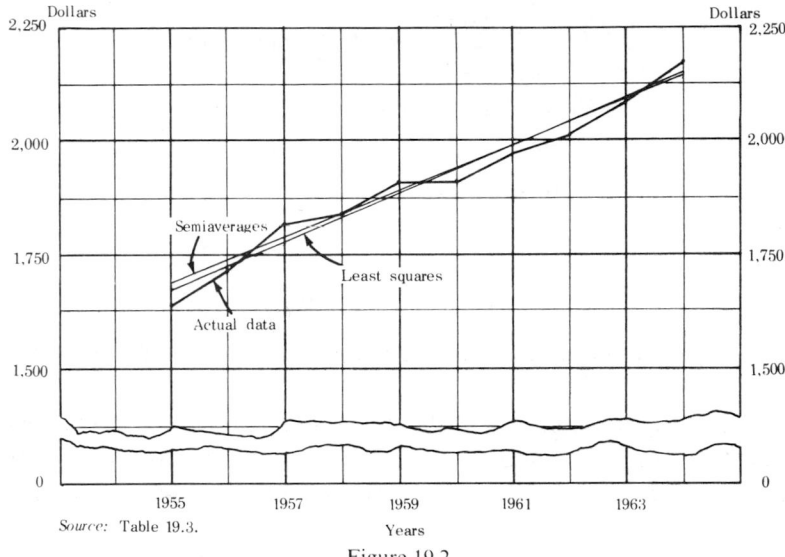

Figure 19.2

PER CAPITA INCOME IN TEXAS, 1955–1964

the same line may be used to define trend, with the X variable representing time, and the Y variable, the value of the series under study such as
sales, inventories, prices, or some other economic series.

The traditional notation in the literature on time series is somewhat
different from that used in Chapter 16 on regression and correlation, but
the principles involved are the same. For example, Formula 16.6

$$x_{1c} = a_{1.2} + b_{12}x_2$$

is the same as Formula 19.3,

$$y_c = a + bx.$$

The normal equations discussed in the technical note may be written
as

$$\Sigma y = na + b\Sigma x$$
$$\Sigma xy = a\Sigma x + b\Sigma x^2.$$

Since the values of x are coded values representing time, it is always
possible to set them up so that $\Sigma x = 0$. When this is done, one term in
each of the normal equations drops out and the equations become

$$a = \frac{\Sigma y}{n} \quad \dots\dots\dots\dots\dots\dots\dots\dots\dots\dots(19.6)$$

$$b = \frac{\Sigma xy}{\Sigma x^2} \quad \dots\dots\dots\dots\dots\dots\dots\dots\dots(19.7)$$

where,
    n is the number of time periods.

The coding of x is done in the following manner:

If n is odd:			If n is even:	
Year	x		Year	x
1	-2		1	-3
2	-1		2	-1
3	0		3	1
4	1		4	3
5	2			
			Total	0
Total	0			
x unit is one year			x unit is one-half year	

➤ *Example.* The computation of a least squares trend line for per capita income in Texas from 1955 through 1964 is shown in Table 19.4, and the trend line is shown in Figure 19.2. Because there is an even number of years, the x unit is taken as one-half year.

$$a = \frac{\Sigma y}{n} = \frac{19,125}{10} = \$1,912.50$$

$$b = \frac{\Sigma xy}{\Sigma x^2} = \frac{8,671}{330} = \$26.28.$$

$$y_c = 1,912.50 + 26.28x$$

origin : January 1, 1960
x unit : one-half year
y unit : per capita income in dollars.

Table 19.4

PER CAPITA INCOME IN TEXAS, 1955–1964

Computation of trend by method of least squares

Year	Per capita income y	x	x^2	xy	Trend values y_c
1955	$1,645	-9	81	$-14,805$	$1,675.98
1956	1,732	-7	49	$-12,124$	1,728.54
1957	1,815	-5	25	$-9,075$	1,781.10
1958	1,843	-3	9	$-5,529$	1,833.66
1959	1,918	-1	1	$-1,918$	1,886.22
1960	1,917	1	1	1,917	1,938.78
1961	1,973	3	9	5,919	1,991.34
1962	2,019	5	25	10,095	2,043.90
1963	2,088	7	49	14,616	2,096.46
1964	2,175	9	81	19,575	2,149.02
Total	$19,125	0	330	8,671	

Source: Table 19.3.

Nonlinear Trend

In the discussion of linear trend, it was assumed that a straight line would best describe the trend in the time series when plotted on an arithmetic chart. The trend equation

$$y_c = a + bx$$

causes y to increase by the amount of b for each unit increase in x. This is called an *arithmetic progression*. When the increase is not constant from one time period to another, some other kind of trend equation is called for. There are a great many equations that might be used to describe a nonlinear trend. Only a few of the most important will be considered here.

Exponential Trend Equations. The trend equation

$$y_c = ab^x$$

causes y to increase by a constant rate rather than a constant amount as in the linear equation. It is the equation for a *geometric progression* and is called an *exponential equation*. It may be written in logarithmic form as

$$\log y_c = \log a + \log bx \quad \dots\dots\dots\dots\dots\text{(19.8)}$$

The normal equations that may be used to compute the two constants, $\log a$ and $\log b$, are:

$$\Sigma(\log y) = n(\log a) + (\log b)\Sigma x$$
$$\Sigma(x\log y) = (\log a)\Sigma x + (\log b)\Sigma x^2.$$

If the x values assigned to the time series are selected so that $\Sigma x = 0$, one term in each of the equations above will drop out and the equations may be simplified to:

$$\log a = \frac{\Sigma(\log y)}{n} \quad \dots\dots\dots\dots\dots\text{(19.9)}$$

$$\log b = \frac{\Sigma(x\log y)}{\Sigma x^2} \quad \dots\dots\dots\dots\dots\text{(19.10)}$$

The equation shown by Formula 19.8 will produce a straight line when the points are plotted on a *semilogarithmic chart*. A semilogarithmic chart is one in which the y axis is laid out according to the logarithms of the numbers on the y scale. The x axis, which is time, remains on an arithmetic scale. Because the same vertical distance anywhere on the chart shows the same percentage of change, this type of chart is ideal for plotting a series with a relatively stable percent of increase from one time period to the next.

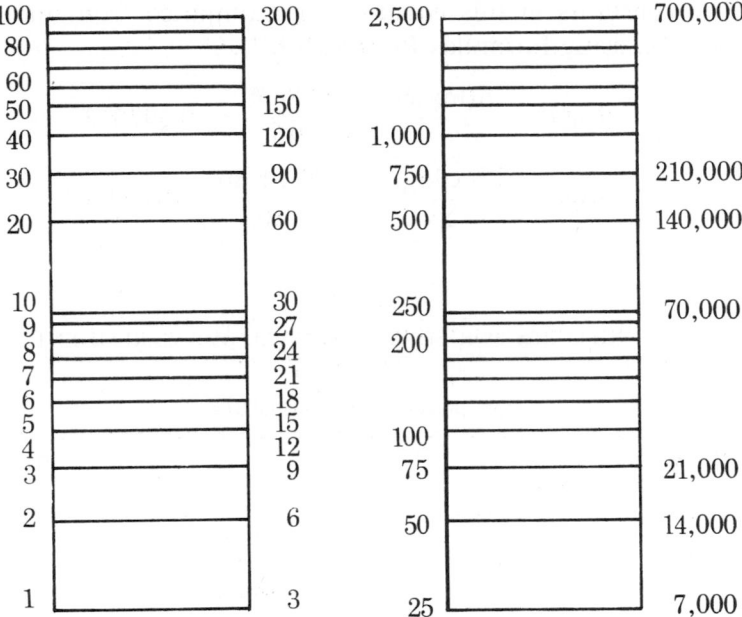

Figure 19.3

SAMPLE LOGARITHMIC SCALES, TWO-CYCLE PAPER

Semilogarithmic chart paper, drawn with the number of cycles needed, can be readily purchased. Figure 19.3 shows examples of four possible scales that might be set up on two-cycle paper. The user need only follow these rules in setting up his scale for the *y* axis:

1. The first numbered line (in the first cycle) may be labeled with any positive value that is convenient to show the data. The value cannot be zero.
2. The second numbered line is double the value of the first.
3. For each additional numbered line in that cycle, add the difference between the values of the first and second lines.
4. The value of the top line in a cycle is always 10 times the value of the bottom line in that cycle.
5. No part of the vertical scale may be omitted.

➤ *Example.* Expenditures by United States residents for foreign travel for a period of nine years are shown in Table 19.5. When these data are plotted on a semilogarithmic chart (Figure 19.4), they fall into a linear pattern that can be described very closely by the exponential trend equation

$$\log y_c = 0.397629 + 0.033664x.$$

The constants in this equation are computed from the data in Table 19.5, using Formulas 19.9 and 19.10:

$$\log a = \frac{\Sigma(\log y)}{n} = \frac{3.578658}{9} = 0.397629$$

$$\log b = \frac{\Sigma(x \log y)}{\Sigma x^2} = \frac{2.019986}{60} = 0.033664.$$

Table 19.5

EXPENDITURES FOR FOREIGN TRAVEL BY U.S. RESIDENTS, 1956–1964

Computation of exponential trend

Year	Expenditures* y	$\log y$	x	x^2	$x \log y$	$\log y_c$	Trend values* y_c
1956	1.81	0.257679	−4	16	−1.030716	0.262973	1.83
1957	1.96	0.292256	−3	9	−0.876768	0.296637	1.98
1958	2.14	0.330414	−2	4	−0.660828	0.330301	2.14
1959	2.38	0.376577	−1	1	−0.376577	0.363965	2.31
1960	2.59	0.413300	0	0	0	0.396729	2.50
1961	2.60	0.414973	1	1	0.414973	0.431293	2.70
1962	2.88	0.459392	2	4	0.918784	0.464957	2.92
1963	3.20	0.505150	3	9	1.515450	0.498621	3.15
1964	3.38	0.528917	4	16	2.115668	0.532285	3.41
Total	...	3.578658	0	60	2.019986	...	...

*Billions of dollars.
Source: United States Department of Commerce, Office of Business Economics, *Survey of Current Business*, June, 1965 (Vol. 45, No. 6), p. 25.

Polynomial Trend Equations. Polynomial trend equations take the form

$$y_c = a + bx + cx^2 + dx^3 + \ldots + jx^n \quad \ldots\ldots\ldots(19.11)$$

where,
a is the value of y_c when $x = 0$
b is the slope of the line at the origin
c is the rate of change in the slope at the origin
d is the change in the rate of change, etc.
n is a positive integer.

The straight line is a special case in which the value of c is zero, which means there is no change in the slope and the only two terms to the right of the equality sign are a and bx. It is said to be a *first-degree curve*.

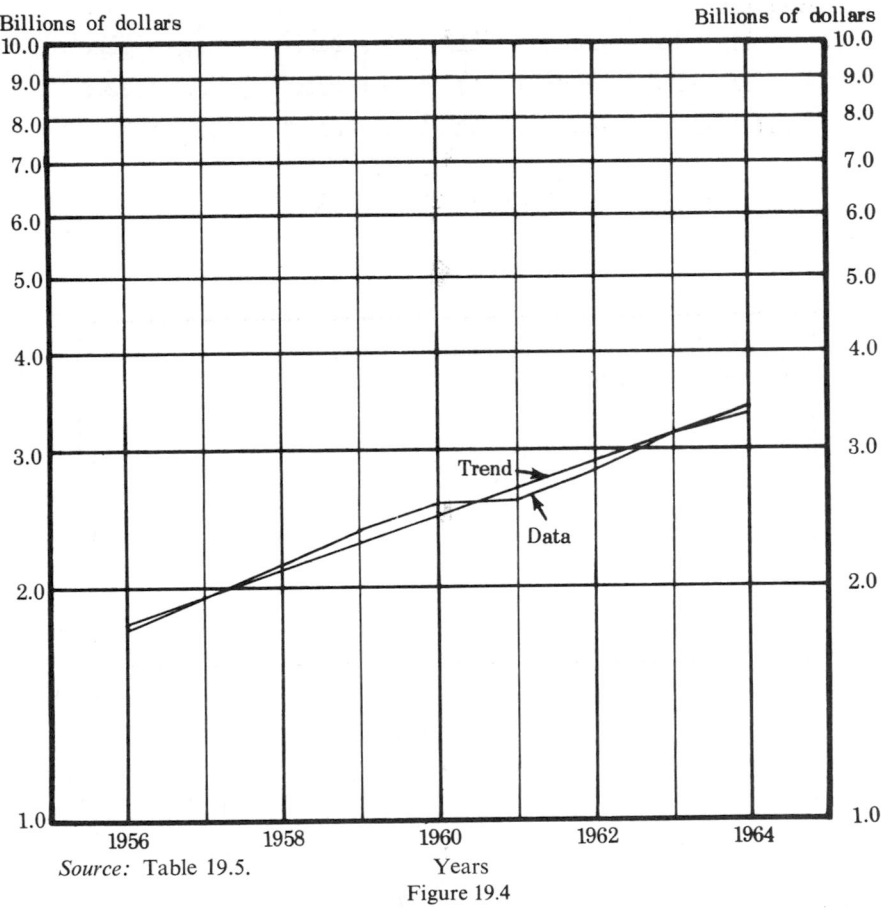

Source: Table 19.5.

Figure 19.4

EXPENDITURES FOR FOREIGN TRAVEL BY U.S.
RESIDENTS, 1956–1964

When the term cx^2 is added, the equation will produce a curved trend line such as that shown in Figure 19.5. Since x is carried to the second power, this is a *second-degree curve*. A *third-degree curve* tends to change direction twice and a *fourth-degree curve* three times.

While it may be possible to have a polynomial trend equation fit the data quite closely by increasing the degree of the curve, there is no advantage in doing this since the equation will no longer be describing trend but will also be describing other fluctuations such as cyclical or even erratic. As a practical matter, curves more complex than the third degree are seldom used to describe trend.

All polynomial trend equations may be fitted by the method of least squares. An nth degree polynomial requires $n + 1$ equations, which may be written as follows:

Equation

$$\text{I.}\quad \Sigma y = na \quad\ + b\Sigma x \quad\ + c\Sigma x^2 \quad\ + \ldots + j\Sigma x^n$$

$$\text{II.}\quad \Sigma xy = a\Sigma x \ + b\Sigma x^2 \ \ + c\Sigma x^3 \ \ + \ldots + j\Sigma x^{n+1}$$

$$\text{III.}\quad \Sigma x^2 y = a\Sigma x^2 + b\Sigma x^3 \ \ + c\Sigma x^4 \ \ + \ldots + j\Sigma x^{n+2}$$

$$\ldots$$

$$n+1\quad \Sigma x^n y = a\Sigma x^n + b\Sigma x^{n+1} + c\Sigma x^{n+2} + \ldots + j\Sigma x^{2n}$$

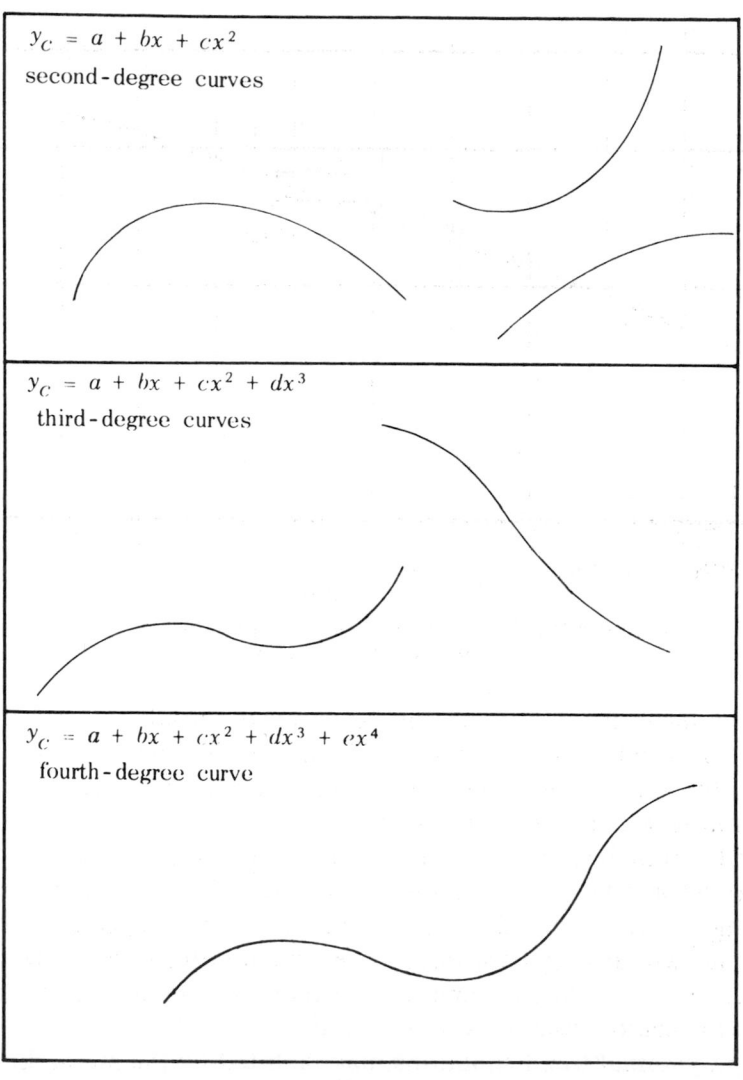

$y_C = a + bx + cx^2$

second-degree curves

$y_C = a + bx + cx^2 + dx^3$

third-degree curves

$y_C = a + bx + cx^2 + dx^3 + ex^4$

fourth-degree curve

Figure 19.5

TYPICAL FORMS OF POLYNOMIAL TREND LINES

Excellent computer programs are available in almost all computer libraries for polynomial curve fitting.

➤ *Example.* An average of the weekly claims for unemployment compensation insurance in Texas for 1947 through 1964 is shown in Table 19.6. The data are plotted in Figure 19.6. A computer program[1] was used to fit polynomial trend equations for the first through the sixth degree family of curves for the 18 annual averages. The results are:

Degree of curve	*Equation*
First	$y_c = 1,435.77 + 405.40x$
Second	$y_c = 1,481.99 + 391.53x + 0.730x^2$
Third	$y_c = 4,799.26 - 1,458.32x + 237.68x^2 - 8.31x^3$
Fourth	$y_c = 2,063.55 + 871.23x - 280.10x^2 + 33.28x^3 - 1.09x^4$
Fifth	$y_c = -458.11 + 3,735.93x - 1,221.29x^2 + 159.23x^3 - 8.42x^4 + 0.15x^5$
Sixth	$y_c = 619.50 + 2,339.60x - 662.33x^2 + 60.55x^3 + 0.17x^4 - 0.21x^5 + 0.0059x^6.$

Table 19.6

AVERAGE WEEKLY CLAIMS FOR UNEMPLOYMENT
COMPENSATION INSURANCE IN TEXAS, 1947–1964

Year	Average weekly claims as of the 16th of the month
1947	$2,615.33
1948	2,162.58
1949	4,213.00
1950	3,724.67
1951	1,872.42
1952	2,122.92
1953	3,173.33
1954	4,930.33
1955	3,746.58
1956	4,346.83
1957	5,405.25
1958	9,024.83
1959	7,374.17
1960	8,699.33
1961	9,436.08
1962	7,902.50
1963	7,813.75
1964	6,603.00

Source: Bureau of Business Research, The University of Texas.

---

[1] W. R. Graves, "Polynomial Curve Fitting (Card)," a computer program for I.B.M. 1620 Computer. *I.B.M. Systems Reference Library* (White Plains, N.Y.: International Business Machines Corporation, 1965), C20-1603-2, p. 60.

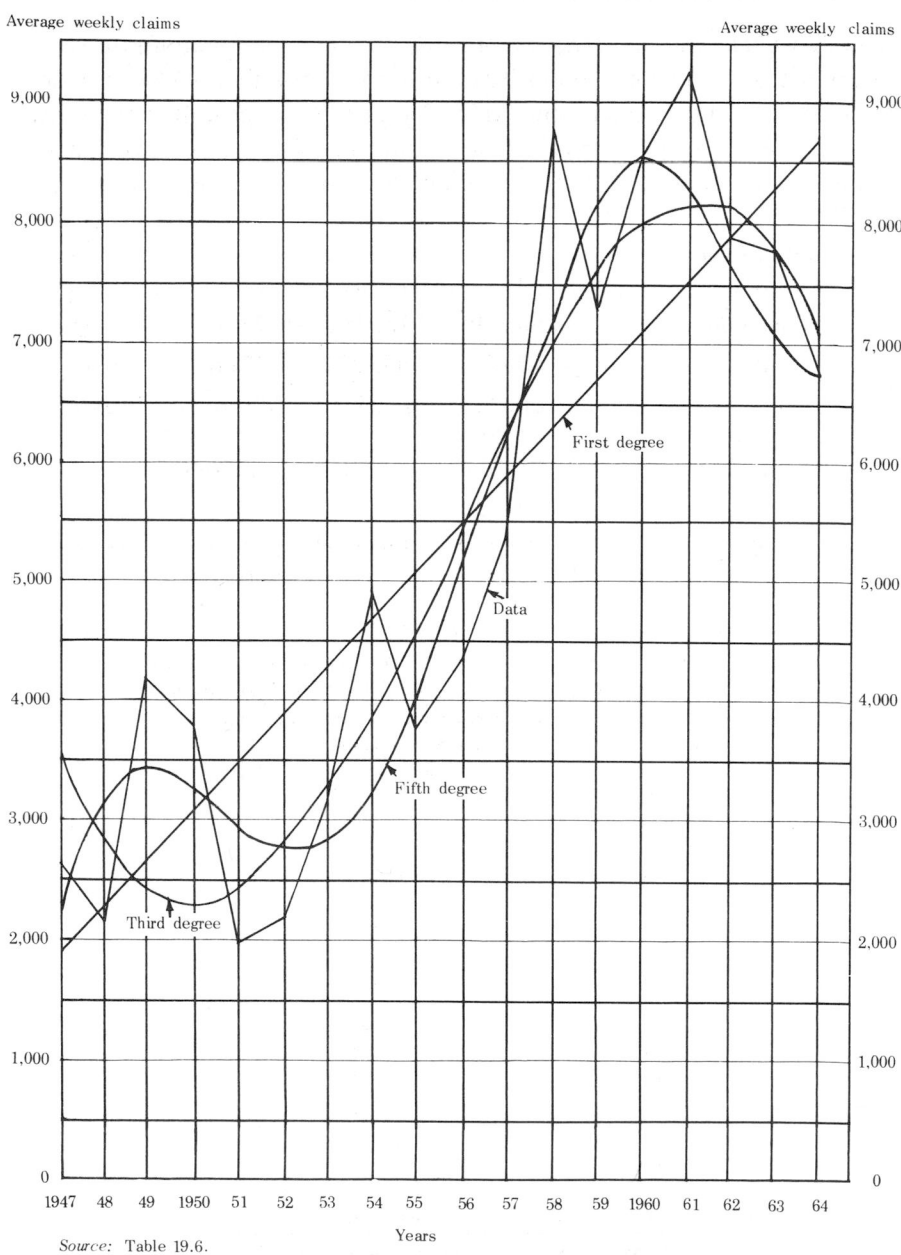

Figure 19.6

AVERAGE WEEKLY CLAIMS FOR UNEMPLOYMENT INSURANCE IN TEXAS,
1947–1964

The first-, third-, and fifth-degree curves are shown in Figure 19.6. The second-degree curve was not plotted as it differs only slightly from the first. The sixth-degree curve is quite similar to the fifth. One of the dangers in using a computer program is that the higher degree polynomial curves are so easy to compute that the investigator may be tempted to use a curve that measures forces other than trend.

Growth Curves. The linear and nonlinear trends just described frequently will give excellent fits to time series that do not exceed more than about 25 or 30 years in length. However, such trend equations may be inadequate to describe growth for longer economic time series. There is considerable evidence to show that many of the so-called *growth curves* that have an upper limit are frequently more appropriate to describe the trends in long time series. Three of the more important types of curves are mentioned here, with examples given for the latter two.

MODIFIED EXPONENTIAL. The formula for the modified exponential trend is written as follows:

$$y_c = a + bc^x \quad\ldots\ldots\ldots\ldots\ldots\ldots\ldots\ldots(\textbf{19.12})$$

This formula will be recognized as a modification of the exponential trend equation $y_c = ab^x$ to which a constant has been added. For this curve the amount of growth (or decline) decreases by a constant percentage per unit of time. The constant, a, is either the upper or the lower limit, or asymptote, of the curve.

GOMPERTZ CURVE. One of the most common of the growth curves is the *Gompertz curve*, which was developed for use in actuarial science and was first applied to the field of economics by Ray B. Prescott in 1922. The Gompertz curve has been used extensively by the National Industrial Conference Board in their studies of long time-growth patterns of states. The formula takes the form

$$y_c = ab^{c^x}$$

but is usually transformed to the logarithmic form

$$\log y_c = \log a + (\log b)c^x \quad\ldots\ldots\ldots\ldots\ldots(\textbf{19.13})$$

A simple approximation of this function can be made by dividing the time series into three equal parts. Values of x are assigned to each time period, with the origin ($x = 0$) being the first time period.

The constants of the Gompertz curve are estimated using the following formulas:

$$c^n = \frac{S_3 - S_2}{S_2 - S_1} \quad \dots\dots\dots\dots\dots\dots(19.14)$$

$$\log b = \frac{(S_2 - S_1)(c - 1)}{(c^n - 1)^2} \quad \dots\dots\dots\dots\dots(19.15)$$

$$\log a = \frac{1}{n}\left(S_1 - \frac{S_2 - S_1}{c^n - 1}\right) \quad \dots\dots\dots\dots(19.16)$$

where,

log a is the logarithm of the maximum value that the curve approaches

$(\log b)c^x$ measures the amount by which the trend value falls short of the maximum at a given point in time

S_1, S_2, and S_3 are the subtotals of log y for each of the three subperiods

n is the number of time periods in each subperiod.

➤ **Example.** In Table 19.7 a Gompertz curve is computed for the figures for marketed natural gas produced in Texas from 1947 through 1961. The constants in the equation are arrived at below:

$$c^n = \frac{S_3 - S_2}{S_2 - S_1} = \frac{3.679979 - 3.170877}{3.170877 - 1.824366} = 0.378090$$

$$\log c = \frac{\log 0.378090}{5} = 9.915519 - 10$$

$$c = 0.82323$$

$$\log b = \frac{(S_2 - S_1)(c - 1)}{(c^n - 1)^2} = \frac{(1.346511)(-0.17677)}{(-0.62191)^2} = -0.61540$$

$$\log a = \frac{1}{n}\left(S_1 - \frac{S_2 - S_1}{c^n - 1}\right) = \frac{1}{5}\left(1.824366 - \frac{1.346511}{-0.62191}\right)$$

$$\log a = 0.79790.$$

The trend values, y_c, computed above and shown in the last column in Table 19.7 are plotted in Figure 19.7 to show the shape of the curve. It is clear from looking at the figure that the rate of growth is constantly decreasing with time.

LOGISTIC CURVE. The logistic curve is often called the *Pearl-Reed growth curve* because of the extensive use made of this curve by Raymond

Table 19.7

GOMPERTZ CURVE FITTED TO MARKETED NATURAL GAS PRODUCED
IN TEXAS, 1947–1961

(Billions of cubic feet)

Year	x	y	log y	Subperiod totals	c^x	(log $b)c^x$	log $y_c =$ (log $b)c^x$ + log a	y_c
1947	0	1.8	0.255273		1.00000	−0.61540	0.18250	1.52
1948	1	2.0	0.301030		0.82323	−0.50744	0.29046	1.97
1949	2	2.3	0.361728	$S_1 = 1.824366$	0.67771	−0.41774	0.38016	2.40
1950	3	2.6	0.414973		0.55791	−0.34390	0.45400	2.84
1951	4	3.1	0.491362		0.45929	−0.28311	0.51479	3.27
1952	5	3.8	0.579784		0.37810	−0.23268	0.56522	3.67
1953	6	4.1	0.612784		0.31126	−0.19155	0.60635	4.04
1954	7	4.4	0.643453	$S_2 = 3.170877$	0.25624	−0.15769	0.64021	4.37
1955	8	4.6	0.662758		0.21094	−0.12981	0.66809	4.66
1956	9	4.7	0.672098		0.17365	−0.10686	0.69104	4.91
1957	10	5.0	0.698970		0.14295	−0.08797	0.70993	5.13
1958	11	5.2	0.716003		0.11768	−0.07242	0.72516	5.31
1959	12	5.2	0.716003	$S_3 = 3.679979$	0.09688	−0.05962	0.73828	5.47
1960	13	5.9	0.770852		0.07975	−0.04908	0.74882	5.61
1961	14	6.0	0.778151		0.06565	−0.04040	0.75750	5.72

Source of data: U.S. Bureau of Mines.

Pearl and L. J. Reed in their studies of population growth. It resembles the Gompertz curve in its shape and is really a modified exponential curve, except that the formula computes the value of $\dfrac{1}{y_c}$ rather than y_c. The equation is

$$\frac{1}{y_c} = a + bc^x \quad \dots\dots\dots\dots\dots\dots(19.17)$$

Computations are simplified somewhat by multiplying $\dfrac{1}{y}$ by a suitable power of 10 to control the size of the fractions being used. Formula 19.14 may be used to compute the value of c^n. The values of the other constants in the equation are computed as follows:

$$b = \frac{(S_2 - S_1)(c - 1)}{(c^n - 1)^2} \quad \dots\dots\dots\dots\dots(19.18)$$

$$a = \frac{1}{n}\left(S_1 - \frac{S_2 - S_1}{c^n - 1}\right) \quad \dots\dots\dots\dots(19.19)$$

The notation is the same as that used in the formulas for the Gompertz curve, and the values of x are assigned in the same way.

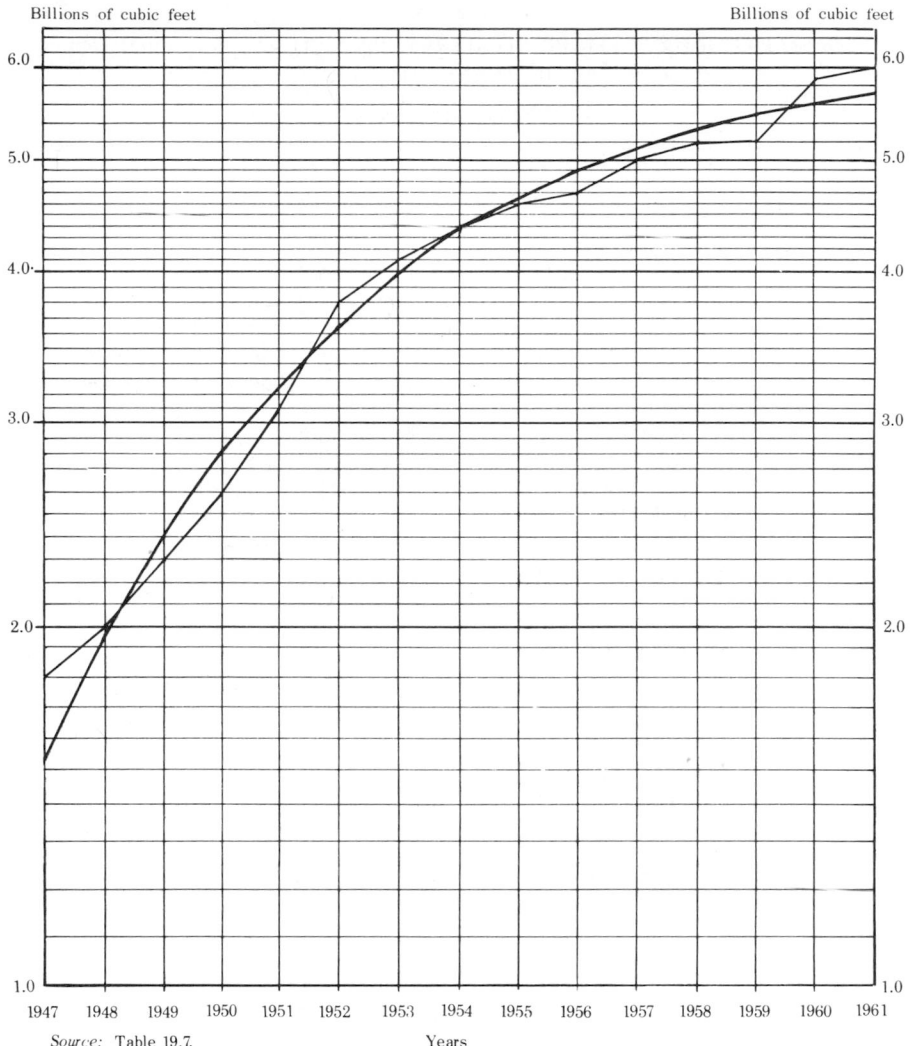

Figure 19.7

GOMPERTZ CURVE FITTED TO MARKETED NATURAL GAS PRODUCED
IN TEXAS, 1947–1961

➤ *Example.* A logistic curve is fitted to marketed natural gas produced
in Texas from 1947 through 1961. The figures are shown in Table 19.8.
The curve is not shown in a figure, but the student may compare the
trend values with those of the Gompertz curve and see that the two
curves are almost identical. The constants in the equation are computed as follows:

$$c^n = c^5 = \frac{S_3 - S_2}{S_2 - S_1} = \frac{9.20 - 11.64}{11.64 - 21.99} = 0.2358$$

$$\log c = \frac{\log 0.2358}{5} = 0.87451 - 1$$

$$c = 0.749$$

$$b = \frac{(S_2 - S_1)(c - 1)}{(c^n - 1)^2}$$

$$= \frac{(-10.35)(-0.251)}{(-0.7642)^2} = 4.45$$

$$a = \frac{1}{n}\left(S_1 - \frac{S_2 - S_1}{c^n - 1}\right)$$

$$= \frac{1}{5}\left(21.99 - \frac{-10.35}{-0.7642}\right) = 1.69.$$

Table 19.8

LOGISTIC CURVE FITTED TO MARKETED NATURAL GAS PRODUCED
IN TEXAS, 1947–1961

(Billions of cubic feet)

Year	x	y	$\dfrac{10}{y}$	Subperiod totals	c^x	bc^x	$a + bc^x$	$\dfrac{10}{a + bc^x} = y_c$
1947	0	1.8	5.56		1.000	4.450	6.14	1.63
1948	1	2.0	5.00		0.749	3.333	5.02	1.99
1949	2	2.3	4.35	$S_1 = 21.99$	0.561	2.496	4.19	2.39
1950	3	2.6	3.85		0.420	1.869	3.56	2.81
1951	4	3.1	3.23		0.315	1.402	3.09	3.24
1952	5	3.8	2.63		0.236	1.050	2.74	3.65
1953	6	4.1	2.44		0.177	0.788	2.48	4.03
1954	7	4.4	2.27	$S_2 = 11.64$	0.133	0.592	2.28	4.39
1955	8	4.6	2.17		0.100	0.445	2.14	4.67
1956	9	4.7	2.13		0.075	0.334	2.02	4.95
1957	10	5.0	2.00		0.056	0.249	1.94	5.15
1958	11	5.2	1.92		0.042	0.187	1.88	5.32
1959	12	5.2	1.92	$S_3 = 9.20$	0.032	0.142	1.83	5.46
1960	13	5.9	1.69		0.024	0.107	1.80	5.56
1961	14	6.0	1.67		0.018	0.080	1.77	5.65

Source of data: Table 19.7.

$c = 0.749$

$b = 4.45$

$a = 1.69.$

STUDY QUESTIONS

19-1. Explain briefly the meaning of each of the following terms:
a. time series
b. decomposition
c. econometrics
d. trend
e. seasonal variation
f. cyclical variation
g. erratic variation
h. multiplicative time-series model
i. additive time-series model
j. arithmetic progression
k. geometric progression
l. exponential equation
m. semilogarithmic chart
n. first-degree curve
o. second-degree curve
p. growth curve
q. modified exponential curve
r. Gompertz curve

19-2. Why is the average businessman interested in the analysis of time-series data?

19-3. What are some of the unique problems that arise when dealing with the analysis of time-series data?

19-4. What are the four types of fluctuations in a time series? Give an example of each.

19-5. Distinguish between the ways of expressing the four types of fluctuations in the multiplicative and the additive time-series models.

19-6. What would you use as a null hypothesis in a runs test for trend? What would be the alternate hypothesis? What constitutes a run?

19-7. What are the difficulties involved in using a moving average to measure trend?

19-8. How does a least-squares trend line differ from a least-squares regression equation for two variables? What do these two equations have in common?

19-9. When would you use an exponential equation to describe the trend in a time series?

19-10. How many times does a fifth-degree polynomial equation tend to change direction? What danger lies in using such an equation to describe trend?

19-11. When is a growth curve a good measure of trend?

PROBLEMS

19-1. The following table gives expenditures at motion picture theaters in millions of dollars.
   a. Plot the series on an arithmetic chart.
   b. Use a one-sample runs test to test the hypothesis that there is no trend.
   c. How can you account for the drop in the series in the early 1930's, the increase in the early 1940's, and the decline after 1956? Would you explain these changes in the direction of the series as cyclical fluctuations?

EXPENDITURES AT MOTION PICTURE THEATERS
IN THE UNITED STATES, 1929–1964

(Millions of dollars)

Year	Expenditures	Year	Expenditures
1929	720	1947	1,594
1930	732	1948	1,506
1931	719	1949	1,451
1932	527	1950	1,376
1933	482	1951	1,310
1934	518	1952	1,246
1935	556	1953	1,187
1936	626	1954	1,228
1937	676	1955	1,326
1938	663	1956	1,394
1939	659	1957	1,126
1940	735	1958	992
1941	809	1959	958
1942	1,022	1960	951
1943	1,275	1961	921
1944	1,341	1962	903
1945	1,450	1963	900
1946	1,692	1964	923

Source: Survey of Current Business, November, 1965.

19-2. The table at the top of page 682 shows industrial electric power consumption in Texas.
   a. Plot the series on an arithmetic chart.
   b. Use a one-sample runs test to test the hypothesis that there is no trend.

19-3. Using the data in Problem 19-1:
   a. Compute a three-year moving average of expenditures at motion picture theaters.
   b. Plot the moving average on the original data plotted in Problem 19-1(a).

19-4. Using the data in Problem 19-2:
   a. Compute a five-period moving average of industrial electric power consumption.
   b. Plot the moving average on the original data plotted in Problem 19-2(a).

INDUSTRIAL ELECTRIC POWER CONSUMPTION IN TEXAS
1961–1964

(In millions of KWH)

Month	Years			
	1961	1962	1963	1964
January	2,248.80	2,569.90	2,810.20	3,132.50
February	2,184.00	2,548.60	2,671.40	3,021.30
March	2,316.70	2,654.00	2,839.60	3,100.00
April	2,402.30	2,660.50	2,958.60	3,114.40
May	2,494.40	2,830.70	3,043.90	3,298.90
June	2,494.40	2,838.40	3,991.60	4,276.50
July	2,574.40	2,944.20	3,167.60	3,418.50
August	2,674.90	3,010.20	3,248.00	3,511.00
September	2,303.80	3,054.70	3,170.20	3,437.70
October	2,530.70	2,972.00	3,195.50	3,356.60
November	2,522.80	2,915.30	3,111.20	3,293.10
December	2,556.40	2,795.80	3,121.90	3,418.90

Source: The Bureau of Business Research, The University of Texas.

19-5. The following table shows production of natural gasoline in the United States.

a. Plot the data on an arithmetic chart.

b. Compute a linear trend equation by the method of semiaverages and plot the trend line on the chart drawn in (a).

c. Compute a first-degree polynomial trend equation (straight line) by the method of least squares. Plot the new trend line on the original data.

d. In your opinion which trend line (b or c) appears to fit the data best?

PRODUCTION OF NATURAL GASOLINE IN THE
UNITED STATES, 1953–1966

Year	Millions of gallons daily
1953	10.8
1954	11.2
1955	12.2
1956	12.1
1957	12.3
1958	11.9
1959	11.6
1960	12.2
1961	12.8
1962	13.1
1963	13.4
1964	14.4
1965*	14.7
1966†	15.0

*Preliminary.   †Estimate.

Source: Oil and Gas Journal, January 31, 1966.

19-6. Using the data in Problem 19-1 for the years 1947 through 1964, compute the following straight-line trend equations and use each to estimate expenditures in motion picture theaters in 1966:
   a. Method of semiaverages.
   b. Method of least squares.

19-7. The following table shows the sales for a hypothetical company.
   a. Plot the series on an arithmetic chart. Would a straight-line trend fit the data?
   b. Plot the same series on a semilogarithmic chart. Would a straight-line trend fitted to logarithms fit the data?
   c. Compute an exponential trend equation and plot it on the chart called for in (b.).

SALES OF THE COMFORTABLE SHOE COMPANY,
1951–1965

Year	Sales in dollars
1951	23,100
1952	30,050
1953	33,010
1954	35,500
1955	44,900
1956	59,230
1957	64,200
1958	70,122
1959	73,025
1960	80,000
1961	95,000
1962	121,000
1963	139,550
1964	153,000
1965	182,175

Source: Company records.

19-8. The table at the top of page 684 shows the population of the United States from 1900 through 1960 and projected to 1970:
   a. Plot the series on a semilogarithmic chart.
   b. Compute an exponential trend equation to fit the series and use it to estimate the population in the United States in the year 2000.

19-9. Using the data in Problem 19-1 for the years 1939 through 1953:
   a. Plot the data on an arithmetic chart.
   b. Compute a second-degree polynomial trend equation and plot it on the original data.
   c. In your opinion is the second-degree curve a proper description of trend for this series? What are the dangers involved in using this equation to esimate expenditures in 1955?

POPULATION IN THE UNITED STATES, 1900–1960,
AND PROJECTED TO 1970

Year	Population (thousands)
1900	76,094
1910	92,407
1920	106,446
1930	123,188
1940	132,594
1950	152,271
1960	180,676
1970	208,996

Source: United States Bureau of the Census.

19-10. Using the entire time series given in Problem 19-1 and a polynomial curve fit program from your computer center library:

  a. Punch the data on IBM cards using the format called for in the writeup of the program.

  b. Run the program to compute polynomial trend equations from the first through the sixth degree.

  c. Plot the original data and the trend equations on an arithmetic chart and compare the trend lines to see how each fits the data.

19-11. The following table gives hypothetical sales figures for a period of 12 years.

  a. Plot the series on a semilogarithmic chart.

  b. Compute a Gompertz curve to describe the trend in the data and plot on the chart drawn in (a).

  c. Compute a logistic (Pearl-Reed) curve to describe the trend in the data and plot on the chart drawn in (a).

ANNUAL SALES OF GASTON
MANUFACTURING CO., 1954–1965

Year	Sales in thousands of dollars
1954	140
1955	210
1956	250
1957	330
1958	400
1959	540
1960	590
1961	650
1962	710
1963	750
1964	760
1965	770

Source: Company records.

19-12. The following table shows the amount of industrial life insurance purchased in the United States for a period of 21 years.

a. Plot the series on a semilogarithmic chart.

b. Compute a Gompertz curve and plot it on the chart called for in (a).

c. Compute a logistic curve and plot it on the chart called for in (a).

PURCHASES OF INDUSTRIAL LIFE INSURANCE
IN THE UNITED STATES, 1944–1964

(Millions of dollars)

Year	Amount
1944	3,200
1945	3,430
1946	4,340
1947	4,575
1948	4,600
1949	4,930
1950	5,402
1951	5,461
1952	5,987
1953	6,506
1954	6,846
1955	6,342
1956	6,531
1957	6,766
1958	6,982
1959	6,859
1960	6,880
1961	7,000
1962	7,046
1963	7,154
1964	7,212

Source: Life Insurance Fact Book, 1965. Institute
of Life Insurance.

SELECTED READINGS

Brown, Robert Goodell. *Smoothing, Forecasting and Prediction.* Englewood Cliffs, N.J.: Prentice-Hall, Inc., 1963.

> Section III, Smoothing Techniques, develops the techniques of exponential smoothing, including multiple smoothing for higher order polynomials

Croxton, Frederick E., and Dudley J. Cowden. *Applied General Statistics.* 2d ed. Englewood Cliffs, N.J.: Prentice-Hall, Inc., 1955.

> Chapters 11 through 16 give an excellent discussion of the classical approach to time-series analysis. Chapter 22 discusses the correlation of time series.

Brennan, Michael J., Jr. *Preface to Econometrics.* 2d ed. Cincinnati: South-Western Publishing Company, 1965.

> The author introduces the student to the subject of econometrics as the application of modern statistical methods to economic theory expressed in mathematical terms.

Gaston, J. Frank. *Growth Patterns in Industry: A Reexamination.* New York: The National Industrial Conference Board, 1961.

> An excellent example of the use of the Gompertz curve in the analysis of the growth of 32 specific industries in the United States.

Chapter 20

Time Series: Periodic Analysis and Forecasting

SEASONAL VARIATION

The Nature of Seasonal Forces

It has already been pointed out that one of the types of fluctuations found in time-series data is the seasonal component. If a time series has in it regular recurring periodic fluctuations, these fluctuations can be measured and expressed as an *index of seasonal variation.* Many economic and business series have distinct seasonal patterns that are pronounced enough to measure with some precision. Once measured, they can be used to predict future behavior of the series.

Computation of an Index of Seasonal Variation

While there are many techniques available for computing an index of seasonal variation, many of the simpler methods were devised prior to the development of electronic computers and were designed to sacrifice precision for ease of computation. Any acceptable modern method for computing such an index probably will be programmed for a computer solution. The method should be designed to meet the following criteria:

1. It should measure only the seasonal forces in the data. It should not be influenced by the forces of trend or cycle that may be present.
2. It should modify the erratic fluctuations in the data with an acceptable system of averaging.
3. It should recognize slowly changing seasonal patterns that may be present and modify the index to keep up with these changes.

One method that meets the criteria above is called the *ratio of two-item average of a 12-month moving average.* The ratios computed by this method are called *specific seasonals.* In terms of the multiplicative time-series model, $y = T \times S \times C \times E$, a specific seasonal is a measure of the seasonal and the erratic components in the series.

$$SS = \frac{y}{\text{moving average}} = \frac{T \times S \times C \times E}{T \times C} = S \times E,$$

where,

SS is used to represent a specific seasonal.

The moving average technique eliminates the effects of the trend and the cyclical components by comparing the y value for each month with the year in which that month is centered. A two-item average is necessary to adjust for the awkward fact that a year has an even rather than an odd number of months.

An arithmetic mean of the specific seasonals for each month would be one way to eliminate much of the erratic component still left in the data and to get a measure of the seasonal importance of that month. An even better device is to compute a least squares trend line for the specific seasonals for each month. This means a total of 12 trend equations, one for each month. The value of y_c on the trend line for January at any point in time (x) will be a measure of the seasonal importance of January at that time. The use of a trend line takes care both of the problem of smoothing (averaging) the erratic component and at the same time adjusting for any long-term shifts in the seasonal pattern. If the importance of a particular month in the seasonal pattern is not changing, the b value of the trend equation of specific seasonals for that month will be zero.

If, for a given year, the total of the trend values (Σy_c) for each month is 1,200, these 12 trend values constitute the index of seasonal variation for that year. If the total is not equal to 1,200, each of the trend values should be modified by multiplying it by a *leveling factor*, which is computed as follows:

$$\text{leveling factor} = \frac{1,200}{\text{total of the 12 trend values}}.$$

The steps to be followed in using this method are best demonstrated by a computer flow diagram such as that shown in Figure 20.1.

➤ *Example.* The Bureau of Business Research of The University of Texas collects and publishes figures monthly on residential construction authorized in Texas. These figures come from building permits issued for building within incorporated areas of Texas cities. Because there is a distinct seasonal pattern in these data, an index of seasonal variation is computed using the method of ratio of two-item average of a 12-month moving average. The data then are adjusted for seasonal variation by dividing the data for each month by the seasonal index for that month and multiplying the quotient by 100. Table 20.1

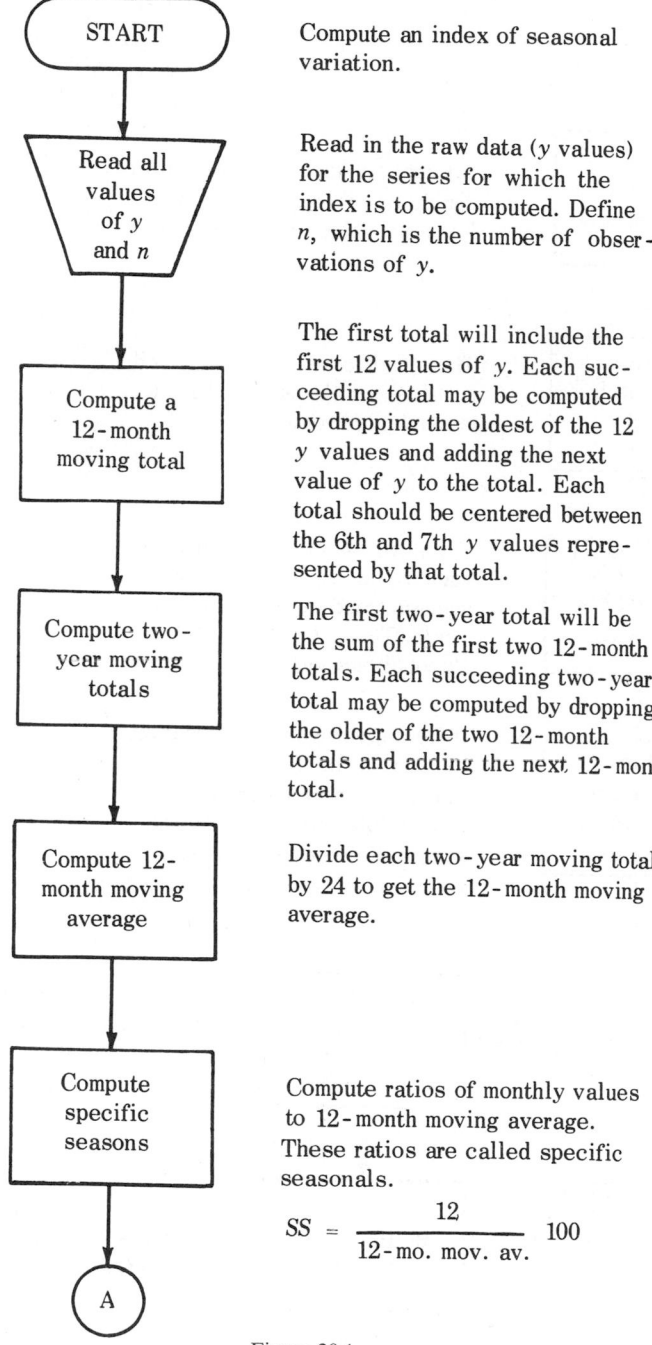

START

Compute an index of seasonal variation.

Read all values of y and n

Read in the raw data (y values) for the series for which the index is to be computed. Define n, which is the number of observations of y.

Compute a 12-month moving total

The first total will include the first 12 values of y. Each succeeding total may be computed by dropping the oldest of the 12 y values and adding the next value of y to the total. Each total should be centered between the 6th and 7th y values represented by that total.

Compute two-year moving totals

The first two-year total will be the sum of the first two 12-month totals. Each succeeding two-year total may be computed by dropping the older of the two 12-month totals and adding the next 12-month total.

Compute 12-month moving average

Divide each two-year moving total by 24 to get the 12-month moving average.

Compute specific seasons

Compute ratios of monthly values to 12-month moving average. These ratios are called specific seasonals.

$$SS = \frac{12}{\text{12-mo. mov. av.}}\ 100$$

A

Figure 20.1

A FLOW DIAGRAM FOR COMPUTING AN INDEX OF SEASONAL VARIATION BY THE METHOD OF RATIO OF TWO-ITEM AVERAGE OF A 12-MONTH MOVING AVERAGE

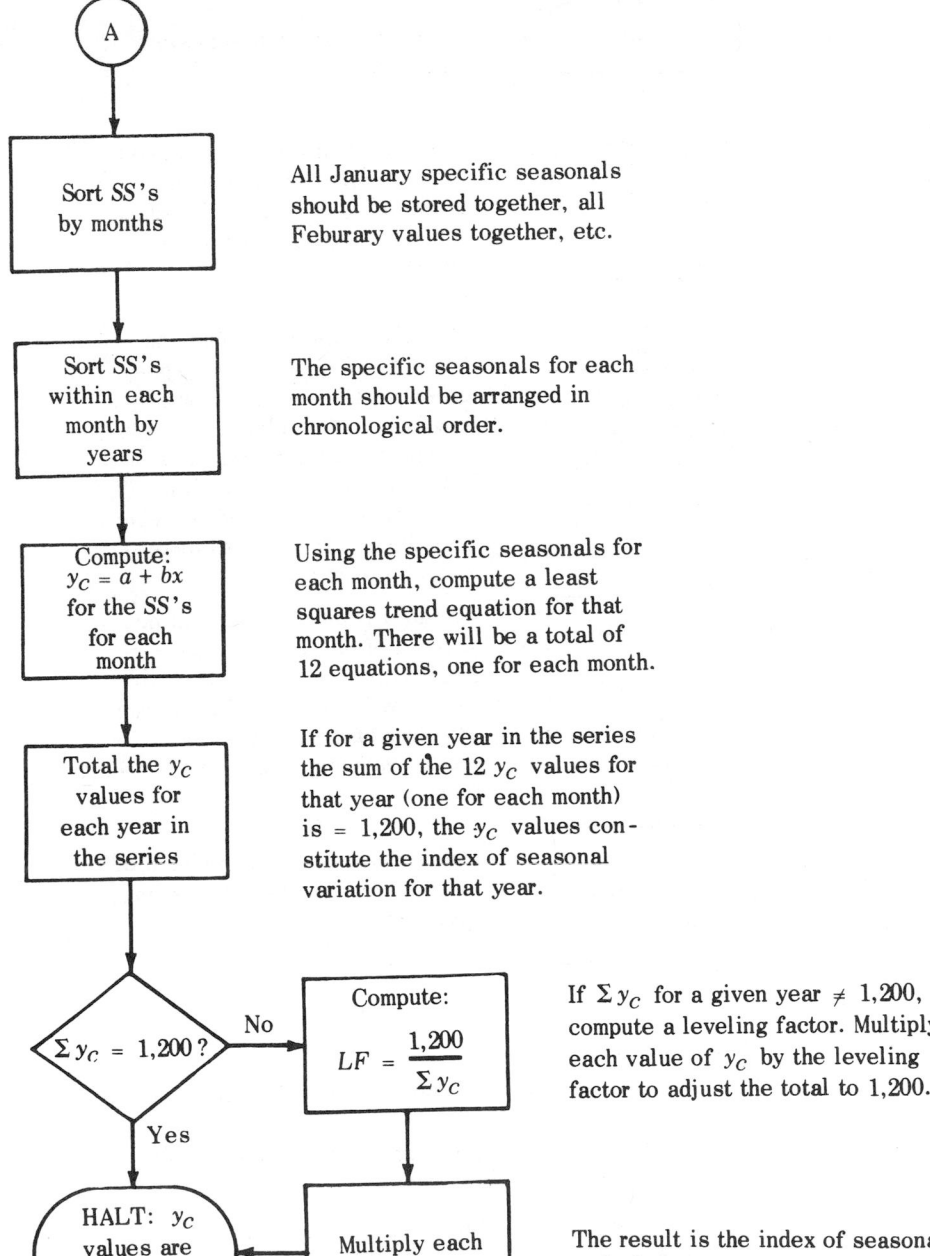

All January specific seasonals should be stored together, all Feburary values together, etc.

The specific seasonals for each month should be arranged in chronological order.

Using the specific seasonals for each month, compute a least squares trend equation for that month. There will be a total of 12 equations, one for each month.

If for a given year in the series the sum of the 12 y_c values for that year (one for each month) is = 1,200, the y_c values constitute the index of seasonal variation for that year.

If Σy_c for a given year $\neq$ 1,200, compute a leveling factor. Multiply each value of y_c by the leveling factor to adjust the total to 1,200.

The result is the index of seasonal variation.

Figure 20.1 *(continued)*

A FLOW DIAGRAM FOR COMPUTING AN INDEX OF SEASONAL VARIATION
BY THE METHOD OF RATIO OF TWO-ITEM AVERAGE OF A 12-MONTH
MOVING AVERAGE

shows the original data, the index of seasonal variation for that month, and the seasonally adjusted figures for 1947 through 1964. The work was done on a Control Data Corporation 6600 Computer, following the steps in the flow diagram shown in Figure 20.1.

Table 20.2 demonstrates how the specific seasonals might be computed using an electric calculator. A total of 204 specific seasonals made available by the computer are shown in Table. 20.3. These were arranged chronologically by months prior to fitting a least squares trend equation of the first degree. Table 20.4 shows the 12 trend equations and the projected index of seasonal variation for 1965. The student will note that seven of the months are becoming less important each year in the seasonal pattern, while the remaining five months (March, April, July, August, and November) are of growing importance.

Table 20.1

RESIDENTIAL CONSTRUCTION AUTHORIZED IN TEXAS, 1947–1964

(Thousands of dollars)

Month	Data	Seasonal index	Seasonally adjusted data
		1947	
January	9,983.00	108.65	9,188.45
February	13,546.00	102.72	13,187.79
March	16,017.00	117.96	13,578.20
April	18,910.00	101.73	18,589.03
May	17,041.00	109.16	15,610.89
June	20,606.00	103.48	19,913.37
July	21,353.00	100.55	21,237.10
August	23,244.00	103.54	22,448.83
September	23,003.00	102.53	22,436.16
October	24,180.00	82.46	29,323.99
November	20,797.00	82.77	25,127.24
December	20,057.00	84.47	23,744.42
		1948	
January	27,530.00	107.96	25,499.97
February	23,397.00	102.39	22,850.15
March	29,858.00	118.37	25,223.55
April	31,129.00	102.48	30,374.53
May	21,717.00	109.15	19,896.30
June	23,364.00	103.38	22,599.95
July	26,475.00	100.89	26,241.76
August	23,155.00	103.98	22,268.36
September	23,118.00	102.04	22,654.81
October	18,477.00	83.31	22,177.99
November	16,600.00	82.42	20,141.04
December	15,232.00	83.61	18,217.76

Table 20.1 (Continued)

Month	Data	Seasonal index	Seasonally adjusted data
		1949	
January	13,962.00	107.27	13,015.20
February	16,942.00	102.07	16,598.39
March	21,747.00	118.79	18,307.74
April	19,816.00	103.24	19,193.91
May	23,431.00	109.14	21,468.57
June	24,187.00	103.28	23,418.12
July	21,719.00	101.23	21,454.70
August	28,150.00	104.42	26,958.17
September	27,102.00	101.56	26,684.99
October	24,145.00	84.17	28,687.18
November	32,511.00	82.07	39,613.35
December	26,171.00	82.75	31,626.16
		1950	
January	35,531.00	106.59	33,334.81
February	41,587.00	101.75	40,872.89
March	48,855.00	119.20	40,986.36
April	41,499.00	104.00	39,903.54
May	48,384.00	109.13	44,335.72
June	47,459.00	103.19	45,993.71
July	52,020.00	101.57	51,213.43
August	46,802.00	104.86	44,632.65
September	38,820.00	101.08	38,404.90
October	34,614.00	85.02	40,712.45
November	34,387.00	81.72	42,077.58
December	40,701.00	81.89	49,701.11
		1951	
January	56,086.00	105.90	52,960.29
February	39,172.00	101.42	38,621.97
March	45,349.00	119.61	37,913.89
April	35,982.00	104.76	34,348.57
May	42,538.00	109.12	38,982.43
June	62,933.00	103.09	61,047.61
July	20,829.00	101.92	20,437.03
August	24,592.00	105.30	23,354.26
September	37,835.00	100.60	37,609.71
October	23,607.00	85.87	27,490.02
November	23,024.00	81.37	28,293.73
December	20,057.00	81.03	24,751.95
		1952	
January	36,693.00	105.22	34,874.07
February	40,342.00	101.10	39,902.61
March	48,221.00	120.02	40,176.52
April	41,921.00	105.51	39,730.81
May	36,764.00	109.11	33,694.14
June	33,687.00	102.99	32,708.70
July	27,712.00	102.26	27,099.29
August	32,311.00	105.74	30,557.24
September	33,274.00	100.12	33,235.04
October	36,851.00	86.73	42,489.88
November	29,442.00	81.03	36,336.03
December	30,499.00	80.17	38,041.74

Table 20.1 (Continued)

Month	Data	Seasonal index	Seasonally adjusted data
		1953	
January	36,313.00	104.53	34,739.48
February	36,587.00	100.78	36,304.49
March	43,525.00	120.44	36,139.79
April	36,047.00	106.27	33,920.31
May	32,547.00	109.10	29,832.00
June	30,267.00	102.89	29,415.85
July	25,749.00	102.60	25,095.52
August	23,714.00	106.18	22,334.06
September	24,442.00	99.64	24,531.43
October	24,602.00	87.58	28,089.94
November	25,295.00	80.68	31,352.61
December	25,534.00	79.31	32,193.97
		1954	
January	28,007.00	103.84	26,970.45
February	37,384.00	100.46	37,214.60
March	49,730.00	120.85	41,151.07
April	46,855.00	107.03	43,778.77
May	42,896.00	109.09	39,321.31
June	47,562.00	102.80	46,268.30
July	50,896.00	102.95	49,439.04
August	54,312.00	106.62	50,940.75
September	55,532.00	99.15	56,006.01
October	47,242.00	88.44	53,418.82
November	51,965.00	80.33	64,688.44
December	55,217.00	78.45	70,381.80
		1955	
January	55,073.00	103.16	53,387.52
February	56,616.00	100.13	56,541.24
March	66,104.00	121.26	54,514.41
April	58,947.00	107.78	54,690.04
May	64,819.00	109.08	59,422.84
June	57,195.00	102.70	55,692.07
July	47,597.00	103.29	46,080.95
August	51,859.00	107.06	48,440.40
September	44,963.00	98.67	45,568.20
October	49,526.00	89.29	55,465.83
November	39,574.00	79.98	49,477.82
December	32,847.00	77.59	42,331.83
		1956	
January	41,755.00	102.47	40,748.15
February	42,304.00	99.81	42,384.84
March	49,163.00	121.67	40,406.19
April	40,740.00	108.54	37,534.27
May	48,876.00	109.07	44,811.19
June	36,752.00	102.60	35,820.24
July	38,183.00	103.63	36,844.46
August	43,318.00	107.50	40,297.07
September	32,144.00	98.19	32,736.48
October	34,806.00	90.14	38,611.13
November	26,605.00	79.64	33,408.49
December	23,807.00	76.73	31,025.08

Table 20.1 (Continued)

Month	Data	Seasonal index	Seasonally adjusted data
		1957	
January	47,659.00	101.78	46,823.31
February	44,408.00	99.49	44,637.28
March	42,485.00	122.08	34,799.76
April	45,735.00	109.30	41,844.39
May	48,216.00	109.06	44,210.14
June	44,762.00	102.50	43,668.63
July	53,994.00	103.98	51,929.34
August	45,740.00	107.94	42,376.98
September	46,970.00	97.71	48,071.60
October	43,994.00	91.00	48,345.62
November	32,904.00	79.29	41,499.56
December	39,035.00	75.88	51,446.23
		1958	
January	51,298.00	101.10	50,740.54
February	45,022.00	99.16	45,401.82
March	58,190.00	122.50	47,503.43
April	64,559.00	110.05	58,660.79
May	65,257.00	109.05	59,840.83
June	70,287.00	102.41	68,635.38
July	74,150.00	104.32	71,080.16
August	73,864.00	108.38	68,155.78
September	66,639.00	97.23	68,539.80
October	65,403.00	91.85	71,204.11
November	55,850.00	78.94	70,750.17
December	58,336.00	75.02	77,764.73
		1959	
January	72,715.00	100.41	72,416.24
February	65,599.00	98.84	66,368.54
March	77,044.00	122.91	62,683.97
April	77,630.00	110.81	70,055.77
May	65,245.00	109.04	59,835.31
June	66,012.00	102.31	64,522.22
July	68,882.00	104.66	65,813.90
August	63,907.00	108.81	58,730.21
September	63,823.00	96.75	65,970.32
October	53,834.00	92.71	58,069.14
November	42,351.00	78.59	53,887.23
December	42,739.00	74.16	57,633.35
		1960	
January	55,073.00	99.73	55,224.04
February	53,593.00	98.52	54,399.42
March	73,022.00	123.32	59,213.04
April	61,929.00	111.57	55,507.54
May	57,117.00	109.03	52,386.03
June	54,037.00	102.21	52,867.81
July	46,365.00	105.00	44,155.17
August	52,492.00	109.25	48,045.93
September	48,948.00	96.26	50,848.01
October	42,645.00	93.56	45,580.09
November	40,911.00	78.24	52,286.38
December	35,788.00	73.30	48,825.72

Table 20.1 (Concluded)

Month	Data	Seasonal index	Seasonally adjusted data
		1961	
January	48,572.00	99.04	49,042.59
February	46,924.00	98.19	47,786.69
March	64,735.00	123.73	52,318.30
April	59,705.00	112.33	53,153.55
May	63,955.00	109.02	58,663.03
June	56,758.00	102.11	55,582.91
July	63,312.00	105.35	60,098.18
August	73,228.00	109.69	66,757.20
September	58,688.00	95.78	61,272.67
October	60,658.00	94.41	64,246.55
November	52,193.00	77.90	67,003.20
December	41,415.00	72.44	57,172.87
		1962	
January	63,263.00	98.35	64,321.45
February	65,676.00	97.87	67,104.09
March	78,494.00	124.15	63,227.59
April	76,507.00	113.08	67,655.99
May	73,995.00	109.01	67,878.49
June	72,084.00	102.02	70,659.01
July	67,008.00	105.69	63,400.21
August	73,531.00	110.13	66,766.08
September	61,252.00	95.30	64,272.78
October	62,678.00	95.27	65,791.10
November	58,954.00	77.55	76,022.12
December	48,833.00	71.58	68,222.53
		1963	
January	65,035.00	97.67	66,587.53
February	67,692.00	97.55	69,392.84
March	83,952.00	124.56	67,400.30
April	74,327.00	113.84	65,291.22
May	82,497.00	109.00	75,684.64
June	63,819.00	101.92	62,617.18
July	81,679.00	106.03	77,031.39
August	79,371.00	110.57	71,782.52
September	63,291.00	94.82	66,749.68
October	68,776.00	96.12	71,550.77
November	52,876.00	77.20	68,491.61
December	49,665.00	70.72	70,227.84
		1964	
January	71,948.00	96.98	74,186.60
February	67,885.00	97.23	69,821.78
March	87,170.00	124.97	69,753.05
April	74,487.00	114.60	64,999.65
May	68,309.00	108.99	62,673.99
June	71,091.00	101.82	69,818.96
July	70,431.00	106.38	66,209.32
August	65,758.00	111.01	59,235.74
September	66,413.00	94.34	70,399.86
October	62,463.00	96.98	64,410.99
November	56,538.00	76.85	73,566.49
December	47,165.00	69.86	67,512.95

Source: Bureau of Business Research, The University of Texas.

Table 20.2

RESIDENTIAL CONSTRUCTION AUTHORIZED IN TEXAS: WORK SHEET
FOR THE COMPUTATION OF SPECIFIC SEASONALS FOR AN INDEX
OF SEASONAL VARIATION

Year and month	Construction (thousands of dollars) y	12-month moving total, centered	Two-year moving total	12-month moving average, centered	Ratio to 12-month moving average, SS
1947 Jan.	9,983				
Feb.	13,546				
Mar.	16,017				
Apr.	18,910				
May	17,041				
June	20,606	228,739			
July	21,353	246,284	475,023	19,793	107.88
Aug.	23,244	256,135	502,419	20,934	111.03
Sept.	23,003	269,976	526,111	21,921	104.93
Oct.	24,180	282,195	552,171	23,007	105.10
Nov.	20,797	286,871	569,066	23,711	87.71
Dec.	20,057	etc.	etc.	etc.	etc.
1948 Jan.	27,530				
Feb.	23,397				
Mar.	29,858				
Apr.	31,129				
May	21,717				
etc.					

Source: Bureau of Business Research, The University of Texas.

CYCLICAL FLUCTUATIONS

Cyclical fluctuations, which have been defined as wavelike fluctuations about trend, are more difficult to measure than either the trend or the seasonal components. The very fact that the length and the amplitude of the cycle may vary substantially from one cycle to the next makes any kind of direct measurement hazardous. While it is possible to compute averages both of length and of amplitude, the dispersion about these averages is so great as to render them virtually useless. Nevertheless, the businessman is vitally concerned with the measurement of cyclical fluctuations, particularly as they affect his own business. Such measurements are usually made indirectly, as may be seen from the discussion that follows.

Table 20.3

RESIDENTIAL CONSTRUCTION AUTHORIZED IN TEXAS*

Specific seasonals, July, 1947–June, 1964

Year	Jan.	Feb.	Mar.	April	May	June
1948	113.06	95.27	121.57	127.96	90.81	99.26
1949	69.59	84.40	106.35	95.04	107.73	105.77
1950	97.29	107.85	122.67	101.83	117.25	113.13
1951	130.99	96.50	114.44	91.96	111.37	170.73
1952	112.61	121.54	144.70	124.45	106.55	95.68
1953	107.76	110.00	133.79	113.88	105.09	98.94
1954	81.11	101.45	126.15	112.47	98.13	103.25
1955	98.31	101.49	119.67	107.38	118.99	107.86
1956	96.13	99.10	117.62	100.22	123.74	95.26
1957	119.14	108.94	102.42	107.66	111.80	101.68
1958	98.13	82.93	103.39	111.32	109.05	114.10
1959	106.95	97.40	115.30	117.23	100.10	103.20
1960	97.32	97.14	135.03	116.86	108.86	103.69
1961	94.58	88.66	119.45	107.86	113.05	99.09
1962	97.16	100.61	120.02	116.64	112.19	108.32
1963	95.53	98.20	121.21	106.79	118.53	91.98
1964	103.91	99.53	128.62	110.13	101.16	105.20

Year	July	Aug.	Sept.	Oct.	Nov.	Dec.
1947	107.88	111.03	104.93	105.10	87.71	83.50
1948	116.26	105.55	108.38	90.04	82.50	75.30
1949	89.67	107.66	95.75	79.59	100.71	76.32
1950	119.83	105.97	88.39	79.49	79.84	93.63
1951	59.19	71.42	109.35	67.51	65.83	59.84
1952	77.78	91.13	94.79	106.31	85.98	89.90
1953	85.72	79.77	81.42	80.07	80.03	77.94
1954	105.10	107.85	107.12	89.09	95.45	99.03
1955	92.35	102.92	91.60	104.00	85.66	73.51
1956	99.30	111.69	83.29	90.35	68.74	61.03
1957	120.50	101.67	102.85	93.39	67.70	77.49
1958	117.15	113.56	99.92	96.15	81.46	85.30
1959	110.07	104.18	105.19	89.94	71.95	73.66
1960	89.93	102.91	97.15	85.38	81.60	70.82
1961	108.93	123.04	96.41	97.61	82.50	64.39
1962	100.12	109.60	90.88	92.81	86.95	72.02
1963	117.18	113.39	90.23	97.86	75.86	71.55

Source of data: Table 20.1.

*Computer computations are carried to eight significant digits but are truncated to two decimal places for printout.

Table 20.4

RESIDENTIAL CONSTRUCTION AUTHORIZED IN TEXAS

(Thousands of dollars)

Trend equations of specific seasonals

		a		b
January	y_c =	109.5633	+	$-0.6859x$
February	y_c =	103.2557	+	$-0.3219x$
March	y_c =	117.7956	+	$0.4154x$
April	y_c =	101.1815	+	$0.7607x$
May	y_c =	109.4003	+	$-0.0081x$
June	y_c =	103.7932	+	$-0.0958x$
July	y_c =	100.4131	+	$0.3456x$
August	y_c =	103.3192	+	$0.4423x$
September	y_c =	103.2247	+	$-0.4811x$
October	y_c =	81.7752	+	$0.8575x$
November	y_c =	83.2893	+	$-0.3472x$
December	y_c =	85.5093	+	$-0.8600x$

Base = 56,792.72 beginning with month 121,
and ending with month 156

Index of seasonal variation projected to 1965

Month	Index
January	96.30
February	96.90
March	125.38
April	115.35
May	108.98
June	101.72
July	106.72
August	111.45
September	93.86
October	97.83
November	76.51
December	69.00

Source: Bureau of Business Research, The University
of Texas.

A Runs Test for Cycle

A runs test for cycle similar to that used to test for trend may be used as a nonparametric test for a significant wavelike pattern that may be identified as a cyclical component. A one-sample runs test using Formulas 13.12, 13.13, and 13.14 is appropriate. If an increase from one time period to the next is treated as a plus ($+$) and a decrease is treated as a minus ($-$), a *run* may be defined as a series of $+$'s or a series of $-$'s. If the time-series data contain a cyclical pattern, there should be long groups of positive signs followed by long groups of negative signs. For a given number of observations, a cyclical pattern will produce substantially fewer runs than would be expected from a random series.

Decomposition of Time Series

The classical approach to measuring cyclical fluctuations has been to measure and remove the forces exerted by the trend and the seasonal components, thus leaving a measure of cyclical and erratic. Erratic fluctuations probably cannot be removed altogether, but they can be modified by a moving average. The decomposition of the multiplicative time-series model may be shown as follows:

Original data $(y) = T \times S \times C \times E$

$$\text{Data adjusted for seasonal} = \frac{T \times S \times C \times E}{S} = T \times C \times E$$

$$\text{Data adjusted for seasonal and trend} = \frac{T \times C \times E}{T} = C \times E$$

A moving average of the values of $C \times E$ gives an estimate of C.

➤ *Example.* To demonstrate the technique of decomposition of a time series, the theoretical data shown in Table 20.5 are first deseasonalized, then detrended, and finally smoothed with a three-period moving average to give an index of cycle. Columns (2), (4), and (5) are in the original units of the data. The values in Columns (3), (6), and (8) are index numbers with a base $= 100.00$. In the example it is assumed that an index of seasonal variation is available on a quarterly basis and that a least squares trend equation for a straight line has already been computed to give the trend values by quarters. The data in Table 20.5 are shown also in Figure 20.2. Graph A in that figure shows the original series; graph B shows the trend line and the series after adjustment for seasonal variation; graph C shows the series after adjustment for both trend and seasonal; and graph D shows the estimate of cycle. The shading in graph D is intended to emphasize the swings above and below 100%, which represents normal for cycle.

Table 20.5

COMPUTATION OF A MEASURE OF CYCLE BY ELIMINATING SEASONAL
AND TREND AND BY MODIFYING ERRATIC FLUCTUATIONS

Year and quarter (1)		Original data $y =$ $T \times S \times C \times E$ (2)	I.S.V. S (3)	$T \times C \times E$ (4)	Trend T (5)	$C \times E$ (6)	3-qr. moving total (7)	3-qr. moving average C (8)
1959	1	274.4	108	254.1	242	105.0	...	...
	2	262.4	96	273.3	244	112.0	328.5	109.5
	3	224.9	82	274.3	246	111.5	324.0	108.0
	4	284.1	114	249.2	248	100.5	309.0	103.0
1960	1	261.9	108	242.5	250	97.0	294.0	98.0
	2	233.5	96	243.2	252	96.5	285.0	95.0
	3	190.6	82	232.4	254	91.5	282.0	94.0
	4	274.3	114	240.6	256	94.0	286.5	95.5
1961	1	281.4	108	260.6	258	101.0	292.5	97.5
	2	243.4	96	253.5	260	97.5	300.0	100.0
	3	218.0	82	265.9	262	101.5	310.5	103.5
	4	335.6	114	294.4	264	111.5	321.0	107.0
1962	1	310.3	108	287.3	266	108.0	330.0	110.0
	2	284.3	96	296.1	268	110.5	342.0	114.0
	3	273.5	82	333.5	270	123.5	354.0	118.0
	4	372.1	114	326.4	272	120.0	...	...

One of the greatest uncertainties in the decomposition approach lies in the choice of the equation to represent trend. A good example is to be found in the data shown in Figure 19.6 on page 674. Here, three possible trend lines have been plotted on a time series representing average weekly claims for unemployment insurance. Quite obviously, any measure of cycle computed for these data based on one trend equation would vary substantially from any other based on a different trend equation. A high-degree polynomial would be measuring both trend and cycle, so one could not measure cycle by taking out trend.

The problem of forecasting the critical turns in the business cycle is discussed briefly in Chapter 21 in the discussion of a diffusion index.

ERRATIC FLUCTUATIONS

In Chapter 19 erratic fluctuations were defined as a random component. This category includes a great number of factors, some of which can be identified and others cannot. For example, unusual increases or decreases in sales due to strikes, fire, weather, special promotions can all be classed as erratic. A very pronounced erratic fluctuation produced by a national emergency such as a war may be difficult to distinguish from the trend component if the war lasts long enough. Many small erratic fluctuations have no known cause.

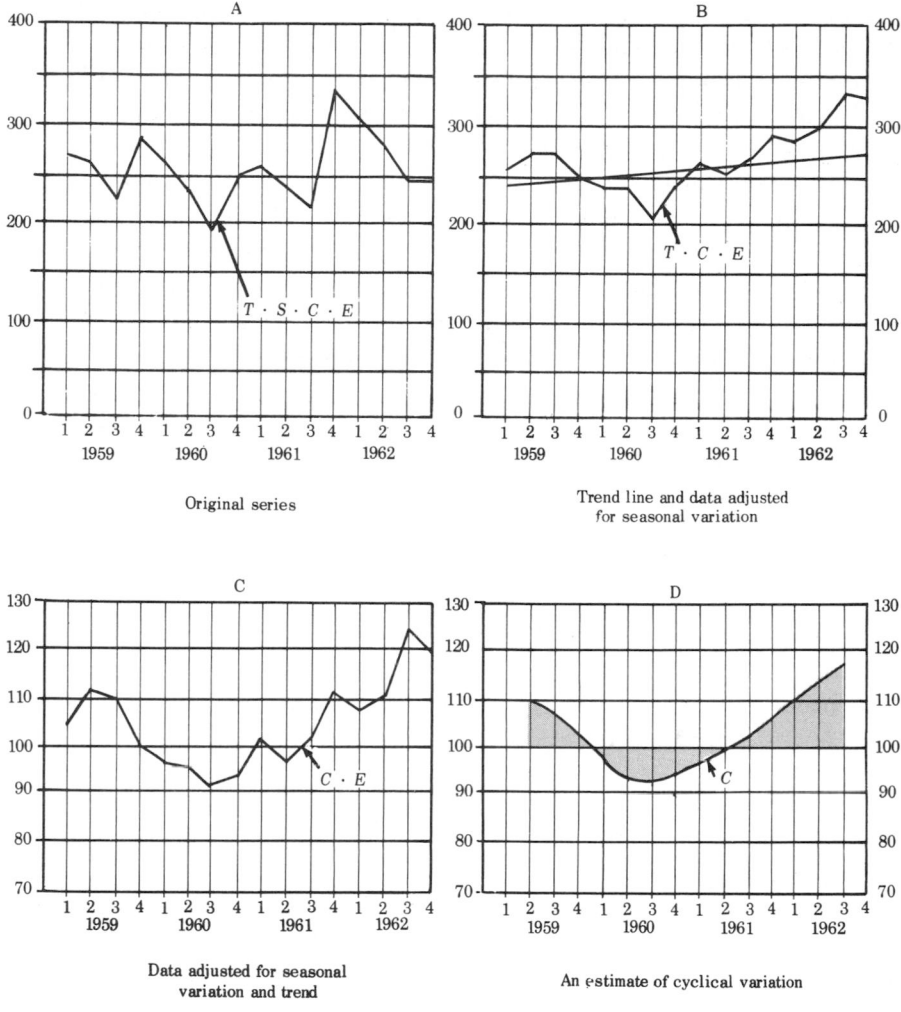

Figure 20.2

COMPUTATION OF CYCLE BY ELIMINATING SEASONAL AND TREND AND
MODIFYING ERRATIC FLUCTUATIONS

CORRELATION OF TIME SERIES

Some of the unique problems connected with time-series analysis were
mentioned at the beginning of this chapter. One of these problems centers
on the correlation of time series.

Because time-series data consist of observations of a variable at different points in time, there is usually a mutual dependence of successive
observations. It is this lack of independence that may seriously affect

the interpretation of the least squares estimates of population parameters. In the regression equation (Formula 16.17), $x_1 = a_{1.2} + b_{12}x_2 + e$, x_1 and e are assumed to be random variables, but not x_2. The validity of traditional statistical tests is dependent upon the assumption that the successive values of e are independent of one another and are normally distributed. If this is not true, the sample cannot be treated as a random sample, and the traditional tests of significance are not applicable.

An observed value of x_1 in an economic time series is usually correlated with, and not independent of, the value of that same variable in the previous time period. This type of correlation is called *autocorrelation*. This term is used to describe the lead or lag correlation of a particular time series with itself. When there is a lead or lag correlation between two different time series, this is usually referred to as *serial correlation*.

One way in which the researcher may remove autocorrelation in order to make his observations mutually independent is to eliminate trend from the original data and work with the deviations about trend. If strong cyclical or seasonal components are present in the data, they may also cause autocorrelation. Adjustment for these forces may be necessary.

A lengthy discussion of the problems with and the techniques for handling autocorrelation is not possible here, but the student can find additional material in specialized books on regression and correlation, time-series analysis and econometrics.

EXPONENTIAL SMOOTHING

New methods are being sought constantly to project time-series data into the future. One of the most exciting of the recently developed techniques is *exponential smoothing*, which is a term applied to a special type of weighted moving average useful in sales and inventory forecasting.[1]

The chief advantage of this technique lies in the simplicity of using the model in a digital computer. Only five computer instructions are necessary and can be used repeatedly for each degree of smoothing. The data to be stored are quite brief, the computations are quick and simple, and the smoothing constant can be adjusted at will as current information indicates a need for a change. In brief, exponential smoothing overcomes almost *all the problems* connected with forecasting with a moving average.

---

[1] Robert G. Brown and Richard F. Meyer, "The Fundamental Theorem of Exponential Smoothing," *Operations Research*, Volume 9, No. 5 (September–October, 1961), pp. 673–687.

The Nature of Exponential Smoothing

It will be remembered that one of the fundamental problems in using a moving average is the cumbersome job of keeping track of past observations in order to adjust the moving totals.

➤ *Example.* In the case of a three-month moving average:

Time period (t)	Value (x)	Moving average ($\bar{x}$)
1	10	
2	8	
3	12	$\bar{x}_{t=3} = \dfrac{10 + 8 + 12}{3} = 10$
4	13	$\bar{x}_{t=4} = \dfrac{8 + 12 + 13}{3} = 11.$

In order to compute the moving average for time period four, it was necessary to use data for time periods two, three, and four. Even if the new average had been computed as

$$\bar{x}_{t-4} = \bar{x}_{t-3} + \tfrac{1}{3}(13 - 10) = 11,$$

it is still necessary to remember the value of x for time period one.

In exponential smoothing, only the old average is retained and the new average is estimated as

new average $= \alpha$ (new value) $+ (1 - \alpha)$ old average,

or, the simple exponential smoothing equation is

$$S_t(x) = \alpha x_t + (1 - \alpha)s_{t-1}(x) \quad \dots\dots\dots\dots(20.1)$$

where,

x_t is the value of the series in time period t

$S_t(x)$ is the smoothed value (moving average) of the series in time period t

$S_{t-1}(x)$ is the smoothed value (moving average) of the series in time period just previous to period t

α is the smoothing constant, $0 < \alpha < 1$.

The value $S_{t-1}(x)$ represents the average experience to date for a series. In time period t a new observation x_t becomes available. If S_t is greater than the old average, the new average will be greater than the old, and conversely. The function $S_t(x)$ is a linear combination of all past observations, and the weight given to all previous observations decreases geometrically with age.

➤ *Example.* If the value of the smoothing constant is $\alpha = 0.4$, then

Time period	Weight
t	0.4
$t - 1$	0.24
$t - 2$	0.144
$t - 3$	0.0864
etc.	0.1296 (all other).

The weight given to the most recent observation is 0.4 and the weight given to all previous observations is 0.6, which is $1 - \alpha$.

For higher degrees of smoothing, the nth order function may be defined as

$$S_t^n(x) = \alpha S_t^{n-1}(x) + (1 - \alpha)S_{t-1}^n(x) \ldots\ldots\ldots\ldots(20.2)$$

Applications have been found in industry for the first three degrees of smoothing, but only simple exponential smoothing will be illustrated here.

Exponential smoothing deals with equally spaced observations in a time series. The time span between successive observations is the *sampling interval.* The appropriate length of the sampling interval depends on the individual series being forecast. It may vary from a few hours in forecasting stock market prices to quarterly data in estimating inventory demands in a very stable industry. If the interval chosen is too short, the cost of making the projections may be excessive; and if the interval is too long, changes in the data pattern will not be reflected as quickly as might be desirable.

Value of the Smoothing Constant

The value of the smoothing constant determines in large part the responsiveness of the smoothing process to changes in current demand. A large smoothing constant will cause the process to adjust rapidly to a change in trend. However, the very fact that it is so sensitive to change will also cause it to react to some of the erratic fluctuations in the data. A small smoothing constant will be less sensitive to important changes in the data but will be influenced less by random changes also. If a significant change in trend is anticipated, the value of the smoothing constant may be increased without difficulty in the computer program. Management need not predict the direction or the magnitude of the change but only the fact that one may take place.

The value of α affects the smoothed estimate or forecast in the same way that the length of the averaging period affects a moving average. The relationship between the smoothing constant and the number of time periods represented by the average is shown in the following formulas and by example in Table 20.6:

$$N = \frac{2}{\alpha} - 1 \quad \dots\dots\dots\dots\dots\dots\dots(20.3)$$

$$\alpha = \frac{2}{N + 1} \quad \dots\dots\dots\dots\dots\dots\dots(20.4)$$

where,

N is the number of observations in a moving average.

Table 20.6

SMOOTHING CONSTANTS AND
EQUIVALENT MOVING AVERAGES

N	α
3	0.500
4	0.400
5	0.333
7	0.250
9	0.200
19	0.100
199	0.010

Adjustment for Trend

Since exponential smoothing, like any other moving average, lags behind a systematic trend in the data, it is necessary to correct the system for a steadily rising or falling demand. A simple procedure is available to utilize information stored in the computer to measure a trend and to compensate for it. This procedure uses the differences between successive forecasts as estimates of trend. Exponential smoothing is used on successive differences to compute an average trend. The estimate of trend is adjusted by the smoothing constant and the adjusted value is then added to each new forecast to correct the forecast for trend. The three steps to be taken to adjust for trend are:

1. Change in average = new average − old average or,

$$C_t = S_t(x) - S_{t-1}(x) \quad \dots\dots\dots\dots\dots(20.5)$$

    where,

    C_t is the change in the smoothed value between time period t and the previous time period.

2. New trend = α (change in average) + $(1 - \alpha)$ old trend or,

$$T_t = \alpha C_t + (1 - \alpha)T_{t-1} \quad \dots\dots\dots\dots(20.6)$$

    where,

    T_t is the estimated trend for time period t

    T_{t-1} is the estimate of trend for the previous time period.

3. Expected demand (forecast) $=$ new average $+ \dfrac{(1 - \alpha)}{\alpha}$ (new trend) or,

$$D_{t+1} = S_t(x) + \frac{(1 - \alpha)}{\alpha} T_t \quad \dots\dots\dots\dots\dots\text{(20.7)}$$

where,

    D_{t+1} is the expected demand or the forecast for the next time period.

This method of correcting for trend still has some lag and requires several sampling intervals to compensate fully for a rise or fall in demand resulting from trend. The number of sampling intervals required is dependent upon the smoothing constant. It is for this reason that the smoothing constant should be increased in anticipation of a change in trend.

Adjustment for Seasonal Variation

Before any steps are taken to apply exponential smoothing for seasonal variation, one must make certain a definite seasonal pattern exists and has been measured by computing an index of seasonal variation. Adjustment for seasonal variation should be made only if the seasonal variation exceeds in magnitude the erratic fluctuations in the data.

Once the index of seasonal variation is at hand, the forecast can be adjusted as follows:

    adjusted expected demand $=$ expected demand times the index of seasonal variation for the month of the forecast or,

$$AD_{t+1} = D_{t+1}(I.S.V_{t+1}) \quad \dots\dots\dots\dots\dots\text{(20.8)}$$

where,

    AD_{t+1} is the expected demand for period $t + 1$ adjusted for seasonal variation

    $I.S.V_{t+1}$ is the index of seasonal variation for period $t + 1$.

The adjusted forecast is not stored in the computer or used in any subsequent computations. To prevent distortion in future forecasts, the adjusting process should be kept outside the exponential smoothing system.

Estimating Initial Conditions

Before exponential smoothing can begin, the initial values for the average and for trend must be estimated in some fashion. The most common method used to get the estimate for the average is to use an average of past demand. If a trend equation has been fitted to past observations, the slope of this trend line will provide an initial estimate of trend. Often, a value of $\alpha = 0.50$ is used for the first three time periods forecast to correct automatically the system for any larger error in estimates of appropriate starting conditions.

Forecast Errors

The multiplicity of unpredictable influences on demand means that actual demand will fluctuate around the average, creating errors in the forecast of demand. Assuming that these errors are serially independent and normally distributed, the probability that an error of any given magnitude will occur can be calculated once the mean and the standard deviation of the error have been estimated. Error may be expressed as

$$e = D_{t+1} - x_{t+1} \dots\dots\dots\dots\dots\dots\dots(20.9)$$

where,
   e is the error in the forecast.

➤ *Example.* Table 20.7 shows the exponential smoothing of the net market value of automobile stocks in the United States from 1953 through 1959. The initial value of the average was taken as the average for the period from 1946 through 1952, seven years. The initial value for trend was set at zero. Both beginning estimates were too small, which accounts for the fact that the expected demand is too small for the first five forecasts. This situation is corrected by the sixth forecast. More realistic estimates and a larger value of α would have made the adjustment possible much more quickly.

Exponential Smoothing with a Computer

Even simple exponential smoothing such as that shown in Table 20.7 can be exceedingly tedious when done by hand. Higher degrees of smoothing are not worthwhile if they must be done by hand or on a calculator.

Exponential smoothing formulas require that only a few values be stored in memory; square roots are avoided; and very few divisions are necessary. These characteristics make for very simple and rapid computer solutions. Figure 20.3 illustrates by a flow diagram the program required for simple exponential smoothing.

Since the system provides for estimates of trend, it is possible to extrapolate trend as far into the future as the forecaster desires, keeping in mind all the assumptions that must be made concerning the shape of the trend line and the likelihood that the forces presently at work will continue to influence future growth.

Table 20.7

EXPONENTIAL SMOOTHING OF NET MARKET VALUE OF AUTOMOBILE STOCKS IN THE UNITED STATES, 1953–1959

(In current dollars)

Year, Dec. 31 (1)	Market value (Bil. of $'s) x (2)	Average $S(x)$ (3)	Change in average C (4)	Trend T (5)	Expected demand D (6)	Error in estimate e (7)
Initial estimates	...	31.44	...	0	...	...
1953	44.5	34.71	3.27	0.82	37.17	−6.63
1954	43.8	36.98	2.27	1.19	40.55	−5.85
1955	46.4	39.34	2.36	1.48	43.78	−9.82
1956	53.6	42.91	3.57	2.00	48.91	−4.79
1957	53.7	45.61	2.70	2.18	52.15	−2.85
1958	55.0	47.96	2.35	2.23	54.65	0.45
1959	54.2	49.52	1.56	2.06	55.70	

Source: Survey of Current Business, U.S. Department of Commerce, Office of Business Economics, Vol. 45, No. 10, Oct., 1965, p. 25.

$$\alpha = 0.25 \qquad 1 - \alpha = 0.75 \qquad \frac{1 - \alpha}{\alpha} = 3$$

To compute the expected value for 1954:

1. $S_{t=1953}(x) = \alpha x_{t=1953} + (1 - \alpha)S_{t-1=1952}(x)$

    34.71 $= (0.25)(44.5) + (0.75)(31.44)$

2. $C_{t=1953} \quad = S_{t=1953}(x) - S_{t-1=1952}(x)$

    3.27 $= 34.71 - 31.44$

3. $T_{t=1953} \quad = \alpha C_{t=1953} + (1 - \alpha)T_{t-1=1952}$

    0.82 $= (0.25)(3.27) + (0.75)(0)$

4. $D_{t+1=1954} = S_{t=1953}(x) + \dfrac{(1 - \alpha)}{\alpha} T_{t=1953}$

    34.17 $= 34.71 + 3(0.82)$

5. $e \qquad\qquad = D_{t+1=1954} - x_{t+1=1954}$

    −6.63 $= 37.17 - 43.8.$

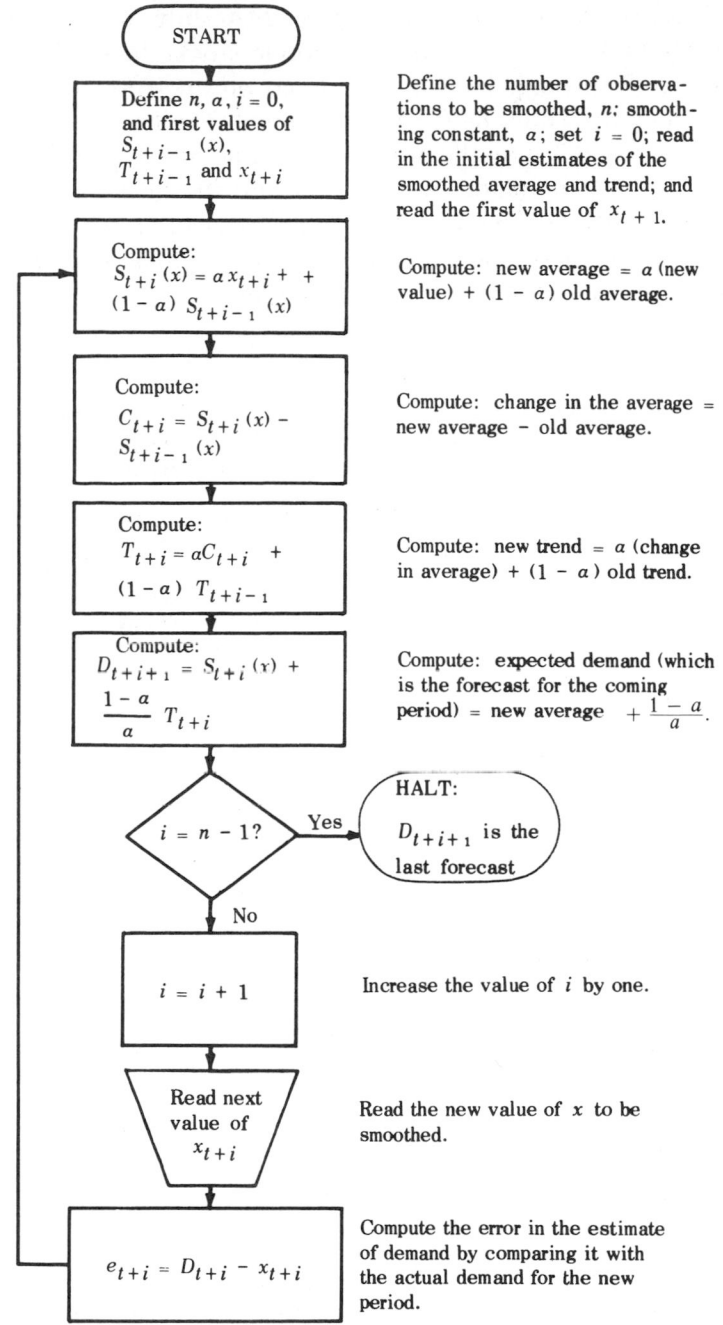

Define the number of observations to be smoothed, n; smoothing constant, a; set $i = 0$; read in the initial estimates of the smoothed average and trend; and read the first value of x_{t+1}.

Compute: new average $= a$ (new value) $+ (1 - a)$ old average.

Compute: change in the average $=$ new average $-$ old average.

Compute: new trend $= a$ (change in average) $+ (1 - a)$ old trend.

Compute: expected demand (which is the forecast for the coming period) $=$ new average $+ \frac{1-a}{a}$.

Increase the value of i by one.

Read the new value of x to be smoothed.

Compute the error in the estimate of demand by comparing it with the actual demand for the new period.

Figure 20.3

A FLOW DIAGRAM FOR COMPUTING SIMPLE EXPONENTIAL SMOOTHING
OF A TIME SERIES OF n OBSERVATIONS

➤ *Example.* Table 20.8 and Figure 20.4 show simple exponential smoothing for the value of automobile stocks in the United States from 1949 through 1964 as computed on an IBM 1620 Computer. Two smoothed lines have been computed. The first of the lines uses a value of $\alpha = 0.25$ and the other uses a value of $\alpha = 0.50$. In both cases trend was extrapolated for six years into the future using a second-degree parabola. The fact that these forecasts are so different when different values of α are used makes one skeptical of forecasts made too far into the future with this technique.

Table 20.8

COMPUTER EXPONENTIAL SMOOTHING OF NET MARKET VALUE OF
AUTOMOBILE STOCKS IN THE UNITED STATES, 1949–1964,
WITH EXTRAPOLATED VALUES TO 1970

(Billions of current dollars)

Year	Observed x_t	$\alpha = 0.25$ Forecast D_t	$\alpha = 0.25$ Error e_t	$\alpha = 0.50$ Forecast D_t	$\alpha = 0.50$ Error e_t
1949	25.5	28.6	+3.1	31.3	+5.8
1950	35.6	28.3	−7.3	26.8	−8.8
1951	41.7	34.2	−7.5	35.2	−6.5
1952	43.5	41.0	−2.5	42.3	−1.2
1953	44.5	45.3	+0.8	44.6	+0.1
1954	43.8	47.6	+3.8	45.1	+1.3
1955	46.4	47.8	+1.4	43.9	−2.5
1956	53.6	49.0	−4.6	45.9	−7.7
1957	53.7	53.7	0	53.2	−0.5
1958	55.0	55.8	+0.8	54.3	−0.7
1959	54.2	57.2	+3.0	55.2	+1.0
1960	50.6	57.0	+6.4	54.2	+3.6
1961	55.8	54.1	−1.7	50.4	−5.4
1962	61.3	55.5	−5.8	54.9	−6.4
1963	67.9	60.0	−7.9	61.2	−6.7
1964	76.8	65.8	−11.0	68.5	−8.3
1965	...	74.4	...	77.7	...
1966	...	76.1	...	80.3	...
1967	...	78.0	...	84.3	...
1968	...	80.1	...	89.6	...
1969	...	82.5	...	96.2	...
1970	...	85.0	...	104.2	...

Source of original data: Survey of Current Business, U.S. Department of Commerce, Office of Business Economics, Vol. 45, No. 10, Oct., 1965, p. 25.

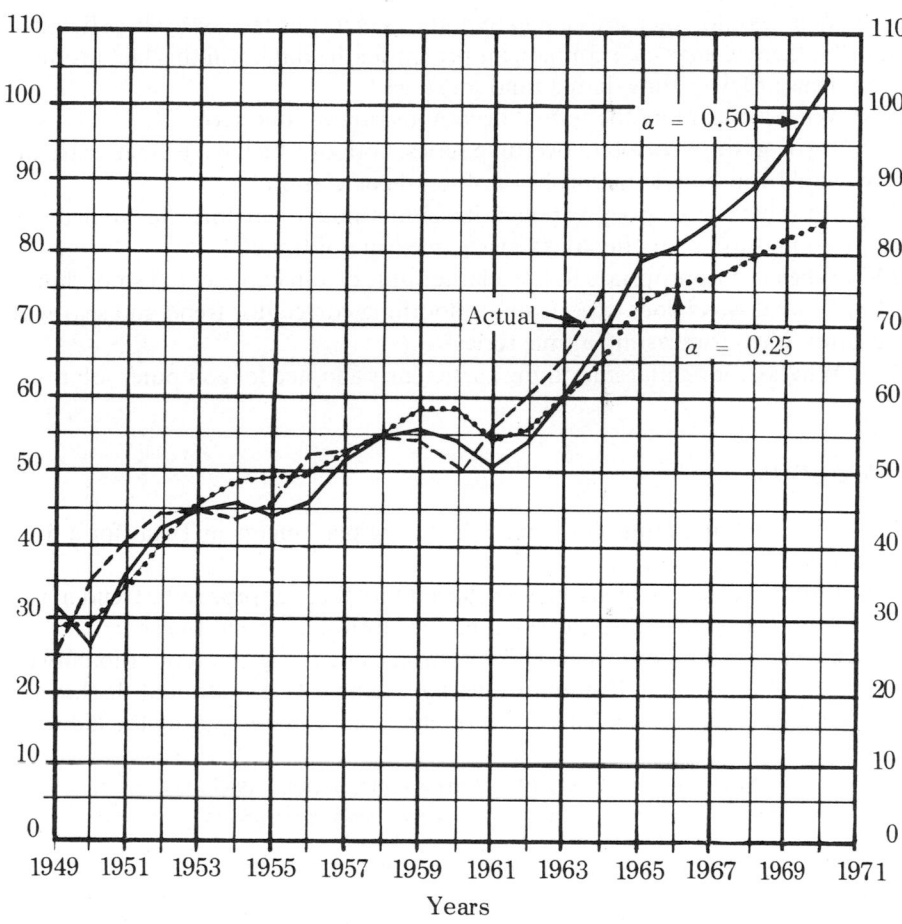

Source of data: Table 20.8.

Figure 20.4

NET MARKET VALUE OF AUTOMOBILE STOCKS IN THE UNITED STATES,
1949–1964, WITH PROJECTIONS TO 1970 USING EXPONENTIAL
SMOOTHING WITH TWO VALUES OF α

(Billions of current dollars)

STUDY QUESTIONS

20-1. Explain briefly the meaning of each of the following terms:

a. index of seasonal variation
b. specific seasonal
c. leveling factor
d. autocorrelation
e. serial correlation
f. exponential smoothing
g. sampling interval

20-2. What are the criteria that should be met in an acceptable method of computing an index of seasonal variation?

20-3. What would you use as a null hypothesis in a runs test for cyclical fluctuations? If there is a cyclical component present in the data, will this fact produce more runs or fewer runs than a random series?

20-4. What is meant by the term, "decomposition of time series"?

20-5. If you wish to correlate two time series, both of which have positive trend, how would you handle the problem of serial correlation?

20-6. In what ways does exponential smoothing overcome the difficulties involved in using a moving average as a measure of trend?

20-7. When is it appropriate to use a large value of α in exponential smoothing?

20-8. In what ways does exponential smoothing correct for trend and seasonal variation when forecasting a time series?

20-9. Why is exponential smoothing particularly adapted for computer solution?

PROBLEMS

20-1. The following table shows manufacturing placements in Texas for a five-year period.

    a. Plot the series on an arithmetic chart. Does there appear to be trend in the data? Can you see any seasonal pattern from looking at the chart?

    b. Compute an index of seasonal variation using the method of ratio of two-item average of a 12-month moving average. Use a straight arithmetic mean of specific seasonals and a leveling factor in computing the index.

MANUFACTURING PLACEMENTS IN TEXAS, 1960–1964

Month	1960	1961	Year 1962	1963	1964
January	4,674.00	3,811.00	5,419.00	3,856.00	5,083.00
February	5,364.00	4,081.00	6,106.00	4,359.00	5,568.00
March	5,589.00	4,772.00	6,401.00	5,126.00	6,162.00
April	6,315.00	5,361.00	7,343.00	6,041.00	6,888.00
May	6,698.00	6,650.00	7,515.00	6,312.00	7,144.00
June	7,098.00	7,096.00	7,697.00	6,291.00	7,521.00
July	5,971.00	5,793.00	6,846.00	5,146.00	6,421.00
August	6,212.00	6,430.00	7,308.00	5,419.00	6,463.00
September	6,436.00	6,860.00	7,620.00	6,268.00	7,028.00
October	5,550.00	7,802.00	6,479.00	5,722.00	6,480.00
November	5,502.00	6,812.00	4,413.00	4,797.00	7,072.00
December	3,592.00	4,589.00	3,467.00	3,897.00	4,425.00

Source: Bureau of Business Research, The University of Texas.

20-2. The table on page 713 shows sales for a period of eight years for a printing company.

    a. Compute an index of seasonal variation using the method of ratio of two-item average of a 12-month moving average. Use an arithmetic mean of specific seasonals and a leveling factor, if necessary.

SALES OF THE APEX PRINTING COMPANY, 1958–1965

(Thousands of dollars)

Month	1958	1959	1960	1961	1962	1963	1964	1965
				Year				
January	13.7	14.5	16.9	19.8	21.9	25.6	24.1	23.4
February	16.9	19.1	21.6	24.0	25.3	28.8	28.1	28.4
March	17.5	21.6	24.0	25.7	31.8	35.2	32.6	35.0
April	16.6	17.9	20.3	23.0	27.1	28.4	26.9	27.9
May	15.4	17.7	19.2	21.5	25.1	27.4	25.7	26.3
June	15.2	16.3	18.8	21.3	24.5	26.1	25.1	25.7
July	13.7	13.1	16.6	18.3	20.7	24.2	22.8	24.4
August	14.1	13.7	16.4	19.6	21.3	25.9	24.2	22.6
September	14.3	15.3	16.8	20.1	22.7	25.3	24.1	22.8
October	14.8	15.6	18.1	20.7	20.8	25.5	25.1	23.3
November	13.4	12.9	15.7	17.8	20.6	24.5	21.5	22.9
December	13.6	13.1	15.9	17.9	19.8	22.5	21.6	22.1

Source: Company sales records.

b. Compute a first-degree least squares trend equation to the specific seasonals for January to determine if there is any shift taking place in the seasonal importance of January. Use the equation to estimate the seasonal index for January in 1966.

20-3. Using the data in Problem 19-1:

a. Compute a straight-line trend by the method of least squares or use the one computed in Problem 19-10(b).

b. Adjust the original series for trend by dividing the observation for each year by the trend value for that year and multiplying the result by 100 to express as an index.

c. Use a three-year moving average to obtain an index of the business cycle in the series.

20-4. Using the data in Problem 20-2:

a. Compute a least squares trend equation (first-degree polynomial) and use it to adjust the series for trend.

b. Use the index of seasonal variation computed in Problem 20-2(b) to de-seasonalize the adjusted series computed in (a).

c. Use a three-month moving total to smooth the erratic fluctuations and to produce a measure of cycle.

20-5. Using the data in Problem 19-5:

a. Use Formulas 20.1, 20.5, 20.6, and 20.7 to apply exponential smoothing to the series. Use a value of $\alpha = 0.25$. Use as initial estimates an average of 10 million gallons daily and a trend of 0.4 million daily. Forecast production for 1967.

b. Repeat the steps called for in (a) using a value for $\alpha = 0.40$ and compare the results.

20-6. Using the data in Problem 20-2 and a computer program for exponential smoothing from your computer center library:

    a. Punch the data on IBM cards using the format called for in the write-up of the program.

    b. Run the program with different values of α to compare results. Which value of α, if any, seems to consistently provide the best predictions?

SELECTED READINGS

Brown, Robert Goodell. *Smoothing, Forecasting and Prediction.* Englewood Cliffs, N.J.: Prentice-Hall, Inc., 1963.

    Section III, Smoothing Techniques, develops the techniques of exponential smoothing, including multiple smoothing for higher order polynomials.

Croxton, Frederick E., and Dudley J. Cowden. *Applied General Statistics.* 2d ed. Englewood Cliffs, N.J.: Prentice-Hall, Inc., 1955.

    Chapters 11 through 16 give an excellent discussion of the classical approach to time-series analysis. Chapter 22 discusses the correlation of time series.

Brennan, Michael J., Jr. *Preface to Econometrics.* 2d ed. Cincinnati: South-Western Publishing Company, 1966.

    The author introduces the student to the subject of econometrics as the application of modern statistical methods to economic theory expressed in mathematical terms.

Chapter 21

Index Numbers of Business Change

THE CONCEPT OF AN INDEX NUMBER

Index numbers are barometers of business change. Every economic variable that affects the businessman, whether it is sales, prices, or the purchasing power of the money he uses changes over time, and these changes can be expressed as index numbers.

In its simplest form an index number is a ratio of two numbers, expressed as a percent. When changes in only one variable are involved, such as the number of automobiles produced in the United States each year, it is a simple matter to express the number produced each year as a percent of the number produced in some given base year. On the other hand, to compute a "cost of living" index can be a complex, costly, and difficult task involving many technical decisions. Such an index must consider all the important goods and services bought by thousands of consumers in dozens of cities and communities.

In both cases cited above, the purpose of the index is to give a quick, overall picture of changes taking place.

The purpose of this chapter is to summarize briefly the basic techniques and theory of index numbers and to examine a few of the more important indexes produced by private and governmental agencies to see how these indexes are put together and what they measure.

Definition

An *index number* is a percentage relative that compares economic measures in a given period with those same measures at a fixed time period in the past.

Kinds of Index Numbers

The usefulness of any index number lies in the types of questions it can answer. Each index number is designed for a particular purpose, and it is this purpose that determines its method of construction. In this chapter four basic types of index numbers will be considered. These are the value index, price index, quantity index, and diffusion index.

Value Index. The simplest kind of index number is the value index. It compares total value in some period with total value in the base period. For example, an index of department store sales would be a value index. Total value would be the sum of the price of each item times the number sold. This type of index is seldom used because it is difficult to determine just what changes it measures. If the index rises, one is not sure whether it has risen because of an increase in prices or because of an increase in volume. It may be the result of both.

Price Index. Principal emphasis in this chapter will be on indexes of prices. Most of the classic formulas will be discussed as well as such well-known indexes as the Index of Consumer Prices, Dow-Jones Stock Averages, and Standard & Poor's "500" Price Indexes. All of these are designed to measure changes in prices while holding measures of quantity constant.

Quantity Index.   A quantity index measures changes in volume of goods produced, bought, or consumed. For almost every formula for a price index, there is a corresponding one to measure changes in quantities. For this reason, the discussion of quantity indexes here will not be as extensive as that of price indexes.

Diffusion Index. A diffusion index is a simple measure that summarizes changes in a group of economic series. It expresses, for a given group, the percent of the series that has risen over given spans of time. The turning points in such an index tend to lead turning points in the aggregate business cycle, and the index foretells how widespread the change will be.

Decisions on Index-Number Construction

Just as a builder spends a great deal of time and effort designing and planning a building before he turns the first spade of dirt, so the statistician must carefully design an index number to meet the need that originally called for its creation. The design must first take into account the uses to which the index will be put. If it is a price index, it may be concerned with measuring prices of only a few commodities or of a great many. It may be concerned with price changes on a nationwide basis or with changes in a restricted area only.

Once the basic decisions are made concerning how the index number will be used, it is possible to decide what data are to be used, how they are to be collected, and how often. While sampling techniques are seldom used to determine which items should be priced, random samples of prices themselves may be called for. Other decisions that must be made include the choice of a base period, a method of weighting the components for the index, and finally the actual method of construction. These critical decision areas and several others not yet mentioned will be discussed in greater detail as some of the classic formulas of index-number construction are discussed in later sections of this chapter.

HOW INDEX NUMBERS ARE USED

Index numbers have a great many uses and new ones are being added constantly as the businessman and the general public become more familiar with them. A quick review of three of the more common uses will help to put later discussions in a more understandable context. These uses are:

1. *Measure changes that have taken place from one time period to another.* Measuring economic changes over time is basic to success in business. Such a barometer tells what has happened in the past, and its careful study may foretell much of the future.
2. *Combine changes in several series.* A builder concerned with price changes in several commodities with which he builds may wish to summarize changes in costs of lumber, glass, steel, and many other materials. Since these materials are measured in many different kinds of units for pricing such as board feet, pounds, and gallons, they cannot be added and compared directly. An index number can be designed, however, that combines relative changes in all the series into a single measure of overall change.
3. *Devalue a time series in terms of constant dollars.* The purchasing power of the dollar is constantly changing. Over the short run these changes may be small, but over a long period of time they can be substantial. If a series such as wage rates is divided by its equivalent "cost of living" index for each period, the resulting series is said to be expressed in *constant dollars.*

CONSTRUCTING INDEX NUMBERS OF PRICES

There are dozens of ways to construct a price index. The approach here is to begin with the simplest methods and to progress to the more complicated methods in an attempt to overcome the limitations of each method just discussed.

Simple Relatives

If an index of prices is wanted for a single series such as wheat, it is necessary only to express each price as a fixed-base relative. Such an index would be expressed as

$$P = \frac{p_i}{p_o} \, 100 \quad \ldots\ldots\ldots\ldots\ldots\ldots\ldots\ldots\text{(21.1)}$$

where,

    P is a price index

    p is a price

    p_o is a price in the base year

    p_i is a price in the given year (i.e., p_{64} is a price in 1964).

➤ *Example.* If the average price of wheat in the United States was $2.41 per bushel in 1962, $2.33 per bushel in 1963, and $1.71 per bushel in 1964, the following price index might be constructed using 1962 as the base year:

$$P\,(1962) = \frac{p_o}{p_o} \, 100 = \frac{\$2.41}{2.41} \, 100 = 100.0$$

$$P\,(1963) = \frac{p_{63}}{p_o} \, 100 = \frac{\$2.33}{2.41} \, 100 = 96.7$$

$$P\,(1964) = \frac{p_{64}}{p_o} \, 100 = \frac{\$1.71}{2.41} \, 100 = 71.0.$$

The price index for 1964 merely says that the average price of wheat in 1964 was 71 % of the average price of wheat in 1962.

The principal limitation to the above approach is that only one commodity is considered. When more than one series is involved, averages of price relatives must be considered.

Simple Averages of Price Relatives

If the assumption is made that all the series being considered are of equal importance, the only problem is the selection of a method of averaging the price relatives. While, theoretically, any average might be used, the choice usually narrows to the arithmetic mean, the geometric mean, or the harmonic mean. It should be noted, however, that each average gives a different answer; the appropriate one to use will have to be determined by the nature of the problem. The formulas are given below.

An Arithmetic Mean of Price Relatives.

$$P = \frac{\sum \frac{p_i}{p_o} \, 100}{n} \quad \ldots\ldots\ldots\ldots\ldots\ldots\text{(21.2)}$$

A Geometric Mean of Price Relatives.

$$P = \text{antilog} \ \frac{\sum \log \frac{p_i}{p_o} \ 100}{n} \quad \text{.................(21.3)}$$

A Harmonic Mean of Price Relatives.

$$P = \frac{n}{\sum \dfrac{1}{\dfrac{p_i}{p_o} \ 100}} \quad \text{.................(21.4)}$$

where,

    n is the number of different series in the index.

➤ *Example.* Data in Table 21.1 are prices of three food products in the United States for three given years. In Table 21.2 these prices have been expressed as price relatives using Formula 21.1.

Table 21.1

PRICES OF THREE FOOD PRODUCTS IN THE UNITED STATES
1962–1964

Product	Unit	Price per unit (in dollars)		
		1962	1963	1964
Beef[1]	per pound	0.464	0.417	0.408
Rice[2]	per pound	0.094	0.093	0.083
Wheat[3]	per bushel	2.410	2.330	1.710

[1] Includes veal. Wholesale price.
[2] Wholesale price.
[3] Average of all grades.
Source: Survey of Current Business.

Table 21.2

PRICE RELATIVES
(1962 = 100.0)

Product	1962	1963	1964
Beef	100.0	89.9	87.9
Rice	100.0	98.9	88.3
Wheat	100.0	96.7	71.0

The price relatives for 1964 have been combined into price indexes in Table 21.3 using all three of the means. It should be noted that the arithmetic mean gives the highest price index for 1964, the geometric mean the next highest, and the harmonic mean the lowest index.

Table 21.3

UNWEIGHTED PRICE INDEXES FOR 1964
(1962 = 100.0)

Product	$\dfrac{p_{64}}{p_o} 100$	$\log \dfrac{p_{64}}{p_o} 100$	$\dfrac{1}{\dfrac{p_{64}}{p_o} 100}$
Beef	87.9	1.943989	0.011377
Rice	88.3	1.945961	0.011325
Wheat	71.0	1.851258	0.014085
Totals	247.2	5.741208	0.036787

Arithmetic mean of price relatives:

$$P = \frac{\sum \dfrac{p_i}{p_o} 100}{n} = \frac{247.2}{3} = 82.4.$$

Geometric mean of price relatives:

$$P = \text{antilog} \frac{\sum \log \dfrac{p_i}{p_o} 100}{n} = \text{antilog} \frac{5.741208}{3} = 82.0.$$

Harmonic mean of price relatives:

$$P = \frac{n}{\sum \dfrac{1}{\dfrac{p_i}{p_o} 100}} = \frac{3}{0.036787} = 81.6.$$

Weighted Averages of Price Relatives

The assumption made in the previous section that all the series being averaged are of equal importance is one which can seldom be made in actual practice. Some of the series are almost always more important than others, and their relative positions need to be recognized with an appropriate system of weighting when their respective price changes are combined into an index.

➤ *Example.* The relative importance of beef, rice, and wheat in the United States economy can be seen from a study of the data in Table 21.4. In 1962 the value of beef was more than twice that of wheat and almost 10 times that of rice. By 1964 the importance of beef in relation to wheat and rice was even greater than in 1962.

Table 21.4

VALUE OF PRODUCTION OF THREE FOOD PRODUCTS
IN THE UNITED STATES, 1962–1964

Product	Value* (billions of dollars)		
	1962	1963	1964
Beef	5.8464	5.6712	6.2832
Rice	0.6204	0.6510	0.6059
Wheat	2.6510	2.5630	2.2230

*Value is the product of average price times quantity produced.
Source: Survey of Current Business.

The decision to use some system of weights in averaging price ratios is a next logical step. In taking such a step, the statistician wants to be sure that the system of weights he uses accurately represents the relative importance of each series to be included in the index; and, of course, the weights must be in units that can be added.

While it is possible to assign weights to each series arbitrarily, this action involves a matter of judgment and is usually avoided as being too subjective. Some system that uses the relative values of the products in some given period is most commonly used. In the examples that follow, base-year values are used in two cases and given-year values are used in one. The relative advantage of each system is discussed later in the section entitled "Weights."

Weighted Arithmetic Mean of Price Relatives. A price index using a weighted arithmetic mean of price relatives can be computed as

$$P = \frac{\sum w \frac{p_i}{p_o} 100}{\sum w} \qquad \dots\dots\dots\dots\dots\dots(21.5)$$

where,

w is any system of weights.

If the weights used are base-year values, then w is $p_o q_o$ and the formula becomes

$$P = \frac{\sum p_o q_o \frac{p_i}{p_o} 100}{\sum p_o q_o} \qquad \dots\dots\dots\dots\dots(21.6)$$

➤ *Example.* The figures in Table 21.5 show the production of the three food products, beef, rice, and wheat, in the United States for three given years. The data for 1962 are used to provide a system of weights to compute a price index for 1964. The computation of the index is shown in Table 21.6.

Table 21.5

PRODUCTION OF THREE FOOD PRODUCTS IN
THE UNITED STATES, 1962–1964

Product	Unit	Amount produced (billions)		
		1962	1963	1964
Beef[1]	Pounds	12.6	13.6	15.4
Rice[2]	Pounds	6.6	7.0	7.3
Wheat[3]	Bushels	1.1	1.1	1.3

[1] Includes veal. Inspected slaughter.
[2] Crop estimate reported in 100-lb. bags. Shown here as pounds.
[3] Crop estimate.
Source: Survey of Current Business.

Table 21.6

WEIGHTED ARITHMETIC MEAN OF PRICE RELATIVES, 1964
(Using base-year values as weights)

(1962 = 100.0)

Product	$\dfrac{p_{64}}{p_o} 100$	p_o	q_o	$p_o q_o$	$p_o q_o \dfrac{p_{64}}{p_o} 100$
Beef	87.9	0.464	12.6	5.8464	513.8986
Rice	88.3	0.094	6.6	0.6204	54.7813
Wheat	71.0	2.410	1.1	2.6510	188.2210
Totals				9.1178	756.9009

$$P = \frac{\sum p_o q_o \dfrac{p_i}{p_o} 100}{\sum p_o q_o} = \frac{756.9009}{9.1178} = 83.0.$$

Weighted Geometric Mean of Price Relatives. In the discussion of the arithmetic mean in Chapter 2, it was pointed out that its one greatest weakness lies in the fact that it is unduly influenced by extremes. This may mean that a price index computed using an arithmetic mean will have an upward bias. Since the geometric mean is a more conservative average, it may be used to combine the price relatives into a price index.

The formula for a weighted geometric mean of price relatives may be written as

$$P = \text{antilog} \frac{\sum w \log \frac{p_i}{p_o} 100}{\sum w} \quad \ldots\ldots\ldots\ldots\ldots(21.7)$$

If the weights are base-year values, then w becomes $p_o q_o$ and the formula can be written

$$P = \text{antilog} \frac{\sum p_o q_o \log \frac{p_i}{p_o} 100}{\sum p_o q_o} \quad \ldots\ldots\ldots\ldots(21.8)$$

➤ *Example.* A price index for beef, rice, and wheat for 1964, using 1962 as the base year, is computed in Table 21.7, which follows. The system of weights, base-year values, is the same as the previous example.

Table 21.7

WEIGHTED GEOMETRIC MEAN OF PRICE RELATIVES, 1964
(Using base-year weights)

$(1962 = 100.0)$

Product	$\frac{p_{64}}{p_o} 100$	$\log \frac{p_{64}}{p_o} 100$	$p_o q_o$	$p_o q_o \log \frac{p_{64}}{p_o} 100$
Beef	87.9	1.943989	5.8464	11.365337
Rice	88.3	1.945961	0.6204	1.207274
Wheat	71.0	1.851258	2.6510	4.907685
Totals			9.1178	17.480296

$$P = \text{antilog} \frac{\sum p_o q_o \log \frac{p_i}{p_o} 100}{\sum p_o q_o} = \text{antilog} \frac{17.480296}{9.1178}$$

$$P = \text{antilog } 1.917162 = 82.6.$$

Weighted Harmonic Mean of Price Relatives. The harmonic mean is an even more conservative average than the geometric mean. It may also be used in computing a price index. While any system of weights may be used, the formula shown here uses given-year weights. This index computed with a harmonic mean will be shown later to be the same as Paasche's price index.

The formula for a weighted harmonic mean of price relatives is written

$$P = \frac{\Sigma w}{\Sigma w \dfrac{p_o}{p_i} \dfrac{1}{100}} \quad \dots\dots\dots\dots\dots\dots\dots\dots\text{(21.9)}$$

If the weights used are given-year values, the w is $p_i q_i$ and the formula becomes

$$P = \frac{\Sigma p_i q_i}{\Sigma p_i q_i \dfrac{p_o}{p_i} \dfrac{1}{100}} \quad \dots\dots\dots\dots\dots\dots\text{(21.10)}$$

➤ *Example.* The same data employed in previous examples are utilized here to compute a price index for 1964 using a weighted harmonic mean of price relatives weighted with given-year (1964) values. The computations are shown in Table 21.8.

Table 21.8

WEIGHTED HARMONIC MEAN OF PRICE RELATIVES, 1964
(Using given-year weights)

(1962 = 100.0)

Product	q_{64}	p_o	p_{64}	$p_{64}q_{64}$	$\dfrac{p_o}{p_{64}}$	$\dfrac{p_o}{p_{64}}\dfrac{1}{100}$	$p_{64}q_{64}\dfrac{p_o}{p_{64}}\dfrac{1}{100}$
Beef	15.4	0.464	0.408	6.2832	1.137	0.01137	0.07144
Rice	7.3	0.094	0.083	0.6059	1.133	0.01133	0.00686
Wheat	1.3	2.410	1.710	2.2230	1.409	0.01409	0.03132
Totals				9.1121			0.10962

$$P = \frac{\Sigma p_{64}q_{64}}{\Sigma p_{64}q_{64} \dfrac{p_o}{p_{64}} \dfrac{1}{100}} = \frac{9.1121}{0.10962} = 83.1.$$

Weighted Aggregates

The aggregate formulas for computing price indexes are basically no different from the weighted averages of price relatives just discussed. These new formulas have different names and they can be applied without first computing price relatives, but the index numbers they produce are the same.

Laspeyres' Price Index. The numerator of Formula 21.6 can be simplified by cancelling the term p_o. The resulting formula is that for Laspeyres' price index. It is written as

$$P_L = \frac{\Sigma p_i q_o}{\Sigma p_o q_o} \; 100 \qquad ....(21.11)$$

➤ *Example.* Laspeyres' price index is computed for 1964 in Table 21.9 and the value arrived at can be seen to be the same as that shown in Table 21.6.

Table 21.9

LASPEYRES' PRICE INDEX, 1964
(Using base-year weights)

(1962 = 100.0)

Product	p_o	p_{64}	q_o	$p_o q_o$	$p_{64} q_o$
Beef	0.464	0.408	12.6	5.8464	5.1408
Rice	0.094	0.083	6.6	0.6204	0.5478
Wheat	2.410	1.710	1.1	2.6510	1.8810
Totals				9.1178	7.5696

$$P_L = \frac{\Sigma p_{64} q_o}{\Sigma p_o q_o} \; 100 = \frac{7.5696}{9.1178} \; 100 = 83.0.$$

Paasche's Price Index. Another well-known but less used price index is Paasche's price index. This index corresponds to the harmonic mean of price relatives weighted with given-year values (see Formula 21.10). The fact that Paasche's formula requires that new weights, q_i, be found for each new year of the index presents some practical problems. Not only is it difficult and costly to secure the quantity information required for weights, but the index when computed can only be compared with the base period and not with other years of the index.

The formula for Paasche's price index is

$$P_P = \frac{\Sigma p_i q_i}{\Sigma p_o q_i} \; 100.........................(21.12)$$

➤ *Example.* Paasche's price index is computed for 1964 in Table 21.10. It should be noted that the index is the same as that computed in Table 21.8 using Formula 21.10.

Table 21.10

PAASCHE'S PRICE INDEX, 1964

(1962 = 100.0)

Product	q_{64}	p_o	p_{64}	$p_{64}q_{64}$	p_oq_{64}
Beef	15.4	0.464	0.408	6.2832	7.1456
Rice	7.3	0.094	0.083	0.6059	0.6862
Wheat	1.3	2.410	1.710	2.2230	3.1330
Totals				9.1121	10.9648

$$P_P = \frac{\Sigma p_i q_i}{\Sigma p_o q_i} \, 100 = \frac{9.1121}{10.9648} \, 100 = 83.1.$$

Other Systems of Weights. So far only values in the base year or for a single given year have been used as weights. As a practical matter, any combination of years may be used as weights. In the formula below, the base-year quantities are combined with given-year quantities to provide weights.

$$P = \frac{\Sigma p_i (q_o + q_i)}{\Sigma p_o (q_o + q_i)} \, 100 \quad \ldots\ldots\ldots\ldots\ldots (21.13)$$

➤ *Example.* In Table 21.11 a price index for 1964 is computed using the method of aggregates and using quantities in both the base year and the year of the index as weights.

Table 21.11

PRICE INDEX, WEIGHTED AGGREGATES METHOD, 1964
(Using base- and given-year quantities as weights)

(1962 = 100.0)

Product	p_{64}	p_o	q_o	q_{64}	$q_o + q_{64}$	$p_{64}(q_o + q_{64})$	$p_o(q_o + q_{64})$
Beef	0.408	0.464	12.6	15.4	28.0	11.4240	12.9920
Rice	0.083	0.094	6.6	7.3	13.9	1.1537	1.3066
Wheat	1.710	2.410	1.1	1.3	2.4	4.1040	5.7840
Totals						16.6817	20.0826

$$P = \frac{\Sigma p_{64}(q_o + q_{64})}{\Sigma p_o(q_o + q_{64})} \, 100 = \frac{16.6817}{20.0826} \, 100 = 83.1.$$

Chain Index Numbers

All the index-number formulas just discussed use a fixed-base period. In each case, the price index for a given period made it possible to compare prices in that period with prices in some fixed period. It is often more convenient and practical to compute an index that has as its base the time period just past. This is particularly true with such indexes as the Consumer Price Index or the Wholesale Price Index published by the Bureau of Labor Statistics of the United States Department of Labor. The samples of information will vary from one month to another and even the products being priced may change over time. It is much easier to get information that is strictly comparable for two adjoining time periods than it is to get comparable information over longer periods of time. A *chain index* is one that has a moving base, which is the period immediately preceding the period of the index.

The formula for a chain price index for a current period, i, based on prices in the previous period, $i - 1$, may be written

$$P_{i-1,\ i} = \frac{\Sigma p_i q_a}{\Sigma p_{i-1} q_a} \ 100 \quad \ldots\ldots\ldots\ldots\ldots\ldots(21.14)$$

where,

p_i is the price in a current period

p_{i-1} is the price in a period immediately preceding period p_i

q_a is a quantity in a fixed-weight period.

This formula is a modified Laspeyres'-type index formula.

➤ *Example.* In Table 21.12 a chain price index is computed for 1963, with 1962 as the base year. In Table 21.13 a chain price index is computed for 1964, with 1963 as the base year. The quantity, q_a, is the quantity in 1962.

Table 21.12

CHAIN PRICE INDEX, 1963
(Using 1962 quantities as q_a)

(1962 = 100.0)

Product	p_{62}	p_{63}	q_a	$p_{62}q_a$	$p_{63}q_a$
Beef	0.464	0.417	12.6	5.8464	5.2542
Rice	0.094	0.093	6.6	0.6204	0.6138
Wheat	2.410	2.330	1.1	2.6510	2.5630
Totals				9.1178	8.4310

$$P_{62-63} = \frac{\Sigma p_{63} q_a}{\Sigma p_{62} q_a} \ 100 = \frac{8.4310}{9.1178} \ 100 = 92.5.$$

Table 21.13

CHAIN PRICE INDEX, 1964
(Using 1962 quantities as q_a)

(1963 = 100.0)

Product	p_{63}	p_{64}	q_a	$p_{63}q_a$	$p_{64}q_a$
Beef	0.417	0.408	12.6	5.2542	5.1408
Rice	0.093	0.083	6.6	0.6138	0.5478
Wheat	2.330	1.710	1.1	2.5630	1.8810
Totals				8.4310	7.5696

$$P_{63-64} = \frac{\Sigma p_{64}q_a}{\Sigma p_{63}q_a} = \frac{7.5696}{8.4310} = 89.8.$$

To convert a chain index to a fixed-base index, the index for period i is computed in this fashion:

$$P_i = P_{i-1}\frac{\Sigma p_i q_a}{\Sigma p_{i-1}q_a} \quad\dots\dots\dots\dots\dots(21.15)$$

Since

$$\frac{\Sigma p_i q_a}{\Sigma p_{i-1}q_a} \text{ is } \frac{p_{i-1,\,i}}{100},$$

then,

$$P_i = \frac{[P_{i-1}]\cdot[P_{i-1,\,i}]}{100} \quad\dots\dots\dots\dots\dots(21.16)$$

➤**Example.** Using the data in the previous example, it can be shown that the price index for 1964 with 1962 as a base is

$$P_{62-64} = \frac{P_{62-63}\cdot P_{63-64}}{100} = \frac{92.47 \times 89.78}{100} = 83.0.$$

This may be seen more clearly as

$$P_{62-64} = \frac{\dfrac{8.4310}{9.1178}\,100 \times \dfrac{7.5696}{8.4310}\,100}{100} = 83.0.$$

This price index is the same as Laspeyres' price index computed in Table 21.6. While only two chain index numbers were used in this example, a chain series of any length can be converted to a series of price index numbers with a common base by the same procedure.

Since the Consumer Price Index is an excellent example of a chain index number, a brief explanation of how it is compiled is appropriate here. This index is a statistical measure of changes in the prices of a fixed "market basket" of goods and services bought by city wage earners and clerical workers.

The index covers prices of almost everything people buy for living, including food, clothing, transportation, medical and personal care, reading, recreation, and many other goods and services. A total of some 400 items make up the market basket.

The decision as to what items to include in the basket as well as their relative importance was determined by a consumer expenditure survey in 1960–1961. This survey, conducted in 66 cities in the United States, recorded in great detail the kinds, qualities, and amounts of all goods and services bought by 4,344 urban families and 517 single workers. This information was used as the basis for establishing the weights in the index.

The prices themselves are obtained periodically by personal visit to a representative sample of about 16,500 stores, restaurants, and service establishments. Rental rates are obtained from about 34,000 tenants. Other price information is secured in a variety of ways.

The base period of the index is taken as 1957–1959. This is changed from time to time, but the index is also still published regularly using the old bases of 1939 and 1947–1949.

A standard chain index formula such as Formula 21.15 is used to calculate the Consumer Price Index from prices for the market-basket items. The weights are represented by the q_a values in the formula. Average price changes from the previous pricing period to the current month are expressed in percentage terms for each item. The percentage changes of all goods and services are combined using the formula. The chain index number thus produced is multiplied by the index number for the previous month and divided by 100 to secure a fixed-base index number with 1957–1959 as the base.

Fisher's Ideal Index

Professor Irving Fisher published in 1927 an extensive work on index numbers in which he tested a variety of formulas in an attempt to find an ideal index number.[1] The index that he selected was one which best met his tests of consistency of behavior and is frequently called Fisher's "ideal" index number. It is a geometric average of Paasche's and Laspeyres' price indexes and may be written as

---

[1] Irving Fisher, *The Making of Index Numbers* (Boston: Houghton Mifflin Company, 1927), p. 220.

$$P_F = \sqrt{P_L \cdot P_P} \quad \text{or it may be written as}$$

$$P_F = \sqrt{\frac{\Sigma p_i q_o}{\Sigma p_o q_o} \cdot \frac{\Sigma p_i q_i}{\Sigma p_o q_i}} \; 100 \quad \ldots\ldots\ldots\ldots\ldots\ldots(21.17)$$

➤ *Example.* Fisher's ideal price index for 1964 with 1962 = 100 is computed in Table 21.14. It is first shown as the geometric average of Paasche's and Laspeyres' price indexes derived earlier in this chapter. The same index is also computed using Fisher's formula. The figures are shown in Table 21.14.

Table 21.14

FISHER'S IDEAL PRICE INDEX, 1964

(1962 = 100.0)

Product	$p_o q_o$	$p_{64} q_o$	$p_{64} q_{64}$	$p_o q_{64}$
Beef	5.8464	5.1408	6.2832	7.1456
Rice	0.6204	0.5478	0.6059	0.6862
Wheat	2.6510	1.8810	2.2230	3.1330
Totals	9.1178	7.5696	9.1121	10.9648

$$P_F = \sqrt{P_L \cdot P_P} = \sqrt{(83.0)(83.1)} = \sqrt{6,897.3} = 83.1$$

and also

$$P_F = \sqrt{\frac{\Sigma p_i q_o}{\Sigma p_o q_o} \cdot \frac{\Sigma p_i q_i}{\Sigma p_o q_i}} \; 100 = \sqrt{\frac{7.5696}{9.1178} \cdot \frac{9.1121}{10.9648}} \; 100 = \sqrt{0.68992}\,(100)$$

$$= 83.1.$$

Other Price Indexes

There are many price indexes of interest to the businessman, in addition to the Consumer Price Index already discussed. A few of the more popular ones are discussed here.

Wholesale Price Index. This index is also published by the Bureau of Labor Statistics of the United States Department of Labor and is designed to measure average changes in prices of all commodities sold in the primary markets of the United States. The goods priced for the index include some 2,100 items representing manufacturing, agriculture, forestry, fishing, mining, quarrying, well operation, and gas and electric public utilities. Prices are at the wholesale rather than the retail level.

The index is computed using the formula

$$P_i = P_{i-1} \left[\frac{\sum q_a p_{i-1} \frac{p_i}{p_{i-1}}}{\sum q_a p_{i-1}} \right] \text{ which simplifies to}$$

$$P_i = P_{i-1} \left[\frac{\sum p_i q_a}{\sum p_{i-1} q_a} \right] \text{ which is Formula 21.15.}$$

The reference base for the index is 1957–1959 = 100.0. The weights ($q_a p_{i-1}$) are computed as the amounts (q_a) of these goods sold in 1958 times the prices (p_{i-1}) in the previous period.

Dow-Jones Stock Averages. Dow-Jones & Company computes four price indexes. One is for 30 industrial common stocks, one is for 20 railroad common stocks, one is for 15 utility common stocks, and the fourth is a composite of the first three.

When the company first began publishing its index of closing industrial stock prices in 1897, there were only 12 stocks used, and the index was computed as:

$$P = \frac{\Sigma(12 \text{ closing prices})}{12}.$$

As additional stocks were added to the list, the formula for the index was changed by increasing the size of the denominator so that it was always the same as the total number of stocks whose prices were being averaged.

Serious problems began to arise with the index when some of the corporations whose stocks were included in the average had stock splits.

➤ ***Example.*** Imagine a simplified example with only two stocks: Stock *A* is worth $8 a share and Stock *B* is worth $10. The index is

$$P = \frac{\$8 + \$10}{2} = \$9.$$

If Stock *B* splits two for one so that a share now sells for $5, the index when next computed drops to

$$P = \frac{\$8 + \$5}{2} = \$6.50$$

even though the total market value of the two stocks is the same.

The method first used to overcome this distortion was to multiply the price of each split share by the amount of the split so that the index was

$$P = \frac{\$8 + 2(\$5)}{2} = \$9.$$

This method became too cumbersome to use in time, and in 1928 a new method was adopted to handle stock splits. This method is still in use and works as follows. The evening before the split takes place two calculations are made:

1. The index for that day is computed as before.
2. The total value of all stock prices is calculated as if the split had taken place (i.e., using the new price of the split stock). This new total is divided by the index computed in 1 above. The quotient is the new divisor that will be used to compute the index the next night.

➤ *Example.* In the previous example, the index before the stock split is

$$P = \frac{\$8 + \$10}{2} = \$9.$$

The divisor for the index after the stock split is computed as the sum of $8 and $5 divided by the old index of $9. The new divisor is $\frac{13}{9}$ = 1.44. The next day, if there is no other change in prices

$$P = \frac{\$13}{1.44} = \$9.$$

While the industrial index includes 30 stocks, the divisor for the index has shrunk from 30 to 2.078 (summer, 1968) as a result of numerous stock splits. This fact explains why the Dow-Jones Industrial Common Stock Average is much higher than the average price of the stocks used to compute the index.

Standard & Poor's "500" Price Index. A more scientifically constructed index of common stock prices is computed by Standard & Poor's Corporation. This index covers 500 stocks representing 93 individual categories that comprise the four main groups of industrials, rails, utilities, and the 500-stock composite.

The formula used to compute the index is a modified Paasche formula with a base period of 1941–1943 = 10.0. A system of weights is used to reflect the relative market importance of each stock in the index. The price of each stock multiplied by the number of shares outstanding gives the current market value of that particular issue. This market value determines the relative importance of each stock. The formula used is

$$P = \frac{\Sigma p_i q_i}{\Sigma p_o q_o} 10$$

where,

p_i is current market price

p_o is average price in the base period

q_i is number of shares currently outstanding

q_o is number of shares outstanding in the base period.

The problem of stock dividends and stock splits is handled by simply changing the weighting factor to equal the number of shares of stock outstanding after the dividend or stock split has become effective.

The Standard & Poor's Index has three distinct advantages over the Dow-Jones Index:

1. It weights the price changes in stock based on their relative importance in the market.
2. It results in an index level that is more in line with the average value of the stock included.
3. It includes a much larger sample of stock prices.

CONSTRUCTING INDEX NUMBERS OF QUANTITIES

Just as an index number of prices measures the changing cost of a fixed quantity of goods, so an index number of quantities measures the changing volume of goods produced, sold, or consumed at fixed prices. In the one index, quantity is held constant to allow a measure of changing price, while in the other, price is held constant to measure changes in quantity. Because of the similarity in the design of the two types of index numbers, most of the space in this chapter is devoted to indexes of price, and the discussion of quantity indexes is confined to the following formulas.

Weighted Averages of Quantity Relatives

Arithmetic Mean. A weighted arithmetic mean of quantity relatives may be computed as

$$Q = \frac{\sum w \frac{q_i}{q_o} 100}{\sum w} \quad \dots\dots\dots\dots\dots\dots(21.18)$$

where,

Q is a quantity index

q is a quantity

q_i is a quantity in the given year

q_o is a quantity in the base year

w is any system of weights.

If base-year weights are used, the formula becomes

$$Q = \frac{\sum p_o q_o \frac{q_i}{q_o} 100}{\sum p_o q_o} \quad \dots\dots\dots\dots\dots(21.19)$$

Geometric Mean. A weighted geometric mean of quantity relatives using base-year values as weights may be computed as

$$Q = \text{antilog} \frac{\sum p_o q_o \log \frac{q_i}{q_o} 100}{\sum p_o q_o} \quad \dots\dots\dots\dots(21.20)$$

Harmonic Mean. The weighted harmonic mean of quantity relatives weighted with given-year values is shown below as Paasche's quantity index.

Weighted Aggregates

Laspeyres' Quantity Index.

$$Q_L = \frac{\sum q_i p_o}{\sum q_o p_o} 100 \quad \dots\dots\dots\dots\dots(21.21)$$

Paasche's Quantity Index.

$$Q_P = \frac{\sum q_i p_i}{\sum q_o p_i} 100 \quad \dots\dots\dots\dots\dots(21.22)$$

Fisher's Ideal Quantity Index.

$$Q_F = \sqrt{Q_L \cdot Q_P} \dots\dots\dots\dots\dots(21.23)$$

SOME PROBLEMS OF INDEX-NUMBER CONSTRUCTION

The imposing array of index-number formulas just discussed may leave the student somewhat confused as to their relative merits. Certainly the formulas themselves give little indication of the many practical problems involved in their use. The very fact that there are many formulas suggests that there is no best one to use. The one selected for a particular index will depend on the particular problems associated with that index.

Commodities to be Included

The purpose for which the index is being computed is basic in determining the commodities to be included. However, it may be said without reservation that a sufficiently large number of relevant items must be selected to obtain a reliable index. Among other things, the Dow-Jones Stock Average suffers as an index because it measures price changes in only 30 stocks. It is doubtful that the group of stocks is sufficiently large for the index to be representative of what is happening to the prices of industrial stocks in general. This is in contrast to the Standard & Poor's "500" Stock Average, which is computed from considerably more data.

The vast amount of data going into index numbers produced by the federal government can be judged by the figures already given for the Consumer Price Index and the Wholesale Price Index. These involve hundreds of commodities priced at thousands of locations.

Quality and Price

To insure that a price index reflects only changes in price and not changes in quality, detailed specifications are required to describe the items to be priced. For example, in the Consumer Price Index the specifications for a man's shirt to be priced, carefully describe the style, fabric, yarn, thread count, finish, construction, and size range, and require that the shirt be a nationally advertised brand. When an agent prices a shirt in a store, he must first examine it carefully to make sure the price he records is for a shirt that meets fully the specifications.

In spite of the use of specifications to try to insure against the confusing of quality changes with price changes, certain quality changes take place that cannot be handled in this manner. For example, a product that has been priced in the past may be taken off the market and replaced with a new product of different quality.

Problems of changing quality are handled in one of three basic ways:

1. *Direct comparison.* This method assumes that qualities are identical and that quality differences are insignificant.
2. *Linking.* This method requires prices for both qualities for at least one date. The old quality product measures price change up to the date of introduction, and the new quality product from that date forward.
3. *Adjustment for quality difference.* This method reduces or increases the price in the current period by the value of the quality difference and then compares the adjusted current price directly with the price of the former item in the preceding period.

These three methods can best be further explained by an example showing how the three methods are employed by the Bureau of Labor Statistics in constructing the Consumer Price Index.[2]

---

[2] Ethel D. Hoover, "The CPI and Problems of Quality Change," *Monthly Labor Review* (Washington, D.C.: Bureau of Labor Statistics), Vol. 84 (November, 1961), pp. 1175–1185.

➤ *Example.* The three methods of computing price changes are illustrated in the following tabulation:

Method	Base period	Period 1	Period 2
1. *Direct comparison*			
reported price	$1.25	$1.60	$1.75
price relative	...	$\dfrac{1.60}{1.25}100 = 128.0$	$\dfrac{1.75}{1.60}100 = 109.4$
price index	100.0	128.0	$\dfrac{128.0 \times 109.4}{100} = 140.0$
2. *Linking*			
reported price			
quality I	$1.00	$1.30	$...
quality II	...	0.80	0.92
price relative	...	$\dfrac{1.30}{1.00}100 = 130.0$	$\dfrac{0.92}{0.80}100 = 115.0$
price index	100.0	130.0	$\dfrac{130.0 \times 115.0}{100} = 149.5$
3. *Adjustment for quality difference*			
reported price			
quality I	$1.00	$...	$...
quality II	...	1.50	1.80
value of quality difference between I and II	...	0.25	...
price relative	...	$\dfrac{1.50 - 0.25}{1.00}100 = 125.0$	$\dfrac{1.80}{1.50}100 = 120.0$
price index	100.0	125.0	$\dfrac{125.0 \times 120.0}{100} = 150.0$

The Base Period

The selection of a base period for an index involves one overriding consideration. It should be a period in the past that is considered to be relatively "normal." Since it is difficult to find any one year that is entirely normal, most index numbers computed by the federal government use a period of several years. The period 1957–1959 has now generally replaced the base period of 1947–1949, which was used as the base for several years. The period from 1947 to 1949, inclusive, fell between World War II and the Korean War and was neither a time of unusual economic boom nor depression. It now seems necessary to shift the base period for most index numbers about every 10 years to keep pace with our rapidly changing economy.

When the base for an index number is shifted from one period to another, the change can be made by dividing the index number for each year of the old index by the value of that index at the time of the new base.

➤ *Example.* The conversion from an index with a base of 1960 = 100.0 to an index with a base of 1963 = 100.0 can be accomplished as follows:

Year	Old index (1960 = 100.0)	New index (1963 = 100.0)
1960	100.0	$\dfrac{100.0}{125.0} 100 = 80.0$
1961	115.0	$\dfrac{115.0}{125.0} 100 = 92.0$
1962	122.0	$\dfrac{122.0}{125.0} 100 = 97.6$
1963	125.0	$\dfrac{125.0}{125.0} 100 = 100.0$
1964	130.2	$\dfrac{130.2}{125.0} 100 = 104.2$
1965	132.1	$\dfrac{132.1}{125.0} 100 = 105.7$

The Selection of an Average

The statistician has several averages he can use in computing an index number. In selecting one to use, he should strive to choose an average that is both accurate and simple. The median and the mode are generally unsatisfactory as they are highly unstable unless the items being averaged are very numerous. It is the arithmetic, harmonic, and geometric means that are most often considered.

Arithmetic Mean. It can be shown that if an arithmetic mean and constant weights are used to compute two index numbers, computing forward and backward between two dates, the resulting indexes are not reciprocals of each other, and their product is always greater than 100.0. For this reason the arithmetic mean is said to have an upward bias.

➤ *Example.* The upward bias of the arithmetic mean in averaging price relatives is shown in the following computations in which only two commodities are used and in which each product is assumed to have the same weight:

	Price		Price relatives: $\dfrac{p_i}{p_o}100$	
Product	1960	1965	1960 = 100.0	1965 = 100.0
A	\$.20	\$.22	110.00	90.91
B	0.60	0.50	83.33	120.00
			193.33	210.91

$$P(1960 = 100.0) = \frac{193.33}{2} = 96.7 \text{ (Formula 21.2)}$$

$$P(1965 = 100.0) = \frac{210.91}{2} = 105.5 \text{ (Formula 21.2)}$$

$$\frac{96.7 \times 105.5}{100} = 102 > 100.0.$$

Harmonic Mean. It can further be shown that if the harmonic mean is used to compute the same two index numbers, their product is always less than 100. Thus, the harmonic mean has a downward bias.

➤ **Example.** Using the data in the previous example and averaging the price relatives using the harmonic mean produce the results shown below:

	$\dfrac{p_i}{p_o}100$		$\dfrac{1}{\dfrac{p_i}{p_o}100}$	
Product	1960 = 100.0	1965 = 100.0	1960 = 100.0	1965 = 100.0
A	110.00	90.91	0.0090909	0.0109999
B	83.33	120.00	0.0120005	0.0083333
			0.0210914	0.0193332

$$P(1960 = 100.0) = \frac{2}{0.0210914} = 94.8 \text{ (Formula 21.4)}$$

$$P(1965 = 100.0) = \frac{2}{0.0193332} = 103.4 \text{ (Formula 21.4)}$$

$$\frac{94.8 \times 103.4}{100} = 98.0 < 100.0.$$

Geometric Mean. The geometric means give consistent results. The product of geometric means with constant weights, computed forward and backward, always equals 100.0.

➤ **Example.** For the same data just used, the geometric mean of price relatives reveals the following:

Product	$\dfrac{p_i}{p_o} 100$		$\log \dfrac{p_i}{p_o} 100$	
	1960 = 100.0	1965 = 100.0	1960 = 100.0	1965 = 100.0
A	110.00	90.91	2.041393	1.958612
B	83.33	120.00	1.920801	2.079181
			3.962194	4.037793

$$P(1960 = 100.0) = \text{antilog} \frac{3.962194}{2} = \text{antilog } 1.981097 =$$

$$= 95.74 \text{ (Formula 21.3)}$$

$$P(1965 = 100.0) = \text{antilog} \frac{4.037793}{2} = \text{antilog } 2.018896 =$$

$$= 104.45 \text{ (Formula 21.3)}$$

$$\frac{95.74 \times 104.45}{100} = 100.00.$$

Since the geometric mean alone is free of bias, one might conclude that it is the only appropriate average to use in computing index numbers. However, there is still another problem to be considered along with the type of average when one speaks of bias. This is the problem of weights, which is considered next.

Weights

It has already been recognized that it is seldom possible to obtain a useful average of price relatives without weighting the relatives in proportion to the quantities they represent. In other words, a realistic price index must be a weighted index; and as the only unit that is common to all commodities is value, it is necessary to use weights based on values.

Values in the Base Period As Weights. Values in the base period are often used as weights. This is logical since the base period is selected as a normal period, and the value relationships should be normal. This system of weights has the added advantage of being a fixed period in the past so that index numbers computed in the future can be compared with one another.

There is one disadvantage to this system of weights. As time passes, values change, and in a price index too much weight will be given to those items that have the smallest rise in price, or the largest drop when prices are falling. Generally, base-year weights have a downward bias.

➤ *Example.* If the prices of two products, *A* and *B*, are recorded for two years as shown below, the 1960 values are equal. In this example, it is assumed that the price for A increases much faster than that for B but that the quantities remain constant. By 1965 the value of A is much greater than the value of B. If values for 1960 are used as weights to compute a price index for 1965, the index is 310. If, on the other hand, values for 1965 are used as weights for the price index for 1965, the index is 426.5. The difference in the two index numbers (each with the same base period of $1960 = 100.0$) lies in the weights used.

Product	Price 1960 p_o	Price 1965 p_i	$q_o = q_i$	Value 1960 $p_o q_o$	Value 1965 $p_i q_i$	$\dfrac{p_i}{p_o}100$	$p_o q_o \dfrac{p_i}{p_o}100$	$p_i q_i \dfrac{p_i}{p_o}100$
A	\$1.	\$5.00	10	\$10.	\$50.	500.0	5,000	25,000
B	1.	1.20	10	10.	12.	120.0	1,200	1,440
				20.	62.		6,200	26,440

$$P(1960 = 100.0; \text{base-year weights}) = \frac{6{,}200}{20} = 310.0$$

$$P(1960 = 100.0; \text{given-year weights}) = \frac{26{,}440}{62} = 426.5.$$

Values in the Year of the Index As Weights. If values in the given years are used as weights, it is possible to overcome the bias discussed in connection with base-year weights. But other problems result. Since new quantities as well as new prices must be secured each year, many more data are needed, and the computation of the index becomes more costly. Further, each index number when computed may be compared only with the base period.

Arbitrary Values As Weights. Some indexes use values that are neither base-year nor given-year values but are determined by averaging several years or by otherwise establishing weights. For example, the weights for the Consumer Price Index were established by a consumer expenditures survey in 1960–1961, while the base period of the index is 1957–1959.

Weight Correlation Bias. Another problem of bias is encountered in index-number construction. This one, which is highly complex in nature, is the bias that is introduced on account of correlation between weights and the relatives to which they are applied. This type of bias is called *weight correlation bias.* An intensive study on weight correlation bias was made by Dr. Warren M. Persons and the results were published in 1928.[3]

---

[3] Warren M. Persons, *The Construction of Index Numbers* (Boston: Houghton-Mifflin Company, 1928).

Persons found that if there is no correlation between prices and quantities or if there is positive correlation, base-year weights produce a downward bias and given-year weights produce an upward bias. If there is negative correlation between prices and quantities, the bias may be either upward or downward or offsetting, depending on the relative strength of each series.

COMPUTERS AND INDEX NUMBERS

It can be fairly stated that the present volume, accuracy, and timeliness of modern-day index numbers would be impossible without the use of digital computers.

➤ *Example.* The daily stock price indexes published by Standard & Poor's Corporation are heavily dependent on electronic equipment. Ticker tape is fed directly into computers and indexes are obtained almost instantaneously. The same Ultronic Systems, which provide electronic stock quotations to brokers, transmit stock price readings to S & P throughout the day, updating them every five minutes. This makes it possible for the indexes for the main groups to appear hourly on the tickers of the American Stock Exchange, the Commodity News Service, the Cotton Exchange Ticker, the Pacific Coast Stock Exchange, and the Montreal Stock Exchange.

Government price indexes are likewise heavily dependent upon computers to handle vast amounts of data very rapidly.

➤ *Example.* The Wholesale Price Index is computed following a flow diagram similar to that shown in Figure 21.1.

➤ *Example.* The United States Department of Commerce uses computers (1) to adjust raw data used in indexes, (2) to compile diffusion indexes, (3) to chart data, and (4) to do research in the field of index numbers.

Nearly all major series and component series handled by the department are analyzed for the presence (or absence) of seasonal variation. The Commerce Department uses a Sperry Rand 1105 computer, which analyzes an economic time series consisting of 288 months of data in approximately 40 seconds. The compilation of diffusion indexes over various time spans and consisting of as many as 80 components can be handled by the computer in less than five minutes. Work of this nature would not be practical in terms of time or money without the use of computers. Further, large amounts of basic data can now be compiled as empirical evidence to support or refute untested hypotheses and open new channels of investigation.

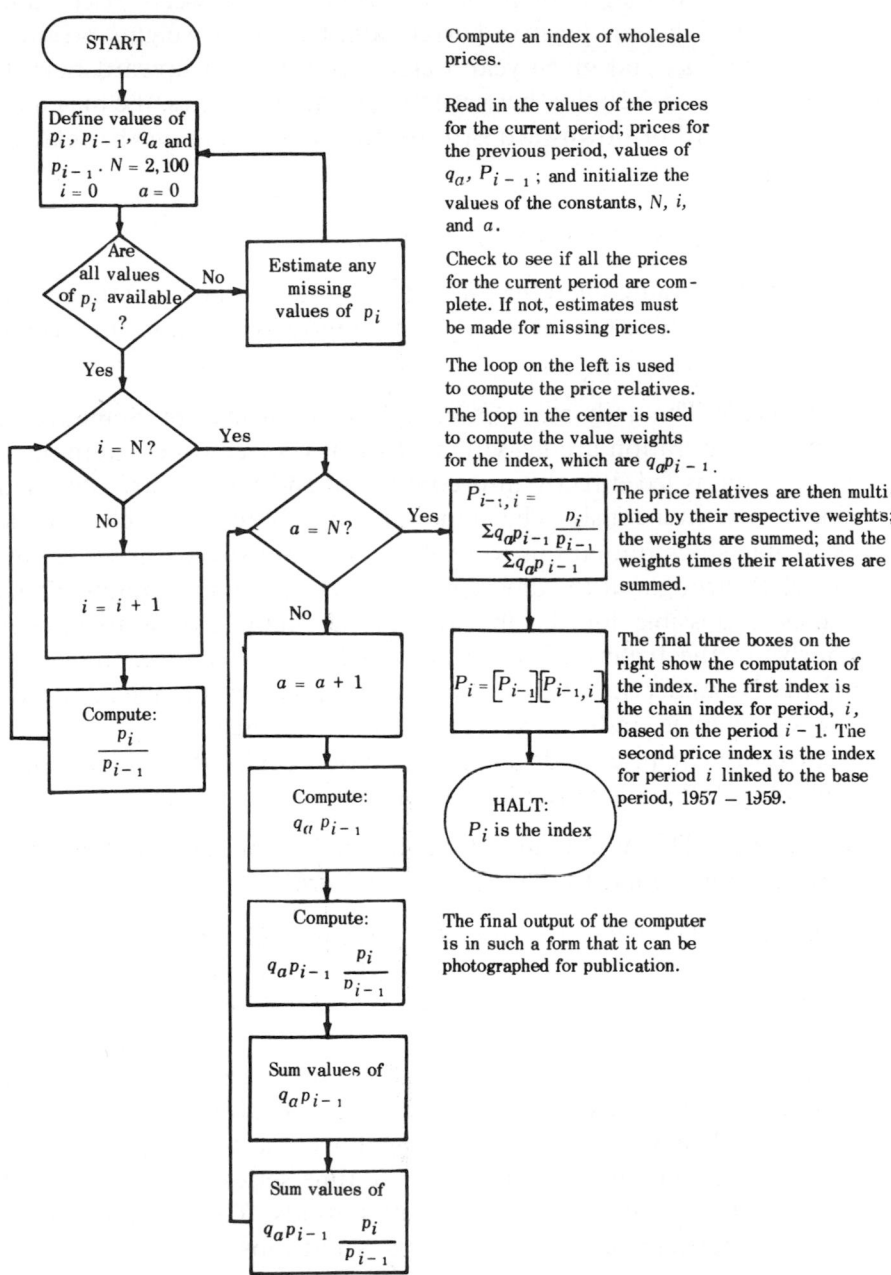

Compute an index of wholesale prices.

Read in the values of the prices for the current period; prices for the previous period, values of q_a, P_{i-1}; and initialize the values of the constants, N, i, and a.

Check to see if all the prices for the current period are complete. If not, estimates must be made for missing prices.

The loop on the left is used to compute the price relatives. The loop in the center is used to compute the value weights for the index, which are $q_a p_{i-1}$.

The price relatives are then multiplied by their respective weights; the weights are summed; and the weights times their relatives are summed.

The final three boxes on the right show the computation of the index. The first index is the chain index for period, i, based on the period $i-1$. The second price index is the index for period i linked to the base period, 1957 – 1959.

The final output of the computer is in such a form that it can be photographed for publication.

Figure 21.1

A FLOW DIAGRAM FOR COMPUTING A PRICE
INDEX FROM A SAMPLE OF 2,100
WHOLESALE PRICES

While it is clear that the businessman must still make many decisions under uncertainty, it is equally clear that index numbers provide him with some guideposts he can use in making his decisions. The computer is helping to make these guideposts more numerous and more accurate than ever before.

STUDY QUESTIONS

21-1. Explain briefly the meaning of each of the following terms:

a. index number	h. chain index number
b. value index	i. market basket of goods and services
c. price index	j. Fisher's ideal index
d. quantity index	k. linking
e. diffusion index	l. base period
f. constant dollars	m. weight correlation bias
g. price relative	

21-2. Give three uses of index numbers.

21-3. What kinds of averages may be used to combine price relatives into a price index?

21-4. What weights are normally used to compute Laspeyres' price index?

21-5. Why is Paasche's price index formula used less frequently than Laspeyres' price index?

21-6. What type of formula is used to compute the Wholesale Price Index?

21-7. What system of weights is used to compute the Consumer Price Index? How were these weights determined?

21-8. Why did Fisher consider his index to be "ideal"?

21-9. If you were to compare the formulas for Standard & Poor's "500" Price Index with that used for the Dow-Jones Stock Averages, which would you consider to be the better measure of changes in stock prices? Why?

21-10. What things need to be considered in determining the commodities to be used for a price index?

21-11. Under what conditions would it be necessary to use the "adjustment for quality difference" method rather than the "linking" method to handle a substantial change in quality of an item considered for a price index? If you could use either method, which would you prefer? Why?

21-12. What base period is currently used for most federally constructed index numbers? Why is this a logical base?

21-13. What kind of bias might you expect in an index number computed using an arithmetic mean of price relatives? A harmonic mean? A geometric mean?

21-14. What kind of bias results from using base-year values as weights in a price index?

21-15. What are some of the disadvantages of using given-year values as weights in a price index?

21-16. Discuss the role of computers in the production of index numbers.

PROBLEMS

21-1.

VALUE OF LIFE INSURANCE IN FORCE
IN THE UNITED STATES. 1958
TO 1963

(Billions of dollars)

Year	Value
1958	288
1959	316
1960	340
1961	364
1962	389
1963	419

Source: *Life Insurance Fact
Book*, 1964 (New York: Institute of Life Insurance), p. 25.

a. Compute a value index for the series using 1960 = 100.0.
b. Can the fact that the index is rising be attributed to (1) more people buying
   policies, (2) policies getting larger on the average, (3) both, or (4) cannot be
   determined from the information given?
c. Can you suggest a way in which the value index might be divided into two
   series to measure better what kind of changes are taking place?

21-2. Compute the price index for the three petroleum products shown below,
using 1958 as the base. Use the method of aggregates (arithmetic mean with
base-year values as weights).

PRICE PER GALLON AND SALES IN GALLONS
FOR THREE PETROLEUM PRODUCTS

Product	Price per gallon		Sales in gallons	
	1958	1965	1958	1965
Fuel oil	$0.14	$0.15	4,500	7,800
Gasoline	0.28	0.25	8,250	11,630
Lubricants	0.30	0.33	550	720

21-3.

NUMBER AND PRICE OF THREE MODELS OF LAWN MOWERS SOLD BY A HARDWARE STORE
1960 AND 1965

Model of lawn mower	1960		1965	
	Number sold	price	Number sold	price
Model I	225	$35	315	$38
Model II	300	54	420	62
Self-propelled	75	105	95	90

Using 1960 as the base period, compute the following indexes of prices for 1965:

a. An arithmetic mean of price relatives.
b. A geometric mean of price relatives.
c. A harmonic mean of price relatives.

21-4. Use the data in Problem 21-3 to compute the following indexes of prices for 1965 with 1960 = 100.0:

a. Arithmetic mean of price relatives weighted with base-year values.
b. Geometric mean of price relatives weighted with base-year values.
c. Harmonic mean of price relatives weighted with base-year values.

21-5. Use the data in Problem 21-3 to compute the following indexes of prices for 1965 with 1960 = 100.0:

a. Harmonic mean of price relatives weighted with given-year values.
b. Paasche's price index.
c. Laspeyres' price index.
d. Fisher's ideal index.

21-6. Construct a price index and a quantity index of grains for 1966 using 1960 as the base. Use Laspeyres' formula in each case.

PRICE AND PRODUCTION FOR THREE GRAINS
1960 AND 1966

Commodity	1960		1966	
	Price (per bu)	Production (1,000 bu)	Price (per bu)	Production (1,000 bu)
Wheat	$1.40	500	$1.20	450
Corn	0.90	400	1.00	330
Oats	0.45	250	0.55	150

21-7.

PRODUCTION AND PRICE FOR THREE COMMODITIES
1955 AND 1965

Commodity	Unit	Production (1,000 units)		Price per unit	
		1955	1965	1955	1965
Peaches	bushels	1,500	2,000	$2.75	$4.25
Pecans	pounds	8,000	9,100	0.20	0.35
Oranges	boxes	3,540	4,200	2.10	1.50

Using 1955 as the base period, compute the following indexes of prices for 1965:
a. An arithmetic mean of price relatives.
b. A geometric mean of price relatives.
c. A harmonic mean of price relatives.

21-8. Use the data in Problem 21-7 to compute the following indexes of prices for 1965 with 1955 = 100.0:
a. An arithmetic mean of price relatives weighted with base-year values.
b. A geometric mean of price relatives weighted with base-year values.

21-9. Use the data in Problem 21-7 to compute the following indexes of prices for 1965 with 1955 = 100.0:
a. A harmonic mean of price relatives weighted with given-year values.
b. Paasche's price index.
c. Laspeyres' price index.
d. Fisher's ideal index.

21-10. For the series below compute the values of the new index using 1964 as the base year from the old index that has 1959 as its base:

INDEX FOR THE YEARS 1957–1965

Year	Old index (1959 = 100.0)	New index (1964 = 100.0)
1957	79.2	
1958	84.6	
1959	100.0	
1960	111.0	
1961	116.7	
1962	123.8	
1963	154.6	
1964	163.0	100.0
1965	172.5	

21-11. Given the following price index : (1960 = 100.0)

1958	1959	1960	1961	1962	1963	1964
87.2	97.3	100.0	112.0	120.2	123.7	124.8

a. Shift the base to 1958 = 100.0.
b. Shift the base to 1962 = 100.0.

21-12. In the series below, the values of the new index with a base of 1965 are given. Compute the values of the old index with 1960 as the base.

INDEX FOR THE YEARS 1959–1966

Year	Old index (1960 = 100.0)	New index (1965 = 100.0)
1959		133.5
1960	100.0	131.7
1961		125.2
1962		120.0
1963		118.6
1964		105.3
1965		100.0
1966		98.0

21-13. Judging from the data below, are the real wages of the employees of Company *A* keeping pace with the cost of living? What is the exact situation in 1964?

CONSUMER PRICE INDEX AND AVERAGE WEEKLY EARNINGS
IN COMPANY *A*, 1960–1964

Year	Consumer Price Index 1957–1959 = 100.0	Average weekly earnings in Company *A*
1960	103.1	$61.50
1961	104.2	61.75
1962	105.4	62.20
1963	106.7	63.20
1964	108.1	64.75

21-14. In January, 1965, the Consumer Price Index for Detroit stood at 104.0 (1957–1959 = 100.0). On the same date the index for San Francisco was 110.6. What does this tell you about the relative cost of living in the two cities?

21-15.

NUMBER OF HEAD AND PRICE PER HEAD OF LIVESTOCK
1960, 1961, AND 1965

Livestock	Number of head (thousands)			Price per head (dollars)		
	1960	1961	1965	1960	1961	1965
Cattle	1,250	1,300	1,500	$124	$120	$132
Sheep	1,800	1,900	2,000	15	16	17
Hogs	1,600	1,650	1,860	16	18	17

Using the data above:

a. Compute an index of livestock prices for 1965 using 1960 and 1961 quantities as base-year quantities and 1960 prices as base-year prices. Use Formula 21.13.

b. Compute a quantity index for livestock for 1965 using 1960 and 1961 prices as base-year prices and 1960 quantities as base-year quantities. Modify Formula 21.13 to make it a quantity index formula to use in this problem.

21-16.

PRICES OF FOUR COMMODITIES
1960–1965.

Commodity	Weights q_a	Prices					
		1960	1961	1962	1963	1964	1965
A	0.2	$1.00	$1.10	$1.05	$1.11	$1.18	$1.20
B	0.4	0.26	0.30	0.35	0.42	0.55	0.60
C	0.1	0.58	0.56	0.52	0.50	0.50	0.45
D	0.3	2.00	2.05	2.10	2.25	2.50	2.65

Using the values of q_a as weights:

a. Compute chain price index numbers for 1961 through 1965.

b. Use the values from (a) to compute P_{60-62}, P_{60-63}, P_{60-64}, and P_{60-65}.

c. Compare the value of P_{60-65} computed in (b) with an arithmetic mean of price relatives using $1960 = 100.0$ and the values of q_a as weights.

21-17.

PRICES OF THREE DAIRY PRODUCTS
1963–1966

Dairy product	Unit	Weights q_a	Prices			
			1963	1964	1965	1966
Milk	quart	0.5	$0.20	$0.21	$0.23	$0.25
Butter	pound	0.2	0.82	0.85	0.83	0.80
Eggs	dozen	0.3	0.60	0.58	0.59	0.61

Using the values of q_a as weights:

a. Compute chain price index numbers for 1964 through 1966.
b. Using 1964 = 100.0, compute P_{64-65}, P_{64-66}, and P_{64-63}.

21-18. Assume that one of the products selected for a price index has a substantial change in quality.

a. If you have the following information, compute the index using the "linking" method:

Reported price	Base period	Period 1	Period 2
Quality I	$5.00	$6.00	$...
Quality II	...	9.00	10.00

b. If you have the following information, compute the index using the "adjustment of quality difference" method:

Price for:	Base period	Period 1	Period 2
Quality I	$5.00	...	...
Quality II	...	$9.00	$10.00
Value of the difference between I & II	...	3.00	...

21-19. Draw flow diagrams to show how you would solve the following problems on a computer:
a. Problem 21-1(a).
b. Problem 21-3(a).
c. Problem 21-6.

SELECTED READINGS

Ekeblad, Frederick A. *The Statistical Method in Business*. New York: John Wiley & Sons, Inc., 1952.

Chapter 19 entitled, "Index Numbers: the Comparison of Group Characteristics," is a good introduction to the use of index numbers in business.

Fisher, Irving. *The Making of Index Numbers*. Boston: Houghton Mifflin Company, 1927.

A definitive work on index numbers. In this book Professor Fisher examines and tests for reliability many different formulas for computing index numbers.

Persons, Warren Milton. *The Construction of Index Numbers*. Boston: Houghton Mifflin Company, 1928.

A short but highly instructive book on the construction of index numbers of prices. Special attention is given to the problems of bias resulting from the type of average used and from correlation between quantities and prices.

Stockton, John R. *Introduction to Business and Economic Statistics*. 3d ed. Cincinnati: South-Western Publishing Company, 1966.

Chapter 16 has a clear, readable introduction to the subject of index numbers, and Chapter 17 discusses some of the more important business and economic barometers of interest to the businessman.

Contents

Glossary of Symbols

PART I—A REVIEW OF DESCRIPTIVE STATISTICS

X	A random variable.
μ	Arithmetic mean of a random variable.
N	Number of values of a variable.
k	Number of classes in a frequency distribution.
$\log n$	Logarithm of number of observations to be included in a frequency distribution.
Σ	The Greek letter *sigma*, meaning "the sum of."
f	Number of values of a variable falling in a particular class in a frequency distribution.
m	Value of the midpoint of a class of a frequency distribution.
w	Weight assigned each value of a variable.
A	Midpoint of some arbitrarily selected class interval.
d	Deviation of the midpoint of a class from A, expressed in class interval units.
i	Class interval of a frequency distribution, when all the classes are the same size.
G	Geometric mean.
$\log$	Logarithm.
r	Average rate of change.
P_N	Value at the end of the time period.
P_O	Value at the beginning of the time period.
N	Number of time periods for which the average rate of change is being computed.
H	Harmonic mean.
Md	Median.
L_{Md}	Real lower limit of the class in which the median falls.
$F_{L_{Md}}$	Cumulative frequency less than the lower limit of the class in which the median falls.

1

f_{Md}	Frequency of the class in which the median falls.
i_{Md}	Class interval of the class in which the median falls.
Mo_E	Empirical mode.
Mo	Mode.
L_{Mo}	Real lower limit of the class in which the mode falls.
d_1	The difference between the number of items in the modal class and the class that immediately precedes it.
d_2	The difference between the number of items in the modal class and the class that immediately follows it.
i_{Mo}	Class interval of the class in which the mode falls.
Q_1	First quartile.
Q_3	Third quartile.
L_{Q_1}	Real lower limit of the first quartile class.
L_{Q_3}	Real lower limit of the third quartile class.
$F_{L_{Q1}}$	Cumulative frequency less than the lower limit of the first quartile class.
$F_{L_{Q3}}$	Cumulative frequency less than the lower limit of the third quartile class.
f_{Q_1}	Frequency of the first quartile class.
f_{Q_3}	Frequency of the third quartile class.
i_{Q_1}	Class interval of the first quartile class.
i_{Q_3}	Class interval of the third quartile class.
D_3	Third decile.
L_{D_3}	Real lower limit of the third decile class.
$F_{L_{D3}}$	Cumulative frequency less than the lower limit of the third decile class.
f_{D_3}	Frequency of the third decile class.
i_{D_3}	Class interval of the third decile class.
P_{75}	Seventy-fifth percentile.
$L_{P_{75}}$	Real lower limit of the 75th percentile class.

F_{LP75}	Cumulative frequency less than the lower limit of the 75th percentile class.
f_{P75}	Frequency of the 75th percentile class.
i_{P75}	Class interval of the 75th percentile class.
QR	Interquartile range.
Q	Quartile deviation.
AD	Average deviation.
σ	Standard deviation of a universe of items.
σ^2	Variance of a universe of items.
V	Coefficient of variation.
V_Q	Coefficient of quartile variation.
Sk	Skewness.
M_1	First moment about the mean.
M_2	Second moment about the mean (also known as the variance).
M_3	Third moment about the mean.
M_4	Fourth moment about the mean.
β_1	Beta one. A measure of relative skewness.
α_3	Alpha three. A measure of relative skewness.
β_2	Beta two. A measure of relative kurtosis.
α_4	Alpha four. A measure of relative kurtosis.

PART III—PROBABILITY AND PROBABILITY DISTRIBUTIONS

n	Number of distinct objects from which groups are drawn.
r	Number of distinct objects drawn from a total of n objects.
$_nP_r$	Number of permutations of n things taken r at a time.
$_nC_r$	Number of combinations of n things taken r at a time.
$P(A)$	Probability of A.

$P(A')$	Probability that A will not occur.
$\cup$	Union of subsets.
$\cap$	Intersection of subsets.
$P(A \mid B)$	Probability of event A relative to an event B.
$E(X)$	Expected value of X.
MR	Marginal revenue.
ML	Marginal loss.
P_c	Computed or critical probability.
pdf	Probability density function.
M'_k	k^{th} moment about the origin of a random variable X.
M'_0	Zero-order moment about the origin, which expresses the total area of the probability distribution.
M'_1	First-order moment that is the expected value of the random variable X.
μ	Expected value of a random variable.
M_k	k^{th} moment about the mathematical expectation of a random variable X.
M_2	Variance of a distribution.
$P(r \mid n, p)$	Probability of r successes in n Bernoulli trials, given the probability p of a success.
π	Long-run or universe fraction of successes from Bernoulli trials.
$\text{Var}(r)$	Variance of the number of successes from Bernoulli trials.
σ_r	Standard deviation of a Bernoulli process.
$\text{Var}(p)$	Variance of the proportion of successes from Bernoulli trials.
σ_p	Standard deviation of the proportion of successes from Bernoulli trials.
k	Number of successes per unit of space.
t	A given amount of space.
λ	Expected number of successes in a given amount of space.
r'	A specified value of the number of successes r.

$P(r \mid \lambda)$ — Poisson probability of r successes given a value of λ.

$P(c \mid N, r, n)$ — Hypergeometric probability of c defectives in a sample given N, r, and n.

$n_1, n_2, \ldots, n_k$ — Number of items in each of k groups.

$P(n \mid r, p)$ — Probability that n trials will be required to obtained r successes, given a probability p.

$\tilde{r}$ — A specified value of the number of successes.

$\tilde{n}$ — A specified number of trials.

$f(X)$ — A function of the variable X.

$\int$ — Integral symbol.

e — The base of natural logarithms.

β — The reciprocal of the average number of successes.

$f(t)$ — Exponential density function.

$P(t)$ — Exponential probability of no success prior to the interval t.

$f(r)$ — Normal density function.

β_2 — Relative kurtosis (not to be confused with the parameter of the exponential distribution).

Y — Ordinate of the normal curve.

z — Deviation in standard deviation units.

$f(U)$ — Unit normal density function.

$f(t)$ — Gamma density function (exponential density function is a special case of the gamma).

$\tilde{\mu}$ — A specified value of μ.

$d.f.$ — Degrees of freedom.

f_e — Expected frequency.

$E(L_w)$ — Expected length of a waiting line.

$E(T_w)$ — Expected waiting time of a unit.

$E(U)$ — Expected utilization of a facility.

$P(D)$ — Probability of delay.

$E(T_s)$	Expected total time a unit is in the system.
$P(n)$	Probability of n units in the system.
$P(0)$	Probability of no units in the system.
$P(m)$	Probability that m units are waiting or being served, finite input source.

PART IV—SAMPLING

$\bar{\bar{x}}$	Mean of several sample means.
$s_{\bar{x}}$	Standard deviation of sample means.
Md_{Md}	Median of sample medians.
$\bar{s}$	Average of sample standard deviations.
s_{Md}	Standard deviation of sample medians.
s_s	Standard deviation of sample standard deviations.
$\sigma_{\bar{x}}$	Standard error of sample means.
σ_{Md}	Standard error of sample medians.
σ_s	Standard error of sample standard deviations.
$E(s^2)$	Expected value of a sample variance.
s^2	Sample variance.
$\hat{\sigma}^2$	Unbiased estimate of the universe variance.
$\hat{\sigma}$	Unbiased estimate of the universe standard deviation.
$\hat{\sigma}_{\bar{x}}$	Unbiased estimate of the standard error of the mean.
p	Sample proportion.
$\hat{\sigma}_p$	Unbiased estimate of the standard error of the proportion.
$\theta, \hat{\theta}$	A random variable and its estimator.
α	Level of confidence.
z_α	Number of standard errors associated with a level of confidence.
σ_{percent}	Standard error of the percent.

f	Sampling fraction.
$\bar{R}$	Average of several sample ranges.
d_2	Ratio of the average sample range to the universe standard deviation.
A_2	Factor for estimating $3\sigma_{\bar{x}}$ from the average sample range.
$UCL_{\bar{x}}$	Upper control limit for sample means.
$LCL_{\bar{x}}$	Lower control limit for sample means.
D_3	Factor for computing the upper control limit of sample ranges.
D_4	Factor for computing the lower control limit of sample ranges.
UCL_R	Upper control limit for sample ranges.
LCL_R	Lower control limit for sample ranges.
p'	Estimated universe proportion.
UCL_p	Upper control limit for sample proportions.
LCL_p	Lower control limit for sample proportions.
$\bar{c}$	Expected number of defects per unit.
σ_c	Standard deviation of the number of defects per unit.
UCL_c	Upper control limit for defects per unit.
LCL_c	Lower control limit for defects per unit.
t	Student's t distribution.
t_α	Value of t for a given level of significance, α.
f	Sampling fraction, $\dfrac{n}{N}$.
L	Number of strata in a stratified sample.
N_h	Number of listing units in the universe for the hth strata.
n_h	Number of listing units in the sample for the hth strata.
μ_h	Universe mean of the items in the hth strata.
$\bar{x}_h$	Sample mean of the items in the hth strata.
X_{hi}	The ith member of the universe from the hth strata.
x_{hi}	The ith member of the sample from the hth strata.

μ_{St} Universe mean of the stratified sample.

$\bar{x}_{St}$ Sample mean of the stratified sample.

σ_h^2 Universe variance of the hth strata.

$\hat{\sigma}_h^2$ Unbiased estimate of the universe variance of the hth strata from a sample.

$\sigma_{\bar{x}_{St}}$ Universe standard error of the mean for a stratified sample.

$\hat{\sigma}_{\bar{x}_{St}}$ Unbiased estimate of the universe standard error of the mean for a stratified sample.

π_h Universe percent of a given characteristic in the hth strata.

p_h Sample percent of a given characteristic in the hth strata.

π_{St} Universe percentage of a given characteristic of a stratified sample.

p_{St} Sample percentage of a given characteristic of a stratified sample.

$\sigma_{p_h}^2$ Universe variance of the percentage of the hth strata.

$\hat{\sigma}_{p_h}^2$ Unbiased estimate of universe variance of the percentage for the hth strata from a sample.

$\sigma_{p_{St}}$ Universe standard error of the percent of a stratified sample.

$\hat{\sigma}_{p_{St}}$ Unbiased estimate of universe standard error of the percent of a stratified sample.

C Total cost of the sample survey.

C_h Cost per sample unit for the hth stratum.

M Number of primary sampling units in the universe.

m Number of primary sampling units in the cluster sample.

N_i Number of listing units in the universe of the ith primary unit.

n_i Number of listing units in the sample of the ith primary unit.

N Total number of listing units in the universe.

n Total number of listing units in the sample.

X_i Cluster total of the universe of the listing units in the ith primary unit.

x_i Cluster total of the sample of the listing units in the ith primary unit.

μ_i Universe mean of the ith primary unit.

$\bar{x}_i$ Sample mean of the ith primary unit.

μ Overall universe mean.

$\bar{\bar{x}}$ Overall sample mean.

σ_b^2 Universe variance between primary units.

$\hat{\sigma}_b^2$ Unbiased estimate of universe variance between primary units from a cluster sample.

σ_i^2 Universe variance of listing units within the ith primary unit.

$\hat{\sigma}_i^2$ Unbiased estimate of universe variance within the ith primary unit from a sample.

σ_w^2 Universe variance within primary units.

$\hat{\sigma}_w^2$ Unbiased estimate of universe variance within primary units of a cluster sample.

$\text{Var}(\bar{\bar{x}})$ Universe variance of the sample mean of a two-stage cluster sample.

$\hat{\sigma}_{\bar{\bar{x}}}^2$ Unbiased estimate of universe variance of the sample mean of a two-stage cluster sample.

$\sigma_{\bar{\bar{x}}}$ Universe standard error of the mean of a two-stage cluster sample.

$\hat{\sigma}_{\bar{\bar{x}}}$ Unbiased estimate of universe standard error of the mean of a two-stage cluster sample.

$\bar{N}$ Average number of universe listing units per primary unit.

$\bar{n}$ Average number of sample listing units per primary unit in a two-stage cluster sample.

δ Intraclass correlation between elementary units with primary units in a two-stage cluster sample.

C_1 Cost per primary unit included in a cluster sample.

C_2 Cost per listing unit included in a cluster sample.

PART V—INFERENCE

H_1 Null hypothesis.

H_2 Alternate hypothesis.

W_1	State of the world when H_1 is true.
W_2	State of the world when H_1 is false.
A_1	Action taken when H_1 is accepted.
A_2	Action taken when H_1 is rejected.
$\bar{x}_c$	Critical value of a sample mean.
α	Level of significance, which is the probability of a Type I error.
β	Probability of a Type II error.
$P(A_2 \mid W_1)$	Probability of a Type I error.
$P(A_1 \mid W_2)$	Probability of a Type II error.
$\sigma_{\bar{x}_1 - \bar{x}_2}$	Standard error of the difference between two sample means.
$\hat{\sigma}_{\bar{x}_1 - \bar{x}_2}$	Unbiased estimate of the standard error of the difference between two sample means.
p_c	Critical value of a sample percent.
$\hat{\sigma}_{p_1 - p_2}$	Unbiased estimate of the standard error of the difference between two sample percents.
χ^2	The chi-square distribution.
f_o	An observed frequency.
f_e	An expected frequency.
F_o	Cumulative frequency of an observed distribution.
F_e	Cumulative frequency of an expected distribution.
D	Maximum absolute difference between F_o and F_e.
T	Sum of the positive ranks or the negative ranks, whichever is the smaller for the Wilcoxon matched-pairs signed-ranks test.
μ_T	Mean of T for the Wilcoxon matched-pairs signed-ranks test.
σ_T	Standard error of T.
n_1	Number of items in the first sample in a Mann-Whitney U test.
n_2	Number of items in the second sample in a Mann-Whitney U test.
R_1	Total of the ranks assigned to values of the first sample in the Mann-Whitney U test.

U	The statistic in the Mann-Whitney U test.
μ_U	Mean of U for the Mann-Whitney U test.
σ_U	Standard error of U.
R	Observed number of runs in a one-sample runs test.
μ_R	Mean of R in a one-sample runs test.
σ_R	Standard error of R.
F	The statistic F.
χ^2	Chi-square.
x_{ij}	i^{th} observation of the jth sample.
ε	Sampling error.
$\hat{\sigma}_\varepsilon^2$	Variance of the sampling error.
θ_j	Measure of bias in an observed value.
$\hat{\sigma}_c^2$	Unbiased estimate of a universe variance obtained from the dispersion of column means.
r	Number of rows (samples).
$\underset{i}{\Sigma}$	Summation of all i items in a column.
$\underset{j}{\Sigma}$	Summation of all j columns.
$\bar{x}_j$	Mean of the jth column.
c	Number of columns.
MSC	Mean sum of squares for all columns.
MSE	Mean square error.
SST	Total sum of squares.
C	Correction factor.
SSC	Sum of squares between columns (samples).
n_j	Number of observations in the jth sample.
x_{ij}	i^{th} observation of the jth sample.
$T._j$	Total of the observations of the jth sample.
c	Number of samples (columns).

T	Grand total of all observations in all c samples.
θ_j	Effect of the jth sample.
ε_{ij}	Effect of the sampling error on the ith observation of the jth sample.
N	Total number of observations in all samples.
SSC	Between columns sum of squares.
SSE	Error sum of squares.
SST	Total sum of squares.
MSC	Mean square of columns.
MSE	Mean square error.
C	Correction factor.
$T_{i.}$	Total of the ith row.
$T_{..}$	Grand total of the observations in all samples.
τ_i	Effect of the ith row.
SSR	Between rows sum of squares.
MSR	Mean square of rows.
F_R	Variance ratio for row differences.
F_C	Variance ratio for column differences.
n	Number of observations per cell.
γ_{ij}	Interaction of the ith row with the jth column.
x_{ijk}	k^{th} observation of the ith row and the jth column.
$T_{i..}$	Total of all observations in the ith row, with n observations per cell.
$T_{.j.}$	Total of all observations in the jth column, with n observations per cell.
$T_{...}$	Grand total of all observations, n observations per cell.
ε_{ijk}	Effect of sampling error on the kth observation in the ith row and the jth column.
SSI	Interaction sum of squares.
MSI	Mean square of interactions.

T_{ij}	Total for the cell in the ith row and the jth column.
SSM	Between means sum of squares.
F_I	Variance ratio for interaction differences.
A, B, C, etc.	Treatments in a Latin square, or factors in a factorial experiment.
$x_{ij(k)}$	k^{th} treatment of the ith row and the jth column of a Latin square.
T_k	Total of observations for the kth treatment.
γ_k	Effect of the kth treatment.
$\varepsilon_{ij(k)}$	Effect of sampling error on the kth treatment of the ith row and the jth column.
Tr	Treatment.
$SS(Tr)$	Between treatments sum of squares.
$MS(Tr)$	Mean square of treatments.
F_{Tr}	Variance ratio for treatment differences.
0 and 1	Levels of factors in a 2^3 factorial experiment.
x_{ijkl}	An observation of x taken from the ith level of A, the jth level of B, the kth level of C, and the lth replicate.
l	Combination used when all factors are at level 0.
rp	Replicate.
ε_{ijkl}	Effect of a sampling error on the lth replicate of the ith level of A, the jth level of B, and the kth level of C.
α_i	Effect of the ith level of A.
β_j	Effect of the jth level of B.
γ_k	Effect of the kth level of C.
$(\alpha\beta)_{ij}$	Interaction of the ith level of A with the jth level of B.
$(\alpha\gamma)_{ik}$	Interaction of the ith level of A with the kth level of C.
$(\beta\gamma)_{jk}$	Interaction of the jth level of B with the kth level of C.
$(\alpha\beta\gamma)_{ijk}$	Interaction of the ith level of A with the jth level of B with the kth level of C.
ρ_1	Effect of the lth replicate.

AB, AC,
  and *BC*   Two-factor interactions.

ABC   Three-factor interaction.

SSA   Sum of squares, factor *A*.

SSB   Sum of squares, factor *B*.

SSC   Sum of squares, factor *C*.

SS(AB)   Sum of squares, *A* interaction *B*.

SS(AC)   Sum of squares, *A* interaction *C*.

SS(BC)   Sum of squares, *B* interaction *C*.

SS(ABC)   Sum of squares, *A* interaction *B* interaction *C*.

MSA, etc. Mean square, factor *A*, etc.

F_A, F_B, F_C Variance ratios for main effects.

F_{AB}, F_{AC}, F_{BC} Variance ratios for two-factor interactions.

F_{ABC} Variance ratio for three-factor interactions.

T_a, T_b, T_c Totals for main effects.

T_{ab}, T_{ac}, T_{bc} Totals for two-factor interactions.

T_{abc} Total for three-factor interaction.

T_I Grand total, 2^3 factorial experiment.

PART VI—REGRESSION AND CORRELATION

X_{1c} Computed value of a variable.

$\alpha_{1.2}$ Constant term of the universe line of regression.

β_{12} Regression coefficient for the analysis of two variables.

ε Error of estimating a random variable with a regression line.

$\sigma^2_{1.2}$ Variance of the deviations of X_1 from X_{1c}.

$a_{1.2}$ Unbiased estimate of $\alpha_{1.2}$ obtained from sample data.

b_{12} Unbiased estimate of β_{12} obtained from sample data.

$\sigma_{1.2}$ Standard error of the estimates of x_1, based on x_2.

$\hat{\sigma}_{1.2}$ — Estimated standard error of the estimate.

$E(b_{12})$ — Expected value of the regression coefficient.

$\sigma_{b_{12}}$ — Standard error of estimating β_{12} with b_{12}.

$\hat{\sigma}_{b_{12}}$ — Estimated standard error of a regression coefficient.

$\hat{\sigma}_{(\bar{x}_1 \mid x_2)}$ — Estimated standard error of a regression line.

$\hat{\sigma}_{(x_1 \mid x_2)}$ — Estimated standard error of an estimated value of X_1.

ρ_{12} — Correlation coefficient based on a universe of observations.

ρ_{12}^2 — Universe coefficient of determination.

$1 - \rho_{12}^2$ — Universe coefficient of nondetermination.

r_{12}^2 — Estimated determination coefficient that is a point estimate ρ_{12}^2.

$\sigma_{r_{12}}$ — Standard error of an estimated correlation coefficient.

r_{rank} — Coefficient of rank correlation.

$x_{1c \, . \, x_2 x_2^2}$ — Expected value of x_1 computed by use of a quadratic regression equation.

c_{12} — Regression coefficient based on squared values of x_2.

$\mathbf{A}^{-1}$ — Inverse of a square matrix.

$\mathbf{I}$ — Identity matrix.

$\dfrac{1}{x_1}$ — Reciprocal of an observation of x_1.

$I^2_{x_1 \, . \, x_2 x_2^2}$ — Index of determination for a second-order polynomial.

$I^2_{x_1 \, . \, x_2 x_2^2 \cdots \cdot x_2^k}$ — Index of determination for a kth order polynomial.

$r^2_{x_1 x_2 \, . \, x_2}$ — Proportion of the unassociated sum of squares for the first-order polynomial that is associated with the addition of x_2^2 as an independent variable.

$I_{\log x_1 \, . \, x_2}$ — Index of correlation for the logarithms of x_1 and x_2.

$I_{\left(\frac{1}{x_1}\right) . \, x_2}$ — Index of correlation for the reciprocals of x_1 and x_2.

A_{12} — Proportion of the variation of X_1, associated with the variation of X_2.

U_{12} — Proportion of the variation of X_1 not associated with the variation of X_2.

$\sigma^2_{1.23}$ — Variance of estimating X_1 given values of X_2 and X_3 as independent variables.

$\sigma^2_{1.234}$ — Variance of estimating X_1 given values of X_2, X_3, and X_4 as independent variables.

$a_{1.23}$ — Unbiased estimate of the universe constant term $\alpha_{1.23}$ for a trivariate regression equation.

$b_{12.3}$ — Unbiased estimate of the universe regression coefficient $\beta_{12.3}$ that reflects the expected change in x_1 with a unit change in x_2, with the effects of x_3 held constant.

$b_{13.2}$ — Unbiased estimate of the universe regression coefficient $\beta_{13.2}$ that reflects the expected change in x_1 with a unit change in x_3, with the effects of x_2 held constant.

ε^2 — Sum of the squared deviations of x_1 from x_{1c} that is minimized by the least squares method.

Σd^2_1 — Sum of the squared deviations of the sample observations of variable x_1 from $\bar{x}_1$.

Σd^2_2 — Sum of the squared deviations of the sample observations of variable x_2 from $\bar{x}_2$.

Σd^2_3 — Sum of the squared deviations of the sample observations of variable x_3 from $\bar{x}_3$.

Σd_{12} — Sum of the cross-products of x_1 and x_2 expressed as deviations from the respective means.

Σd_{13} — Sum of the cross-products of x_1 and x_3 expressed as deviations from the respective means.

Σd_{23} — Sum of the cross-products of x_2 and x_3 expressed as deviations from the respective means.

$\Sigma u^2_{1.23}$ — Variation of x_1 not associated with the variation of independent variables x_2 or x_3.

$\hat{\sigma}_{1.23}$ — Estimated standard error of the estimate of x_1 based on its regression on independent variables x_2 and x_3.

$\hat{\sigma}_{a_{1.23}}$ — Unbiased estimate of the standard error of the constant term for trivariate regression.

$\hat{\sigma}_{b_{12.3}}$ — Unbiased estimate of the standard error of the universe regression coefficient $\beta_{12.3}$.

$\hat{\sigma}_{b_{13.2}}$ — Unbiased estimate of the standard error of the universe regression coefficient $\beta_{13.2}$.

c_{ii}	Element on the ith row and i^{th} column on the principal diagonal of the moment matrix of observed sums of squares and cross-products that are expressed as deviations from the respective means.
$R^2_{1.23}$	Unbiased estimate of the universe coefficient of multiple determination for the correlation of x_1 with x_2 and x_3.
a_{ij}	Element on the ith row and j^{th} column of the moment matrix.
$R_{1.23}$	Unbiased estimate of the universe coefficient of multiple correlation for the correlation of x_1 with x_2 and x_3.
$r^2_{12.3}$	First-order partial determination coefficient for the correlation of x_1 and x_2 with the effects of x_3 held constant.
$r^2_{13.2}$	First-order partial determination coefficient for the correlation of x_1 and x_3 with the effects of x_2 held constant.
$a_{1.234}$	Unbiased estimate of the constant term $\alpha_{1.234}$ for the multiple regression of x_1 on x_2, x_3, and x_4.
$\hat{\sigma}^2_{1.234}$	Unbiased estimate of the variance of the estimate of x_1 given values of x_2, x_3, and x_4.
$x_{1c.234}$	Predicted value of x_1 based on the multiple regression of x_1 on x_2, x_3, and x_4.
$\hat{\sigma}_{1.234}$	Unbiased estimate of the standard error of the estimate of x_1 given values of x_2, x_3, and x_4.
$b_{12.34}$	Unbiased estimate of the universe regression coefficient $\beta_{12.34}$.
$b_{13.24}$	Unbiased estimate of the universe regression coefficient $\beta_{13.24}$.
$b_{14.23}$	Unbiased estimate of the universe regression coefficient $\beta_{14.23}$.
$\hat{\sigma}_{b_{1i.jk}}$	Unbiased estimate of the standard error of the regression coefficient $\beta_{1i.jk}$.
$R^2_{1.234}$	Unbiased estimate of the universe multiple determination coefficient.
$r^2_{14.23}$	Unbiased estimate of the second-order partial correlation coefficient.

PART VII—TIME SERIES AND INDEX NUMBERS

T	Trend component of a time series.
S	Seasonal component of a time series.
C	Cyclical component of a time series.
E	Erratic component of a time series.
a	y-intercept at the origin.
b	Slope of a trend line.
y_c	Trend values for the y variable.
S_1	Sum of the y values for the first half of a time series.
S_2	Sum of the y values for the second half of a time series.
n	Number of time periods in a time series.
c	Rate of change in the slope of a polynomial trend line at the origin.
d	Change in the rate of change in the slope of a polynomial trend line at the origin.
S_1	Sum of the y values for the first third of a time series – Gompertz curve.
S_2	Sum of the y values for the second third of a time series – Gompertz curve.
S_3	Sum of the y values for the third third of a time series – Gompertz curve.
x_t	Value of the time series in time period t.
$S_t(x)$	Smoothed value (moving average) of the series in time period t.
$S_{t-1}(x)$	Smoothed value (moving average) of the series in the period previous to t.
α	Smoothing constant.
N	Number of observations in a moving average.
C_t	Change in the smoothed value between time period t and the previous time period.
T_t	Estimated trend for time period t.
T_{t-1}	Estimated trend for the previous time period.

D_{t+1}	Expected demand (forecast) for the next time period.
AD_{t+1}	Expected demand for the next time period adjusted for seasonal variation.
$I.S.V._{t+1}$	Index of seasonal variation for the next time period.
e	Error in the forecast.
P	A price index.
p	A price.
p_o	A price in the base year.
p_i	A price in the given year or in the current period (i.e., p_{68} is a price in 1968).
p_{i-1}	A price in the period immediately preceding period p_i.
n	The number of different series in the index.
w	Weight assigned to each series in the index.
Q	A quantity index.
q	A quantity.
q_o	A quantity in the base year.
q_i	A quantity in the given year (i.e., q_{68} is a quantity in 1968).
q_a	A quantity in a fixed-weight period.

Glossary of Formulas

PART I—A REVIEW OF DESCRIPTIVE STATISTICS

**Formula
Number**   **Page**

**Formula
Number**   **Page**

PART III—PROBABILITY AND PROBABILITY DISTRIBUTIONS

**Formula
Number**   **Page**

(6.2) $_nP_r = \dfrac{n!}{(n-r)!}$ .... number of permutations of n different
objects taken r at a
time 136

(6.3) $_nC_r = \begin{pmatrix} n \\ r \end{pmatrix} = \dfrac{n!}{r!(n-r)!}$ .... number of combinations of n different
objects taken r at a
time 139

(6.4) $\begin{pmatrix} n+1 \\ r \end{pmatrix} = \begin{pmatrix} n \\ r-1 \end{pmatrix} + \begin{pmatrix} n \\ r \end{pmatrix}$ .... Pascal's rule for the
number of combina-
tions of n different
objects taken r at a
time 140

(6.5) $0 \le P(A) \le 1$ .... probability that event
A will occur is equal to
or less than one and
equal to or greater
than zero 146

(6.6) $P(A') = 1 - P(A)$ .... probability that event
A will not occur is one
minus the probability
that it will occur 146

(6.7) $P(A_1 \cup A_2 \cup \ldots \cup A_k) = P(A_1) + P(A_2) + \ldots + P(A_k)$
special rule of addi-
tion for probability of
occurrence of k mutu-
ally exclusive events... 157

(6.8) $P(B_1 \cup B_2) = P(B_1) + P(B_2) - P(B_1 \cap B_2)$ ...
general rule of addi-
tion for probability of
occurrence of two
events that may or
may not be mutually
exclusive 158

(6.9) $P(A_1 \cap A_2 \cap \ldots \cap A_k) = P(A_1) \cdot P(A_2) \cdot \ldots \cdot P(A_k)$
special rule of multi-
plication for probabil-
ity of occurrence of k
independent events ... 158

(6.10) $P(A \mid B) = \dfrac{P(A \cap B)}{P(B)}$ .... conditional probability that event A will
occur given that event
B has already occur-
red...................... 160

**Formula
Number**   **Page**

(6.11) $P(A \cap B) = P(B) \cdot P(A \mid B)$ ....general rule of multiplication for probabil-
ity of occurrence of A
and B, which may or
may not be indepen-
dent 163

(6.12) $P(B) = P(A_1) \cdot P(B \mid A_1) + P(A_2) \cdot P(B \mid A_2)$
$+ \ldots + P(A_k) \cdot P(B \mid A_k)$ ....rule of elimination for
$A_1, A_2, \ldots, A_k$ mutually
exclusive events 163

(6.13) $P(H_i \mid E) = \dfrac{P(H_i \cap E)}{P(H_1 \cap E) + P(H_2 \cap E) + \ldots + P(H_k \cap E)}$
Bayes' theorem 165

(6.14) $E(X) = X_1 P(X_1) + X_2 P(X_2) + \ldots + X_n P(X_n)$
mathematical expec-
tation 168

(6.15) $pMR = (1 - p)ML$ ....equality of marginal
expected values 174

(6.16) $p_c = \dfrac{ML}{ML + MR}$ ....critical probability ... 174

(7.1) $M'_k = E(X^k) = \Sigma X_i^k P_i$ ....the kth order moment
about the origin of a
random variable X... 187

(7.2) $M_k = E(X_i - \mu)^k = \Sigma(X_i - \mu)^k P_i$ ....the kth moment of a
discrete random vari-
able X about $E(X)$ ... 188

(7.3) $P(r \mid n, p) = \dbinom{n}{r} p^r q^{n-r}$ ....binomial probability
density function 191

(7.4) $P(r \mid n, \pi) = \dbinom{n}{r} \pi^r (1 - \pi)^{n-r}$ ....binomial probability
of r successes in n
Bernoulli trials......... 197

(7.5) $E(r) = n\pi$ ....mean of the binomial
distribution 198

(7.6) $\text{Var}(r) = n\pi(1 - \pi)$.................................variance of the binomial distribution 198

(7.7) $\sigma_r = \sqrt{n\pi(1 - \pi)}$.................................standard deviation of
the binomial distribu-
tion 198

(7.8) $E(p) = \pi$ ....mean of a sampling
distribution of p 199

**Formula
Number**   **Page**

**Formula
Number**   **Page**

(8.16) $E(T_w) = \dfrac{a}{s(s-a)} = \dfrac{E(L_w)}{a}$ ....expected waiting time, Poisson arrivals and exponential service times...................... 263

(8.17) $E(T_s) = \dfrac{1}{s-a} = E(T_w) + \dfrac{1}{s}$ ....expected total time in the system, Poisson arrivals and exponential service times...... 264

(8.18) $P(n) = \left(1 - \dfrac{a}{s}\right)\left(\dfrac{a}{s}\right)^n$ ....probability of n units in the system, Poisson arrivals and exponential service times 264

(8.19) $P(O) = \dfrac{1}{\left[\dfrac{\left(\dfrac{a}{s}\right)^M}{M!\left[1 - \dfrac{\left(\dfrac{a}{s}\right)}{M}\right]} + 1 + \dfrac{\left(\dfrac{a}{s}\right)^1}{1!} + \dfrac{\left(\dfrac{a}{s}\right)^2}{2!} + \ldots + \dfrac{\left(\dfrac{a}{s}\right)^{M-1}}{(M-1)!}\right]}$

probability of no units in the system, multiple facilities 266

(8.20) $E(L_w) = \dfrac{\left(\dfrac{a}{s}\right)^{M+1}}{(M-1)!\left[M - \left(\dfrac{a}{s}\right)\right]^2} P(O)$.........expected length of a waiting line, multiple facilities 266

(8.21) $E(L_s) = E(L_w) + \left(\dfrac{a}{s}\right)$ ....expected number of units in the system, multiple facilities...... 266

(8.22) $E(T_w) = \dfrac{E(L_w)}{a}$ ....expected waiting time, multiple facilities...... 266

(8.23) $E(T_s) = E(T_w) + \dfrac{1}{s} = \dfrac{E(L_s)}{a}$ ....expected total time in the system, multiple facilities 266

(8.24) $E(U) = \dfrac{a}{sM}$ ....expected utilization of the system, multiple facilities 266

(8.25) $P(D) = 1 - \dfrac{a}{sM}$.....................................probability of delay, multiple facilities...... 266

(8.26)

$P(m) = \dfrac{1}{\left[1 + \dfrac{1}{1!}\left(\dfrac{s}{a}\right)^1 + \dfrac{1}{2!}\left(\dfrac{s}{a}\right)^2 + \ldots + \dfrac{1}{m!}\left(\dfrac{s}{a}\right)^m\right]}$

probability that m units are waiting or being served, finite input source 268

**Formula
Number** **Page**

(8.27) $P(m - k) = \dfrac{1}{k!}\left(\dfrac{s}{a}\right)^k P(m)$.........................probability of $m - k$ units waiting or being served, finite input source 268

(8.28) $E(L_w) = m - \dfrac{a + s}{a}[1 - P(O)]$...............expected length of the waiting line, finite input source 268

(8.29) $E(T_w) = \dfrac{1}{s}\left[\dfrac{m}{1 - P(O)} - \dfrac{a + s}{a}\right]$...............expected waiting time, finite input source ... 268

PART IV—SAMPLING

(9.1) $P(|x - \mu| \geq k\sigma) \leq \dfrac{1}{k^2}$...........................Tchebycheff's inequality.............. 288

(9.2) $E(\bar{x}) = \mu$ ....expected value of a sample mean 289

(9.3) $\sigma_{\bar{x}} = \dfrac{\sigma}{\sqrt{n}}$ ....standard error of the mean..................... 289

(9.4) $\sigma_{Md} = 1.25\,\dfrac{\sigma}{\sqrt{n}}$ ....standard error of the median 291

(9.5) $\sigma_s = \dfrac{\sigma}{\sqrt{2n}}$..standard error of the standard deviation ... 293

(9.6) $\sigma_s = \sqrt{\dfrac{M_4 - M_2^2}{4M_2 \cdot n}}$ ....standard error of the standard deviation ... 293

(9.7) $E(s^2) = \dfrac{n - 1}{n}\,\sigma^2$.....................................expected value of a sample variance 294

(9.8) $s^2 = \dfrac{\overset{n}{\underset{1}{\Sigma}}(x_i - \bar{x})^2}{n}$ ....sample variance 294

(9.9) $\hat{\sigma}^2 = \dfrac{n}{n - 1}\,s^2$ ....unbiased estimate of universe variance...... 294

**Formula
Number** Page

**Formula
Number**   **Page**

(9.23) $\sigma_{\bar{x}}^2 = \dfrac{\sigma^2}{n}(1 - f)$ .... variance of the standard error of the mean
with finite correction $\quad$ 315

(9.24) $\sigma_{\bar{x}} = \dfrac{\sigma}{\sqrt{n}}\sqrt{1 - f}$ .... standard error of the
mean with finite cor-
rection 315

(9.25) $\hat{\sigma}_{\bar{x}} = \dfrac{s}{\sqrt{n - 1}}\sqrt{1 - f}$ .... estimated standard
error of the mean with
finite correction 316

(9.26) $\hat{\sigma}_p = \sqrt{1 - f}(100)\sqrt{\dfrac{p(1 - p)}{n - 1}}$ .... estimated standard
error of the propor-
tion with finite cor-
rection 317

(9.27) $d_2 = \dfrac{\bar{R}}{\sigma}$ .... ratio of the average
sample range to the
universe standard de-
viation 319

(9.28) $A_2 = \dfrac{3}{d_2\sqrt{n}}$ .... factor for estimating
$3\sigma_{\bar{x}}$ from the average
sample range 320

(9.29) $UCL_{\bar{x}} = \bar{x} + A_2\bar{R}$ .... upper control limit for
sample means 320

(9.30) $LCL_{\bar{x}} = \bar{x} - A_2\bar{R}$ .... lower control limits
for sample means ... 320

(9.31) $UCL_R = D_4\bar{R}$ .... upper control limit for 323
sample ranges ....

(9.32) $LCL_R = D_3\bar{R}$ .... lower control limit for
sample ranges 323

(9.33) $UCL_p = p' + 3\hat{\sigma}_p$ .... upper control limit of
sample proportions... 325

(9.34) $LCL_p = p' = 3\hat{\sigma}_p$ .... lower control limit of
sample proportions... 325

(9.35) $UCL_c = \bar{c} + 3\sigma_c$ .... upper control limit for
defects per unit......... 328

(9.36) $LCL_c = \bar{c} - 3\sigma_c$ .... lower control limit for
defects per unit......... 328

**Formula
Number**   **Page**

PART V—INFERENCE

Formula
Number
                                                                                                           Page

(11.5) $z = \dfrac{(\bar{x}_1 - \bar{x}_2) - (\mu_1 - \mu_2)}{\sigma_{\bar{x}_1 - \bar{x}_2}}$ .... deviation of differences in two sample means from an assumed difference of zero in the two universe means in units of the standard error of the difference 399

(11.6) $\hat{\sigma}_{\bar{x}_1 - \bar{x}_2} = \sqrt{\dfrac{n_1 s_1^2 + n_2 s_2^2}{n_1 + n_2 - 2}} \sqrt{\dfrac{n_1 + n_2}{n_1 n_2}}$ .... estimated standard error of the difference between two sample means 401

(11.7) $t = \dfrac{(\bar{x}_1 - \bar{x}_2) - (\mu_1 - \mu_2)}{\hat{\sigma}_{\bar{x}_1 - \bar{x}_2}}$ .... deviation of differences in two sample means from an assumed difference of zero in the two universe means in units of the estimated standard error of the difference 401

(12.1) $z = \dfrac{p_c - \pi}{\sigma_p}$ .... deviation of a critical value of a sample percent from a universe percent in units of standard error of percent 408

(12.2) $z = \dfrac{r - \frac{1}{2} - E(r)}{\sigma_r}$ .... deviation of an observed number of successes from an expected number of successes in units of the standard deviation of r 418

(12.3) $z = \dfrac{p - \pi}{\sigma_p}$ .... deviation of a sample percent from a universe percent in units of the standard error of percent 419

(12.4) $\hat{\sigma}_{p_1 - p_2} = \sqrt{\dfrac{\hat{\pi}(1 - \hat{\pi})}{n_1} + \dfrac{\hat{\pi}(1 - \hat{\pi})}{n_2}}$ .... estimated standard error of the difference between two sample percents 420

(12.5) $\hat{\pi} = \dfrac{x_1 + x_2}{n_1 + n_2}$ .... an estimate of a universe percent made from the results of two samples 420

**Formula
Number**   **Page**

(12.6) $z = \dfrac{(p_1 - p_2) - (\pi_1 - \pi_2)}{\hat{\sigma}_{p_1 - p_2}}$ ....deviation of differ- 420
ences in two sample
percents from an
assumed difference of
zero in the two uni-
verse percents in units
of the standard error
of the difference ......

(13.1) $\chi^2 = \sum \dfrac{(f_o - f_e)^2}{f_e}$ ....chi-square............... 424

(13.2) $\chi^2 = \sum \dfrac{(|f_o - f_e| - \frac{1}{2})^2}{f_e}$ ....chi-square using
Yates' correction for
continuity............... 433

(13.3) $z = \sqrt{2\chi^2} - \sqrt{2(d.f.) - 1}$ .... computation of z for
a chi-square test in-
volving more than 30
degrees of freedom ... 434

(13.4) $D = \text{maximum} \, |F_o - F_e|$ .... maximum absolute
difference between F_o
and F_e in a Kolmo-
gorov-Smirnov one-
sample test 436

(13.5) $\mu_T = \dfrac{n(n + 1)}{4}$ .... mean of the theoretical sampling distribu-
tion of T for the Wil-
coxon matched-pairs
signed-ranks test...... 444

(13.6) $\sigma_T = \sqrt{\dfrac{n(n + 1)(2n + 1)}{24}}$ .... standard deviation of
the theoretical sam-
pling distribution of T.
This is the standard
error of T............... 444

(13.7) $z = \dfrac{T - \mu_T}{\sigma_T}$ .... deviation of sample T
from μ_T in units of the
standard error of T.... 444

(13.8) $U = n_1 n_2 + \dfrac{n_1(n_2 + 1)}{2} - R_1$ .... the statistic in the
Mann-Whitney U test 446

(13.9) $\mu_U = \dfrac{n_1 n_2}{2}$ .... mean of a theoretical
sampling distribution
of U for the Mann-
Whitney U test......... 446

**Formula
Number**   **Page**

(13.10) $\sigma_U = \sqrt{\dfrac{n_1 n_2 (n_1 + n_2 + 1)}{12}}$ .... standard deviation of
a theoretical sampling
distribution of U for a
Mann-Whitney U test.
This is the standard
error of U 446

(13.11) $z = \dfrac{U - \mu_U}{\sigma_U}$ .... deviation of sample U
from μ_U in units of the
standard error of U... 446

(13.12) $\mu_R = \dfrac{2n_1 n_2}{n_1 + n_2} + 1$ .... mean of a theoretical
sampling distribution
of R for a one-sample
runs test. 448

(13.13) $\sigma_R = \sqrt{\dfrac{2n_1 n_2 (2n_1 n_2 - n_1 - n_2)}{(n_1 + n_2)^2 (n_1 + n_2 - 1)}}$ .... standard error of R... 448

(13.14) $z = \dfrac{R - \mu_R}{\sigma_R}$ .... deviation of sample R
from μ_R in units of the
standard error of R... 448

(14.1) $\chi^2 = \dfrac{(n-1)\hat{\sigma}^2}{\sigma^2}$ .... significance test of a
sample variance 462

(14.2) $\chi^2 = \dfrac{ns^2}{\sigma^2}$ .... significance test of a
sample variance 462

(14.3) $F = \dfrac{\dfrac{n_1 s_1^2}{(n_1 - 1)}}{\dfrac{n_2 s_2^2}{(n_2 - 1)}}$ .... the statistic F 464

(14.4) $F = \dfrac{\hat{\sigma}_1^2}{\hat{\sigma}_2^2}$ .... ratio of two estimates
of a universe variance 464

(14.5) $g(F) = \dfrac{\left(\dfrac{d.f._1 + d.f._2 - 2}{2}\right)!}{\left(\dfrac{d.f._1 - 2}{2}\right)! \left(\dfrac{d.f._2 - 2}{2}\right)!} \left(\dfrac{d.f._1}{d.f._2}\right)^{\frac{d.f._1}{2}} \dfrac{F^{\frac{d.f._1 - 2}{2}}}{\left(1 + \dfrac{d.f._1 F}{d.f._2}\right)^{\frac{d.f._1 + d.f._2}{2}}}$

density function of the
statistic F 464

**Formula
Number**
                                                                      Page

$(14.6)\ \hat{\sigma}^2 = n\hat{\sigma}_{\bar{x}}^2$ ....unbiased estimate of a
universe variance...... 473

$(14.7)\ \hat{\sigma}_{\bar{x}}^2 = \dfrac{\sum\limits_{j}(\bar{x}_j - \bar{x})^2}{c - 1}$ ....unbiased estimate of
the variance of sample
means obtained from
the dispersion be-
tween sample means 473

$(14.8)\ \hat{\sigma}_c^2 = \dfrac{r\sum\limits_{j}(\bar{x}_j - \bar{x})^2}{c - 1}$ ....unbiased estimate of a
universe variance ob-
tained from the dis-
persion of column
means 474

$(14.9)\ \hat{\sigma}_\varepsilon^2 = \dfrac{\sum\limits_{i}\sum\limits_{j}(x_{ij} - \bar{x}_j)^2}{c(r - 1)}$ ....unbiased estimate of a
universe variance ob-
tained from the de-
viations of the obser-
vations of all samples 476

$(14.10)\ F = \dfrac{\hat{\sigma}_c^2}{\hat{\sigma}_\varepsilon^2}$ ....ratio of two unbiased
estimates of a universe
variance 477

$(14.11)\ SST = \sum\limits_{i}\sum\limits_{j}x_{ij}^2 - \dfrac{(\sum\limits_{i}\sum\limits_{j}x_{ij})^2}{(c)(r)}$ ....sum of squared deviations................. 479

$(14.12)\ SSC = \dfrac{\sum\limits_{j}(\sum\limits_{i}x_{ij})^2}{r} - C$ ....sum of squared
deviations between
columns 479

$(14.13)\ SSE = SST - SSC$ ....residual (error) sum
of squares.............. 479

$(15.1)\ C = \dfrac{T^2}{N}$ ....correction factor, one-
way analysis........... 490

$(15.2)\ SSC = \sum\limits_{j=1}^{c}\dfrac{T_{.j}^2}{n_j} - C$ ....between columns sum
of squares, one-way
analysis................. 490

$(15.3)\ SST = \sum\limits_{i=1}^{r}\sum\limits_{j=1}^{c}x_{ij}^2 - C$ ....total sum of squares... 490

$(15.4)\ SSE = SST - SSC$ ....error sum of squares,
one-way analysis...... 490

PART VI—REGRESSION AND CORRELATION

**Formula
Number**

(16.11) $\sigma_{1.2} = \sqrt{\dfrac{\Sigma(X_1 - X_{1c})^2}{N}}$ ....standard error of the
estimate 549

(16.12) $\hat{\sigma}_{1.2} = \sqrt{\dfrac{\Sigma(x_1 - x_{1c})^2}{n-2}}$ ....estimated standard
error of the estimate... 550

(16.13) $\hat{\sigma}_{1.2} = \sqrt{\dfrac{\Sigma x_1^2 - a_{1.2}\Sigma x_1 - b_{12}\Sigma x_1 x_2}{n-2}}$ ......estimated standard
error of the estimate... 551

(16.14) $\sigma_{b_{12}} = \dfrac{\sigma_{1.2}}{\sqrt{\Sigma(x_2 - \bar{x}_2)^2}}$ ....standard error of a
regression coefficient 552

(16.15) $\hat{\sigma}_{b_{12}} = \dfrac{\hat{\sigma}_{1.2}}{\sqrt{\Sigma(x_2 - \bar{x}_2)^2}}$ ....estimated standard
error of a regression
coefficient.............. 552

(16.16) $\hat{\sigma}_{b_{12}} = \dfrac{\hat{\sigma}_{1.2}}{\sqrt{\Sigma x_2^2 - \dfrac{(\Sigma x_2)^2}{n}}}$ ....estimated standard
error of a regression
coefficient.............. 553

(16.17) $t = \dfrac{b_{12} - \beta_{12}}{\hat{\sigma}_{b_{12}}}$ ....value of t for a test of
significance of a re-
gression coefficient... 553

(16.18) $\hat{\sigma}_{(\bar{x}_1 \mid x_2)} = \hat{\sigma}_{1.2}\sqrt{\dfrac{1}{n} + \dfrac{(x_2' - \bar{x}_2)^2}{\Sigma x_2^2 - \dfrac{(\Sigma x_2)^2}{n}}}$ ......estimated standard
error of an estimated
mean.................... 554

(16.19) $\hat{\sigma}_{(x_1 \mid x_2)} = \hat{\sigma}_{1.2}\sqrt{1 + \dfrac{1}{n} + \dfrac{(X_2 - \bar{x}_2)^2}{\Sigma x_2^2 - \dfrac{(\Sigma x_2)^2}{n}}}$ estimated standard
error of an estimated
value of X_1 557

(16.20) $\rho_{12} = \dfrac{cov(X_1, X_2)}{\sigma_{x_1}\sigma_{x_2}}$ ....universe coefficient of
correlation 560

(16.21) $\rho_{12}^2 = \dfrac{\Sigma(X_{1c} - \bar{X}_1)^2}{\Sigma(X_1 - \bar{X}_1)^2}$ ....universe coefficient of
determination as the
ratio of associated to
total sum of squares... 561

(16.22) $1 - \rho_{12}^2 = \dfrac{\Sigma(X_1 - X_{1c})^2}{\Sigma(X_1 - \bar{X}_1)^2}$ ....universe coefficient of
nondetermination ... 562

**Formula
Number**

**Formula
Number**   **Page**

(18.13) $r_{12.3}^2 = \dfrac{R_{1.23}^2 - r_{13}^2}{1 - r_{13}^2}$ ....first-order partial
determination coeffi-
cient of the correlation
of x_1 with x_2 and x_3
held constant 640

(18.14) $r_{13.2}^2 = \dfrac{R_{1.23}^2 - r_{12}^2}{1 - r_{12}^2}$ ....first-order partial
determination coeffi-
cient of the correlation
of x_1 with x_3 and x_2
held constant 640

(18.15) $a_{1.234} = \bar{x}_1 - b_{12.34}\bar{x}_2 - b_{13.24}\bar{x}_3 - b_{14.23}\bar{x}_4$

estimate of the uni-
verse constant term
$\alpha_{1.234}$ 642

(18.16) $\hat{\sigma}_{1.234}^2 = \dfrac{\Sigma d_1^2 - b_{12.34}\Sigma d_{12} - b_{13.24}\Sigma d_{13} - b_{14.23}\Sigma d_{14}}{n - 4}$

estimate of the vari-
ance of estimating x_1
from $x_2, x_3,$ and x_4 ... 642

(18.17) $R_{1.23\ldots r}^2 = \dfrac{\begin{array}{c}b_{12.3}\ldots,\Sigma d_{12} + b_{13.2}\ldots,\Sigma d_{13} + \ldots \\ + b_{1r.2}\ldots_{r-1}\Sigma d_{1r}\end{array}}{\Sigma d_1^2}$

estimate of the uni-
verse determination
coefficient for the cor-
relation of x_1 with x_2,
$x_3,$ and x_4.............. 646

(18.18) $r_{14.23}^2 = \dfrac{R_{1.234}^2 - R_{1.23}^2}{1 - R_{1.23}^2}$.......................second-order partial
determination coeffi-
cient of the correlation
of x_1 with x_4 where x_2
and x_3 are held con-
stant 648

PART VII—TIME SERIES AND INDEX NUMBERS

(19.1) $y = T \times S \times C \times E$ ....multiplicative time-
series model............ 659

(19.2) $y = T + S + C + E$ ....additive time-series
model 659

(19.3) $y_c = a + bx$ ....equation for straight-
line trend 660

Formula
Number   **Page**

**Formula
Number**

SQUARES — SQUARE ROOTS — RECIPROCALS

n	n^2	$\sqrt{n}$	$\sqrt{10n}$	$1/n$	n	n^2	$\sqrt{n}$	$\sqrt{10n}$	$1/n$
1.00	1.0000	1.00000	3.16228	1.000000	**1.50**	2.2500	1.22474	3.87298	.666667
1.01	1.0201	1.00499	3.17805	.990099	1.51	2.2801	1.22882	3.88587	.662252
1.02	1.0404	1.00995	3.19374	.980392	1.52	2.3104	1.23288	3.89872	.657895
1.03	1.0609	1.01489	3.20936	.970874	1.53	2.3409	1.23693	3.91152	.653595
1.04	1.0816	1.01980	3.22490	.961538	1.54	2.3716	1.24097	3.92428	.649351
1.05	1.1025	1.02470	3.24037	.952381	1.55	2.4025	1.24499	3.93700	.645161
1.06	1.1236	1.02956	3.25576	.943396	1.56	2.4336	1.24900	3.94968	.641026
1.07	1.1449	1.03441	3.27109	.934579	1.57	2.4649	1.25300	3.96232	.636943
1.08	1.1664	1.03923	3.28634	.925926	1.58	2.4964	1.25698	3.97492	.632911
1.09	1.1881	1.04403	3.30151	.917431	1.59	2.5281	1.26095	3.98748	.628931
1.10	1.2100	1.04881	3.31662	.909091	**1.60**	2.5600	1.26491	4.00000	.625000
1.11	1.2321	1.05357	3.33167	.900901	1.61	2.5921	1.26886	4.01248	.621118
1.12	1.2544	1.05830	3.34664	.892857	1.62	2.6244	1.27279	4.02492	.617284
1.13	1.2769	1.06301	3.36155	.884956	1.63	2.6569	1.27671	4.03733	.613497
1.14	1.2996	1.06771	3.37639	.877193	1.64	2.6896	1.28062	4.04969	.609756
1.15	1.3225	1.07238	3.39116	.869565	1.65	2.7225	1.28452	4.06202	.606061
1.16	1.3456	1.07703	3.40588	.862069	1.66	2.7556	1.28841	4.07431	.602410
1.17	1.3689	1.08167	3.42053	.854701	1.67	2.7889	1.29228	4.08656	.598802
1.18	1.3924	1.08628	3.43511	.847458	1.68	2.8224	1.29615	4.09878	.595238
1.19	1.4161	1.09087	3.44964	.840336	1.69	2.8561	1.30000	4.11096	.591716
1.20	1.4400	1.09545	3.46410	.833333	**1.70**	2.8900	1.30384	4.12311	.588235
1.21	1.4641	1.10000	3.47851	.826446	1.71	2.9241	1.30767	4.13521	.584795
1.22	1.4884	1.10454	3.49285	.819672	1.72	2.9584	1.31149	4.14729	.581395
1.23	1.5129	1.10905	3.50714	.813008	1.73	2.9929	1.31529	4.15933	.578035
1.24	1.5376	1.11355	3.52136	.806452	1.74	3.0276	1.31909	4.17133	.574713
1.25	1.5625	1.11803	3.53553	.800000	1.75	3.0625	1.32288	4.18330	.571429
1.26	1.5876	1.12250	3.54965	.793651	1.76	3.0976	1.32665	4.19524	.568182
1.27	1.6129	1.12694	3.56371	.787402	1.77	3.1329	1.33041	4.20714	.564972
1.28	1.6384	1.13137	3.57771	.781250	1.78	3.1684	1.33417	4.21900	.561798
1.29	1.6641	1.13578	3.59166	.775194	1.79	3.2041	1.33791	4.23084	.558659
1.30	1.6900	1.14018	3.60555	.769231	**1.80**	3.2400	1.34164	4.24264	.555556
1.31	1.7161	1.14455	3.61939	.763359	1.81	3.2761	1.34536	4.25441	.552486
1.32	1.7424	1.14891	3.63318	.757576	1.82	3.3124	1.34907	4.26615	.549451
1.33	1.7689	1.15326	3.64692	.751880	1.83	3.3489	1.35277	4.27785	.546448
1.34	1.7956	1.15758	3.66060	.746269	1.84	3.3856	1.35647	4.28952	.543478
1.35	1.8225	1.16190	3.67423	.740741	1.85	3.4225	1.36015	4.30116	.540541
1.36	1.8496	1.16619	3.68782	.735294	1.86	3.4596	1.36382	4.31277	.537634
1.37	1.8769	1.17047	3.70135	.729927	1.87	3.4969	1.36748	4.32435	.534759
1.38	1.9044	1.17473	3.71484	.724638	1.88	3.5344	1.37113	4.33590	.531915
1.39	1.9321	1.17898	3.72827	.719424	1.89	3.5721	1.37477	4.34741	.529101
1.40	1.9600	1.18322	3.74166	.714286	**1.90**	3.6100	1.37840	4.35890	.526316
1.41	1.9881	1.18743	3.75500	.709220	1.91	3.6481	1.38203	4.37035	.523560
1.42	2.0164	1.19164	3.76829	.704225	1.92	3.6864	1.38564	4.38178	.520833
1.43	2.0449	1.19583	3.78153	.699301	1.93	3.7249	1.38924	4.39318	.518135
1.44	2.0736	1.20000	3.79473	.694444	1.94	3.7636	1.39284	4.40454	.515464
1.45	2.1025	1.20416	3.80789	.689655	1.95	3.8025	1.39642	4.41588	.512821
1.46	2.1316	1.20830	3.82099	.684932	1.96	3.8416	1.40000	4.42719	.510204
1.47	2.1609	1.21244	3.83406	.680272	1.97	3.8809	1.40357	4.43847	.507614
1.48	2.1904	1.21655	3.84708	.675676	1.98	3.9204	1.40712	4.44972	.505051
1.49	2.2201	1.22066	3.86005	.671141	1.99	3.9601	1.41067	4.46094	.502513
1.50	2.2500	1.22474	3.87298	.666667	**2.00**	4.0000	1.41421	4.47214	.500000
n	n^2	$\sqrt{n}$	$\sqrt{10n}$	$1/n$	n	n^2	$\sqrt{n}$	$\sqrt{10n}$	$1/n$

SQUARES — SQUARE ROOTS — RECIPROCALS (*Continued*)

n	*n*²	$\sqrt{n}$	$\sqrt{10n}$	1/*n*	*n*	*n*²	$\sqrt{n}$	$\sqrt{10n}$	1/*n*
2.00	4.0000	1.41421	4.47214	.500000	**2.50**	6.2500	1.58114	5.00000	.400000
2.01	4.0401	1.41774	4.48330	.497512	2.51	6.3001	1.58430	5.00999	.398406
2.02	4.0804	1.42127	4.49444	.495050	2.52	6.3504	1.58745	5.01996	.396825
2.03	4.1209	1.42478	4.50555	.492611	2.53	6.4009	1.59060	5.02991	.395257
2.04	4.1616	1.42829	4.51664	.490196	2.54	6.4516	1.59374	5.03984	.393701
2.05	4.2025	1.43178	4.52769	.487805	2.55	6.5025	1.59687	5.04975	.392157
2.06	4.2436	1.43527	4.53872	.485437	2.56	6.5536	1.60000	5.05964	.390625
2.07	4.2849	1.43875	4.54973	.483092	2.57	6.6049	1.60312	5.06952	.389105
2.08	4.3264	1.44222	4.56070	.480769	2.58	6.6564	1.60624	5.07937	.387597
2.09	4.3681	1.44568	4.57165	.478469	2.59	6.7081	1.60935	5.08920	.386100
2.10	4.4100	1.44914	4.58258	.476190	**2.60**	6.7600	1.61245	5.09902	.384615
2.11	4.4521	1.45258	4.59347	.473934	2.61	6.8121	1.61555	5.10882	.383142
2.12	4.4944	1.45602	4.60435	.471698	2.62	6.8644	1.61864	5.11859	.381679
2.13	4.5369	1.45945	4.61519	.469484	2.63	6.9169	1.62173	5.12835	.380228
2.14	4.5796	1.46287	4.62601	.467290	2.64	6.9696	1.62481	5.13809	.378788
2.15	4.6225	1.46629	4.63681	.465116	2.65	7.0225	1.62788	5.14782	.377358
2.16	4.6656	1.46969	4.64758	.462963	2.66	7.0756	1.63095	5.15752	.375940
2.17	4.7089	1.47309	4.65833	.460829	2.67	7.1289	1.63401	5.16720	.374532
2.18	4.7524	1.47648	4.66905	.458716	2.68	7.1824	1.63707	5.17687	.373134
2.19	4.7961	1,47986	4.67974	.456621	2.69	7.2361	1.64012	5.18652	.371747
2.20	4.8400	1.48324	4.69042	.454545	**2.70**	7.2900	1.64317	5.19615	.370370
2.21	4.8841	1.48661	4.70106	.452489	2.71	7.3441	1.64621	5.20577	.369004
2.22	4.9284	1.48997	4.71169	.450450	2.72	7.3984	1.64924	5.21536	.367647
2.23	4.9729	1.49332	4.72229	.448430	2.73	7.4529	1.65227	5.22494	.366300
2.24	5.0176	1.49666	4.73286	.446429	2.74	7.5076	1.65529	5.23450	.364964
2.25	5.0625	1.50000	4.74342	.444444	2.75	7.5625	1.65831	5.24404	.363636
2.26	5.1076	1.50333	4.75395	.442478	2.76	7.6176	1.66132	5.25357	.362319
2.27	5.1529	1.50665	4.76445	.440529	2.77	7.6729	1.66433	5.26308	.361011
2.28	5.1984	1.50997	4.77493	.438596	2.78	7.7284	1.66733	5.27257	.359712
2.29	5.2441	1.51327	4.78539	.436681	2.79	7.7841	1.67033	5.28205	.358423
2.30	5.2900	1.51658	4.79583	.434783	**2.80**	7.8400	1.67332	5.29150	.357143
2.31	5.3361	1.51987	4.80625	.432900	2.81	7.8961	1.67631	5.30094	.355872
2.32	5.3824	1.52315	4.81664	.431034	2.82	7.9524	1.67929	5.31037	.354610
2.33	5.4289	1.52643	4.82701	.429185	2.83	8.0089	1.68226	5.31977	.353357
2.34	5.4756	1.52971	4.83735	.427350	2.84	8.0656	1.68523	5.32917	.352113
2.35	5.5225	1.53297	4.84768	.425532	2.85	8.1225	1.68819	5.33854	.350877
2.36	5.5696	1.53623	4.85798	.423729	2.86	8.1796	1.69115	5.34790	.349650
2.37	5.6169	1.53948	4.86826	.421941	2.87	8.2369	1.69411	5.35724	.348432
2.38	5.6644	1.54272	4.87852	.420168	2.88	8.2944	1.69706	5.36656	.347222
2.39	5.7121	1.54596	4.88876	.418410	2.89	8.3521	1.70000	5.37587	.346021
2.40	5.7600	1.54919	4.89898	.416667	**2.90**	8.4100	1.70294	5.38516	.344828
2.41	5.8081	1.55242	4.90918	.414938	2.91	8.4681	1.70587	5.39444	.343643
2.42	5.8564	1.55563	4.91935	.413223	2.92	8.5264	1.70880	5.40370	.342466
2.43	5.9049	1.55885	4.92950	.411523	2.93	8.5849	1.71172	5.41295	.341297
2.44	5.9536	1.56205	4.93964	.409836	2.94	8.6436	1.71464	5.42218	.340136
2.45	6.0025	1.56525	4.94975	.408163	2.95	8.7025	1.71756	5.43139	.338983
2.46	6.0516	1.56844	4.95984	.406504	2.96	8.7616	1.72047	5.44059	.337838
2.47	6.1009	1.57162	4.96991	.404858	2.97	8.8209	1.72337	5.44977	.336700
2.48	6.1504	1.57480	4.97996	.403226	2.98	8.8804	1.72627	5.45894	.335570
2.49	6.2001	1.57797	4.98999	.401606	2.99	8.9401	1.72916	5.46809	.334448
2.50	6.2500	1.58114	5.00000	.400000	**3.00**	9.0000	1.73205	5.47723	.333333
n	*n*²	$\sqrt{n}$	$\sqrt{10n}$	1/*n*	*n*	*n*²	$\sqrt{n}$	$\sqrt{10n}$	1/*n*

SQUARES — SQUARE ROOTS — RECIPROCALS (*Continued*)

n	n^2	$\sqrt{n}$	$\sqrt{10n}$	$1/n$	n	n^2	$\sqrt{n}$	$\sqrt{10n}$	$1/n$
3.00	9.0000	1.73205	5.47723	.333333	3.50	12.2500	1.87083	5.91608	.285714
3.01	9.0601	1.73494	5.48635	.332226	3.51	12.3201	1.87350	5.92453	.284900
3.02	9.1204	1.73781	5.49545	.331126	3.52	12.3904	1.87617	5.93296	.284091
3.03	9.1809	1.74069	5.50454	.330033	3.53	12.4609	1.87883	5.94138	.283286
3.04	9.2416	1.74356	5.51362	.328947	3.54	12.5316	1.88149	5.94979	.282486
3.05	9.3025	1.74642	5.52268	.327869	3.55	12.6025	1.88414	5.95819	.281690
3.06	9.3636	1.74929	5.53173	.326797	3.56	12.6736	1.88680	5.96657	.280899
3.07	9.4249	1.75214	5.54076	.325733	3.57	12.7449	1.88944	5.97495	.280112
3.08	9.4864	1.75499	5.54977	.324675	3.58	12.8164	1.89209	5.98331	.279330
3.09	9.5481	1.75784	5.55878	.323625	3.59	12.8881	1.89473	5.99166	.278552
3.10	9.6100	1.76068	5.56776	.322581	3.60	12.9600	1.89737	6.00000	.277778
3.11	9.6721	1.76352	5.57674	.321543	3.61	13.0321	1.90000	6.00833	.277008
3.12	9.7344	1.76635	5.58570	.320513	3.62	13.1044	1.90263	6.01664	.276243
3.13	9.7969	1.76918	5.59464	.319489	3.63	13.1769	1.90526	6.02495	.275482
3.14	9.8596	1.77200	5.60357	.318471	3.64	13.2496	1.90788	6.03324	.274725
3.15	9.9225	1.77482	5.61249	.317460	3.65	13.3225	1.91050	6.04152	.273973
3.16	9.9856	1.77764	5.62139	.316456	3.66	13.3956	1.91311	6.04979	.273224
3.17	10.0489	1.78045	5.63028	.315457	3.67	13.4689	1.91572	6.05805	.272480
3.18	10.1124	1.78326	5.63915	.314465	3.68	13.5424	1.91833	6.06630	.271739
3.19	10.1761	1.78606	5.64801	.313480	3.69	13.6161	1.92094	6.07454	.271003
3.20	10.2400	1.78885	5.65685	.312500	3.70	13.6900	1.92354	6.08276	.270270
3.21	10.3041	1.79165	5.66569	.311526	3.71	13.7641	1.92614	6.09098	.269542
3.22	10.3684	1.79444	5.67450	.310559	3.72	13.8384	1.92873	6.09918	.268817
3.23	10.4329	1.79722	5.68331	.309598	3.73	13.9129	1.93132	6.10737	.268097
3.24	10.4976	1.80000	5.69210	.308642	3.74	13.9876	1.93391	6.11555	.267380
3.25	10.5625	1.80278	5.70088	.307692	3.75	14.0625	1.93649	6.12372	.266667
3.26	10.6276	1.80555	5.70964	.306748	3.76	14.1376	1.93907	6.13188	.265957
3.27	10.6929	1.80831	5.71839	.305810	3.77	14.2129	1.94165	6.14003	.265252
3.28	10.7584	1.81108	5.72713	.304878	3.78	14.2884	1.94422	6.14817	.264550
3.29	10.8241	1.81384	5.73585	.303951	3.79	14.3641	1.94679	6.15630	.263852
3.30	10.8900	1.81659	5.74456	.303030	3.80	14.4400	1.94936	6.16441	.263158
3.31	10.9561	1.81934	5.75326	.302115	3.81	14.5161	1.95192	6.17252	.262467
3.32	11.0224	1.82209	5.76194	.301205	3.82	14.5924	1.95448	6.18061	.261780
3.33	11.0889	1.82483	5.77062	.300300	3.83	14.6689	1.95704	6.18870	.261097
3.34	11.1556	1.82757	5.77927	.299401	3.84	14.7456	1.95959	6.19677	.260417
3.35	11.2225	1.83030	5.78792	.298507	3.85	14.8225	1.96214	6.20484	.259740
3.36	11.2896	1.83303	5.79655	.297619	3.86	14.8996	1.96469	6.21289	.259067
3.37	11.3569	1.83576	5.80517	.296736	3.87	14.9769	1.96723	6.22093	.258398
3.38	11.4244	1.83848	5.81378	.295858	3.88	15.0544	1.96977	6.22896	.257732
3.39	11.4921	1.84120	5.82237	.294985	3.89	15.1321	1.97231	6.23699	.257069
3.40	11.5600	1.84391	5.83095	.294118	3.90	15.2100	1.97484	6.24500	.256410
3.41	11.6281	1.84662	5.83952	.293255	3.91	15.2881	1.97737	6.25300	.255754
3.42	11.6964	1.84932	5.84808	.292398	3.92	15.3664	1.97990	6.26099	.255102
3.43	11.7649	1.85203	5.85662	.291545	3.93	15.4449	1.98242	6.26897	.254453
3.44	11.8336	1.85472	5.86515	.290698	3.94	15.5236	1.98494	6.27694	.253807
3.45	11.9025	1.85742	5.87367	.289855	3.95	15.6025	1.98746	6.28490	.253165
3.46	11.9716	1.86011	5.88218	.289017	3.96	15.6816	1.98997	6.29285	.252525
3.47	12.0409	1.86279	5.89067	.288184	3.97	15.7609	1.99249	6.30079	.251889
3.48	12.1104	1.86548	5.89915	.287356	3.98	15.8408	1.99499	6.30872	.251256
3.49	12.1801	1.86815	5.90762	.286533	3.99	15.9201	1.99750	6.31664	.250627
3.50	12.2500	1.87083	5.91608	.285714	4.00	16.0000	2.00000	6.32456	.250000
n	n^2	$\sqrt{n}$	$\sqrt{10n}$	$1/n$	n	n^2	$\sqrt{n}$	$\sqrt{10n}$	$1/n$

SQUARES — SQUARE ROOTS — RECIPROCALS (*Continued*)

n	*n*²	$\sqrt{n}$	$\sqrt{10n}$	1/*n*	*n*	*n*²	$\sqrt{n}$	$\sqrt{10n}$	1/*n*
4.00	16.0000	2.00000	6.32456	.250000	**4.50**	20.2500	2.12132	6.70820	.222222
4.01	16.0801	2.00250	6.33246	.249377	4.51	20.3401	2.12368	6.71565	.221729
4.02	16.1604	2.00499	6.34035	.248756	4.52	20.4304	2.12603	6.72309	.221239
4.03	16.2409	2.00749	6.34823	.248139	4.53	20.5209	2.12838	6.73053	.220751
4.04	16.3216	2.00998	6.35610	.247525	4.54	20.6116	2.13073	6.73795	.220264
4.05	16.4025	2.01246	6.36396	.246914	4.55	20.7025	2.13307	6.74537	.219780
4.06	16.4836	2.01494	6.37181	.246305	4.56	20.7936	2.13542	6.75278	.219298
4.07	16.5649	2.01742	6.37966	.245700	4.57	20.8849	2.13776	6.76018	.218818
4.08	16.6464	2.01990	6.38749	.245098	4.58	20.9764	2.14009	6.76757	.218341
4.09	16.7281	2.02237	6.39531	.244499	4.59	21.0681	2.14243	6.77495	.217865
4.10	16.8100	2.02485	6.40312	.243902	**4.60**	21.1600	2.14476	6.78233	.217391
4.11	16.8921	2.02731	6.41093	.243309	4.61	21.2521	2.14709	6.78970	.216920
4.12	16.9744	2.02978	6.41872	.242718	4.62	21.3444	2.14942	6.79706	.216450
4.13	17.0569	2.03224	6.42651	.242131	4.63	21.4369	2.15174	6.80441	.215983
4.14	17.1396	2.03470	6.43428	.241546	4.64	21.5296	2.15407	6.81175	.215517
4.15	17.2225	2.03715	6.44205	.240964	4.65	21.6225	2.15639	6.81909	.215054
4.16	17.3056	2.03961	6.44981	.240385	4.66	21.7156	2.15870	6.82642	.214592
4.17	17.3889	2.04206	6.45755	.239808	4.67	21.8089	2.16102	6.83374	.214133
4.18	17.4724	2.04450	6.46529	.239234	4.68	21.9024	2.16333	6.84105	.213675
4.19	17.5561	2.04695	6.47302	.238663	4.69	21.9961	2.16564	6.84836	.213220
4.20	17.6400	2.04939	6.48074	.238095	**4.70**	22.0900	2.16795	6.85565	.212766
4.21	17.7241	2.05183	6.48845	.237530	4.71	22.1841	2.17025	6.86294	.212314
4.22	17.8084	2.05426	6.49615	.236967	4.72	22.2784	2.17256	6.87023	.211864
4.23	17.8929	2.05670	6.50384	.236407	4.73	22.3729	2.17486	6.87750	.211416
4.24	17.9776	2.05913	6.51153	.235849	4.74	22.4676	2.17715	6.88477	.210970
4.25	18.0625	2.06155	6.51920	.235294	4.75	22.5625	2.17945	6.89202	.210526
4.26	18.1476	2.06398	6.52687	.234742	4.76	22.6576	2.18174	6.89928	.210084
4.27	18.2329	2.06640	6.53452	.234192	4.77	22.7529	2.18403	6.90652	.209644
4.28	18.3184	2.06882	6.54217	.233645	4.78	22.8484	2.18632	6.91375	.209205
4.29	18.4041	2.07123	6.54981	.233100	4.79	22.9441	2.18861	6.92098	.208768
4.30	18.4900	2.07364	6.55744	.232558	**4.80**	23.0400	2.19089	6.92820	.208333
4.31	18.5761	2.07605	6.56506	.232019	4.81	23.1361	2.19317	6.93542	.207900
4.32	18.6624	2.07846	6.57267	.231481	4.82	23.2324	2.19545	6.94262	.207469
4.33	18.7489	2.08087	6.58027	.230947	4.83	23.3289	2.19773	6.94982	.207039
4.34	18.8356	2.08327	6.58787	.230415	4.84	23.4256	2.20000	6.95701	.206612
4.35	18.9225	2.08567	6.59545	.229885	4.85	23.5225	2.20227	6.96419	.206186
4.36	19.0096	2.08806	6.60303	.229358	4.86	23.6196	2.20454	6.97137	.205761
4.37	19.0969	2.09045	6.61060	.228833	4.87	23.7169	2.20681	6.97854	.205339
4.38	19.1844	2.09284	6.61816	.228311	4.88	23.8144	2.20907	6.98570	.204918
4.39	19.2721	2.09523	6.62571	.227790	4.89	23.9121	2.21133	6.99285	.204499
4.40	19.3600	2.09762	6.63325	.227273	**4.90**	24.0100	2.21359	7.00000	.204082
4.41	19.4481	2.10000	6.64078	.226757	4.91	24.1081	2.21585	7.00714	.203666
4.42	19.5364	2.10238	6.64831	.226244	4.92	24.2064	2.21811	7.01427	.203252
4.43	19.6249	2.10476	6.65582	.225734	4.93	24.3049	2.22036	7.02140	.202840
4.44	19.7136	2.10713	6.66333	.225225	4.94	24.4036	2.22261	7.02851	.202429
4.45	19.8025	2.10950	6.67083	.224719	4.95	24.5025	2.22486	7.03562	.202020
4.46	19.8916	2.11187	6.67832	.224215	4.96	24.6016	2.22711	7.04273	.201613
4.47	19.9809	2.11424	6.68581	.223714	4.97	24.7009	2.22935	7.04982	.201207
4.48	20.0704	2.11660	6.69328	.223214	4.98	24.8004	2.23159	7.05691	.200803
4.49	20.1601	2.11896	6.70075	.222717	4.99	24.9001	2.23383	7.06399	.200401
4.50	20.2500	2.12132	6.70820	.222222	**5.00**	25.0000	2.23607	7.07107	.200000
n	*n*²	$\sqrt{n}$	$\sqrt{10n}$	1/*n*	*n*	*n*²	$\sqrt{n}$	$\sqrt{10n}$	1/*n*

SQUARES — SQUARE ROOTS — RECIPROCALS (*Continued*)

n	*n*²	√*n*	√10*n*	1/*n*	*n*	*n*²	√*n*	√10*n*	1/*n*
5.00	25.0000	2.23607	7.07107	.200000	**5.50**	30.2500	2.34521	7.41620	.181818
5.01	25.1001	2.23830	7.07814	.199601	5.51	30.3601	2.34734	7.42294	.181488
5.02	25.2004	2.24054	7.08520	.199203	5.52	30.4704	2.34947	7.42967	.181159
5.03	25.3009	2.24277	7.09225	.198807	5.53	30.5809	2.35160	7.43640	.180832
5.04	25.4016	2.24499	7.09930	.198413	5.54	30.6916	2.35372	7.44312	.180505
5.05	25.5025	2.24722	7.10634	.198020	5.55	30.8025	2.35584	7.44983	.180180
5.06	25.6036	2.24944	7.11337	.197628	5.56	30.9136	2.35797	7.45654	.179856
5.07	25.7049	2.25167	7.12039	.197239	5.57	31.0249	2.36008	7.46324	.179533
5.08	25.8064	2.25389	7.12741	.196850	5.58	31.1364	2.36220	7.46994	.179211
5.09	25.9081	2.25610	7.13442	.196464	5.59	31.2481	2.36432	7.47663	.178891
5.10	26.0100	2.25832	7.14143	.196078	**5.60**	31.3600	2.36643	7.48331	.178571
5.11	26.1121	2.26053	7.14843	.195695	5.61	31.4721	2.36854	7.48999	.178253
5.12	26.2144	2.26274	7.15542	.195312	5.62	31.5844	2.37065	7.49667	.177936
5.13	26.3169	2.26495	7.16240	.194932	5.63	31.6969	2.37276	7.50333	.177620
5.14	26.4196	2.26716	7.16938	.194553	5.64	31.8096	2.37487	7.50999	.177305
5.15	26.5225	2.26936	7.17635	.194175	5.65	31.9225	2.37697	7.51665	.176991
5.16	26.6256	2.27156	7.18331	.193798	5.66	32.0356	2.37908	7.52330	.176678
5.17	26.7289	2.27376	7.19027	.193424	5.67	32.1489	2.38118	7.52994	.176367
5.18	26.8324	2.27596	7.19722	.193050	5.68	32.2624	2.38328	7.53658	.176056
5.19	26.9361	2.27816	7.20417	.192678	5.69	32.3761	2.38537	7.54321	.175747
5.20	27.0400	2.28035	7.21110	.192308	**5.70**	32.4900	2.38747	7.54983	.175439
5.21	27.1441	2.28254	7.21803	.191939	5.71	32.6041	2.38956	7.55645	.175131
5.22	27.2484	2.28473	7.22496	.191571	5.72	32.7184	2.39165	7.56307	.174825
5.23	27.3529	2.28692	7.23187	.191205	5.73	32.8329	2.39374	7.56968	.174520
5.24	27.4576	2.28910	7.23878	.190840	5.74	32.9476	2.39583	7.57628	.174216
5.25	27.5625	2.29129	7.24569	.190476	5.75	33.0625	2.39792	7.58288	.173913
5.26	27.6676	2.29347	7.25259	.190114	5.76	33.1776	2.40000	7.58947	.173611
5.27	27.7729	2.29565	7.25948	.189753	5.77	33.2929	2.40208	7.59605	.173310
5.28	27.8784	2.29783	7.26636	.189394	5.78	33.4084	2.40416	7.60263	.173010
5.29	27.9841	2.30000	7.27324	.189036	5.79	33.5241	2.40624	7.60920	.172712
5.30	28.0900	2.30217	7.28011	.188679	**5.80**	33.6400	2.40832	7.61577	.172414
5.31	28.1961	2.30434	7.28697	.188324	5.81	33.7561	2.41039	7.62234	.172117
5.32	28.3024	2.30651	7.29383	.187970	5.82	33.8724	2.41247	7.62889	.171821
5.33	28.4089	2.30868	7.30068	.187617	5.83	33.9889	2.41454	7.63544	.171527
5.34	28.5156	2.31084	7.30753	.187266	5.84	34.1056	2.41661	7.64199	.171233
5.35	28.6225	2.31301	7.31437	.186916	5.85	34.2225	2.41868	7.64853	.170940
5.36	28.7296	2.31517	7.32120	.186567	5.86	34.3396	2.42074	7.65506	.170649
5.37	28.8369	2.31733	7.32803	.186220	5.87	34.4569	2.42281	7.66159	.170358
5.38	28.9444	2.31948	7.33485	.185874	5.88	34.5744	2.42487	7.66812	.170068
5.39	29.0521	2.32164	7.34166	.185529	5.89	34.6921	2.42693	7.67463	.169779
5.40	29.1600	2.32379	7.34847	.185185	**5.90**	34.8100	2.42899	7.68115	.169492
5.41	29.2681	2.32594	7.35527	.184843	5.91	34.9281	2.43105	7.68765	.169205
5.42	29.3764	2.32809	7.36206	.184502	5.92	35.0464	2.43311	7.69415	.168919
5.43	29.4849	2.33024	7.36885	.184162	5.93	35.1649	2.43516	7.70065	.168634
5.44	29.5936	2.33238	7.37564	.183824	5.94	35.2836	2.43721	7.70714	.168350
5.45	29.7025	2.33452	7.38241	.183486	5.95	35.4025	2.43926	7.71362	.168067
5.46	29.8116	2.33666	7.38918	.183150	5.96	35.5216	2.44131	7.72010	.167785
5.47	29.9209	2.33880	7.39594	.182815	5.97	35.6409	2.44336	7.72658	.167504
5.48	30.0304	2.34094	7.40270	.182482	5.98	35.7604	2.44540	7.73305	.167224
5.49	30.1401	2.34307	7.40945	.182149	5.99	35.8801	2.44745	7.73951	.166945
5.50	30.2500	2.34521	7.41620	.181818	**6.00**	36.0000	2.44949	7.74597	.166667
n	*n*²	√*n*	√10*n*	1/*n*	*n*	*n*²	√*n*	√10*n*	1/*n*

SQUARES — SQUARE ROOTS — RECIPROCALS (*Continued*)

n	n²	√n	√10n	1/n	n	n²	√n	√10n	1/n
6.00	36.0000	2.44949	7.74597	.166667	**6.50**	42.2500	2.54951	8.06226	.153846
6.01	36.1201	2.45153	7.75242	.166389	6.51	42.3801	2.55147	8.06846	.153610
6.02	36.2404	2.45357	7.75887	.166113	6.52	42.5104	2.55343	8.07465	.153374
6.03	36.3609	2.45561	7.76531	.165837	6.53	42.6409	2.55539	8.08084	.153139
6.04	36.4816	2.45764	7.77174	.165563	6.54	42.7716	2.55734	8.08703	.152905
6.05	36.6025	2.45967	7.77817	.165289	6.55	42.9025	2.55930	8.09321	.152672
6.06	36.7236	2.46171	7.78460	.165017	6.56	43.0336	2.56125	8.09938	.152439
6.07	36.8449	2.46374	7.79102	.164745	6.57	43.1649	2.56320	8.10555	.152207
6.08	36.9664	2.46577	7.79744	.164474	6.58	43.2964	2.56515	8.11172	.151976
6.09	37.0881	2.46779	7.80385	.164204	6.59	43.4281	2.56710	8.11788	.151745
6.10	37.2100	2.46982	7.81025	.163934	**6.60**	43.5600	2.56905	8.12404	.151515
6.11	37.3321	2.47184	7.81665	.163666	6.61	43.6921	2.57099	8.13019	.151286
6.12	37.4544	2.47386	7.82304	.163399	6.62	43.8244	2.57294	8.13634	.151057
6.13	37.5769	2.47588	7.82943	.163132	6.63	43.9569	2.57488	8.14248	.150830
6.14	37.6996	2.47790	7.83582	.162866	6.64	44.0896	2.57682	8.14862	.150602
6.15	37.8225	2.47992	7.84219	.162602	6.65	44.2225	2.57876	8.15475	.150376
6.16	37.9456	2.48193	7.84857	.162338	6.66	44.3556	2.58070	8.16088	.150150
6.17	38.0689	2.48395	7.85493	.162075	6.67	44.4889	2.58263	8.16701	.149925
6.18	38.1924	2.48596	7.86130	.161812	6.68	44.6224	2.58457	8.17313	.149701
6.19	38.3161	2.48797	7.86766	.161551	6.69	44.7561	2.58650	8.17924	.149477
6.20	38.4400	2.48998	7.87401	.161290	**6.70**	44.8900	2.58844	8.18535	.149254
6.21	38.5641	2.49199	7.88036	.161031	6.71	45.0241	2.59037	8.19146	.149031
6.22	38.6884	2.49399	7.88670	.160772	6.72	45.1584	2.59230	8.19756	.148810
6.23	38.8129	2.49600	7.89303	.160514	6.73	45.2929	2.59422	8.20366	.148588
6.24	38.9376	2.49800	7.89937	.160256	6.74	45.4276	2.59615	8.20975	.148368
6.25	39.0625	2.50000	7.90569	.160000	6.75	45.5625	2.59808	8.21584	.148148
6.26	39.1876	2.50200	7.91202	.159744	6.76	45.6976	2.60000	8.22192	.147929
6.27	39.3129	2.50400	7.91833	.159490	6.77	45.8329	2.60192	8.22800	.147710
6.28	39.4384	2.50599	7.92465	.159236	6.78	45.9684	2.60384	8.23408	.147493
6.29	39.5641	2.50799	7.93095	.158983	6.79	46.1041	2.60576	8.24015	.147275
6.30	39.6900	2.50998	7.93725	.158730	**6.80**	46.2400	2.60768	8.24621	.147059
6.31	39.8161	2.51197	7.94355	.158479	6.81	46.3761	2.60960	8.25227	.146843
6.32	39.9424	2.51396	7.94984	.158228	6.82	46.5124	2.61151	8.25833	.146628
6.33	40.0689	2.51595	7.95613	.157978	6.83	46.6489	2.61343	8.26438	.146413
6.34	40.1956	2.51794	7.96241	.157729	6.84	46.7856	2.61534	8.27043	.146199
6.35	40.3225	2.51992	7.96869	.157480	6.85	46.9225	2.61725	8.27647	.145985
6.36	40.4496	2.52190	7.97496	.157233	6.86	47.0596	2.61916	8.28251	.145773
6.37	40.5769	2.52389	7.98123	.156986	6.87	47.1969	2.62107	8.28855	.145560
6.38	40.7044	2.52587	7.98749	.156740	6.88	47.3344	2.62298	8.29458	.145349
6.39	40.8321	2.52784	7.99375	.156495	6.89	47.4721	2.62488	8.30060	.145138
6.40	40.9600	2.52982	8.00000	.156250	**6.90**	47.6100	2.62679	8.30662	.144928
6.41	41.0881	2.53180	8.00625	.156006	6.91	47.7481	2.62869	8.31264	.144718
6.42	41.2164	2.53377	8.01249	.155763	6.92	47.8864	2.63059	8.31865	.144509
6.43	41.3449	2.53574	8.01873	.155521	6.93	48.0249	2.63249	8.32466	.144300
6.44	41.4736	2.53772	8.02496	.155280	6.94	48.1636	2.63439	8.33067	.144092
6.45	41.6025	2.53969	8.03119	.155039	6.95	48.3025	2.63629	8.33667	.143885
6.46	41.7316	2.54165	8.03741	.154799	6.96	48.4416	2.63818	8.34266	.143678
6.47	41.8609	2.54362	8.04363	.154560	6.97	48.5809	2.64008	8.34865	.143472
6.48	41.9904	2.54558	8.04984	.154321	6.98	48.7204	2.64197	8.35464	.143266
6.49	42.1201	2.54755	8.05605	.154083	6.99	48.8601	2.64386	8.36062	.143062
6.50	42.2500	2.54951	8.06226	.153846	**7.00**	49.0000	2.64575	8.36660	.142857
n	n²	√n	√10n	1/n	n	n²	√n	√10n	1/n

SQUARES — SQUARE ROOTS — RECIPROCALS (*Continued*)

n	n²	√n	√10n	1/n	n	n²	√n	√10n	1/n
7.00	49.0000	2.64575	8.36660	.142857	**7.50**	56.2500	2.73861	8.66025	.133333
7.01	49.1401	2.64764	8.37257	.142653	7.51	56.4001	2.74044	8.66603	.133156
7.02	49.2804	2.64953	8.37854	.142450	7.52	56.5504	2.74226	8.67179	.132979
7.03	49.4209	2.65141	8.38451	.142248	7.53	56.7009	2.74408	8.67756	.132802
7.04	49.5616	2.65330	8.39047	.142045	7.54	56.8516	2.74591	8.68332	.132626
7.05	49.7025	2.65518	8.39643	.141844	7.55	57.0025	2.74773	8.68907	.132450
7.06	49.8436	2.65707	8.40238	.141643	7.56	57.1536	2.74955	8.69483	.132275
7.07	49.9849	2.65895	8.40833	.141443	7.57	57.3049	2.75136	8.70057	.132100
7.08	50.1264	2.66083	8.41427	.141243	7.58	57.4564	2.75318	8.70632	.131926
7.09	50.2681	2.66271	8.42021	.141044	7.59	57.6081	2.75500	8.71206	.131752
7.10	50.4100	2.66458	8.42615	.140845	**7.60**	57.7600	2.75681	8.71780	.131579
7.11	50.5521	2.66646	8.43208	.140647	7.61	57.9121	2.75862	8.72353	.131406
7.12	50.6944	2.66833	8.43801	.140449	7.62	58.0644	2.76043	8.72926	.131234
7.13	50.8369	2.67021	8.44393	.140252	7.63	58.2169	2.76225	8.73499	.131062
7.14	50.9796	2.67208	8.44985	.140056	7.64	58.3696	2.76405	8.74071	.130890
7.15	51.1225	2.67395	8.45577	.139860	7.65	58.5225	2.76586	8.74643	.130719
7.16	51.2656	2.67582	8.46168	.139665	7.66	58.6756	2.76767	8.75214	.130548
7.17	51.4089	2.67769	8.46759	.139470	7.67	58.8289	2.76948	8.75785	.130378
7.18	51.5524	2.67955	8.47349	.139276	7.68	58.9824	2.77128	8.76356	.130208
7.19	51.6961	2.68142	8.47939	.139082	7.69	59.1361	2.77308	8.76926	.130039
7.20	51.8400	2.68328	8.48528	.138889	**7.70**	59.2900	2.77489	8.77496	.129870
7.21	51.9841	2.68514	8.49117	.138696	7.71	59.4441	2.77669	8.78066	.129702
7.22	52.1284	2.68701	8.49706	.138504	7.72	59.5984	2.77849	8.78635	.129534
7.23	52.2729	2.68887	8.50294	.138313	7.73	59.7529	2.78029	8.79204	.129366
7.24	52.4176	2.69072	8.50882	.138122	7.74	59.9076	2.78209	8.79773	.129199
7.25	52.5625	2.69258	8.51469	.137931	7.75	60.0625	2.78388	8.80341	.129032
7.26	52.7076	2.69444	8.52056	.137741	7.76	60.2176	2.78568	8.80909	.128866
7.27	52.8529	2.69629	8.52643	.137552	7.77	60.3729	2.78747	8.81476	.128700
7.28	52.9984	2.69815	8.53229	.137363	7.78	60.5284	2.78927	8.82043	.128535
7.29	53.1441	2.70000	8.53815	.137174	7.79	60.6841	2.79106	8.82610	.128370
7.30	53.2900	2.70185	8.54400	.136986	**7.80**	60.8400	2.79285	8.83176	.128205
7.31	53.4361	2.70370	8.54985	.136799	7.81	60.9961	2.79464	8.83742	.128041
7.32	53.5824	2.70555	8.55570	.136612	7.82	61.1524	2.79643	8.84308	.127877
7.33	53.7289	2.70740	8.56154	.136426	7.83	61.3089	2.79821	8.84873	.127714
7.34	53.8756	2.70924	8.56738	.136240	7.84	61.4656	2.80000	8.85438	.127551
7.35	54.0225	2.71109	8.57321	.136054	7.85	61.6225	2.80179	8.86002	.127389
7.36	54.1696	2.71293	8.57904	.135870	7.86	61.7796	2.80357	8.86566	.127226
7.37	54.3169	2.71477	8.58487	.135685	7.87	61 9369	2.80535	8.87130	.127065
7.38	54.4644	2.71662	8.59069	.135501	7.88	62.0944	2.80713	8.87694	.126904
7.39	54.6121	2.71846	8.59651	.135318	7.89	62.2521	2.80891	8.88257	.126743
7.40	54.7600	2.72029	8.60233	.135135	**7.90**	62.4100	2.81069	8.88819	.126582
7.41	54.9081	2.72213	8.60814	.134953	7.91	62.5681	2.81247	8.89382	.126422
7.42	55.0564	2.72397	8.61394	.134771	7.92	62.7264	2.81425	8.89944	.126263
7.43	55.2049	2.72580	8.61974	.134590	7.93	62.8849	2.81603	8.90505	.126103
7.44	55.3536	2.72764	8.62554	.134409	7.94	63.0436	2.81780	8.91067	.125945
7.45	55.5025	2.72947	8.63134	.134228	7.95	63.2025	2.81957	8.91628	.125786
7.46	55.6516	2.73130	8.63713	.134048	7.96	63.3616	2.82135	8.92188	.125628
7.47	55.8009	2.73313	8.64292	.133869	7.97	63.5209	2.82312	8.92749	.125471
7.48	55.9504	2.73496	8.64870	.133690	7.98	63.6804	2.82489	8.93308	.125313
7.49	56.1001	2.73679	8.65448	.133511	7.99	63.8401	2.82666	8.93868	.125156
7.50	56.2500	2.73861	8.66025	.133333	**8.00**	64.0000	2.82843	8.94427	.125000
n	n²	√n	√10n	1/n	n	n²	√n	√10n	1/n

SQUARES — SQUARE ROOTS — RECIPROCALS (*Continued*)

n	*n*²	√*n*	√10*n*	1/*n*		*n*	*n*²	√*n*	√10*n*	1/*n*
8.00	64.0000	2.82843	8.94427	.125000		**8.50**	72.2500	2.91548	9.21954	.117647
8.01	64.1601	2.83019	8.94986	.124844		8.51	72.4201	2.91719	9.22497	.117509
8.02	64.3204	2.83196	8.95545	.124688		8.52	72.5904	2.91890	9.23038	.117371
8.03	64.4809	2.83373	8.96103	.124533		8.53	72.7609	2.92062	9.23580	.117233
8.04	64.6416	2.83549	8.96660	.124378		8.54	72.9316	2.92233	9.24121	.117096
8.05	64.8025	2.83725	8.97218	.124224		8.55	73.1025	2.92404	9.24662	.116959
8.06	64.9636	2.83901	8.97775	.124069		8.56	73.2736	2.92575	9.25203	.116822
8.07	65.1249	2.84077	8.98332	.123916		8.57	73.4449	2.92746	9.25743	.116686
8.08	65.2864	2.84253	8.98888	.123762		8.58	73.6164	2.92916	9.26283	.116550
8.09	65.4481	2.84429	8.99444	.123609		8.59	73.7881	2.93087	9.26823	.116414
8.10	65.6100	2.84605	9.00000	.123457		**8.60**	73.9600	2.93258	9.27362	.116279
8.11	65.7721	2.84781	9.00555	.123305		8.61	74.1321	2.93428	9.27901	.116144
8.12	65.9344	2.84956	9.01110	.123153		8.62	74.3044	2.93598	9.28440	.116009
8.13	66.0969	2.85132	9.01665	.123001		8.63	74.4769	2.93769	9.28978	.115875
8.14	66.2596	2.85307	9.02219	.122850		8.64	74.6496	2.93939	9.29516	.115741
8.15	66.4225	2.85482	9.02774	.122699		8.65	74.8225	2.94109	9.30054	.115607
8.16	66.5856	2.85657	9.03327	.122549		8.66	74.9956	2.94279	9.30591	.115473
8.17	66.7489	2.85832	9.03881	.122399		8.67	75.1689	2.94449	9.31128	.115340
8.18	66.9124	2.86007	9.04434	.122249		8.68	75.3424	2.94618	9.31665	.115207
8.19	67.0761	2.86182	9.04986	.122100		8.69	75.5161	2.94788	9.32202	.115075
8.20	67.2400	2.86356	9.05539	.121951		**8.70**	75.6900	2.94958	9.32738	.114943
8.21	67.4041	2.86531	9.06091	.121803		8.71	75.8641	2.95127	9.33274	.114811
8.22	67.5684	2.86705	9.06642	.121655		8.72	76.0384	2.95296	9.33809	.114679
8.23	67.7329	2.86880	9.07193	.121507		8.73	76.2129	2.95466	9.34345	.114548
8.24	67.8976	2.87054	9.07744	.121359		8.74	76.3876	2.95635	9.34880	.114416
8.25	68.0625	2.87228	9.08295	.121212		8.75	76.5625	2.95804	9.35414	.114286
8.26	68.2276	2.87402	9.08845	.121065		8.76	76.7376	2.95973	9.35949	.114155
8.27	68.3929	2.87576	9.09395	.120919		8.77	76.9129	2.96142	9.36483	.114025
8.28	68.5584	2.87750	9.09945	.120773		8.78	77.0884	2.96311	9.37017	.113895
8.29	68.7241	2.87924	9.10494	.120627		8.79	77.2641	2.96479	9.37550	.113766
8.30	68.8900	2.88097	9.11043	.120482		**8.80**	77.4400	2.96648	9.38083	.113636
8.31	69.0561	2.88271	9.11592	.120337		8.81	77.6161	2.96816	9.38616	.113507
8.32	69.2224	2.88444	9.12140	.120192		8.82	77.7924	2.96985	9.39149	.113379
8.33	69.3889	2.88617	9.12688	.120048		8.83	77.9689	2.97153	9.39681	.113250
8.34	69.5556	2.88791	9.13236	.119904		8.84	78.1456	2.97321	9.40213	.113122
8.35	69.7225	2.88964	9.13783	.119760		8.85	78.3225	2.97489	9.40744	.112994
8.36	69.8896	2.89137	9.14330	.119617		8.86	78.4996	2.97658	9.41276	.112867
8.37	70.0569	2.89310	9.14877	.119474		8.87	78.6769	2.97825	9.41807	.112740
8.38	70.2244	2.89482	9.15423	.119332		8.88	78.8544	2.97993	9.42338	.112613
8.39	70.3921	2.89655	9.15969	.119190		8.89	79.0321	2.98161	9.42868	.112486
8.40	70.5600	2.89828	9.16515	.119048		**8.90**	79.2100	2.98329	9.43398	.112360
8.41	70.7281	2.90000	9.17061	.118906		8.91	79.3881	2.98496	9.43928	.112233
8.42	70.8964	2.90172	9.17606	.118765		8.92	79.5664	2.98664	9.44458	.112108
8.43	71.0649	2.90345	9.18150	.118624		8.93	79.7449	2.98831	9.44987	.111982
8.44	71.2336	2.90517	9.18695	.118483		8.94	79.9236	2.98998	9.45516	.111857
8.45	71.4025	2.90689	9.19239	.118343		8.95	80.1025	2.99166	9.46044	.111732
8.46	71.5716	2.90861	9.19783	.118203		8.96	80.2816	2.99333	9.46573	.111607
8.47	71.7409	2.91033	9.20326	.118064		8.97	80.4609	2.99500	9.47101	.111483
8.48	71.9104	2.91204	9.20869	.117925		8.98	80.6404	2.99666	9.47629	.111359
8.49	72.0801	2.91376	9.21412	.117786		8.99	80.8201	2.99833	9.48156	.111235
8.50	72.2500	2.91548	9.21954	.117647		**9.00**	81.0000	3.00000	9.48683	.111111
n	*n*²	√*n*	√10*n*	1/*n*		*n*	*n*²	√*n*	√10*n*	1/*n*

SQUARES — SQUARE ROOTS — RECIPROCALS (*Concluded*)

n	n²	√n	√10n	1/n	n	n²	√n	√10n	1/n
9.00	81.0000	3.00000	9.48683	.111111	**9.50**	90.2500	3.08221	9.74679	.105263
9.01	81.1801	3.00167	9.49210	.110988	9.51	90.4401	3.08383	9.75192	.105152
9.02	81.3604	3.00333	9.49737	.110865	9.52	90.6304	3.08545	9.75705	.105042
9.03	81.5409	3.00500	9.50263	.110742	9.53	90.8209	3.08707	9.76217	.104932
9.04	81.7216	3.00666	9.50789	.110619	9.54	91.0116	3.08869	9.76729	.104822
9.05	81.9025	3.00832	9.51315	.110497	9.55	91.2025	3.09031	9.77241	.104712
9.06	82.0836	3.00998	9.51840	.110375	9.56	91.3936	3.09192	9.77753	.104603
9.07	82.2649	3.01164	9.52365	.110254	9.57	91.5849	3.09354	9.78264	.104493
9.08	82.4464	3.01330	9.52890	.110132	9.58	91.7764	3.09516	9.78775	.104384
9.09	82.6281	3.01496	9.53415	.110011	9.59	91.9681	3.09677	9.79285	.104275
9.10	82.8100	3.01662	9.53939	.109890	**9.60**	92.1600	3.09839	9.79796	.104167
9.11	82.9921	3.01828	9.54463	.109769	9.61	92.3521	3.10000	9.80306	.104058
9.12	83.1744	3.01993	9.54987	.109649	9.62	92.5444	3.10161	9.80816	.103950
9.13	83.3569	3.02159	9.55510	.109529	9.63	92.7369	3.10322	9.81326	.103842
9.14	83.5396	3.02324	9.56033	.109409	9.64	92.9296	3.10483	9.81835	.103734
9.15	83.7225	3.02490	9.56556	.109290	9.65	93.1225	3.10644	9.82344	.103627
9.16	83.9056	3.02655	9.57079	.109170	9.66	93.3156	3.10805	9.82853	.103520
9.17	84.0889	3.02820	9.57601	.109051	9.67	93.5089	3.10966	9.83362	.103413
9.18	84.2724	3.02985	9.58123	.108932	9.68	93.7024	3.11127	9.83870	.103306
9.19	84.4561	3.03150	9.58645	.108814	9.69	93.8961	3.11288	9.84378	.103199
9.20	84.6400	3.03315	9.59166	.108696	**9.70**	94.0900	3.11448	9.84886	.103093
9.21	84.8241	3.03480	9.59687	.108578	9.71	94.2841	3.11609	9.85393	.102987
9.22	85.0084	3.03645	9.60208	.108460	9.72	94.4784	3.11769	9.85901	.102881
9.23	85.1929	3.03809	9.60729	.108342	9.73	94.6729	3.11929	9.86408	.102775
9.24	85.3776	3.03974	9.61249	.108225	9.74	94.8676	3.12090	9.86914	.102669
9.25	85.5625	3.04138	9.61769	.108108	9.75	95.0625	3.12250	9.87421	.102564
9.26	85.7476	3.04302	9.62289	.107991	9.76	95.2576	3.12410	9.87927	.102459
9.27	85.9329	3.04467	9.62808	.107875	9.77	95.4529	3.12570	9.88433	.102354
9.28	86.1184	3.04631	9.63328	.107759	9.78	95.6484	3.12730	9.88939	.102249
9.29	86.3041	3.04795	9.63846	.107643	9.79	95.8441	3.12890	9.89444	.102145
9.30	86.4900	3.04959	9.64365	.107527	**9.80**	96.0400	3.13050	9.89949	.102041
9.31	86.6761	3.05123	9.64883	.107411	9.81	96.2361	3.13209	9.90454	.101937
9.32	86.8624	3.05287	9.65401	.107296	9.82	96.4324	3.13369	9.90959	.101833
9.33	87.0489	3.05450	9.65919	.107181	9.83	96.6289	3.13528	9.91464	.101729
9.34	87.2356	3.05614	9.66437	.107066	9.84	96.8256	3.13688	9.91968	.101626
9.35	87.4225	3.05778	9.66954	.106952	9.85	97.0225	3.13847	9.92472	.101523
9.36	87.6096	3.05941	9.67471	.106838	9.86	97.2196	3.14006	9.92975	.101420
9.37	87.7969	3.06105	9.67988	.106724	9.87	97.4169	3.14166	9.93479	.101317
9.38	87.9844	3.06268	9.68504	.106610	9.88	97.6144	3.14325	9.93982	.101215
9.39	88.1721	3.06431	9.69020	.106496	9.89	97.8121	3.14484	9.94485	.101112
9.40	88.3600	3.06594	9.69536	.106383	**9.90**	98.0100	3.14643	9.94987	.101010
9.41	88.5481	3.06757	9.70052	.106270	9.91	98.2081	3.14802	9.95490	.100908
9.42	88.7364	3.06920	9.70567	.106157	9.92	98.4064	3.14960	9.95992	.100806
9.43	88.9249	3.07083	9.71082	.106045	9.93	98.6049	3.15119	9.96494	.100705
9.44	89.1136	3.07246	9.71597	.105932	9.94	98.8036	3.15278	9.96995	.100604
9.45	89.3025	3.07409	9.72111	.105820	9.95	99.0025	3.15436	9.97497	.100503
9.46	89.4916	3.07571	9.72625	.105708	9.96	99.2016	3.15595	9.97998	.100402
9.47	89.6809	3.07734	9.73139	.105597	9.97	99.4009	3.15753	9.98499	.100301
9.48	89.8704	3.07896	9.73653	.105485	9.98	99.6004	3.15911	9.98999	.100200
9.49	90.0601	3.08058	9.74166	.105374	9.99	99.8001	3.16070	9.99500	.100100
9.50	90.2500	3.08221	9.74679	.105263	**10.00**	100.000	3.16228	10.0000	.100000
n	n²	√n	√10n	1/n	n	n²	√n	√10n	1/n

LOGARITHMS OF NUMBERS 1,000–1,499 †
Six-Place Mantissas

N	0	1	2	3	4	5	6	7	8	9	D#
100	00 0000	0434	0868	1301	1734	2166	2598	3029	3461	3891	434
01	4321	4751	5181	5609	6038	6466	6894	7321	7748	8174	430
02	00 8600	9026	9451	9876	*0300	*0724	*1147	*1570	*1993	*2415	426
03	01 2837	3259	3680	4100	4521	4940	5360	5779	6197	6616	422
04	01 7033	7451	7868	8284	8700	9116	9532	9947	*0361	*0775	418
05	02 1189	1603	2016	2428	2841	3252	3664	4075	4486	4896	414
06	5306	5715	6125	6533	6942	7350	7757	8164	8571	8978	410
07	02 9384	9789	*0195	*0600	*1004	*1408	*1812	*2216	*2619	*3021	406
08	03 3424	3826	4227	4628	5029	5430	5830	6230	6629	7028	402
09	03 7426	7825	8223	8620	9017	9414	9811	*0207	*0602	*0998	399
110	04 1393	1787	2182	2576	2969	3362	3755	4148	4540	4932	395
11	5323	5714	6105	6495	6885	7275	7664	8053	8442	8830	391
12	04 9218	9606	9993	*0380	*0766	*1153	*1538	*1924	*2309	*2694	388
13	05 3078	3463	3846	4230	4613	4996	5378	5760	6142	6524	385
14	05 6905	7286	7666	8046	8426	8805	9185	9563	9942	*0320	381
15	06 0698	1075	1452	1829	2206	2582	2958	3333	3709	4083	377
16	4458	4832	5206	5580	5953	6326	6699	7071	7443	7815	374
17	06 8186	8557	8928	9298	9668	*0038	*0407	*0776	*1145	*1514	371
18	07 1882	2250	2617	2985	3352	3718	4085	4451	4816	5182	368
19	5547	5912	6276	6640	7004	7368	7731	8094	8457	8819	365
120	07 9181	9543	9904	*0266	*0626	*0987	1347	*1707	*2067	*2426	362
21	08 2785	3144	3503	3861	4219	4576	4934	5291	5647	6004	359
22	6360	6716	7071	7426	7781	8136	8490	8845	9198	9552	356
23	08 9905	*0258	*0611	*0963	*1315	*1667	*2018	*2370	*2721	*3071	353
24	09 3422	3772	4122	4471	4820	5169	5518	5866	6215	6562	350
25	09 6910	7257	7604	7951	8298	8644	8990	9335	9681	*0026	347
26	10 0371	0715	1059	1403	1747	2091	2434	2777	3119	3462	344
27	3804	4146	4487	4828	5169	5510	5851	6191	6531	6871	342
28	10 7210	7549	7888	8227	8565	8903	9241	9579	9916	*0253	339
29	11 0590	0926	1263	1599	1934	2270	2605	2940	3275	3609	337
130	3943	4277	4611	4944	5278	5611	5943	6276	6608	6940	334
31	11 7271	7603	7934	8265	8595	8926	9256	9586	9915	*0245	332
32	12 0574	0903	1231	1560	1888	2216	2544	2871	3198	3525	329
33	3852	4178	4504	4830	5156	5481	5806	6131	6456	6781	326
34	12 7105	7429	7753	8076	8399	8722	9045	9368	9690	*0012	324
35	13 0334	0655	0977	1298	1619	1939	2260	2580	2900	3219	322
36	3539	3858	4177	4496	4814	5133	5451	5769	6086	6403	319
37	6721	7037	7354	7671	7987	8303	8618	8934	9249	9564	317
38	13 9879	*0194	*0508	*0822	*1136	*1450	*1763	*2076	*2389	*2702	315
39	14 3015	3327	3639	3951	4263	4574	4885	5196	5507	5818	312
140	6128	6438	6748	7058	7367	7676	7985	8294	8603	8911	310
41	14 9219	9527	9835	*0142	*0449	*0756	*1063	*1370	*1676	*1982	308
42	15 2288	2594	2900	3205	3510	3815	4120	4424	4728	5032	306
43	5336	5640	5943	6246	6549	6852	7154	7457	7759	8061	304
44	15 8362	8664	8965	9266	9567	9868	*0168	*0469	*0769	*1068	302
45	16 1368	1667	1967	2266	2564	2863	3161	3460	3758	4055	300
46	4353	4650	4947	5244	5541	5838	6134	6430	6726	7022	297
47	16 7317	7613	7908	8203	8497	8792	9086	9380	9674	9968	296
48	17 0262	0555	0848	1141	1434	1726	2019	2311	2603	2895	293
49	3186	3478	3769	4060	4351	4641	4932	5222	5512	5802	292
N	0	1	2	3	4	5	6	7	8	9	D

*Prefix first two places on next line.
Example: The mantissa for number (N) 1072 is *03 0195.*

#The *highest difference* between adjacent mantissas on the *individual line.* It is also the *lowest difference* between adjacent mantissas on the *preceding line* in many cases.
†With permission of Stephen P. Shao, MATHEMATICS OF FINANCE, Copyright, 1962, South-Western Publishing Co.

LOGARITHMS OF NUMBERS 1,500–1,999
Six-Place Mantissas

N	0	1	2	3	4	5	6	7	8	9	D
150	17 6091	6381	6670	6959	7248	7536	7825	8113	8401	8689	290
51	17 8977	9264	9552	9839	*0126	*0413	*0699	*0986	*1272	*1558	288
52	18 1844	2129	2415	2700	2985	3270	3555	3839	4123	4407	286
53	4691	4975	5259	5542	5825	6108	6391	6674	6956	7239	284
54	18 7521	7803	8084	8366	8647	8928	9209	9490	9771	*0051	282
55	19 0332	0612	0892	1171	1451	1730	2010	2289	2567	2846	280
56	3125	3403	3681	3959	4237	4514	4792	5069	5346	5623	278
57	5900	6176	6453	6729	7005	7281	7556	7832	8107	8382	277
58	19 8657	8932	9206	9481	9755	*0029	*0303	*0577	*0850	*1124	275
59	20 1397	1670	1943	2216	2488	2761	3033	3305	3577	3848	273
160	4120	4391	4663	4934	5204	5475	5746	6016	6286	6556	272
61	6826	7096	7365	7634	7904	8173	8441	8710	8979	9247	270
62	20 9515	9783	*0051	*0319	*0586	*0853	*1121	*1388	*1654	*1921	268
63	21 2188	2454	2720	2986	3252	3518	3783	4049	4314	4579	266
64	4844	5109	5373	5638	5902	6166	6430	6694	6957	7221	265
65	21 7484	7747	8010	8273	8536	8798	9060	9323	9585	9846	263
66	22 0108	0370	0631	0892	1153	1414	1675	1936	2196	2456	262
67	2716	2976	3236	3496	3755	4015	4274	4533	4792	5051	260
68	5309	5568	5826	6084	6342	6600	6858	7115	7372	7630	259
69	22 7887	8144	8400	8657	8913	9170	9426	9682	9938	*0193	257
170	23 0449	0704	0960	1215	1470	1724	1979	2234	2488	2742	256
71	2996	3250	3504	3757	4011	4264	4517	4770	5023	5276	254
72	5528	5781	6033	6285	6537	6789	7041	7292	7544	7795	253
73	23 8046	8297	8548	8799	9049	9299	9550	9800	*0050	*0300	251
74	24 0549	0799	1048	1297	1546	1795	2044	2293	2541	2790	250
75	3038	3286	3534	3782	4030	4277	4525	4772	5019	5266	248
76	5513	5759	6006	6252	6499	6745	6991	7237	7482	7728	247
77	24 7973	8219	8464	8709	8954	9198	9443	9687	9932	*0176	246
78	25 0420	0664	0908	1151	1395	1638	1881	2125	2368	2610	244
79	2853	3096	3338	3580	3822	4064	4306	4548	4790	5031	243
180	5273	5514	5755	5996	6237	6477	6718	6958	7198	7439	241
81	25 7679	7918	8158	8398	8637	8877	9116	9355	9594	9833	240
82	26 0071	0310	0548	0787	1025	1263	1501	1739	1976	2214	239
83	2451	2688	2925	3162	3399	3636	3873	4109	4346	4582	237
84	4818	5054	5290	5525	5761	5996	6232	6467	6702	6937	236
85	7172	7406	7641	7875	8110	8344	8578	8812	9046	9279	235
86	26 9513	9746	9980	*0213	*0446	*0679	*0912	*1144	*1377	*1609	234
87	27 1842	2074	2306	2538	2770	3001	3233	3464	3696	3927	232
88	4158	4389	4620	4850	5081	5311	5542	5772	6002	6232	231
89	6462	6692	6921	7151	7380	7609	7838	8067	8296	8525	230
190	27 8754	8982	9211	9439	9667	9895	*0123	*0351	*0578	*0806	229
91	28 1033	1261	1488	1715	1942	2169	2396	2622	2849	3075	228
92	3301	3527	3753	3979	4205	4431	4656	4882	5107	5332	226
93	5557	5782	6007	6232	6456	6681	6905	7130	7354	7578	225
94	28 7802	8026	8249	8473	8696	8920	9143	9366	9589	9812	224
95	29 0035	0257	0480	0702	0925	1147	1369	1591	1813	2034	223
96	2256	2478	2699	2920	3141	3363	3584	3804	4025	4246	222
97	4466	4687	4907	5127	5347	5567	5787	6007	6226	6446	221
98	6665	6884	7104	7323	7542	7761	7979	8198	8416	8635	220
99	29 8853	9071	9289	9507	9725	9943	*0161	*0378	*0595	*0813	218
N	0	1	2	3	4	5	6	7	8	9	D

LOGARITHMS OF NUMBERS 2,000–2,499
Six-Place Mantissas

N	0	1	2	3	4	5	6	7	8	9	D
200	30 1030	1247	1464	1681	1898	2114	2331	2547	2764	2980	217
01	3196	3412	3628	3844	4059	4275	4491	4706	4921	5136	216
02	5351	5566	5781	5996	6211	6425	6639	6854	7068	7282	215
03	7496	7710	7924	8137	8351	8564	8778	8991	9204	9417	214
04	30 9630	9843	*0056	*0268	*0481	*0693	*0906	*1118	*1330	*1542	213
05	31 1754	1966	2177	2389	2600	2812	3023	3234	3445	3656	212
06	3867	4078	4289	4499	4710	4920	5130	5340	5551	5760	211
07	5970	6180	6390	6599	6809	7018	7227	7436	7646	7854	210
08	31 8063	8272	8481	8689	8898	9106	9314	9522	9730	9938	209
09	32 0146	0354	0562	0769	0977	1184	1391	1598	1805	2012	208
210	2219	2426	2633	2839	3046	3252	3458	3665	3871	4077	207
11	4282	4488	4694	4899	5105	5310	5516	5721	5926	6131	206
12	6336	6541	6745	6950	7155	7359	7563	7767	7972	8176	205
13	32 8380	8583	8787	8991	9194	9398	9601	9805	*0008	*0211	204
14	33 0414	0617	0819	1022	1225	1427	1630	1832	2034	2236	203
15	2438	2640	2842	3044	3246	3447	3649	3850	4051	4253	202
16	4454	4655	4856	5057	5257	5458	5658	5859	6059	6260	201
17	6460	6660	6860	7060	7260	7459	7659	7858	8058	8257	200
18	33 8456	8656	8855	9054	9253	9451	9650	9849	*0047	*0246	200
19	34 0444	0642	0841	1039	1237	1435	1632	1830	2028	2225	199
220	2423	2620	2817	3014	3212	3409	3606	3802	3999	4196	198
21	4392	4589	4785	4981	5178	5374	5570	5766	5962	6157	197
22	6353	6549	6744	6939	7135	7330	7525	7720	7915	8110	196
23	34 8305	8500	8694	8889	9083	9278	9472	9666	9860	*0054	195
24	35 0248	0442	0636	0829	1023	1216	1410	1603	1796	1989	194
25	2183	2375	2568	2761	2954	3147	3339	3532	3724	3916	193
26	4108	4301	4493	4685	4876	5068	5260	5452	5643	5834	192
27	6026	6217	6408	6599	6790	6981	7172	7363	7554	7744	191
28	7935	8125	8316	8506	8696	8886	9076	9266	9456	9646	191
29	35 9835	*0025	*0215	*0404	*0593	*0783	*0972	*1161	*1350	*1539	190
230	36 1728	1917	2105	2294	2482	2671	2859	3048	3236	3424	189
31	3612	3800	3988	4176	4363	4551	4739	4926	5113	5301	188
32	5488	5675	5862	6049	6236	6423	6610	6796	6983	7169	187
33	7356	7542	7729	7915	8101	8287	8473	8659	8845	9030	187
34	36 9216	9401	9587	9772	9958	*0143	*0328	*0513	*0698	*0883	186
35	37 1068	1253	1437	1622	1806	1991	2175	2360	2544	2728	185
36	2912	3096	3280	3464	3647	3831	4015	4198	4382	4565	184
37	4748	4932	5115	5298	5481	5664	5846	6029	6212	6394	184
38	6577	6759	6942	7124	7306	7488	7670	7852	8034	8216	183
39	37 8398	8580	8761	8943	9124	9306	9487	9668	9849	*0030	182
240	38 0211	0392	0573	0754	0934	1115	1296	1476	1656	1837	181
41	2017	2197	2377	2557	2737	2917	3097	3277	3456	3636	180
42	3815	3995	4174	4353	4533	4712	4891	5070	5249	5428	180
43	5606	5785	5964	6142	6321	6499	6677	6856	7034	7212	179
44	7390	7568	7746	7923	8101	8279	8456	8634	8811	8989	178
45	38 9166	9343	9520	9698	9875	*0051	*0228	*0405	*0582	*0759	178
46	39 0935	1112	1288	1464	1641	1817	1993	2169	2345	2521	177
47	2697	2873	3048	3224	3400	3575	3751	3926	4101	4277	176
48	4452	4627	4802	4977	5152	5326	5501	5676	5850	6025	175
49	6199	6374	6548	6722	6896	7071	7245	7419	7592	7766	175
N	0	1	2	3	4	5	6	7	8	9	D

LOGARITHMS OF NUMBERS 2,500–2,999
Six-Place Mantissas

N	0	1	2	3	4	5	6	7	8	9	D
250	39 7940	8114	8287	8461	8634	8808	8981	9154	9328	9501	174
51	39 9674	9847	*0020	*0192	*0365	*0538	*0711	*0883	*1056	*1228	173
52	40 1401	1573	1745	1917	2089	2261	2433	2605	2777	2949	172
53	3121	3292	3464	3635	3807	3978	4149	4320	4492	4663	172
54	4834	5005	5176	5346	5517	5688	5858	6029	6199	6370	171
55	6540	6710	6881	7051	7221	7391	7561	7731	7901	8070	171
56	8240	8410	8579	8749	8918	9087	9257	9426	9595	9764	170
57	40 9933	*0102	*0271	*0440	*0609	*0777	*0946	*1114	*1283	*1451	169
58	41 1620	1788	1956	2124	2293	2461	2629	2796	2964	3132	169
59	3300	3467	3635	3803	3970	4137	4305	4472	4639	4806	168
260	4973	5140	5307	5474	5641	5808	5974	6141	6308	6474	167
61	6641	6807	6973	7139	7306	7472	7638	7804	7970	8135	167
62	8301	8467	8633	8798	8964	9129	9295	9460	9625	9791	166
63	41 9956	*0121	*0286	*0451	*0616	*0781	*0945	*1110	*1275	*1439	165
64	42 1604	1768	1933	2097	2261	2426	2590	2754	2918	3082	165
65	3246	3410	3574	3737	3901	4065	4228	4392	4555	4718	164
66	4882	5045	5208	5371	5534	5697	5860	6023	6186	6349	163
67	6511	6674	6836	6999	7161	7324	7486	7648	7811	7973	163
68	8135	8297	8459	8621	8783	8944	9106	9268	9429	9591	162
69	42 9752	9914	*0075	*0236	*0398	*0559	*0720	*0881	*1042	*1203	162
270	43 1364	1525	1685	1846	2007	2167	2328	2488	2649	2809	161
71	2969	3130	3290	3450	3610	3770	3930	4090	4249	4409	161
72	4569	4729	4888	5048	5207	5367	5526	5685	5844	6004	160
73	6163	6322	6481	6640	6799	6957	7116	7275	7433	7592	159
74	7751	7909	8067	8226	8384	8542	8701	8859	9017	9175	159
75	43 9333	9491	9648	9806	9964	*0122	*0279	*0437	*0594	*0752	158
76	44 0909	1066	1224	1381	1538	1695	1852	2009	2166	2323	158
77	2480	2637	2793	2950	3106	3263	3419	3576	3732	3889	157
78	4045	4201	4357	4513	4669	4825	4981	5137	5293	5449	156
79	5604	5760	5915	6071	6226	6382	6537	6692	6848	7003	156
280	7158	7313	7468	7623	7778	7933	8088	8242	8397	8552	155
81	44 8706	8861	9015	9170	9324	9478	9633	9787	9941	*0095	155
82	45 0249	0403	0557	0711	0865	1018	1172	1326	1479	1633	154
83	1786	1940	2093	2247	2400	2553	2706	2859	3012	3165	154
84	3318	3471	3624	3777	3930	4082	4235	4387	4540	4692	153
85	4845	4997	5150	5302	5454	5606	5758	5910	6062	6214	153
86	6366	6518	6670	6821	6973	7125	7276	7428	7579	7731	152
87	7882	8033	8184	8336	8487	8638	8789	8940	9091	9242	152
88	45 9392	9543	9694	9845	9995	*0146	*0296	*0447	*0597	*0748	151
89	46 0898	1048	1198	1348	1499	1649	1799	1948	2098	2248	151
290	2398	2548	2697	2847	2997	3146	3296	3445	3594	3744	150
91	3893	4042	4191	4340	4490	4639	4788	4936	5085	5234	149
92	5383	5532	5680	5829	5977	6126	6274	6423	6571	6719	149
93	6868	7016	7164	7312	7460	7608	7756	7904	8052	8200	148
94	8347	8495	8643	8790	8938	9085	9233	9380	9527	9675	148
95	46 9822	9969	*0116	*0263	*0410	*0557	*0704	*0851	*0998	*1145	147
96	47 1292	1438	1585	1732	1878	2025	2171	2318	2464	2610	147
97	2756	2903	3049	3195	3341	3487	3633	3779	3925	4071	147
98	4216	4362	4508	4653	4799	4944	5090	5235	5381	5526	146
99	5671	5816	5962	6107	6252	6397	6542	6687	6832	6976	146
N	0	1	2	3	4	5	6	7	8	9	D

LOGARITHMS OF NUMBERS 3,000–3,499
Six-Place Mantissas

N	0	1	2	3	4	5	6	7	8	9	D
300	47 7121	7266	7411	7555	7700	7844	7989	8133	8278	8422	145
01	47 8566	8711	8855	8999	9143	9287	9431	9575	9719	9863	145
02	48 0007	0151	0294	0438	0582	0725	0869	1012	1156	1299	144
03	1443	1586	1729	1872	2016	2159	2302	2445	2588	2731	144
04	2874	3016	3159	3302	3445	3587	3730	3872	4015	4157	143
05	4300	4442	4585	4727	4869	5011	5153	5295	5437	5579	143
06	5721	5863	6005	6147	6289	6430	6572	6714	6855	6997	142
07	7138	7280	7421	7563	7704	7845	7986	8127	8269	8410	142
08	8551	8692	8833	8974	9114	9255	9396	9537	9677	9818	141
09	48 9958	*0099	*0239	*0380	*0520	*0661	*0801	*0941	*1081	*1222	141
310	49 1362	1502	1642	1782	1922	2062	2201	2341	2481	2621	140
11	2760	2900	3040	3179	3319	3458	3597	3737	3876	4015	140
12	4155	4294	4433	4572	4711	4850	4989	5128	5267	5406	139
13	5544	5683	5822	5960	6099	6238	6376	6515	6653	6791	139
14	6930	7068	7206	7344	7483	7621	7759	7897	8035	8173	139
15	8311	8448	8586	8724	8862	8999	9137	9275	9412	9550	138
16	49 9687	9824	9962	*0099	*0236	*0374	*0511	*0648	*0785	*0922	138
17	50 1059	1196	1333	1470	1607	1744	1880	2017	2154	2291	137
18	2427	2564	2700	2837	2973	3109	3246	3382	3518	3655	137
19	3791	3927	4063	4199	4335	4471	4607	4743	4878	5014	136
320	5150	5286	5421	5557	5693	5828	5964	6099	6234	6370	136
21	6505	6640	6776	6911	7046	7181	7316	7451	7586	7721	136
22	7856	7991	8126	8260	8395	8530	8664	8799	8934	9068	135
23	50 9203	9337	9471	9606	9740	9874	*0009	*0143	*0277	*0411	135
24	51 0545	0679	0813	0947	1081	1215	1349	1482	1616	1750	134
25	1883	2017	2151	2284	2418	2551	2684	2818	2951	3084	134
26	3218	3351	3484	3617	3750	3883	4016	4149	4282	4415	133
27	4548	4681	4813	4946	5079	5211	5344	5476	5609	5741	133
28	5874	6006	6139	6271	6403	6535	6668	6800	6932	7064	133
29	7196	7328	7460	7592	7724	7855	7987	8119	8251	8382	132
330	8514	8646	8777	8909	9040	9171	9303	9434	9566	9697	132
31	51 9828	9959	*0090	*0221	*0353	*0484	*0615	*0745	*0876	*1007	132
32	52 1138	1269	1400	1530	1661	1792	1922	2053	2183	2314	131
33	2444	2575	2705	2835	2966	3096	3226	3356	3486	3616	131
34	3746	3876	4006	4136	4266	4396	4526	4656	4785	4915	130
35	5045	5174	5304	5434	5563	5693	5822	5951	6081	6210	130
36	6339	6469	6598	6727	6856	6985	7114	7243	7372	7501	130
37	7630	7759	7888	8016	8145	8274	8402	8531	8660	8788	129
38	52 8917	9045	9174	9302	9430	9559	9687	9815	9943	*0072	129
39	53 0200	0328	0456	0584	0712	0840	0968	1096	1223	1351	128
340	1479	1607	1734	1862	1990	2117	2245	2372	2500	2627	128
41	2754	2882	3009	3136	3264	3391	3518	3645	3772	3899	128
42	4026	4153	4280	4407	4534	4661	4787	4914	5041	5167	127
43	5294	5421	5547	5674	5800	5927	6053	6180	6306	6432	127
44	6558	6685	6811	6937	7063	7189	7315	7441	7567	7693	127
45	7819	7945	8071	8197	8322	8448	8574	8699	8825	8951	126
46	53 9076	9202	9327	9452	9578	9703	9829	9954	*0079	*0204	126
47	54 0329	0455	0580	0705	0830	0955	1080	1205	1330	1454	126
48	1579	1704	1829	1953	2078	2203	2327	2452	2576	2701	125
49	2825	2950	3074	3199	3323	3447	3571	3696	3820	3944	125
N	0	1	2	3	4	5	6	7	8	9	D

LOGARITHMS OF NUMBERS 3,500–3,999
Six-Place Mantissas

N	0	1	2	3	4	5	6	7	8	9	D
350	54 4068	4192	4316	4440	4564	4688	4812	4936	5060	5183	124
51	5307	5431	5555	5678	5802	5925	6049	6172	6296	6419	124
52	6543	6666	6789	6913	7036	7159	7282	7405	7529	7652	124
53	7775	7898	8021	8144	8267	8389	8512	8635	8758	8881	123
54	54 9003	9126	9249	9371	9494	9616	9739	9861	9984	*0106	123
55	55 0228	0351	0473	0595	0717	0840	0962	1084	1206	1328	123
56	1450	1572	1694	1816	1938	2060	2181	2303	2425	2547	122
57	2668	2790	2911	3033	3155	3276	3398	3519	3640	3762	122
58	3883	4004	4126	4247	4368	4489	4610	4731	4852	4973	122
59	5094	5215	5336	5457	5578	5699	5820	5940	6061	6182	121
360	6303	6423	6544	6664	6785	6905	7026	7146	7267	7387	121
61	7507	7627	7748	7868	7988	8108	8228	8349	8469	8589	121
62	8709	8829	8948	9068	9188	9308	9428	9548	9667	9787	120
63	55 9907	*0026	*0146	*0265	*0385	*0504	*0624	*0743	*0863	*0982	120
64	56 1101	1221	1340	1459	1578	1698	1817	1936	2055	2174	120
65	2293	2412	2531	2650	2769	2887	3006	3125	3244	3362	119
66	3481	3600	3718	3837	3955	4074	4192	4311	4429	4548	119
67	4666	4784	4903	5021	5139	5257	5376	5494	5612	5730	119
68	5848	5966	6084	6202	6320	6437	6555	6673	6791	6909	118
69	7026	7144	7262	7379	7497	7614	7732	7849	7967	8084	118
370	8202	8319	8436	8554	8671	8788	8905	9023	9140	9257	118
71	56 9374	9491	9608	9725	9842	9959	*0076	*0193	*0309	*0426	117
72	57 0543	0660	0776	0893	1010	1126	1243	1359	1476	1592	117
73	1709	1825	1942	2058	2174	2291	2407	2523	2639	2755	117
74	2872	2988	3104	3220	3336	3452	3568	3684	3800	3915	116
75	4031	4147	4263	4379	4494	4610	4726	4841	4957	5072	116
76	5188	5303	5419	5534	5650	5765	5880	5996	6111	6226	116
77	6341	6457	6572	6687	6802	6917	7032	7147	7262	7377	116
78	7492	7607	7722	7836	7951	8066	8181	8295	8410	8525	115
79	8639	8754	8868	8983	9097	9212	9326	9441	9555	9669	115
380	57 9784	9898	*0012	*0126	*0241	*0355	*0469	*0583	*0697	*0811	115
81	58 0925	1039	1153	1267	1381	1495	1608	1722	1836	1950	114
82	2063	2177	2291	2404	2518	2631	2745	2858	2972	3085	114
83	3199	3312	3426	3539	3652	3765	3879	3992	4105	4218	114
84	4331	4444	4557	4670	4783	4896	5009	5122	5235	5348	113
85	5461	5574	5686	5799	5912	6024	6137	6250	6362	6475	113
86	6587	6700	6812	6925	7037	7149	7262	7374	7486	7599	113
87	7711	7823	7935	8047	8160	8272	8384	8496	8608	8720	113
88	8832	8944	9056	9167	9279	9391	9503	9615	9726	9838	112
89	58 9950	*0061	*0173	*0284	*0396	*0507	*0619	*0730	*0842	*0953	112
390	59 1065	1176	1287	1399	1510	1621	1732	1843	1955	2066	112
91	2177	2288	2399	2510	2621	2732	2843	2954	3064	3175	111
92	3286	3397	3508	3618	3729	3840	3950	4061	4171	4282	111
93	4393	4503	4614	4724	4834	4945	5055	5165	5276	5386	111
94	5496	5606	5717	5827	5937	6047	6157	6267	6377	6487	111
95	6597	6707	6817	6927	7037	7146	7256	7366	7476	7586	110
96	7695	7805	7914	8024	8134	8243	8353	8462	8572	8681	110
97	8791	8900	9009	9119	9228	9337	9446	9556	9665	9774	110
98	9883	9992	*0101	*0210	*0319	*0428	*0537	*0646	*0755	*0864	109
99	60 0973	1082	1191	1299	1408	1517	1625	1734	1843	1951	109
N	0	1	2	3	4	5	6	7	8	9	D

LOGARITHMS OF NUMBERS 4,000–4,499
Six-Place Mantissas

N	0	1	2	3	4	5	6	7	8	9	D
400	60 2060	2169	2277	2386	2494	2603	2711	2819	2928	3036	109
01	3144	3253	3361	3469	3577	3686	3794	3902	4010	4118	109
02	4226	4334	4442	4550	4658	4766	4874	4982	5089	5197	108
03	5305	5413	5521	5628	5736	5844	5951	6059	6166	6274	108
04	6381	6489	6596	6704	6811	6919	7026	7133	7241	7348	108
05	7455	7562	7669	7777	7884	7991	8098	8205	8312	8419	108
06	8526	8633	8740	8847	8954	9061	9167	9274	9381	9488	107
07	60 9594	9701	9808	9914	*0021	*0128	*0234	*0341	*0447	*0554	107
08	61 0660	0767	0873	0979	1086	1192	1298	1405	1511	1617	107
09	1723	1829	1936	2042	2148	2254	2360	2466	2572	2678	107
410	2784	2890	2996	3102	3207	3313	3419	3525	3630	3736	106
11	3842	3947	4053	4159	4264	4370	4475	4581	4686	4792	106
12	4897	5003	5108	5213	5319	5424	5529	5634	5740	5845	106
13	5950	6055	6160	6265	6370	6476	6581	6686	6790	6895	106
14	7000	7105	7210	7315	7420	7525	7629	7734	7839	7943	105
15	8048	8153	8257	8362	8466	8571	8676	8780	8884	8989	105
16	61 9093	9198	9302	9406	9511	9615	9719	9824	9928	*0032	105
17	62 0136	0240	0344	0448	0552	0656	0760	0864	0968	1072	104
18	1176	1280	1384	1488	1592	1695	1799	1903	2007	2110	104
19	2214	2318	2421	2525	2628	2732	2835	2939	3042	3146	104
420	3249	3353	3456	3559	3663	3766	3869	3973	4076	4179	104
21	4282	4385	4488	4591	4695	4798	4901	5004	5107	5210	104
22	5312	5415	5518	5621	5724	5827	5929	6032	6135	6238	103
23	6340	6443	6546	6648	6751	6853	6956	7058	7161	7263	103
24	7366	7468	7571	7673	7775	7878	7980	8082	8185	8287	103
25	8389	8491	8593	8695	8797	8900	9002	9104	9206	9308	103
26	62 9410	9512	9613	9715	9817	9919	*0021	*0123	*0224	*0326	102
27	63 0428	0530	0631	0733	0835	0936	1038	1139	1241	1342	102
28	1444	1545	1647	1748	1849	1951	2052	2153	2255	2356	102
29	2457	2559	2660	2761	2862	2963	3064	3165	3266	3367	102
430	3468	3569	3670	3771	3872	3973	4074	4175	4276	4376	101
31	4477	4578	4679	4779	4880	4981	5081	5182	5283	5383	101
32	5484	5584	5685	5785	5886	5986	6087	6187	6287	6388	101
33	6488	6588	6688	6789	6889	6989	7089	7189	7290	7390	101
34	7490	7590	7690	7790	7890	7990	8090	8190	8290	8389	100
35	8489	8589	8689	8789	8888	8988	9088	9188	9287	9387	100
36	63 9486	9586	9686	9785	9885	9984	*0084	*0183	*0283	*0382	100
37	64 0481	0581	0680	0779	0879	0978	1077	1177	1276	1375	100
38	1474	1573	1672	1771	1871	1970	2069	2168	2267	2366	100
39	2465	2563	2662	2761	2860	2959	3058	3156	3255	3354	99
440	3453	3551	3650	3749	3847	3946	4044	4143	4242	4340	99
41	4439	4537	4636	4734	4832	4931	5029	5127	5226	5324	99
42	5422	5521	5619	5717	5815	5913	6011	6110	6208	6306	99
43	6404	6502	6600	6698	6796	6894	6992	7089	7187	7285	98
44	7383	7481	7579	7676	7774	7872	7969	8067	8165	8262	98
45	8360	8458	8555	8653	8750	8848	8945	9043	9140	9237	98
46	64 9335	9432	9530	9627	9724	9821	9919	*0016	*0113	*0210	98
47	65 0308	0405	0502	0599	0696	0793	0890	0987	1084	1181	97
48	1278	1375	1472	1569	1666	1762	1859	1956	2053	2150	97
49	2246	2343	2440	2536	2633	2730	2826	2923	3019	3116	97
N	0	1	2	3	4	5	6	7	8	9	D

LOGARITHMS OF NUMBERS 4,500–4,999
Six-Place Mantissas

N	0	1	2	3	4	5	6	7	8	9	D
450	65 3213	3309	3405	3502	3598	3695	3791	3888	3984	4080	97
51	4177	4273	4369	4465	4562	4658	4754	4850	4946	5042	97
52	5138	5235	5331	5427	5523	5619	5715	5810	5906	6002	97
53	6098	6194	6290	6386	6482	6577	6673	6769	6864	6960	96
54	7056	7152	7247	7343	7438	7534	7629	7725	7820	7916	96
55	8011	8107	8202	8298	8393	8488	8584	8679	8774	8870	96
56	8965	9060	9155	9250	9346	9441	9536	9631	9726	9821	96
57	65 9916	*0011	*0106	*0201	*0296	*0391	*0486	*0581	*0676	*0771	95
58	66 0865	0960	1055	1150	1245	1339	1434	1529	1623	1718	95
59	1813	1907	2002	2096	2191	2286	2380	2475	2569	2663	95
460	2758	2852	2947	3041	3135	3230	3324	3418	3512	3607	95
61	3701	3795	3889	3983	4078	4172	4266	4360	4454	4548	95
62	4642	4736	4830	4924	5018	5112	5206	5299	5393	5487	94
63	5581	5675	5769	5862	5956	6050	6143	6237	6331	6424	94
64	6518	6612	6705	6799	6892	6986	7079	7173	7266	7360	94
65	7453	7546	7640	7733	7826	7920	8013	8106	8199	8293	94
66	8386	8479	8572	8665	8759	8852	8945	9038	9131	9224	94
67	66 9317	9410	9503	9596	9689	9782	9875	9967	*0060	*0153	93
68	67 0246	0339	0431	0524	0617	0710	0802	0895	0988	1080	93
69	1173	1265	1358	1451	1543	1636	1728	1821	1913	2005	93
470	2098	2190	2283	2375	2467	2560	2652	2744	2836	2929	93
71	3021	3113	3205	3297	3390	3482	3574	3666	3758	3850	93
72	3942	4034	4126	4218	4310	4402	4494	4586	4677	4769	92
73	4861	4953	5045	5137	5228	5320	5412	5503	5595	5687	92
74	5778	5870	5962	6053	6145	6236	6328	6419	6511	6602	92
75	6694	6785	6876	6968	7059	7151	7242	7333	7424	7516	92
76	7607	7698	7789	7881	7972	8063	8154	8245	8336	8427	92
77	8518	8609	8700	8791	8882	8973	9064	9155	9246	9337	91
78	67 9428	9519	9610	9700	9791	9882	9973	*0063	*0154	*0245	91
79	68 0336	0426	0517	0607	0698	0789	0879	0970	1060	1151	91
480	1241	1332	1422	1513	1603	1693	1784	1874	1964	2055	91
81	2145	2235	2326	2416	2506	2596	2686	2777	2867	2957	91
82	3047	3137	3227	3317	3407	3497	3587	3677	3767	3857	90
83	3947	4037	4127	4217	4307	4396	4486	4576	4666	4756	90
84	4845	4935	5025	5114	5204	5294	5383	5473	5563	5652	90
85	5742	5831	5921	6010	6100	6189	6279	6368	6458	6547	90
86	6636	6726	6815	6904	6994	7083	7172	7261	7351	7440	90
87	7529	7618	7707	7796	7886	7975	8064	8153	8242	8331	90
88	8420	8509	8598	8687	8776	8865	8953	9042	9131	9220	89
89	68 9309	9398	9486	9575	9664	9753	9841	9930	*0019	*0107	89
490	69 0196	0285	0373	0462	0550	0639	0728	0816	0905	0993	89
91	1081	1170	1258	1347	1435	1524	1612	1700	1789	1877	89
92	1965	2053	2142	2230	2318	2406	2494	2583	2671	2759	89
93	2847	2935	3023	3111	3199	3287	3375	3463	3551	3639	88
94	3727	3815	3903	3991	4078	4166	4254	4342	4430	4517	88
95	4605	4693	4781	4868	4956	5044	5131	5219	5307	5394	88
96	5482	5569	5657	5744	5832	5919	6007	6094	6182	6269	88
97	6356	6444	6531	6618	6706	6793	6880	6968	7055	7142	88
98	7229	7317	7404	7491	7578	7665	7752	7839	7926	8014	88
99	8101	8188	8275	8362	8449	8535	8622	8709	8796	8883	87
N	0	1	2	3	4	5	6	7	8	9	D

LOGARITHMS OF NUMBERS 5,000–5,499
Six-Place Mantissas

N	0	1	2	3	4	5	6	7	8	9	D
500	69 8970	9057	9144	9231	9317	9404	9491	9578	9664	9751	87
01	69 9838	9924	*0011	*0098	*0184	*0271	*0358	*0444	*0531	*0617	87
02	70 0704	0790	0877	0963	1050	1136	1222	1309	1395	1482	87
03	1568	1654	1741	1827	1913	1999	2086	2172	2258	2344	87
04	2431	2517	2603	2689	2775	2861	2947	3033	3119	3205	86
05	3291	3377	3463	3549	3635	3721	3807	3893	3979	4065	86
06	4151	4236	4322	4408	4494	4579	4665	4751	4837	4922	86
07	5008	5094	5179	5265	5350	5436	5522	5607	5693	5778	86
08	5864	5949	6035	6120	6206	6291	6376	6462	6547	6632	86
09	6718	6803	6888	6974	7059	7144	7229	7315	7400	7485	86
510	7570	7655	7740	7826	7911	7996	8081	8166	8251	8336	86
11	8421	8506	8591	8676	8761	8846	8931	9015	9100	9185	85
12	70 9270	9355	9440	9524	9609	9694	9779	9863	9948	*0033	85
13	71 0117	0202	0287	0371	0456	0540	0625	0710	0794	0879	85
14	0963	1048	1132	1217	1301	1385	1470	1554	1639	1723	85
15	1807	1892	1976	2060	2144	2229	2313	2397	2481	2566	85
16	2650	2734	2818	2902	2986	3070	3154	3238	3323	3407	85
17	3491	3575	3659	3742	3826	3910	3994	4078	4162	4246	84
18	4330	4414	4497	4581	4665	4749	4833	4916	5000	5084	84
19	5167	5251	5335	5418	5502	5586	5669	5753	5836	5920	84
520	6003	6087	6170	6254	6337	6421	6504	6588	6671	6754	84
21	6838	6921	7004	7088	7171	7254	7338	7421	7504	7587	84
22	7671	7754	7837	7920	8003	8086	8169	8253	8336	8419	84
23	8502	8585	8668	8751	8834	8917	9000	9083	9165	9248	83
24	71 9331	9414	9497	9580	9663	9745	9828	9911	9994	*0077	83
25	72 0159	0242	0325	0407	0490	0573	0655	0738	0821	0903	83
26	0986	1068	1151	1233	1316	1398	1481	1563	1646	1728	83
27	1811	1893	1975	2058	2140	2222	2305	2387	2469	2552	83
28	2634	2716	2798	2881	2963	3045	3127	3209	3291	3374	83
29	3456	3538	3620	3702	3784	3866	3948	4030	4112	4194	82
530	4276	4358	4440	4522	4604	4685	4767	4849	4931	5013	82
31	5095	5176	5258	5340	5422	5503	5585	5667	5748	5830	82
32	5912	5993	6075	6156	6238	6320	6401	6483	6564	6646	82
33	6727	6809	6890	6972	7053	7134	7216	7297	7379	7460	82
34	7541	7623	7704	7785	7866	7948	8029	8110	8191	8273	82
35	8354	8435	8516	8597	8678	8759	8841	8922	9003	9084	82
36	9165	9246	9327	9408	9489	9570	9651	9732	9813	9893	81
37	72 9974	*0055	*0136	*0217	*0298	*0378	*0459	*0540	*0621	*0702	81
38	73 0782	0863	0944	1024	1105	1186	1266	1347	1428	1508	81
39	1589	1669	1750	1830	1911	1991	2072	2152	2233	2313	81
540	2394	2474	2555	2635	2715	2796	2876	2956	3037	3117	81
41	3197	3278	3358	3438	3518	3598	3679	3759	3839	3919	81
42	3999	4079	4160	4240	4320	4400	4480	4560	4640	4720	81
43	4800	4880	4960	5040	5120	5200	5279	5359	5439	5519	80
44	5599	5679	5759	5838	5918	5998	6078	6157	6237	6317	80
45	6397	6476	6556	6635	6715	6795	6874	6954	7034	7113	80
46	7193	7272	7352	7431	7511	7590	7670	7749	7829	7908	80
47	7987	8067	8146	8225	8305	8384	8463	8543	8622	8701	80
48	8781	8860	8939	9018	9097	9177	9256	9335	9414	9493	80
49	73 9572	9651	9731	9810	9889	9968	*0047	*0126	*0205	*0284	80
N	0	1	2	3	4	5	6	7	8	9	D

LOGARITHMS OF NUMBERS 5,500–5,999
Six-Place Mantissas

N	0	1	2	3	4	5	6	7	8	9	D
550	74 0363	0442	0521	0600	0678	0757	0836	0915	0994	1073	79
51	1152	1230	1309	1388	1467	1546	1624	1703	1782	1860	79
52	1939	2018	2096	2175	2254	2332	2411	2489	2568	2647	79
53	2725	2804	2882	2961	3039	3118	3196	3275	3353	3431	79
54	3510	3588	3667	3745	3823	3902	3980	4058	4136	4215	79
55	4293	4371	4449	4528	4606	4684	4762	4840	4919	4997	79
56	5075	5153	5231	5309	5387	5465	5543	5621	5699	5777	78
57	5855	5933	6011	6089	6167	6245	6323	6401	6479	6556	78
58	6634	6712	6790	6868	6945	7023	7101	7179	7256	7334	78
59	7412	7489	7567	7645	7722	7800	7878	7955	8033	8110	78
560	8188	8266	8343	8421	8498	8576	8653	8731	8808	8885	78
61	8963	9040	9118	9195	9272	9350	9427	9504	9582	9659	78
62	74 9736	9814	9891	9968	*0045	*0123	*0200	*0277	*0354	*0431	78
63	75 0508	0586	0663	0740	0817	0894	0971	1048	1125	1202	78
64	1279	1356	1433	1510	1587	1664	1741	1818	1895	1972	77
65	2048	2125	2202	2279	2356	2433	2509	2586	2663	2740	77
66	2816	2893	2970	3047	3123	3200	3277	3353	3430	3506	77
67	3583	3660	3736	3813	3889	3966	4042	4119	4195	4272	77
68	4348	4425	4501	4578	4654	4730	4807	4883	4960	5036	77
69	5112	5189	5265	5341	5417	5494	5570	5646	5722	5799	77
570	5875	5951	6027	6103	6180	6256	6332	6408	6484	6560	77
71	6636	6712	6788	6864	6940	7016	7092	7168	7244	7320	76
72	7396	7472	7548	7624	7700	7775	7851	7927	8003	8079	76
73	8155	8230	8306	8382	8458	8533	8609	8685	8761	8836	76
74	8912	8988	9063	9139	9214	9290	9366	9441	9517	9592	76
75	75 9668	9743	9819	9894	9970	*0045	*0121	*0196	*0272	*0347	76
76	76 0422	0498	0573	0649	0724	0799	0875	0950	1025	1101	76
77	1176	1251	1326	1402	1477	1552	1627	1702	1778	1853	76
78	1928	2003	2078	2153	2228	2303	2378	2453	2529	2604	76
79	2679	2754	2829	2904	2978	3053	3128	3203	3278	3353	75
580	3428	3503	3578	3653	3727	3802	3877	3952	4027	4101	75
81	4176	4251	4326	4400	4475	4550	4624	4699	4774	4848	75
82	4923	4998	5072	5147	5221	5296	5370	5445	5520	5594	75
83	5669	5743	5818	5892	5966	6041	6115	6190	6264	6338	75
84	6413	6487	6562	6636	6710	6785	6859	6933	7007	7082	75
85	7156	7230	7304	7379	7453	7527	7601	7675	7749	7823	75
86	7898	7972	8046	8120	8194	8268	8342	8416	8490	8564	74
87	8638	8712	8786	8860	8934	9008	9082	9156	9230	9303	74
88	76 9377	9451	9525	9599	9673	9746	9820	9894	9968	*0042	74
89	77 0115	0189	0263	0336	0410	0484	0557	0631	0705	0778	74
590	0852	0926	0999	1073	1146	1220	1293	1367	1440	1514	74
91	1587	1661	1734	1808	1881	1955	2028	2102	2175	2248	74
92	2322	2395	2468	2542	2615	2688	2762	2835	2908	2981	74
93	3055	3128	3201	3274	3348	3421	3494	3567	3640	3713	74
94	3786	3860	3933	4006	4079	4152	4225	4298	4371	4444	74
95	4517	4590	4663	4736	4809	4882	4955	5028	5100	5173	73
96	5246	5319	5392	5465	5538	5610	5683	5756	5829	5902	73
97	5974	6047	6120	6193	6265	6338	6411	6483	6556	6629	73
98	6701	6774	6846	6919	6992	7064	7137	7209	7282	7354	73
99	7427	7499	7572	7644	7717	7789	7862	7934	8006	8079	73
N	0	1	2	3	4	5	6	7	8	9	D

LOGARITHMS OF NUMBERS 6,000–6,499
Six-Place Mantissas

N	0	1	2	3	4	5	6	7	8	9	D
600	77 8151	8224	8296	8368	8441	8513	8585	8658	8730	8802	73
01	8874	8947	9019	9091	9163	9236	9308	9380	9452	9524	73
02	77 9596	9669	9741	9813	9885	9957	*0029	*0101	*0173	*0245	73
03	78 0317	0389	0461	0533	0605	0677	0749	0821	0893	0965	72
04	1037	1109	1181	1253	1324	1396	1468	1540	1612	1684	72
05	1755	1827	1899	1971	2042	2114	2186	2258	2329	2401	72
06	2473	2544	2616	2688	2759	2831	2902	2974	3046	3117	72
07	3189	3260	3332	3403	3475	3546	3618	3689	3761	3832	72
08	3904	3975	4046	4118	4189	4261	4332	4403	4475	4546	72
09	4617	4689	4760	4831	4902	4974	5045	5116	5187	5259	72
610	5330	5401	5472	5543	5615	5686	5757	5828	5899	5970	72
11	6041	6112	6183	6254	6325	6396	6467	6538	6609	6680	71
12	6751	6822	6893	6964	7035	7106	7177	7248	7319	7390	71
13	7460	7531	7602	7673	7744	7815	7885	7956	8027	8098	71
14	8168	8239	8310	8381	8451	8522	8593	8663	8734	8804	71
15	8875	8946	9016	9087	9157	9228	9299	9369	9440	9510	71
16	78 9581	9651	9722	9792	9863	9933	*0004	*0074	*0144	*0215	71
17	79 0285	0356	0426	0496	0567	0637	0707	0778	0848	0918	71
18	0988	1059	1129	1199	1269	1340	1410	1480	1550	1620	71
19	1691	1761	1831	1901	1971	2041	2111	2181	2252	2322	71
620	2392	2462	2532	2602	2672	2742	2812	2882	2952	3022	70
21	3092	3162	3231	3301	3371	3441	3511	3581	3651	3721	70
22	3790	3860	3930	4000	4070	4139	4209	4279	4349	4418	70
23	4488	4558	4627	4697	4767	4836	4906	4976	5045	5115	70
24	5185	5254	5324	5393	5463	5532	5602	5672	5741	5811	70
25	5880	5949	6019	6088	6158	6227	6297	6366	6436	6505	70
26	6574	6644	6713	6782	6852	6921	6990	7060	7129	7198	70
27	7268	7337	7406	7475	7545	7614	7683	7752	7821	7890	70
28	7960	8029	8098	8167	8236	8305	8374	8443	8513	8582	70
29	8651	8720	8789	8858	8927	8996	9065	9134	9203	9272	69
630	79 9341	9409	9478	9547	9616	9685	9754	9823	9892	9961	69
31	80 0029	0098	0167	0236	0305	0373	0442	0511	0580	0648	69
32	0717	0786	0854	0923	0992	1061	1129	1198	1266	1335	69
33	1404	1472	1541	1609	1678	1747	1815	1884	1952	2021	69
34	2089	2158	2226	2295	2363	2432	2500	2568	2637	2705	69
35	2774	2842	2910	2979	3047	3116	3184	3252	3321	3389	69
36	3457	3525	3594	3662	3730	3798	3867	3935	4003	4071	69
37	4139	4208	4276	4344	4412	4480	4548	4616	4685	4753	69
38	4821	4889	4957	5025	5093	5161	5229	5297	5365	5433	68
39	5501	5569	5637	5705	5773	5841	5908	5976	6044	6112	68
640	6180	6248	6316	6384	6451	6519	6587	6655	6723	6790	68
41	6858	6926	6994	7061	7129	7197	7264	7332	7400	7467	68
42	7535	7603	7670	7738	7806	7873	7941	8008	8076	8143	68
43	8211	8279	8346	8414	8481	8549	8616	8684	8751	8818	68
44	8886	8953	9021	9088	9156	9223	9290	9358	9425	9492	68
45	80 9560	9627	9694	9762	9829	9896	9964	*0031	*0098	*0165	68
46	81 0233	0300	0367	0434	0501	0569	0636	0703	0770	0837	68
47	0904	0971	1039	1106	1173	1240	1307	1374	1441	1508	68
48	1575	1642	1709	1776	1843	1910	1977	2044	2111	2178	67
49	2245	2312	2379	2445	2512	2579	2646	2713	2780	2847	67
N	0	1	2	3	4	5	6	7	8	9	D

LOGARITHMS OF NUMBERS 6,500–6,999
Six-Place Mantissas

N	0	1	2	3	4	5	6	7	8	9	D
650	81 2913	2980	3047	3114	3181	3247	3314	3381	3448	3514	67
51	3581	3648	3714	3781	3848	3914	3981	4048	4114	4181	67
52	4248	4314	4381	4447	4514	4581	4647	4714	4780	4847	67
53	4913	4980	5046	5113	5179	5246	5312	5378	5445	5511	67
54	5578	5644	5711	5777	5843	5910	5976	6042	6109	6175	67
55	6241	6308	6374	6440	6506	6573	6639	6705	6771	6838	67
56	6904	6970	7036	7102	7169	7235	7301	7367	7433	7499	67
57	7565	7631	7698	7764	7830	7896	7962	8028	8094	8160	67
58	8226	8292	8358	8424	8490	8556	8622	8688	8754	8820	66
59	8885	8951	9017	9083	9149	9215	9281	9346	9412	9478	66
660	81 9544	9610	9676	9741	9807	9873	9939	*0004	*0070	*0136	66
61	82 0201	0267	0333	0399	0464	0530	0595	0661	0727	0792	66
62	0858	0924	0989	1055	1120	1186	1251	1317	1382	1448	66
63	1514	1579	1645	1710	1775	1841	1906	1972	2037	2103	66
64	2168	2233	2299	2364	2430	2495	2560	2626	2691	2756	66
65	2822	2887	2952	3018	3083	3148	3213	3279	3344	3409	66
66	3474	3539	3605	3670	3735	3800	3865	3930	3996	4061	66
67	4126	4191	4256	4321	4386	4451	4516	4581	4646	4711	65
68	4776	4841	4906	4971	5036	5101	5166	5231	5296	5361	65
69	5426	5491	5556	5621	5686	5751	5815	5880	5945	6010	65
670	6075	6140	6204	6269	6334	6399	6464	6528	6593	6658	65
71	6723	6787	6852	6917	6981	7046	7111	7175	7240	7305	65
72	7369	7434	7499	7563	7628	7692	7757	7821	7886	7951	65
73	8015	8080	8144	8209	8273	8338	8402	8467	8531	8595	65
74	8660	8724	8789	8853	8918	8982	9046	9111	9175	9239	65
75	9304	9368	9432	9497	9561	9625	9690	9754	9818	9882	65
76	82 9947	*0011	*0075	*0139	*0204	*0268	*0332	*0396	*0460	*0525	65
77	83 0589	0653	0717	0781	0845	0909	0973	1037	1102	1166	65
78	1230	1294	1358	1422	1486	1550	1614	1678	1742	1806	64
79	1870	1934	1998	2062	2126	2189	2253	2317	2381	2445	64
680	2509	2573	2637	2700	2764	2828	2892	2956	3020	3083	64
81	3147	3211	3275	3338	3402	3466	3530	3593	3657	3721	64
82	3784	3848	3912	3975	4039	4103	4166	4230	4294	4357	64
83	4421	4484	4548	4611	4675	4739	4802	4866	4929	4993	64
84	5056	5120	5183	5247	5310	5373	5437	5500	5564	5627	64
85	5691	5754	5817	5881	5944	6007	6071	6134	6197	6261	64
86	6324	6387	6451	6514	6577	6641	6704	6767	6830	6894	64
87	6957	7020	7083	7146	7210	7273	7336	7399	7462	7525	64
88	7588	7652	7715	7778	7841	7904	7967	8030	8093	8156	64
89	8219	8282	8345	8408	8471	8534	8597	8660	8723	8786	63
690	8849	8912	8975	9038	9101	9164	9227	9289	9352	9415	63
91	83 9478	9541	9604	9667	9729	9792	9855	9918	9981	*0043	63
92	84 0106	0169	0232	0294	0357	0420	0482	0545	0608	0671	63
93	0733	0796	0859	0921	0984	1046	1109	1172	1234	1297	63
94	1359	1422	1485	1547	1610	1672	1735	1797	1860	1922	63
95	1985	2047	2110	2172	2235	2297	2360	2422	2484	2547	63
96	2609	2672	2734	2796	2859	2921	2983	3046	3108	3170	63
97	3233	3295	3357	3420	3482	3544	3606	3669	3731	3793	63
98	3855	3918	3980	4042	4104	4166	4229	4291	4353	4415	63
99	4477	4539	4601	4664	4726	4788	4850	4912	4974	5036	63
N	0	1	2	3	4	5	6	7	8	9	D

LOGARITHMS OF NUMBERS 7,000–7,499
Six-Place Mantissas

N	0	1	2	3	4	5	6	7	8	9	D
700	84 5098	5160	5222	5284	5346	5408	5470	5532	5594	5656	62
01	5718	5780	5842	5904	5966	6028	6090	6151	6213	6275	62
02	6337	6399	6461	6523	6585	6646	6708	6770	6832	6894	62
03	6955	7017	7079	7141	7202	7264	7326	7388	7449	7511	62
04	7573	7634	7696	7758	7819	7881	7943	8004	8066	8128	62
05	8189	8251	8312	8374	8435	8497	8559	8620	8682	8743	62
06	8805	8866	8928	8989	9051	9112	9174	9235	9297	9358	62
07	84 9419	9481	9542	9604	9665	9726	9788	9849	9911	9972	62
08	85 0033	0095	0156	0217	0279	0340	0401	0462	0524	0585	62
09	0646	0707	0769	0830	0891	0952	1014	1075	1136	1197	62
710	1258	1320	1381	1442	1503	1564	1625	1686	1747	1809	62
11	1870	1931	1992	2053	2114	2175	2236	2297	2358	2419	61
12	2480	2541	2602	2663	2724	2785	2846	2907	2968	3029	61
13	3090	3150	3211	3272	3333	3394	3455	3516	3577	3637	61
14	3698	3759	3820	3881	3941	4002	4063	4124	4185	4245	61
15	4306	4367	4428	4488	4549	4610	4670	4731	4792	4852	61
16	4913	4974	5034	5095	5156	5216	5277	5337	5398	5459	61
17	5519	5580	5640	5701	5761	5822	5882	5943	6003	6064	61
18	6124	6185	6245	6306	6366	6427	6487	6548	6608	6668	61
19	6729	6789	6850	6910	6970	7031	7091	7152	7212	7272	61
720	7332	7393	7453	7513	7574	7634	7694	7755	7815	7875	61
21	7935	7995	8056	8116	8176	8236	8297	8357	8417	8477	61
22	8537	8597	8657	8718	8778	8838	8898	8958	9018	9078	61
23	9138	9198	9258	9318	9379	9439	9499	9559	9619	9679	61
24	85 9739	9799	9859	9918	9978	*0038	*0098	*0158	*0218	*0278	60
25	86 0338	0398	0458	0518	0578	0637	0697	0757	0817	0877	60
26	0937	0996	1056	1116	1176	1236	1295	1355	1415	1475	60
27	1534	1594	1654	1714	1773	1833	1893	1952	2012	2072	60
28	2131	2191	2251	2310	2370	2430	2489	2549	2608	2668	60
29	2728	2787	2847	2906	2966	3025	3085	3144	3204	3263	60
730	3323	3382	3442	3501	3561	3620	3680	3739	3799	3858	60
31	3917	3977	4036	4096	4155	4214	4274	4333	4392	4452	60
32	4511	4570	4630	4689	4748	4808	4867	4926	4985	5045	60
33	5104	5163	5222	5282	5341	5400	5459	5519	5578	5637	60
34	5696	5755	5814	5874	5933	5992	6051	6110	6169	6228	60
35	6287	6346	6405	6465	6524	6583	6642	6701	6760	6819	60
36	6878	6937	6996	7055	7114	7173	7232	7291	7350	7409	59
37	7467	7526	7585	7644	7703	7762	7821	7880	7939	7998	59
38	8056	8115	8174	8233	8292	8350	8409	8468	8527	8586	59
39	8644	8703	8762	8821	8879	8938	8997	9056	9114	9173	59
740	9232	9290	9349	9408	9466	9525	9584	9642	9701	9760	59
41	86 9818	9877	9935	9994	*0053	*0111	*0170	*0228	*0287	*0345	59
42	87 0404	0462	0521	0579	0638	0696	0755	0813	0872	0930	59
43	0989	1047	1106	1164	1223	1281	1339	1398	1456	1515	59
44	1573	1631	1690	1748	1806	1865	1923	1981	2040	2098	59
45	2156	2215	2273	2331	2389	2448	2506	2564	2622	2681	59
46	2739	2797	2855	2913	2972	3030	3088	3146	3204	3262	59
47	3321	3379	3437	3495	3553	3611	3669	3727	3785	3844	59
48	3902	3960	4018	4076	4134	4192	4250	4308	4366	4424	58
49	4482	4540	4598	4656	4714	4772	4830	4888	4945	5003	58
N	0	1	2	3	4	5	6	7	8	9	D

LOGARITHMS OF NUMBERS 7,500–7,999
Six-Place Mantissas

N	0	1	2	3	4	5	6	7	8	9	D
750	87 5061	5119	5177	5235	5293	5351	5409	5466	5524	5582	58
51	5640	5698	5756	5813	5871	5929	5987	6045	6102	6160	58
52	6218	6276	6333	6391	6449	6507	6564	6622	6680	6737	58
53	6795	6853	6910	6968	7026	7083	7141	7199	7256	7314	58
54	7371	7429	7487	7544	7602	7659	7717	7774	7832	7889	58
55	7947	8004	8062	8119	8177	8234	8292	8349	8407	8464	58
56	8522	8579	8637	8694	8752	8809	8866	8924	8981	9039	58
57	9096	9153	9211	9268	9325	9383	9440	9497	9555	9612	58
58	87 9669	9726	9784	9841	9898	9956	*0013	*0070	*0127	*0185	58
59	88 0242	0299	0356	0413	0471	0528	0585	0642	0699	0756	58
760	0814	0871	0928	0985	1042	1099	1156	1213	1271	1328	58
61	1385	1442	1499	1556	1613	1670	1727	1784	1841	1898	57
62	1955	2012	2069	2126	2183	2240	2297	2354	2411	2468	57
63	2525	2581	2638	2695	2752	2809	2866	2923	2980	3037	57
64	3093	3150	3207	3264	3321	3377	3434	3491	3548	3605	57
65	3661	3718	3775	3832	3888	3945	4002	4059	4115	4172	57
66	4229	4285	4342	4399	4455	4512	4569	4625	4682	4739	57
67	4795	4852	4909	4965	5022	5078	5135	5192	5248	5305	57
68	5361	5418	5474	5531	5587	5644	5700	5757	5813	5870	57
69	5926	5983	6039	6096	6152	6209	6265	6321	6378	6434	57
770	6491	6547	6604	6660	6716	6773	6829	6885	6942	6998	57
71	7054	7111	7167	7223	7280	7336	7392	7449	7505	7561	57
72	7617	7674	7730	7786	7842	7898	7955	8011	8067	8123	57
73	8179	8236	8292	8348	8404	8460	8516	8573	8629	8685	57
74	8741	8797	8853	8909	8965	9021	9077	9134	9190	9246	57
75	9302	9358	9414	9470	9526	9582	9638	9694	9750	9806	56
76	88 9862	9918	9974	*0030	*0086	*0141	*0197	*0253	*0309	*0365	56
77	89 0421	0477	0533	0589	0645	0700	0756	0812	0868	0924	56
78	0980	1035	1091	1147	1203	1259	1314	1370	1426	1482	56
79	1537	1593	1649	1705	1760	1816	1872	1928	1983	2039	56
780	2095	2150	2206	2262	2317	2373	2429	2484	2540	2595	56
81	2651	2707	2762	2818	2873	2929	2985	3040	3096	3151	56
82	3207	3262	3318	3373	3429	3484	3540	3595	3651	3706	56
83	3762	3817	3873	3928	3984	4039	4094	4150	4205	4261	56
84	4316	4371	4427	4482	4538	4593	4648	4704	4759	4814	56
85	4870	4925	4980	5036	5091	5146	5201	5257	5312	5367	56
86	5423	5478	5533	5588	5644	5699	5754	5809	5864	5920	56
87	5975	6030	6085	6140	6195	6251	6306	6361	6416	6471	56
88	6526	6581	6636	6692	6747	6802	6857	6912	6967	7022	56
89	7077	7132	7187	7242	7297	7352	7407	7462	7517	7572	55
790	7627	7682	7737	7792	7847	7902	7957	8012	8067	8122	55
91	8176	8231	8286	8341	8396	8451	8506	8561	8615	8670	55
92	8725	8780	8835	8890	8944	8999	9054	9109	9164	9218	55
93	9273	9328	9383	9437	9492	9547	9602	9656	9711	9766	55
94	89 9821	9875	9930	9985	*0039	*0094	*0149	*0203	*0258	*0312	55
95	90 0367	0422	0476	0531	0586	0640	0695	0749	0804	0859	55
96	0913	0968	1022	1077	1131	1186	1240	1295	1349	1404	55
97	1458	1513	1567	1622	1676	1731	1785	1840	1894	1948	55
98	2003	2057	2112	2166	2221	2275	2329	2384	2438	2492	55
99	2547	2601	2655	2710	2764	2818	2873	2927	2981	3036	55
N	0	1	2	3	4	5	6	7	8	9	D

LOGARITHMS OF NUMBERS 8,000–8,499
Six-Place Mantissas

N	0	1	2	3	4	5	6	7	8	9	D
800	90 3090	3144	3199	3253	3307	3361	3416	3470	3524	3578	55
01	3633	3687	3741	3795	3849	3904	3958	4012	4066	4120	55
02	4174	4229	4283	4337	4391	4445	4499	4553	4607	4661	55
03	4716	4770	4824	4878	4932	4986	5040	5094	5148	5202	54
04	5256	5310	5364	5418	5472	5526	5580	5634	5688	5742	54
05	5796	5850	5904	5958	6012	6066	6119	6173	6227	6281	54
06	6335	6389	6443	6497	6551	6604	6658	6712	6766	6820	54
07	6874	6927	6981	7035	7089	7143	7196	7250	7304	7358	54
08	7411	7465	7519	7573	7626	7680	7734	7787	7841	7895	54
09	7949	8002	8056	8110	8163	8217	8270	8324	8378	8431	54
810	8485	8539	8592	8646	8699	8753	8807	8860	8914	8967	54
11	9021	9074	9128	9181	9235	9289	9342	9396	9449	9503	54
12	90 9556	9610	9663	9716	9770	9823	9877	9930	9984	*0037	54
13	91 0091	0144	0197	0251	0304	0358	0411	0464	0518	0571	54
14	0624	0678	0731	0784	0838	0891	0944	0998	1051	1104	54
15	1158	1211	1264	1317	1371	1424	1477	1530	1584	1637	54
16	1690	1743	1797	1850	1903	1956	2009	2063	2116	2169	54
17	2222	2275	2328	2381	2435	2488	2541	2594	2647	2700	54
18	2753	2806	2859	2913	2966	3019	3072	3125	3178	3231	54
19	3284	3337	3390	3443	3496	3549	3602	3655	3708	3761	53
820	3814	3867	3920	3973	4026	4079	4132	4184	4237	4290	53
21	4343	4396	4449	4502	4555	4608	4660	4713	4766	4819	53
22	4872	4925	4977	5030	5083	5136	5189	5241	5294	5347	53
23	5400	5453	5505	5558	5611	5664	5716	5769	5822	5875	53
24	5927	5980	6033	6085	6138	6191	6243	6296	6349	6401	53
25	6454	6507	6559	6612	6664	6717	6770	6822	6875	6927	53
26	6980	7033	7085	7138	7190	7243	7295	7348	7400	7453	53
27	7506	7558	7611	7663	7716	7768	7820	7873	7925	7978	53
28	8030	8083	8135	8188	8240	8293	8345	8397	8450	8502	53
29	8555	8607	8659	8712	8764	8816	8869	8921	8973	9026	53
830	9078	9130	9183	9235	9287	9340	9392	9444	9496	9549	53
31	91 9601	9653	9706	9758	9810	9862	9914	9967	*0019	*0071	53
32	92 0123	0176	0228	0280	0332	0384	0436	0489	0541	0593	53
33	0645	0697	0749	0801	0853	0906	0958	1010	1062	1114	53
34	1166	1218	1270	1322	1374	1426	1478	1530	1582	1634	52
35	1686	1738	1790	1842	1894	1946	1998	2050	2102	2154	52
36	2206	2258	2310	2362	2414	2466	2518	2570	2622	2674	52
37	2725	2777	2829	2881	2933	2985	3037	3089	3140	3192	52
38	3244	3296	3348	3399	3451	3503	3555	3607	3658	3710	52
39	3762	3814	3865	3917	3969	4021	4072	4124	4176	4228	52
840	4279	4331	4383	4434	4486	4538	4589	4641	4693	4744	52
41	4796	4848	4899	4951	5003	5054	5106	5157	5209	5261	52
42	5312	5364	5415	5467	5518	5570	5621	5673	5725	5776	52
43	5828	5879	5931	5982	6034	6085	6137	6188	6240	6291	52
44	6342	6394	6445	6497	6548	6600	6651	6702	6754	6805	52
45	6857	6908	6959	7011	7062	7114	7165	7216	7268	7319	52
46	7370	7422	7473	7524	7576	7627	7678	7730	7781	7832	52
47	7883	7935	7986	8037	8088	8140	8191	8242	8293	8345	52
48	8396	8447	8498	8549	8601	8652	8703	8754	8805	8857	52
49	8908	8959	9010	9061	9112	9163	9215	9266	9317	9368	52
N	0	1	2	3	4	5	6	7	8	9	D

LOGARITHMS OF NUMBERS 8,500–8,999
Six-Place Mantissas

N	0	1	2	3	4	5	6	7	8	9	D
850	92 9419	9470	9521	9572	9623	9674	9725	9776	9827	9879	52
51	92 9930	9981	*0032	*0083	*0134	*0185	*0236	*0287	*0338	*0389	51
52	93 0440	0491	0542	0592	0643	0694	0745	0796	0847	0898	51
53	0949	1000	1051	1102	1153	1204	1254	1305	1356	1407	51
54	1458	1509	1560	1610	1661	1712	1763	1814	1865	1915	51
55	1966	2017	2068	2118	2169	2220	2271	2322	2372	2423	51
56	2474	2524	2575	2626	2677	2727	2778	2829	2879	2930	51
57	2981	3031	3082	3133	3183	3234	3285	3335	3386	3437	51
58	3487	3538	3589	3639	3690	3740	3791	3841	3892	3943	51
59	3993	4044	4094	4145	4195	4246	4296	4347	4397	4448	51
860	4498	4549	4599	4650	4700	4751	4801	4852	4902	4953	51
61	5003	5054	5104	5154	5205	5255	5306	5356	5406	5457	51
62	5507	5558	5608	5658	5709	5759	5809	5860	5910	5960	51
63	6011	6061	6111	6162	6212	6262	6313	6363	6413	6463	51
64	6514	6564	6614	6665	6715	6765	6815	6865	6916	6966	51
65	7016	7066	7117	7167	7217	7267	7317	7367	7418	7468	51
66	7518	7568	7618	7668	7718	7769	7819	7869	7919	7969	51
67	8019	8069	8119	8169	8219	8269	8320	8370	8420	8470	51
68	8520	8570	8620	8670	8720	8770	8820	8870	8920	8970	50
69	9020	9070	9120	9170	9220	9270	9320	9369	9419	9469	50
870	93 9519	9569	9619	9669	9719	9769	9819	9869	9918	9968	50
71	94 0018	0068	0118	0168	0218	0267	0317	0367	0417	0467	50
72	0516	0566	0616	0666	0716	0765	0815	0865	0915	0964	50
73	1014	1064	1114	1163	1213	1263	1313	1362	1412	1462	50
74	1511	1561	1611	1660	1710	1760	1809	1859	1909	1958	50
75	2008	2058	2107	2157	2207	2256	2306	2355	2405	2455	50
76	2504	2554	2603	2653	2702	2752	2801	2851	2901	2950	50
77	3000	3049	3099	3148	3198	3247	3297	3346	3396	3445	50
78	3495	3544	3593	3643	3692	3742	3791	3841	3890	3939	50
79	3989	4038	4088	4137	4186	4236	4285	4335	4384	4433	50
880	4483	4532	4581	4631	4680	4729	4779	4828	4877	4927	50
81	4976	5025	5074	5124	5173	5222	5272	5321	5370	5419	50
82	5469	5518	5567	5616	5665	5715	5764	5813	5862	5912	50
83	5961	6010	6059	6108	6157	6207	6256	6305	6354	6403	50
84	6452	6501	6551	6600	6649	6698	6747	6796	6845	6894	50
85	6943	6992	7041	7090	7140	7189	7238	7287	7336	7385	50
86	7434	7483	7532	7581	7630	7679	7728	7777	7826	7875	49
87	7924	7973	8022	8070	8119	8168	8217	8266	8315	8364	49
88	8413	8462	8511	8560	8609	8657	8706	8755	8804	8853	49
89	8902	8951	8999	9048	9097	9146	9195	9244	9292	9341	49
890	9390	9439	9488	9536	9585	9634	9683	9731	9780	9829	49
91	94 9878	9926	9975	*0024	*0073	*0121	*0170	*0219	*0267	*0316	49
92	95 0365	0414	0462	0511	0560	0608	0657	0706	0754	0803	49
93	0851	0900	0949	0997	1046	1095	1143	1192	1240	1289	49
94	1338	1386	1435	1483	1532	1580	1629	1677	1726	1775	49
95	1823	1872	1920	1969	2017	2066	2114	2163	2211	2260	49
96	2308	2356	2405	2453	2502	2550	2599	2647	2696	2744	49
97	2792	2841	2889	2938	2986	3034	3083	3131	3180	3228	49
98	3276	3325	3373	3421	3470	3518	3566	3615	3663	3711	49
99	3760	3808	3856	3905	3953	4001	4049	4098	4146	4194	49
N	0	1	2	3	4	5	6	7	8	9	D

LOGARITHMS OF NUMBERS 9,000–9,499
Six-Place Mantissas

N	0	1	2	3	4	5	6	7	8	9	D
900	95 4243	4291	4339	4387	4435	4484	4532	4580	4628	4677	49
01	4725	4773	4821	4869	4918	4966	5014	5062	5110	5158	49
02	5207	5255	5303	5351	5399	5447	5495	5543	5592	5640	49
03	5688	5736	5784	5832	5880	5928	5976	6024	6072	6120	48
04	6168	6216	6265	6313	6361	6409	6457	6505	6553	6601	48
05	6649	6697	6745	6793	6840	6888	6936	6984	7032	7080	48
06	7128	7176	7224	7272	7320	7368	7416	7464	7512	7559	48
07	7607	7655	7703	7751	7799	7847	7894	7942	7990	8038	48
08	8086	8134	8181	8229	8277	8325	8373	8421	8468	8516	48
09	8564	8612	8659	8707	8755	8803	8850	8898	8946	8994	48
910	9041	9089	9137	9185	9232	9280	9328	9375	9423	9471	48
11	9518	9566	9614	9661	9709	9757	9804	9852	9900	9947	48
12	95 9995	*0042	*0090	*0138	*0185	*0233	*0280	*0328	*0376	*0423	48
13	96 0471	0518	0566	0613	0661	0709	0756	0804	0851	0899	48
14	0946	0994	1041	1089	1136	1184	1231	1279	1326	1374	48
15	1421	1469	1516	1563	1611	1658	1706	1753	1801	1848	48
16	1895	1943	1990	2038	2085	2132	2180	2227	2275	2322	48
17	2369	2417	2464	2511	2559	2606	2653	2701	2748	2795	48
18	2843	2890	2937	2985	3032	3079	3126	3174	3221	3268	48
19	3316	3363	3410	3457	3504	3552	3599	3646	3693	3741	48
920	3788	3835	3882	3929	3977	4024	4071	4118	4165	4212	48
21	4260	4307	4354	4401	4448	4495	4542	4590	4637	4684	48
22	4731	4778	4825	4872	4919	4966	5013	5061	5108	5155	48
23	5202	5249	5296	5343	5390	5437	5484	5531	5578	5625	47
24	5672	5719	5766	5813	5860	5907	5954	6001	6048	6095	47
25	6142	6189	6236	6283	6329	6376	6423	6470	6517	6564	47
26	6611	6658	6705	6752	6799	6845	6892	6939	6986	7033	47
27	7080	7127	7173	7220	7267	7314	7361	7408	7454	7501	47
28	7548	7595	7642	7688	7735	7782	7829	7875	7922	7969	47
29	8016	8062	8109	8156	8203	8249	8296	8343	8390	8436	47
930	8483	8530	8576	8623	8670	8716	8763	8810	8856	8903	47
31	8950	8996	9043	9090	9136	9183	9229	9276	9323	9369	47
32	9416	9463	9509	9556	9602	9649	9695	9742	9789	9835	47
33	96 9882	9928	9975	*0021	*0068	*0114	*0161	*0207	*0254	*0300	47
34	97 0347	0393	0440	0486	0533	0579	0626	0672	0719	0765	47
35	0812	0858	0904	0951	0997	1044	1090	1137	1183	1229	47
36	1276	1322	1369	1415	1461	1508	1554	1601	1647	1693	47
37	1740	1786	1832	1879	1925	1971	2018	2064	2110	2157	47
38	2203	2249	2295	2342	2388	2434	2481	2527	2573	2619	47
39	2666	2712	2758	2804	2851	2897	2943	2989	3035	3082	47
940	3128	3174	3220	3266	3313	3359	3405	3451	3497	3543	47
41	3590	3636	3682	3728	3774	3820	3866	3913	3959	4005	47
42	4051	4097	4143	4189	4235	4281	4327	4374	4420	4466	47
43	4512	4558	4604	4650	4696	4742	4788	4834	4880	4926	46
44	4972	5018	5064	5110	5156	5202	5248	5294	5340	5386	46
45	5432	5478	5524	5570	5616	5662	5707	5753	5799	5845	46
46	5891	5937	5983	6029	6075	6121	6167	6212	6258	6304	46
47	6350	6396	6442	6488	6533	6579	6625	6671	6717	6763	46
48	6808	6854	6900	6946	6992	7037	7083	7129	7175	7220	46
49	7266	7312	7358	7403	7449	7495	7541	7586	7632	7678	46
N	0	1	2	3	4	5	6	7	8	9	D

LOGARITHMS OF NUMBERS 9,500–9,999
Six-Place Mantissas

N	0	1	2	3	4	5	6	7	8	9	D
950	97 7724	7769	7815	7861	7906	7952	7998	8043	8089	8135	46
51	8181	8226	8272	8317	8363	8409	8454	8500	8546	8591	46
52	8637	8683	8728	8774	8819	8865	8911	8956	9002	9047	46
53	9093	9138	9184	9230	9275	9321	9366	9412	9457	9503	46
54	97 9548	9594	9639	9685	9730	9776	9821	9867	9912	9958	46
55	98 0003	0049	0094	0140	0185	0231	0276	0322	0367	0412	46
56	0458	0503	0549	0594	0640	0685	0730	0776	0821	0867	46
57	0912	0957	1003	1048	1093	1139	1184	1229	1275	1320	46
58	1366	1411	1456	1501	1547	1592	1637	1683	1728	1773	46
59	1819	1864	1909	1954	2000	2045	2090	2135	2181	2226	46
960	2271	2316	2362	2407	2452	2497	2543	2588	2633	2678	46
61	2723	2769	2814	2859	2904	2949	2994	3040	3085	3130	46
62	3175	3220	3265	3310	3356	3401	3446	3491	3536	3581	46
63	3626	3671	3716	3762	3807	3852	3897	3942	3987	4032	46
64	4077	4122	4167	4212	4257	4302	4347	4392	4437	4482	45
65	4527	4572	4617	4662	4707	4752	4797	4842	4887	4932	45
66	4977	5022	5067	5112	5157	5202	5247	5292	5337	5382	45
67	5426	5471	5516	5561	5606	5651	5696	5741	5786	5830	45
68	5875	5920	5965	6010	6055	6100	6144	6189	6234	6279	45
69	6324	6369	6413	6458	6503	6548	6593	6637	6682	6727	45
970	6772	6817	6861	6906	6951	6996	7040	7085	7130	7175	45
71	7219	7264	7309	7353	7398	7443	7488	7532	7577	7622	45
72	7666	7711	7756	7800	7845	7890	7934	7979	8024	8068	45
73	8113	8157	8202	8247	8291	8336	8381	8425	8470	8514	45
74	8559	8604	8648	8693	8737	8782	8826	8871	8916	8960	45
75	9005	9049	9094	9138	9183	9227	9272	9316	9361	9405	45
76	9450	9494	9539	9583	9628	9672	9717	9761	9806	9850	45
77	98 9895	9939	9983	*0028	*0072	*0117	*0161	*0206	*0250	*0294	45
78	99 0339	0383	0428	0472	0516	0561	0605	0650	0694	0738	45
79	0783	0827	0871	0916	0960	1004	1049	1093	1137	1182	45
980	1226	1270	1315	1359	1403	1448	1492	1536	1580	1625	45
81	1669	1713	1758	1802	1846	1890	1935	1979	2023	2067	45
82	2111	2156	2200	2244	2288	2333	2377	2421	2465	2509	45
83	2554	2598	2642	2686	2730	2774	2819	2863	2907	2951	45
84	2995	3039	3083	3127	3172	3216	3260	3304	3348	3392	45
85	3436	3480	3524	3568	3613	3657	3701	3745	3789	3833	45
86	3877	3921	3965	4009	4053	4097	4141	4185	4229	4273	44
87	4317	4361	4405	4449	4493	4537	4581	4625	4669	4713	44
88	4757	4801	4845	4889	4933	4977	5021	5065	5108	5152	44
89	5196	5240	5284	5328	5372	5416	5460	5504	5547	5591	44
990	5635	5679	5723	5767	5811	5854	5898	5942	5986	6030	44
91	6074	6117	6161	6205	6249	6293	6337	6380	6424	6468	44
92	6512	6555	6599	6643	6687	6731	6774	6818	6862	6906	44
93	6949	6993	7037	7080	7124	7168	7212	7255	7299	7343	44
94	7386	7430	7474	7517	7561	7605	7648	7692	7736	7779	44
95	7823	7867	7910	7954	7998	8041	8085	8129	8172	8216	44
96	8259	8303	8347	8390	8434	8477	8521	8564	8608	8652	44
97	8695	8739	8782	8826	8869	8913	8956	9000	9043	9087	44
98	9131	9174	9218	9261	9305	9348	9392	9435	9479	9522	44
99	99 9565	9609	9652	9696	9739	9783	9826	9870	9913	9957	44
N	0	1	2	3	4	5	6	7	8	9	D

Table C >> 77

BINOMIAL PROBABILITY DISTRIBUTION

$$P(r \mid n, p) = \binom{n}{r} p^r q^{n-r}$$

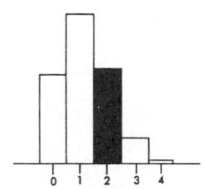

$$P(r = 2 \mid n = 4, p = 0.3) = 0.2646$$

n = 1

r \ p	.01	.02	.03	.04	.05	.06	.07	.08	.09	.10
0	.9900	.9800	.9700	.9600	.9500	.9400	.9300	.9200	.9100	.9000
1	.0100	.0200	.0300	.0400	.0500	.0600	.0700	.0800	.0900	.1000
	.11	.12	.13	.14	.15	.16	.17	.18	.19	.20
0	.8900	.8800	.8700	.8600	.8500	.8400	.8300	.8200	.8100	.8000
1	.1100	.1200	.1300	.1400	.1500	.1600	.1700	.1800	.1900	.2000
	.21	.22	.23	.24	.25	.26	.27	.28	.29	.30
0	.7900	.7800	.7700	.7600	.7500	.7400	7300	.7200	.7100	.7000
1	.2100	.2200	.2300	.2400	.2500	.2600	.2700	.2800	.2900	.3000
	.31	.32	.33	.34	.35	.36	.37	.38	.39	.40
0	.6900	.6800	.6700	.6600	.6500	.6400	.6300	.6200	.6100	.6000
1	.3100	.3200	.3300	.3400	.3500	.3600	.3700	.3800	.3900	.4000
	.41	.42	.43	.44	.45	.46	.47	.48	.49	.50
0	.5900	.5800	.5700	.5600	.5500	.5400	.5300	.5200	.5100	.5000
1	.4100	.4200	.4300	.4400	.4500	.4600	.4700	.4800	.4900	.5000

n = 2

r \ p	.01	.02	.03	.04	.05	.06	.07	.08	.09	.10
0	.9801	.9604	.9409	.9216	.9025	.8836	.8649	.8464	.8281	.8100
1	.0198	.0392	.0582	.0768	.0950	.1128	.1302	.1472	.1638	.1800
2	.0001	.0004	.0009	.0016	.0025	.0036	.0049	.0064	.0081	.0100
	.11	.12	.13	.14	.15	.16	.17	.18	.19	.20
0	.7921	.7744	.7569	.7396	.7225	.7056	.6889	.6724	.6561	.6400
1	.1958	.2112	.2262	.2408	.2550	.2688	.2822	.2952	.3078	.3200
2	.0121	.0144	.0169	.0196	.0225	.0256	.0289	.0324	.0361	.0400
	.21	.22	.23	.24	.25	.26	.27	.28	.29	.30
0	.6241	.6084	.5929	.5776	.5625	.5476	.5329	.5184	.5041	.4900
1	.3318	.3432	.3542	.3648	.3750	.3848	.3942	.4032	.4118	.4200
2	.0441	.0484	.0529	.0576	.0625	.0676	.0729	.0784	.0841	.0900
	.31	.32	.33	.34	.35	.36	.37	.38	.39	.40
0	.4761	.4624	.4489	.4356	.4225	.4096	.3969	.3844	.3721	.3600
1	.4278	.4352	.4422	.4488	.4550	.4608	.4662	.4712	.4758	.4800
2	.0961	.1024	.1089	.1156	.1225	.1296	.1369	.1444	.1521	.1600
	.41	.42	.43	.44	.45	.46	.47	.48	.49	.50
0	.3481	.3364	.3249	.3136	.3025	.2916	.2809	.2704	.2601	.2500
1	.4838	.4872	.4902	.4928	.4950	.4968	.4982	.4992	.4998	.5000
2	.1681	.1764	.1849	.1936	.2025	.2116	.2209	.2304	.2401	.2500

n = 3

p r	.01	.02	.03	.04	.05	.06	.07	.08	.09	.10
0	.9704	.9412	.9127	.8847	.8574	.8306	.8044	.7787	.7536	.7290
1	.0294	.0576	.0847	.1106	.1354	.1590	.1816	.2031	.2236	.2430
2	.0003	.0012	.0026	.0046	.0071	.0102	.0137	.0177	.0221	.0270
3	.0000	.0000	.0000	.0001	.0001	.0002	.0003	.0005	.0007	.0010

	.11	.12	.13	.14	.15	.16	.17	.18	.19	.20
0	.7050	.6815	.6585	.6361	.6141	.5927	.5718	.5514	.5314	.5120
1	.2614	.2788	.2952	.3106	.3251	.3387	.3513	.3631	.3740	.3840
2	.0323	.0380	.0441	.0506	.0574	.0645	.0720	.0797	.0877	.0960
3	.0013	.0017	.0022	.0027	.0034	.0041	.0049	.0058	.0069	.0080

	.21	.22	.23	.24	.25	.26	.27	.28	.29	.30
0	.4930	.4746	.4565	.4390	.4219	.4052	.3890	.3732	.3579	.3430
1	.3932	.4015	.4091	.4159	.4219	.4271	.4316	.4355	.4386	.4410
2	.1045	.1133	.1222	.1313	.1406	.1501	.1597	.1693	.1791	.1890
3	.0093	.0106	.0122	.0138	.0156	.0176	.0197	.0220	.0244	.0270

	.31	.32	.33	.34	.35	.36	.37	.38	.39	.40
0	.3285	.3144	.3008	.2875	.2746	.2621	.2500	.2383	.2270	.2160
1	.4428	.4439	.4444	.4443	.4436	.4424	.4406	.4382	.4354	.4320
2	.1989	.2089	.2189	.2289	.2389	.2488	.2587	.2686	.2783	.2880
3	.0298	.0328	.0359	.0393	.0429	.0467	.0507	.0549	.0593	.0640

	.41	.42	.43	.44	.45	.46	.47	.48	.49	.50
0	.2054	.1951	.1852	.1756	.1664	.1575	.1489	.1406	.1327	.1250
1	.4282	.4239	.4191	.4140	.4084	.4024	.3961	.3894	.3823	.3750
2	.2975	.3069	.3162	.3252	.3341	.3428	.3512	.3594	.3674	.3750
3	.0689	.0741	.0795	.0852	.0911	.0973	.1038	.1106	.1176	.1250

n = 4

p r	.01	.02	.03	.04	.05	.06	.07	.08	.09	.10
0	.9606	.9224	.8853	.8493	.8145	.7807	.7481	.7164	.6857	.6561
1	.0388	.0753	.1095	.1416	.1715	.1993	.2252	.2492	.2713	.2916
2	.0006	.0023	.0051	.0088	.0135	.0191	.0254	.0325	.0402	.0486
3	.0000	.0000	.0001	.0002	.0005	.0008	.0013	.0019	.0027	.0036
4	.0000	.0000	.0000	.0000	.0000	.0000	.0000	.0000	.0001	.0001

	.11	.12	.13	.14	.15	.16	.17	.18	.19	.20
0	.6274	.5997	.5729	.5470	.5220	.4979	.4746	.4521	.4305	.4096
1	.3102	.3271	.3424	.3562	.3685	.3793	.3888	.3970	.4039	.4096
2	.0575	.0669	.0767	.0870	.0975	.1084	.1195	.1307	.1421	.1536
3	.0047	.0061	.0076	.0094	.0115	.0138	.0163	.0191	.0222	.0256
4	.0001	.0002	.0003	.0004	.0005	.0007	.0008	.0010	.0013	.0016

	.21	.22	.23	.24	.25	.26	.27	.28	.29	.30
0	.3895	.3702	.3515	.3336	.3164	.2999	.2840	.2687	.2541	.2401
1	.4142	.4176	.4200	.4214	.4219	.4214	.4201	.4180	.4152	.4116
2	.1651	.1767	.1882	.1996	.2109	.2221	.2331	.2439	.2544	.2646
3	.0293	.0332	.0375	.0420	.0469	.0520	.0575	.0632	.0693	.0756
4	.0019	.0023	.0028	.0033	.0039	.0046	.0053	.0061	.0071	.0081

	.31	.32	.33	.34	.35	.36	.37	.38	.39	.40
0	.2267	.2138	.2015	.1897	.1785	.1678	.1575	.1478	.1385	.1296
1	.4074	.4025	.3970	.3910	.3845	.3775	.3701	.3623	.3541	.3456
2	.2745	.2841	.2933	.3021	.3105	.3185	.3260	.3330	.3396	.3456
3	.0822	.0891	.0963	.1038	.1115	.1194	.1276	.1361	.1447	.1536
4	.0092	.0105	.0119	.0134	.0150	.0168	.0187	.0209	.0231	.0256

	.41	.42	.43	.44	.45	.46	.47	.48	.49	.50
0	.1212	.1132	.1056	.0983	.0915	.0850	.0789	.0731	.0677	.0625
1	.3368	.3278	.3185	.3091	.2995	.2897	.2799	.2700	.2600	.2500
2	.3511	.3560	.3604	.3643	.3675	.3702	.3723	.3738	.3747	.3750
3	.1627	.1719	.1813	.1908	.2005	.2102	.2201	.2300	.2400	.2500
4	.0283	.0311	.0342	.0375	.0410	.0448	.0488	.0531	.0576	.0625

Table C >> **79**

n = 5

p r	.01	.02	.03	.04	.05	.06	.07	.08	.09	.10
0	.9510	.9039	.8587	.8154	.7738	.7339	.6957	.6591	.6240	.5905
1	.0480	.0922	.1328	.1699	.2036	.2342	.2618	.2866	.3086	.3280
2	.0010	.0038	.0082	.0142	.0214	.0299	.0394	.0498	.0610	.0729
3	.0000	.0001	.0003	.0006	.0011	.0019	.0030	.0043	.0060	.0081
4	.0000	.0000	.0000	.0000	.0000	.0001	.0001	.0002	.0003	.0004

	.11	.12	.13	.14	.15	.16	.17	.18	.19	.20
0	.5584	.5277	.4984	.4704	.4437	.4182	.3939	.3707	.3487	.3277
1	.3451	.3598	.3724	.3829	.3915	.3983	.4034	.4069	.4089	.4096
2	.0853	.0981	.1113	.1247	.1382	.1517	.1652	.1786	.1919	.2048
3	.0105	.0134	.0166	.0203	.0244	.0289	.0338	.0392	.0450	.0512
4	.0007	.0009	.0012	.0017	.0022	.0028	.0035	.0043	.0053	.0064
5	.0000	.0000	.0000	.0001	.0001	.0001	.0001	.0002	.0002	.0003

	.21	.22	.23	.24	.25	.26	.27	.28	.29	.30
0	.3077	.2887	.2707	.2536	.2373	.2219	.2073	.1935	.1804	.1681
1	.4090	.4072	.4043	.4003	.3955	.3898	.3834	.3762	.3685	.3602
2	.2174	.2297	.2415	.2529	.2637	.2739	.2836	.2926	.3010	.3087
3	.0578	.0648	.0721	.0798	.0879	.0962	.1049	.1138	.1229	.1323
4	.0077	.0091	.0108	.0126	.0146	.0169	.0194	.0221	.0251	.0284
5	.0004	.0005	.0006	.0008	.0010	.0012	.0014	.0017	.0021	.0024

	.31	.32	.33	.34	.35	.36	.37	.38	.39	.40
0	.1564	.1454	.1350	.1252	.1160	.1074	.0992	.0916	.0845	.0778
1	.3513	.3421	.3325	.3226	.3124	.3020	.2914	.2808	.2700	.2592
2	.3157	.3220	.3275	.3323	.3364	.3397	.3423	.3441	.3452	.3456
3	.1418	.1515	.1613	.1712	.1811	.1911	.2010	.2109	.2207	.2304
4	.0319	.0357	.0397	.0441	.0488	.0537	.0590	.0646	.0706	.0768
5	.0029	.0034	.0039	.0045	.0053	.0060	.0069	.0079	.0090	.0102

	.41	.42	.43	.44	.45	.46	.47	.48	.49	.50
0	.0715	.0656	.0602	.0551	.0503	.0459	.0418	.0380	.0345	.0312
1	.2484	.2376	.2270	.2164	.2059	.1956	.1854	.1755	.1657	.1562
2	.3452	.3442	.3424	.3400	.3369	.3332	.3289	.3240	.3185	.3125
3	.2399	.2492	.2583	.2671	.2757	.2838	.2916	.2990	.3060	.3125
4	.0834	.0902	.0974	.1049	.1128	.1209	.1293	.1380	.1470	.1562
5	.0116	.0131	.0147	.0165	.0185	.0206	.0229	.0255	.0282	.0312

n = 6

p r	.01	.02	.03	.04	.05	.06	.07	.08	.09	.10
0	.9415	.8858	.8330	.7828	.7351	.6899	.6470	.6064	.5679	.5314
1	.0571	.1085	.1546	.1957	.2321	.2642	.2922	.3164	.3370	.3543
2	.0014	.0055	.0120	.0204	.0305	.0422	.0550	.0688	.0833	.0984
3	.0000	.0002	.0005	.0011	.0021	.0036	.0055	.0080	.0110	.0146
4	.0000	.0000	.0000	.0000	.0001	.0002	.0003	.0005	.0008	.0012
5	.0000	.0000	.0000	.0000	.0000	.0000	.0000	.0000	.0000	.0001

	.11	.12	.13	.14	.15	.16	.17	.18	.19	.20
0	.4970	.4644	.4336	.4046	.3771	.3513	.3269	.3040	.2824	.2621
1	.3685	.3800	.3888	.3952	.3993	.4015	.4018	.4004	.3975	.3932
2	.1139	.1295	.1452	.1608	.1762	.1912	.2057	.2197	.2331	.2458
3	.0188	.0236	.0289	.0349	.0415	.0486	.0562	.0643	.0729	.0819
4	.0017	.0024	.0032	.0043	.0055	.0069	.0086	.0106	.0128	.0154
5	.0001	.0001	.0002	.0003	.0004	.0005	.0007	.0009	.0012	.0015
6	.0000	.0000	.0000	.0000	.0000	.0000	.0000	.0000	.0000	.0001

	.21	.22	.23	.24	.25	.26	.27	.28	.29	.30
0	.2431	.2252	.2084	.1927	.1780	.1642	.1513	.1393	.1281	.1176
1	.3877	.3811	.3735	.3651	.3560	.3462	.3358	.3251	.3139	.3025
2	.2577	.2687	.2789	.2882	.2966	.3041	.3105	.3160	.3206	.3241
3	.0913	.1011	.1111	.1214	.1318	.1424	.1531	.1639	.1746	.1852
4	.0182	.0214	.0249	.0287	.0330	.0375	.0425	.0478	.0535	.0595
5	.0019	.0024	.0030	.0036	.0044	.0053	.0063	.0074	.0087	.0102
6	.0001	.0001	.0001	.0002	.0002	.0003	.0004	.0005	.0006	.0007

n = 6 (Continued)

r \ p	.31	.32	.33	.34	.35	.36	.37	.38	.39	.40
0	.1079	.0989	.0905	.0827	.0754	.0687	.0625	.0568	.0515	.0467
1	.2909	.2792	.2673	.2555	.2437	.2319	.2203	.2089	.1976	.1866
2	.3267	.3284	.3292	.3290	.3280	.3261	.3235	.3201	.3159	.3110
3	.1957	.2061	.2162	.2260	.2355	.2446	.2533	.2616	.2693	.2765
4	.0660	.0727	.0799	.0873	.0951	.1032	.1116	.1202	.1291	.1382
5	.0119	.0137	.0157	.0180	.0205	.0232	.0262	.0295	.0330	.0369
6	.0009	.0011	.0013	.0015	.0018	.0022	.0026	.0030	.0035	.0041

r \ p	.41	.42	.43	.44	.45	.46	.47	.48	.49	.50
0	.0422	.0381	.0343	.0308	.0277	.0248	.0222	.0198	.0176	.0156
1	.1759	.1654	.1552	.1454	.1359	.1267	.1179	.1095	.1014	.0938
2	.3055	.2994	.2928	.2856	.2780	.2699	.2615	.2527	.2436	.2344
3	.2831	.2891	.2945	.2992	.3032	.3065	.3091	.3110	.3121	.3125
4	.1475	.1570	.1666	.1763	.1861	.1958	.2056	.2153	.2249	.2344
5	.0410	.0455	.0503	.0554	.0609	.0667	.0729	.0795	.0864	.0938
6	.0048	.0055	.0063	.0073	.0083	.0095	.0108	.0122	.0138	.0156

n = 7

r \ p	.01	.02	.03	.04	.05	.06	.07	.08	.09	.10
0	.9321	.8681	.8080	.7514	.6983	.6485	.6017	.5578	.5168	.4783
1	.0659	.1240	.1749	.2192	.2573	.2897	.3170	.3396	.3578	.3720
2	.0020	.0076	.0162	.0274	.0406	.0555	.0716	.0886	.1061	.1240
3	.0000	.0003	.0008	.0019	.0036	.0059	.0090	.0128	.0175	.0230
4	.0000	.0000	.0000	.0001	.0002	.0004	.0007	.0011	.0017	.0026
5	.0000	.0000	.0000	.0000	.0000	.0000	.0000	.0001	.0001	.0002

r \ p	.11	.12	.13	.14	.15	.16	.17	.18	.19	.20
0	.4423	.4087	.3773	.3479	.3206	.2951	.2714	.2493	.2288	.2097
1	.3827	.3901	.3946	.3965	.3960	.3935	.3891	.3830	.3756	.3670
2	.1419	.1596	.1769	.1936	.2097	.2248	.2391	.2523	.2643	.2753
3	.0292	.0363	.0441	.0525	.0617	.0714	.0816	.0923	.1033	.1147
4	.0036	.0049	.0066	.0086	.0109	.0136	.0167	.0203	.0242	.0287
5	.0003	.0004	.0006	.0008	.0012	.0016	.0021	.0027	.0034	.0043
6	.0000	.0000	.0000	.0000	.0001	.0001	.0001	.0002	.0003	.0004

r \ p	.21	.22	.23	.24	.25	.26	.27	.28	.29	.30
0	.1920	.1757	.1605	.1465	.1335	.1215	.1105	.1003	.0910	.0824
1	.3573	.3468	.3356	.3237	.3115	.2989	.2860	.2731	.2600	.2471
2	.2850	.2935	.3007	.3067	.3115	.3150	.3174	.3186	.3186	.3177
3	.1263	.1379	.1497	.1614	.1730	.1845	.1956	.2065	.2169	.2269
4	.0336	.0389	.0447	.0510	.0577	.0648	.0724	.0803	.0886	.0972
5	.0054	.0066	.0080	.0097	.0115	.0137	.0161	.0187	.0217	.0250
6	.0005	.0006	.0008	.0010	.0013	.0016	.0020	.0024	.0030	.0036
7	.0000	.0000	.0000	.0000	.0001	.0001	.0001	.0001	.0002	.0002

r \ p	.31	.32	.33	.34	.35	.36	.37	.38	.39	.40
0	.0745	.0672	.0606	.0546	.0490	.0440	.0394	.0352	.0314	.0280
1	.2342	.2215	.2090	.1967	.1848	.1732	.1619	.1511	.1407	.1306
2	.3156	.3127	.3088	.3040	.2985	.2922	.2853	.2778	.2698	.2613
3	.2363	.2452	.2535	.2610	.2679	.2740	.2793	.2838	.2875	.2903
4	.1062	.1154	.1248	.1345	.1442	.1541	.1640	.1739	.1838	.1935
5	.0286	.0326	.0369	.0416	.0466	.0520	.0578	.0640	.0705	.0774
6	.0043	.0051	.0061	.0071	.0084	.0098	.0113	.0131	.0150	.0172
7	.0003	.0003	.0004	.0005	.0006	.0008	.0009	.0011	.0014	.0016

r \ p	.41	.42	.43	.44	.45	.46	.47	.48	.49	.50
0	.0249	.0221	.0195	.0173	.0152	.0134	.0117	.0103	.0090	.0078
1	.1211	.1119	.1032	.0950	.0872	.0798	.0729	.0664	.0604	.0547
2	.2524	.2431	.2336	.2239	.2140	.2040	.1940	.1840	.1740	.1641
3	.2923	.2934	.2937	.2932	.2918	.2897	.2867	.2830	.2786	.2734
4	.2031	.2125	.2216	.2304	.2388	.2468	.2543	.2612	.2676	.2734
5	.0847	.0923	.1003	.1086	.1172	.1261	.1353	.1447	.1543	.1641
6	.0196	.0223	.0252	.0284	.0320	.0358	.0400	.0445	.0494	.0547
7	.0019	.0023	.0027	.0032	.0037	.0044	.0051	.0059	.0068	.0078

Table C >> **81**

n = 8

r \ p	.01	.02	.03	.04	.05	.06	.07	.08	.09	.10
0	.9227	.8508	.7837	.7214	.6634	.6096	.5596	.5132	.4703	.4305
1	.0746	.1389	.1939	.2405	.2793	.3113	.3370	.3570	.3721	.3826
2	.0026	.0099	.0210	.0351	.0515	.0695	.0888	.1087	.1288	.1488
3	.0001	.0004	.0013	.0029	.0054	.0089	.0134	.0189	.0255	.0331
4	.0000	.0000	.0001	.0002	.0004	.0007	.0013	.0021	.0031	.0046
5	.0000	.0000	.0000	.0000	.0000	.0000	.0001	.0001	.0002	.0004

r \ p	.11	.12	.13	.14	.15	.16	.17	.18	.19	.20
0	.3937	.3596	.3282	.2992	.2725	.2479	.2252	.2044	.1853	.1678
1	.3892	.3923	.3923	.3897	.3847	.3777	.3691	.3590	.3477	.3355
2	.1684	.1872	.2052	.2220	.2376	.2518	.2646	.2758	.2855	.2936
3	.0416	.0511	.0613	.0723	.0839	.0959	.1084	.1211	.1339	.1468
4	.0064	.0087	.0115	.0147	.0185	.0228	.0277	.0332	.0393	.0459
5	.0006	.0009	.0014	.0019	.0026	.0035	.0045	.0058	.0074	.0092
6	.0000	.0001	.0001	.0002	.0002	.0003	.0003	.0005	.0009	.0011
7	.0000	.0000	.0000	.0000	.0000	.0000	.0000	.0000	.0001	.0001

r \ p	.21	.22	.23	.24	.25	.26	.27	.28	.29	.30
0	.1517	.1370	.1236	.1113	.1001	.0899	.0806	.0722	.0646	.0576
1	.3226	.3092	.2953	.2812	.2670	.2527	.2386	.2247	.2110	.1977
2	.3002	.3052	.3087	.3108	.3115	.3108	.3089	.3058	.3017	.2965
3	.1596	.1722	.1844	.1963	.2076	.2184	.2285	.2379	.2464	.2541
4	.0530	.0607	.0689	.0775	.0865	.0959	.1056	.1156	.1258	.1361
5	.0113	.0137	.0165	.0196	.0231	.0270	.0313	.0360	.0411	.0467
6	.0015	.0019	.0025	.0031	.0038	.0047	.0058	.0070	.0084	.0100
7	.0001	.0002	.0002	.0003	.0004	.0005	.0006	.0008	.0010	.0012
8	.0000	.0000	.0000	.0000	.0000	.0000	.0000	.0000	.0001	.0001

r \ p	.31	.32	.33	.34	.35	.36	.37	.38	.39	.40
0	.0514	.0457	.0406	.0360	.0319	.0281	.0248	.0218	.0192	.0168
1	.1847	.1721	.1600	.1484	.1373	.1267	.1166	.1071	.0981	.0896
2	.2904	.2835	.2758	.2675	.2587	.2494	.2397	.2297	.2194	.2090
3	.2609	.2668	.2717	.2756	.2786	.2805	.2815	.2815	.2806	.2787
4	.1465	.1569	.1673	.1775	.1875	.1973	.2067	.2157	.2242	.2322
5	.0527	.0591	.0659	.0732	.0808	.0888	.0971	.1058	.1147	.1239
6	.0118	.0139	.0162	.0188	.0217	.0250	.0285	.0324	.0367	.0413
7	.0015	.0019	.0023	.0028	.0033	.0040	.0048	.0057	.0067	.0079
8	.0001	.0001	.0001	.0002	.0002	.0003	.0004	.0004	.0005	.0007

r \ p	.41	.42	.43	.44	.45	.46	.47	.48	.49	.50
0	.0147	.0128	.0111	.0097	.0084	.0072	.0062	.0053	.0046	.0039
1	.0816	.0742	.0672	.0608	.0548	.0493	.0442	.0395	.0352	.0312
2	.1985	.1880	.1776	.1672	.1569	.1469	.1371	.1275	.1183	.1094
3	.2759	.2723	.2679	.2627	.2568	.2503	.2431	.2355	.2273	.2188
4	.2397	.2465	.2526	.2580	.2627	.2627	.2665	.2695	.2717	.2730	.2734
5	.1332	.1428	.1525	.1622	.1719	.1816	.1912	.2006	.2098	.2188
6	.0463	.0517	.0575	.0637	.0703	.0774	.0848	.0926	.1008	.1094
7	.0092	.0107	.0124	.0143	.0164	.0188	.0215	.0244	.0277	.0312
8	.0008	.0010	.0012	.0014	.0017	.0020	.0024	.0028	.0033	.0039

n = 9

r \ p	.01	.02	.03	.04	.05	.06	.07	.08	.09	.10
0	.9135	.8337	.7602	.6925	.6302	.5730	.5204	.4722	.4279	.3874
1	.0830	.1531	.2116	.2597	.2985	.3292	.3525	.3695	.3809	.3874
2	.0034	.0125	.0262	.0433	.0629	.0840	.1061	.1285	.1507	.1722
3	.0001	.0006	.0019	.0042	.0077	.0125	.0186	.0261	.0348	.0446
4	.0000	.0000	.0001	.0003	.0006	.0012	.0021	.0034	.0052	.0074
5	.0000	.0000	.0000	.0000	.0000	.0001	.0002	.0003	.0005	.0008
6	.0000	.0000	.0000	.0000	.0000	.0000	.0000	.0000	.0000	.0001

n = 9 (Continued)

r \ p	.11	.12	.13	.14	.15	.16	.17	.18	.19	.20
0	.3504	.3165	.2855	.2573	.2316	.2082	.1869	.1676	.1501	.1342
1	.3897	.3884	.3840	.3770	.3679	.3569	.3446	.3312	.3169	.3020
2	.1927	.2119	.2295	.2455	.2597	.2720	.2823	.2908	.2973	.3020
3	.0556	.0674	.0800	.0933	.1069	.1209	.1349	.1489	.1627	.1762
4	.0103	.0138	.0179	.0228	.0283	.0345	.0415	.0490	.0573	.0661
5	.0013	.0019	.0027	.0037	.0050	.0066	.0085	.0108	.0134	.0165
6	.0001	.0002	.0003	.0004	.0006	.0008	.0012	.0016	.0021	.0028
7	.0000	.0000	.0000	.0000	.0000	.0001	.0001	.0001	.0002	.0003

r \ p	.21	.22	.23	.24	.25	.26	.27	.28	.29	.30
0	.1199	.1069	.0952	.0846	.0751	.0665	.0589	.0520	.0458	.0404
1	.2867	.2713	.2558	.2404	.2253	.2104	.1960	.1820	.1685	.1556
2	.3049	.3061	.3056	.3037	.3003	.2957	.2899	.2831	.2754	.2668
3	.1891	.2014	.2130	.2238	.2336	.2424	.2502	.2569	.2624	.2668
4	.0754	.0852	.0954	.1060	.1168	.1278	.1388	.1499	.1608	.1715
5	.0200	.0240	.0285	.0335	.0389	.0449	.0513	.0583	.0657	.0735
6	.0036	.0045	.0057	.0070	.0087	.0105	.0127	.0151	.0179	.0210
7	.0004	.0005	.0007	.0010	.0012	.0016	.0020	.0025	.0031	.0039
8	.0000	.0000	.0001	.0001	.0001	.0001	.0002	.0002	.0003	.0004

r \ p	.31	.32	.33	.34	.35	.36	.37	.38	.39	.40
0	.0355	.0311	.0272	.0238	.0207	.0180	.0156	.0135	.0117	.0101
1	.1433	.1317	.1206	.1102	.1004	.0912	.0826	.0747	.0673	.0605
2	.2576	.2478	.2376	.2270	.2162	.2052	.1941	.1831	.1721	.1612
3	.2701	.2721	.2731	.2729	.2716	.2693	.2660	.2618	.2567	.2508
4	.1820	.1921	.2017	.2109	.2194	.2272	.2344	.2407	.2462	.2508
5	.0818	.0904	.0994	.1086	.1181	.1278	.1376	.1475	.1574	.1672
6	.0245	.0284	.0326	.0373	.0424	.0479	.0539	.0603	.0671	.0743
7	.0047	.0057	.0069	.0082	.0098	.0116	.0136	.0158	.0184	.0212
8	.0005	.0007	.0008	.0011	.0013	.0016	.0020	.0024	.0029	.0035
9	.0000	.0000	.0000	.0001	.0001	.0001	.0001	.0002	.0002	.0003

r \ p	.41	.42	.43	.44	.45	.46	.47	.48	.49	.50
0	.0087	.0074	.0064	.0054	.0046	.0039	.0033	.0028	.0023	.0020
1	.0542	.0484	.0431	.0383	.0339	.0299	.0263	.0231	.0202	.0176
2	.1506	.1402	.1301	.1204	.1110	.1020	.0934	.0853	.0776	.0703
3	.2442	.2369	.2291	.2207	.2119	.2027	.1933	.1837	.1739	.1641
4	.2545	.2573	.2592	.2601	.2600	.2590	.2571	.2543	.2506	.2461
5	.1769	.1863	.1955	.2044	.2128	.2207	.2280	.2347	.2408	.2461
6	.0819	.0900	.0983	.1070	.1160	.1253	.1348	.1445	.1542	.1641
7	.0244	.0279	.0318	.0360	.0407	.0458	.0512	.0571	.0635	.0703
8	.0042	.0051	.0060	.0071	.0083	.0097	.0114	.0132	.0153	.0176
9	.0003	.0004	.0005	.0006	.0008	.0009	.0011	.0014	.0016	.0020

n = 10

r \ p	.01	.02	.03	.04	.05	.06	.07	.08	.09	.10
0	.9044	.8171	.7374	.6648	.5987	.5386	.4840	.4344	.3894	.3487
1	.0914	.1667	.2281	.2770	.3151	.3438	.3643	.3777	.3851	.3874
2	.0042	.0153	.0317	.0519	.0746	.0988	.1234	.1478	.1714	.1937
3	.0001	.0008	.0026	.0058	.0105	.0168	.0248	.0343	.0452	.0574
4	.0000	.0000	.0001	.0004	.0010	.0019	.0033	.0052	.0078	.0112
5	.0000	.0000	.0000	.0000	.0001	.0001	.0003	.0005	.0009	.0015
6	.0000	.0000	.0000	.0000	.0000	.0000	.0000	.0000	.0001	.0001

r \ p	.11	.12	.13	.14	.15	.16	.17	.18	.19	.20
0	.3118	.2785	.2484	.2213	.1969	.1749	.1552	.1374	.1216	.1074
1	.3854	.3798	.3712	.3603	.3474	.3331	.3178	.3017	.2852	.2684
2	.2143	.2330	.2496	.2639	.2759	.2856	.2929	.2980	.3010	.3020
3	.0706	.0847	.0995	.1146	.1298	.1450	.1600	.1745	.1883	.2013
4	.0153	.0202	.0260	.0326	.0401	.0483	.0573	.0670	.0773	.0881
5	.0023	.0033	.0047	.0064	.0085	.0111	.0141	.0177	.0218	.0264
6	.0002	.0004	.0006	.0009	.0012	.0018	.0024	.0032	.0043	.0055
7	.0000	.0000	.0000	.0001	.0001	.0002	.0003	.0004	.0006	.0008
8	.0000	.0000	.0000	.0000	.0000	.0000	.0000	.0000	.0001	.0001

Table C >> **83**

n = 10 (Continued)

r \ p	.21	.22	.23	.24	.25	.26	.27	.28	.29	.30
0	.0947	.0834	.0733	.0643	.0563	.0492	.0430	.0374	.0326	.0282
1	.2517	.2351	.2188	.2030	.1877	.1730	.1590	.1456	.1330	.1211
2	.3011	.2984	.2942	.2885	.2816	.2735	.2646	.2548	.2444	.2335
3	.2134	.2244	.2343	.2429	.2503	.2563	.2609	.2642	.2662	.2668
4	.0993	.1108	.1225	.1343	.1460	.1576	.1689	.1798	.1903	.2001
5	.0317	.0375	.0439	.0509	.0584	.0664	.0750	.0839	.0933	.1029
6	.0070	.0088	.0109	.0134	.0162	.0195	.0231	.0272	.0317	.0368
7	.0011	.0014	.0019	.0024	.0031	.0039	.0049	.0060	.0074	.0090
8	.0001	.0002	.0002	.0003	.0004	.0005	.0007	.0009	.0011	.0014
9	.0000	.0000	.0000	.0000	.0000	.0000	.0001	.0001	.0001	.0001

r \ p	.31	.32	.33	.34	.35	.36	.37	.38	.39	.40
0	.0245	.0211	.0182	.0157	.0135	.0115	.0098	.0084	.0071	.0060
1	.1099	.0995	.0898	.0808	.0725	.0649	.0578	.0514	.0456	.0403
2	.2222	.2107	.1990	.1873	.1757	.1642	.1529	.1419	.1312	.1209
3	.2662	.2644	.2614	.2573	.2522	.2462	.2394	.2319	.2237	.2150
4	.2093	.2177	.2253	.2320	.2377	.2424	.2461	.2487	.2503	.2508
5	.1128	.1229	.1332	.1434	.1536	.1636	.1734	.1829	.1920	.2007
6	.0422	.0482	.0547	.0616	.0689	.0767	.0849	.0934	.1023	.1115
7	.0108	.0130	.0154	.0181	.0212	.0247	.0285	.0327	.0374	.0425
8	.0018	.0023	.0028	.0035	.0043	.0052	.0063	.0075	.0090	.0106
9	.0002	.0002	.0003	.0004	.0005	.0006	.0008	.0010	.0013	.0016
10	.0000	.0000	.0000	.0000	.0000	.0000	.0000	.0001	.0001	.0001

r \ p	.41	.42	.43	.44	.45	.46	.47	.48	.49	.50
0	.0051	.0043	.0036	.0030	.0025	.0021	.0017	.0014	.0012	.0010
1	.0355	.0312	.0273	.0238	.0207	.0180	.0155	.0133	.0114	.0098
2	.1111	.1017	.0927	.0843	.0763	.0688	.0619	.0554	.0494	.0439
3	.2058	.1963	.1865	.1765	.1665	.1564	.1464	.1364	.1267	.1172
4	.2503	.2488	.2462	.2427	.2384	.2331	.2271	.2204	.2130	.2051
5	.2087	.2162	.2229	.2289	.2340	.2383	.2417	.2441	.2456	.2461
6	.1209	.1304	.1401	.1499	.1596	.1692	.1786	.1878	.1966	.2051
7	.0480	.0540	.0604	.0673	.0746	.0824	.0905	.0991	.1080	.1172
8	.0125	.0147	.0171	.0198	.0229	.0263	.0301	.0343	.0389	.0439
9	.0019	.0024	.0029	.0035	.0042	.0050	.0059	.0070	.0083	.0098
10	.0001	.0002	.0002	.0003	.0003	.0004	.0005	.0006	.0008	.0010

n = 11

r \ p	.01	.02	.03	.04	.05	.06	.07	.08	.09	.10
0	.8953	.8007	.7153	.6382	.5688	.5063	.4501	.3996	.3544	.3138
1	.0995	.1798	.2433	.2925	.3293	.3555	.3727	.3823	.3855	.3835
2	.0050	.0183	.0376	.0609	.0867	.1135	.1403	.1662	.1906	.2131
3	.0002	.0011	.0035	.0076	.0137	.0217	.0317	.0434	.0566	.0710
4	.0000	.0000	.0002	.0006	.0014	.0028	.0048	.0075	.0112	.0158
5	.0000	.0000	.0000	.0000	.0001	.0002	.0005	.0009	.0015	.0025
6	.0000	.0000	.0000	.0000	.0000	.0000	.0000	.0001	.0002	.0003

r \ p	.11	.12	.13	.14	.15	.16	.17	.18	.19	.20
0	.2775	.2451	.2161	.1903	.1673	.1469	.1288	.1127	.0985	.0859
1	.3773	.3676	.3552	.3408	.3248	.3078	.2901	.2721	.2541	.2362
2	.2332	.2507	.2654	.2774	.2866	.2932	.2971	.2987	.2980	.2953
3	.0865	.1025	.1190	.1355	.1517	.1675	.1826	.1967	.2097	.2215
4	.0214	.0280	.0356	.0441	.0536	.0638	.0748	.0864	.0984	.1107
5	.0037	.0053	.0074	.0101	.0132	.0170	.0214	.0265	.0323	.0388
6	.0005	.0007	.0011	.0016	.0023	.0032	.0044	.0058	.0076	.0097
7	.0000	.0001	.0001	.0002	.0003	.0004	.0006	.0009	.0013	.0017
8	.0000	.0000	.0000	.0000	.0000	.0000	.0001	.0001	.0001	.0002

n = 11 (Continued)

r \ p	.21	.22	.23	.24	.25	.26	.27	.28	.29	.30
0	.0748	.0650	.0564	.0489	.0422	.0364	.0314	.0270	.0231	.0198
1	.2187	.2017	.1854	.1697	.1549	.1408	.1276	.1153	.1038	.0932
2	.2907	.2845	.2768	.2680	.2581	.2474	.2360	.2242	.2121	.1998
3	.2318	.2407	.2481	.2539	.2581	.2608	.2619	.2616	.2599	.2568
4	.1232	.1358	.1482	.1603	.1721	.1832	.1937	.2035	.2123	.2201
5	.0459	.0536	.0620	.0709	.0803	.0901	.1003	.1108	.1214	.1321
6	.0122	.0151	.0185	.0224	.0268	.0317	.0371	.0431	.0496	.0566
7	.0023	.0030	.0039	.0050	.0064	.0079	.0098	.0120	.0145	.0173
8	.0003	.0004	.0006	.0008	.0011	.0014	.0018	.0023	.0030	.0037
9	.0000	.0000	.0001	.0001	.0001	.0002	.0002	.0003	.0004	.0005

r \ p	.31	.32	.33	.34	.35	.36	.37	.38	.39	.40
0	.0169	.0144	.0122	.0104	.0088	.0074	.0062	.0052	.0044	.0036
1	.0834	.0744	.0662	.0587	.0518	.0457	.0401	.0351	.0306	.0266
2	.1874	.1751	.1630	.1511	.1395	.1284	.1177	.1075	.0978	.0887
3	.2526	.2472	.2408	.2335	.2254	.2167	.2074	.1977	.1876	.1774
4	.2269	.2326	.2372	.2406	.2428	.2438	.2436	.2423	.2399	.2365
5	.1427	.1533	.1636	.1735	.1830	.1920	.2003	.2079	.2148	.2207
6	.0641	.0721	.0806	.0894	.0985	.1080	.1176	.1274	.1373	.1471
7	.0206	.0242	.0283	.0329	.0379	.0434	.0494	.0558	.0627	.0701
8	.0046	.0057	.0070	.0085	.0102	.0122	.0145	.0171	.0200	.0234
9	.0007	.0009	.0011	.0015	.0018	.0023	.0028	.0035	.0043	.0052
10	.0001	.0001	.0001	.0001	.0002	.0003	.0003	.0004	.0005	.0007

r \ p	.41	.42	.43	.44	.45	.46	.47	.48	.49	.50
0	.0030	.0025	.0021	.0017	.0014	.0011	.0009	.0008	.0006	.0005
1	.0231	.0199	.0171	.0147	.0125	.0107	.0090	.0076	.0064	.0054
2	.0801	.0721	.0646	.0577	.0513	.0454	.0401	.0352	.0308	.0269
3	.1670	.1566	.1462	.1359	.1259	.1161	.1067	.0976	.0888	.0806
4	.2321	.2267	.2206	.2136	.2060	.1978	.1892	.1801	.1707	.1611
5	.2258	.2299	.2329	.2350	.2360	.2359	.2348	.2327	.2296	.2256
6	.1569	.1664	.1757	.1846	.1931	.2010	.2083	.2148	.2206	.2256
7	.0779	.0861	.0947	.1036	.1128	.1223	.1319	.1416	.1514	.1611
8	.0271	.0312	.0357	.0407	.0462	.0521	.0585	.0654	.0727	.0806
9	.0063	.0075	.0090	.0107	.0126	.0148	.0173	.0201	.0233	.0269
10	.0009	.0011	.0014	.0017	.0021	.0025	.0031	.0037	.0045	.0054
11	.0001	.0001	.0001	.0001	.0002	.0002	.0002	.0003	.0004	.0005

n = 12

r \ p	.01	.02	.03	.04	.05	.06	.07	.08	.09	.10
0	.8864	.7847	.6938	.6127	.5404	.4759	.4186	.3677	.3225	.2824
1	.1074	.1922	.2575	.3064	.3413	.3645	.3781	.3837	.3827	.3766
2	.0060	.0216	.0438	.0702	.0988	.1280	.1565	.1835	.2082	.2301
3	.0002	.0015	.0045	.0098	.0173	.0272	.0393	.0532	.0686	.0852
4	.0000	.0001	.0003	.0009	.0021	.0039	.0067	.0104	.0153	.0213
5	.0000	.0000	.0000	.0001	.0002	.0004	.0008	.0014	.0024	.0038
6	.0000	.0000	.0000	.0000	.0000	.0000	.0001	.0001	.0003	.0005

r \ p	.11	.12	.13	.14	.15	.16	.17	.18	.19	.20
0	.2470	.2157	.1880	.1637	.1422	.1234	.1069	.0924	.0798	.0687
1	.3663	.3529	.3372	.3197	.3012	.2821	.2627	.2434	.2245	.2062
2	.2490	.2647	.2771	.2863	.2924	.2955	.2960	.2939	.2897	.2835
3	.1026	.1203	.1380	.1553	.1720	.1876	.2021	.2151	.2265	.2362
4	.0285	.0369	.0464	.0569	.0683	.0804	.0931	.1062	.1195	.1329
5	.0056	.0081	.0111	.0148	.0193	.0245	.0305	.0373	.0449	.0532
6	.0008	.0013	.0019	.0028	.0040	.0054	.0073	.0096	.0123	.0155
7	.0001	.0001	.0002	.0004	.0006	.0009	.0013	.0018	.0025	.0033
8	.0000	.0000	.0000	.0000	.0001	.0001	.0002	.0002	.0004	.0005
9	.0000	.0000	.0000	.0000	.0000	.00000	.0000	.0000	.0000	.0001

Table C >> **85**

n = 12 (Continued)

p \ r	.21	.22	.23	.24	.25	.26	.27	.28	.29	.30
0	.0591	.0507	.0434	.0371	.0317	.0270	.0229	.0194	.0164	.0138
1	.1885	.1717	.1557	.1407	.1267	.1137	.1016	.0906	.0804	.0712
2	.2756	.2663	.2558	.2444	.2323	.2197	.2068	.1937	.1807	.1678
3	.2442	.2503	.2547	.2573	.2581	.2573	.2549	.2511	.2460	.2397
4	.1460	.1589	.1712	.1828	.1936	.2034	.2122	.2197	.2261	.2311
5	.0621	.0717	.0818	.0924	.1032	.1143	.1255	.1367	.1477	.1585
6	.0193	.0236	.0285	.0340	.0401	.0469	.0542	.0620	.0704	.0792
7	.0044	.0057	.0073	.0092	.0115	.0141	.0172	.0207	.0246	.0291
8	.0007	.0010	.0014	.0018	.0024	.0031	.0040	.0050	.0063	.0078
9	.0001	.0001	.0002	.0003	.0004	.0005	.0007	.0009	.0011	.0015
10	.0000	.0000	.0000	.0000	.0000	.0001	.0001	.0001	.0001	.0002

p \ r	.31	.32	.33	.34	.35	.36	.37	.38	.39	.40
0	.0116	.0098	.0082	.0068	.0057	.0047	.0039	.0032	.0027	.0022
1	.0628	.0552	.0484	.0422	.0368	.0319	.0276	.0237	.0204	.0174
2	.1552	.1429	.1310	.1197	.1088	.0986	.0890	.0800	.0716	.0639
3	.2324	.2241	.2151	.2055	.1954	.1849	.1742	.1634	.1526	.1419
4	.2349	.2373	.2384	.2382	.2367	.2340	.2302	.2254	.2195	.2128
5	.1688	.1787	.1879	.1963	.2039	.2106	.2163	.2210	.2246	.2270
6	.0885	.0981	.1079	.1180	.1281	.1382	.1482	.1580	.1675	.1766
7	.0341	.0396	.0456	.0521	.0591	.0666	.0746	.0830	.0918	.1009
8	.0096	.0116	.0140	.0168	.0199	.0234	.0274	.0318	.0367	.0420
9	.0019	.0024	.0031	.0038	.0048	.0059	.0071	.0087	.0104	.0125
10	.0003	.0003	.0005	.0006	.0008	.0010	.0013	.0016	.0020	.0025
11	.0000	.0000	.0000	.0001	.0001	.0001	.0001	.0002	.0002	.0003

p \ r	.41	.42	.43	.44	.45	.46	.47	.48	.49	.50
0	.0018	.0014	.0012	.0010	.0008	.0006	.0005	.0004	.0003	.0002
1	.0148	.0126	.0106	.0090	.0075	.0063	.0052	.0043	.0036	.0029
2	.0567	.0502	.0442	.0388	.0339	.0294	.0255	.0220	.0189	.0161
3	.1314	.1211	.1111	.1015	.0923	.0836	.0754	.0676	.0604	.0537
4	.2054	.1973	.1886	.1794	.1700	.1602	.1504	.1405	.1306	.1208
5	.2284	.2285	.2276	.2256	.2225	.2184	.2134	.2075	.2008	.1934
6	.1851	.1931	.2003	.2068	.2124	.2171	.2208	.2234	.2250	.2256
7	.1103	.1198	.1295	.1393	.1489	.1585	.1678	.1768	.1853	.1934
8	.0479	.0542	.0611	.0684	.0762	.0844	.0930	.1020	.1113	.1208
9	.0148	.0175	.0205	.0239	.0277	.0319	.0367	.0418	.0475	.0537
10	.0031	.0038	.0046	.0056	.0068	.0082	.0098	.0116	.0137	.0161
11	.0004	.0005	.0006	.0008	.0010	.0013	.0016	.0019	.0024	.0029
12	.0000	.0000	.0000	.0001	.0001	.0001	.0001	.0001	.0002	.0002

n = 13

p \ r	.01	.02	.03	.04	.05	.06	.07	.08	.09	.10
0	.8775	.7690	.6730	.5882	.5133	.4474	.3893	.3383	.2935	.2542
1	.1152	.2040	.2706	.3186	.3512	.3712	.3809	.3824	.3773	.3672
2	.0070	.0250	.0502	.0797	.1109	.1422	.1720	.1995	.2239	.2448
3	.0003	.0019	.0057	.0122	.0214	.0333	.0475	.0636	.0812	.0997
4	.0000	.0001	.0004	.0013	.0028	.0053	.0089	.0138	.0201	.0277
5	.0000	.0000	.0000	.0001	.0003	.0006	.0012	.0022	.0036	.0055
6	.0000	.0000	.0000	.0000	.0000	.0001	.0001	.0003	.0005	.0008
7	.0000	.0000	.0000	.0000	.0000	.0000	.0000	.0000	.0000	.0001

p \ r	.11	.12	.13	.14	.15	.16	.17	.18	.19	.20
0	.2198	.1898	.1636	.1408	.1209	.1037	.0887	.0758	.0646	.0550
1	.3532	.3364	.3178	.2979	.2774	.2567	.2362	.2163	.1970	.1787
2	.2619	.2753	.2849	.2910	.2937	.2934	.2903	.2848	.2773	.2680
3	.1187	.1376	.1561	.1737	.1900	.2049	.2180	.2293	.2385	.2457
4	.0367	.0469	.0583	.0707	.0838	.0976	.1116	.1258	.1399	.1535
5	.0082	.0115	.0157	.0207	.0266	.0335	.0412	.0497	.0591	.0691
6	.0013	.0021	.0031	.0045	.0063	.0085	.0112	.0145	.0185	.0230
7	.0002	.0003	.0005	.0007	.0011	.0016	.0023	.0032	.0043	.0058
8	.0000	.0000	.0001	.0001	.0001	.0002	.0004	.0005	.0008	.0011
9	.0000	.0000	.0000	.0000	.0000	.0000	.0000	.0001	.0001	.0001

n = 13 (Continued)

r \ p	.21	.22	.23	.24	.25	.26	.27	.28	.29	.30
0	.0467	.0396	.0334	.0282	.0238	.0200	.0167	.0140	.0117	.0097
1	.1613	.1450	.1299	.1159	.1029	.0911	.0804	.0706	.0619	.0540
2	.2573	.2455	.2328	.2195	.2059	.1921	.1784	.1648	.1516	.1388
3	.2508	.2539	.2550	.2542	.2517	.2475	.2419	.2351	.2271	.2181
4	.1667	.1790	.1904	.2007	.2097	.2174	.2237	.2285	.2319	.2337
5	.0797	.0909	.1024	.1141	.1258	.1375	.1489	.1600	.1705	.1803
6	.0283	.0342	.0408	.0480	.0559	.0644	.0734	.0829	.0928	.1030
7	.0075	.0096	.0122	.0152	.0186	.0226	.0272	.0323	.0379	.0442
8	.0015	.0020	.0027	.0036	.0047	.0060	.0075	.0094	.0116	.0142
9	.0002	.0003	.0005	.0006	.0009	.0012	.0015	.0020	.0026	.0034
10	.0000	.0000	.0001	.0001	.0001	.0002	.0002	.0003	.0004	.0006
11	.0000	.0000	.0000	.0000	.0000	.0000	.0000	.0000	.0000	.0001

r \ p	.31	.32	.33	.34	.35	.36	.37	.38	.39	.40
0	.0080	.0066	.0055	.0045	.0037	.0030	.0025	.0020	.0016	.0013
1	.0469	.0407	.0351	.0302	.0259	.0221	.0188	.0159	.0135	.0113
2	.1265	.1148	.1037	.0933	.0836	.0746	.0663	.0586	.0516	.0453
3	.2084	.1981	.1874	.1763	.1651	.1538	.1427	.1317	.1210	.1107
4	.2341	.2331	.2307	.2270	.2222	.2163	.2095	.2018	.1934	.1845
5	.1893	.1974	.2045	.2105	.2154	.2190	.2215	.2227	.2226	.2214
6	.1134	.1239	.1343	.1446	.1546	.1643	.1734	.1820	.1898	.1968
7	.0509	.0583	.0662	.0745	.0833	.0924	.1019	.1115	.1213	.1312
8	.0172	.0206	.0244	.0288	.0336	.0390	.0449	.0513	.0582	.0656
9	.0043	.0054	.0067	.0082	.0101	.0122	.0146	.0175	.0207	.0243
10	.0008	.0010	.0013	.0017	.0022	.0027	.0034	.0043	.0053	.0065
11	.0001	.0001	.0002	.0002	.0003	.0004	.0006	.0007	.0009	.0012
12	.0000	.0000	.0000	.0000	.0000	.0000	.0001	.0001	.0001	.0001

r \ p	.41	.42	.43	.44	.45	.46	.47	.48	.49	.50
0	.0010	.0008	.0007	.0005	.0004	.0003	.0003	.0002	.0002	.0001
1	.0095	.0079	.0066	.0054	.0045	.0037	.0030	.0024	.0020	.0016
2	.0395	.0344	.0298	.0256	.0220	.0188	.0160	.0135	.0114	.0095
3	.1007	.0913	.0823	.0739	.0660	.0587	.0519	.0457	.0401	.0349
4	.1750	.1653	.1553	.1451	.1350	.1250	.1151	.1055	.0962	.0873
5	.2189	.2154	.2108	.2053	.1989	.1917	.1838	.1753	.1664	.1571
6	.2029	.2080	.2121	.2151	.2169	.2177	.2173	.2158	.2131	.2095
7	.1410	.1506	.1600	.1690	.1775	.1854	.1927	.1992	.2048	.2095
8	.0735	.0818	.0905	.0996	.1089	.1185	.1282	.1379	.1476	.1571
9	.0284	.0329	.0379	.0435	.0495	.0561	.0631	.0707	.0788	.0873
10	.0079	.0095	.0114	.0137	.0162	.0191	.0224	.0261	.0303	.0349
11	.0015	.0019	.0024	.0029	.0036	.0044	.0054	.0066	.0079	.0095
12	.0002	.0002	.0003	.0004	.0005	.0006	.0008	.0010	.0013	.0016
13	.0000	.0000	.0000	.0000	.0000	.0000	.0001	.0001	.0001	.0001

n = 14

r \ p	.01	.02	.03	.04	.05	.06	.07	.08	.09	.10
0	.8687	.7536	.6528	.5647	.4877	.4205	.3620	.3112	.2670	.2288
1	.1229	.2153	.2827	.3294	.3593	.3758	.3815	.3788	.3698	.3559
2	.0081	.0286	.0568	.0892	.1229	.1559	.1867	.2141	.2377	.2570
3	.0003	.0023	.0070	.0149	.0259	.0398	.0562	.0745	.0940	.1142
4	.0000	.0001	.0006	.0017	.0037	.0070	.0116	.0178	.0256	.0349
5	.0000	.0000	.0000	.0001	.0004	.0009	.0018	.0031	.0051	.0078
6	.0000	.0000	.0000	.0000	.0000	.0001	.0002	.0004	.0008	.0013
7	.0000	.0000	.0000	.0000	.0000	.0000	.0000	.0000	.0001	.0002

r \ p	.11	.12	.13	.14	.15	.16	.17	.18	.19	.20
0	.1956	.1670	.1423	.1211	.1028	.0871	.0736	.0621	.0523	.0440
1	.3385	.3188	.2977	.2759	.2539	.2322	.2112	.1910	.1719	.1539
2	.2720	.2826	.2892	.2919	.2912	.2875	.2811	.2725	.2620	.2501
3	.1345	.1542	.1728	.1901	.2056	.2190	.2303	.2393	.2459	.2501
4	.0457	.0578	.0710	.0851	.0998	.1147	.1297	.1444	.1586	.1720
5	.0113	.0158	.0212	.0277	.0352	.0437	.0531	.0634	.0744	.0860
6	.0021	.0032	.0048	.0068	.0093	.0125	.0163	.0209	.0262	.0322
7	.0003	.0005	.0008	.0013	.0019	.0027	.0038	.0052	.0070	.0092
8	.0000	.0001	.0001	.0002	.0003	.0005	.0007	.0010	.0014	.0020
9	.0000	.0000	.0000	.0000	.0000	.0001	.0001	.0001	.0002	.0003

Table C >> **87**

n = 14 (Continued)

r \ p	.21	.22	.23	.24	.25	.26	.27	.28	.29	.30
0	.0369	.0309	.0258	.0214	.0178	.0148	.0122	.0101	.0083	.0068
1	.1372	.1218	.1077	.0948	.0832	.0726	.0632	.0548	.0473	.0407
2	.2371	.2234	.2091	.1946	.1802	.1659	.1519	.1385	.1256	.1134
3	.2521	.2520	.2499	.2459	.2402	.2331	.2248	.2154	.2052	.1943
4	.1843	.1955	.2052	.2135	.2202	.2252	.2286	.2304	.2305	.2290
5	.0980	.1103	.1226	.1348	.1468	.1583	.1691	.1792	.1883	.1963
6	.0391	.0466	.0549	.0639	.0734	.0834	.0938	.1045	.1153	.1262
7	.0119	.0150	.0188	.0231	.0280	.0335	.0397	.0464	.0538	.0618
8	.0028	.0037	.0049	.0064	.0082	.0103	.0128	.0158	.0192	.0232
9	.0005	.0007	.0010	.0013	.0018	.0024	.0032	.0041	.0052	.0066
10	.0001	.0001	.0001	.0002	.0003	.0004	.0006	.0008	.0011	.0014
11	.0000	.0000	.0000	.0000	.0000	.0001	.0001	.0001	.0002	.0002

r \ p	.31	.32	.33	.34	.35	.36	.37	.38	.39	.40
0	.0055	.0045	.0037	.0030	.0024	.0019	.0016	.0012	.0010	.0008
1	.0349	.0298	.0253	.0215	.0181	.0152	.0128	.0106	.0088	.0073
2	.1018	.0911	.0811	.0719	.0634	.0557	.0487	.0424	.0367	.0317
3	.1830	.1715	.1598	.1481	.1366	.1253	.1144	.1039	.0940	.0845
4	.2261	.2219	.2164	.2098	.2022	.1938	.1848	.1752	.1652	.1549
5	.2032	.2088	.2132	.2161	.2178	.2181	.2170	.2147	.2112	.2066
6	.1369	.1474	.1575	.1670	.1759	.1840	.1912	.1974	.2026	.2066
7	.0703	.0793	.0886	.0983	.1082	.1183	.1283	.1383	.1480	.1574
8	.0276	.0326	.0382	.0443	.0510	.0582	.0659	.0742	.0828	.0918
9	.0083	.0102	.0125	.0152	.0183	.0218	.0258	.0303	.0353	.0408
10	.0019	.0024	.0031	.0039	.0049	.0061	.0076	.0093	.0113	.0136
11	.0003	.0004	.0006	.0007	.0010	.0013	.0016	.0021	.0026	.0033
12	.0000	.0000	.0001	.0001	.0001	.0002	.0002	.0003	.0004	.0005
13	.0000	.0000	.0000	.0000	.0000	.0000	.0000	.0000	.0000	.0001

r \ p	.41	.42	.43	.44	.45	.46	.47	.48	.49	.50
0	.0006	.0005	.0004	.0003	.0002	.0002	.0001	.0001	.0001	.0001
1	.0060	.0049	.0040	.0033	.0027	.0021	.0017	.0014	.0011	.0009
2	.0272	.0233	.0198	.0168	.0141	.0118	.0099	.0082	.0008	.0056
3	.0757	.0674	.0597	.0527	.0462	.0403	.0350	.0303	.0260	.0222
4	.1446	.1342	.1239	.1138	.1040	.0945	.0854	.0768	.0687	.0611
5	.2009	.1943	.1869	.1788	.1701	.1610	.1515	.1418	.1320	.1222
6	.2094	.2111	.2115	.2108	.2088	.2057	.2015	.1963	.1902	.1833
7	.1663	.1747	.1824	.1892	.1952	.2003	.2043	.2071	.2089	.2095
8	.1011	.1107	.1204	.1301	.1398	.1493	.1585	.1673	.1756	.1833
9	.0469	.0534	.0605	.0682	.0762	.0848	.0937	.1030	.1125	.1222
10	.0163	.0193	.0228	.0268	.0312	.0361	.0415	.0475	.0540	.0611
11	.0041	.0051	.0063	.0076	.0093	.0112	.0134	.0160	.0189	.0222
12	.0007	.0009	.0012	.0015	.0019	.0024	.0030	.0037	.0045	.0056
13	.0001	.0001	.0001	.0002	.0002	.0003	.0004	.0005	.0007	.0009
14	.0000	.0000	.0000	.0000	.0000	.0000	.0000	.0000	.0000	.0001

n = 15

r \ p	.01	.02	.03	.04	.05	.06	.07	.08	.09	.10
0	.8601	.7386	.6333	.5421	.4633	.3953	.3367	.2863	.2430	.2059
1	.1303	.2261	.2938	.3388	.3658	.3785	.3801	.3734	.3605	.3432
2	.0092	.0323	.0636	.0988	.1348	.1691	.2003	.2273	.2496	.2669
3	.0004	.0029	.0085	.0178	.0307	.0468	.0653	.0857	.1070	.1285
4	.0000	.0002	.0008	.0022	.0049	.0090	.0148	.0223	.0317	.0428
5	.0000	.0000	.0001	.0002	.0006	.0013	.0024	.0043	.0069	.0105
6	.0000	.0000	.0000	.0000	.0000	.0001	.0003	.0006	.0011	.0019
7	.0000	.0000	.0000	.0000	.0000	.0000	.0000	.0001	.0001	.0003

n = 15 (Continued)

r \ p	.11	.12	.13	.14	.15	.16	.17	.18	.19	.20
0	.1741	.1470	.1238	.1041	.0874	.0731	.0611	.0510	.0424	.0352
1	.3228	.3006	.2775	.2542	.2312	.2090	.1878	.1678	.1492	.1319
2	.2793	.2870	.2903	.2897	.2856	.2787	.2692	.2578	.2449	.2309
3	.1496	.1696	.1880	.2044	.2184	.2300	.2389	.2452	.2489	.2501
4	.0555	.0694	.0843	.0998	.1156	.1314	.1468	.1615	.1752	.1876
5	.0151	.0208	.0277	.0357	.0449	.0551	.0662	.0780	.0904	.1032
6	.0031	.0047	.0069	.0097	.0132	.0175	.0226	.0285	.0353	.0430
7	.0005	.0008	.0013	.0020	.0030	.0043	.0059	.0081	.0107	.0138
8	.0001	.0001	.0002	.0003	.0005	.0008	.0012	.0018	.0025	.0035
9	.0000	.0000	.0000	.0000	.0001	.0001	.0002	.0003	.0005	.0007
10	.0000	.0000	.0000	.0000	.0000	.0000	.0000	.0000	.0001	.0001

r	.21	.22	.23	.24	.25	.26	.27	.28	.29	.30
0	.0291	.0241	.0198	.0163	.0134	.0109	.0089	.0072	.0059	.0047
1	.1162	.1018	.0889	.0772	.0668	.0576	.0494	.0423	.0360	.0305
2	.2162	.2010	.1858	.1707	.1559	.1416	.1280	.1150	.1029	.0916
3	.2490	.2457	.2405	.2336	.2252	.2156	.2051	.1939	.1821	.1700
4	.1986	.2079	.2155	.2213	.2252	.2273	.2276	.2262	.2231	.2186
5	.1161	.1290	.1416	.1537	.1651	.1757	.1852	.1935	.2005	.2061
6	.0514	.0606	.0705	.0809	.0917	.1029	.1142	.1254	.1365	.1472
7	.0176	.0220	.0271	.0329	.0393	.0465	.0543	.0627	.0717	.0811
8	.0047	.0062	.0081	.0104	.0131	.0163	.0201	.0244	.0293	.0348
9	.0010	.0014	.0019	.0025	.0034	.0045	.0058	.0074	.0093	.0116
10	.0002	.0002	.0003	.0005	.0007	.0009	.0013	.0017	.0023	.0030
11	.0000	.0000	.0000	.0001	.0001	.0002	.0002	.0003	.0004	.0006
12	.0000	.0000	.0000	.0000	.0000	.0000	.0000	.0000	.0001	.0001

r	.31	.32	.33	.34	.35	.36	.37	.38	.39	.40
0	.0038	.0031	.0025	.0020	.0016	.0012	.0010	.0008	.0006	.0005
1	.0258	.0217	.0182	.0152	.0126	.0104	.0086	.0071	.0058	.0047
2	.0811	.0715	.0627	.0547	.0476	.0411	.0354	.0303	.0259	.0219
3	.1579	.1457	.1338	.1222	.1110	.1002	.0901	.0805	.0716	.0634
4	.2128	.2057	.1977	.1888	.1792	.1692	.1587	.1481	.1374	.1268
5	.210	.2130	.2142	.2140	.2123	.2093	.2051	.1997	.1933	.1859
6	.1575	.1671	.1759	.1837	.1906	.1963	.2008	.2040	.2059	.2066
7	.0910	.1011	.1114	.1217	.1319	.1419	.1516	.1608	.1693	.1771
8	.0409	.0476	.0549	.0627	.0710	.0798	.0890	.0985	.1082	.1181
9	.0143	.0174	.0210	.0251	.0298	.0349	.0407	.0470	.0538	.0612
10	.0038	.0049	.0062	.0078	.0096	.0118	.0143	.0173	.0206	.0245
11	.0008	.0011	.0014	.0018	.0024	.0030	.0038	.0048	.0060	.0074
12	.0001	.0002	.0002	.0003	.0004	.0006	.0007	.0010	.0013	.0016
13	.0000	.0000	.0000	.0000	.0001	.0001	.0001	.0001	.0002	.0003

r	.41	.42	.43	.44	.45	.46	.47	.48	.49	.50
0	.0004	.0003	.0002	.0002	.0001	.0001	.0001	.0001	.0000	.0000
1	.0038	.0031	.0025	.0020	.0016	.0012	.0010	.0008	.0006	.0005
2	.0185	.0156	.0130	.0108	.0090	.0074	.0060	.0049	.0040	.0032
3	.0558	.0489	.0426	.0369	.0318	.0272	.0232	.0197	.0166	.0139
4	.1163	.1061	.0963	.0869	.0780	.0696	.0617	.0545	.0478	.0417
5	.1778	.1691	.1598	.1502	.1404	.1304	.1204	.1106	.1010	.0916
6	.2060	.2041	.2010	.1967	.1914	.1851	.1780	.1702	.1617	.1527
7	.1840	.1900	.1949	.1987	.2013	.2028	.2030	.2020	.1997	.1964
8	.1279	.1376	.1470	.1561	.1647	.1727	.1800	.1864	.1919	.1964
9	.0691	.0775	.0863	.0954	.1048	.1144	.1241	.1338	.1434	.1527
10	.0288	.0337	.0390	.0450	.0515	.0585	.0661	.0741	.0827	.0916
11	.0091	.0111	.0134	.0161	.0191	.0226	.0266	.0311	.0361	.0417
12	.0021	.0027	.0034	.0042	.0052	.0064	.0079	.0096	.0116	.0139
13	.0003	.0004	.0006	.0008	.0010	.0013	.0016	.0020	.0026	.0032
14	.0000	.0000	.0001	.0001	.0001	.0002	.0002	.0003	.0004	.0005

Table C >> **89**

n = 16

r\p	.01	.02	.03	.04	.05	.06	.07	.08	.09	.10
0	.8515	.7238	.6143	.5204	.4401	.3716	.3131	.2634	.2211	.1853
1	.1376	.2363	.3040	.3469	.3706	.3795	.3771	.3665	.3499	.3294
2	.0104	.0362	.0705	.1084	.1463	.1817	.2129	.2390	.2596	.2745
3	.0005	.0034	.0102	.0211	.0359	.0541	.0748	.0970	.1198	.1423
4	.0000	.0002	.0010	.0029	.0061	.0112	.0183	.0274	.0385	.0514
5	.0000	.0000	.0001	.0003	.0008	.0017	.0033	.0057	.0091	.0137
6	.0000	.0000	.0000	.0000	.0001	.0002	.0005	.0009	.0017	.0028
7	.0000	.0000	.0000	.0000	.0000	.0000	.0000	.0001	.0002	.0004
8	.0000	.0000	.0000	.0000	.0000	.0000	.0000	.0000	.0000	.0001

r\p	.11	.12	.13	.14	.15	.16	.17	.18	.19	.20
0	.1550	.1293	.1077	.0895	.0743	.0614	.0507	.0418	.0343	.0281
1	.3065	.2822	.2575	.2332	.2097	.1873	.1662	.1468	.1289	.1126
2	.2841	.2886	.2886	.2847	.2775	.2675	.2554	.2416	.2267	.2111
3	.1638	.1837	.2013	.2163	.2285	.2378	.2441	.2475	.2482	.2463
4	.0658	.0814	.0977	.1144	.1311	.1472	.1625	.1766	.1892	.2001
5	.0195	.0266	.0351	.0447	.0555	.0673	.0799	.0930	.1065	.1201
6	.0044	.0067	.0096	.0133	.0180	.0235	.0300	.0374	.0458	.0550
7	.0008	.0013	.0020	.0031	.0045	.0064	.0088	.0117	.0153	.0197
8	.0001	.0002	.0003	.0006	.0009	.0014	.0020	.0029	.0041	.0055
9	.0000	.0000	.0000	.0001	.0001	.0002	.0004	.0006	.0008	.0012
10	.0000	.0000	.0000	.0000	.0000	.0000	.0001	.0001	.0001	.0002

r\p	.21	.22	.23	.24	.25	.26	.27	.28	.29	.30
0	.0230	.0188	.0153	.0124	.0100	.0081	.0065	.0052	.0042	.0033
1	.0979	.0847	.0730	.0626	.0535	.0455	.0385	.0325	.0273	.0228
2	.1952	.1792	.1635	.1482	.1336	.1198	.1068	.0947	.0835	.0732
3	.2421	.2359	.2279	.2185	.2079	.1964	.1843	.1718	.1591	.1465
4	.2092	.2162	.2212	.2242	.2252	.2243	.2215	.2171	.2112	.2040
5	.1334	.1464	.1586	.1699	.1802	.1891	.1966	.2026	.2071	.2099
6	.0650	.0757	.0869	.0984	.1101	.1218	.1333	.1445	.1551	.1649
7	.0247	.0305	.0371	.0444	.0524	.0611	.0704	.0803	.0905	.1010
8	.0074	.0097	.0125	.0158	.0197	.0242	.0293	.0351	.0416	.0487
9	.0017	.0024	.0033	.0044	.0058	.0075	.0096	.0121	.0151	.0185
10	.0003	.0005	.0007	.0010	.0014	.0019	.0025	.0033	.0043	.0056
11	.0000	.0001	.0001	.0002	.0002	.0004	.0005	.0007	.0010	.0013
12	.0000	.0000	.0000	.0000	.0000	.0001	.0001	.0001	.0002	.0002

r\p	.31	.32	.33	.34	.35	.36	.37	.38	.39	.40
0	.0026	.0021	.0016	.0013	.0010	.0008	.0006	.0005	.0004	.0003
1	.0190	.0157	.0130	.0107	.0087	.0071	.0058	.0047	.0038	.0030
2	.0639	.0555	.0480	.0413	.0353	.0301	.0255	.0215	.0180	.0150
3	.1341	.1220	.1103	.0992	.0888	.0790	.0699	.0615	.0538	.0468
4	.1958	.1865	.1766	.1662	.1553	.1444	.1333	.1224	.1118	.1014
5	.2111	.2107	.2088	.2054	.2008	.1949	.1879	.1801	.1715	.1623
6	.1739	.1818	.1885	.1940	.1982	.2010	.2024	.2024	.2010	.1983
7	.1116	.1222	.1326	.1428	.1524	.1615	.1698	.1772	.1836	.1889
8	.0564	.0647	.0735	.0827	.0923	.1022	.1122	.1222	.1320	.1417
9	.0225	.0271	.0322	.0379	.0442	.1511	.0586	.0666	.0750	.0840
10	.0071	.0089	.0111	.0137	.0167	.0201	.0241	.0286	.0336	.0392
11	.0017	.0023	.0030	.0038	.0049	.0062	.0077	.0095	.0117	.0142
12	.0003	.0004	.0006	.0008	.0011	.0014	.0019	.0024	.0031	.0040
13	.0000	.0001	.0001	.0001	.0002	.0003	.0003	.0005	.0006	.0008
14	.0000	.0000	.0000	.0000	.0000	.0000	.0000	.0001	.0001	.0001

r\p	.41	.42	.43	.44	.45	.46	.47	.48	.49	.50
0	.0002	.0002	.0001	.0001	.0001	.0001	.0000	.0000	.0000	.0000
1	.0024	.0019	.0015	.0012	.0009	.0007	.0005	.0004	.0003	.0002
2	.0125	.0103	.0085	.0069	.0056	.0046	.0037	.0029	.0023	.0018
3	.0405	.0349	.0299	.0254	.0215	.0181	.0151	.0126	.0104	.0085
4	.0915	.0821	.0732	.0649	.0572	.0501	.0436	.0378	.0325	.0278
5	.1526	.1426	.1325	.1224	.1123	.1024	.0929	.0837	.0749	.0667
6	.1944	.1894	.1833	.1762	.1684	.1600	.1510	.1416	.1319	.1222
7	.1930	.1959	.1975	.1978	.1969	.1947	.1912	.1867	.1811	.1746
8	.1509	.1596	.1676	.1749	.1812	.1865	.1908	.1939	.1958	.1964
9	.0932	.1027	.1124	.1221	.1318	.1413	.1504	.1591	.1672	.1746
10	.0453	.0521	.0594	.0672	.0755	.0842	.0934	.1028	.1124	.1222
11	.0172	.0206	.0244	.0288	.0337	.0391	.0452	.0518	.0589	.0667
12	.0050	.0062	.0077	.0094	.0115	.0139	.0167	.0199	.0236	.0278
13	.0011	.0014	.0018	.0023	.0029	.0036	.0046	.0057	.0070	.0085
14	.0002	.0002	.0003	.0004	.0005	.0007	.0009	.0011	.0014	.0018
15	.0000	.0000	.0000	.0000	.0001	.0001	.0001	.0001	.0002	.0002

n = 17

r \ p	.01	.02	.03	.04	.05	.06	.07	.08	.09	.10
0	.8429	.7093	.5958	.4996	.4181	.3493	.2912	.2423	.2012	.1668
1	.1447	.2461	.3133	.3539	.3741	.3790	.3726	.3582	.3383	.3150
2	.0117	.0402	.0775	.1180	.1575	.1935	.2244	.2492	.2677	.2800
3	.0006	.0041	.0120	.0246	.0415	.0618	.0844	.1083	.1324	.1556
4	.0000	.0003	.0013	.0036	.0076	.0138	.0222	.0330	.0458	.0605
5	.0000	.0000	.0001	.0004	.0010	.0023	.0044	.0075	.0118	.0175
6	.0000	.0000	.0000	.0000	.0001	.0003	.0007	.0013	.0023	.0039
7	.0000	.0000	.0000	.0000	.0000	.0000	.0001	.0002	.0004	.0007
8	.0000	.0000	.0000	.0000	.0000	.0000	.0000	.0000	.0000	.0001

r \ p	.11	.12	.13	.14	.15	.16	.17	.18	.19	.20
0	.1379	.1138	.0937	.0770	.0631	.0516	.0421	.0343	.0278	.0225
1	.2898	.2638	.2381	.2131	.1893	.1671	.1466	.1279	.1109	.0957
2	.2865	.2878	.2846	.2775	.2673	.2547	.2402	.2245	.2081	.1914
3	.1771	.1963	.2126	.2259	.2359	.2425	.2460	.2464	.2441	.2393
4	.0766	.0937	.1112	.1287	.1457	.1617	.1764	.1893	.2004	.2093
5	.0246	.0332	.0432	.0545	.0668	.0801	.0939	.1081	.1222	.1361
6	.0061	.0091	.0129	.0177	.0236	.0305	.0385	.0474	.0573	.0680
7	.0012	.0019	.0030	.0045	.0065	.0091	.0124	.0164	.0211	.0267
8	.0002	.0003	.0006	.0009	.0014	.0022	.0032	.0045	.0062	.0084
9	.0000	.0000	.0001	.0002	.0003	.0004	.0006	.0010	.0015	.0021
10	.0000	.0000	.0000	.0000	.0000	.0001	.0001	.0002	.0003	.0004
11	.0000	.0000	.0000	.0000	.0000	.0000	.0000	.0000	.0000	.0001

r \ p	.21	.22	.23	.24	.25	.26	.27	.28	.29	.30
0	.0182	.0146	.0118	.0094	.0075	.0060	.0047	.0038	.0030	.0023
1	.0822	.0702	.0597	.0505	.0426	.0357	.0299	.0248	.0206	.0169
2	.1747	.1584	.1427	.1277	.1136	.1005	.0883	.0772	.0672	.0581
3	.2322	.2234	.2131	.2016	.1893	.1765	.1634	.1502	.1372	.1245
4	.2161	.2205	.2228	.2228	.2209	.2170	.2115	.2044	.1961	.1868
5	.1493	.1617	.1730	.1830	.1914	.1982	.2033	.2067	.2083	.2081
6	.0794	.0912	.1034	.1156	.1276	.1393	.1504	.1608	.1701	.1784
7	.0332	.0404	.0485	.0573	.0668	.0769	.0874	.0982	.1092	.1201
8	.0110	.0143	.0181	.0226	.0279	.0338	.0404	.0478	.0558	.0644
9	.0029	.0040	.0054	.0071	.0093	.0119	.0150	.0186	.0228	.0276
10	.0006	.0009	.0013	.0018	.0025	.0033	.0044	.0058	.0074	.0095
11	.0001	.0002	.0002	.0004	.0005	.0007	.0010	.0014	.0019	.0026
12	.0000	.0000	.0000	.0001	.0001	.0001	.0002	.0003	.0004	.0006
13	.0000	.0000	.0000	.0000	.0000	.0000	.0000	.0000	.0001	.0001

r \ p	.31	.32	.33	.34	.35	.36	.37	.38	.39	.40
0	.0018	.0014	.0011	.0009	.0007	.0005	.0004	.0003	.0002	.0002
1	.0139	.0114	.0093	.0075	.0060	.0048	.0039	.0031	.0024	.0019
2	.0500	.0428	.0364	.0309	.0260	.0218	.0182	.0151	.0125	.0102
3	.1123	.1007	.0898	.0795	.0701	.0614	.0534	.0463	.0398	.0341
4	.1766	.1659	.1547	.1434	.1320	.1208	.1099	.0993	.0892	.0796
5	.2063	.2030	.1982	.1921	.1849	.1767	.1677	.1582	.1482	.1379
6	.1854	.1910	.1952	.1979	.1991	.1988	.1970	.1939	.1895	.1839
7	.1309	.1413	.1511	.1602	.1685	.1757	.1818	.1868	.1904	.1927
8	.0735	.0831	.0930	.1032	.1134	.1235	.1335	.1431	.1521	.1606
9	.0330	.0391	.0458	.0531	.0611	.0695	.0784	.0877	.0973	.1070
10	.0119	.0147	.0181	.0219	.0263	.0313	.0368	.0430	.0498	.0571
11	.0034	.0044	.0057	.0072	.0090	.0112	.0138	.0168	.0202	.0242
12	.0008	.0010	.0014	.0018	.0024	.0031	.0040	.0051	.0065	.0081
13	.0001	.0002	.0003	.0004	.0005	.0007	.0009	.0012	.0016	.0021
14	.0000	.0000	.0000	.0001	.0001	.0001	.0002	.0002	.0003	.0004
15	.0000	.0000	.0000	.0000	.0000	.0000	.0000	.0000	.0000	.0001

Table C >> 91

n = 17 (Continued)

r \ p	.41	.42	.43	.44	.45	.46	.47	.48	.49	.50
0	.0001	.0001	.0001	.0001	.0000	.0000	.0000	.0000	.0000	.0000
1	.0015	.0012	.0009	.0007	.0005	.0004	.0003	.0002	.0002	.0001
2	.0084	.0068	.0055	.0044	.0035	.0028	.0022	.0017	.0013	.0010
3	.0290	.0246	.0207	.0173	.0144	.0119	.0097	.0079	.0064	.0052
4	.0706	.0622	.0546	.0475	.0411	.0354	.0302	.0257	.0217	.0182
5	.1276	.1172	.1070	.0971	.0875	.0784	.0697	.0616	.0541	.0472
6	.1773	.1697	.1614	.1525	.1432	.1335	.1237	.1138	.1040	.0944
7	.1936	.1932	.1914	.1883	.1841	.1787	.1723	.1650	.1570	.1484
8	.1682	.1748	.1805	.1850	.1883	.1903	.1910	.1904	.1886	.1855
9	.1169	.1266	.1361	.1453	.1540	.1621	.1694	.1758	.1812	.1855
10	.0650	.0733	.0822	.0914	.1008	.1105	.1202	.1298	.1393	.1484
11	.0287	.0338	.0394	.0457	.0525	.0599	.0678	.0763	.0851	.0944
12	.0100	.0122	.0149	.0179	.0215	.0255	.0301	.0352	.0409	.0472
13	.0027	.0034	.0043	.0054	.0068	.0084	.0103	.0125	.0151	.0182
14	.0005	.0007	.0009	.0012	.0016	.0020	.0026	.0033	.0041	.0052
15	.0001	.0001	.0001	.0002	.0003	.0003	.0005	.0006	.0008	.0010
16	.0000	.0000	.0000	.0000	.0000	.0000	.0001	.0001	.0001	.0001

n = 18

r \ p	.01	.02	.03	.04	.05	.06	.07	.08	.09	.10
0	.8345	.6951	.5780	.4796	.3972	.3283	.2708	.2229	.1831	.1501
1	.1517	.2554	.3217	.3597	.3763	.3772	.3669	.3489	.3260	.3002
2	.0130	.0443	.0846	.1274	.1683	.2047	.2348	.2579	.2741	.2835
3	.0007	.0048	.0140	.0283	.0473	.0697	.0942	.1196	.1446	.1680
4	.0000	.0004	.0016	.0044	.0093	.0167	.0266	.0390	.0536	.0700
5	.0000	.0000	.0001	.0005	.0014	.0030	.0056	.0095	.0148	.0218
6	.0000	.0000	.0000	.0000	.0002	.0004	.0009	.0018	.0032	.0052
7	.0000	.0000	.0000	.0000	.0000	.0000	.0001	.0003	.0005	.0010
8	.0000	.0000	.0000	.0000	.0000	.0000	.0000	.0000	.0001	.0002

r \ p	.11	.12	.13	.14	.15	.16	.17	.18	.19	.20
0	.1227	.1002	.0815	.0662	.0536	.0434	.0349	.0281	.0225	.0180
1	.2731	.2458	.2193	.1940	.1704	.1486	.1288	.1110	.0951	.0811
2	.2869	.2850	.2785	.2685	.2556	.2407	.2243	.2071	.1897	.1723
3	.1891	.2072	.2220	.2331	.2406	.2445	.2450	.2425	.2373	.2297
4	.0877	.1060	.1244	.1423	.1592	.1746	.1882	.1996	.2087	.2153
5	.0303	.0405	.0520	.0649	.0787	.0931	.1079	.1227	.1371	.1507
6	.0081	.0120	.0168	.0229	.0301	.0384	.0479	.0584	.0697	.0816
7	.0017	.0028	.0043	.0064	.0091	.0126	.0168	.0220	.0280	.0350
8	.0003	.0005	.0009	.0014	.0022	.0033	.0047	.0066	.0090	.0120
9	.0000	.0001	.0001	.0003	.0004	.0007	.0011	.0016	.0024	.0033
10	.0000	.0000	.0000	.0000	.0001	.0001	.0002	.0003	.0005	.0008
11	.0000	.0000	.0000	.0000	.0000	.0000	.0000	.0001	.0001	.0001

r \ p	.21	.22	.23	.24	.25	.26	.27	.28	.29	.30
0	.0144	.0114	.0091	.0072	.0056	.0044	.0035	.0027	.0021	.0016
1	.0687	.0580	.0487	.0407	.0338	.0280	.0231	.0189	.0155	.0126
2	.1553	.1390	.1236	.1092	.0958	.0836	.0725	.0626	.0537	.0458
3	.2202	.2091	.1969	.1839	.1704	.1567	.1431	.1298	.1169	.1046
4	.2195	.2212	.2205	.2177	.2130	.2065	.1985	.1892	.1790	.1681
5	.1634	.1747	.1845	.1925	.1988	.2031	.2055	.2061	.2048	.2017
6	.0941	.1067	.1194	.1317	.1436	.1546	.1647	.1736	.1812	.1873
7	.0429	.0516	.0611	.0713	.0820	.0931	.1044	.1157	.1269	.1376
8	.0157	.0200	.0251	.0310	.0376	.0450	.0531	.0619	.0713	.0811
9	.0046	.0063	.0083	.0109	.0139	.0176	.0218	.0267	.0323	.0386
10	.0011	.0016	.0022	.0031	.0042	.0056	.0073	.0094	.0119	.0149
11	.0002	.0003	.0005	.0007	.0010	.0014	.0020	.0026	.0035	.0046
12	.0000	.0001	.0001	.0001	.0002	.0003	.0004	.0006	.0008	.0012
13	.0000	.0000	.0000	.0000	.0000	.0000	.0001	.0001	.0002	.0002

n = 18 (Continued)

r \ p	.31	.32	.33	.34	.35	.36	.37	.38	.39	.40
0	.0013	.0010	.0007	.0006	.0004	.0003	.0002	.0002	.0001	.0001
1	.0102	.0082	.0066	.0052	.0042	.0033	.0026	.0020	.0016	.0012
2	.0388	.0327	.0275	.0229	.0190	.0157	.0129	.0105	.0086	.0069
3	.0930	.0822	.0722	.0630	.0547	.0471	.0404	.0344	.0292	.0246
4	.1567	.1450	.1333	.1217	.1104	.0994	.0890	.0791	.0699	.0614
5	.1971	.1911	.1838	.1755	.1664	.1566	.1463	.1358	.1252	.1146
6	.1919	.1948	.1962	.1959	.1941	.1908	.1862	.1803	.1734	.1655
7	.1478	.1572	.1656	.1730	.1792	.1840	.1875	.1895	.1900	.1892
8	.0913	.1017	.1122	.1226	.1327	.1423	.1514	.1597	.1671	.1734
9	.0456	.0532	.0614	.0701	.0794	.0890	.0988	.1087	.1187	.1284
10	.0184	.0225	.0272	.0325	.0385	.0450	.0522	.0600	.0683	.0771
11	.0060	.0077	.0097	.0122	.0151	.0184	.0223	.0267	.0318	.0374
12	.0016	.0021	.0028	.0037	.0047	.0060	.0076	.0096	.0118	.0145
13	.0003	.0005	.0006	.0009	.0012	.0016	.0021	.0027	.0035	.0045
14	.0001	.0001	.0001	.0002	.0002	.0003	.0004	.0006	.0008	.0011
15	.0000	.0000	.0000	.0000	.0000	.0000	.0001	.0001	.0001	.0002

r \ p	.41	.42	.43	.44	.45	.46	.47	.48	.49	.50
0	.0001	.0001	.0000	.0000	.0000	.0000	.0000	.0000	.0000	.0000
1	.0009	.0007	.0005	.0004	.0003	.0002	.0002	.0001	.0001	.0001
2	.0055	.0044	.0035	.0028	.0022	.0017	.0013	.0010	.0008	.0006
3	.0206	.0171	.0141	.0116	.0095	.0077	.0062	.0050	.0039	.0031
4	.0536	.0464	.0400	.0342	.0291	.0246	.0206	.0172	.0142	.0117
5	.1042	.0941	.0844	.0753	.0666	.0586	.0512	.0444	.0382	.0327
6	.1569	.1477	.1380	.1281	.1181	.1081	.0983	.0887	.0796	.0708
7	.1869	.1833	.1785	.1726	.1657	.1579	.1494	.1404	.1310	.1214
8	.1786	.1825	.1852	.1864	.1864	.1850	.1822	.1782	.1731	.1669
9	.1379	.1469	.1552	.1628	.1694	.1751	.1795	.1828	.1848	.1855
10	.0862	.0957	.1054	.1151	.1248	.1342	.1433	.1519	.1598	.1669
11	.0436	.0504	.0578	.0658	.0742	.0831	.0924	.1020	.1117	.1214
12	.0177	.0213	.0254	.0301	.0354	.0413	.0478	.1549	.0626	.0708
13	.0057	.0071	.0089	.0109	.0134	.0162	.0196	.0234	.0278	.0327
14	.0014	.0018	.0024	.0031	.0039	.0049	.0062	.0077	.0095	.0117
15	.0003	.0004	.0005	.0006	.0009	.0011	.0015	.0019	.0024	.0031
16	.0000	.0000	.0001	.0001	.0001	.0002	.0002	.0003	.0004	.0006
17	.0000	.0000	.0000	.0000	.0000	.0000	.0000	.0000	.0000	.0001

n = 19

r \ p	.01	.02	.03	.04	.05	.06	.07	.08	.09	.10
0	.8262	.6812	.5606	.4604	.3774	.3086	.2519	.2051	.1666	.1351
1	.1586	.2642	.3294	.3645	.3774	.3743	.3602	.3389	.3131	.2852
2	.0144	.0485	.0917	.1367	.1787	.2150	.2440	.2652	.2787	.2852
3	.0008	.0056	.0161	.0323	.0533	.0778	.1041	.1307	.1562	.1796
4	.0000	.0005	.0020	.0054	.0112	.0199	.0313	.0455	.0618	.0798
5	.0000	.0000	.0002	.0007	.0018	.0038	.0071	.0119	.0183	.0266
6	.0000	.0000	.0000	.0001	.0002	.0006	.0012	.0024	.0042	.0069
7	.0000	.0000	.0000	.0000	.0000	.0001	.0002	.0004	.0008	.0014
8	.0000	.0000	.0000	.0000	.0000	.0000	.0000	.0001	.0001	.0002

r \ p	.11	.12	.13	.14	.15	.16	.17	.18	.19	.20
0	.1092	.0881	.0709	.0569	.0456	.0364	.0290	.0230	.0182	.0144
1	.2565	.2284	.2014	.1761	.1529	.1318	.1129	.0961	.0813	.0685
2	.2854	.2803	.2708	.2581	.2428	.2259	.2081	.1898	.1717	.1540
3	.1999	.2166	.2293	.2381	.2428	.2439	.2415	.2361	.2282	.2182
4	.0988	.1181	.1371	.1550	.1714	.1858	.1979	.2073	.2141	.2182
5	.0366	.0483	.0614	.0757	.0907	.1062	.1216	.1365	.1507	.1636
6	.0106	.0154	.0214	.0288	.0374	.0472	.0581	.0699	.0825	.0955
7	.0024	.0039	.0059	.0087	.0122	.0167	.0221	.0285	.0359	.0443
8	.0004	.0008	.0013	.0021	.0032	.0048	.0068	.0094	.0126	.0166
9	.0001	.0001	.0002	.0004	.0007	.0011	.0017	.0025	.0036	.0051
10	.0000	.0000	.0000	.0001	.0001	.0002	.0003	.0006	.0009	.0013
11	.0000	.0000	.0000	.0000	.0000	.0000	.0001	.0001	.0002	.0003

Table C >> **93**

n = 19 (Continued)

r \ p	.21	.22	.23	.24	.25	.26	.27	.28	.29	.30
0	.0113	.0089	.0070	.0054	.0042	.0033	.0025	.0019	.0015	.0011
1	.0573	.0477	.0396	.0326	.0268	.0219	.0178	.0144	.0116	.0093
2	.1371	.1212	.1064	.0927	.0803	.0692	.0592	.0503	.0426	.0358
3	.2065	.1937	.1800	.1659	.1517	.1377	.1240	.1109	.0985	.0869
4	.2196	.2185	.2151	.2096	.2023	.1935	.1835	.1726	.1610	.1491
5	.1751	.1849	.1928	.1986	.2023	.2040	.2036	.2013	.1973	.1916
6	.1086	.1217	.1343	.1463	.1574	.1672	.1757	.1827	.1880	.1916
7	.0536	.0637	.0745	.0858	.0974	.1091	.1207	.1320	.1426	.1525
8	.0214	.0270	.0334	.0406	.0487	.0575	.0670	.0770	.0874	.0981
9	.0069	.0093	.0122	.0157	.0198	.0247	.0303	.0366	.0436	.0514
10	.0018	.0026	.0036	.0050	.0066	.0087	.0112	.0142	.0178	.0220
11	.0004	.0006	.0009	.0013	.0018	.0025	.0034	.0045	.0060	.0077
12	.0001	.0001	.0002	.0003	.0004	.0006	.0008	.0012	.0016	.0022
13	.0000	.0000	.0000	.0000	.0001	.0001	.0002	.0002	.0004	.0005
14	.0000	.0000	.0000	.0000	.0000	.0000	.0000	.0000	.0001	.0001

r \ p	.31	.32	.33	.34	.35	.36	.37	.38	.39	.40
0	.0009	.0007	.0005	.0004	.0003	.0002	.0002	.0001	.0001	.0001
1	.0074	.0059	.0046	.0036	.0029	.0022	.0017	.0013	.0010	.0008
2	.0299	.0249	.0206	.0169	.0138	.0112	.0091	.0073	.0058	.0046
3	.0762	.0664	.0574	.0494	.0422	.0358	.0302	.0253	.0211	.0175
4	.1370	.1249	.1131	.1017	.0909	.0806	.0710	.0621	.0540	.0467
5	.1846	.1764	.1672	.1572	.1468	.1360	.1251	.1143	.1036	.0933
6	.1935	.1936	.1921	.1890	.1844	.1785	.1714	.1634	.1546	.1451
7	.1615	.1692	.1757	.1808	.1844	.1865	.1870	.1860	.1835	.1797
8	.1088	.1195	.1298	.1397	.1489	.1573	.1647	.1710	.1760	.1797
9	.0597	.0687	.0782	.0880	.0980	.1082	.1182	.1281	.1375	.1464
10	.0268	.0323	.0385	.0453	.0528	.0608	.0694	.0785	.0879	.0976
11	.0099	.0124	.0155	.0191	.0233	.0280	.0334	.0394	.0460	.0532
12	.0030	.0039	.0051	.0066	.0083	.0105	.0131	.0161	.0196	.0237
13	.0007	.0010	.0014	.0018	.0024	.0032	.0041	.0053	.0067	.0085
14	.0001	.0002	.0003	.0004	.0006	.0008	.0010	.0014	.0018	.0024
15	.0000	.0000	.0000	.0001	.0001	.0001	.0002	.0003	.0004	.0005
16	.0000	.0000	.0000	.0000	.0000	.0000	.0000	.0000	.0001	.0001

r \ p	.41	.42	.43	.44	.45	.46	.47	.48	.49	.50
0	.0000	.0000	.0000	.0000	.0000	.0000	.0000	.0000	.0000	.0000
1	.0006	.0004	.0003	.0002	.0002	.0001	.0001	.0001	.0001	.0000
2	.0037	.0029	.0022	.0017	.0013	.0010	.0008	.0006	.0004	.0003
3	.0144	.0118	.0096	.0077	.0062	.0049	.0039	.0031	.0024	.0018
4	.0400	.0341	.0289	.0243	.0203	.0168	.0138	.0113	.0092	.0074
5	.0834	.0741	.0653	.0572	.0497	.0429	.0368	.0313	.0265	.0222
6	.1353	.1252	.1150	.1049	.0949	.0853	.0751	.0674	.0593	.0518
7	.1746	.1683	.1611	.1530	.1443	.1350	.1254	.1156	.1058	.0961
8	.1820	.1829	.1823	.1803	.1771	.1725	.1668	.1601	.1525	.1442
9	.1546	.1618	.1681	.1732	.1771	.1796	.1808	.1806	.1791	.1762
10	.1074	.1172	.1268	.1361	.1449	.1530	.1603	.1667	.1721	.1762
11	.0611	.0694	.0783	.0875	.0970	.1066	.1163	.1259	.1352	.1442
12	.0283	.0335	.0394	.0458	.0529	.0606	.0688	.0775	.0866	.0961
13	.0106	.0131	.0160	.0194	.0233	.0278	.0328	.0385	.0448	.0518
14	.0032	.0041	.0052	.0065	.0082	.0101	.0125	.0152	.0185	.0222
15	.0007	.0010	.0013	.0017	.0022	.0029	.0037	.0047	.0059	.0074
16	.0001	.0002	.0002	.0003	.0005	.0006	.0008	.0011	.0014	.0018
17	.0000	.0000	.0000	.0000	.0001	.0001	.0001	.0002	.0002	.0003

n = 20

r \ p	.01	.02	.03	.04	.05	.06	.07	.08	.09	.10
0	.8179	.6676	.5438	.4420	.3585	.2901	.2342	.1887	.1516	.1216
1	.1652	.2725	.3364	.3683	.3774	.3703	.3526	.3282	.3000	.2702
2	.0159	.0528	.0988	.1458	.1887	.2246	.2521	.2711	.2818	.2852
3	.0010	.0065	.0183	.0364	.0596	.0860	.1139	.1414	.1672	.1901
4	.0000	.0006	.0024	.0065	.0133	.0233	.0364	.0523	.0703	.0898
5	.0000	.0000	.0002	.0009	.0022	.0048	.0088	.0145	.0222	.0319
6	.0000	.0000	.0000	.0001	.0003	.0008	.0017	.0032	.0055	.0089
7	.0000	.0000	.0000	.0000	.0000	.0001	.0002	.0005	.0011	.0020
8	.0000	.0000	.0000	.0000	.0000	.0000	.0000	.0001	.0002	.0004
9	.0000	.0000	.0000	.0000	.0000	.0000	.0000	.0000	.0000	.0001

					n = 20 (Continued)					
r \ p	.11	.12	.13	.14	.15	.16	.17	.18	.19	.20
0	.0972	.0776	.0617	.0490	.0388	.0306	.0241	.0189	.0148	.0115
1	.2403	.2115	.1844	.1595	.1368	.1165	.0986	.0829	.0693	.0576
2	.2822	.2740	.2618	.2466	.2293	.2109	.1919	.1730	.1545	.1369
3	.2093	.2242	.2347	.2409	.2428	.2410	.2358	.2278	.2175	.2054
4	.1099	.1299	.1491	.1666	.1821	.1951	.2053	.2125	.2168	.2182
5	.0435	.0567	.0713	.1868	.1028	.1189	.1345	.1493	.1627	.1746
6	.0134	.0193	.0266	.0353	.0454	.0566	.0689	.0819	.0954	.1091
7	.0033	.0053	.0080	.0115	.0160	.0216	.0282	.0360	.0448	.0545
8	.0007	.0012	.0019	.0030	.0046	.0067	.0094	.0128	.0171	.0222
9	.0001	.0002	.0004	.0007	.0011	.0017	.0026	.0038	.0053	.0074
10	.0000	.0000	.0001	.0001	.0002	.0004	.0006	.0009	.0014	.0020
11	.0000	.0000	.0000	.0000	.0000	.0001	.0001	.0002	.0003	.0005
12	.0000	.0000	.0000	.0000	.0000	.0000	.0000	.0000	.0001	.0001

	.21	.22	.23	.24	.25	.26	.27	.28	.29	.30
0	.0090	.0069	.0054	.0041	.0032	.0024	.0018	.0014	.0011	.0008
1	.0477	.0392	.0321	.0261	.0211	.0170	.0137	.0109	.0087	.0068
2	.1204	.1050	.0910	.0783	.0669	.0569	.0480	.0403	.0336	.0278
3	.1920	.1777	.1631	.1484	.1339	.1199	.1065	.0940	.0823	.0716
4	.2169	.2131	.2070	.1991	.1897	.1790	.1675	.1553	.1429	.1304
5	.1845	.1923	.1979	.2012	.2023	.2013	.1982	.1933	.1868	.1789
6	.1226	.1356	.1478	.1589	.1686	.1768	.1833	.1879	.1907	.1916
7	.0652	.0765	.0883	.1003	.1124	.1242	.1356	.1462	.1558	.1643
8	.0282	.0351	.0429	.0515	.0609	.0709	.0815	.0924	.1034	.1144
9	.0100	.0132	.0171	.0217	.0271	.0332	.0402	.0479	.0563	.0654
10	.0029	.0041	.0056	.0075	.0099	.0128	.0163	.0205	.0253	.0308
11	.0007	.0010	.0015	.0022	.0030	.0041	.0055	.0072	.0094	.0120
12	.0001	.0002	.0003	.0005	.0008	.0011	.0015	.0021	.0029	.0039
13	.0000	.0000	.0001	.0001	.0002	.0002	.0003	.0005	.0007	.0010
14	.0000	.0000	.0000	.0000	.0000	.0000	.0001	.0001	.0001	.0002

	.31	.32	.33	.34	.35	.36	.37	.38	.39	.40
0	.0006	.0004	.0003	.0002	.0002	.0001	.0001	.0001	.0001	.0000
1	.0054	.0042	.0033	.0025	.0020	.0015	.0011	.0009	.0007	.0005
2	.0229	.0188	.0153	.0124	.0100	.0080	.0064	.0050	.0040	.0031
3	.0619	.0531	.0453	.0383	.0323	.0270	.0224	.0185	.0152	.0123
4	.1181	.1062	.0947	.0839	.0738	.0645	.0559	.0482	.0412	.0350
5	.1698	.1599	.1493	.1384	.1272	.1161	.1051	.0945	.0843	.0746
6	.1907	.1881	.1839	.1782	.1712	.1632	.1543	.1447	.1347	.1244
7	.1714	.1770	.1811	.1836	.1844	.1836	.1812	.1774	.1722	.1659
8	.1251	.1354	.1450	.1537	.1614	.1678	.1730	.1767	.1790	.1797
9	.0750	.0849	.0952	.1056	.1158	.1259	.1354	.1444	.1526	.1597
10	.0370	.0440	.0516	.0598	.0686	.0779	.0875	.0974	.1073	.1171
11	.0151	.0188	.0231	.0280	.0336	.0398	.0467	.0542	.0624	.0710
12	.0051	.0066	.0085	.0108	.0136	.0168	.0206	.0249	.0299	.0355
13	.0014	.0019	.0026	.0034	.0045	.0058	.0074	.0094	.0118	.0146
14	.0003	.0005	.0006	.0009	.0012	.0016	.0022	.0029	.0038	.0049
15	.0001	.0001	.0001	.0002	.0003	.0004	.0005	.0007	.0010	.0013
16	.0000	.0000	.0000	.0000	.0000	.0001	.0001	.0001	.0002	.0003

	.41	.42	.43	.44	.45	.46	.47	.48	.49	.50
0	.0000	.0000	.0000	.0000	.0000	.0000	.0000	.0000	.0000	.0000
1	.0004	.0003	.0002	.0001	.0001	.0001	.0001	.0000	.0000	.0000
2	.0024	.0018	.0014	.0011	.0008	.0006	.0005	.0003	.0002	.0002
3	.0100	.0080	.0064	.0051	.0040	.0031	.0024	.0019	.0014	.0011
4	.0295	.0247	.0206	.0170	.0139	.0113	.0092	.0074	.0059	.0046
5	.0656	.0573	.0496	.0427	.0365	.0309	.0260	.0217	.0180	.0148
6	.1140	.1037	.0936	.0839	.0746	.0658	.0577	.0501	.0432	.0370
7	.1585	.1502	.1413	.1318	.1221	.1122	.1023	.0925	.0830	.0739
8	.1790	.1768	.1732	.1683	.1623	.1553	.1474	.1388	.1296	.1201
9	.1658	.1707	.1742	.1763	.1771	.1763	.1742	.1708	.1661	.1602
10	.1268	.1359	.1446	.1524	.1593	.1652	.1700	.1734	.1755	.1762
11	.0801	.0895	.0991	.1089	.1185	.1280	.1370	.1455	.1533	.1602
12	.0417	.0486	.0561	.0642	.0727	.0818	.0911	.1007	.1105	.1201
13	.0178	.0217	.0260	.0310	.0366	.0429	.0497	.0572	.0653	.0739
14	.0062	.0078	.0098	.0122	.0150	.0183	.0221	.0264	.0314	.0370
15	.0017	.0023	.0030	.0038	.0049	.0062	.0078	.0098	.0121	.0148
16	.0004	.0005	.0007	.0009	.0013	.0017	.0022	.0028	.0036	.0046
17	.0001	.0001	.0001	.0002	.0002	.0003	.0005	.0006	.0008	.0011
18	.0000	.0000	.0000	.0000	.0000	.0000	.0001	.0001	.0001	.0002

Table C >> **95**

n = 25

r \ p	.01	.02	.03	.04	.05	.06	.07	.08	.09	.10
0	.7778	.6035	.4670	.3604	.2774	.2129	.1630	.1244	.0946	.0718
1	.1964	.3079	.3611	.3754	.3650	.3398	.3066	.2704	.2340	.1994
2	.0238	.0754	.1340	.1877	.2305	.2602	.2770	.2821	.2777	.2659
3	.0018	.0118	.0318	.0600	.0930	.1273	.1598	.1881	.2106	.2265
4	.0001	.0013	.0054	.0137	.0269	.0447	.0662	.0899	.1145	.1384
5	.0000	.0001	.0007	.0024	.0060	.0120	.0209	.0329	.0476	.0646
6	.0000	.0000	.0001	.0003	.0010	.0026	.0052	.0095	.0157	.0239
7	.0000	.0000	.0000	.0000	.0001	.0004	.0011	.0022	.0042	.0072
8	.0000	.0000	.0000	.0000	.0000	.0001	.0002	.0004	.0009	.0018
9	0	.0000	.0000	.0000	.0000	.0000	.0000	.0001	.0002	.0004
10	0	.0000	.0000	.0000	.0000	.0000	.0000	.0000	.0000	.0001

r \ p	.11	.12	.13	.14	.15	.16	.17	.18	.19	.20
0	.0543	.0409	.0308	.0230	.0172	.0128	.0095	.0070	.0052	.0038
1	.1678	.1395	.1149	.0938	.0759	.0609	.0486	.0384	.0302	.0236
2	.2488	.2283	.2060	.1832	.1607	.1392	.1193	.1012	.0851	.0708
3	.2358	.2387	.2360	.2286	.2174	.2033	.1874	.1704	.1530	.1358
4	.1603	.1790	.1940	.2047	.2110	.2130	.2111	.2057	.1974	.1867
5	.0832	.1025	.1217	.1399	.1564	.1704	.1816	.1897	.1945	.1960
6	.0343	.0466	.0606	.0759	.0920	.1082	.1240	.1388	.1520	.1633
7	.0115	.0173	.0246	.0336	.0441	.0559	.0689	.0827	.0968	.1108
8	.0032	.0053	.0083	.0123	.0175	.0240	.0318	.0408	.0511	.0623
9	.0007	.0014	.0023	.0038	.0058	.0086	.0123	.0169	.0226	.0294
10	.0001	.0003	.0006	.0010	.0016	.0026	.0040	.0059	.0085	.0118
11	.0000	.0001	.0001	.0002	.0004	.0007	.0011	.0018	.0027	.0040
12	.0000	.0000	.0000	.0000	.0001	.0002	.0003	.0005	.0007	.0012
13	.0000	.0000	.0000	.0000	.0000	.0000	.0001	.0001	.0002	.0003
14	.0000	.0000	.0000	.0000	.0000	.0000	.0000	.0000	.0000	.0001

r \ p	.21	.22	.23	.24	.25	.26	.27	.28	.29	.30
0	.0028	.0020	.0015	.0010	.0008	.0005	.0004	.0003	.0002	.0001
1	.0183	.0141	.0109	.0083	.0063	.0047	.0035	.0026	.0020	.0014
2	.0585	.0479	.0389	.0314	.0251	.0199	.0157	.0123	.0096	.0074
3	.1192	.1035	.0891	.0759	.0641	.0537	.0446	.0367	.0300	.0243
4	.1742	.1606	.1463	.1318	.1175	.1037	.0906	.0785	.0673	.0572
5	.1945	.1903	.1836	.1749	.1645	.1531	.1408	.1282	.1155	.1030
6	.1724	.1789	.1828	.1841	.1828	.1793	.1736	.1661	.1572	.1472
7	.1244	.1369	.1482	.1578	.1654	.1709	.1743	.1754	.1743	.1712
8	.0744	.0869	.0996	.1121	.1241	.1351	.1450	.1535	.1602	.1651
9	.0373	.0463	.0562	.0669	.0781	.0897	.1013	.1127	.1236	.1336
10	.0159	.0209	.0269	.0338	.0417	.0504	.0600	.0701	.0808	.0916
11	.0058	.0080	.0109	.0145	.0189	.0242	.0302	.0372	.0450	.0536
12	.0018	.0026	.0038	.0054	.0074	.0099	.0130	.0169	.0214	.0268
13	.0005	.0007	.0011	.0017	.0025	.0035	.0048	.0066	.0088	.0115
14	.0001	.0002	.0003	.0005	.0007	.0010	.0015	.0022	.0031	.0042
15	.0000	.0000	.0001	.0001	.0002	.0003	.0004	.0006	.0009	.0013
16	.0000	.0000	.0000	.0000	.0000	.0001	.0001	.0002	.0002	.0004
17	.0000	.0000	.0000	.0000	.0000	.0000	.0000	.0000	.0001	.0001

r \ p	.31	.32	.33	.34	.35	.36	.37	.38	.39	.40
0	.0001	.0001	.0000	.0000	.0000	.0000	.0000	.0000	.0000	.0000
1	.0011	.0008	.0006	.0004	.0003	.0002	.0001	.0001	.0001	.0000
2	.0057	.0043	.0033	.0025	.0018	.0014	.0010	.0007	.0005	.0004
3	.0195	.0156	.0123	.0097	.0076	.0058	.0045	.0034	.0026	.0019
4	.0482	.0403	.0334	.0274	.0224	.0181	.0145	.0115	.0091	.0071
5	.0910	.0797	.0691	.0594	.0506	.0427	.0357	.0297	.0244	.0199
6	.1363	.1250	.1134	.1020	.0908	.0801	.0700	.0606	.0520	.0442
7	.1662	.1596	.1516	.1426	.1327	.1222	.1115	.1008	.0902	.0800
8	.1680	.1690	.1681	.1652	.1607	.1547	.1474	.1390	.1298	.1200
9	.1426	.1502	.1563	.1608	.1635	.1644	.1635	.1609	.1567	.1511
10	.1025	.1131	.1232	.1325	.1409	.1479	.1536	.1578	.1603	.1612
11	.0628	.0726	.0828	.0931	.1034	.1135	.1230	.1319	.1398	.1465
12	.0329	.0399	.0476	.0560	.0650	.0745	.0843	.0943	.1043	.1140
13	.0148	.0188	.0234	.0288	.0350	.0419	.0495	.0578	.0667	.0760
14	.0057	.0076	.0099	.0127	.0161	.0202	.0249	.0304	.0365	.0434
15	.0019	.0026	.0036	.0048	.0064	.0083	.0107	.0136	.0171	.0212
16	.0005	.0008	.0011	.0015	.0021	.0029	.0039	.0052	.0068	.0088
17	.0001	.0002	.0003	.0004	.0006	.0009	.0012	.0017	.0023	.0031
18	.0000	.0000	.0001	.0001	.0001	.0002	.0003	.0005	.0007	.0009
19	.0000	.0000	.0000	.0000	.0000	.0000	.0001	.0001	.0002	.0002

					n = 25 (Continued)					
p r	.41	.42	.43	.44	.45	.46	.47	.48	.49	.50
0	.0000	.0000	.0000	.0000	.0000	.0000	.0000	.0000	.0000	.0000
1	.0000	.0000	.0000	.0000	.0000	.0000	.0000	.0000	.0000	.0000
2	.0003	.0002	.0001	.0001	.0001	.0000	.0000	.0000	.0000	.0000
3	.0014	.0011	.0008	.0006	.0004	.0003	.0002	.0001	.0001	.0001
4	.0055	.0042	.0032	.0024	.0018	.0014	.0010	.0007	.0005	.0004
5	.0161	.0129	.0102	.0081	.0063	.0049	.0037	.0028	.0021	.0016
6	.0372	.0311	.0257	.0211	.0172	.0138	.0110	.0087	.0068	.0053
7	.0703	.0611	.0527	.0450	.0381	.0319	.0265	.0218	.0178	.0143
8	.1099	.0996	.0895	.0796	.0701	.0612	.0529	.0453	.0384	.0322
9	.1442	.1363	.1275	.1181	.1084	.0985	.o886	.0790	.0697	.0609
10	.1603	.1579	.1539	.1485	.1419	.1342	.1257	.1166	.1071	.0974
11	.1519	.1559	.1583	.1591	.1583	.1559	.1521	.1468	.1404	.1328
12	.1232	.1317	.1393	.1458	.1511	.1550	.1573	.1581	.1573	.1550
13	.0856	.0954	.1051	.1146	.1236	.1320	.1395	.1460	.1512	.1550
14	.0510	.0592	.0680	.0772	.0867	.0964	.1060	.1155	.1245	.1328
15	.0260	.0314	.0376	.0445	.0520	.0602	.0690	.0782	.0877	.0974
16	.0113	.0142	.0177	.0218	.0266	.0321	.0382	.0451	.0527	.0609
17	.0042	.0055	.0071	.0091	.0115	.0145	.0179	.0220	.0268	.0322
18	.0013	.0018	.0024	.0032	.0042	.0055	.0071	.0090	.0114	.0143
19	.0003	.0005	.0007	.0009	.0013	.0017	.0023	.0031	.0040	.0053
20	.0001	.0001	.0001	.0002	.0003	.0004	.0006	.0009	.0012	.0016
21	.0000	.0000	.0000	.0000	.0001	.0001	.0001	.0002	.0003	.0004
22	.0000	.0000	.0000	.0000	.0000	.0000	.0000	.0000	.0000	.0001

					n = 30					
p r	.01	.02	.03	.04	.05	.06	.07	.08	.09	.10
0	.7397	.5455	.4010	.2939	.2146	.1563	.1134	.0820	.0591	.0424
1	.2242	.3340	.3721	.3673	.3389	.2992	.2560	.2138	.1752	.1413
2	.0328	.0988	.1669	.2219	.2586	.2769	.2794	.2696	.2513	.2277
3	.0031	.0188	.0482	.0863	.1270	.1650	.1963	.2188	.2319	.2361
4	.0002	.0026	.0101	.0243	.0451	.0711	.0997	.1284	.1548	.1771
5	.0000	.0003	.0016	.0053	.0124	.0236	.0390	.0581	.0796	.1023
6	.0000	.0000	.0002	.0009	.0027	.0063	.0122	.0210	.0328	.0474
7	.0000	.0000	.0000	.0001	.0005	.0014	.0032	.0063	.0111	.0180
8	.0000	.0000	.0000	.0000	.0001	.0003	.0007	.0016	.0032	.0058
9	0	.0000	.0000	.0000	.0000	.0000	.0001	.0003	.0008	.0016
10	0	.0000	.0000	.0000	.0000	.0000	.0000	.0001	.0002	.0004
11	0	0	.0000	.0000	.0000	.0000	.0000	.0000	.0000	.0001
12	0	0	.0000	.0000	.0000	.0000	.0000	.0000	.0000	.0000
13	0	0	0	.0000	.0000	.^000	.0000	.0000	.0000	.0000

	.11	.12	.13	.14	.15	.16	.17	.18	.19	.20
0	.0303	.0216	.0153	.0108	.0076	.0054	.0037	.0026	.0018	.0012
1	.1124	.0884	.0687	.0529	.0404	.0306	.0230	.0171	.0126	.0093
2	.2015	.1747	.1489	.1249	.1034	.0844	.0682	.0544	.0430	.0337
3	.2324	.2224	.2077	.1898	.1703	.1501	.1303	.1115	.0942	.0785
4	.1939	.2047	.2095	.2086	.2028	.1930	.1802	.1652	.1491	.1325
5	.1246	.1451	.1628	.1766	.1861	.1912	.1919	.1886	.1819	.1723
6	.0642	.0825	.1013	.1198	.1368	.1517	.1638	.1725	.1777	.1795
7	.0272	.0386	.0519	.0668	.0828	.0991	.1150	.1298	.1429	.1538
8	.0097	.0151	.0223	.0313	.0420	.0543	.0677	.0819	.0964	.1106
9	.0029	.0050	.0081	.0125	.0181	.0253	.0339	.0440	.0553	.0676
10	.0008	.0014	.0026	.0043	.0067	.0101	.0146	.0203	.0272	.0355
11	.0002	.0004	.0007	.0013	.0022	.0035	.0054	.0081	.0116	.0161
12	.0000	.0001	.0002	.0003	.0006	.0011	.0018	.0028	.0043	.0064
13	.0000	.0000	.0000	.0001	.0001	.0003	.0005	.0009	.0014	.0022
14	.0000	.0000	.0000	.0000	.0000	.0001	.0001	.0002	.0004	.0007
15	.0000	.0000	.0000	.0000	.0000	.0000	.0000	.0001	.0001	.0002

Table C>> **97**

n = 30 (Continued)

p / r	.21	.22	.23	.24	.25	.26	.27	.28	.29	.30
0	.0008	.0006	.0004	.0003	.0002	.0001	.0001	.0001	.0000	.0000
1	.0068	.0049	.0035	.0025	.0018	.0013	.0009	.0006	.0004	.0003
2	.0261	.0200	.0153	.0115	.0086	.0064	.0047	.0035	.0025	.0018
3	.0647	.0528	.0426	.0340	.0269	.0210	.0163	.0125	.0095	.0072
4	.1161	.1005	.0858	.0724	.0604	.0499	.0407	.0329	.0263	.0208
5	.1605	.1473	.1333	.1189	.1047	.0911	.0783	.0665	.0559	.0464
6	.1778	.1732	.1659	.1565	.1455	.1334	.1207	.1078	.0951	.0829
7	.1621	.1674	.1699	.1694	.1662	.1606	.1530	.1437	.1332	.1219
8	.1239	.1358	.1459	.1538	.1593	.1623	.1627	.1607	.1564	.1501
9	.0805	.0936	.1065	.1187	.1298	.1394	.1471	.1527	.1562	.1573
10	.0449	.0554	.0668	.0787	.0909	.1028	.1143	.1247	.1339	.1416
11	.0217	.0284	.0363	.0452	.0551	.0657	.0768	.0882	.0995	.1103
12	.0091	.0127	.0172	.0226	.0291	.0365	.0450	.0543	.0643	.0749
13	.0034	.0050	.0071	.0099	.0134	.0178	.0230	.0292	.0364	.0444
14	.0011	.0017	.0026	.0038	.0054	.0076	.0103	.0138	.0180	.0231
15	.0003	.0005	.0008	.0013	.0019	.0028	.0041	.0057	.0079	.0106
16	.0001	.0001	.0002	.0004	.0006	.0009	.0014	.0021	.0030	.0042
17	.0000	.0000	.0001	.0001	.0002	.0003	.0004	.0007	.0010	.0015
18	.0000	.0000	.0000	.0000	.0000	.0001	.0001	.0002	.0003	.0005
19	.0000	.0000	.0000	.0000	.0000	.0000	.0000	.0000	.0001	.0001

r	.31	.32	.33	.34	.35	.36	.37	.38	.39	.40
0	.0000	.0000	.0000	.0000	.0000	.0000	.0000	.0000	.0000	.0000
1	.0002	.0001	.0001	.0001	.0000	.0000	.0000	.0000	.0000	.0000
2	.0013	.0009	.0006	.0004	.0003	.0002	.0001	.0001	.0001	.0000
3	.0054	.0040	.0029	.0021	.0015	.0011	.0008	.0006	.0004	.0003
4	.0163	.0127	.0098	.0074	.0056	.0042	.0031	.0023	.0017	.0012
5	.0382	.0311	.0250	.0199	.0157	.0123	.0095	.0073	.0055	.0041
6	.0715	.0609	.0513	.0428	.0353	.0288	.0233	.0186	.0147	.0115
7	.1101	.0983	.0867	.0756	.0652	.0556	.0469	.0391	.0323	.0263
8	.1422	.1330	.1228	.1120	.1009	.0899	.0792	.0689	.0593	.0505
9	.1562	.1530	.1478	.1410	.1328	.1236	.1136	.1032	.0927	.0823
10	.1474	.1512	.1529	.1526	.1502	.1460	.1402	.1329	.1245	.1152
11	.1204	.1293	.1369	.1429	.1471	.1493	.1497	.1481	.1447	.1390
12	.0856	.0964	.1068	.1166	.1254	.1330	.1392	.1437	.1465	.1474
13	.0533	.1628	.1728	.0831	.0935	.1036	.1132	.1219	.1296	.1360
14	.0291	.0359	.0436	.0520	.0611	.0708	.0807	.0908	.1007	.1101
15	.0139	.0180	.0229	.0286	.0351	.0425	.0506	.0593	.0686	.0783
16	.0059	.0079	.0106	.0138	.0177	.0224	.0278	.0341	.0411	.0489
17	.0022	.0031	.0043	.0059	.0079	.0104	.0135	.0172	.0217	.0269
18	.0007	.0010	.0015	.0022	.0031	.0042	.0057	.0076	.0100	.0129
19	.0002	.0003	.0005	.0007	.0010	.0015	.0021	.0029	.0040	.0054
20	.0000	.0001	.0001	.0002	.0003	.0005	.0007	.0010	.0014	.0020
21	.0000	.0000	.0000	.0000	.0001	.0001	.0002	.0003	.0004	.0006
22	.0000	.0000	.0000	.0000	.0000	.0000	.0000	.0001	.0001	.0002

r	.41	.42	.43	.44	.45	.46	.47	.48	.49	.50
0	.0000	.0000	.0000	.0000	.0000	.0000	.0000	.0000	.0000	.0000
1	.0000	.0000	.0000	.0000	.0000	.0000	.0000	.0000	.0000	.0000
2	.0000	.0000	.0000	.0000	.0000	.0000	.0000	.0000	.0000	.0000
3	.0002	.0001	.0001	.0001	.0000	.0000	.0000	.0000	.0000	.0000
4	.0009	.0006	.0004	.0003	.0002	.0001	.0001	.0001	.0000	.0000
5	.0031	.0023	.0017	.0012	.0008	.0006	.0004	.0003	.0002	.0001
6	.0089	.0068	.0052	.0039	.0029	.0021	.0015	.0011	.0008	.0006
7	.0213	.0170	.0134	.0105	.0081	.0062	.0047	.0035	.0026	.0019
8	.0425	.0354	.0291	.0237	.0191	.0152	.0120	.0093	.0072	.0055
9	.0722	.0626	.0537	.0456	.0382	.0317	.0260	.0210	.0168	.0133
10	.1054	.0952	.0851	.0752	.0656	.0567	.0483	.0408	.0340	.0280
11	.1331	.1254	.1167	.1074	.0976	.0877	.0779	.0684	.0593	.0509
12	.1465	.1438	.1394	.1336	.1265	.1183	.1094	.1000	.0903	.0806
13	.1409	.1442	.1456	.1453	.1433	.1396	.1344	.1278	.1201	.1115
14	.1189	.1268	.1334	.1387	.1424	.1444	.1447	.1432	.1401	.1354
15	.0881	.0979	.1074	.1162	.1242	.1312	.1369	.1410	.1436	.1445
16	.0574	.0665	.0759	.0856	.0953	.1048	.1138	.1221	.1293	.1354
17	.0329	.0396	.0472	.0554	.0642	.0735	.0831	.0928	.1023	.1115
18	.0165	.0207	.0257	.0314	.0379	.0452	.0532	.0619	.0710	.0806
19	.0072	.0095	.0122	.0156	.0196	.0243	.0298	.0361	.0431	.0509
20	.0028	.0038	.0051	.0067	.0088	.0114	.0145	.0183	.0228	.0280
21	.0009	.0013	.0018	.0025	.0034	.0046	.0061	.0080	.0104	.0133
22	.0003	.0004	.0006	.0008	.0012	.0016	.0022	.0030	.0041	.0055
23	.0001	.0001	.0001	.0002	.0003	.0005	.0007	.0010	.0014	.0019
24	.0000	.0000	.0000	.0001	.0001	.0001	.0002	.0003	.0004	.0006
25	.0000	.0000	.0000	.0000	.0000	.0000	.0000	.0001	.0001	.0001

n = 40

p r	.01	.02	.03	.04	.05	.06	.07	.08	.09	.10
0	.6690	.4457	.2957	.1954	.1285	.0842	.0549	.0356	.0230	.0148
1	.2703	.3638	.3658	.3256	.2706	.2149	.1652	.1238	.0910	.0657
2	.0532	.1448	.2206	.2646	.2777	.2675	.2425	.2100	.1754	.1423
3	.0068	.0374	.0864	.1396	.1851	.2162	.2312	.2313	.2198	.2003
4	.0006	.0071	.0247	.0538	.0901	.1277	.1609	.1860	.2011	.2059
5	.0000	.0010	.0055	.0161	.0342	.0587	.0872	.1165	.1432	.1647
6	.0000	.0001	.0010	.0039	.0105	.0218	.0383	.0591	.0826	.1068
7	.0000	.0000	.0001	.0008	.0027	.0068	.0140	.0250	.0397	.0576
8	.0000	.0000	.0000	.0001	.0006	.0018	.0043	.0090	.0162	.0264
9	.0000	.0000	.0000	.0000	.0001	.0004	.0012	.0028	.0057	.0104
10	0	.0000	.0000	.0000	.0000	.0001	.0003	.0007	.0017	.0036
11	0	.0000	.0000	.0000	.0000	.0000	.0001	.0002	.0005	.0011
12	0	0	.0000	.0000	.0000	.0000	.0000	.0000	.0001	.0003
13	0	0	.0000	.0000	.0000	.0000	.0000	.0000	.0000	.0001
14	0	0	0	.0000	.0000	.0000	.0000	.0000	.0000	.0000
15	0	0	0	.0000	.0000	.0000	.0000	.0000	.0000	.0000
16	0	0	0	0	.0000	.0000	.0000	.0000	.0000	.0000
17	0	0	0	0	0	.0000	.0000	.0000	.0000	.0000
18	0	0	0	0	0	0	.0000	.0000	.0000	.0000

	.11	.12	.13	.14	.15	.16	.17	.18	.19	.20
0	.0095	.0060	.0038	.0024	.0015	.0009	.0006	.0004	.0002	.0001
1	.0467	.0328	.0228	.0156	.0106	.0071	.0047	.0031	.0020	.0013
2	.1126	.0873	.0663	.0496	.0365	.0265	.0190	.0134	.0094	.0065
3	.1763	.1507	.1255	.1022	.0816	.0639	.0492	.0373	.0279	.0205
4	.2016	.1901	.1735	.1539	.1332	.1126	.0932	.0757	.0604	.0475
5	.1794	.1867	.1867	.1804	.1692	.1544	.1375	.1197	.1021	.0854
6	.1293	.1485	.1627	.1713	.1742	.1715	.1642	.1533	.1397	.1246
7	.0777	.0983	.1181	.1355	.1493	.1587	.1634	.1634	.1592	.1513
8	.0396	.0553	.0728	.0910	.1087	.1247	.1381	.1480	.1540	.1560
9	.0174	.0268	.0387	.0527	.0682	.0844	.1005	.1155	.1284	.1386
10	.0067	.0113	.0179	.0266	.0373	.0499	.0638	.0786	.0934	.1075
11	.0022	.0042	.0073	.0118	.0180	.0259	.0357	.0470	.0597	.0733
12	.0007	.0014	.0026	.0046	.0077	.0119	.0176	.0250	.0339	.0443
13	.0002	.0004	.0008	.0016	.0029	.0049	.0078	.0118	.0171	.0238
14	.0000	.0001	.0002	.0005	.0010	.0018	.0031	.0050	.0077	.0115
15	.0000	.0000	.0001	.0001	.0003	.0006	.0011	.0019	.0031	.0050
16	.0000	.0000	.0000	.0000	.0001	.0002	.0003	.0007	.0012	.0019
17	.0000	.0000	.0000	.0000	.0000	.0000	.0001	.0002	.0004	.0007
18	.0000	.0000	.0000	.0000	.0000	.0000	.0000	.0001	.0001	.0002
19	.0000	.0000	.0000	.0000	.0000	.0000	.0000	.0000	.0000	.0001

	.21	.22	.23	.24	.25	.26	.27	.28	.29	.30
0	.0001	.0000	.0000	.0000	.0000	.0000	.0000	.0000	.0000	.0000
1	.0009	.0005	.0003	.0002	.0001	.0001	.0001	.0000	.0000	.0000
2	.0044	.0030	.0020	.0013	.0009	.0006	.0004	.0002	.0001	.0001
3	.0149	.0107	.0076	.0053	.0037	.0025	.0017	.0011	.0008	.0005
4	.0367	.0279	.0210	.0155	.0113	.0082	.0058	.0041	.0029	.0020
5	.0702	.0567	.0451	.0353	.0272	.0207	.0155	.0115	.0084	.0061
6	.1088	.0933	.0786	.0650	.0530	.0424	.0335	.0261	.0200	.0151
7	.1405	.1278	.1140	.0997	.0857	.0724	.0602	.0493	.0397	.0315
8	.1541	.1487	.1404	.1299	.1179	.1050	.0919	.0790	.0669	.0557
9	.1456	.1491	.1492	.1459	.1397	.1312	.1208	.1093	.0972	.0849
10	.1200	.1304	.1381	.1428	.1444	.1429	.1385	.1318	.1230	.1128
11	.0870	.1003	.1125	.1230	.1312	.1369	.1397	.1397	.1370	.1319
12	.0559	.0684	.0812	.0939	.1057	.1162	.1249	.1313	.1353	.1366
13	.0320	.0415	.0523	.0638	.0759	.0880	.0995	.1100	.1190	.1261
14	.0164	.0226	.0301	.0389	.0488	.0596	.0710	.0825	.0937	.1042
15	.0076	.0110	.0156	.0213	.0282	.0363	.0455	.0556	.0664	.0774
16	.0031	.0049	.0073	.0105	.0147	.0199	.0263	.0338	.0424	.0518
17	.0012	.0019	.0031	.0047	.0069	.0099	.0137	.0186	.0244	.0314
18	.0004	.0007	.0012	.0019	.0029	.0044	.0065	.0092	.0127	.0172
19	.0001	.0002	.0004	.0007	.0011	.0018	.0028	.0042	.0060	.0085
20	.0000	.0001	.0001	.0002	.0004	.0007	.0011	.0017	.0026	.0038
21	.0000	.0000	.0000	.0001	.0001	.0002	.0004	.0006	.0010	.0016
22	.0000	.0000	.0000	.0000	.0000	.0001	.0001	.0002	.0004	.0006
23	.0000	.0000	.0000	.0000	.0000	.0000	.0000	.0001	.0001	.0002
24	.0000	.0000	.0000	.0000	.0000	.0000	.0000	.0000	.0000	.0001

Table C >> **99**

n = 40 (Continued)

r \ p	.31	.32	.33	.34	.35	.36	.37	.38	.39	.40
0	.0000	.0000	.0000	.0000	.0000	.0000	.0000	.0000	.0000	.0000
1	.0000	.0000	.0000	.0000	.0000	.0000	.0000	.0000	.0000	.0000
2	.0001	.0000	.0000	.0000	.0000	.0000	.0000	.0000	.0000	.0000
3	.0003	.0002	.0001	.0001	.0001	.0000	.0000	.0000	.0000	.0000
4	.0013	.0009	.0006	.0004	.0003	.0002	.0001	.0001	.0000	.0000
5	.0043	.0030	.0021	.0014	.0010	.0007	.0004	.0003	.0002	.0001
6	.0113	.0083	.0061	.0043	.0031	.0021	.0015	.0010	.0007	.0005
7	.0247	.0190	.0145	.0109	.0080	.0059	.0042	.0030	.0021	.0015
8	.0457	.0369	.0294	.0231	.0179	.0136	.0102	.0076	.0056	.0040
9	.0730	.0618	.0515	.0423	.0342	.0272	.0214	.0166	.0126	.0095
10	.1017	.0902	.0786	.0675	.0571	.0475	.0389	.0315	.0250	.0196
11	.1246	.1157	.1056	.0948	.0838	.0729	.0624	.0526	.0437	.0357
12	.1353	.1316	.1257	.1181	.1090	.0990	.0885	.0779	.0675	.0576
13	.1309	.1334	.1334	.1310	.1265	.1200	.1120	.1028	.0929	.0827
14	.1134	.1210	.1267	.1302	.1313	.1302	.1269	.1216	.1146	.1063
15	.0883	.0987	.1082	.1162	.1226	.1269	.1291	.1291	.1270	.1228
16	.0620	.0726	.0832	.0935	.1031	.1116	.1185	.1237	.1268	.1279
17	.0393	.0482	.0579	.0680	.0784	.0886	.0983	.1070	.1145	.1204
18	.0226	.0290	.0364	.0448	.0539	.0637	.0737	.0838	.0935	.1026
19	.0117	.0158	.0208	.0267	.0336	.0415	.0501	.0595	.0692	.0792
20	.0055	.0078	.0107	.0144	.0190	.0245	.0309	.0383	.0465	.0554
21	.0024	.0035	.0050	.0071	.0097	.0131	.0173	.0223	.0283	.0352
22	.0009	.0014	.0021	.0032	.0045	.0064	.0088	.0118	.0156	.0203
23	.0003	.0005	.0008	.0013	.0019	.0028	.0040	.0057	.0078	.0106
24	.0001	.0002	.0003	.0005	.0007	.0011	.0017	.0025	.0035	.0050
25	.0000	.0001	.0001	.0002	.0003	.0004	.0006	.0010	.0014	.0021
26	.0000	.0000	.0000	.0000	.0001	.0001	.0002	.0003	.0005	.0008
27	.0000	.0000	.0000	.0000	.0000	.0000	.0001	.0001	.0002	.0003
28	.0000	.0000	.0000	.0000	.0000	.0000	.0000	.0000	.0001	.0001

r \ p	.41	.42	.43	.44	.45	.46	.47	.48	.49	.50
0	.0000	.0000	.0000	.0000	.0000	.0000	0	0	0	0
1	.0000	.0000	.0000	.0000	.0000	.0000	.0000	.0000	.0000	.0000
2	.0000	.0000	.0000	.0000	.0000	.0000	.0000	.0000	.0000	.0000
3	.0000	.0000	.0000	.0000	.0000	.0000	.0000	.0000	.0000	.0000
4	.0000	.0000	.0000	.0000	.0000	.0000	.0000	.0000	.0000	.0000
5	.0001	.0000	.0000	.0000	.0000	.0000	.0000	.0000	.0000	.0000
6	.0003	.0002	.0001	.0001	.0000	.0000	.0000	.0000	.0000	.0000
7	.0010	.0007	.0004	.0003	.0002	.0001	.0001	.0000	.0000	.0000
8	.0029	.0020	.0014	.0009	.0006	.0004	.0003	.0002	.0001	.0001
9	.0071	.0052	.0037	.0026	.0018	.0013	.0009	.0006	.0004	.0002
10	.0152	.0116	.0087	.0064	.0047	.0034	.0024	.0017	.0011	.0008
11	.0288	.0229	.0179	.0138	.0105	.0078	.0058	.0042	.0030	.0021
12	.0484	.0400	.0326	.0262	.0207	.0161	.0124	.0093	.0069	.0051
13	.0724	.0624	.0530	.0443	.0365	.0296	.0236	.0186	.0144	.0109
14	.0970	.0871	.0771	.0671	.0575	.0486	.0404	.0330	.0266	.0211
15	.1168	.1094	.1008	.0914	.0816	.0717	.0621	.0529	.0443	.0366
16	.1269	.1238	.1188	.1122	.1043	.0955	.0860	.0763	.0665	.0572
17	.1245	.1265	.1265	.1245	.1205	.1148	.1077	.0994	.0903	.0807
18	.1105	.1171	.1220	.1250	.1260	.1250	.1220	.1172	.1108	.1031
19	.0889	.0982	.1065	.1137	.1194	.1233	.1253	.1253	.1233	.1194
20	.0649	.0746	.0844	.0938	.1025	.1103	.1166	.1214	.1244	.1254
21	.0429	.0515	.0606	.0702	.0799	.0895	.0985	.1067	.1138	.1194
22	.0258	.0322	.0395	.0476	.0565	.0658	.0754	.0851	.0944	.1031
23	.0140	.0182	.0233	.0293	.0362	.0439	.0524	.0615	.0710	.0807
24	.0069	.0094	.0125	.0163	.0210	.0265	.0329	.0402	.0483	.0572
25	.0031	.0043	.0060	.0082	.0110	.0144	.0187	.0237	.0297	.0366
26	.0012	.0018	.0026	.0037	.0052	.0071	.0096	.0126	.0165	.0211
27	.0004	.0007	.0010	.0015	.0022	.0031	.0044	.0061	.0082	.0109
28	.0001	.0002	.0004	.0006	.0008	.0012	.0018	.0026	.0037	.0051
29	.0000	.0001	.0001	.0002	.0003	.0004	.0007	.0010	.0015	.0021
30	.0000	.0000	.0000	.0001	.0001	.0001	.0002	.0003	.0005	.0008
31	.0000	.0000	.0000	.0000	.0000	.0000	.0001	.0001	.0002	.0002
32	.0000	.0000	.0000	.0000	.0000	.0000	.0000	.0000	.0000	.0001

n = 50

r \ p	.01	.02	.03	.04	.05	.06	.07	.08	.09	.10
0	.6050	.3642	.2181	.1299	.0769	.0453	.0266	.0155	.0090	.0052
1	.3056	.3716	.3372	.2706	.2025	.1447	.0999	.0672	.0443	.0286
2	.0756	.1858	.2555	.2762	.2611	.2262	.1843	.1433	.1073	.0779
3	.0122	.0607	.1264	.1842	.2199	.2311	.2219	.1993	.1698	.1386
4	.0015	.0145	.0459	.0902	.1360	.1733	.1963	.2037	.1973	.1809
5	.0001	.0027	.0131	.0346	.0658	.1018	.1359	.1629	.1795	.1849
6	.0000	.0004	.0030	.0108	.0260	.0487	.0767	.1063	.1332	.1541
7	.0000	.0001	.0006	.0028	.0086	.0195	.0363	.0581	.0828	.1076
8	.0000	.0000	.0001	.0006	.0024	.0067	.0147	.0271	.0440	.0643
9	.0000	.0000	.0000	.0001	.0006	.0020	.0052	.0110	.0203	.0333
10	.0000	.0000	.0000	.0000	.0001	.0005	.0016	.0039	.0082	.0152
11	0	.0000	.0000	.0000	.0000	.0001	.0004	.0012	.0030	.0061
12	0	.0000	.0000	.0000	.0000	.0000	.0001	.0004	.0010	.0022
13	0	0	.0000	.0000	.0000	.0000	.0000	.0001	.0003	.0007
14	0	0	.0000	.0000	.0000	.0000	.0000	.0000	.0001	.0002
15	0	0	0	.0000	.0000	.0000	.0000	.0000	.0000	.0001
16	0	0	0	.0000	.0000	.0000	.0000	.0000	.0000	.0000
17	0	0	0	0	.0000	.0000	.0000	.0000	.0000	.0000
18	0	0	0	0	0	.0000	.0000	.0000	.0000	.0000
19	0	0	0	0	0	.0000	.0000	.0000	.0000	.0000
20	0	0	0	0	0	0	.0000	.0000	.0000	.0000
21	0	0	0	0	0	0	0	.0000	.0000	.0000
22	0	0	0	0	0	0	0	0	.0000	.0000
23	0	0	0	0	0	0	0	0	0	.0000

r	.11	.12	.13	.14	.15	.16	.17	.18	.19	.20
0	.0029	.0017	.0009	.0005	.0003	.0002	.0001	.0000	.0000	.0000
1	.0182	.0114	.0071	.0043	.0026	.0016	.0009	.0005	.0003	.0002
2	.0552	.0382	.0259	.0172	.0113	.0073	.0046	.0029	.0018	.0011
3	.1091	.0833	.0619	.0449	.0319	.0222	.0151	.0102	.0067	.0044
4	.1584	.1334	.1086	.0858	.0661	.0496	.0364	.0262	.0185	.0128
5	.1801	.1674	.1493	.1286	.1072	.0869	.0687	.0530	.0400	.0295
6	.1670	.1712	.1674	.1570	.1419	.1242	.1055	.0872	.0703	.0554
7	.1297	.1467	.1572	.1606	.1575	.1358	.1358	.1203	.1037	.0870
8	.0862	.1075	.1263	.1406	.1493	.1523	.1495	.1420	.1307	.1169
9	.0497	.0684	.0880	.1068	.1230	.1353	.1429	.1454	.1431	.1364
10	.0252	.0383	.0539	.0713	.0890	.1057	.1200	.1309	.1376	.1398
11	.0113	.0190	.0293	.0422	.0571	.0732	.0894	.1045	.1174	.1271
12	.0045	.0084	.0142	.0223	.0328	.0453	.0595	.0745	.0895	.1033
13	.0016	.0034	.0062	.0106	.0169	.0252	.0356	.0478	.0613	.0755
14	.0005	.0012	.0025	.0046	.0079	.0127	.0193	.0277	.0380	.0499
15	.0002	.0004	.0009	.0018	.0033	.0058	.0095	.0146	.0214	.0299
16	.0000	.0001	.0003	.0006	.00p3	.0024	.0042	.0070	.0110	.0164
17	.0000	.0000	.0001	.0002	.0005	.0009	.0017	.0031	.0052	.0082
18	.0000	.0000	.0000	.0001	.0001	.0003	.0007	.0012	.0022	.0037
19	.0000	.0000	.0000	.0000	.0000	.0001	.0002	.0005	.0009	.0016
20	.0000	.0000	.0000	.0000	.0000	.0000	.0001	.0002	.0003	.0006
21	.0000	.0000	.0000	.0000	.0000	.0000	.0000	.0000	.0001	.0002
22	.0000	.0000	.0000	.0000	.0000	.0000	.0000	.0000	.0000	.0001
23	.0000	.0000	.0000	.0000	.0000	.0000	.0000	.0000	.0000	.0000

r	.21	.22	.23	.24	.25	.26	.27	.28	.29	.30
0	.0000	.0000	.0000	.0000	.0000	.0000	.0000	.0000	.0000	.0000
1	.0001	.0001	.0000	.0000	.0000	.0000	.0000	.0000	.0000	.0000
2	.0007	.0004	.0002	.0001	.0001	.0000	.0000	.0000	.0000	.0000
3	.0028	.0018	.0011	.0007	.0004	.0002	.0001	.0001	.0000	.0000
4	.0088	.0059	.0039	.0025	.0016	.0010	.0006	.0004	.0002	.0001
5	.0214	.0152	.0106	.0073	.0049	.0033	.0021	.0014	.0009	.0006
6	.0427	.0322	.0238	.0173	.0123	.0087	.0060	.0040	.0027	.0018
7	.0713	.0571	.0447	.0344	.0259	.0191	.0139	.0099	.0069	.0048
8	.1019	.0865	.0718	.0583	.0463	.0361	.0276	.0207	.0152	.0110
9	.1263	.1139	.1001	.0859	.0721	.0592	.0476	.0375	.0290	.0220
10	.1377	.1317	.1226	.1113	.0985	.0852	.0721	.0598	.0485	.0386
11	.1331	.1351	.1332	.1278	.1194	.1089	.0970	.0845	.0721	.0602
12	.1150	.1238	.1293	.1311	.1294	.1244	.1166	.1068	.0957	.0838
13	.0894	.1021	.1129	.1210	.1261	.1277	.1261	.1215	.1142	.1050
14	.0628	.0761	.0891	.1010	.1110	.1186	.1233	.1248	.1233	.1189

*Table C >> *101

n = 50 (Continued)

r\p	.21	.22	.23	.24	.25	.26	.27	.28	.29	.30
15	.0400	.0515	.0639	.0766	.0888	.1000	.1094	.1165	.1209	.1223
16	.0233	.0318	.0417	.0529	.0648	.0769	.0885	.0991	.1080	.1147
17	.0124	.0179	.0249	.0334	.0432	.0540	.0655	.0771	.0882	.0983
18	.0060	.0093	.0137	.0193	.0264	.0348	.0444	.0550	.0661	.0772
19	.0027	.0044	.0069	.0103	.0148	.0206	.0277	.0360	.0454	.0558
20	.0011	.0019	.0032	.0050	.0077	.0112	.0159	.0217	.0288	.0370
21	.0004	.0008	.0014	.0023	.0036	.0056	.0084	.0121	.0168	.0227
22	.0001	.0003	.0005	.0009	.0016	.0026	.0041	.0062	.0090	.0128
23	.0000	.0001	.0002	.0004	.0006	.0011	.0018	.0029	.0045	.0067
24	.0000	.0000	.0001	.0001	.0002	.0004	.0008	.0013	.0021	.0032
25	.0000	.0000	.0000	.0000	.0001	.0002	.0003	.0005	.0009	.0014
26	.0000	.0000	.0000	.0000	.0000	.0001	.0001	.0002	.0003	.0006
27	.0000	.0000	.0000	.0000	.0000	.0000	.0000	.0001	.0001	.0002
28	.0000	.0000	.0000	.0000	.0000	.0000	.0000	.0000	.0000	.0001

r\p	.31	.32	.33	.34	.35	.36	.37	.38	.39	.40
0	.0000	.0000	.0000	.0000	.0000	.0000	.0000	.0000	.0000	0
1	.0000	.0000	.0000	.0000	.0000	.0000	.0000	.0000	.0000	.0000
2	.0000	.0000	.0000	.0000	.0000	.0000	.0000	.0000	.0000	.0000
3	.0000	.0000	.0000	.0000	.0000	.0000	.0000	.0000	.0000	.0000
4	.0001	.0000	.0000	.0000	.0000	.0000	.0000	.0000	.0000	.0000
5	.0003	.0002	.0001	.0001	.0000	.0000	.0000	.0000	.0000	.0000
6	.0011	.0007	.0005	.0003	.0002	.0001	.0001	.0000	.0000	.0000
7	.0032	.0022	.0014	.0009	.0006	.0004	.0002	.0001	.0001	.0000
8	.0078	.0055	.0037	.0025	.0017	.0011	.0007	.0004	.0003	.0002
9	.0164	.0120	.0086	.0061	.0042	.0029	.0019	.0013	.0008	.0005
10	.0301	.0231	.0174	.0128	.0093	.0066	.0046	.0032	.0022	.0014
11	.0493	.0395	.0311	.0240	.0182	.0136	.0099	.0071	.0050	.0035
12	.0719	.0604	.0498	.0402	.0319	.0248	.0189	.0142	.0105	.0076
13	.0944	.0831	.0717	.0606	.0502	.0408	.0325	.0255	.0195	.0147
14	.1121	.1034	.0933	.0825	.0714	.0607	.0505	.0412	.0330	.0260
15	.1209	.1168	.1103	.1020	.0923	.0819	.0712	.0606	.0507	.0415
16	.1188	.1202	.1189	.1149	.1088	.1008	.0914	.0813	.0709	.0606
17	.1068	.1132	.1171	.1184	.1171	.1133	.1074	.0997	.0906	.0808
18	.0880	.0976	.1057	.1118	.1156	.1169	.1156	.1120	.1062	.0987
19	.0666	.0774	.0877	.0970	.1048	.1107	.1144	.1156	.1144	.1109
20	.0463	.0564	.0670	.0775	.0875	.0965	.1041	.1098	.1134	.1146
21	.0297	.0379	.0471	.0570	.0673	.0770	.0074	.0062	.1035	.1091
22	.0176	.0235	.0306	.0387	.0478	.0575	.0676	.0777	.0873	.0959
23	.0096	.0135	.0183	.0243	.0313	.0394	.0484	.0580	.0679	.0778
24	.0049	.0071	.0102	.0141	.0190	.0249	.0319	.0400	.0489	.0584
25	.0023	.0035	.0052	.0075	.0106	.0146	.0195	.0255	.0325	.0405
26	.0010	.0016	.0025	.0037	.0055	.0079	.0110	.0150	.0200	.0259
27	.0004	.0007	.0011	.0017	.0026	.0039	.0058	.0082	.0113	.0154
28	.0001	.0003	.0004	.0007	.0012	.0018	.0028	.0041	.0060	.0084
29	.0000	.0001	.0002	.0003	.0005	.0008	.0012	.0019	.0029	.0043
30	.0000	.0000	.0001	.0001	.0002	.0003	.0005	.0008	.0013	.0020
31	.0000	.0000	.0000	.0000	.0001	.0001	.0002	.0003	.0005	.0009
32	.0000	.0000	.0000	.0000	.0000	.0000	.0001	.0001	.0002	.0003
33	.0000	.0000	.0000	.0000	.0000	.0000	.0000	.0000	.0001	.0001

r\p	.41	.42	.43	.44	.45	.46	.47	.48	.49	.50
0	0	0	0	0	0	0	0	0	0	0
1	.0000	.0000	.0000	0	0	0	0	0	0	0
2	.0000	.0000	.0000	.0000	.0000	.0000	.0000	0	0	0
3	.0000	.0000	.0000	.0000	.0000	.0000	.0000	.0000	.0000	.0000
4	.0000	.0000	.0000	.0000	.0000	.0000	.0000	.0000	.0000	.0000
5	.0000	.0000	.0000	.0000	.0000	.0000	.0000	.0000	.0000	.0000
6	.0000	.0000	.0000	.0000	.0000	.0000	.0000	.0000	.0000	.0000
7	.0000	.0000	.0000	.0000	.0000	.0000	.0000	.0000	.0000	.0000
8	.0001	.0001	.0000	.0000	.0000	.0000	.0000	.0000	.0000	.0000
9	.0003	.0002	.0001	.0001	.0000	.0000	.0000	.0000	.0000	.0000
10	.0009	.0006	.0004	.0002	.0001	.0001	.0001	.0000	.0000	.0000
11	.0024	.0016	.0010	.0007	.0004	.0003	.0002	.0001	.0001	.0000
12	.0054	.0037	.0026	.0017	.0011	.0007	.0005	.0003	.0002	.0001
13	.0109	.0079	.0057	.0040	.0027	.0018	.0012	.0008	.0005	.0003
14	.0200	.0152	.0113	.0082	.0059	.0041	.0029	.0019	.0013	.0008

n = 50 (Continued)

r \ p	.41	.42	.43	.44	.45	.46	.47	.48	.49	.50
15	.0334	.0264	.0204	.0155	.0116	.0085	.0061	.0043	.0030	.0020
16	.0508	.0418	.0337	.0267	.0207	.0158	.0118	.0086	.0062	.0044
17	.0706	.0605	.0508	.0419	.0339	.0269	.0209	.0159	.0119	.0087
18	.0899	.0803	.0703	.0604	.0508	.0420	.0340	.0270	.0210	.0160
19	.1053	.0979	.0893	.0799	.0700	.0602	.0507	.0419	.0340	.0270
20	.1134	.1099	.1044	.0973	.0888	.0795	.0697	.0600	.0506	.0419
21	.1126	.1137	.1126	.1092	.1038	.0967	.0884	.0791	.0695	.0598
22	.1031	.1086	.1119	.1131	.1119	.1086	.1033	.0963	.0880	.0788
23	.0872	.0957	.1028	.1082	.1115	.1126	.1115	.1082	.1029	.0960
24	.0682	.0780	.0872	.0956	.1026	.1079	.1112	.1124	.1112	.1080
25	.0493	.0587	.0684	.0781	.0873	.0956	.1026	.1079	.1112	.1123
26	.0329	.0409	.0497	.0590	.0687	.0783	.0875	.0957	.1027	.1080
27	.0203	.0263	.0333	.0412	.0500	.0593	.0690	.0786	.0877	.0960
28	.0116	.0157	.0206	.0266	.0336	.0415	.0502	.0596	.0692	.0788
29	.0061	.0086	.0118	.0159	.0208	.0268	.0338	.0417	.0504	.0598
30	.0030	.0044	.0062	.0087	.0119	.0160	.0210	.0270	.0339	.0419
31	.0013	.0020	.0030	.0044	.0063	.0088	.0120	.0161	.0210	.0270
32	.0006	.0009	.0014	.0021	.0031	.0044	.0063	.0088	.0120	.0160
33	.0002	.0003	.0006	.0009	.0014	.0021	.0031	.0044	.0063	.0087
34	.0001	.0001	.0002	.0003	.0006	.0009	.0014	.0020	.0030	.0044
35	.0000	.0000	.0001	.0001	.0002	.0003	.0005	.0009	.0013	.0020
36	.0000	.0000	.0000	.0000	.0001	.0001	.0002	.0003	.0005	.0008
37	.0000	.0000	.0000	.0000	.0000	.0000	.0001	.0001	.0002	.0003
38	.0000	.0000	.0000	.0000	.0000	.0000	.0000	.0000	.0001	.0001

n = 75

r \ p	.01	.02	.03	.04	.05	.06	.07	.08	.09	.10
0	.4706	.2198	.1018	.0468	.0213	.0097	.0043	.0019	.0008	.0004
1	.3565	.3364	.2362	.1463	.0843	.0462	.0244	.0125	.0063	.0031
2	.1332	.2540	.2703	.2255	.1641	.1091	.0680	.0404	.0230	.0127
3	.0327	.1261	.2034	.2287	.2101	.1695	.1246	.0854	.0554	.0343
4	.0060	.0463	.1132	.1715	.1991	.1947	.1688	.1337	.0985	.0685
5	.0009	.0134	.0497	.1015	.1488	.1765	.1804	.1651	.1384	.1081
6	.0001	.0032	.0179	.0493	.0914	.1314	.1584	.1674	.1597	.1402
7	.0000	.0006	.0055	.0203	.0474	.0827	.1176	.1435	.1557	.1535
8	.0000	.0001	.0014	.0072	.0212	.0449	.0752	.1061	.1309	.1450
9	.0000	.0000	.0003	.0022	.0083	.0213	.0421	.0687	.0964	.1199
10	.0000	.0000	.0001	.0006	.0029	.0090	.0209	.0394	.0629	.0880
11	.0000	.0000	.0000	.0002	.0009	.0034	.0093	.0203	.0368	.0578
12	0	.0000	.0000	.0000	.0003	.0012	.0037	.0094	.0194	.0342
13	0	.0000	.0000	.0000	.0001	.0004	.0014	.0040	.0093	.0184
14	0	.0000	.0000	.0000	.0000	.0001	.0005	.0015	.0041	.0091
15	0	.0000	.0000	.0000	.0000	.0000	.0001	.0005	.0016	.0041
16	0	0	.0000	.0000	.0000	.0000	.0000	.0002	.0006	.0017
17	0	0	.0000	.0000	.0000	.0000	.0000	.0001	.0002	.0007
18	0	0	0	.0000	.0000	.0000	.0000	.0000	.0001	.0002
19	0	0	0	.0000	.0000	.0000	.0000	.0000	.0000	.0001
20	0	0	0	0	.0000	.0000	.0000	.0000	.0000	.0000
21	0	0	0	0	.0000	.0000	.0000	.0000	.0000	.0000
22	0	0	0	0	0	.0000	.0000	.0000	.0000	.0000
23	0	0	0	0	0	.0000	.0000	.0000	.0000	.0000
24	0	0	0	0	0	0	.0000	.0000	.0000	.0000
25	0	0	0	0	0	0	.0000	.0000	.0000	.0000
26	0	0	0	0	0	0	0	.0000	.0000	.0000
27	0	0	0	0	0	0	0	0	.0000	.0000
28	0	0	0	0	0	0	0	0	.0000	.0000
29	0	0	0	0	0	0	0	0	0	.0000
30	0	0	0	0	0	0	0	0	0	0
31	0	0	0	0	0	0	0	0	0	0
32	0	0	0	0	0	0	0	0	0	0
33	0	0	0	0	0	0	0	0	0	0
34	0	0	0	0	0	0	0	0	0	0
35	0	0	0	0	0	0	0	0	0	0

Table C >> **103**

n = 75 (Continued)

r \ p	.11	.12	.13	.14	.15	.16	.17	.18	.19	.20
0	.0002	.0001	.0000	.0000	.0000	.0000	.0000	.0000	.0000	.0000
1	.0015	.0007	.0003	.0001	.0001	.0000	.0000	.0000	.0000	.0000
2	.0068	.0035	.0018	.0009	.0004	.0002	.0001	.0000	.0000	.0000
3	.0204	.0117	.0066	.0036	.0019	.0010	.0005	.0002	.0001	.0001
4	.0454	.0288	.0176	.0104	.0060	.0034	.0018	.0010	.0005	.0003
5	.0797	.0558	.0374	.0241	.0150	.0091	.0053	.0030	.0017	.0009
6	.1149	.0888	.0652	.0458	.0309	.0201	.0127	.0077	.0046	.0027
7	.1400	.1193	.0961	.0735	.0538	.0378	.0256	.0167	.0106	.0065
8	.1470	.1383	.1220	.1018	.0807	.0612	.0446	.0313	.0212	.0139
9	.1353	.1404	.1357	.1233	.1060	.0868	.0679	.0511	.0370	.0258
10	.1104	.1264	.1339	.1325	.1235	.1091	.0919	.0740	.0572	.0426
11	.0806	.1018	.1182	.1275	.1288	.1228	.1112	.0960	.0793	.0630
12	.0531	.0741	.0942	.1107	.1212	.1248	.1214	.1124	.0992	.0840
13	.0318	.0489	.0682	.0873	.1037	.1152	.1205	.1195	.1128	.1017
14	.0174	.0296	.0451	.0629	.0810	.0971	.1093	.1162	.1172	.1126
15	.0088	.0164	.0274	.0417	.0581	.0752	.0911	.1037	.1118	.1145
16	.0041	.0084	.0154	.0254	.0385	.0537	.0699	.0854	.0983	.1073
17	.0017	.0040	.0080	.0144	.0236	.0355	.0497	.0650	.0800	.0931
18	.0007	.0017	.0038	.0075	.0134	.0218	.0328	.0460	.0605	.0750
19	.0003	.0007	.0017	.0037	.0071	.0125	.0202	.0303	.0426	.0563
20	.0001	.0003	.0007	.0017	.0035	.0066	.0116	.0186	.0280	.0394
21	.0000	.0001	.0003	.0007	.0016	.0033	.0062	.0107	.0172	.0258
22	.0000	.0000	.0001	.0003	.0007	.0016	.0031	.0058	.0099	.0158
23	.0000	.0000	.0000	.0001	.0003	.0007	.0015	.0029	.0053	.0091
24	.0000	.0000	.0000	.0000	.0001	.0003	.0007	.0014	.0027	.0049
25	.0000	.0000	.0000	.0000	.0000	.0001	.0003	.0006	.0013	.0025
26	.0000	.0000	.0000	.0000	.0000	.0000	.0001	.0003	.0006	.0012
27	.0000	.0000	.0000	.0000	.0000	.0000	.0000	.0001	.0002	.0005
28	.0000	.0000	.0000	.0000	.0000	.0000	.0000	.0000	.0001	.0002
29	.0000	.0000	.0000	.0000	.0000	.0000	.0000	.0000	.0000	.0001
30	.0000	.0000	.0000	.0000	.0000	.0000	.0000	.0000	.0000	.0000
31	0	.0000	.0000	.0000	.0000	.0000	.0000	.0000	.0000	.0000
32	0	.0000	.0000	.0000	.0000	.0000	.0000	.0000	.0000	.0000
33	0	0	.0000	.0000	.0000	.0000	.0000	.0000	.0000	.0000
34	0	0	0	.0000	.0000	.0000	.0000	.0000	.0000	.0000
35	0	0	0	0	.0000	.0000	.0000	.0000	.0000	.0000

r	.21	.22	.23	.24	.25	.26	.27	.28	.29	.30
0	.0000	.0000	.0000	.0000	.0000	.0000	.0000	.0000	0	0
1	.0000	.0000	.0000	.0000	.0000	.0000	.0000	.0000	.0000	.0000
2	.0000	.0000	.0000	.0000	.0000	.0000	.0000	.0000	.0000	.0000
3	.0000	.0000	.0000	.0000	.0000	.0000	.0000	.0000	.0000	.0000
4	.0001	.0001	.0000	.0000	.0000	.0000	.0000	.0000	.0000	.0000
5	.0005	.0002	.0001	.0001	.0000	.0000	.0000	.0000	.0000	.0000
6	.0015	.0008	.0004	.0002	.0001	.0001	.0000	.0000	.0000	.0000
7	.0039	.0023	.0013	.0007	.0004	.0002	.0001	.0001	.0000	.0000
8	.0088	.0055	.0033	.0019	.0011	.0006	.0003	.0002	.0001	.0000
9	.0175	.0115	.0073	.0045	.0027	.0016	.0009	.0005	.0003	.0001
10	.0307	.0213	.0144	.0094	.0060	.0037	.0022	.0013	.0007	.0004
11	.0481	.0355	.0254	.0176	.0118	.0077	.0049	.0030	.0018	.0011
12	.0683	.0535	.0404	.0296	.0209	.0144	.0096	.0062	.0039	.0024
13	.0879	.0731	.0585	.0453	.0338	.0245	.0172	.0118	.0078	.0050
14	.1035	.0913	.0774	.0633	.0500	.0381	.0282	.0202	.0141	.0095
15	.1119	.1047	.0940	.0813	.0677	.0545	.0424	.0320	.0234	.0166
16	.1116	.1107	.1053	.0962	.0846	.0718	.0589	.0467	.0359	.0267
17	.1029	.1084	.1092	.1055	.0979	.0876	.0756	.0630	.0508	.0397
18	.0881	.0985	.1051	.1073	.1052	.0991	.0900	.0789	.0669	.0549
19	.0703	.0834	.0942	.1017	.1052	.1045	.0999	.0921	.0820	.0705
20	.0523	.0658	.0788	.0899	.0982	.1028	.1035	.1003	.0938	.0846
21	.0364	.0486	.0616	.0744	.0857	.0946	.1002	.1021	.1003	.0950
22	.0238	.0337	.0452	.0576	.0701	.0816	.0910	.0975	.1005	.1000
23	.0146	.0219	.0311	.0419	.0539	.0661	.0776	.0874	.0946	.0987
24	.0084	.0134	.0201	.0287	.0389	.0503	.0622	.0736	.0838	.0917
25	.0045	.0077	.0123	.0185	.0265	.0360	.0469	.0584	.0698	.0801
26	.0023	.0042	.0070	.0112	.0170	.0244	.0334	.0437	.0548	.0660
27	.0011	.0021	.0038	.0064	.0103	.0155	.0224	.0308	.0406	.0514
28	.0005	.0010	.0020	.0035	.0059	.0094	.0142	.0206	.0285	.0377
29	.0002	.0005	.0009	.0018	.0032	.0053	.0085	.0130	.0188	.0262

n = 75 (Continued)

r \ p	.21	.22	.23	.24	.25	.26	.27	.28	.29	.30
30	.0001	.0002	.0004	.0009	.0016	.0029	.0048	.0077	.0118	.0172
31	.0000	.0001	.0002	.0004	.0008	.0015	.0026	.0044	.0070	.0107
32	.0000	.0000	.0001	.0002	.0004	.0007	.0013	.0023	.0039	.0063
33	.0000	.0000	.0000	.0001	.0002	.0003	.0006	.0012	.0021	.0035
34	.0000	.0000	.0000	.0000	.0001	.0001	.0003	.0006	.0011	.0019
35	.0000	.0000	.0000	.0000	.0000	.0001	.0001	.0003	.0005	.0009
36	.0000	.0000	.0000	.0000	.0000	.0000	.0001	.0001	.0002	.0004
37	.0000	.0000	.0000	.0000	.0000	.0000	.0000	.0000	.0001	.0002
38	.0000	.0000	.0000	.0000	.0000	.0000	.0000	.0000	.0000	.0001

r \ p	.31	.32	.33	.34	.35	.36	.37	.38	.39	.40
0	0	0	0	0	0	0	0	0	0	0
1	.0000	0	0	0	0	0	0	0	0	0
2	.0000	.0000	.0000	.0000	0	0	0	0	0	0
3	.0000	.0000	.0000	.0000	.0000	.0000	0	0	0	0
4	.0000	.0000	.0000	.0000	.0000	.0000	.0000	.0000	.0000	0
5	.0000	.0000	.0000	.0000	.0000	.0000	.0000	.0000	.0000	.0000
6	.0000	.0000	.0000	.0000	.0000	.0000	.0000	.0000	.0000	.0000
7	.0000	.0000	.0000	.0000	.0000	.0000	.0000	.0000	.0000	.0000
8	.0000	.0000	.0000	.0000	.0000	.0000	.0000	.0000	.0000	.0000
9	.0001	.0000	.0000	.0000	.0000	.0000	.0000	.0000	.0000	.0000
10	.0002	.0001	.0001	.0000	.0000	.0000	.0000	.0000	.0000	.0000
11	.0006	.0003	.0002	.0001	.0001	.0000	.0000	.0000	.0000	.0000
12	.0014	.0008	.0005	.0003	.0001	.0001	.0000	.0000	.0000	.0000
13	.0032	.0019	.0011	.0007	.0004	.0002	.0001	.0001	.0000	.0000
14	.0063	.0040	.0025	.0015	.0009	.0005	.0003	.0002	.0001	.0000
15	.0115	.0077	.0050	.0032	.0020	.0012	.0007	.0004	.0002	.0001
16	.0193	.0136	.0093	.0061	.0040	.0025	.0015	.0009	.0005	.0003
17	.0301	.0222	.0158	.0110	.0074	.0049	.0031	.0019	.0012	.0007
18	.0436	.0336	.0251	.0182	.0129	.0088	.0059	.0038	.0024	.0015
19	.0588	.0474	.0371	.0282	.0208	.0149	.0104	.0070	.0046	.0030
20	.0739	.0625	.0512	.0407	.0314	.0235	.0171	.0121	.0083	.0056
21	.0870	.0770	.0660	.0549	.0442	.0346	.0263	.0194	.0139	.0097
22	.0959	.0890	.0798	.0694	.0585	.0478	.0379	.0292	.0218	.0159
23	.0993	.0965	.0906	.0824	.0725	.0619	.0513	.0412	.0321	.0244
24	.0967	.0984	.0967	.0919	.0846	.0755	.0652	.0547	.0445	.0352
25	.0886	.0944	.0972	.0966	.0930	.0866	.0782	.0684	.0581	.0479
26	.0765	.0855	.0920	.0957	.0963	.0937	.0883	.0806	.0714	.0614
27	.0624	.0730	.0823	.0895	.0941	.0956	.0941	.0897	.0829	.0742
28	.0481	.0589	.0695	.0790	.0868	.0922	.0947	.0942	.0908	.0848
29	.0350	.0449	.0554	.0660	.0758	.0841	.0902	.0936	.0941	.0917
30	.0241	.0324	.0419	.0521	.0626	.0725	.0812	.0880	.0922	.0937
31	.0157	.0221	.0299	.0390	.0489	.0592	.0692	.0783	.0856	.0907
32	.0097	.0143	.0203	.0276	.0362	.0458	.0559	.0659	.0753	.0831
33	.0057	.0088	.0130	.0185	.0254	.0336	.0428	.0527	.0627	.0722
34	.0032	.0051	.0079	.0118	.0169	.0233	.0310	.0399	.0495	.0595
35	.0017	.0028	.0046	.0071	.0107	.0154	.0214	.0286	.0371	.0464
36	.0008	.0015	.0025	.0041	.0064	.0096	.0139	.0195	.0263	.0344
37	.0004	.0007	.0013	.0022	.0036	.0057	.0086	.0126	.0178	.0242
38	.0002	.0003	.0006	.0011	.0019	.0032	.0051	.0077	.0114	.0161
39	.0001	.0002	.0003	.0006	.0010	.0017	.0028	.0045	.0069	.0102
40	.0000	.0001	.0001	.0003	.0005	.0009	.0015	.0025	.0040	.0061
41	.0000	.0000	.0001	.0001	.0002	.0004	.0007	.0013	.0022	.0035
42	.0000	.0000	.0000	.0000	.0001	.0002	.0004	.0006	.0011	.0019
43	.0000	.0000	.0000	.0000	.0000	.0001	.0002	.0003	.0005	.0010
44	.0000	.0000	.0000	.0000	.0000	.0000	.0001	.0001	.0003	.0005
45	.0000	.0000	.0000	.0000	.0000	.0000	.0000	.0001	.0001	.0002
46	.0000	.0000	.0000	.0000	.0000	.0000	.0000	.0000	.0000	.0001

r \ p	.41	.42	.43	.44	.45	.46	.47	.48	.49	.50
0	0	0	0	0	0	0	0	0	0	0
1	0	0	0	0	0	0	0	0	0	0
2	0	0	0	0	0	0	0	0	0	0
3	0	0	0	0	0	0	0	0	0	0
4	0	0	0	0	0	0	0	0	0	0
5	.0000	0	0	0	0	0	0	0	0	0
6	.0000	.0000	.0000	0	0	0	0	0	0	0
7	.0000	.0000	.0000	.0000	.0000	0	0	0	0	0
8	.0000	.0000	.0000	.0000	.0000	.0000	0	0	0	0
9	.0000	.0000	.0000	.0000	.0000	.0000	.0000	.0000	0	0

Table C>>**105**

n = 75 (Continued)

r \ p	.41	.42	.43	.44	.45	.46	.47	.48	.49	.50
10	.0000	.0000	.0000	.0000	.0000	.0000	.0000	.0000	.0000	.0000
11	.0000	.0000	.0000	.0000	.0000	.0000	.0000	.0000	.0000	.0000
12	.0000	.0000	.0000	.0000	.0000	.0000	.0000	.0000	.0000	.0000
13	.0000	.0000	.0000	.0000	.0000	.0000	.0000	.0000	.0000	.0000
14	.0000	.0000	.0000	.0000	.0000	.0000	.0000	.0000	.0000	.0000
15	.0001	.0000	.0000	.0000	.0000	.0000	.0000	.0000	.0000	.0000
16	.0002	.0001	.0000	.0000	.0000	.0000	.0000	.0000	.0000	.0000
17	.0004	.0002	.0001	.0001	.0000	.0000	.0000	.0000	.0000	.0000
18	.0009	.0005	.0003	.0002	.0001	.0000	.0000	.0000	.0000	.0000
19	.0019	.0011	.0007	.0004	.0002	.0001	.0001	.0000	.0000	.0000
20	.0036	.0023	.0014	.0008	.0005	.0003	.0002	.0001	.0000	.0000
21	.0066	.0043	.0028	.0017	.0010	.0006	.0004	.0002	.0001	.0001
22	.0112	.0077	.0051	.0033	.0021	.0013	.0008	.0004	.0003	.0001
23	.0179	.0128	.0089	.0060	.0040	.0025	.0016	.0009	.0006	.0003
24	.0270	.0201	.0146	.0103	.0070	.0047	.0030	.0019	.0012	.0007
25	.0383	.0298	.0225	.0165	.0117	.0081	.0055	.0036	.0023	.0014
26	.0512	.0414	.0326	.0249	.0185	.0133	.0093	.0063	.0042	.0027
27	.0645	.0544	.0446	.0355	.0274	.0206	.0150	.0106	.0073	.0049
28	.0769	.0676	.0577	.0478	.0384	.0300	.0228	.0168	.0120	.0083
29	.0866	.0793	.0705	.0609	.0510	.0415	.0327	.0251	.0187	.0135
30	.0923	.0881	.0816	.0733	.0639	.0541	.0445	.0355	.0275	.0207
31	.0931	.0926	.0893	.0836	.0760	.0670	.0573	.0476	.0384	.0300
32	.0889	.0922	.0927	.0903	.0854	.0784	.0699	.0604	.0507	.0413
33	.0805	.0870	.0911	.0925	.0911	.0871	.0807	.0727	.0635	.0538
34	.0691	.0778	.0849	.0898	.0921	.0916	.0884	.0829	.0753	.0665
35	.0563	.0660	.0750	.0826	.0882	.0914	.0919	.0896	.0848	.0779
36	.0434	.0531	.0629	.0721	.0802	.0865	.0905	.0919	.0905	.0865
37	.0318	.0405	.0500	.0597	.0692	.0777	.0846	.0894	.0917	.0912
38	.0221	.0294	.0377	.0469	.0566	.0662	.0750	.0825	.0881	.0912
39	.0146	.0202	.0270	.0350	.0439	.0535	.0631	.0723	.0803	.0865
40	.0091	.0131	.0183	.0247	.0324	.0410	.0504	.0600	.0694	.0779
41	.0054	.0081	.0118	.0166	.0226	.0298	.0381	.0473	.0569	.0665
42	.0030	.0048	.0072	.0106	.0150	.0206	.0274	.0354	.0443	.0538
43	.0016	.0026	.0042	.0064	.0094	.0134	.0186	.0250	.0327	.0413
44	.0008	.0014	.0023	.0036	.0056	.0083	.0120	.0168	.0228	.0300
45	.0004	.0007	.0012	.0020	.0032	.0049	.0073	.0107	.0151	.0207
46	.0002	.0003	.0006	.0010	.0017	.0027	.0042	.0064	.0095	.0135
47	.0001	.0001	.0003	.0005	.0008	.0014	.0023	.0037	.0056	.0083
48	.0000	.0001	.0001	.0002	.0004	.0007	.0012	.0020	.0031	.0049
49	.0000	.0000	.0000	.0001	.0002	.0003	.0006	.0010	.0017	.0027
50	.0000	.0000	.0000	.0000	.0001	.0001	.0003	.0005	.0008	.0014
51	.0000	.0000	.0000	.0000	.0000	.0001	.0001	.0002	.0004	.0007
52	.0000	.0000	.0000	.0000	.0000	.0000	.0000	.0001	.0002	.0003
53	.0000	.0000	.0000	.0000	.0000	.0000	.0000	.0000	.0001	.0001
54	.0000	.0000	.0000	.0000	.0000	.0000	.0000	.0000	.0000	.0001

n = 100

r \ p	.01	.02	.03	.04	.05	.06	.07	.08	.09	.10
0	.3660	.1326	.0476	.0169	.0059	.0021	.0007	.0002	.0001	.0000
1	.3697	.2707	.1471	.0703	.0312	.0131	.0053	.0021	.0008	.0003
2	.1849	.2734	.2252	.1450	.0812	.0414	.0198	.0090	.0039	.0016
3	.0610	.1823	.2275	.1973	.1396	.0864	.0486	.0254	.0125	.0059
4	.0149	.0902	.1706	.1994	.1781	.1338	.0888	.0536	.0301	.0159
5	.0029	.0353	.1013	.1595	.1800	.1639	.1283	.0895	.0571	.0339
6	.0005	.0114	.0496	.1052	.1500	.1657	.1529	.1233	.0895	.0596
7	.0001	.0031	.0206	.0589	.1060	.1420	.1545	.1440	.1188	.0889
8	.0000	.0007	.0074	.0285	.0649	.1054	.1352	.1455	.1366	.1148
9	.0000	.0002	.0023	.0121	.0349	.0687	.1040	.1293	.1381	.1304
10	.0000	.0000	.0007	.0046	.0167	.0399	.0712	.1024	.1243	.1319
11	.0000	.0000	.0002	.0016	.0072	.0209	.0439	.0728	.1006	.1199
12	.0000	.0000	.0000	.0005	.0028	.0099	.0245	.0470	.0738	.0988
13	.0000	.0000	.0000	.0001	.0010	.0043	.0125	.0276	.0494	.0743
14	0	.0000	.0000	.0000	.0003	.0017	.0058	.0149	.0304	.0513
15	0	.0000	.0000	.0000	.0001	.0006	.0025	.0074	.0172	.0327
16	0	.0000	.0000	.0000	.0000	.0002	.0010	.0034	.0090	.0193
17	0	.0000	.0000	.0000	.0000	.0001	.0004	.0015	.0044	.0106
18	0	0	.0000	.0000	.0000	.0000	.0001	.0006	.0020	.0054
19	0	0	.0000	.0000	.0000	.0000	.0000	.0002	.0009	.0026

n = 100 (Continued)

r \ p	.01	.02	.03	.04	.05	.06	.07	.08	.09	.10
20	0	0	.0000	.0000	.0000	.0000	.0000	.0001	.0003	.0012
21	0	0	0	.0000	.0000	.0000	.0000	.0000	.0001	.0005
22	0	0	0	.0000	.0000	.0000	.0000	.0000	.0000	.0002
23	0	0	0	0	.0000	.0000	.0000	.0000	.0000	.0001
24	0	0	0	0	.0000	.0000	.0000	.0000	.0000	.0000
25	0	0	0	0	.0000	.0000	.0000	.0000	.0000	.0000
26	0	0	0	0	0	.0000	.0000	.0000	.0000	.0000
27	0	0	0	0	0	.0000	.0000	.0000	.0000	.0000
28	0	0	0	0	0	0	.0000	.0000	.0000	.0000
29	0	0	0	0	0	0	.0000	.0000	.0000	.0000
30	0	0	0	0	0	0	0	.0000	.0000	.0000
31	0	0	0	0	0	0	0	.0000	.0000	.0000
32	0	0	0	0	0	0	0	0	.0000	.0000
33	0	0	0	0	0	0	0	0	.0000	.0000
34	0	0	0	0	0	0	0	0	0	.0000
35	0	0	0	0	0	0	0	0	0	0
36	0	0	0	0	0	0	0	0	0	0
37	0	0	0	0	0	0	0	0	0	0
38	0	0	0	0	0	0	0	0	0	0
39	0	0	0	0	0	0	0	0	0	0
40	0	0	0	0	0	0	0	0	0	0
41	0	0	0	0	0	0	0	0	0	0
42	0	0	0	0	0	0	0	0	0	0
43	0	0	0	0	0	0	0	0	0	0
44	0	0	0	0	0	0	0	0	0	0
45	0	0	0	0	0	0	0	0	0	0
46	0	0	0	0	0	0	0	0	0	0
47	0	0	0	0	0	0	0	0	0	0
48	0	0	0	0	0	0	0	0	0	0

	.11	.12	.13	.14	.15	.16	.17	.18	.19	.20
0	.0000	.0000	.0000	.0000	.0000	.0000	.0000	.0000	.0000	.0000
1	.0001	.0000	.0000	.0000	.0000	.0000	.0000	.0000	.0000	.0000
2	.0007	.0003	.0001	.0000	.0000	.0000	.0000	.0000	.0000	.0000
3	.0027	.0012	.0005	.0002	.0001	.0000	.0000	.0000	.0000	.0000
4	.0080	.0038	.0018	.0008	.0003	.0001	.0001	.0000	.0000	.0000
5	.0189	.0100	.0050	.0024	.0011	.0005	.0002	.0001	.0000	.0000
6	.0369	.0215	.0119	.0063	.0031	.0015	.0007	.0003	.0001	.0001
7	.0613	.0394	.0238	.0137	.0075	.0039	.0020	.0009	.0004	.0002
8	.0881	.0625	.0414	.0259	.0153	.0086	.0047	.0024	.0012	.0006
9	.1112	.0871	.0632	.0430	.0276	.0168	.0098	.0054	.0029	.0015
10	.1251	.1080	.0860	.0637	.0444	.0292	.0182	.0108	.0062	.0034
11	.1265	.1205	.1051	.0849	.0640	.0454	.0305	.0194	.0118	.0069
12	.1160	.1219	.1165	.1025	.0838	.0642	.0463	.0316	.0206	.0128
13	.0970	.1125	.1179	.1130	.1001	.0827	.0642	.0470	.0327	.0216
14	.0745	.0954	.1094	.1143	.1098	.0979	.0817	.0641	.0476	.0335
15	.0528	.0745	.0938	.1067	.1111	.1070	.0960	.0807	.0640	.0481
16	.0347	.0540	.0744	.0922	.1041	.1082	.1044	.0941	.0798	.0638
17	.0212	.0364	.0549	.0742	.0908	.1019	.1057	.1021	.0924	.0789
18	.0121	.0229	.0379	.0557	.0739	.0895	.0998	.1033	.1000	.0909
19	.0064	.0135	.0244	.0391	.0563	.0736	.0882	.0979	.1012	.0981
20	.0032	.0074	.0148	.0258	.0402	.0567	.0732	.0870	.0962	.0993
21	.0015	.0039	.0084	.0160	.0270	.0412	.0571	.0728	.0859	.0946
22	.0007	.0019	.0045	.0094	.0171	.0282	.0420	.0574	.0724	.0849
23	.0003	.0009	.0023	.0052	.0103	.0182	.0292	.0427	.0576	.0720
24	.0001	.0004	.0011	.0027	.0058	.0111	.0192	.0301	.0433	.0577
25	.0000	.0002	.0005	.0013	.0031	.0064	.0119	.0201	.0309	.0439
26	.0000	.0001	.0002	.0006	.0016	.0035	.0071	.0127	.0209	.0316
27	.0000	.0000	.0001	.0003	.0008	.0018	.0040	.0076	.0134	.0217
28	.0000	.0000	.0000	.0001	.0004	.0009	.0021	.0044	.0082	.0141
29	.0000	.0000	.0000	.0000	.0002	.0004	.0011	.0024	.0048	.0088
30	.0000	.0000	.0000	.0000	.0001	.0002	.0005	.0012	.0027	.0052
31	.0000	.0000	.0000	.0000	.0000	.0001	.0002	.0006	.0014	.0029
32	.0000	.0000	.0000	.0000	.0000	.0000	.0001	.0003	.0007	.0016
33	.0000	.0000	.0000	.0000	.0000	.0000	.0000	.0001	.0003	.0008
34	.0000	.0000	.0000	.0000	.0000	.0000	.0000	.0001	.0002	.0004
35	.0000	.0000	.0000	.0000	.0000	.0000	.0000	.0000	.0001	.0002
36	.0000	.0000	.0000	.0000	.0000	.0000	.0000	.0000	.0000	.0001
37	0	.0000	.0000	.0000	.0000	.0000	.0000	.0000	.0000	.0000
38	0	.0000	.0000	.0000	.0000	.0000	.0000	.0000	.0000	.0000
39	0	0	.0000	.0000	.0000	.0000	.0000	.0000	.0000	.0000

Table C»107

n = 100 (Continued)

r \ p	.11	.12	.13	.14	.15	.16	.17	.18	.19	.20
40	0	0	0	.0000	.0000	.0000	.0000	.0000	.0000	.0000
41	0	0	0	.0000	.0000	.0000	.0000	.0000	.0000	.0000
42	0	0	0	.0	.0000	.0000	.0000	.0000	.0000	.0000
43	0	0	0	0	0	.0000	.0000	.0000	.0000	.0000
44	0	0	0	0	0	.0000	.0000	.0000	.0000	.0000
45	0	0	0	0	0	0	.0000	.0000	.0000	.0000
46	0	0	0	0	0	0	0	.0000	.0000	.0000
47	0	0	0	0	0	0	0	.0000	.0000	.0000
48	0	0	0	0	0	0	0	0	.0000	.0000

r \ p	.21	.22	.23	.24	.25	.26	.27	.28	.29	.30
0	.0000	.0000	0	0	0	0	0	0	0	0
1	.0000	.0000	.0000	.0000	0	0	0	0	0	0
2	.0000	.0000	.0000	.0000	.0000	.0000	.0000	0	0	0
3	.0000	.0000	.0000	.0000	.0000	.0000	.0000	.0000	.0000	0
4	.0000	.0000	.0000	.0000	.0000	.0000	.0000	.0000	.0000	.0000
5	.0000	.0000	.0000	.0000	.0000	.0000	.0000	.0000	.0000	.0000
6	.0000	.0000	.0000	.0000	.0000	.0000	.0000	.0000	.0000	.0000
7	.0001	.0000	.0000	.0000	.0000	.0000	.0000	.0000	.0000	.0000
8	.0003	.0001	.0001	.0000	.0000	.0000	.0000	.0000	.0000	.0000
9	.0007	.0003	.0002	.0001	.0000	.0000	.0000	.0000	.0000	.0000
10	.0018	.0009	.0004	.0002	.0001	.0000	.0000	.0000	.0000	.0000
11	.0038	.0021	.0011	.0005	.0003	.0001	.0000	.0000	.0000	.0000
12	.0076	.0043	.0024	.0012	.0006	.0003	.0001	.0001	.0000	.0000
13	.0136	.0082	.0048	.0027	.0014	.0007	.0004	.0002	.0001	.0000
14	.0225	.0144	.0089	.0052	.0030	.0016	.0009	.0004	.0002	.0001
15	.0343	.0233	.0152	.0095	.0057	.0033	.0018	.0010	.0005	.0002
16	.0484	.0350	.0241	.0159	.0100	.0061	.0035	.0020	.0011	.0006
17	.0636	.0487	.0356	.0248	.0165	.0106	.0065	.0038	.0022	.0012
18	.0780	.0634	.0490	.0361	.0254	.0171	.0111	.0069	.0041	.0024
19	.0895	.0772	.0631	.0492	.0365	.0259	.0177	.0115	.0072	.0044
20	.0963	.0881	.0764	.0629	.0493	.0369	.0264	.0182	.0120	.0076
21	.0975	.0947	.0869	.0756	.0626	.0494	.0373	.0269	.0186	.0124
22	.0931	.0959	.0932	.0858	.0749	.0623	.0495	.0376	.0273	.0190
23	.0839	.0917	.0944	.0919	.0847	.0743	.0621	.0495	.0378	.0277
24	.0716	.0830	.0905	.0931	.0906	.0837	.0736	.0618	.0496	.0380
25	.0578	.0712	.0822	.0893	.0918	.0894	.0828	.0731	.0615	.0496
26	.0444	.0579	.0708	.0814	.0883	.0906	.0883	.0819	.0725	.0613
27	.0323	.0448	.0580	.0704	.0806	.0873	.0896	.0873	.0812	.0720
28	.0224	.0329	.0451	.0580	.0701	.0799	.0864	.0886	.0864	.0804
29	.0148	.0231	.0335	.0455	.0580	.0697	.0793	.0855	.0876	.0856
30	.0093	.0154	.0237	.0340	.0458	.0580	.0694	.0787	.0847	.0868
31	.0056	.0098	.0160	.0242	.0344	.0460	.0580	.0691	.0781	.0840
32	.0032	.0060	.0103	.0165	.0248	.0349	.0462	.0579	.0688	.0776
33	.0018	.0035	.0063	.0107	.0170	.0252	.0352	.0464	.0579	.0685
34	.0009	.0019	.0037	.0067	.0112	.0175	.0257	.0356	.0466	.0579
35	.0005	.0010	.0021	.0040	.0070	.0116	.0179	.0261	.0359	.0468
36	.0002	.0005	.0011	.0023	.0042	.0073	.0120	.0183	.0265	.0362
37	.0001	.0003	.0006	.0012	.0024	.0045	.0077	.0123	.0187	.0268
38	.0000	.0001	.0003	.0006	.0013	.0026	.0047	.0079	.0127	.0191
39	.0000	.0001	.0001	.0003	.0007	.0015	.0028	.0049	.0082	.0130
40	.0000	.0000	.0001	.0002	.0004	.0008	.0016	.0029	.0051	.0085
41	.0000	.0000	.0000	.0001	.0002	.0004	.0008	.0017	.0031	.0053
42	.0000	.0000	.0000	.0000	.0001	.0002	.0004	.0009	.0018	.0032
43	.0000	.0000	.0000	.0000	.0000	.0001	.0002	.0005	.0010	.0019
44	.0000	.0000	.0000	.0000	.0000	.0000	.0001	.0002	.0005	.0010
45	.0000	.0000	.0000	.0000	.0000	.0000	.0000	.0001	.0003	.0005
46	.0000	.0000	.0000	.0000	.0000	.0000	.0000	.0001	.0001	.0003
47	.0000	.0000	.0000	.0000	.0000	.0000	.0000	.0000	.0001	.0001
48	.0000	.0000	.0000	.0000	.0000	.0000	.0000	.0000	.0000	.0001

r \ p	.31	.32	.33	.34	.35	.36	.37	.38	.39	.40
0	0	0	0	0	0	0	0	0	0	0
1	0	0	0	0	0	0	0	0	0	0
2	0	0	0	0	0	0	0	0	0	0
3	0	0	0	0	0	0	0	0	0	0
4	0	0	0	0	0	0	0	0	0	0
5	.0000	.0000	0	0	0	0	0	0	0	0
6	.0000	.0000	.0000	.0000	0	0	0	0	0	0
7	.0000	.0000	.0000	.0000	.0000	0	0	0	0	0
8	.0000	.0000	.0000	.0000	.0000	.0000	.0000	0	0	0
9	.0000	.0000	.0000	.0000	.0000	.0000	.0000	.0000	0	0

n = 100 (Continued)

r \ p	.31	.32	.33	.34	.35	.36	.37	.38	.39	.40
10	.0000	.0000	.0000	.0000	.0000	.0000	.0000	.0000	.0000	.0000
11	.0000	.0000	.0000	.0000	.0000	.0000	.0000	.0000	.0000	.0000
12	.0000	.0000	.0000	.0000	.0000	.0000	.0000	.0000	.0000	.0000
13	.0000	.0000	.0000	.0000	.0000	.0000	.0000	.0000	.0000	.0000
14	.0000	.0000	.0000	.0000	.0000	.0000	.0000	.0000	.0000	.0000
15	.0001	.0001	.0000	.0000	.0000	.0000	.0000	.0000	.0000	.0000
16	.0003	.0001	.0001	.0000	.0000	.0000	.0000	.0000	.0000	.0000
17	.0006	.0003	.0002	.0001	.0000	.0000	.0000	.0000	.0000	.0000
18	.0013	.0007	.0004	.0002	.0001	.0000	.0000	.0000	.0000	.0000
19	.0025	.0014	.0008	.0004	.0002	.0001	.0000	.0000	.0000	.0000
20	.0046	.0027	.0015	.0008	.0004	.0002	.0001	.0001	.0000	.0000
21	.0079	.0049	.0029	.0016	.0009	.0005	.0002	.0001	.0001	.0000
22	.0127	.0082	.0051	.0030	.0017	.0010	.0005	.0003	.0001	.0001
23	.0194	.0131	.0085	.0053	.0032	.0018	.0010	.0006	.0003	.0001
24	.0280	.0198	.0134	.0088	.0055	.0033	.0019	.0011	.0006	.0003
25	.0382	.0283	.0201	.0137	.0090	.0057	.0035	.0020	.0012	.0006
26	.0496	.0384	.0286	.0204	.0140	.0092	.0059	.0036	.0021	.0012
27	.0610	.0495	.0386	.0288	.0207	.0143	.0095	.0060	.0037	.0022
28	.0715	.0608	.0495	.0387	.0290	.0209	.0145	.0097	.0062	.0038
29	.0797	.0710	.0605	.0495	.0388	.0292	.0211	.0147	.0098	.0063
30	.0848	.0791	.0706	.0603	.0494	.0389	.0294	.0213	.0149	.0100
31	.0860	.0840	.0785	.0702	.0601	.0494	.0389	.0295	.0215	.0151
32	.0833	.0853	.0834	.0779	.0698	.0599	.0493	.0390	.0296	.0217
33	.0771	.0827	.0846	.0827	.0774	.0694	.0597	.0493	.0390	.0297
34	.0683	.0767	.0821	.0840	.0821	.0769	.0691	.0595	.0492	.0391
35	.0578	.0680	.0763	.0816	.0834	.0816	.0765	.0688	.0593	.0491
36	.0469	.0578	.0678	.0759	.0811	.0829	.0811	.0761	.0685	.0591
37	.0365	.0471	.0578	.0676	.0755	.0806	.0824	.0807	.0757	.0682
38	.0272	.0367	.0472	.0577	.0674	.0752	.0802	.0820	.0803	.0754
39	.0194	.0275	.0369	.0473	.0577	.0672	.0749	.0799	.0816	.0799
40	.0133	.0197	.0277	.0372	.0474	.0577	.0671	.0746	.0795	.0812
41	.0087	.0136	.0200	.0280	.0373	.0475	.0577	.0670	.0744	.0792
42	.0055	.0090	.0138	.0203	.0282	.0375	.0476	.0576	.0668	.0742
43	.0033	.0057	.0092	.0141	.0205	.0285	.0377	.0477	.0576	.0667
44	.0019	.0035	.0059	.0094	.0143	.0207	.0287	.0378	.0477	.0576
45	.0011	.0020	.0036	.0060	.0096	.0145	.0210	.0289	.0380	.0478
46	.0006	.0011	.0021	.0037	.0062	.0098	.0147	.0212	.0290	.0381
47	.0003	.0006	.0012	.0022	.0038	.0063	.0099	.0149	.0213	.0292
48	.0001	.0003	.0007	.0012	.0023	.0039	.0064	.0101	.0151	.0215
49	.0001	.0002	.0003	.0007	.0013	.0023	.0040	.0066	.0102	.0152
50	.0000	.0001	.0002	.0004	.0007	.0013	.0024	.0041	.0067	.0103
51	.0000	.0000	.0001	.0002	.0004	.0007	.0014	.0025	.0042	.0068
52	.0000	.0000	.0000	.0001	.0002	.0004	.0008	.0014	.0025	.0042
53	.0000	.0000	.0000	.0000	.0001	.0002	.0004	.0008	.0015	.0026
54	.0000	.0000	.0000	.0000	.0000	.0001	.0002	.0004	.0008	.0015
55	.0000	.0000	.0000	.0000	.0000	.0000	.0001	.0002	.0004	.0008
56	.0000	.0000	.0000	.0000	.0000	.0000	.0000	.0001	.0002	.0004
57	.0000	.0000	.0000	.0000	.0000	.0000	.0000	.0001	.0001	.0002
58	.0000	.0000	.0000	.0000	.0000	.0000	.0000	.0000	.0001	.0001
59	.0000	.0000	.0000	.0000	.0000	.0000	.0000	.0000	.0000	.0001

r	.41	.42	.43	.44	.45	.46	.47	.48	.49	.50
0	0	0	0	0	0	0	0	0	0	0
1	0	0	0	0	0	0	0	0	0	0
2	0	0	0	0	0	0	0	0	0	0
3	0	0	0	0	0	0	0	0	0	0
4	0	0	0	0	0	0	0	0	0	0
5	0	0	0	0	0	0	0	0	0	0
6	0	0	0	0	0	0	0	0	0	0
7	0	0	0	0	0	0	0	0	0	0
8	0	0	0	0	0	0	0	0	0	0
9	0	0	0	0	0	0	0	0	0	0
10	0	0	0	0	0	0	0	0	0	0
11	.0000	0	0	0	0	0	0	0	0	0
12	.0000	.0000	0	0	0	0	0	0	0	0
13	.0000	.0000	.0000	.0000	0	0	0	0	0	0
14	.0000	.0000	.0000	.0000	.0000	0	0	0	0	0

Table C >> **109**

				n = 100 (Continued)					
p r	.41	.42	.43	.44	.45	.46	.47	.48	.49	.50
15	.0000	.0000	.0000	.0000	.0000	.0000	. 0	0	0	0
16	.0000	.0000	.0000	.0000	.0000	.0000	.0000	.0000	0	0
17	.0000	.0000	.0000	.0000	.0000	.0000	.0000	.0000	.0000	0
18	.0000	.0000	.0000	.0000	.0000	.0000	.0000	.0000	.0000	.0000
19	.0000	.0000	.0000	.0000	.0000	.0000	.0000	.0000	.0000	.0000
20	.0000	.0000	.0000	.0000	.0000	.0000	.0000	.0000	.0000	.0000
21	.0000	.0000	.0000	.0000	.0000	.0000	.0000	.0000	.0000	.0000
22	.0000	.0000	.0000	.0000	.0000	.0000	.0000	.0000	.0000	.0000
23	.0001	.0000	.0000	.0000	.0000	.0000	.0000	.0000	.0000	.0000
24	.0002	.0001	.0000	.0000	.0000	.0000	.0000	.0000	.0000	.0000
25	.0003	.0002	.0001	.0000	.0000	.0000	.0000	.0000	.0000	.0000
26	.0007	.0003	.0002	.0001	.0000	.0000	.0000	.0000	.0000	.0000
27	.0013	.0007	.0004	.0002	.0001	.0000	.0000	.0000	.0000	.0000
28	.0023	.0013	.0007	.0004	.0002	.0001	.0000	.0000	.0000	.0000
29	.0039	.0024	.0014	.0008	.0004	.0002	.0001	.0000	.0000	.0000
30	.0065	.0040	.0024	.0014	.0008	.0004	.0002	.0001	.0001	.0000
31	.0102	.0066	.0041	.0025	.0014	.0008	.0004	.0002	.0001	.0001
32	.0152	.0103	.0067	.0042	.0025	.0015	.0008	.0004	.0002	.0001
33	.0218	.0154	.0104	.0068	.0043	.0026	.0015	.0008	.0004	.0002
34	.0298	.0219	.0155	.0105	.0069	.0043	.0026	.0015	.0009	.0005
35	.0391	.0299	.0220	.0156	.0106	.0069	.0044	.0026	.0015	.0009
36	.0491	.0391	.0300	.0221	.0157	.0107	.0070	.0044	.0027	.0016
37	.0590	.0490	.0391	.0300	.0222	.0157	.0107	.0070	.0044	.0027
38	.0680	.0588	.0489	.0391	.0301	.0222	.0158	.0108	.0071	.0045
39	.0751	.0677	.0587	.0489	.0391	.0301	.0223	.0158	.0108	.0071
40	.0796	.0748	.0675	.0586	.0488	.0391	.0301	.0223	.0159	.0108
41	.0809	.0793	.0745	.0673	.0584	.0487	.0391	.0301	.0223	.0159
42	.0790	.0806	.0790	.0672	.0672	.0583	.0487	.0390	.0301	.0223
43	.0740	.0787	.0804	.0788	.0741	.0670	.0582	.0486	.0390	.0301
44	.0666	.0739	.0785	.0802	.0786	.0739	.0669	.0581	.0485	.0390
45	.0576	.0666	.0737	.0784	.0800	.0784	.0738	.0668	.0580	.0485
46	.0479	.0576	.0665	.0736	.0782	.0798	.0783	.0737	.0667	.0580
47	.0382	.0480	.0576	.0665	.0736	.0781	.0797	.0781	.0736	.0666
48	.0293	.0383	.0480	.0577	.0665	.0735	.0781	.0797	.0781	.0735
49	.0216	.0295	.0384	.0481	.0577	.0664	.0735	.0780	.0796	.0780
50	.0153	.0218	.0296	.0385	.0482	.0577	.0665	.0735	.0780	.0796
51	.0104	.0155	.0219	.0297	.0386	.0482	.0578	.0665	.0735	.0780
52	.0068	.0105	.0156	.0220	.0298	.0387	.0483	.0578	.0665	.0735
53	.0043	.0069	.0106	.0156	.0221	.0299	.0388	.0483	.0579	.0666
54	.0026	.0044	.0070	.0107	.0157	.0221	.0299	.0388	.0484	.0580
55	.0015	.0026	.0044	.0070	.0108	.0158	.0222	.0300	.0389	.0485
56	.0008	.0015	.0027	.0044	.0071	.0108	.0158	.0222	.0300	.0390
57	.0005	.0009	.0016	.0027	.0045	.0071	.0108	.0158	.0223	.0301
58	.0002	.0005	.0009	.0016	.0027	.0045	.0071	.0108	.0159	.0223
59	.0001	.0002	.0005	.0009	.0016	.0027	.0045	.0071	.0109	.0159
60	.0001	.0001	.0002	.0005	.0009	.0016	.0027	.0045	.0071	.0108
61	.0000	.0001	.0001	.0002	.0005	.0009	.0016	.0027	.0045	.0071
62	.0000	.0000	.0001	.0001	.0002	.0005	.0009	.0016	.0027	.0045
63	.0000	.0000	.0000	.0001	.0001	.0002	.0005	.0009	.0016	.0027
64	.0000	.0000	.0000	.0000	.0001	.0001	.0002	.0005	.0009	.0016
65	.0000	.0000	.0000	.0000	.0000	.0001	.0001	.0002	.0005	.0009
66	.0000	.0000	.0000	.0000	.0000	.0000	.0001	.0001	.0002	.0005
67	.0000	.0000	.0000	.0000	.0000	.0000	.0000	.0001	.0001	.0002
68	.0000	.0000	.0000	.0000	.0000	.0000	.0000	.0000	.0001	.0001
69	.0000	.0000	.0000	.0000	.0000	.0000	.0000	.0000	.0000	.0001

CUMULATIVE BINOMIAL PROBABILITY DISTRIBUTION

$$P(r \geq \tilde{r} \mid n, p) = \sum_{r=\tilde{r}}^{n} \binom{n}{r} p^r q^{n-r}$$

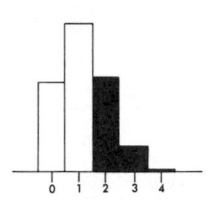

$$P(r \geq 2 \mid n = 4, p = 0.30) = 0.3483$$

n = 1

p \\ r	.01	.02	.03	.04	.05	.06	.07	.08	.09	.10
1	.0100	.0200	.0300	.0400	.0500	.0600	.0700	.0800	.0900	.1000

	.11	.12	.13	.14	.15	.16	.17	.18	.19	.20
1	.1100	.1200	.1300	.1400	.1500	.1600	.1700	.1800	.1900	.2000

	.21	.22	.23	.24	.25	.26	.27	.28	.29	.30
1	.2100	.2200	.2300	.2400	.2500	.2600	.2700	.2800	.2900	.3000

	.31	.32	.33	.34	.35	.36	.37	.38	.39	.40
1	.3100	.3200	.3300	.3400	.3500	.3600	.3700	.3800	.3900	.4000

	.41	.42	.43	.44	.45	.46	.47	.48	.49	.50
1	.4100	.4200	.4300	.4400	.4500	.4600	.4700	.4800	.4900	.5000

n = 2

p \\ r	.01	.02	.03	.04	.05	.06	.07	.08	.09	.10
1	.0199	.0396	.0591	.0784	.0975	.1164	.1351	.1536	.1719	.1900
2	.0001	.0004	.0009	.0016	.0025	.0036	.0049	.0064	.0081	.0100

	.11	.12	.13	.14	.15	.16	.17	..18	.19	.20
1	.2079	.2256	.2431	.2604	.2775	.2944	.3111	.3276	.3439	.3600
2	.0121	.0144	.0169	.0196	.0225	.0256	.0289	.0324	.0361	.0400

	.21	.22	.23	.24	.25	.26	.27	.28	.29	.30
1	.3759	.3916	.4071	.4224	.4375	.4524	.4671	.4816	.4959	.5100
2	.0441	.0484	.0529	.0576	.0625	.0676	.0729	.0784	.0841	.0900

	.31	.32	.33	.34	.35	.36	.37	.38	.39	.40
1	.5239	.5376	.5511	.5644	.5775	.5904	.6031	.6156	.6279	.6400
2	.0961	.1024	.1089	.1156	.1225	.1296	.1369	.1444	.1521	.1600

	.41	.42	.43	.44	.45	.46	.47	.48	.49	.50
1	.6519	.6636	.6751	.6864	.6975	.7084	.7191	.7296	.7399	.7500
2	.1681	.1764	.1849	.1936	.2025	.2116	.2209	.2304	.2401	.2500

n = 3

p \\ r	.01	.02	.03	.04	.05	.06	.07	.08	.09	.10
1	.0297	.0588	.0873	.1153	.1426	.1694	.1956	.2213	.2264	.2710
2	.0003	.0012	.0026	.0047	.0072	.0104	.0140	.0182	.0228	.0280
3	.0000	.0000	.0000	.0001	.0001	.0002	.0003	.0005	.0007	.0010

n = 3 (Continued)

p / r	.11	.12	.13	.14	.15	.16	.17	.18	.19	.20
1	.2950	.3185	.3415	.3639	.3859	.4073	.4282	.4486	.4686	.4880
2	.0336	.0397	.0463	.0533	.0608	.0686	.0769	.0855	.0946	.1040
3	.0013	.0017	.0022	.0027	.0034	.0041	.0049	.0058	.0069	.0080

r	.21	.22	.23	.24	.25	.26	.27	.28	.29	.30
1	.5070	.5254	.5435	.5610	.5781	.5948	.6110	.6268	.6421	.6570
2	.1138	.1239	.1344	.1452	.1562	.1676	.1793	.1913	.2035	.2160
3	.0093	.0106	.0122	.0138	.0156	.0176	.0197	.0220	.0244	.0270

r	.31	.32	.33	.34	.35	.36	.37	.38	.39	.40
1	.6715	.6856	.6992	.7125	.7254	.7379	.7500	.7617	.7730	.7840
2	.2287	.2417	.2548	.2682	.2818	.2955	.3094	.3235	.3377	.3520
3	.0298	.0328	.0359	.0393	.0429	.0467	.0507	.0549	.0593	.0640

r	.41	.42	.43	.44	.45	.46	.47	.48	.49	.50
1	.7946	.8049	.8148	.8244	.8336	.8425	.8511	.8594	.8673	.8750
2	.3665	.3810	.3957	.4104	.4252	.4401	.4551	.4700	.4850	.5000
3	.0689	.0741	.0797	.0852	.0911	.0973	.1038	.1106	.1176	.1250

n = 4

p / r	.01	.02	.03	.04	.05	.06	.07	.08	.09	.10
1	.0394	.0776	.1147	.1507	.1855	.2193	.2519	.2836	.3143	.3439
2	.0006	.0023	.0052	.0091	.0140	.0199	.0267	.0344	.0430	.0523
3	.0000	.0000	.0001	.0002	.0005	.0008	.0013	.0019	.0027	.0037
4	.0000	.0000	.0000	.0000	.0000	.0000	.0000	.0000	.0001	.0001

r	.11	.12	.13	.14	.15	.16	.17	.18	.19	.20
1	.3726	.4003	.4271	.4530	.4780	.5021	.5254	.5479	.5695	.5904
2	.0624	.0732	.0847	.0968	.1095	.1228	.1366	.1509	.1656	.1808
3	.0049	.0063	.0079	.0098	.0120	.0144	.0171	.0202	.0235	.0272
4	.0001	.0002	.0003	.0004	.0005	.0007	.0008	.0010	.0013	.0016

r	.21	.22	.23	.24	.25	.26	.27	.28	.29	.30
1	.6105	.6298	.6485	.6664	.6836	.7001	.7160	.7313	.7459	.7599
2	.1963	.2122	.2285	.2450	.2617	.2787	.2959	.3132	.3307	.3483
3	.0312	.0356	.0403	.0453	.0508	.0566	.0628	.0694	.0763	.0837
4	.0019	.0023	.0028	.0033	.0039	.0046	.0053	.0061	.0071	.0081

r	.31	.32	.33	.34	.35	.36	.37	.38	.39	.40
1	.7733	.7862	.7985	.8103	.8215	.8322	.8425	.8522	.8615	.8704
2	.3660	.3837	.4015	.4193	.4370	.4547	.4724	.4900	.5075	.5248
3	.0915	.0996	.1082	.1171	.1265	.1362	.1464	.1569	.1679	.1792
4	.0092	.0105	.0119	.0134	.0150	.0168	.0187	.0209	.0231	.0256

r	.41	.42	.43	.44	.45	.46	.47	.48	.49	.50
1	.8788	.8868	.8944	.9017	.9085	.9150	.9211	.9269	.9323	.9375
2	.5420	.5590	.5759	.5926	.6090	.6252	.6412	.6569	.6724	.6875
3	.1909	.2030q	.2155	.2283	.2415	.2550	.2689	.2831	.2977	.3125
4	.0283	.0311	.0342	.0375	.0410	.0448	.0488	.0531	.0576	.0625

n = 5

p / r	.01	.02	.03	.04	.05	.06	.07	.08	.09	.10
1	.0490	.0961	.1413	.1846	.2262	.2661	.3043	.3409	.3760	.4095
2	.0010	.0038	.0085	.0148	.0226	.0319	.0425	.0544	.0674	.0815
3	.0000	.0001	.0003	.0006	.0012	.0020	.0031	.0045	.0063	.0086
4	.0000	.0000	.0000	.0000	.0000	.0001	.0001	.0002	.0003	.0005

r	.11	.12	.13	.14	.15	.16	.17	.18	.19	.20
1	.4416	.4723	.5016	.5296	.5563	.5818	.6061	.6293	.6513	.6723
2	.0965	.1125	.1292	.1467	.1648	.1835	.2027	.2224	.2424	.2627
3	.0112	.0143	.0179	.0220	.0266	.0318	.0375	.0437	.0505	.0579
4	.0007	.0009	.0013	.0017	.0022	.0029	.0036	.0045	.0055	.0067
5	.0000	.0000	.0000	.0001	.0001	.0001	.0001	.0002	.0002	.0003

n = 5 (Continued)

r \ p	.21	.22	.23	.24	.25	.26	.27	.28	.29	.30
1	.6923	.7113	.7293	.7464	.7627	.7781	.7927	.8065	.8196	.8319
2	.2833	.3041	.3251	.3461	.3672	.3883	.4093	.4303	.4511	.4718
3	.0659	.0744	.0836	.0933	.1035	.1143	.1257	.1376	.1501	.1631
4	.0081	.0097	.0114	.0134	.0156	.0181	.0208	.0238	.0272	.0308
5	.0004	.0005	.0006	.0008	.0010	.0012	.0014	.0017	.0021	.0024

r \ p	.31	..32	.33	.34	.35	.36	.37	.38	.39	.40
1	.8436	.8546	.8650	.8748	.8840	.8926	.9008	.9084	.9155	.9222
2	.4923	.5125	.5325	.5522	.5716	.5906	.6093	.6276	.6455	.6630
3	.1766	.1905	.2050	.2199	.2352	.2509	.2670	.2835	.3003	.3174
4	.0347	.0390	.0436	.0486	.0540	.0598	.0660	.0726	.0796	.0870
5	.0029	.0034	.0039	.0045	.0053	.0060	.0069	.0079	.0090	.0102

r \ p	.41	.42	.43	.44	.45	.46	.47	.48	.49	.50
1	.9285	.9344	.9398	.9449	.9497	.9541	.9582	.9620	.9655	.9688
2	.6801	.6967	.7129	.7286	.7438	.7585	.7728	.7865	.7998	.8125
3	.3349	.3525	.3705	.3886	.4069	.4253	.4439	.4625	.4813	.5000
4	.0949	.1033	.1121	.1214	.1312	.1415	.1522	.1635	.1752	.1875
5	.0116	.0131	.0147	.0165	.0185	.0206	.0229	.0255	.0282	.0312

n = 6

r \ p	.01	.02	.03	.04	.05	.06	..07	.08	.09	.10
1	.0585	.1142	.1670	.2172	.2649	.3101	.3530	.3936	.4321	.4686
2	.0015	.0057	.0125	.0216	.0328	.0459	.0608	.0773	.0952	.1143
3	.0000	.0002	.0005	.0012	.0022	.0038	.0058	.0085	.0118	.0158
4	.0000	.0000	.0000	.0000	.0001	.0002	.0003	.0005	.0008	.0013
5	.0000	.0000	.0000	.0000	.0000	.0000	.0000	.0000	.0000	.0001

r \ p	.11	.12	.13	.14	.15	.16	.17	.18	.19	.20
1	.5030	.5356	.5664	.5954	.6229	.6487	.6731	.6960	.7176	.7379
2	.1345	.1556	.1776	.2003	.2235	.2472	.2713	.2956	.3201	.3446
3	.0206	.0261	.0324	.0395	.0476	.0560	.0655	.0759	.0870	.0989
4	.0018	.0025	.0034	.0045	.0059	.0075	.0094	.0116	.0141	.0170
5	.0001	.0001	.0002	.0003	.0004	.0005	.0007	.0010	.0013	.0016
6	.0000	.0000	.0000	.0000	.0000	.0000	.0000	.0000	.0000	.0001

r \ p	.21	.22	.23	.24	.25	.26	.27	.28	.29	.30
1	.7569	.7748	.7916	.8073	.8220	.8358	.8487	.8607	.8719	.8824
2	.3692	.3937	.4180	.4422	.4661	.4896	.5128	.5356	.5580	.5798
3	.1115	.1250	.1391	.1539	.1694	.1856	.2023	.2196	.2374	.2557
4	.0202	.0239	.0280	.0326	.0376	.0431	.0492	.0557	.0628	.0705
5	.0020	.0025	.0031	.0038	.0046	.0056	.0067	.0079	.0093	.0109
6	.0001	.0001	.0001	.0002	.0002	.0003	.0004	.0005	.0006	.0007

r \ p	.31	.32	.33	.34	.35	.36	.37	.38	.39	.40
1	.8921	.9011	.9095	.9173	.9246	.9313	.9375	.9432	.9485	.9533
2	.6012	.6220	.6422	.6619	.6809	.6994	.7172	.7343	.7508	.7667
3	.2744	.2936	.3130	.3328	.3529	.3732	.3937	.4143	.4350	.4557
4	.0787	.0875	.0969	.1069	.1174	.1286	.1404	.1527	.1657	.1792
5	.0127	.0148	.0170	.0195	.0223	.0254	.0288	.0325	.0365	.0410
6	.0009	.0011	.0013	.0015	.0018	.0022	.0026	.0030	.0035	.0041

r \ p	.41	.42	.43	.44	.45	.46	.47	.48	.49	.50
1	.9578	.9619	.9657	.9692	.9723	.9752	.9778	.9802	.9824	.9844
2	.7819	.7965	.8105	.8238	.8364	.8485	.8599	.8707	.8810	.8906
3	.4764	.4971	.5177	.5382	.5585	.5786	.5985	.6180	.6373	.6562
4	.1933	.2080	.2232	.2390	.2553	.2721	.2893	.3070	.3252	.3438
5	.0458	.0510	.0566	.0627	.0692	.0762	.0837	.0917	.1003	.1094
6	.0048	.0055	.0063	.0073	.0083	.0095	.0108	.0122	.0138	.0156

n = 7

r \ p	.01	.02	.03	.04	.05	.06	.07	.08	.09	.10
1	.0679	.1319	.1920	.2486	.3017	.3515	.3983	.4422	.4832	.5217
2	.0020	.0079	.0171	.0294	.0444	.0618	.0813	.1026	.1255	.1497
3	.0000	.0003	.0009	.0020	.0038	.0063	.0097	.0140	.0193	.0257
4	.0000	.0000	.0000	.0001	.0002	.0004	.0007	.0012	.0018	.0027
5	.0000	.0000	.0000	.0000	.0000	.0000	.0000	.0001	.0001	.0002

n = 7 (Continued)

r\p	.11	.12	.13	.14	.15	.16	.17	.18	.29	.20
1	.5577	.5913	.6227	.6521	.6794	.7049	.7286	.7507	.7712	.7903
2	.1750	.2012	.2281	.2556	.2834	.3115	.3396	.3677	.3956	.4233
3	.0331	.0416	.0513	.0620	.0738	.0866	.1005	.1154	.1313	.1480
4	.0039	.0054	.0072	.0094	.0121	.0153	.0189	.0231	.0279	.0333
5	.0003	.0004	.0006	.0009	.0012	.0017	.0022	.0029	.0037	.0047
6	.0000	.0000	.0000	.0000	.0001	.0001	.0001	.0002	.0003	.0004

r\p	.21	.22	.23	.24	.25	.26	.27	.28	.29	.30
1	.8080	.8243	.8395	.8535	.8665	.8785	.8895	.8997	.9090	.9176
2	.4506	.4775	.5040	.5298	.5551	.5796	.6035	.6266	.6490	.6706
3	.1657	.1841	.2033	.2231	.2436	.2646	.2861	.3081	.3304	.3529
4	.0394	.0461	.0536	.0617	.0706	.0802	.0905	.1016	.1134	.1260
5	.0058	.0072	.0088	.0107	.0129	.0153	.0181	.0213	.0248	.0288
6	.0005	.0006	.0008	.0011	.0013	.0017	.0021	.0026	.0031	.0038
7	.0000	.0000	.0000	.0000	.0001	.0001	.0001	.0001	.0002	.0002

r\p	.31	.32	.33	.34	.35	.36	.37	.38	.39	.40
1	.9255	.9328	.9394	.9454	.9510	.9560	.9606	.9648	.9686	.9720
2	.6914	.7113	.7304	.7487	.7662	.7828	.7987	.8137	.8279	.8414
3	.3757	.3987	.4217	.4447	.4677	.4906	.5134	.5359	.5581	.5801
4	.1394	.1534	.1682	.1837	.1998	.2167	.2341	.2521	.2707	.2898
5	.0332	.0380	.0434	.0492	.0556	.0625	.0701	.0782	.0869	.0963
6	.0046	.0055	.0065	.0077	.0090	.0105	.0123	.0142	.0164	.0188
7	.0003	.0003	.0004	.0005	.0006	.0008	.0009	.0011	.0014	.0016

r\p	.41	.42	.43	.44	.45	.46	.47	.48	.49	.50
1	.9751	.9779	.9805	.9827	.9848	.9866	.9883	.9897	.9910	.9922
2	.8541	.8660	.8772	.8877	.8976	.9068	.9153	.9233	.9307	.9375
3	.6017	.6229	.6436	.6638	.6836	.7027	.7213	.7393	.7567	.7734
4	.3094	.3294	.3498	.3706	.3917	.4131	.4346	.4563	.4781	.5000
5	.1063	.1169	.1282	.1402	.1529	.1663	.1803	.1951	.2105	.2266
6	.0216	.0246	.0279	.0316	.0357	.0402	.0451	.0504	.0562	.0625
7	.0019	.0023	.0027	.0032	.0037	.0044	.0051	.0059	.0068	.0078

n = 8

r\p	.01	.02	.03	.04	.05	.06	.07	.08	.09	.10
1	.0773	.1492	.2163	.2786	.3366	.3904	.4404	.4868	.5297	.5695
2	.0027	.0103	.0223	.0381	.0572	.0792	.1035	.1298	.1577	.1869
3	.0001	.0004	.0013	.0031	.0058	.0096	.0147	.0211	.0289	.0381
4	.0000	.0000	.0001	.0002	.0004	.0007	.0013	.0022	.0034	.0050
5	.0000	.0000	.0000	.0000	.0000	.0000	.0001	.0001	.0003	.0004

r\p	.11	.12	.13	.14	.15	.16	.17	.18	.19	.20
1	.6063	.6404	.6718	.7008	.7275	.7521	.7748	.7956	.8147	.8322
2	.2171	.2480	.2794	.3111	.3428	.3744	.4057	.4366	.4670	.4967
3	.0487	.0608	.0743	.0891	.1052	.1226	.1412	.1608	.1815	.2031
4	.0071	.0097	.0129	.0168	.0214	.0267	.0328	.0397	.0476	.0563
5	.0007	.0010	.0015	.0021	.0029	.0038	.0050	.0065	.0083	.0104
6	.0000	.0001	.0001	.0002	.0002	.0004	.0005	.0007	.0009	.0012
7	.0000	.0000	.0000	.0000	.0000	.0000	.0000	.0000	.0001	.0001

r\p	.21	.22	.23	.24	.25	.26	.27	.28	.29	.30
1	.8483	.8630	.8764	.8887	.8999	.9101	.9194	.9278	.9354	.9424
2	.5257	.5538	.5811	.6075	.6329	.6573	.6807	.7031	.7244	.7447
3	.2255	.2486	.2724	.2967	.3215	.3465	.3718	.3973	.4228	.4482
4	.0659	.0765	.0880	.1004	.1138	.1281	.1433	.1594	.1763	.1941
5	.0129	.0158	.0191	.0230	.0273	.0322	.0377	.0438	.0505	.0580
6	.0016	.0021	.0027	.0034	.0042	.0052	.0064	.0078	.0094	.0113
7	.0001	.0002	.0002	.0003	.0004	.0005	.0006	.0008	.0010	.0013
8	.0000	.0000	.0000	.0000	.0000	.0000	.0000	.0000	.0001	.0001

r\p	.31	.32	.33	.34	.35	.36	.37	.38	.39	.40
1	.9486	.9543	.9594	.9640	.9681	.9719	.9752	.9782	.9808	.9832
2	.7640	.7822	.7994	.8156	.8309	.8452	.8586	.8711	.8828	.8936
3	.4736	.4987	.5236	.5481	.5722	.5958	.6189	.6415	.6634	.6846
4	.2126	.2319	.2519	.2724	.2936	.3153	.3374	.3599	.3828	.4059
5	.0661	.0750	.0846	.0949	.1061	.1180	.1307	.1443	.1586	.1737
6	.0134	.0159	.0187	.9218	.0253	.0293	.0336	.0385	.0439	.0498
7	.0016	.0020	.0024	.0030	.0036	.0043	.0051	.0061	.0072	.0085
8	.0001	.0001	.0001	.0002	.0002	.0003	.0004	.0004	.0005	.0007

n = 8 (Continued)

p r	.41	.42	.43	.44	.45	.46	.47	.48	.49	.50
1	.9853	.9872	.9889	.9903	.9916	.9928	.9938	.9947	.9954	.9961
2	.9037	.9130	.9216	.9295	.9368	.9435	.9496	.9552	.9602	.9648
3	.7052	.7250	.7440	.7624	.7799	.7966	.8125	.8276	.8419	.8555
4	.4292	.4527	.4762	.4996	.5230	.5463	.5694	.5922	.6146	.6367
5	.1895	.2062	.2235	.2416	.2604	.2798	.2999	.3205	.3416	.3633
6	.0563	.0634	.0711	.0794	.0885	.0982	.1086	.1198	.1318	.1445
7	.0100	.0117	.0136	.0157	.0181	.0208	.0239	.0272	.0310	.0352
8	.0008	.0010	.0012	.0014	.0017	.0020	.0024	.0028	.0033	.0039

n = 9

p r	.01	.02	.03	.04	.05	.06	.07	.08	.09	.10
1	.0865	.1663	.2398	.3075	.3698	.4270	.4796	.5278	.5721	.6126
2	.0034	.0131	.0282	.0478	.0712	.0978	.1271	.1583	.1912	.2252
3	.0001	.0006	.0020	.0045	.0084	.0138	.0209	.0298	.0405	.0530
4	.0000	.0000	.0001	.0003	.0006	.0013	.0023	.0037	.0057	.0083
5	.0000	.0000	.0000	.0000	.0000	.0001	.0002	.0003	.0005	.0009
6	.0000	.0000	.0000	.0000	.0000	.0000	.0000	.0000	.0000	.0001

	.11	.12	.13	.14	.15	.16	.17	.18	.19	.20
1	.6496	.6835	.7145	.7427	.7684	.7918	.8131	.8324	.8499	.8658
2	.2599	.2951	.3304	.3657	.4005	.4348	.4685	.5012	.5330	.5638
3	.0672	.0833	.1009	.1202	.1409	.1629	.1861	.2105	.2357	.2618
4	.0117	.0158	.0209	.0269	.0339	.0420	.0512	.0615	.0730	.0856
5	.0014	.0021	.0030	.0041	.0056	.0075	.0098	.0125	.0158	.0196
6	.0001	.0002	.0003	.0004	.0006	.0009	.0013	.0017	.0023	.0031
7	.0000	.0000	.0000	.0000	.0000	.0001	.0001	.0002	.0002	.0003

	.21	.22	.23	.24	.25	.26	.27	.28	.29	.30
1	.8801	.8931	.9048	.9154	.9249	.9335	.9411	.9480	.9542	.9596
2	.5934	.6218	.6491	.6750	.6997	.7230	.7452	.7660	.7856	.8040
3	.2885	.3158	.3434	.3713	.3993	.4273	.4552	.4829	.5102	.5372
4	.0994	.0114	.1304	.1475	.1657	.1849	.2050	.2260	.2478	.2703
5	.0240	.0291	.0350	.0416	.0489	.0571	.0662	.0762	.0870	.0988
6	.0040	.0051	.0065	.0081	.0100	.0122	.0149	.0179	.0213	.0253
7	.0004	.0006	.0008	.0010	.0013	.0017	.0022	.0028	.0035	.0043
8	.0000	.0000	.0001	.0001	.0001	.0001	.0002	.0003	.0003	.0004

	.31	.32	.33	.34	.35	.36	.37	.38	.39	.40
1	.9645	.9689	.9728	.9762	.9793	.9820	.9844	.9865	.9883	.9899
2	.8212	.8372	.8522	.8661	.8789	.8908	.9017	.9118	.9210	.9295
3	.5636	.5894	.6146	.6390	.6627	.6856	.7076	.7287	.7489	.7682
4	.2935	.3173	.3415	.3662	.3911	.4163	.4416	.4669	.4922	.5174
5	.1115	.1252	.1398	.1553	.1717	.1890	.2072	.2262	.2460	.2666
6	.0298	.0348	.0404	.0467	.0536	.0612	.0696	.0787	.0886	.0994
7	.0053	.0064	.0078	.0094	.0112	.0133	.0157	.0184	.0215	.0250
8	.0006	.0007	.0009	.0011	.0014	.0017	.0021	.0026	.0031	.0038
9	.0000	.0000	.0000	.0001	.0001	.0001	.0001	.0002	.0002	.0003

	.41	.42	.43	.44	.45	.46	.47	.48	.49	.50
1	.9913	.9926	.9936	.9946	.9954	.9961	.9967	.9972	.9977	.9980
2	.9372	.9442	.9505	.0563	.9615	.9662	.9704	.9741	.9775	.9805
3	.7866	.8039	.8204	.8359	.8505	.8642	.8769	.8889	.8999	.9102
4	.5424	.5670	.5913	.6152	.6386	.6614	.6836	.7052	.7260	.7461
5	.2878	.3097	.3322	.3551	.3786	.4024	.4265	.4509	.4754	.5000
6	.1109	.1233	.1366	.1508	.1658	.1817	.1985	.2161	.2346	.2539
7	.0290	.0334	.0383	.0437	.0498	.0564	.0637	.0717	.0804	.0898
8	.0046	.0055	.0065	.0077	.0091	.0107	.0125	.0145	.0169	.0195
9	.0003	.0004	.0005	.0006	.0008	.0009	.0011	.0014	.0016	.0020

n = 10

p r	.01	.02	.03	.04	.05	.06	.07	.08	.09	.10
1	.0956	.1829	.2626	.3352	.4013	.4614	.5160	.5656	.6106	.6513
2	.0043	.0162	.0345	.0582	.0861	.1176	.1517	.1879	.2254	.2639
3	.0001	.0009	.0028	.0062	.0115	.0188	.0283	.0401	.0540	.0702
4	.0000	.0000	.0001	.0004	.0010	.0020	.0036	.0058	.0088	.0128
5	.0000	.0000	.0000	.0000	.0001	.0002	.0003	.0006	.0010	.0016
6	.0000	.0000	.0000	.0000	.0000	.0000	.0000	.0000	.0001	.0001

	.11	.12	.13	.14	.15	.16	.17	.18	.19	.20
1	.6882	.7215	.7516	.7787	.8031	.8251	.8448	.8626	.8784	.8926
2	.3028	.3417	.3804	.4184	.4557	.4920	.5270	.5608	.5932	.6242
3	.0884	.1087	.1308	.1545	.1798	.2064	.2341	.2628	.2922	.3222
4	.0178	.0239	.0313	.0400	.0500	.0614	.0741	.0883	.1039	.1209
5	.0025	.0037	.0053	.0073	.0099	.0130	.0168	.0213	.0266	.0328
6	.0003	.0004	.0006	.0010	.0014	.0020	.0027	.0037	.0049	.0064
7	.0000	.0000	.0001	.0001	.0001	.0002	.0003	.0004	.0006	.0009
8	.0000	.0000	.0000	.0000	.0000	.0000	.0000	.0000	.0001	.0001

	.21	.22	.23	.24	.25	.26	.27	.28	.29	.30
1	.9053	.9166	.9267	.9357	.9437	.9508	.9570	.9626	.9674	.9718
2	.6536	.6815	.7079	.7327	.7560	.7778	.7981	.8170	.8345	.8507
3	.3526	.3831	.4137	.4442	.4744	.5042	.5335	.5622	.5901	.6172
4	.1391	.1587	.1794	.2012	.2241	.2479	.2726	.2979	.3239	.3504
5	.0399	.0479	.0569	.0670	.0781	.0904	.1037	.1181	.1337	.1503
6	.0082	.0104	.0130	.0161	.0197	.0239	.0287	.0342	.0404	.0473
7	.0012	.0016	.0021	.0027	.0035	.0045	.0056	.0070	.0087	.0106
8	.0001	.0002	.0002	.0003	.0004	.0006	.0007	.0010	.0012	.0016
9	.0000	.0000	.0000	.0000	.0000	.0000	.0001	.0001	.0001	.0001

	.31	.32	.33	.34	.35	.36	.37	.38	.39	.40
1	.9755	.9789	.9818	.9843	.9865	.9885	.9902	.9916	.9929	.9940
2	.8656	.8794	.8920	.9035	.9140	.9236	.9323	.9402	.9473	.9536
3	.6434	.6687	.6930	.7162	.7384	.7595	.7794	.7983	.8160	.8327
4	.3772	.4044	.4316	.4589	.4862	.5132	.5400	.5664	.5923	.6177
5	.1679	.1867	.2064	.2270	.2485	.2708	.2939	.3177	.3420	.3669
6	.0551	.0637	.0732	.0836	.0949	.1072	.1205	.1348	.1500	.1662
7	.0129	.0155	.0185	.0220	.0260	.0305	.0356	.0413	.0477	.0548
8	.0020	.0025	.0032	.0039	.0048	.0059	.0071	.0086	.0103	.0123
9	.0002	.0003	.0003	.0004	.0005	.0007	.0009	.0011	.0014	.0017
10	.0000	.0000	.0000	.0000	.0000	.0000	.0000	.0001	.0001	.0001

	.41	.42	.43	.44	.45	.46	.47	.48	.49	.50
1	.9949	.9957	.9964	.9970	.9975	.9979	.9983	.9986	.9988	.9990
2	.9594	.9645	.9691	.9731	.9767	.9799	.9827	.9852	.9874	.9892
3	.8483	.8628	.8764	.8889	.9004	.9111	.9209	.9298	.9379	.9453
4	.6425	.6665	.6898	.7123	.7340	.7547	.7745	.7933	.8112	.8281
5	.3922	.4178	.4436	.4696	.4956	.5216	.5474	.5730	.5982	.6230
6	.1834	.2016	.2207	.2407	.2616	.2832	.3057	.3288	.3526	.3770
7	.0626	.0712	.0806	.0908	.1020	.1141	.1271	.1410	.1560	.1719
8	.0146	.0172	.0202	.0236	.0274	.0317	.0366	.0420	.0480	.0547
9	.0021	.0025	.0031	.0037	.0045	.0054	.0065	.0077	.0091	.0107
10	.0001	.0002	.0002	.0003	.0003	.0004	.0005	.0006	.0008	.0010

n = 11

p r	.01	.02	.03	.04	.05	.06	.07	.08	.09	.10
1	.1047	.1993	.2847	.3618	.4312	.4937	.5499	.6004	.6456	.6862
2	.0052	.0195	.0413	.0692	.1019	.1382	.1772	.2181	.2601	.3026
3	.0002	.0012	.0037	.0083	.0152	.0248	.0370	.0519	.0695	.0896
4	.0000	.0000	.0002	.0007	.0016	.0030	.0053	.0085	.0129	.0185
5	.0000	.0000	.0000	.0000	.0001	.0003	.0005	.0010	.0017	.0028
6	.0000	.0000	.0000	.0000	.0000	.0000	.0000	.0001	.0002	.0003

	.11	.12	.13	.14	.15	.16	.17	.18	.19	.20
1	.7225	.7549	.7839	.8097	.8327	.8531	.8712	.8873	.9015	.9141
2	.3452	.3873	.4286	.4689	.5078	.5453	.5811	.6151	.6474	.6779
3	.1120	.1366	.1632	.1915	.2212	.2521	.2839	.3164	.3494	.3826
4	.0256	.0341	.0442	.0560	.0694	.0846	.1013	.1197	.1397	.1611
5	.0042	.0061	.0087	.0119	.0159	.0207	.0266	.0334	.0413	.0504
6	.0005	.0008	.0012	.0018	.0027	.0037	.0051	.0068	.0090	.0117
7	.0000	.0001	.0001	.0002	.0003	.0005	.0007	.0010	.0014	.0020
8	.0000	.0000	.0000	.0000	.0000	.0000	.0001	.0001	.0002	.0002

n = 11 (Continued)

p / r	.21	.22	.23	.24	.25	.26	.27	.28	.29	.30
1	.9252	.9350	.9436	.9511	.9578	.9636	.9686	.9730	.9769	.9802
2	.7065	.7333	.7582	.7814	.8029	.8227	.8410	.8577	.8730	.8870
3	.4158	.4488	.4814	.5134	.5448	.5753	.6049	.6335	.6610	.6873
4	.1840	.2081	.2333	.2596	.2867	.3146	.3430	.3719	.4011	.4304
5	.0607	.0723	.0851	.0992	.1146	.1313	.1493	.1685	.1888	.2103
6	.0148	.0186	.0231	.0283	.0343	.0412	.0490	.0577	.0674	.0782
7	.0027	.0035	.0046	.0059	.0076	.0095	.0119	.0146	.0179	.0216
8	.0003	.0005	.0007	.0009	.0012	.0016	.0021	.0027	.0034	.0043
9	.0000	.0000	.0001	.0001	.0001	.0002	.0002	.0003	.0004	.0006

p / r	.31	.32	.33	.34	.35	.36	.37	.38	.39	.40
1	.9831	.9856	.9878	.9896	.9912	.9926	.9938	.9948	.9956	.9964
2	.8997	.9112	.9216	.9310	.9394	.9470	.9537	.9597	.9650	.9698
3	.7123	.7361	.7587	.7799	.7999	.8186	.8360	.8522	.8672	.8811
4	.4598	.4890	.5179	.5464	.5744	.6019	.6286	.6545	.6796	.7037
5	.2328	.2563	.2807	.3059	.3317	.3581	.3850	.4122	.4397	.4672
6	.0901	.1031	.1171	.1324	.1487	.1661	.1847	.2043	.2249	.2465
7	.0260	.0309	.0366	.0430	.0501	.0581	.0670	.0768	.0876	.0994
8	.0054	.0067	.0082	.0101	.0122	.0148	.0177	.0210	.0249	.0293
9	.0008	.0010	.0013	.0016	.0020	.0026	.0032	.0039	.0048	.0059
10	.0001	.0001	.0001	.0002	.0002	.0003	.0004	.0005	.0006	.0007

p / r	.41	.42	.43	.44	.45	.46	.47	.48	.49	.50
1	.9970	.9975	.9979	.9983	.9986	.9989	.9991	.9992	.9994	.9995
2	.9739	.9776	.9808	.9836	.9861	.9882	.9900	.9916	.9930	.9941
3	.8938	.9055	.9162	.9260	.9348	.9428	.9499	.9564	.9622	.9673
4	.7269	.7490	.7700	.7900	.8089	.8266	.8433	.8588	.8733	.8867
5	.4948	.5223	.5495	.5764	.6029	.6288	.6541	.6787	.7026	.7256
6	.2690	.2924	.3166	.3414	.3669	.3929	.4193	.4460	.4729	.5000
7	.1121	.1260	.1408	.1568	.1738	.1919	.2110	.2312	.2523	.2744
8	.0343	.0399	.0461	.0532	.0610	.0696	.0791	.0895	.1009	.1133
9	.0072	.0087	.0104	.0125	.0148	.0175	.0206	.0241	.0282	.0327
10	.0009	.0012	.0014	.0018	.0022	.0027	.0033	.0040	.0049	.0059
11	.0001	.0001	.0001	.0001	.0002	.0002	.0002	.0003	.0004	.0005

n = 12

p / r	.01	.02	.03	.04	.05	.06	.07	.08	.09	.10
1	.1136	.2153	.3062	.3873	.4596	.5241	.5814	.6323	.6775	.7176
2	.0062	.0231	.0486	.0809	.1184	.1595	.2033	.2487	.2948	.3410
3	.0002	.0015	.0048	.0107	.0196	.0316	.0468	.0652	.0866	.1109
4	.0000	.0001	.0003	.0010	.0022	.0043	.0075	.0120	.0180	.0256
5	.0000	.0000	.0000	.0001	.0002	.0004	.0009	.0016	.0027	.0043
6	.0000	.0000	.0000	.0000	.0000	.0000	.0001	.0002	.0003	.0005
7	.0000	.0000	.0000	.0000	.0000	.0000	.0000	.0000	.0000	.0001

p / r	.11	.12	.13	.14	.15	.16	.17	.18	.19	.20
1	.7530	.7843	.8120	.8363	.8578	.8766	.8931	.9076	.9202	.9313
2	.3867	.4314	.4748	.5166	.5565	.5945	.6304	.6641	.6957	.7251
3	.1377	.1667	.1977	.2303	.2642	.2990	.3344	.3702	.4060	.4417
4	.0351	.0464	.0597	.0750	.0922	.1114	.1324	.1552	.1795	.2054
5	.0065	.0095	.0133	.0181	.0239	.0310	.0393	.0489	.0600	.0726
6	.0009	.0014	.0022	.0033	.0046	.0065	.0088	.0116	.0151	.0194
7	.0001	.0002	.0003	.0004	.0007	.0010	.0015	.0021	.0029	.0039
8	.0000	.0000	.0000	.0000	.0001	.0001	.0002	.0003	.0004	.0006
9	.0000	.0000	.0000	.0000	.0000	.0000	.0000	.0000	.0000	.0001

p / r	.21	.22	.23	.24	.25	.26	.27	.28	.29	.30
1	.9409	.9493	.9566	.9629	.9683	.9730	.9771	.9806	.9836	.9862
2	.7524	.7776	.8009	.8222	.8416	.8594	.8755	.8900	.9032	.9150
3	.4768	.5114	.5450	.5778	.6093	.6397	.6687	.6963	.7225	.7472
4	.2326	.2610	.2904	.3205	.3512	.3824	.4137	.4452	.4765	.5075
5	.0866	.1021	.1192	.1377	.1576	.1790	.2016	.2254	.2504	.2763
6	.0245	.0304	.0374	.0453	.0544	.0646	.0760	.0887	.1026	.1178
7	.0052	.0068	.0089	.0113	.0143	.0178	.0219	.0267	.0322	.0386
8	.0008	.0011	.0016	.0021	.0028	.0036	.0047	.0060	.0076	.0095
9	.0001	.0001	.0002	.0003	.0004	.0005	.0007	.0010	.0013	.0017
10	.0000	.0000	.0000	.0000	.0000	.0001	.0001	.0001	.0002	.0002

n = 12 (Continued)

r \ p	.31	.32	.33	.34	.35	.36	.37	.38	.39	.40
1	.9884	.9902	.9918	.9932	.9943	.9953	.9961	.9968	.9973	.9978
2	.9256	.9350	.9435	.9509	.9576	.9634	.9685	.9730	.9770	.9804
3	.7704	.7922	.8124	.8313	.8487	.8648	.8795	.8931	.9054	.9166
4	.5381	.5681	.5973	.6258	.6533	.6799	.7053	.7296	.7528	.7747
5	.3032	.3308	.3590	.3876	.4167	.4459	.4751	.5043	.5332	.5618
6	.1343	.1521	.1711	.1913	.2127	.2352	.2588	.2833	.3087	.3348
7	.0458	.0540	.0632	.0734	.0846	.0970	.1106	.1253	.1411	.1582
8	.0118	.0144	.0176	.0213	.0255	.0304	.0359	.0422	.0493	.0573
9	.0022	.0028	.0036	.0045	.0056	.0070	.0086	.0104	.0127	.0153
10	.0003	.0004	.0005	.0007	.0008	.0011	.0014	.0018	.0022	.0028
11	.0000	.0000	.0000	.0001	.0001	.0001	.0001	.0002	.0002	.0003

r \ p	.41	.42	.43	.44	.45	.46	.47	.48	.49	.50
1	.9982	.9986	.9988	.9990	.9992	.9994	.9995	.9996	.9997	.9998
2	.9834	.9860	.9882	.9901	.9917	.9931	.9943	.9953	.9961	.9968
3	.9267	.9358	.9440	.9513	.9579	.9637	.9688	.9733	.9773	.9807
4	.7953	.8147	.8329	.8498	,7555	.8801	.8934	.9057	.9168	.9270
5	.5899	.6175	.6443	.6704	.6956	.7198	.7430	.7652	.7862	.8062
6	.3616	.3889	.4167	.4448	.4731	.5014	.5297	.5577	.5855	.6128
7	.1765	.1959	.2164	.2380	.2607	.2843	.3089	.3343	.3604	.3872
8	.0662	.0760	.0869	.0988	.1117	.1258	.1411	.1575	.1751	.1938
9	.0183	.0218	.0258	.0304	.0356	.0415	.0481	.0555	.0638	.0730
10	.0035	.0043	.0053	.0065	.0079	.0095	.0114	.0137	.0163	.0193
11	.0004	.0005	.0007	.0009	.0011	.0014	.0017	.0021	.0026	.0032
12	.0000	.0000	.0000	.0001	.0001	.0001	.0001	.0001	.0002	.0002

n = 13

r \ p	.01	.02	.03	.04	.05	.06	.07	.08	.09	.10
1	.1225	.2310	.3270	.4118	.4867	.5526	.6107	.6617	.7065	.7458
2	.0072	.0270	.0564	.0932	.1354	.1814	.2298	.2794	.3293	.3787
3	.0003	.0020	.0002	.0135	.0245	.0392	.0578	.0799	.1054	.1339
4	.0000	.0001	.0005	.0014	.0031	.0060	.0103	.0163	.0242	.0342
5	.0000	.0000	.0000	.0001	.0003	.0007	.0013	.0024	.0041	.0065
6	.0000	.0000	.0000	.0000	.0000	.0001	.0001	.0003	.0005	.0009
7	.0000	.0000	.0000	.0000	.0000	.0000	.0000	.0000	.0001	.0001

r \ p	.11	.12	.13	.14	.15	.16	.17	.18	.19	.20
1	.7802	.8102	.8364	.8592	.8791	.8963	.9113	.9242	.9354	.9450
2	.4270	.4738	.5186	.5614	.6017	.6396	.6751	.7080	.7384	.7664
3	.1651	.1985	.2337	.2704	.3080	.3463	.3848	.4231	.4611	.4983
4	.0464	.0609	.0776	.0967	.1180	.1414	.1667	.1939	.2226	.2527
5	.0097	.0139	.0193	.0260	.0342	.0438	.0551	.0681	.0827	.0991
6	.0015	.0024	.0036	.0053	.0075	.0104	.0139	.0183	.0237	.0300
7	.0002	.0003	.0005	.0008	.0013	.0019	.0027	.0038	.0052	.0070
8	.0000	.0000	.0001	.0001	.0002	.0003	.0004	.0006	.0009	.0012
9	.0000	.0000	.0000	.0000	.0000	.0000	.0000	.0001	.0001	.0002

r \ p	.21	.22	.23	.24	.25	.26	.27	.28	.29	.30
1	.9533	.9604	.9666	.9718	.9762	.9800	.9833	.9860	.9883	.9903
2	.7920	.8154	.8367	.8559	.8733	.8889	.9029	.9154	.9265	.9363
3	.5347	.5699	.6039	.6364	.6674	.6968	.7245	.7505	.7749	.7975
4	.2839	.3161	.3489	.3822	.4157	.4493	.4826	.5155	.5478	.5794
5	.1173	.1371	.1585	.1816	.2060	.2319	.2589	.2870	.3160	.3457
6	.0375	.0462	.0562	.0675	.0802	.0944	.1099	.1270	.1455	.1654
7	.0093	.0120	.0154	.0195	.0243	.0299	.0365	.0440	.0527	.0624
8	.0017	.0024	.0032	.0043	.0056	.0073	.0093	.0118	.0147	.0182
9	.0002	.0004	.0005	.0007	.0010	.0013	.0018	.0024	.0031	.0040
10	.0000	.0000	.0001	.0001	.0001	.0002	.0003	.0004	.0005	.0007
11	.0000	.0000	.0000	.0000	.0000	.0000	.0000	.0000	.0001	.0001

r \ p	.31	.32	.33	.34	.35	.36	.37	.38	.39	.40
1	.9920	.9934	.9945	.9955	.9963	.9970	.9975	.9980	.9984	.9987
2	.9450	.9527	.9594	.9653	.9704	.0749	.9787	.9821	.9849	.9874
3	.8185	.8379	.8557	.8720	.8868	.9003	.9125	.9235	.9333	.9421
4	.6101	.6398	.6683	.6957	.7217	.7464	.7698	.7917	.8123	.8314
5	.3760	.4067	.4376	.4686	.4995	.5301	.5603	.5899	.6188	.6470

n = 13 (Continued)

r \ p	.31	.32	.33	.34	.35	.36	.37	.38	.39	.40
6	.1867	.2093	.2331	.2581	.2841	.3111	.3388	.3673	.3962	.4256
7	.0733	.0854	.0988	.1135	.1295	.1468	.1654	.1853	.2065	.2288
8	.0223	.0271	.0326	.0390	.0462	.0544	.0635	.0738	.0851	.0977
9	.0052	.0065	.0082	.0102	.0126	.0154	.0187	.0225	.0270	.0321
10	.0009	.0012	.0015	.0020	.0025	.0032	.0040	.0051	.0063	.0078
11	.0001	.0001	.0002	.0003	.0003	.0005	.0006	.0008	.0010	.0013
12	.0000	.0000	.0000	.0000	.0000	.0000	.0001	.0001	.0001	.0001

r \ p	.41	.42	.43	.44	.45	.46	.47	.48	.49	.50
1	.9990	.9992	.9993	.9995	.9996	.9997	.9997	.9998	.9998	.9999
2	.9895	.9912	.9928	.9940	.9951	.9960	.9967	.9974	.9979	.9983
3	.9499	.9569	.9630	.9684	.9731	.9772	.9808	.9838	.9865	.9888
4	.8492	.8656	.8807	.8945	.9071	.9185	.9288	.9381	.9464	.9539
5	.6742	.7003	.7254	.7493	.7721	.7935	.8137	.8326	.8502	.8666
6	.4552	.4849	.5146	.5441	.5732	.6019	.6299	.6573	.6838	.7095
7	.2524	.2770	.3025	.3290	.3563	.3842	.4127	.4415	.4707	.5000
8	.1114	.1264	.1426	.1600	.1788	.1988	.2200	.2424	.2659	.2905
9	.0379	.0446	.0520	.0605	.0698	.0803	.0918	.1045	.1183	.1334
10	.0096	.0117	.0141	.0170	.0203	.0242	.0287	.0338	.0396	.0461
11	.0017	.0021	.0027	.0033	.0041	.0051	.0063	.0077	.0093	.0112
12	.0002	.0002	.0003	.0004	.0005	.0007	.0009	.0011	.0014	.0017
13	.0000	.0000	.0000	.0000	.0000	.0000	.0001	.0001	.0001	.0001

n = 14

r \ p	.01	.02	.03	.04	.05	.06	.07	.08	.09	.10
1	.1313	.2464	.3472	.4353	.5123	.5795	.6380	.6888	.7330	.7712
2	.0084	.0310	.0645	.1059	.1530	.2037	.2564	.3100	.3632	.4154
3	.0003	.0025	.0077	.0167	.0301	.0478	.0698	.0958	.1255	.1584
4	.0000	.0001	.0006	.0019	.0042	.0080	.0136	.0214	.0315	.0441
5	.0000	.0000	.0000	.0002	.0004	.0010	.0020	.0035	.0059	.0092
6	.0000	.0000	.0000	.0000	.0000	.0001	.0002	.0004	.0008	.0015
7	.0000	.0000	.0000	.0000	.0000	.0000	.0000	.0000	.0001	.0002

r \ p	.11	.12	.13	.14	.15	.16	.17	.18	.19	.20
1	.8044	.8330	.8577	.8789	.8972	.9129	.9264	.9379	.9477	.9560
2	.4658	.5141	.5599	.6031	.6433	.6807	.7152	.7469	.7758	.8021
3	.1938	.2315	.2708	.3111	.3521	.3932	.4341	.4744	.5138	.5519
4	.0594	.0774	.0979	.1210	.1465	.1742	.2038	.2351	.2679	.3018
5	.0137	.0196	.0269	.0359	.0467	.0594	.0741	.0907	.1093	.1298
6	.0024	.0038	.0057	.0082	.0115	.0157	.0209	.0273	.0349	.0439
7	.0003	.0006	.0009	.0015	.0022	.0032	.0046	.0064	.0087	.0116
8	.0000	.0001	.0001	.0002	.0003	.0005	.0008	.0012	.0017	.0024
9	.0000	.0000	.0000	.0000	.0000	.0001	.0001	.0002	.0003	.0004

r \ p	.21	.22	.23	.24	.25	.26	.27	.28	.29	.30
1	.9631	.9691	.9742	.9786	.9822	.9852	.9878	.9899	.9917	.9932
2	.8259	.8473	.8665	.8837	.8990	.9126	.9246	.9352	.9444	.9525
3	.5887	.6239	.6574	.6891	.7189	.7467	.7727	.7967	.8188	.8392
4	.3366	.3719	.4076	.4432	.4787	.5136	.5479	.5813	.6137	.6448
5	.1523	.1765	.2023	.2297	.2585	.2884	.3193	.3509	.3832	.4158
6	.0543	.0662	.0797	.0949	.1117	.1301	.1502	.1718	.1949	.2195
7	.0152	.0196	.0248	.0310	.0383	.0467	.0563	.0673	.0796	.0933
8	.0033	.0045	.0060	.0079	.0103	.0132	.0167	.0208	.0257	.0315
9	.0006	.0008	.0011	.0016	.0022	.0029	.0038	.0050	.0065	.0083
10	.0001	.0001	.0002	.0002	.0003	.0005	.0007	.0009	.0012	.0017
11	.0000	.0000	.0000	.0000	.0000	.0001	.0001	.0001	.0002	.0002

r \ p	.31	.32	.33	.34	.35	.36	.37	.38	.39	.40
1	.9945	.9955	.9963	.9970	.9976	.9981	.9984	.9988	.9990	.9992
2	.9596	.9657	.9710	.9756	.9795	.9828	.9857	.9881	.9902	.9919
3	.8577	.8746	.8899	.9037	.9161	.9271	.9370	.9457	.9534	.9602
4	.6747	.7032	.7301	.7556	.7795	.8018	.8226	.8418	.8595	.8757
5	.4486	.4813	.5138	.5458	.5773	.6080	.6378	.6666	.6943	.7207
6	.2454	.2724	.3006	.3297	.3595	.3899	.4208	.4519	.4831	.5141
7	.1084	.1250	.1431	.1626	.1836	.2059	.2296	.2545	.2805	.3075
8	.0381	.0458	.0545	.0643	.0753	.0876	.1012	.1162	.1325	.1501
9	.0105	.0131	.0163	.0200	.0243	.0294	.0353	.0420	.0497	.0583
10	.0022	.0029	.0037	.0048	.0060	.0076	.0095	.0117	.0144	.0175

n = 14 (Continued)

p / r	.31	.32	.33	.34	.35	.36	.37	.38	.39	.40
11	.0003	.0005	.0006	.0008	.0011	.0014	.0019	.0024	.0031	.0039
12	.0000	.0001	.0001	.0001	.0001	.0002	.0003	.0003	.0005	.0006
13	.0000	.0000	.0000	.0000	.0000	.0000	.0000	.0000	.0000	.0001

p / r	.41	.42	.43	.44	.45	.46	.47	.48	.49	.50
1	.9994	.9995	.9996	.9997	.9998	.9998	.9999	.9999	.9999	.9999
2	.9934	.9946	.9956	.9964	.9971	.9977	.9981	.9985	.9988	.9991
3	.9661	.9713	.9758	.9797	.9830	.9858	.9883	.9903	.9921	.9935
4	.8905	.9039	.9161	.9270	.9368	.9455	.9532	.9601	.9661	.9713
5	.7459	.7697	.7922	.8132	.8328	.8510	.8678	.8833	.8974	.9102
6	.5450	.5754	.6052	.6344	.6627	.6900	.7163	.7415	.7654	.7880
7	.3355	.3643	.3937	.4236	.4539	.4843	.5148	.5451	.5751	.6047
8	.1692	.1896	.2113	.2344	.2586	.2840	.3105	.3380	.3663	.3953
9	.0680	.0789	.0910	.1043	.1189	.1348	.1520	.1707	.1906	.2120
10	.0212	.0255	.0304	.0361	.0426	.0500	.0583	.0677	.0782	.0898
11	.0049	.0061	.0076	.0093	.0114	.0139	.0168	.0202	.0241	.0287
12	.0008	.0010	.0013	.0017	.0022	.0027	.0034	.0042	.0053	.0065
13	.0001	.0001	.0001	.0002	.0003	.0003	.0004	.0006	.0007	.0009
14	.0000	.0000	.0000	.0000	.0000	.0000	.0000	.0000	.0000	.0001

n = 15

p / r	.01	.02	.03	.04	.05	.06	.07	.08	.09	.10
1	.1399	.2614	.3667	.4579	.5367	.6047	.6633	.7137	.7570	.7941
2	.0096	.0353	.0730	.1191	.1710	.2262	.2832	.3403	.3965	.4510
3	.0004	.0030	.0094	.0203	.0362	.0571	.0829	.1130	.1469	.1841
4	.0000	.0002	.0008	.0024	.0055	.0104	.0175	.0273	.0399	.0556
5	.0000	.0000	.0001	.0002	.0006	.0014	.0028	.0050	.0082	.0127
6	.0000	.0000	.0000	.0000	.0001	.0001	.0003	.0007	.0013	.0022
7	.0000	.0000	.0000	.0000	.0000	.0000	.0000	.0001	.0002	.0003

p / r	.11	.12	.13	.14	.15	.16	.17	.18	.19	.20
1	.8259	.8530	.8762	.8959	.9126	.9269	.9389	.9490	.9576	.9648
2	.5031	.5524	.5987	.6417	.6814	.7179	.7511	.7813	.8085	.8329
3	.2238	.2654	.3084	.3520	.3958	.4392	.4819	.5234	.5635	.6020
4	.0742	.0959	.1204	.1476	.1773	.2092	.2429	.2782	.3146	.3518
5	.0187	.0265	.0361	.0478	.0617	.0778	.0961	.1167	.1394	.1642
6	.0037	.0057	.0084	.0121	.0168	.0227	.0300	.0387	.0490	.0611
7	.0006	.0010	.0015	.0024	.0036	.0052	.0074	.0102	.0137	.0181
8	.0001	.0001	.0002	.0004	.0006	.0010	.0014	.0021	.0030	.0042
9	.0000	.0000	.0000	.0000	.0001	.0001	.0002	.0003	.0005	.0008
10	.0000	.0000	.0000	.0000	.0000	.0000	.0000	.0000	.0001	.0001

p / r	.21	.22	.23	.24	.25	.26	.27	.28	.29	.30
1	.9709	.9759	.9802	.9837	.9866	.9891	.9911	.9928	.9941	.9953
2	.8547	.8741	.8913	.9065	.9198	.9315	.9417	.9505	.9581	.9647
3	.6385	.6731	.7055	.7358	.7639	.7899	.8137	.8355	.8553	.8732
4	.3895	.4274	.4650	.5022	.5387	.5742	.6086	.6416	.6732	.7031
5	.1910	.2195	.2495	.2810	.3135	.3469	.3810	.4154	.4500	.4845
6	.0748	.0905	.1079	.1272	.1484	.1713	.1958	.2220	.2495	.2784
7	.0234	.0298	.0374	.0463	.0566	.0684	.0817	.0965	.1130	.1311
8	.0058	.0078	.0104	.0135	.0173	.0219	.0274	.0338	.0413	.0500
9	.0011	.0016	.0023	.0031	.0042	.0056	.0073	.0094	.0121	.0152
10	.0002	.0003	.0004	.0006	.0008	.0011	.0015	.0021	.0028	.0037
11	.0000	.0000	.0001	.0001	.0001	.0002	.0002	.0003	.0005	.0007
12	.0000	.0000	.0000	.0000	.0000	.0000	.0000	.0000	.0001	.0001

p / r	.31	.32	.33	.34	.35	.36	.37	.38	.39	.40
1	.9962	.9969	.9975	.9980	.9984	.9988	.9990	.9992	.9994	.9995
2	.9704	.9752	.9794	.9829	.9858	.9883	.9904	.9922	.9936	.9948
3	.8893	.9038	.9167	.9281	.9383	.9472	.9550	.9618	.9678	.9729
4	.7314	.7580	.7829	.8060	.8273	.8469	.8649	.8813	.8961	.9095
5	.5187	.5523	.5852	.6171	.6481	.6778	.7062	.7332	.7587	.7827
6	.3084	.3393	.3709	.4032	.4357	.4684	.5011	.5335	.5654	.5968
7	.1509	.1722	.1951	.2194	.2452	.2722	.3003	.3295	.3595	.3902
8	.0599	.0711	.0837	.0977	.1132	.1302	.1487	.1687	.1902	.2131
9	.0190	.0236	.0289	.0351	.0422	.0504	.0597	.0702	.0820	.0950
10	.0048	.0062	.0079	.0099	.0124	.0154	.0190	.0232	.0281	.0338
11	.0009	.0012	.0016	.0022	.0028	.0037	.0047	.0059	.0075	.0093
12	.0001	.0002	.0003	.0004	.0005	.0006	.0009	.0011	.0015	.0019
13	.0000	.0000	.0000	.0000	.0001	.0001	.0001	.0002	.0002	.0003

n = 15 (Continued)

r \ p	.41	.42	.43	.44	.45	.46	.47	.48	.49	.50
1	.9996	.9997	.9998	.9998	.9999	.9999	.9999	.9999	1.0000	1.0000
2	.9958	.9966	.9973	.9979	.9983	.9987	.9990	.9992	.9994	.9995
3	.9773	.9811	.9843	.9870	.9893	.9913	.9929	.9943	.9954	.9963
4	.9215	.9322	.9417	.9502	.9576	.9641	.9697	.9746	.9788	.9824
5	.8052	.8261	.8454	.8633	.8796	.8945	.9080	.9201	.9310	.9408
6	.6274	.6570	.6856	.7131	.7392	.7641	.7875	.8095	.8301	.8491
7	.4214	.4530	.4847	.5164	.5478	.5789	.6095	.6394	.6684	.6964
8	.2374	.2630	.2898	.3176	.3465	.3762	.4065	.4374	.4686	.5000
9	.1095	.1254	.1427	.1615	.1818	.2034	.2265	.2510	.2767	.3036
10	.0404	.0479	.0565	.0661	.0769	.0890	.1024	.1171	.1333	.1509
11	.0116	.0143	.0174	.0211	.0255	.0305	.0363	.0430	.0506	.0592
12	.0025	.0032	.0040	.0051	.0063	.0079	.0097	.0119	.0145	.0176
13	.0004	.0005	.0007	.0009	.0011	.00p4	.0018	.0023	.0029	.0037
14	.0000	.0000	.0001	.0001	.0001	.0002	.0002	.0003	.0004	.0005

n = 16

r \ p	.01	.02	.03	.04	.05	.06	.07	.08	.09	.10
1	.1485	.2762	.3857	.4796	.5599	.6284	.6869	.7366	.7789	.8147
2	.0109	.0399	.0818	.1327	.1892	.2489	.3098	.3701	.4289	.4853
3	.0005	.0037	.0113	.0242	.0429	.0673	.0969	.1311	.1694	.2108
4	.0000	.0002	.0011	.0032	.0070	.0132	.0221	.0342	.0496	.0684
5	.0000	.0000	.0001	.0003	.0009	.0019	.0038	.0068	.0111	.0170
6	.0000	.0000	.0000	.0000	.0001	.0002	.0005	.0010	.0019	.0033
7	.0000	.0000	.0000	.0000	.0000	.0000	.0001	.0001	.0003	.0005
8	.0000	.0000	.0000	.0000	.0000	.0000	.0000	.0000	.0000	.0001

r \ p	.11	.12	.13	.14	.15	.16	.17	.18	.19	.20
1	.8450	.8707	.8923	.9105	.9257	.9386	.9493	.9582	.9657	.9719
2	.5386	.5885	.6347	.6773	.7161	.7513	.7830	.8115	.8368	.8593
3	.2545	.2999	.3461	.3926	.4386	.4838	.5277	.5698	.6101	.6482
4	.0907	.1162	.1448	.1763	.2101	.2460	.2836	.3223	.3619	.4019
5	.0248	.0348	.0471	.0618	.0791	.0988	.1211	.1458	.1727	.2018
6	.0053	.0082	.0120	.0171	.0235	.0315	.0412	.0527	.0662	.0817
7	.0009	.0015	.0024	.0038	.0056	.0080	.0112	.0153	.0204	.0267
8	.0001	.0002	.0004	.0007	.0011	.0016	.0024	.0036	.0051	.0070
9	.0000	.0000	.0001	.0001	.0002	.0003	.0004	.0007	.0010	.0015
10	.0000	.0000	.0000	.0000	.0000	.0000	.0001	.0001	.0002	.0002

r \ p	.21	.22	.23	.24	.25	.26	.27	.28	.29	.30
1	.9770	.9812	.9847	.9876	.9900	.9919	.9935	.9948	.9958	.9967
2	.8791	.8965	.9117	.9250	.9365	.9465	.9550	.9623	.9686	.9739
3	.6839	.7173	.7483	.7768	.8029	.8267	.8482	.8677	.8851	.9006
4	.4418	.4814	.5203	.5583	.5950	.6303	.6640	.6959	.7260	.7541
5	.2327	.2652	.2991	.3341	.3698	.4060	.4425	.4788	.5147	.5501
6	.0992	.1188	.1405	.1641	.1897	.2169	.2458	.2761	.3077	.3402
7	.0342	.0432	.0536	.0658	.0796	.0951	.1125	.1317	.1526	.1753
8	.0095	.0127	.0166	.0214	.0271	.0340	.0420	.0514	.0621	.0744
9	.0021	.0030	.0041	.0056	.0075	.0098	.0127	.0163	.0206	.0257
10	.0004	.0006	.0008	.0012	.0016	.0023	.0031	.0041	.0055	.0071
11	.0001	.0001	.0001	.0002	.0003	.0004	.0006	.0008	.0011	.0016
12	.0000	.0000	.0000	.0000	.0000	.0001	.0001	.0001	.0002	.0003

r \ p	.31	.32	.33	.34	.35	.36	.37	.38	.39	.40
1	.9974	.9979	.9984	.9987	.9990	.9992	.9994	.9995	.9996	.9997
2	.9784	.9822	.9854	.9880	.9902	.9921	.9936	.9948	.9959	.9967
3	.9144	.9266	.9374	.9467	.9549	.9620	.9681	.9734	.9778	.9817
4	.7804	.8047	.8270	.8475	.8661	.8830	.8982	.9119	.9241	.9349
5	.5846	.6181	.6504	.6813	.7108	.7387	.7649	.7895	.8123	.8334
6	.3736	.4074	.4416	.4759	.5100	.5438	.5770	.6094	.6408	.6712
7	.1997	.2257	.2531	.2819	.3119	.3428	.3746	.4070	.4398	.4728
8	.0881	.1035	.1205	.1391	.1594	.1813	.2048	.2298	.2562	.2839
9	.0317	.0388	.0470	.0564	.0671	.0791	.0926	.1076	.1242	.1423
10	.0092	.0117	.0148	.0185	.0229	.0280	.0341	.0411	.0491	.0583
11	.0021	.0028	.0037	.0048	.0062	.0079	.0100	.0125	.0155	.0191
12	.0004	.0005	.0007	.0010	.0013	.0017	.0023	.0030	.0038	.0049
13	.0001	.0001	.0001	.0001	.0002	.0003	.0004	.0005	.0007	.0009
14	.0000	.0000	.0000	.0000	.0000	.0000	.0000	.0001	.0001	.0001

n = 16 (Continued)

p r	.41	.42	.43	.44	.45	.46	.47	.48	.49	.50
1	.9998	.9998	.9999	.9999	.9999	.9999	1.0000	1.0000	1.0000	1.0000
2	.9974	.9979	.9984	.9987	.9990	.9992	.9994	.9995	.9997	.9997
3	.9849	.9876	.9899	.9918	.9934	.9947	.9958	.9966	.9973	.9979
4	.9444	.9527	.9600	.9664	.9719	.9766	.9806	.9840	.9869	.9894
5	.8529	.8707	.8869	.9015	.9147	.9265	.9370	.9463	.9544	.9616
6	.7003	.7280	.7543	.7792	.8024	.8241	.8441	.8626	.8795	.8949
7	.5058	.5387	.5711	.6029	.6340	.6641	.6932	.7210	.7476	.7728
8	.3128	.3428	.3736	.4051	.4371	.4694	.5019	.5343	.5665	.5982
9	.1619	.1832	.2060	.2302	.2559	.2829	.3111	.3405	.3707	.4018
10	.0687	.0805	.0936	.1081	.1241	.1416	.1607	.1814	.2036	.2272
11	.0234	.0284	.0342	.0409	.0486	.0574	.0674	.0786	.0911	.1051
12	.0062	.0078	.0098	.0121	.0149	.0183	.0222	.0268	.0322	.0384
13	.0012	.0016	.0021	.0027	.0035	.0044	.0055	.0069	.0086	.0106
14	.0002	.0002	.0003	.0004	.0006	.0007	.0010	.0013	.0016	.0021
15	.0000	.0000	.0000	.0000	.0001	.0001	.0001	.0001	.0002	.0003

n = 17

p r	.01	.02	.03	.04	.05	.06	.07	.08	.09	.10
1	.1571	.2907	.4042	.5004	.5819	.6507	.7088	.7577	.7988	.8332
2	.0123	.0446	.0909	.1465	.2078	.2717	.3362	.3995	.4604	.5182
3	.0006	.0044	.0134	.0286	.0503	.0782	.1118	.1503	.1927	.2382
4	.0000	.0003	.0014	.0040	.0088	.0164	.0273	.0419	.0603	.0826
5	.0000	.0000	.0001	.0004	.0012	.0026	.0051	.0090	.0145	.0221
6	.0000	.0000	.0000	.0000	.0001	.0003	.0007	.0015	.0027	.0047
7	.0000	.0000	.0000	.0000	.0000	.0000	.0001	.0002	.0004	.0008
8	.0000	.0000	.0000	.0000	.0000	.0000	.0000	.0000	.0000	.0001

	.11	.12	.13	.14	.15	.16	.17	.18	.19	.20
1	.8621	.8862	.9063	.9230	.9369	.9484	.9579	.9657	.9722	.9775
2	.5723	.6223	.6682	.7099	.7475	.7813	.8113	.8379	.8613	.8818
3	.2858	.3345	.3836	.4324	.4802	.5266	.5711	.6133	.6532	.6904
4	.1007	.1383	.1710	.2005	.2444	.2841	.3251	.3669	.4091	.4511
5	.0321	.0446	.0598	.0778	.0987	.1224	.1487	.1775	.2087	.2418
6	.0075	.0114	.0166	.0234	.0319	.0423	.0548	.0695	.0864	.1057
7	.0014	.0023	.0037	.0056	.0083	.0118	.0163	.0220	.0291	.0377
8	.0002	.0004	.0007	.0011	.0017	.0027	.0039	.0057	.0080	.0109
9	.0000	.0001	.0001	.0002	.0003	.0005	.0008	.0012	.0018	.0026
10	.0000	.0000	.0000	.0000	.0000	.0001	.0001	.0002	.0003	.0005
11	.0000	.0000	.0000	.0000	.0000	.0000	.0000	.0000	.0000	.0001

	.21	.22	.23	.24	.25	.26	.27	.28	.29	.30
1	.9818	.9854	.9882	.9906	.9925	.9940	.9953	.9962	.9970	.9977
2	.8996	.9152	.9285	.9400	.9499	.9583	.9654	.9714	.9765	.9807
3	.7249	.7567	.7859	.8123	.8363	.8578	.8771	.8942	.9093	.9226
4	.4927	.5333	.5728	.6107	.6470	.6814	.7137	.7440	.7721	.7981
5	.2766	.3128	.3500	.3879	.4261	.4643	.5023	.5396	.5760	.6113
6	.1273	.1510	.1770	.2049	.2347	.2661	.2989	.3329	.3677	.4032
7	.0479	.0598	.0736	.0894	.1071	.1268	.1485	.1721	.1976	.2248
8	.0147	.0194	.0251	.0320	.0402	.0499	.0611	.0739	.0884	.1046
9	.0037	.0051	.0070	.0094	.0124	.0161	.0206	.0261	.0326	.0403
10	.0007	.0011	.0016	.0022	.0031	.0042	.0057	.0075	.0098	.0127
11	.0001	.0002	.0003	.0004	.0006	.0009	.0013	.0018	.0024	.0032
12	.0000	.0000	.0000	.0001	.0001	.0002	.0002	.0003	.0005	.0007
13	.0000	.0000	.0000	.0000	.0000	.0000	.0000	.0000	.0001	.0001

	.31	.32	.33	.34	.35	.36	.37	.38	.39	.40
1	.9982	.9986	.9989	.9991	.9993	.9995	.9996	.9997	.9998	.9998
2	.9843	.9872	.9896	.9917	.9933	.9946	.9957	.9966	.9973	.9979
3	.9343	.9444	.9532	.9608	.9673	.9728	.9775	.9815	.9849	.9877
4	.8219	.8437	.8634	.8812	.8972	.9115	.9241	.9353	.9450	.9536
5	.6453	.6778	.7087	.7378	.7652	.7906	.8142	.8360	.8559	.8740
6	.4390	.4749	.5105	.5458	.5803	.6139	.6465	.6778	.7077	.7361
7	.2536	.2838	.3153	.3479	.3812	.4152	.4495	.4839	.5182	.5522
8	.1227	.1426	.1642	.1877	.2128	.2395	.2676	.2971	.3278	.3595
9	.0492	.0595	.0712	.0845	.0994	.1159	.1341	.1541	.1757	.1989
10	.0162	.0204	.0254	.0314	.0383	.0464	.0557	.0664	.0784	.0919

n = 17 (Continued)

r \ p	.31	.32	.33	.34	.35	.36	.37	.38	.39	.40
11	.0043	.0057	.0074	.0095	.0120	.0151	.0189	.0234	.0286	.0348
12	.0009	.0013	.0017	.0023	.0030	.0040	.0051	.0066	.0084	.0106
13	.0002	.0002	.0003	.0004	.0006	.0008	.0011	.0015	.0019	.0025
14	.0000	.0000	.0000	.0001	.0001	.0001	.0002	.0002	.0003	.0005
15	.0000	.0000	.0000	.0000	.0000	.0000	.0000	.0000	.0000	.0001

r \ p	.41	.42	.43	.44	.45	.46	.47	.48	.49	.50
1	.9999	.9999	.9999	.9999	1.0000	1.0000	1.0000	1.0000	1.0000	1.0000
2	.9984	.9987	.9990	.9992	.9994	.9996	.9997	.9998	.9998	.9999
3	.9900	.9920	.9935	.9948	.9959	.9968	.9975	.9980	.9985	.9988
4	.9610	.9674	.9729	.9776	.9816	.9849	.9877	.9901	.9920	.9936
5	.8904	.9051	.9183	.9301	.9404	.9495	.9575	.9644	.9704	.9755
6	.7628	.7879	.8113	.8330	.8529	.8712	.8878	.9028	.9162	.9283
7	.5856	.6182	.6499	.6805	.7098	.7377	.7641	.7890	.8122	.8338
8	.3920	.4250	.4585	.4921	.5257	.5590	.5918	.6239	.6552	.6855
9	.2238	.2502	.2780	.3072	.3374	.3687	.4008	.4335	.4667	.5000
10	.1070	.1236	.1419	.1618	.1834	.2066	.2314	.2577	.2855	.3145
11	.0420	.0503	.0597	.0705	.0826	.0962	.1112	.1279	.1462	.1662
12	.0133	.0165	.0203	.0248	.0301	.0363	.0434	.0517	.0611	.0717
13	.0033	.0042	.0054	.0069	.0086	.0108	.0134	.0165	.0202	.0245
14	.0006	.0008	.0011	.0014	.0019	.0024	.0031	.0040	.0050	.0064
15	.0001	.0001	.0002	.0002	.0003	.0004	.0005	.0007	.0009	.0012
16	.0000	.0000	.0000	.0000	.0000	.0000	.0001	.0001	.0001	.0001

n = 18

r \ p	.01	.02	.03	.04	.05	.06	.07	.08	.09	.10
1	.1655	.3049	.4220	.5204	.6028	.6717	.7292	.7771	.8169	.8499
2	.0138	.0495	.1003	.1607	.2265	.2945	.3622	.4281	.4909	.5497
3	.0007	.0052	.0157	.0333	.0581	.0898	.1275	.1702	.2168	.2662
4	.0000	.0004	.0018	.0050	.0109	.0201	.0333	.0506	.0723	.0982
5	.0000	.0000	.0002	.0006	.0015	.0034	.0067	.0116	.0187	.0282
6	.0000	.0000	.0000	.0001	.0002	.0005	.0010	.0021	.0038	.0064
7	.0000	.0000	.0000	.0000	.0000	.0000	.0001	.0003	.0006	.0012
8	.0000	.0000	.0000	.0000	.0000	.0000	.0000	.0000	.0001	.0002

r \ p	.11	.12	.13	.14	.15	.16	.17	.18	.19	.20
1	.8773	.8998	.9185	.9338	.9464	.9566	.9651	.9719	.9775	.9820
2	.6042	.6540	.6992	.7398	.7759	.8080	.8362	.8609	.8824	.9009
3	.3173	.3690	.4206	.4713	.5203	.5673	.6119	.6538	.6927	.7287
4	.1282	.1618	.1986	.2382	.2798	.3229	.3669	.4112	.4554	.4990
5	.0405	.0558	.0743	.0959	.1206	.1482	.1787	.2116	.2467	.2836
6	.0102	.0154	.0222	.0310	.0419	.0551	.0708	.0889	.1097	.1329
7	.0021	.0034	.0054	.0081	.0118	.0167	.0229	.0306	.0400	.0513
8	.0003	.0006	.0011	.0017	.0027	.0041	.0060	.0086	.0'20	.0163
9	.0000	.0001	.0002	.0003	.0005	.0008	.0013	.0020	.0030	.0043
10	.0000	.0000	.0000	.0000	.0001	.0001	.0002	.0004	.0006	.0009
11	.0000	.0000	.0000	.0000	.0000	.0000	.0000	.0001	.0001	.0002

r \ p	.21	.22	.23	.24	.25	.26	.27	.28	.29	.30
1	.9856	.9886	.9909	.9928	.9944	.9956	.9965	.9973	.9979	.9984
2	.9169	.9306	.9423	.9522	.9605	.9676	.9735	.9784	.9824	.9858
3	.7616	.7916	.8187	.8430	.8647	.8839	.9009	.9158	.9288	.9400
4	.5414	.5825	.6218	.6591	.6943	.7272	.7578	.7860	.8119	.8354
5	.3220	.3613	.4012	.4414	.4813	.5208	.5594	.5968	.6329	.6673
6	.1586	.1866	.2168	.2488	.2825	.3176	.3538	.3907	.4281	.4656
7	.0645	.0799	.0974	.1171	.1390	.1630	.1891	.2171	.2469	.2783
8	.0217	.0283	.0363	.0458	.0569	.0699	.0847	.1014	.1200	.1407
9	.0060	.0083	.0112	.0148	.0193	.0249	.0316	.0395	.0488	.0596
10	.0014	.0020	.0028	.0039	.0054	.0073	.0097	.0127	.0164	.0210
11	.0003	.0004	.0006	.0009	.0012	.0018	.0025	.0034	.0046	.0061
12	.0000	.0001	.0001	.0002	.0002	.0003	.0005	.0007	.0010	.0014
13	.0000	.0000	.0000	.0000	.0000	.0001	.0001	.0001	.0002	.0003

r \ p	.31	.32	.33	.34	.35	.36	.37	.38	.39	.40
1	.9987	.9990	.9993	.9994	.9996	.9997	.9998	.9998	.9999	.9999
2	.9886	.9908	.9927	.9942	.9954	.9964	.9972	.9978	.9983	.9987
3	.9498	.9581	.9652	.9713	.9764	.9807	.9843	.9873	.9897	.9918
4	.8568	.8759	.8931	.9083	.9217	.9335	.9439	.9528	.9606	.9672
5	.7001	.7309	.7598	.7866	.8114	.8341	.8549	.8737	.8907	.9058

				n = 18 (Continued)						
p r	.31	.32	.33	.34	.35	.36	.37	.38	.39	.40
6	.5029	.5398	.5759	.6111	.6450	.6776	.7086	.7379	.7655	.7912
7	.3111	.3450	.3797	.4151	.4509	.4867	.5224	.5576	.5921	.6257
8	.1633	.1878	.2141	.2421	.2717	.3027	.3349	.3681	.4021	.4366
9	.0720	.0861	.1019	.1196	.1391	.1604	.1835	.2084	.2350	.2632
10	.0264	.0329	.0405	.0494	.0597	.0714	.0847	.0997	.1163	.1347
11	.0080	.0104	.0133	.0169	.0212	.0264	.0325	.0397	.0480	.0576
12	.0020	.0027	.0036	.0047	.0062	.0080	.0102	.0130	.0163	.0203
13	.0004	.0005	.0008	.0011	.0014	.0019	.0026	.0034	.0044	.0058
14	.0001	.0001	.0001	.0002	.0003	.0004	.0005	.0007	.0010	.0013
15	.0000	.0000	.0000	.0000	.0000	.0001	.0001	.0001	.0002	.0002

r	.41	.42	.43	.44	.45	.46	.47	.48	.49	.50
1	.9999	.9999	1.0000	1.0000	1.0000	1.0000	1.0000	1.0000	1.0000	1.0000
2	.9990	.9992	.9994	.9996	.9997	.9998	.9998	.9999	.9999	.9999
3	.9934	.9948	.9959	.9968	.9975	.9981	.9985	.9989	.9991	.9993
4	.9729	.9777	.9818	.9852	.9880	.9904	.9923	.9939	.9952	.9962
5	.9193	.9313	.9418	.9510	.9589	.9658	.9717	.9767	.9810	.9846
6	.8151	.8372	.8573	.8757	.8923	.9072	.9205	.9324	.9428	.9519
7	.6582	.6895	.7193	.7476	.7742	.7991	.8222	.8436	.8632	.8811
8	.4713	.5062	.5408	.5750	.6085	.6412	.6728	.7032	.7322	.7597
9	.2928	.3236	.3556	.3885	.4222	.4562	.4906	.5249	.5591	.5927
10	.1549	.1768	.2004	.2258	.2527	.2812	.3110	.3421	.3742	.4073
11	.0686	.0811	.0951	.1107	.1280	.1470	.1677	.1902	.2144	.2403
12	.0250	.0307	.0372	.0449	.0537	.0638	.0753	.0883	.1028	.1189
13	.0074	.0094	.0118	.0147	.0183	.0225	.0275	.0334	.0402	.0481
14	.0017	.0022	.0029	.0038	.0049	.0063	.0079	.0100	.0125	.0154
15	.0003	.0004	.0006	.0007	.0010	.0013	.0017	.0023	.0029	.0038
16	.0000	.0001	.0001	.0001	.0001	.0002	.0003	.0004	.0005	.0007
17	.0000	.0000	.0000	.0000	.0000	.0000	.0000	.0000	.0001	.0001

					n = 19					
p r	.01	.02	.03	.04	.05	.06	.07	.08	.09	.10
1	.1738	.3188	.4394	.5396	.6226	.6914	.7481	.7949	.8334	.8649
2	.0153	.0546	.1100	.1751	.2453	.3171	.3879	.4560	.5202	.5797
3	.0009	.0061	.0083	.0384	.0665	.1021	.1439	.1908	.2415	.2946
4	.0000	.0005	.0002	.0061	.0132	.0243	.0398	.0602	.0853	.1150
5	.0000	.0000	.0002	.0007	.0020	.0044	.0085	.0147	.0235	.0352
6	.0000	.0000	.0000	.0001	.0002	.0006	.0014	.0029	.0051	.0086
7	.0000	.0000	.0000	.0000	.0000	.0001	.0002	.0004	.0009	.0017
8	.0000	.0000	.0000	.0000	.0000	.0000	.0000	.0001	.0001	.0003

r	.11	.12	.13	.14	.15	.16	.17	.18	.19	.20
1	.8908	.9119	.9291	.9431	.9544	.9636	.9710	.9770	.9818	.9856
2	.6342	.6835	.7277	.7669	.8015	.8318	.8581	.8809	.9004	.9171
3	.3488	.4032	.4568	.5089	.5587	.6059	.6500	.6910	.7287	.7631
4	.1490	.1867	.2275	.2708	.3159	.3620	.4085	.4549	.5005	.5449
5	.0502	.0685	.0904	.1158	.1444	.1762	.2107	.2476	.2864	.3267
6	.0135	.0202	.0290	.0401	.0537	.0700	.0891	.1110	.1357	.1631
7	.0030	.0048	.0076	.0113	.0163	.0228	.0310	.0411	.0532	.0676
8	.0005	.0009	.0016	.0026	.0041	.0061	.0089	.0126	.0173	.0233
9	.0001	.0002	.0003	.0005	.0008	.0014	.0021	.0032	.0047	.0067
10	.0000	.0000	.0000	.0001	.0001	.0002	.0004	.0007	.0010	.0016
11	.0000	.0000	.0000	.0000	.0000	.0000	.0001	.0001	.0002	.0003
12	.0000	.0000	.0000	.0000	.0000	.0000	.0000	.0000	.0000	.0001

r	.21	.22	.23	.24	.25	.26	.27	.28	.29	.30
1	.9887	.9911	.9930	.9946	.9958	.9967	.9975	.9981	.9985	.9989
2	.9313	.9434	.9535	.9619	.9690	.9749	.9797	.9837	.9869	.9896
3	.7942	.8222	.8471	.8692	.8887	.9057	.9205	.9333	.9443	.9538
4	.5877	.6285	.6671	.7032	.7369	.7680	.7965	.8224	.8458	.8668
5	.3681	.4100	.4520	.4936	.5346	.5744	.6129	.6498	.6848	.7178
6	.1929	.2251	.2592	.2950	.3322	.3705	.4093	.4484	.4875	.5261
7	.0843	.1034	.1249	.1487	.1749	.2032	.2336	.2657	.2995	.3345
8	.0307	.0396	.0503	.0629	.0775	.0941	.1129	.1338	.1568	.1820
9	.0093	.0127	.0169	.0222	.0287	.0366	.0459	.0568	.0694	.0839
10	.0023	.0034	.0047	.0066	.0089	.0119	.0156	.0202	.0258	.0326

				n = 19 (Continued)						
r \ p	.21	.22	.23	.24	.25	.26	.27	.28	.29	.30
11	.0005	.0007	.0011	.0016	.0023	.0032	.0044	.0060	.0080	.0105
12	.0001	.0001	.0002	.0003	.0005	.0007	.0010	.0015	.0021	.0028
13	.0000	.0000	.0000	.0001	.0001	.0001	.0002	.0003	.0004	.0006
14	.0000	.0000	.0000	.0000	.0000	.0000	.0000	.0000	.0001	.0001

r	.31	.32	.33	.34	.35	.36	.37	.38	.39	.40
1	.9991	.9993	.9995	.9996	.9997	.9998	.9998	.9999	.9999	.9999
2	.9917	.9935	.9949	.9960	.9969	.9976	.9981	.9986	.9989	.9992
3	.9618	.9686	.9743	.9791	.9830	.9863	.9890	.9913	.9931	.9945
4	.8856	.9022	.9169	.9297	.9409	.9505	.9588	.9659	.9719	.9770
5	.7486	.7773	.8037	.8280	.8500	.8699	.8878	.9038	.9179	.9304
6	.5641	.6010	.6366	.6707	.7032	.7339	.7627	.7895	.8143	.8371
7	.3705	.4073	.4445	.4818	.5188	.5554	.5913	.6261	.6597	.6919
8	.2091	.2381	.2688	.3010	.3344	.3690	.4043	.4401	.4762	.5122
9	.1003	.1186	.1389	.1612	.1855	.2116	.2395	.2691	.3002	.3325
10	.0405	.0499	.0608	.0733	.0875	.1035	.1213	.1410	.1626	.1861
11	.0137	.0176	.0223	.0280	.0347	.0426	.0518	.0625	.0747	.0885
12	.0038	.0051	.0068	.0089	.0114	.0146	.0185	.0231	.0287	.0352
13	.0009	.0012	.0017	.0023	.0031	.0041	.0054	.0070	.0091	.0116
14	.0002	.0002	.0003	.0005	.0007	.0009	.0013	.0017	.0023	.0031
15	.0000	.0000	.0001	.0001	.0001	.0002	.0002	.0003	.0005	.0006
16	.0000	.0000	.0000	.0000	.0000	.0000	.0000	.0000	.0001	.0001

r	.41	.42	.43	.44	.45	.46	.47	.48	.49	.50
1	1.0000	1.0000	1.0000	1.0000	1.0000	1.0000	1.0000	1.0000	1.0000	1.0000
2	.9994	.9995	.9996	.9997	.9998	.9999	.9999	.9999	.9999	1.0000
3	.9957	.9967	.9974	.9980	.9985	.9988	.9991	.9993	.9995	.9996
4	.9813	.9849	.9878	.9903	.9923	.9939	.9952	.9963	.9971	.9978
5	.9413	.9518	.9590	.9660	.9720	.9771	.9814	.9850	.9879	.9904
6	.8579	.8767	.8937	.9088	.9223	.9342	.9446	.9537	.9615	.9682
7	.7226	.7515	.7787	.8039	.8273	.8488	.8684	.8862	.9022	.9165
8	.5480	.5832	.6176	.6509	.6831	.7138	.7430	.7706	.7964	.8204
9	.3660	.4003	.4353	.4706	.5060	.5413	.5762	.6105	.6439	.6762
10	.2114	.2385	.2672	.2974	.3290	.3617	.3954	.4299	.4648	.5000
11	.1040	.1213	.1404	.1613	.1841	.2087	.2351	.2631	.2928	.3238
12	.0429	.0518	.0621	.0738	.0871	.1021	.1187	.1372	.1575	.1796
13	.0146	.0183	.0227	.0280	.0342	.0415	.0500	.0597	.0709	.0835
14	.0040	.0052	.0068	.0086	.0109	.0137	.0171	.0212	.0261	.0318
15	.0009	.0012	.0016	.0021	.0028	.0036	.0046	.0060	.0076	.0096
16	.0001	.0002	.0003	.0004	.0005	.0007	.0010	.0013	.0017	.0022
17	.0000	.0000	.0000	.0001	.0001	.0001	.0001	.0002	.0003	.0004

					n = 20					
r \ p	.01	.02	.03	.04	.05	.06	.07	.08	.09	.10
1	.1821	.3324	.4562	.5580	.6415	.7099	.7658	.8113	.8484	.8784
2	.0169	.0599	.1198	.1897	.2642	.3395	.4131	.4831	.5484	.6083
3	.0010	.0071	.0210	.0439	.0755	.1150	.1610	.2121	.2666	.3231
4	.0000	.0006	.0027	.0074	.0159	.0290	.0471	.0706	.0993	.1330
5	.0000	.0000	.0003	.0010	.0026	.0056	.0107	.0183	.0290	.0432
6	.0000	.0000	.0000	.0001	.0003	.0009	.0019	.0038	.0068	.0113
7	.0000	.0000	.0000	.0000	.0000	.0001	.0003	.0006	.0013	.0024
8	.0000	.0000	.0000	.0000	.0000	.0000	.0000	.0001	.0002	.0004
9	.0000	.0000	.0000	.0000	.0000	.0000	.0000	.0000	.0000	.0001

r	.11	.12	.13	.14	.15	.16	.17	.18	.19	.20
1	.9028	.9224	.9383	.9510	.9612	.9694	.9759	.9811	.9852	.9885
2	.6624	.7109	.7539	.7916	.8244	.8529	.8773	.8982	.9159	.9308
3	.3802	.4369	.4920	.5450	.5951	.6420	.6854	.7252	.7614	.7939
4	.1710	.2127	.2573	.3041	.3523	.4010	.4496	.4974	.5439	.5886
5	.0610	.0827	.1083	.1375	.1702	.2059	.2443	.2849	.3271	.3704
6	.0175	.0260	.0370	.0507	.0673	.0870	.1098	.1356	.1643	.1958
7	.0041	.0067	.0103	.0153	.0219	.0304	.0409	.0537	.0689	.0867
8	.0008	.0014	.0024	.0038	.0059	.0088	.0127	.0177	.0241	.0321
9	.0001	.0002	.0005	.0008	.0013	.0021	.0033	.0049	.0071	.0100
10	.0000	.0000	.0001	.0001	.0002	.0004	.0007	.0011	.0017	.0026
11	.0000	.0000	.0000	.0000	.0000	.0001	.0001	.0002	.0004	.0006
12	.0000	.0000	.0000	.0000	.0000	.0000	.0000	.0000	.0001	.0001

n = 20 (Continued)

r \ p	.21	.22	.23	.24	.25	.26	.27	.28	.29	.30
1	.9910	.9931	.9946	.9959	.9968	.9976	.9982	.9986	.9989	.9992
2	.9434	.9539	.9626	.9698	.9757	.9805	.9845	.9877	.9903	.9924
3	.8230	.8488	.8716	.8915	.9087	.9237	.9365	.9474	.9567	.9645
4	.6310	.6711	.7085	.7431	.7748	.8038	.8300	.8534	.8744	.8929
5	.4142	.4580	.5014	.5439	.5852	.6248	.6625	.6981	.7315	.7625
6	.2297	.2657	.3035	.3427	.3828	.4235	.4643	.5048	.5447	.5836
7	.1071	.1301	.1558	.1838	.2142	.2467	.2810	.3169	.3540	.3920
8	.0419	.0536	.0675	.0835	.1018	.1225	.1455	.1707	.1982	.2277
9	.0138	.0186	.0246	.0320	.0409	.0515	.0640	.0784	.0948	.1133
10	.0038	.0054	.0075	.0103	.0139	.0183	.0238	.0305	.0385	.0480
11	.0009	.0013	.0019	.0028	.0039	.0055	.0074	.0100	.0132	.0171
12	.0002	.0003	.0004	.0006	.0009	.0014	.0019	.0027	.0038	.0051
13	.0000	.0000	.0001	.0001	.0002	.0003	.0004	.0006	.0009	.0013
14	.0000	.0000	.0000	.0000	.0000	.0000	.0001	.0001	.0002	.0003

r \ p	.31	.32	.33	.34	.35	.36	.37	.38	.39	.40
1	.9994	.9996	.9997	.9998	.9998	.9999	.9999	.9999	.9999	1.0000
2	.9940	.9953	.9964	.9972	.9979	.9984	.9988	.9991	.9993	.9995
3	.9711	.9765	.9811	.9848	.9879	.9904	.9924	.9940	.9953	.9964
4	.9092	.9235	.9358	.9465	.9556	.9634	.9700	.9755	.9802	.9840
5	.7911	.8173	.8411	.8626	.8818	.8989	.9141	.9274	.9390	.9490
6	.6213	.6574	.6918	.7242	.7546	.7829	.8090	.8329	.8547	.8744
7	.4305	.4693	.5079	.5460	.5834	.6197	.6547	.6882	.7200	.7500
8	.2591	.2922	.3268	.3624	.3990	.4361	.4735	.5108	.5478	.5841
9	.1340	.1568	.1818	.2087	.2376	.2683	.3005	.3341	.3688	.4044
10	.0591	.0719	.0866	.1032	.1218	.1424	.1650	.1897	.2163	.2447
11	.0220	.0279	.0350	.0434	.0532	.0645	.0775	.0923	.1090	.1275
12	.0069	.0091	.0119	.0154	.0196	.0247	.0308	.0381	.0466	.0565
13	.0018	.0025	.0034	.0045	.0060	.0079	.0102	.0132	.0167	.0210
14	.0004	.0006	.0008	.0011	.0015	.0021	.0028	.0037	.0049	.0065
15	.0001	.0001	.0001	.0002	.0003	.0004	.0006	.0009	.0012	.0016
16	.0000	.0000	.0000	.0000	.0001	.0001	.0001	.0002	.0002.	.0003

r \ p	.41	.42	.43	.44	.45	.46	.47	.48	.49	.50
1	1.0000	1.0000	1.0000	1.0000	1.0000	1.0000	1.0000	1.0000	1.0000	1.0000
2	.9996	.9997	.9998	.9998	.9999	.9999	.9999	1.0000	1.0000	1.0000
3	.9972	.9979	.9984	.9988	.9991	.9993	.9995	.9996	.9997	.9998
4	.9872	.9898	.9920	.9937	.9951	.9962	.9971	.9977	.9983	.9987
5	.9577	.9651	.9714	.9767	.9811	.9848	.9879	.9904	.9924	.9941
6	.8921	.9078	.9217	.9340	.9447	.9539	.9619	.9687	.9745	.9793
7	.7780	.8041	.8281	.8501	.8701	.8881	.9042	.9186	.9312	.9423
8	.6196	.6539	.6868	.7183	.7480	.7759	.8020	.8261	.8482	.8684
9	.4406	.4771	.5136	.5499	.5847	.6207	.6546	.6873	.7186	.7483
10	.2748	.3064	.3394	.3736	.4086	.4443	.4804	.5166	.5525	.5881
11	.1480	.1705	.1949	.2212	.2493	.2791	.3104	.3432	.3771	.4119
12	.0679	.0810	.0958	.1123	.1308	.1511	.1734	.1977	.2238	.2517
13	.0262	.0324	.0397	.0482	.0580	.0694	.0823	.0969	.1133	.1316
14	.0084	.0107	.0136	.0172	.0214	.0265	.0326	.0397	.0480	.0577
15	.0022	.0029	.0038	.0050	.0064	.0083	.0105	.0133	.0166	.0207
16	.0004	.0006	.0008	.0011	.0015	.0020	.0027	.0035	.0046	.0059
17	.0001	.0001	.0001	.0002	.0003	.0004	.0005	.0007	.0010	.0013
18	.0000	.0000	.0000	.0000	.0000	.0001	.0001	.0001	.0001	.0002

n = 25

r \ p	.01	.02	.03	.04	.05	.06	.07	.08	.09	.10
1	.2222	.3965	.5330	.6396	.7226	.7871	.8370	.8756	.9054	.9282
2	.0258	.0886	.1720	.2642	.3576	.4473	.5304	.6053	.6714	.7288
3	.0020	.0132	.0380	.0765	.1271	.1871	.2534	.3232	.3937	.4629
4	.0001	.0014	.0062	.0165	.0341	.0598	.0936	.1351	.1831	.2364
5	.0000	.0001	.0008	.0028	.0072	.0150	.0274	.0451	.0686	.0980
6	.0000	.0000	.0001	.0004	.0012	.0031	.0065	.0123	.0210	.0334
7	.0000	.0000	.0000	.0000	.0002	.0005	.0013	.0028	.0054	.0095
8	.0000	.0000	.0000	.0000	.0000	.0001	.0002	.0005	.0011	.0023
9	.0000	.0000	.0000	.0000	.0000	.0000	.0000	.0001	.0002	.0005
10	.0000	.0000	.0000	.0000	.0000	.0000	.0000	.0000	.0000	.0001

n = 25 (Continued)									

p r	.11	.12	.13	.14	.15	.16	.17	.18	.19	.20
1	.9457	.9591	.9692	.9770	.9828	.9872	.9905	.9930	.9948	.9962
2	.7779	.8195	.8543	.8832	.9069	.9263	.9420	.9546	.9646	.9726
3	.5291	.5912	.6483	.7000	.7463	.7870	.8226	.8533	.8796	.9018
4	.2934	.3525	.4123	.4714	.5289	.5837	.6352	.6829	.7266	.7660
5	.1331	.1734	.1283	.2668	.3179	.3707	.4241	.4772	.5292	.5793
6	.0499	.0709	.0965	.1268	.1615	.2002	.2425	.2875	.3347	.3833
7	.0156	.0243	.0359	.0509	.0695	.0920	.1185	.1488	.1827	.2200
8	.0041	.0070	.0113	.0173	.0255	.0361	.0495	.0661	.0859	.1091
9	.0009	.0017	.0030	.0050	.0080	.0121	.0178	.0252	.0348	.0468
10	.0002	.0004	.0007	.0013	.0021	.0035	.0055	.0083	.0122	.0173
11	.0000	.0001	.0001	.0003	.0005	.0009	.0015	.0024	.0037	.0056
12	.0000	.0000	.0000	.0000	.0001	.0002	.0003	.0006	.0010	.0015
13	.0000	.0000	.0000	.0000	.0000	.0000	.0001	.0001	.0002	.0004
14	.0000	.0000	.0000	.0000	.0000	.0000	.0000	.0000	.0000	.0001

	.21	.22	.23	.24	.25	.26	.27	.28	.29	.30
1	.9972	.9980	.9985	.9990	.9992	.9995	.9996	.9997	.9998	.9999
2	.9789	.9838	.9877	.9907	.9930	.9947	.9961	.9971	.9979	.9984
3	.9204	.9360	.9488	.9593	.9679	.9748	.9804	.9848	.9883	.9910
4	.8013	.8324	.8597	.8834	.9038	.9211	.9358	.9481	.9583	.9668
5	.6270	.6718	.7134	.7516	.7863	.8174	.8452	.8696	.8910	.9095
6	.4325	.4816	.5299	.5767	.6217	.6644	.7044	.7415	.7755	.8065
7	.2601	.3027	.3471	.3927	.4389	.4851	.5308	.5753	.6183	.6593
8	.1358	.1658	.1989	.2349	.2735	.3142	.3565	.3999	.4440	.4882
9	.0614	.0788	.0993	.1228	.1494	.1790	.2115	.2465	.2838	.3231
10	.0240	.0325	.0431	.0560	.0713	.0893	.1101	.1338	.1602	.1894
11	.0082	.0117	.0163	.0222	.0297	.0389	.0502	.0636	.0795	.0978
12	.0024	.0036	.0053	.0076	.0107	.0148	.0199	.0264	.0345	.0442
13	.0006	.0010	.0015	.0023	.0034	.0049	.0069	.0096	.0130	.0175
14	.0001	.0002	.0004	.0006	.0009	.0014	.0021	.0030	.0043	.0060
15	.0000	.0000	.0001	.0001	.0002	.0003	.0005	.0008	.0012	.0018
16	.0000	.0000	.0000	.0000	.0000	.0001	.0001	.0002	.0003	.0005
17	.0000	.0000	.0000	.0000	.0000	.0000	.0000	.0000	.0001	.0001

	.31	.32	.33	.34	.35	.36	.37	.38	.39	.40
1	.9999	.9999	1.0000	1.0000	1.0000	1.0000	1.0000	1.0000	1.0000	1.0000
2	.9989	.9992	.9994	.9996	.9997	.9998	.9998	.9999	.9999	.9999
3	.9932	.9949	.9961	.9971	.9979	.9984	.9989	.9992	.9994	.9996
4	.9737	.9793	.9838	.9874	.9903	.9926	.9944	.9958	.9968	.9976
5	.9254	.9390	.9504	.9600	.9680	.9745	.9799	.9842	.9877	.9905
6	.8344	.8593	.8813	.9006	.9174	.9318	.9441	.9546	.9633	.9706
7	.6981	.7343	.7679	.7987	.8266	.8517	.8742	.8940	.9114	.9264
8	.5319	.5747	.6163	.6561	.6939	.7295	.7626	.7932	.8211	.8464
9	.3639	.4057	.4482	.4908	.5332	.5748	.6152	.6542	.6914	.7265
10	.2213	.2555	.2919	.3300	.3697	.4104	.4517	.4933	.5347	.5754
11	.1188	.1424	.1686	.1975	.2288	.2624	.2981	.3355	.3743	.4142
12	.0560	.0698	.0859	.1044	.1254	.1490	.1751	.2036	.2346	.2677
13	.0230	.0299	.0383	.0485	.0604	.0745	.0907	.1093	.1303	.1538
14	.0083	.0112	.0149	.0196	.0255	.0326	.0412	.0515	.0637	.0778
15	.0026	.0036	.0050	.0069	.0093	.0124	.0163	.0212	.0271	.0344
16	.0007	.0010	.0015	.0021	.0029	.0041	.0056	.0075	.0100	.0132
17	.0002	.0002	.0004	.0005	.0008	.0011	.0016	.0023	.0032	.0043
18	.0000	.0000	.0001	.0001	.0002	.0003	.0004	.0006	.0008	.0012
19	.0000	.0000	.0000	.0000	.0000	.0001	.0001	.0001	.0002	.0003
20	.0000	.0000	.0000	.0000	.0000	.0000	.0000	.0000	.0000	.0001

	.41	.42	.43	.44	.45	.46	.47	.48	.49	.50
1	1.0000	1.0000	1.0000	1.0000	1.0000	1.0000	1.0000	1.0000	1.0000	1.0000
2	1.0000	1.0000	1.0000	1.0000	1.0000	1.0000	1.0000	1.0000	1.0000	1.0000
3	.9997	.9998	.9998	.9999	.9999	1.0000	1.0000	1.0000	1.0000	1.0000
4	.9983	.9987	.9991	.9993	.9995	.9997	.9998	.9998	.9999	.9999
5	.9927	.9945	.9958	.9969	.9977	.9983	.9988	.9991	.9994	.9995
6	.9767	.9816	.9856	.9888	.9914	.9934	.9950	.9963	.9972	.9980
7	.9394	.9505	.9599	.9677	.9742	.9796	.9840	.9876	.9904	.9927
8	.8692	.8894	.9071	.9227	.9361	.9477	.9575	.9658	.9727	.9784
9	.7593	.7897	.8177	.8431	.9660	.8865	.9046	.9205	.9343	.9461
10	.6151	.6535	.6902	.7250	.7576	.7880	.8160	.8415	.8646	.8852

n = 25 (Continued)

r \ p	.41	.42	.43	.44	.45	.46	.47	.48	.49	.50
11	.4548	.4956	.5363	.5765	.6157	.6538	.6902	.7249	.7574	.7878
12	.3029	.3397	.3780	.4174	.4574	.4978	.5382	.5780	.6171	.6550
13	.1797	.2080	.2387	.2715	.3063	.3429	.3808	.4199	.4598	.5000
14	.0941	.1127	.1336	.1569	.1827	.2109	.2413	.2740	.3086	.3450
15	.0431	.0535	.0656	.0797	.0960	.1145	.1353	.1585	.1841	.2122
16	.0171	.0220	.0280	.0353	.0440	.0543	.0663	.0803	.0964	.1148
17	.0058	.0078	.0103	.0134	.0174	.0222	.0281	.0352	.0438	.0539
18	.0017	.0023	.0032	.0044	.0058	.0077	.0102	.0132	.0170	.0216
19	.0004	.0006	.0008	.0012	.0016	.0023	.0031	.0041	.0055	.0073
20	.0001	.0001	.0002	.0003	.0004	.0005	.0008	.0011	.0015	.0020
21	.0000	.0000	.0000	.0000	.0001	.0001	.0002	.0002	.0003	.0005
22	.0000	.0000	.0000	.0000	.0000	.0000	.0000	.0000	.0001	.0001

n = 30

r \ p	.01	.02	.03	.04	.05	.06	.07	.08	.09	.10
1	.2603	.4545	.4990	.7061	.7854	.8437	.8866	.9180	.9409	.9576
2	.0361	.1205	.2269	.3388	.4465	.5445	.6306	.7042	.7657	.8163
3	.0033	.0217	.0601	.1169	.1878	.2676	.3513	.4346	.5145	.5886
4	.0002	.0029	.0119	.0306	.0608	.1026	.1550	.2158	.2825	.3526
5	.0000	.0003	.0019	.0063	.0156	.0315	.0553	.0874	.1277	.1755
6	.0000	.0000	.0002	.0011	.0033	.0079	.0162	.0293	.0481	.0732
7	.0000	.0000	.0000	.0001	.0006	.0017	.0040	.0082	.0152	.0258
8	.0000	.0000	.0000	.0000	.0001	.0003	.0008	.0020	.0041	.0078
9	.0000	.0000	.0000	.0000	.0000	.0000	.0001	.0004	.0010	.0020
10	.0000	.0000	.0000	.0000	.0000	.0000	.0000	.0001	.0002	.0005
11	.0000	.0000	.0000	.0000	.0000	.0000	.0000	.0000	.0000	.0001

r \ p	.11	.12	.13	.14	.15	.16	.17	.18	.19	.20
1	.9697	.9784	.9847	.9892	.9924	.9946	.9963	.9974	.9982	.9988
2	.8573	.8900	.9159	.9362	.9520	.9641	.9733	.9803	.9856	.9895
3	.6558	.7153	.7670	.8113	.8486	.8796	.9051	.9250	.9425	.9558
4	.4234	.4929	.5594	.6215	.6783	.7295	.7748	.8144	.8484	.8773
5	.2295	.2882	.3499	.4129	.4755	.5365	.5947	.6491	.6993	.7448
6	.1049	.1431	.1871	.2363	.2894	.3453	.4028	.4605	.5174	.5725
7	.0407	.0606	.0858	.1165	.1526	.1936	.2390	.2880	.3397	.3930
8	.0136	.0221	.0339	.0497	.0698	.0945	.1240	.1582	.1968	.2392
9	.0039	.0069	.0116	.0184	.0278	.0403	.0563	.0763	.1004	.1287
10	.0010	.0019	.0035	.0059	.0097	.0150	.0224	.0323	.0451	.0611
11	.0002	.0005	.0009	.0017	.0029	.0049	.0078	.0120	.0179	.0256
12	.0000	.0001	.0002	.0004	.0008	.0014	.0024	.0040	.0062	.0095
13	.0000	.0000	.0000	.0001	.0002	.0004	.0007	.0011	.0019	.0031
14	.0000	.0000	.0000	.0000	.0000	.0001	.0002	.0003	.0005	.0009
15	.0000	.0000	.0000	.0000	.0000	.0000	.0000	.0001	.0001	.0002
16	.0000	.0000	.0000	.0000	.0000	.0000	.0000	.0000	.0000	.0001

r \ p	.21	.22	.23	.24	.25	.26	.27	.28	.29	.30
1	.9992	.9994	.9996	.9997	.9998	.9999	.9999	.9999	1.0000	1.0000
2	.9924	.9945	.9961	.9972	.9980	.9986	.9990	.9993	.9995	.9997
3	.9663	.9745	.9808	.9857	.9894	.9922	.9943	.9959	.9970	.9979
4	.9016	.9217	.9383	.9517	.9626	.9712	.9780	.9834	.9875	.9907
5	.7854	.8213	.8525	.8793	.9021	.9213	.9373	.9505	.9612	.9698
6	.6249	.6739	.7192	.7604	.7974	.8302	.8590	.8839	.9053	.9234
7	.4470	.5008	.5533	.6039	.6519	.6969	.7384	.7762	.8102	.8405
8	.2850	.3333	.3834	.4345	.4857	.5362	.5853	.6324	.6770	.7186
9	.1611	.1975	.2376	.2807	.3264	.3739	.4226	.4718	.5206	.5685
10	.0806	.1039	.1311	.1620	.1966	.2346	.2756	.3190	.3645	.4112
11	.0357	.0485	.0642	.0833	.1057	.1317	.1613	.1943	.2305	.2696
12	.0140	.0200	.0280	.0381	.0507	.0660	.0845	.1061	.1310	.1593
13	.0049	.0073	.0108	.0155	.0216	.0295	.0395	.0518	.0667	.0845
14	.0015	.0024	.0037	.0056	.0082	.0117	.0164	.0225	.0303	.0401
15	.0004	.0007	.0011	.0018	.0028	.0041	.0061	.0087	.0123	.0169
16	.0001	.0002	.0003	.0005	.0008	.0013	.0020	.0030	.0044	.0064
17	.0000	.0000	.0001	.0001	.0002	.0004	.0006	.0009	.0014	.0021
18	.0000	.0000	.0000	.0000	.0001	.0001	.0001	.0002	.0004	.0006
19	.0000	.0000	.0000	.0000	.0000	.0000	.0000	.0001	.0001	.0002

n = 30 (Continued)

r \ p	.31	.32	.33	.34	.35	.36	.37	.38	.39	.40
1	1.0000	1.0000	1.0000	1.0000	1.0000	1.0000	1.0000	1.0000	1.0000	1.0000
2	.9998	.9999	.9999	.9999	1.0000	1.0000	1.0000	1.0000	1.0000	1.0000
3	.9985	.9989	.9993	.9995	.9997	.9998	.9998	.9999	.9999	1.0000
4	.9931	.9950	.9963	.9974	.9981	.9987	.9991	.9993	.9995	.9997
5	.9768	.9823	.9866	.9899	.9925	.9944	.9959	.9971	.9979	.9985
6	.9386	.9512	.9615	.9700	.9767	.9822	.9864	.9898	.9924	.9943
7	.8671	.8903	.9102	.9271	.9414	.9533	.9631	.9712	.9776	.9828
8	.7570	.7920	.8235	.8515	.8762	.8977	.9163	.9321	.9454	.9565
9	.6148	.6590	.7007	.7395	.7753	.8078	.8371	.8631	.8861	.9060
10	.4586	.5060	.5529	.5985	.6425	.6842	.7235	.7599	.7934	.8237
11	.3112	.3549	.4000	.4460	.4922	.5382	.5833	.6270	.6689	.7085
12	.1909	.2255	.2631	.3031	.3452	.3889	.4337	.4790	.5242	.5689
13	.1053	.1292	.1563	.1865	.2198	.2559	.2945	.3353	.3778	.4215
14	.0520	.0664	.0835	.1034	.1263	.1523	.1813	.2133	.2481	.2855
15	.0229	.0305	.0399	.0514	.0652	.0815	.1006	.1226	.1475	.1754
16	.0090	.0125	.0170	.0228	.0301	.0391	.0501	.0632	.0788	.0971
17	.0031	.0045	.0065	.0090	.0124	.0167	.0222	.0291	.0377	.0481
18	.0010	.0015	.0022	.0032	.0045	.0063	.0088	.0119	.0160	.0212
19	.0003	.0004	.0006	.0010	.0014	.0021	.0031	.0043	.0060	.0083
20	.0001	.0001	.0002	.0003	.0004	.0006	.0009	.0014	.0020	.0029
21	.0000	.0000	.0000	.0001	.0001	.0002	.0002	.0004	.0006	.0009
22	.0000	.0000	.0000	.0000	.0000	.0000	.0001	.0001	.0001	.0002

r \ p	.41	.42	.43	.44	.45	.46	.47	.48	.49	.50
1	1.0000	1.0000	1.0000	1.0000	1.0000	1.0000	1.0000	1.0000	1.0000	1.0000
2	1.0000	1.0000	1.0000	1.0000	1.0000	1.0000	1.0000	1.0000	1.0000	1.0000
3	1.0000	1.0000	1.0000	1.0000	1.0000	1.0000	1.0000	1.0000	1.0000	1.0000
4	.9998	.9999	.9999	.9999	1.0000	1.0000	1.0000	1.0000	1.0000	1.0000
5	.9989	.9993	.9995	.9996	.9998	.9998	.9999	.9999	1.0000	1.0000
6	.9959	.9970	.9978	.9985	.9989	.9992	.9995	.9996	.9998	.9998
7	.9869	.9901	.9926	.9946	.9960	.9971	.9979	.9985	.9990	.9993
8	.9656	.9731	.9792	.9841	.9879	.9909	.9932	.9950	.9964	.9974
9	.9231	.9378	.9501	.9603	.9688	.9757	.9813	.9857	.9892	.9919
10	.8510	.8751	.8964	.9148	.9306	.9440	.9553	.9647	.9724	.9786
11	.7456	.7799	.8112	.8396	.8650	.8874	.9070	.9239	.9384	.9506
12	.6125	.6545	.6945	.7322	.7673	.7996	.8290	.8555	.8790	.8998
13	.4660	.5107	.5551	.5986	.6408	.6813	.7196	.7555	.7888	.8192
14	.3251	.3666	.4095	.4533	.4975	.5417	.5852	.6277	.6687	.7077
15	.2062	.2398	.2760	.3146	.3552	.3973	.4406	.4845	.5285	.5722
16	.1180	.1419	.1687	.1984	.2309	.2661	.3037	.3434	.3849	.4278
17	.0606	.0754	.0928	.1128	.1356	.1613	.1899	.2214	.2556	.2923
18	.0278	.0358	.0456	.0574	.0714	.0878	.1068	.1286	.1533	.1808
19	.0113	.0151	.0199	.0260	.0334	.0426	.0536	.0668	.0822	.1002
20	.0040	.0056	.0077	.0104	.0138	.0183	.0238	.0307	.0391	.0494
21	.0013	.0018	.0026	.0036	.0050	.0069	.0093	.0124	.0164	.0214
22	.0003	.0005	.0008	.0011	.0016	.0022	.0031	.0043	.0060	.0081
23	.0001	.0001	.0002	.0003	.0004	.0006	.0009	.0013	.0019	.0026
24	.0000	.0000	.0000	.0001	.0001	.0001	.0002	.0003	.0005	.0007
25	.0000	.0000	.0000	.0000	.0000	.0000	.0000	.0001	.0001	.0002

n = 40

r \ p	.01	.02	.03	.04	.05	.06	.07	.08	.09	.10
1	.3310	.5543	.7043	.8046	.8715	.9158	.9451	.9644	.9770	.9852
2	.0607	.1905	.3385	.4790	.6009	.7010	.7799	.8406	.8860	.9195
3	.0075	.0457	.1178	.2145	.3233	.4335	.5375	.6306	.7106	.7772
4	.0007	.0082	.0314	.0748	.1382	.2173	.3063	.3993	.4908	.5769
5	.0000	.0012	.0067	.0210	.0480	.0896	.1454	.2132	.2897	.3710
6	.0000	.0001	.0012	.0049	.0139	.0309	.0581	.0967	.1465	.2063
7	.0000	.0000	.0002	.0010	.0034	.0091	.0199	.0376	.0639	.0995
8	.0000	.0000	.0000	.0002	.0007	.0023	.0059	.0127	.0242	.0419
9	.0000	.0000	.0000	.0000	.0001	.0005	.0015	.0037	.0081	.0155
10	.0000	.0000	.0000	.0000	.0000	.0001	.0003	.0010	.0024	.0051
11	.0000	.0000	.0000	.0000	.0000	.0000	.0001	.0002	.0006	.0015
12	.0000	.0000	.0000	.0000	.0000	.0000	.0000	.0000	.0001	.0004
13	.0000	.0000	.0000	.0000	.0000	.0000	.0000	.0000	.0000	.0001

n = 40 (Continued)

r \ p	.11	.12	.13	.14	.15	.16	.17	.18	.19	.20
1	.9905	.9940	.9962	.9976	.9985	.9991	.9994	.9996	.9998	.9999
2	.9438	.9612	.9734	.9820	.9879	.9919	.9947	.9965	.9977	.9985
3	.8312	.8739	.9071	.9324	.9514	.9655	.9757	.9831	.9884	.9921
4	.6548	.7232	.7816	.8302	.8698	.9016	.9265	.9458	.9605	.9715
5	.4532	.5331	.6080	.6762	.7367	.7890	.8333	.8701	.9000	.9241
6	.2738	.3464	.4213	.4958	.5675	.6346	.6958	.7504	.7980	.8387
7	.1445	.1980	.2586	.3245	.3933	.4631	.5316	.5971	.6583	.7141
8	.0668	.0996	.1405	.1890	.2441	.3044	.3682	.4337	.4991	.5629
9	.0272	.0443	.0677	.0980	.1354	.1797	.2301	.2857	.3451	.4069
10	.0098	.0175	.0290	.0453	.0672	.0952	.1296	.1702	.2167	.2682
11	.0032	.0062	.0111	.0188	.0299	.0454	.0657	.0916	.1233	.1608
12	.0009	.0019	.0038	.0070	.0120	.0194	.0301	.0446	.0636	.0875
13	.0002	.0005	.0012	.0023	.0043	.0075	.0124	.0196	.0297	.0432
14	.0001	.0001	.0003	.0007	.0014	.0026	.0047	.0078	.0126	.0194
15	.0000	.0000	.0001	.0002	.0004	.0008	.0016	.0028	.0048	.0079
16	.0000	.0000	.0000	.0000	.0001	.0002	.0005	.0009	.0017	.0029
17	.0000	.0000	.0000	.0000	.0000	.0001	.0001	.0003	.0005	.0010
18	.0000	.0000	.0000	.0000	.0000	.0000	.0000	.0001	.0002	.0003
19	.0000	.0000	.0000	.0000	.0000	.0000	.0000	.0000	.0000	.0001

r \ p	.21	.22	.23	.24	.25	.26	.27	.28	.29	.30
1	.9999	1.0000	1.0000	1.0000	1.0000	1.0000	1.0000	1.0000	1.0000	1.0000
2	.9991	.9994	.9996	.9998	.9999	.9999	.9999	1.0000	1.0000	1.0000
3	.9946	.9964	.9976	.9984	.9990	.9993	.9996	.9997	.9998	.9999
4	.9797	.9857	.9900	.9931	.9953	.9968	.9979	.9986	.9991	.9994
5	.9430	.9578	.9691	.9776	.9840	.9886	.9920	.9945	.9962	.9974
6	.8729	.9011	.9240	.9423	.9567	.9679	.9765	.9830	.9878	.9914
7	.7640	.8078	.8454	.8773	.9038	.9255	.9430	.9569	.9678	.9762
8	.6235	.6799	.7314	.7775	.8180	.8530	.8828	.9076	.9281	.9447
9	.4694	.5312	.5910	.6476	.7002	.7480	.7909	.8286	.8612	.8890
10	.3238	.3821	.4419	.5017	.5605	.6169	.6701	.7193	.7641	.8041
11	.2038	.2517	.3038	.3589	.4161	.4740	.5315	.5875	.6410	.6913
12	.1167	.1514	.1912	.2359	.2849	.3371	.3918	.4478	.5040	.5504
13	.0609	.0830	.1100	.1421	.1791	.2209	.2669	.3165	.3687	.4228
14	.0289	.0415	.0578	.0782	.1032	.1329	.1674	.2065	.2498	.2968
15	.0124	.0189	.0277	.0394	.0544	.0733	.0964	.1240	.1560	.1926
16	.0049	.0078	.0121	.0181	.0262	.0370	.0509	.0683	.0897	.1151
17	.0017	.0030	.0048	.0076	.0116	.0171	.0246	.0345	.0473	.0633
18	.0006	.0010	.0018	.0029	.0047	.0072	.0109	.0160	.0229	.0320
19	.0002	.0003	.0006	.0010	.0017	.0028	.0044	.0068	.0101	.0148
20	.0000	.0001	.0002	.0003	.0006	.0010	.0016	.0026	.0041	.0063
21	.0000	.0000	.0000	.0001	.0002	.0003	.0005	.0009	.0015	.0024
22	.0000	.0000	.0000	.0000	.0000	.0001	.0002	.0003	.0005	.0009
23	.0000	.0000	.0000	.0000	.0000	.0000	.0000	.0001	.0002	.0003
24	.0000	.0000	.0000	.0000	.0000	.0000	.0000	.0000	.0000	.0001

r \ p	.31	.32	.33	.34	.35	.36	.37	.38	.39	.40
1	1.0000	1.0000	1.0000	1.0000	1.0000	1.0000	1.0000	1.0000	1.0000	1.0000
2	1.0000	1.0000	1.0000	1.0000	1.0000	1.0000	1.0000	1.0000	1.0000	1.0000
3	.9999	1.0000	1.0000	1.0000	1.0000	1.0000	1.0000	1.0000	1.0000	1.0000
4	.9996	.9998	.9998	.9999	.9999	1.0000	1.0000	1.0000	1.0000	1.0000
5	.9983	.9989	.9993	.9995	.9997	.9998	.9999	.9999	1.0000	1.0000
6	.9940	.9958	.9971	.9981	.9987	.9991	.9994	.9996	.9998	.9999
7	.9827	.9875	.9911	.9937	.9956	.9970	.9980	.9986	.9991	.9994
8	.9580	.9685	.9766	.9829	.9876	.9911	.9937	.9956	.9970	.9979
9	.9123	.9315	.9472	.9598	.9697	.9775	.9835	.9880	.9914	.9939
10	.8393	.8697	.8957	.9175	.9356	.9503	.9621	.9715	.9788	.9844
11	.7376	.7796	.8171	.8500	.8785	.9028	.9232	.9400	.9537	.9648
12	.6130	.6639	.7115	.7552	.7947	.8299	.8608	.8874	.9101	.9291
13	.4777	.5323	.5857	.6371	.6857	.7309	.7722	.8095	.8426	.8715
14	.3467	.3989	.4524	.5061	.5592	.6109	.6602	.7067	.7497	.7888
15	.2333	.2779	.3257	.3759	.4279	.4807	.5334	.5851	.6351	.6826
16	.1450	.1791	.2175	.2597	.3054	.3538	.4043	.4560	.5081	.5598
17	.0830	.1065	.1343	.1662	.2022	.2422	.2858	.3323	.3813	.4319
18	.0436	.0583	.0764	.0981	.1239	.1536	.1875	.2253	.2668	.3115
19	.0210	.0293	.0399	.0534	.0699	.0900	.1138	.1415	.1732	.2089
20	.0093	.0135	.0192	.0266	.0363	.0485	.0636	.0820	.1040	.1298

n = 40 (Continued)

p \ r	.31	.32	.33	.34	.35	.36	.37	.38	.39	.40
21	.0038	.0057	.0084	.0122	.0173	.0240	.0327	.0438	.0575	.0744
22	.0014	.0022	.0034	.0051	.0075	.0109	.0154	.0214	.0292	.0392
23	.0005	.0008	.0012	.0020	.0030	.0045	.0066	.0096	.0136	.0189
24	.0001	.0002	.0004	.0007	.0011	.0017	.0026	.0039	.0058	.0083
25	.0000	.0001	.0001	.0002	.0004	.0006	.0009	.0015	.0022	.0034
26	.0000	.0000	.0000	.0001	.0001	.0002	.0003	.0005	.0008	.0012
27	.0000	.0000	.0000	.0000	.0000	.0001	.0001	.0002	.0002	.0004
28	.0000	.0000	.0000	.0000	.0000	.0000	.0000	.0000	.0001	.0001

r \ p	.41	.42	.43	.44	.45	.46	.47	.48	.49	.50
1	1.0000	1.0000	1.0000	1.0000	1.0000	1.0000	1.0000	1.0000	1.0000	1.0000
2	1.0000	1.0000	1.0000	1.0000	1.0000	1.0000	1.0000	1.0000	1.0000	1.0000
3	1.0000	1.0000	1.0000	1.0000	1.0000	1.0000	1.0000	1.0000	1.0000	1.0000
4	1.0000	1.0000	1.0000	1.0000	1.0000	1.0000	1.0000	1.0000	1.0000	1.0000
5	1.0000	1.0000	1.0000	1.0000	1.0000	1.0000	1.0000	1.0000	1.0000	1.0000
6	.9999	.9999	1.0000	1.0000	1.0000	1.0000	1.0000	1.0000	1.0000	1.0000
7	.9996	.9998	.9998	.9999	.9999	1.0000	1.0000	1.0000	1.0000	1.0000
8	.9986	.9991	.9994	.9996	.9998	.9998	.9999	.9999	1.0000	1.0000
9	.9958	.9971	.9980	.9987	.9991	.9994	.9996	.9998	.9999	.9999
10	.9887	.9919	.9943	.9960	.9973	.9981	.9988	.9992	.9995	.9997
11	.9735	.9803	.9856	.9896	.9926	.9948	.9964	.9975	.9983	.9989
12	.9447	.9575	.9677	.9758	.9821	.9869	.9906	.9933	.9953	.9968
13	.8964	.9175	.9351	.9496	.9614	.9708	.9782	.9840	.9884	.9917
14	.8240	.8551	.8821	.9053	.9249	.9413	.9546	.9654	.9740	.9808
15	.7270	.7679	.8051	.8382	.8674	.8927	.9143	.9324	.9474	.9597
16	.6102	.6586	.7043	.7468	.7858	.8209	.8522	.8795	.9031	.9231
17	.4833	.5348	.5855	.6346	.6815	.7255	.7662	.8033	.8365	.8659
18	.3589	.4083	.4590	.5101	.5609	.6107	.6585	.7039	.7463	.7852
19	.2484	.2912	.3370	.3851	.4349	.4857	.5365	.5867	.6354	.6821
20	.1594	.1930	.2305	.2714	.3156	.3624	.4112	.4614	.5122	.5627
21	.0946	.1184	.1461	.1776	.2130	.2521	.2946	.3400	.3878	.4373
22	.0516	.0669	.0855	.1074	.1331	.1627	.1961	.2333	.2740	.3179
23	.0259	.0348	.0460	.0598	.0767	.0969	.1206	.1482	.1796	.2148
24	.0118	.0165	.0226	.0305	.0405	.0530	.0683	.0867	.1086	.1341
25	.0049	.0072	.0102	.0142	.0196	.0265	.0354	.0465	.0602	.0769
26	.0019	.0028	.0042	.0060	.0086	.0121	.0167	.0228	.0305	.0403
27	.0006	.0010	.0015	.0023	.0034	.0050	.0072	.0101	.0140	.0192
28	.0002	.0003	.0005	.0008	.0012	.0019	.0028	.0041	.0058	.0083
29	.0001	.0001	.0002	.0002	.0004	.0006	.0010	.0015	.0022	.0032
30	.0000	.0000	.0000	.0001	.0001	.0002	.0003	.0005	.0007	.0011
31	.0000	.0000	.0000	.0000	.0000	.0000	.0001	.0001	.0002	.0003
32	.0000	.0000	.0000	.0000	.0000	.0000	.0000	.0000	.0001	.0001

n = 50

p \ r	.01	.02	.03	.04	.05	.06	.07	.08	.09	.10
1	.3950	.6358	.7819	.8701	.9231	.9547	.9734	.9845	.9910	.9948
2	.0894	.2642	.4447	.5995	.7206	.8100	.8735	.9173	.9468	.9662
3	.0138	.0784	.1892	.3233	.4595	.5838	.6892	.7740	.8395	.8883
4	.0016	.0178	.0628	.1391	.2396	.3527	.4673	.5747	.6697	.7497
5	.0001	.0032	.0168	.0490	.1036	.1794	.2710	.3711	.4723	.5688
6	.0000	.0005	.0037	.0144	.0378	.0776	.1350	.2081	.2928	.3839
7	.0000	.0001	.0007	.0036	.0118	.0289	.0583	.1019	.1596	.2298
8	.0000	.0000	.0001	.0008	.0032	.0094	.0220	.0438	.0768	.1221
9	.0000	.0000	.0000	.0001	.0008	.0027	.0073	.0167	.0328	.0579
10	.0000	.0000	.0000	.0000	.0002	.0007	.0022	.0056	.0125	.0245
11	.0000	.0000	.0000	.0000	.0000	.0002	.0006	.0017	.0043	.0094
12	.0000	.0000	.0000	.0000	.0000	.0000	.0001	.0005	.0013	.0032
13	.0000	.0000	.0000	.0000	.0000	.0000	.0000	.0001	.0004	.0010
14	.0000	.0000	.0000	.0000	.0000	.0000	.0000	.0000	.0001	.0003
15	.0000	.0000	.0000	.0000	.0000	.0000	.0000	.0000	.0000	.0001

	.11	.12	.13	.14	.15	.16	.17	.18	.19	.20
1	.9971	.9983	.9991	.9995	.9997	.9998	.9999	1.0000	1.0000	1.0000
2	.9788	.9869	.9920	.9951	.9971	.9983	.9990	.9994	.9997	.9998
3	.9237	.9487	.9661	.9779	.9858	.9910	.9944	.9965	.9979	.9987
4	.8146	.8655	.9042	.9330	.9540	.9688	.9792	.9863	.9912	.9943
5	.6562	.7320	.7956	.8472	.8879	.9192	.9428	.9601	.9726	.9815

n = 50 (Continued)

r \ p	.11	.12	.13	.14	.15	.16	.17	.18	.19	.20
6	.4760	.5647	.6463	.7186	.7806	.8323	.8741	.9071	.9327	.9520
7	.3091	.3935	.4789	.5616	.6387	.7081	.7686	.8199	.8624	.8966
8	.1793	.2467	.3217	.4010	.4812	.5594	.6328	.6996	.7587	.8096
9	.0932	.1392	.1955	.2605	.3319	.4071	.4832	.5576	.6280	.6927
10	.0435	.0708	.1074	.1537	.2089	.2718	.3403	.4122	.4849	.5563
11	.0183	.0325	.0535	.0824	.1199	.1661	.2203	.2813	.3473	.4164
12	.0069	.0135	.0242	.0402	.0628	.0929	.1309	.1768	.2300	.2893
13	.0024	.0051	.0100	.0179	.0301	.0475	.0714	.1022	.1405	.1861
14	.0008	.0018	.0037	.0073	.0132	.0223	.0357	.0544	.0791	.1106
15	.0002	.0006	.0013	.0027	.0053	.0096	.0164	.0266	.0411	.0607
16	.0001	.0002	.0004	.0009	.0020	.0038	.0070	.0120	.0197	.0308
17	.0000	.0000	.0001	.0003	.0007	.0014	.0027	.0050	.0087	.0144
18	.0000	.0000	.0000	.0001	.0002	.0005	.0010	.0019	.0036	.0063
19	.0000	.0000	.0000	.0000	.0001	.0001	.0003	.0007	.0013	.0025
20	.0000	.0000	.0000	.0000	.0000	.0000	.0001	.0002	.0005	.0009
21	.0000	.0000	.0000	.0000	.0000	.0000	.0000	.0001	.0002	.0003
22	.0000	.0000	.0000	.0000	.0000	.0000	.0000	.0000	.0000	.0001

r \ p	.21	.22	.23	.24	.25	.26	.27	.28	.29	.30
1	1.0000	1.0000	1.0000	1.0000	1.0000	1.0000	1.0000	1.0000	1.0000	1.0000
2	.9999	.9999	1.0000	1.0000	1.0000	1.0000	1.0000	1.0000	1.0000	1.0000
3	.9992	.9995	.9997	.9998	.9999	1.0000	1.0000	1.0000	1.0000	1.0000
4	.9964	.9978	.9986	.9992	.9995	.9997	.9998	.9999	.9999	1.0000
5	.9877	.9919	.9948	.9967	.9979	.9987	.9992	.9995	.9997	.9998
6	.9663	.9767	.9841	.9893	.9930	.9954	.9970	.9981	.9988	.9993
7	.9236	.9445	.9603	.9720	.9806	.9868	.9911	.9941	.9961	.9975
8	.8523	.8874	.9156	.9377	.9547	.9676	.9772	.9842	.9892	.9927
9	.7505	.8009	.8437	.8794	.9084	.9316	.9497	.9635	.9740	.9817
10	.6241	.6870	.7436	.7934	.8363	.8724	.9021	.9260	.9450	.9598
11	.4864	.5552	.6210	.6822	.7378	.7871	.8299	.8663	.8965	.9211
12	.3533	.4201	.4878	.5544	.6184	.6782	.7329	.7817	.8244	.8610
13	.2383	.2963	.3585	.4233	.4890	.5539	.6163	.6749	.7287	.7771
14	.1490	.1942	.2456	.3023	.3630	.4261	.4901	.5534	.6145	.6721
15	.0862	.1181	.1565	.2013	.2519	.3075	.3669	.4286	.4912	.5532
16	.0462	.0665	.0926	.1247	.1631	.2075	.2575	.3121	.3703	.4308
17	.0229	.0347	.0508	.0718	.0983	.1306	.1689	.2130	.2623	.3161
18	.0105	.0168	.0259	.0384	.0551	.0766	.1034	.1359	.1741	.2178
19	.0045	.0075	.0122	.0191	.0287	.0418	.0590	.0809	.1080	.1406
20	.0018	.0031	.0054	.0088	.0139	.0212	.0314	.0449	.0626	.0848
21	.0006	.0012	.0022	.0038	.0063	.0100	.0155	.0232	.0338	.0478
22	.0002	.0004	.0008	.0015	.0026	.0044	.0071	.0112	.0170	.0251
23	.0001	.0001	.0003	.0006	.0010	.0018	.0031	.0050	.0080	.0123
24	.0000	.0000	.0001	.0002	.0004	.0007	.0012	.0021	.0035	.0056
25	.0000	.0000	.0000	.0001	.0001	.0002	.0004	.0008	.0014	.0024
26	.0000	.0000	.0000	.0000	.0000	.0001	.0002	.0003	.0005	.0009
27	.0000	.0000	.0000	.0000	.0000	.0000	.0001	.0001	.0002	.0003
28	.0000	.0000	.0000	.0000	.0000	.0000	.0000	.0000	.0001	.0001

r \ p	.31	.32	.33	.34	.35	.36	.37	.38	.39	.40
1	1.0000	1.0000	1.0000	1.0000	1.0000	1.0000	1.0000	1.0000	1.0000	1.0000
2	1.0000	1.0000	1.0000	1.0000	1.0000	1.0000	1.0000	1.0000	1.0000	1.0000
3	1.0000	1.0000	1.0000	1.0000	1.0000	1.0000	1.0000	1.0000	1.0000	1.0000
4	1.0000	1.0000	1.0000	1.0000	1.0000	1.0000	1.0000	1.0000	1.0000	1.0000
5	.9999	.9999	1.0000	1.0000	1.0000	1.0000	1.0000	1.0000	1.0000	1.0000
6	.9996	.9997	.9998	.9999	.9999	1.0000	1.0000	1.0000	1.0000	1.0000
7	.9984	.9990	.9994	.9996	.9998	.9999	.9999	1.0000	1.0000	1.0000
8	.9952	.9969	.9980	.9987	.9992	.9995	.9997	.9998	.9999	.9999
9	.9874	.9914	.9942	.9962	.9975	.9984	.9990	.9994	.9996	.9998
10	.9710	.9794	.9856	.9901	.9933	.9955	.9971	.9981	.9988	.9992
11	.9409	.9563	.9683	.9773	.9840	.9889	.9924	.9949	.9966	.9978
12	.8916	.9168	.9371	.9533	.9658	.9753	.9825	.9878	.9916	.9943
13	.8197	.8564	.8874	.9130	.9339	.9505	.9635	.9736	.9811	.9867
14	.7253	.7732	.8157	.8524	.8837	.9097	.9310	.9481	.9616	.9720
15	.6131	.6698	.7223	.7699	.8122	.8491	.8805	.9069	.9286	.9460
16	.4922	.5530	.6120	.6679	.7199	.7672	.8094	.8462	.8779	.9045
17	.3734	.4328	.4931	.5530	.6111	.6664	.7179	.7649	.8070	.8439
18	.2666	.3197	.3760	.4346	.4940	.5531	.6105	.6653	.7164	.7631
19	.1786	.2220	.2703	.3227	.3784	.4362	.4949	.5533	.6101	.6644
20	.1121	.1447	.1826	.2257	.2736	.3255	.3805	.4376	.4957	.5535

n = 50 (Continued)

p r	.31	.32	.33	.34	.35	.36	.37	.38	.39	.40
21	.0657	.0882	.1156	.1482	.1861	.2289	.2764	.3278	.3824	.4390
22	.0360	.0503	.0685	.0912	.1187	.1513	.1890	.2317	.2788	.3299
23	.0184	.0267	.0379	.0525	.0710	.0938	.1214	.1540	.1916	.2340
24	.0087	.0133	.0196	.0282	.0396	.0544	.0730	.0960	.1236	.1562
25	.0039	.0061	.0094	.0141	.0207	.0295	.0411	.0560	.0748	.0978
26	.0016	.0026	.0042	.0066	.0100	.0149	.0216	.0306	.0423	.0573
27	.0006	.0011	.0018	.0029	.0045	.0070	.0106	.0155	.0223	.0314
28	.0002	.0004	.0007	.0012	.0019	.0031	.0048	.0074	.0110	.0160
29	.0001	.0001	.0002	.0004	.0007	.0012	.0020	.0032	.0050	.0076
30	.0000	.0000	.0001	.0002	.0003	.0005	.0008	.0013	.0021	.0034
31	.0000	.0000	.0000	.0000	.0001	.0002	.0003	.0005	.0008	.0014
32	.0000	.0000	.0000	.0000	.0000	.0001	.0001	.0002	.0003	.0005
33	.0000	.0000	.0000	.0000	.0000	.0000	.0000	.0001	.0001	.0002
34	.0000	.0000	.0000	.0000	.0000	.0000	.0000	.0000	.0000	.0001

	.41	.42	.43	.44	.45	.46	.47	.48	.49	.50
1	1.0000	1.0000	1.0000	1.0000	1.0000	1.0000	1.0000	1.0000	1.0000	1.0000
2	1.0000	1.0000	1.0000	1.0000	1.0000	1.0000	1.0000	1.0000	1.0000	1.0000
3	1.0000	1.0000	1.0000	1.0000	1.0000	1.0000	1.0000	1.0000	1.0000	1.0000
4	1.0000	1.0000	1.0000	1.0000	1.0000	1.0000	1.0000	1.0000	1.0000	1.0000
5	1.0000	1.0000	1.0000	1.0000	1.0000	1.0000	1.0000	1.0000	1.0000	1.0000
6	1.0000	1.0000	1.0000	1.0000	1.0000	1.0000	1.0000	1.0000	1.0000	1.0000
7	1.0000	1.0000	1.0000	1.0000	1.0000	1.0000	1.0000	1.0000	1.0000	1.0000
8	1.0000	1.0000	1.0000	1.0000	1.0000	1.0000	1.0000	1.0000	1.0000	1.0000
9	.9999	.9999	1.0000	1.0000	1.0000	1.0000	1.0000	1.0000	1.0000	1.0000
10	.9995	.9997	.9998	.9999	.9999	1.0000	1.0000	1.0000	1.0000	1.0000
11	.9986	.9991	.9994	.9997	.9998	.9999	.9999	1.0000	1.0000	1.0000
12	.9962	.9975	.9984	.9990	.9994	.9996	.9998	.9999	.9999	1.0000
13	.9908	.9938	.9958	.9973	.9982	.9989	.9993	.9996	.9997	.9998
14	.9799	.9858	.9902	.9933	.9955	.9970	.9981	.9988	.9992	.9995
15	.9599	.9707	.9789	.9851	.9896	.9929	.9952	.9968	.9980	.9987
16	.9265	.9443	.9585	.9696	.9780	.9844	.9892	.9926	.9950	.9967
17	.8757	.9025	.9248	.9429	.9573	.9687	.9774	.9839	.9888	.9923
18	.8051	.8421	.8740	.9010	.9235	.9418	.9565	.9680	.9769	.9836
19	.7151	.7617	.8037	.8406	.8727	.8998	.9225	.9410	.9559	.9675
20	.6099	.6638	.7143	.7608	.8026	.8396	.8718	.8991	.9219	.9405
21	.4965	.5539	.6099	.6635	.7138	.7602	.8020	.8391	.8713	.8987
22	.3840	.4402	.4973	.5543	.6100	.6634	.7137	.7599	.8018	.8389
23	.2807	.3316	.3854	.4412	.4981	.5548	.6104	.6636	.7138	.7601
24	.1936	.2359	.2826	.3331	.3866	.4422	.4989	.5554	.6109	.6641
25	.1255	.1580	.1953	.2375	.2840	.3343	.3876	.4431	.4996	.5561
26	.0762	.0992	.1269	.1593	.1966	.2386	.2850	.3352	.3885	.4439
27	.0432	.0584	.0772	.1003	.1279	.1603	.1975	.2395	.2858	.3359
28	.0229	.0321	.0439	.0591	.0780	.1010	.1286	.1609	.1981	.2399
29	.0113	.0164	.0233	.0325	.0444	.0595	.0784	.1013	.1289	.1611
30	.0052	.0078	.0115	.0166	.0235	.0327	.0446	.0596	.0784	.1013
31	.0022	.0034	.0053	.0079	.0116	.0167	.0236	.0327	.0445	.0595
32	.0009	.0014	.0022	.0035	.0053	.0079	.0116	.0166	.0234	.0325
33	.0003	.0005	.0009	.0014	.0022	.0035	.0053	.0078	.0114	.0164
34	.0001	.0002	.0003	.0005	.0009	.0014	.0022	.0034	.0052	.0077
35	.0000	.0001	.0001	.0002	.0003	.0005	.0009	.0014	.0021	.0033
36	.0000	.0000	.0000	.0001	.0001	.0002	.0003	.0005	.0008	.0013
37	.0000	.0000	.0000	.0000	.0000	.0001	.0001	.0002	.0003	.0005
38	.0000	.0000	.0000	.0000	.0000	.0000	.0000	.0001	.0001	.0002

n = 75

p r	.01	.02	.03	.04	.05	.06	.07	.08	.09	.10
1	.5294	.7802	.8982	.9532	.9787	.9903	.9957	.9981	.9992	.9996
2	.1729	.4439	.6620	.8069	.8944	.9441	.9712	.9855	.9929	.9965
3	.0397	.1899	.3917	.5814	.7303	.8350	.9032	.9452	.9699	.9839
4	.0069	.0637	.1882	.3527	.5202	.6655	.7786	.8598	.9145	.9496
5	.0010	.0174	.0750	.1812	.3211	.4708	.6098	.7261	.8160	.8811
6	.0001	.0040	.0253	.0798	.1724	.2943	.4294	.5610	.6776	.7729
7	.0000	.0008	.0073	.0305	.0810	.1629	.2709	.3936	.5179	.6327
8	.0000	.0001	.0019	.0102	.0336	.0802	.1534	.2501	.3622	.4792
9	.0000	.0000	.0004	.0030	.0124	.0353	.0781	.1440	.2313	.3342
10	.0000	.0000	.0001	.0008	.0041	.0140	.0360	.0753	.1350	.2142

n = 75 (Continued)

r \ p	.01	.02	.03	.04	.05	.06	.07	.08	.09	.10
11	.0000	.0000	.0000	.0002	.0012	.0050	.0151	.0359	.0721	.1263
12	.0000	.0000	.0000	.0000	.0003	.0016	.0057	.0157	.0353	.0685
13	.0000	.0000	.0000	.0000	.0001	.0005	.0020	.0063	.0159	.0343
14	.0000	.0000	.0000	.0000	.0000	.0001	.0006	.0023	.0066	.0159
15	.0000	.0000	.0000	.0000	.0000	.0000	.0002	.0008	.0025	.0068
16	.0000	.0000	.0000	.0000	.0000	.0000	.0001	.0002	.0009	.0027
17	.0000	.0000	.0000	.0000	.0000	.0000	.0000	.0001	.0003	.0010
18	.0000	.0000	.0000	.0000	.0000	.0000	.0000	.0000	.0001	.0003
19	.0000	.0000	.0000	.0000	.0000	.0000	.0000	.0000	.0000	.0001

r	.11	.12	.13	.14	.15	.16	.17	.18	.19	.20
1	.9998	.9999	1.0000	1.0000	1.0000	1.0000	1.0000	1.0000	1.0000	1.0000
2	.9984	.9992	.9996	.9998	.9999	1.0000	1.0000	1.0000	1.0000	1.0000
3	.9916	.9957	.9978	.9989	.9995	.9998	.9999	.9999	1.0000	1.0000
4	.9712	.9839	.9913	.9954	.9976	.9988	.9994	.9997	.9999	.9999
5	.9258	.9551	.9736	.9849	.9916	.9954	.9976	.9987	.9994	.9997
6	.8461	.8993	.9362	.9608	.9766	.9864	.9923	.9957	.9977	.9988
7	.7312	.8105	.8710	.9150	.9456	.9662	.9796	.9880	.9931	.9961
8	.5913	.6912	.7749	.8414	.8918	.9284	.9540	.9712	.9825	.9896
9	.4442	.5528	.6529	.7397	.8111	.8672	.9094	.9400	.9613	.9757
10	.3090	.4124	.5171	.6164	.7051	.7804	.8415	.8889	.9243	.9499
11	.1986	.2860	.3833	.4839	.5816	.6713	.7496	.8149	.8671	.9072
12	.1180	.1842	.2651	.3564	.4528	.5485	.6385	.7190	.7878	.8443
13	.0649	.1101	.1708	.2458	.3316	.4237	.5170	.6066	.6886	.7603
14	.0330	.0612	.1026	.1585	.2279	.3086	.3965	.4871	.5758	.6586
15	.0156	.0316	.0575	.0955	.1469	.2114	.2872	.3709	.4586	.5460
16	.0069	.0152	.0301	.0539	.0888	.1362	.1961	.2672	.3468	.4315
17	.0028	.0068	.0147	.0284	.0503	.0824	.1261	.1818	.2485	.3241
18	.0011	.0029	.0067	.0141	.0268	.0469	.0764	.1168	.1685	.2310
19	.0004	.0011	.0029	.0065	.0134	.0251	.0436	.0707	.1080	.1560
20	.0001	.0004	.0012	.0028	.0063	.0126	.0235	.0404	.0654	.0997
21	.0000	.0001	.0004	.0012	.0028	.0060	.0119	.0218	.0374	.0603
22	.0000	.0000	.0002	.0004	.0012	.0027	.0057	.0111	.0202	.0345
23	.0000	.0000	.0001	.0002	.0005	.0011	.0026	.0054	.0104	.0187
24	.0000	.0000	.0000	.0001	.0002	.0005	.0011	.0024	.0050	.0096
25	.0000	.0000	.0000	.0000	.0001	.0002	.0004	.0010	.0023	.0047
26	.0000	.0000	.0000	.0000	.0000	.0001	.0002	.0004	.0010	.0021
27	.0000	.0000	.0000	.0000	.0000	.0000	.0001	.0002	.0004	.0009
28	.0000	.0000	.0000	.0000	.0000	.0000	.0000	.0001	.0002	.0004
29	.0000	.0000	.0000	.0000	.0000	.0000	.0000	.0000	.0001	.0002
30	.0000	.0000	.0000	.0000	.0000	.0000	.0000	.0000	.0000	.0001

r	.21	.22	.23	.24	.25	.26	.27	.28	.29	.30
1	1.0000	1.0000	1.0000	1.0000	1.0000	1.0000	1.0000	1.0000	1.0000	1.0000
2	1.0000	1.0000	1.0000	1.0000	1.0000	1.0000	1.0000	1.0000	1.0000	1.0000
3	1.0000	1.0000	1.0000	1.0000	1.0000	1.0000	1.0000	1.0000	1.0000	1.0000
4	1.0000	1.0000	1.0000	1.0000	1.0000	1.0000	1.0000	1.0000	1.0000	1.0000
5	.9998	.9999	1.0000	1.0000	1.0000	1.0000	1.0000	1.0000	1.0000	1.0000
6	.9994	.9997	.9998	.9999	1.0000	1.0000	1.0000	1.0000	1.0000	1.0000
7	.9979	.9989	.9994	.9997	.9998	.9999	1.0000	1.0000	1.0000	1.0000
8	.9940	.9966	.9981	.9990	.9995	.9997	.9999	.9999	1.0000	1.0000
9	.9851	.9911	.9948	.9971	.9984	.9991	.9995	.9998	.9999	.9999
10	.9677	.9797	.9875	.9925	.9956	.9975	.9986	.9992	.9996	.9998
11	.9370	.9583	.9732	.9831	.9897	.9938	.9964	.9979	.9988	.9994
12	.8889	.9228	.9478	.9656	.9779	.9861	.9915	.9949	.9970	.9983
13	.8206	.8693	.9074	.9360	.9569	.9717	.9819	.9887	.9931	.9959
14	.7327	.7963	.8488	.8908	.9231	.9472	.9647	.9769	.9853	.9909
15	.6291	.7050	.7714	.8275	.8731	.9091	.9365	.9567	.9712	.9813
16	.5172	.6003	.6774	.7462	.8054	.8546	.8940	.9247	.9478	.9647
17	.4057	.4895	.5720	.6500	.7208	.7827	.8352	.8780	.9120	.9380
18	.3028	.3811	.4628	.5445	.6228	.6952	.7596	.8150	.8611	.8983
19	.2146	.2826	.3577	.4372	.5176	.5960	.6696	.7361	.7942	.8434
20	.1443	.1992	.2636	.3355	.4125	.4915	.5696	.6440	.7122	.7729
21	.0920	.1334	.1848	.2456	.3143	.3887	.4662	.5437	.6185	.6882
22	.0556	.0848	.1232	.1712	.2286	.2941	.3659	.4415	.5182	.5932
23	.0318	.0511	.0780	.1136	.1585	.2125	.2749	.3440	.4177	.4933
24	.0173	.0292	.0469	.0717	.1046	.1465	.1974	.2567	.3230	.3945
25	.0089	.0158	.0268	.0430	.0657	.0962	.1352	.1830	.2393	.3029

n = 75 (Continued)

r \ p	.21	.22	.23	.24	.25	.26	.27	.28	.29	.30
26	.0043	.0082	.0145	.0245	.0393	.0602	.0883	.1246	.1695	.2227
27	.0020	.0040	.0075	.0132	.0223	.0358	.0550	.0809	.1147	.1567
28	.0009	.0018	.0036	.0068	.0120	.0203	.0326	.0501	.0740	.1053
29	.0004	.0008	.0017	.0033	.0062	.0109	.0184	.0296	.0456	.0676
30	.0001	.0003	.0007	.0015	.0030	.0056	.0099	.0166	.0268	.0414
31	.0001	.0001	.0003	.0007	.0014	.0027	.0050	.0089	.0150	.0242
32	.0000	.0001	.0001	.0003	.0006	.0013	.0025	.0045	.0080	.0134
33	.0000	.0000	.0000	.0001	.0003	.0006	.0011	.0022	.0040	.0071
34	.0000	.0000	.0000	.0000	.0001	.0002	.0005	.0010	.0020	.0036
35	.0000	.0000	.0000	.0000	.0000	.0001	.0002	.0004	.0009	.0017
36	.0000	.0000	.0000	.0000	.0000	.0000	.0001	.0002	.0004	.0008
37	.0000	.0000	.0000	.0000	.0000	.0000	.0000	.0001	.0002	.0003
38	.0000	.0000	.0000	.0000	.0000	.0000	.0000	.0000	.0001	.0001
39	.0000	.0000	.0000	.0000	.0000	.0000	.0000	.0000	.0000	.0001

r	.31	.32	.33	.34	.35	.36	.37	.38	.39	.40
1	1.0000	1.0000	1.0000	1.0000	1.0000	1.0000	1.0000	1.0000	1.0000	1.0000
2	1.0000	1.0000	1.0000	1.0000	1.0000	1.0000	1.0000	1.0000	1.0000	1.0000
3	1.0000	1.0000	1.0000	1.0000	1.0000	1.0000	1.0000	1.0000	1.0000	1.0000
4	1.0000	1.0000	1.0000	1.0000	1.0000	1.0000	1.0000	1.0000	1.0000	1.0000
5	1.0000	1.0000	1.0000	1.0000	1.0000	1.0000	1.0000	1.0000	1.0000	1.0000
6	1.0000	1.0000	1.0000	1.0000	1.0000	1.0000	1.0000	1.0000	1.0000	1.0000
7	1.0000	1.0000	1.0000	1.0000	1.0000	1.0000	1.0000	1.0000	1.0000	1.0000
8	1.0000	1.0000	1.0000	1.0000	1.0000	1.0000	1.0000	1.0000	1.0000	1.0000
9	1.0000	1.0000	1.0000	1.0000	1.0000	1.0000	1.0000	1.0000	1.0000	1.0000
10	.9999	.9999	1.0000	1.0000	1.0000	1.0000	1.0000	1.0000	1.0000	1.0000
11	.9997	.9998	.9999	1.0000	1.0000	1.0000	1.0000	1.0000	1.0000	1.0000
12	.9991	.9995	.9997	.9999	.9999	1.0000	1.0000	1.0000	1.0000	1.0000
13	.9976	.9986	.9992	.9996	.9998	.9999	.9999	1.0000	1.0000	1.0000
14	.9945	.9967	.9981	.9989	.9994	.9997	.9998	.9999	1.0000	1.0000
15	.9882	.9927	.9956	.9974	.9985	.9992	.9995	.9998	.9999	.9999
16	.9767	.9850	.9906	.9942	.9965	.9980	.9988	.9994	.9997	.9998
17	.9574	.9714	.9813	.9881	.9926	.9955	.9973	.9984	.9991	.9995
18	.9273	.9493	.9655	.9771	.9851	.9906	.9942	.9965	.9979	.9988
19	.8837	.9157	.9404	.9588	.9723	.9818	.9883	.9927	.9955	.9973
20	.8249	.8683	.9033	.9306	.9515	.9669	.9779	.9856	.9909	.9944
21	.7510	.8058	.8521	.8900	.9201	.9434	.9608	.9736	.9826	.9888
22	.6640	.7288	.7860	.8351	.8759	.9088	.9346	.9542	.9687	.9791
23	.5681	.6398	.7062	.7657	.8174	.8610	.8967	.9250	.9469	.9633
24	.4688	.5433	.6156	.6833	.7449	.7991	.8454	.8838	.9147	.9389
25	.3722	.4450	.5189	.5914	.6603	.7236	.7802	.8291	.8702	.9037
26	.2836	.3506	.4217	.4948	.5673	.6371	.7020	.7607	.8121	.8559
27	.2070	.2651	.3297	.3991	.4711	.5434	.6138	.6801	.7407	.7945
28	.1446	.1921	.2474	.3096	.3770	.4478	.5197	.5904	.6579	.7203
29	.0966	.1333	.1780	.2305	.2902	.3556	.4249	.4962	.5671	.6354
30	.0616	.0884	.1225	.1646	.2144	.2715	.3348	.4026	.4730	.5438
31	.0375	.0560	.0807	.1124	.1519	.1990	.2536	.3146	.3807	.4501
32	.0217	.0338	.0507	.0735	.1030	.1398	.1844	.2364	.2951	.3594
33	.0120	.0195	.0305	.0459	.0668	.0941	.1285	.1704	.2199	.2763
34	.0063	.0107	.0174	.0273	.0414	.0605	.0857	.1178	.1572	.2041
35	.0032	.0056	.0095	.0155	.0245	.0372	.0547	.0779	.1077	.1446
36	.0015	.0028	.0050	.0084	.0138	.0218	.0333	.0492	.0706	.0981
37	.0007	.0013	.0025	.0044	.0074	.0122	.0194	.0297	.0442	.0637
38	.0003	.0006	.0012	.0021	.0038	.0065	.0108	.0172	.0265	.0396
39	.0001	.0003	.0005	.0010	.0019	.0033	.0057	.0094	.0151	.0235
40	.0000	.0001	.0002	.0004	.0009	.0016	.0029	.0049	.0082	.0133
41	.0000	.0000	.0001	.0002	.0004	.0007	.0014	.0025	.0043	.0072
42	.0000	.0000	.0000	.0001	.0002	.0003	.0006	.0012	.0021	.0037
43	.0000	.0000	.0000	.0000	.0001	.0001	.0003	.0005	.0010	.0018
44	.0000	.0000	.0000	.0000	.0000	.0001	.0001	.0002	.0004	.0008
45	.0000	.0000	.0000	.0000	.0000	.0000	.0000	.0001	.0002	.0004
46	.0000	.0000	.0000	.0000	.0000	.0000	.0000	.0000	.0001	.0002
47	.0000	.0000	.0000	.0000	.0000	.0000	.0000	.0000	.0000	.0001

r	.41	.42	.43	.44	.45	.46	.47	.48	.49	.50
1	1.0000	1.0000	1.0000	1.0000	1.0000	1.0000	1.0000	1.0000	1.0000	1.0000
2	1.0000	1.0000	1.0000	1.0000	1.0000	1.0000	1.0000	1.0000	1.0000	1.0000
3	1.0000	1.0000	1.0000	1.0000	1.0000	1.0000	1.0000	1.0000	1.0000	1.0000
4	1.0000	1.0000	1.0000	1.0000	1.0000	1.0000	1.0000	1.0000	1.0000	1.0000
5	1.0000	1.0000	1.0000	1.0000	1.0000	1.0000	1.0000	1.0000	1.0000	1.0000

n = 75 (Continued)

r \ p	.41	.42	.43	.44	.45	.46	.47	.48	.49	.50
6	1.0000	1.0000	1.0000	1.0000	1.0000	1.0000	1.0000	1.0000	1.0000	1.0000
7	1.0000	1.0000	1.0000	1.0000	1.0000	1.0000	1.0000	1.0000	1.0000	1.0000
8	1.0000	1.0000	1.0000	1.0000	1.0000	1.0000	1.0000	1.0000	1.0000	1.0000
9	1.0000	1.0000	1.0000	1.0000	1.0000	1.0000	1.0000	1.0000	1.0000	1.0000
10	1.0000	1.0000	1.0000	1.0000	1.0000	1.0000	1.0000	1.0000	1.0000	1.0000
11	1.0000	1.0000	1.0000	1.0000	1.0000	1.0000	1.0000	1.0000	1.0000	1.0000
12	1.0000	1.0000	1.0000	1.0000	1.0000	1.0000	1.0000	1.0000	1.0000	1.0000
13	1.0000	1.0000	1.0000	1.0000	1.0000	1.0000	1.0000	1.0000	1.0000	1.0000
14	1.0000	1.0000	1.0000	1.0000	1.0000	1.0000	1.0000	1.0000	1.0000	1.0000
15	1.0000	1.0000	1.0000	1.0000	1.0000	1.0000	1.0000	1.0000	1.0000	1.0000
16	.9999	1.0000	1.0000	1.0000	1.0000	1.0000	1.0000	1.0000	1.0000	1.0000
17	.9997	.9999	.9999	1.0000	1.0000	1.0000	1.0000	1.0000	1.0000	1.0000
18	.9993	.9996	.9998	.9999	1.0000	1.0000	1.0000	1.0000	1.0000	1.0000
19	.9985	.9991	.9995	.9997	.9999	.9999	1.0000	1.0000	1.0000	1.0000
20	.9966	.9980	.9989	.9994	.9996	.9998	.9999	1.0000	1.0000	1.0000
21	.9930	.9957	.9974	.9985	.9992	.9995	.9998	.9999	.9999	1.0000
22	.9864	.9914	.9947	.9968	.9981	.9989	.9994	.9997	.9998	.9999
23	.9752	.9837	.9895	.9935	.9960	.9976	.9986	.9992	.9996	.9998
24	.9573	.9709	.9806	.9874	.9920	.9951	.9971	.9983	.9990	.9995
25	.9303	.9507	.9660	.9771	.9850	.9904	.9940	.9964	.9979	.9988
26	.8920	.9210	.9436	.9607	.9733	.9823	.9886	.9928	.9956	.9974
27	.8408	.8795	.9110	.9358	.9548	.9690	.9793	.9865	.9914	.9947
28	.7763	.8251	.8664	.9003	.9274	.9484	.9643	.9759	.9841	.9899
29	.6994	.7575	.8087	.8525	.8890	.9184	.9415	.9591	.9721	.9815
30	.6128	.6782	.7382	.7917	.8380	.8770	.9088	.9340	.9535	.9680
31	.5206	.5901	.6566	.7184	.7741	.8228	.8643	.8985	.9259	.9473
32	.4275	.4975	.5673	.6348	.6981	.7559	.8070	.8509	.8876	.9173
33	.3386	.4053	.4746	.5444	.6127	.6774	.7371	.7905	.8369	.8760
34	.2581	.3183	.3835	.4519	.5216	.5904	.6564	.7178	.7734	.8222
35	.1889	.2405	.2986	.3622	.4295	.4988	.5679	.6349	.6980	.7557
36	.1327	.1745	.2236	.2795	.3413	.4073	.4760	.5453	.6132	.6778
37	.0892	.1214	.1608	.2074	.2610	.3208	.3855	.4534	.5227	.5912
38	.0574	.0009	.1108	.1477	.1918	.2431	.3009	.3640	.4310	.5000
39	.0353	.0515	.0730	.1007	.1352	.1770	.2259	.2815	.3429	.4088
40	.0207	.0313	.0460	.0657	.0913	.1235	.1627	.2092	.2626	.3222
41	.0116	.0182	.0277	.0410	.0590	.0825	.1123	.1492	.1932	.2443
42	.0062	.0101	.0159	.0244	.0364	.0527	.0742	.1018	.1363	.1778
43	.0031	.0053	.0087	.0139	.0214	.0321	.0468	.0665	.0920	.1240
44	.0015	.0027	.0045	.0075	.0120	.0186	.0282	.0414	.0593	.0827
45	.0007	.0013	.0022	.0039	.0064	.0103	.0162	.0246	.0365	.0527
46	.0003	.0006	.0011	.0019	.0032	.0054	.0088	.0139	.0214	.0320
47	.0001	.0002	.0005	.0009	.0016	.0027	.0046	.0075	.0119	.0185
48	.0000	.0001	.0002	.0004	.0007	.0013	.0023	.0038	.0063	.0101
49	.0000	.0000	.0001	.0002	.0003	.0006	.0011	.0019	.0032	.0053
50	.0000	.0000	.0000	.0001	.0001	.0002	.0005	.0009	.0015	.0026
51	.0000	.0000	.0000	.0000	.0000	.0001	.0002	.0004	.0007	.0012
52	.0000	.0000	.0000	.0000	.0000	.0000	.0001	.0002	.0003	.0005
53	.0000	.0000	.0000	.0000	.0000	.0000	.0000	.0001	.0001	.0002
54	.0000	.0000	.0000	.0000	.0000	.0000	.0000	.0000	.0000	.0001

n = 100

r \ p	.01	.02	.03	.04	.05	.06	.07	.08	.09	.10
1	.6340	.8674	.9524	.9831	.9941	.9979	.9993	.9998	.9999	1.0000
2	.2642	.5967	.8054	.9128	.9629	.9848	.9940	.9977	.9991	.9997
3	.0794	.3233	.5802	.7679	.8817	.9434	.9742	.9887	.9952	.9981
4	.0184	.1410	.3528	.5705	.7422	.8570	.9256	.9633	.9827	.9922
5	.0034	.0508	.1821	.3711	.5640	.7232	.8368	.9097	.9526	.9763
6	.0005	.0155	.0808	.2116	.3840	.5593	.7086	.8201	.8955	.9424
7	.0001	.0041	.0312	.1064	.2340	.3936	.5557	.6968	.8060	.8828
8	.0000	.0009	.0106	.0475	.1280	.2517	.4012	.5529	.6872	.7939
9	.0000	.0002	.0032	.0190	.0631	.1463	.2660	.4074	.5506	.6791
10	.0000	.0000	.0009	.0068	.0282	.0775	.1620	.2780	.4125	.5487
11	.0000	.0000	.0002	.0022	.0115	.0376	.0908	.1757	.2882	.4168
12	.0000	.0000	.0000	.0007	.0043	.0168	.0469	.1028	.1876	.2970
13	.0000	.0000	.0000	.0002	.0015	.0069	.0224	.0559	.1138	.1982
14	.0000	.0000	.0000	.0000	.0005	.0026	.0099	.0282	.0645	.1239
15	.0000	.0000	.0000	.0000	.0001	.0009	.0041	.0133	.0341	.0726

					n = 100 (Continued)					
r \ p	.01	.02	.03	.04	.05	.06	.07	.08	.09	.10
16	.0000	.0000	.0000	.0000	.0000	.0003	.0016	.0058	.0169	.0399
17	.0000	.0000	.0000	.0000	.0000	.0001	.0006	.0024	.0078	.0206
18	.0000	.0000	.0000	.0000	.0000	.0000	.0002	.0009	.0034	.0100
19	.0000	.0000	.0000	.0000	.0000	.0000	.0001	.0003	.0014	.0046
20	.0000	.0000	.0000	.0000	.0000	.0000	.0000	.0001	.0005	.0020
21	.0000	.0000	.0000	.0000	.0000	.0000	.0000	.0000	.0002	.0008
22	.0000	.0000	.0000	.0000	.0000	.0000	.0000	.0000	.0001	.0003
23	.0000	.0000	.0000	.0000	.0000	.0000	.0000	.0000	.0000	.0001

	.11	.12	.13	.14	.15	.16	.17	.18	.19	.20
1	1.0000	1.0000	1.0000	1.0000	1.0000	1.0000	1.0000	1.0000	1.0000	1.0000
2	.9999	1.0000	1.0000	1.0000	1.0000	1.0000	1.0000	1.0000	1.0000	1.0000
3	.9992	.9997	.9999	1.0000	1.0000	1.0000	1.0000	1.0000	1.0000	1.0000
4	.9966	.9985	.9994	.9998	.9999	1.0000	1.0000	1.0000	1.0000	1.0000
5	.9886	.9947	.9977	.9990	.9996	.9998	.9999	1.0000	1.0000	1.0000
6	.9698	.9848	.9926	.9966	.9984	.9993	.9997	.9999	1.0000	1.0000
7	.9328	.9633	.9808	.9903	.9953	.9978	.9990	.9996	.9998	.9999
8	.8715	.9239	.9569	.9766	.9878	.9939	.9970	.9986	.9994	.9997
9	.7835	.8614	.9155	.9508	.9725	.9853	.9924	.9962	.9982	.9991
10	.6722	.7743	.8523	.9078	.9449	.9684	.9826	.9908	.9953	.9977
11	.5471	.6663	.7663	.8440	.9006	.9393	.9644	.9800	.9891	.9943
12	.4206	.5458	.6611	.7591	.8365	.8939	.9340	.9605	.9773	.9874
13	.3046	.4239	.5446	.6566	.7527	.8297	.8876	.9289	.9567	.9747
14	.2076	.3114	.4268	.5436	.6526	.7469	.8234	.8819	.9241	.9531
15	.1330	.2160	.3173	.4294	.5428	.6490	.7417	.8177	.8765	.9196
16	.0802	.1414	.2236	.3227	.4317	.5420	.6458	.7370	.8125	.8715
17	.0456	.0874	.1492	.2305	.3275	.4338	.5414	.6429	.7327	.8077
18	.0244	.0511	.0942	.1563	.2367	.3319	.4357	.5408	.6403	.7288
19	.0123	.0282	.0564	.1006	.1628	.2424	.3359	.4374	.5403	.6379
20	.0059	.0147	.0319	.0614	.1065	.1689	.2477	.3395	.4391	.5398
21	.0026	.0073	.0172	.0356	.0663	.1121	.1745	.2525	.3429	.4405
22	.0011	.0034	.0088	.0196	.0393	.0710	.1174	.1797	.2570	.3460
23	.0005	.0015	.0042	.0103	.0221	.0428	.0754	.1223	.1846	.2611
24	.0002	.0006	.0020	.0051	.0119	.0246	.0462	.0796	.1270	.1891
25	.0001	.0003	.0009	.0024	.0061	.0135	.0271	.0496	.0837	.1314
26	.0000	.0001	.0004	.0011	.0030	.0071	.0151	.0295	.0528	.0875
27	.0000	.0000	.0001	.0005	.0014	.0035	.0081	.0168	.0318	.0558
28	.0000	.0000	.0001	.0002	.0006	.0017	.0041	.0091	.0184	.0342
29	.0000	.0000	.0000	.0001	.0003	.0008	.0020	.0048	.0102	.0200
30	.0000	.0000	.0000	.0000	.0001	.0003	.0009	.0024	.0054	.0112
31	.0000	.0000	.0000	.0000	.0000	.0001	.0004	.0011	.0027	.0061
32	.0000	.0000	.0000	.0000	.0000	.0001	.0002	.0005	.0013	.0031
33	.0000	.0000	.0000	.0000	.0000	.0000	.0001	.0002	.0006	.0016
34	.0000	.0000	.0000	.0000	.0000	.0000	.0000	.0001	.0003	.0007
35	.0000	.0000	.0000	.0000	.0000	.0000	.0000	.0000	.0001	.0003
36	.0000	.0000	.0000	.0000	.0000	.0000	.0000	.0000	.0000	.0001
37	.0000	.0000	.0000	.0000	.0000	.0000	.0000	.0000	.0000	.0001

	.21	.22	.23	.24	.25	.26	.27	.28	.29	.30
1	1.0000	1.0000	1.0000	1.0000	1.0000	1.0000	1.0000	1.0000	1.0000	1.0000
2	1.0000	1.0000	1.0000	1.0000	1.0000	1.0000	1.0000	1.0000	1.0000	1.0000
3	1.0000	1.0000	1.0000	1.0000	1.0000	1.0000	1.0000	1.0000	1.0000	1.0000
4	1.0000	1.0000	1.0000	1.0000	1.0000	1.0000	1.0000	1.0000	1.0000	1.0000
5	1.0000	1.0000	1.0000	1.0000	1.0000	1.0000	1.0000	1.0000	1.0000	1.0000
6	1.0000	1.0000	1.0000	1.0000	1.0000	1.0000	1.0000	1.0000	1.0000	1.0000
7	1.0000	1.0000	1.0000	1.0000	1.0000	1.0000	1.0000	1.0000	1.0000	1.0000
8	.9999	1.0000	1.0000	1.0000	1.0000	1.0000	1.0000	1.0000	1.0000	1.0000
9	.9996	1.9998	1.9999	1.0000	1.0000	1.0000	1.0000	1.0000	1.0000	1.0000
10	.9989	.9995	.9998	.9999	1.0000	1.0000	1.0000	1.0000	1.0000	1.0000
11	.9971	.9986	.9993	.9997	.9999	.9999	1.0000	1.0000	1.0000	1.0000
12	.9933	.9965	.9983	.9992	.9996	.9998	.9999	1.0000	1.0000	1.0000
13	.9857	.9922	.9959	.9979	.9990	.9995	.9998	.9999	1.0000	1.0000
14	.9721	.9840	.9911	.9953	.9975	.9988	.9994	.9997	.9999	.9999
15	.9496	.9695	.9823	.9900	.9946	.9972	.9986	.9993	.9997	.9998
16	.9153	.9462	.9671	.9806	.9889	.9939	.9967	.9983	.9992	.9996
17	.8668	.9112	.9430	.9647	.9789	.9878	.9932	.9963	.9981	.9990
18	.8032	.8625	.9074	.9399	.9624	.9773	.9867	.9925	.9959	.9978
19	.7252	.7991	.8585	.9038	.9370	.9601	.9757	.9856	.9918	.9955
20	.6358	.7220	.7953	.8547	.9005	.9342	.9580	.9741	.9846	.9911

n = 100 (Continued)

r \ p	.21	.22	.23	.24	.25	.26	.27	.28	.29	.30
21	.5394	.6338	.7189	.7918	.8512	.8973	.9316	.9560	.9726	.9835
22	.4419	.5391	.6320	.7162	.7886	.8479	.8943	.9291	.9540	.9712
23	.3488	.4432	.5388	.6304	.7136	.7856	.8448	.8915	.9267	.9521
24	.2649	.3514	.4444	.5386	.6289	.7113	.7828	.8420	.8889	.9245
25	.1933	.2684	.3539	.4455	.5383	.6276	.7091	.7802	.8393	.8864
26	.1355	.1972	.2717	.3561	.4465	.5381	.6263	.7071	.7778	.8369
27	.0911	.1393	.2009	.2748	.3583	.4475	.5380	.6252	.7053	.7756
28	.0588	.0945	.1429	.2043	.2776	.3602	.4484	.5378	.6242	.7036
29	.0364	.0616	.0978	.1463	.2075	.2803	.3621	.4493	.5377	.6232
30	.0216	.0386	.0643	.1009	.1495	.2105	.2828	.3638	.4501	.5377
31	.0123	.0232	.0406	.0669	.1038	.1526	.2134	.2851	.3654	.4509
32	.0067	.0134	.0247	.0427	.0693	.1065	.1554	.2160	.2873	.3669
33	.0035	.0074	.0144	.0262	.0446	.0717	.1091	.1580	.2184	.2893
34	.0018	.0039	.0081	.0154	.0276	.0465	.0739	.1116	.1605	.2207
35	.0009	.0020	.0044	.0087	.0164	.0290	.0482	.0760	.1139	.1629
36	.0004	.0010	.0023	.0048	.0094	.0174	.0303	.0499	.0780	.1161
37	.0002	.0005	.0011	.0025	.0052	.0101	.0183	.0316	.0515	.0799
38	.0001	.0002	.0005	.0013	.0027	.0056	.0107	.0193	.0328	.0530
39	.0000	.0001	.0002	.0006	.0014	.0030	.0060	.0113	.0201	.0340
40	.0000	.0000	.0001	.0003	.0007	.0015	.0032	.0064	.0119	.0210
41	.0000	.0000	.0000	.0001	.0003	.0008	.0017	.0035	.0068	.0125
42	.0000	.0000	.0000	.0001	.0001	.0004	.0008	.0018	.0037	.0072
43	.0000	.0000	.0000	.0000	.0001	.0002	.0004	.0009	.0020	.0040
44	.0000	.0000	.0000	.0000	.0000	.0001	.0002	.0005	.0010	.0021
45	.0000	.0000	.0000	.0000	.0000	.0000	.0001	.0002	.0005	.0011
46	.0000	.0000	.0000	.0000	.0000	.0000	.0000	.0001	.0002	.0005
47	.0000	.0000	.0000	.0000	.0000	.0000	.0000	.0000	.0001	.0003
48	.0000	.0000	.0000	.0000	.0000	.0000	.0000	.0000	.0000	.0001
49	.0000	.0000	.0000	.0000	.0000	.0000	.0000	.0000	.0000	.0001

r	.31	.32	.33	.34	.35	.36	.37	.38	.39	.40
1	1.0000	1.0000	1.0000	1.0000	1.0000	1.0000	1.0000	1.0000	1.0000	1.0000
2	1.0000	1.0000	1.0000	1.0000	1.0000	1.0000	1.0000	1.0000	1.0000	1.0000
3	1.0000	1.0000	1.0000	1.0000	1.0000	1.0000	1.0000	1.0000	1.0000	1.0000
4	1.0000	1.0000	1.0000	1.0000	1.0000	1.0000	1.0000	1.0000	1.0000	1.0000
5	1.0000	1.0000	1.0000	1.0000	1.0000	1.0000	1.0000	1.0000	1.0000	1.0000
6	1.0000	1.0000	1.0000	1.0000	1.0000	1.0000	1.0000	1.0000	1.0000	1.0000
7	1.0000	1.0000	1.0000	1.0000	1.0000	1.0000	1.0000	1.0000	1.0000	1.0000
8	1.0000	1.0000	1.0000	1.0000	1.0000	1.0000	1.0000	1.0000	1.0000	1.0000
9	1.0000	1.0000	1.0000	1.0000	1.0000	1.0000	1.0000	1.0000	1.0000	1.0000
10	1.0000	1.0000	1.0000	1.0000	1.0000	1.0000	1.0000	1.0000	1.0000	1.0000
11	1.0000	1.0000	1.0000	1.0000	1.0000	1.0000	1.0000	1.0000	1.0000	1.0000
12	1.0000	1.0000	1.0000	1.0000	1.0000	1.0000	1.0000	1.0000	1.0000	1.0000
13	1.0000	1.0000	1.0000	1.0000	1.0000	1.0000	1.0000	1.0000	1.0000	1.0000
14	1.0000	1.0000	1.0000	1.0000	1.0000	1.0000	1.0000	1.0000	1.0000	1.0000
15	.9999	1.0000	1.0000	1.0000	1.0000	1.0000	1.0000	1.0000	1.0000	1.0000
16	.9998	.9999	1.0000	1.0000	1.0000	1.0000	1.0000	1.0000	1.0000	1.0000
17	.9995	.9998	.9999	1.0000	1.0000	1.0000	1.0000	1.0000	1.0000	1.0000
18	.9989	.9995	.9997	.9999	.9999	1.0000	1.0000	1.0000	1.0000	1.0000
19	.9976	.9988	.9994	.9997	.9999	.9999	1.0000	1.0000	1.0000	1.0000
20	.9950	.9973	.9986	.9993	.9997	.9998	.9999	1.0000	1.0000	1.0000
21	.9904	.9946	.9971	.9985	.9992	.9996	.9998	.9999	1.0000	1.0000
22	.9825	.9898	.9942	.9968	.9983	.9991	.9996	.9998	.9999	1.0000
23	.9698	.9816	.9891	.9938	.9966	.9982	.9991	.9995	.9998	.9999
24	.9504	.9685	.9806	.9885	.9934	.9963	.9980	.9990	.9995	.9997
25	.9224	.9487	.9672	.9797	.9879	.9930	.9961	.9979	.9989	.9994
26	.8841	.9204	.9471	.9660	.9789	.9873	.9926	.9958	.9977	.9988
27	.8346	.8820	.9185	.9456	.9649	.9780	.9867	.9922	.9956	.9976
28	.7736	.8325	.8800	.9168	.9442	.9638	.9773	.9862	.9919	.9954
29	.7021	.7717	.8305	.8781	.9152	.9429	.9628	.9765	.9857	.9916
30	.6224	.7007	.7699	.8287	.8764	.9137	.9417	.9618	.9759	.9852
31	.5376	.6216	.6994	.7684	.8270	.8748	.9123	.9405	.9610	.9752
32	.4516	.5376	.6209	.6982	.7669	.8254	.8733	.9110	.9395	.9602
33	.3683	.4523	.5375	.6203	.6971	.7656	.8240	.8720	.9098	.9385
34	.2912	.3696	.4530	.5375	.6197	.6961	.7643	.8227	.8708	.9087
35	.2229	.2929	.3708	.4536	.5376	.6192	.6953	.7632	.8216	.8697
36	.1650	.2249	.2946	.3720	.4542	.5376	.6188	.6945	.7623	.8205
37	.1181	.1671	.2268	.2961	.3731	.4547	.5377	.6184	.6938	.7614
38	.0816	.1200	.1690	.2285	.2976	.3741	.4553	.5377	.6181	.6932
39	.0545	.0833	.1218	.1708	.2301	.2989	.3750	.4558	.5378	.6178
49	.0351	.0558	.0849	.1235	.1724	.2316	.3001	.3759	.4562	.5379

n = 100 (Continued)

r \ p	.31	.32	.33	.34	.35	.36	.37	.38	.39	.40
41	.0218	.0361	.0571	.0863	.1250	.1739	.2330	.3012	.3767	.4567
42	.0131	.0226	.0371	.0583	.0877	.1265	.1753	.2343	.3023	.3775
43	.0075	.0136	.0233	.0380	.0594	.0889	.1278	.1766	.2355	.3033
44	.0042	.0079	.0141	.0240	.0389	.0605	.0901	.1290	.1778	.2365
45	.0023	.0044	.0082	.0146	.0246	.0397	.0614	.0911	.1301	.1789
46	.0012	.0024	.0046	.0085	.0150	.0252	.0405	.0623	.0921	.1311
47	.0006	.0012	.0025	.0048	.0088	.0154	.0257	.0411	.0631	.0930
48	.0003	.0006	.0013	.0026	.0050	.0091	.0158	.0262	.0417	.0638
49	.0001	.0003	.0007	.0014	.0027	.0052	.0094	.0162	.0267	.0423
50	.0001	.0001	.0003	.0007	.0015	.0029	.0054	.0096	.0165	.0271
51	.0000	.0001	.0002	.0003	.0007	.0015	.0030	.0055	.0098	.0168
52	.0000	.0000	.0001	.0002	.0004	.0008	.0016	.0030	.0056	.0100
53	.0000	.0000	.0000	.0001	.0002	.0004	.0008	.0016	.0031	.0058
54	.0000	.0000	.0000	.0000	.0001	.0002	.0004	.0008	.0017	.0032
55	.0000	.0000	.0000	.0000	.0000	.0001	.0002	.0004	.0009	.0017
56	.0000	.0000	.0000	.0000	.0000	.0000	.0001	.0002	.0004	.0009
57	.0000	.0000	.0000	.0000	.0000	.0000	.0000	.0001	.0002	.0004
58	.0000	.0000	.0000	.0000	.0000	.0000	.0000	.0000	.0001	.0002
59	.0000	.0000	.0000	.0000	.0000	.0000	.0000	.0000	.0000	.0001

r	.41	.42	.43	.44	.45	.46	.47	.48	.49	.50
1	1.0000	1.0000	1.0000	1.0000	1.0000	1.0000	1.0000	1.0000	1.0000	1.0000
2	1.0000	1.0000	1.0000	1.0000	1.0000	1.0000	1.0000	1.0000	1.0000	1.0000
3	1.0000	1.0000	1.0000	1.0000	1.0000	1.0000	1.0000	1.0000	1.0000	1.0000
4	1.0000	1.0000	1.0000	1.0000	1.0000	1.0000	1.0000	1.0000	1.0000	1.0000
5	1.0000	1.0000	1.0000	1.0000	1.0000	1.0000	1.0000	1.0000	1.0000	1.0000
6	1.0000	1.0000	1.0000	1.0000	1.0000	1.0000	1.0000	1.0000	1.0000	1.0000
7	1.0000	1.0000	1.0000	1.0000	1.0000	1.0000	1.0000	1.0000	1.0000	1.0000
8	1.0000	1.0000	1.0000	1.0000	1.0000	1.0000	1.0000	1.0000	1.0000	1.0000
9	1.0000	1.0000	1.0000	1.0000	1.0000	1.0000	1.0000	1.0000	1.0000	1.0000
10	1.0000	1.0000	1.0000	1.0000	1.0000	1.0000	1.0000	1.0000	1.0000	1.0000
11	1.0000	1.0000	1.0000	1.0000	1.0000	1.0000	1.0000	1.0000	1.0000	1.0000
12	1.0000	1.0000	1.0000	1.0000	1.0000	1.0000	1.0000	1.0000	1.0000	1.0000
13	1.0000	1.0000	1.0000	1.0000	1.0000	1.0000	1.0000	1.0000	1.0000	1.0000
14	1.0000	1.0000	1.0000	1.0000	1.0000	1.0000	1.0000	1.0000	1.0000	1.0000
15	1.0000	1.0000	1.0000	1.0000	1.0000	1.0000	1.0000	1.0000	1.0000	1.0000
16	1.0000	1.0000	1.0000	1.0000	1.0000	1.0000	1.0000	1.0000	1.0000	1.0000
17	1.0000	1.0000	1.0000	1.0000	1.0000	1.0000	1.0000	1.0000	1.0000	1.0000
18	1.0000	1.0000	1.0000	1.0000	1.0000	1.0000	1.0000	1.0000	1.0000	1.0000
19	1.0000	1.0000	1.0000	1.0000	1.0000	1.0000	1.0000	1.0000	1.0000	1.0000
20	1.0000	1.0000	1.0000	1.0000	1.0000	1.0000	1.0000	1.0000	1.0000	1.0000
21	1.0000	1.0000	1.0000	1.0000	1.0000	1.0000	1.0000	1.0000	1.0000	1.0000
22	1.0000	1.0000	1.0000	1.0000	1.0000	1.0000	1.0000	1.0000	1.0000	1.0000
23	1.0000	1.0000	1.0000	1.0000	1.0000	1.0000	1.0000	1.0000	1.0000	1.0000
24	.9999	.9999	1.0000	1.0000	1.0000	1.0000	1.0000	1.0000	1.0000	1.0000
25	.9997	.9999	.9999	1.0000	1.0000	1.0000	1.0000	1.0000	1.0000	1.0000
26	.9994	.9997	.9999	.9999	1.0000	1.0000	1.0000	1.0000	1.0000	1.0000
27	.9987	.9994	.9997	.9998	.9999	1.0000	1.0000	1.0000	1.0000	1.0000
28	.9975	.9987	.9993	.9997	.9998	.9999	1.0000	1.0000	1.0000	1.0000
29	.9952	.9974	.9986	.9993	.9996	.9998	.9999	1.0000	1.0000	1.0000
30	.9913	.9950	.9972	.9985	.9992	.9996	.9998	.9999	1.0000	1.0000
31	.9848	.9910	.9948	.9971	.9985	.9992	.9996	.9998	.9999	1.0000
32	.9746	.9844	.9907	.9947	.9970	.9984	.9992	.9996	.9998	.9999
33	.9594	.9741	.9840	.9905	.9945	.9969	.9984	.9991	.9996	.9998
34	.9376	.9587	.9736	.9837	.9902	.9944	.9969	.9983	.9991	.9996
35	.9078	.9368	.9581	.9732	.9834	.9900	.9942	.9968	.9983	.9991
36	.8687	.9069	.9361	.9576	.9728	.9831	.9899	.9941	.9967	.9982
37	.8196	.8678	.9061	.9355	.9571	.9724	.9829	.9897	.9941	.9967
38	.7606	.8188	.8670	.9054	.9349	.9567	.9721	.9827	.9896	.9940
39	.6927	.7599	.8181	.8663	.9049	.9345	.9563	.9719	.9825	.9895
40	.6176	.6922	.7594	.8174	.8657	.9044	.9341	.9561	.9717	.9824
41	.5380	.6174	.6919	.7589	.8169	.8653	.9040	.9338	.9558	.9716
42	.4571	.5382	.6173	.6916	.7585	.8165	.8649	.9037	.9335	.9557
43	.3782	.4576	.5383	.6173	.6913	.7582	.8162	.8646	.9035	.9334
44	.3041	.3788	.4580	.5385	.6172	.6912	.7580	.8160	.8645	.9033
45	.2375	.3049	.3794	.4583	.5387	.6173	.6911	.7579	.8159	.8644

	n = 100 (Continued)									
r \ p	.41	.42	.43	.44	.45	.46	.47	.48	.49	.50
46	.1799	.2384	.3057	.3799	.4587	.5389	.6173	.6911	.7579	.8159
47	.1320	.1807	.2391	.3063	.3804	.4590	.5391	.6174	.6912	.7579
48	.0938	.1328	.1815	.2398	.3069	.3809	.4593	.5393	.6176	.6914
49	.0644	.0944	.1335	.1822	.2404	.3074	.3813	.4596	.5395	.6178
50	.0428	.0650	.0950	.1341	.1827	.2409	.3078	.3816	.4599	.5398
51	.0275	.0432	.0655	.0955	.1346	.1832	.2413	.3082	.3819	.4602
52	.0170	.0278	.0436	.0659	.0960	.1350	.1836	.2417	.3084	.3822
53	.0102	.0172	.0280	.0439	.0662	.0963	.1353	.1838	.2419	.3086
54	.0059	.0103	.0174	.0282	.0441	.0664	.0965	.1355	.1840	.2421
55	.0033	.0059	.0104	.0175	.0284	.0443	.0666	.0967	.1356	.1841
56	.0017	.0033	.0060	.0105	.0176	.0285	.0444	.0667	.0967	.1356
57	.0009	.0018	.0034	.0061	.0106	.0177	.0286	.0444	.0667	.0967
58	.0004	.0009	.0018	.0034	.0061	.0106	.0177	.0286	.0444	.0666
59	.0002	.0005	.0009	.0018	.0034	.0061	.0106	.0177	.0285	.0443
60	.0001	.0002	.0005	.0009	.0018	.0034	.0061	.0106	.0177	.0284
61	.0000	.0001	.0002	.0005	.0009	.0018	.0034	.0061	.0106	.0176
62	.0000	.0000	.0001	.0002	.0005	.0009	.0018	.0034	.0061	.0105
63	.0000	.0000	.0000	.0001	.0002	.0005	.0009	.0018	.0034	.0060
64	.0000	.0000	.0000	.0000	.0001	.0002	.0005	.0009	.0018	.0033
65	.0000	.0000	.0000	.0000	.0000	.0001	.0002	.0005	.0009	.0018
66	.0000	.0000	.0000	.0000	.0000	.0000	.0001	.0002	.0004	.0009
67	.0000	.0000	.0000	.0000	.0000	.0000	.0000	.0001	.0002	.0004
68	.0000	.0000	.0000	.0000	.0000	.0000	.0000	.0000	.0001	.0002
69	.0000	.0000	.0000	.0000	.0000	.0000	.0000	.0000	.0000	.0001

VALUES OF $e^{-\lambda}$

With permission of Samuel B. Richmond, STATISTICAL ANALYSIS
Second Edition, Copyright ©, 1964
The Ronald Press Company, New York

λ	$e^{-\lambda}$	λ	$e^{-\lambda}$
0.0	1.00000	2.5	.08208
0.1	.90484	2.6	.07427
0.2	.81873	2.7	.06721
0.3	.74082	2.8	.06081
0.4	.67032	2.9	.05502
0.5	.60653	3.0	.04979
0.6	.54881	3.2	.04076
0.7	.49659	3.4	.03337
0.8	.44933	3.6	.02732
0.9	.40657	3.8	.02237
1.0	.36788	4.0	.01832
1.1	.33287	4.2	.01500
1.2	.30119	4.4	.01228
1.3	.27253	4.6	.01005
1.4	.24660	4.8	.00823
1.5	.22313	5.0	.00674
1.6	.20190	5.5	.00409
1.7	.18268	6.0	.00248
1.8	.16530	6.5	.00150
1.9	.14957	7.0	.00091
2.0	.13534	7.5	.00055
2.1	.12246	8.0	.00034
2.2	.11080	8.5	.00020
2.3	.10026	9.0	.00012
2.4	.09072	10.0	.00005

POISSON PROBABILITY DISTRIBUTION

$$P(r \mid \lambda) = \frac{\lambda^r}{r!} e^{-\lambda}$$

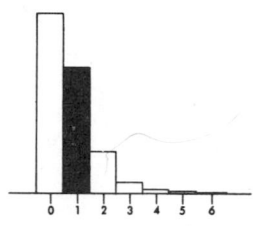

$$P(r = 1 \mid \lambda = 0.7) = 0.3476$$

r	0.10	0.20	0.30	0.40	λ 0.50	0.60	0.70	0.80	0.90	1.00
0	.9048	.8187	.7408	.6703	.6065	.5488	.4966	.4493	.4066	.3679
1	.0905	.1637	.2222	.2681	.3033	.3293	.3476	.3595	.3659	.3679
2	.0045	.0164	.0333	.0536	.0758	.0988	.1217	.1438	.1647	.1839
3	.0002	.0011	.0033	.0072	.0126	.0198	.0284	.0383	.0494	.0613
4	.0000	.0001	.0003	.0007	.0016	.0030	.0050	.0077	.0111	.0153
5	.0000	.0000	.0000	.0001	.0002	.0004	.0007	.0012	.0020	.0031
6	.0000	.0000	.0000	.0000	.0000	.0000	.0001	.0002	.0003	.0005
7	.0000	.0000	.0000	.0000	.0000	.0000	.0000	.0000	.0000	.0001

r	1.10	1.20	1.30	1.40	λ 1.50	1.60	1.70	1.80	1.90	2.00
0	.3329	.3012	.2725	.2466	.2231	.2019	.1827	.1653	.1496	.1353
1	.3662	.3614	.3543	.3452	.3347	.3230	.3106	.2975	.2842	.2707
2	.2014	.2169	.2303	.2417	.2510	.2584	.2640	.2678	.2700	.2707
3	.0738	.0867	.0998	.1128	.1255	.1378	.1496	.1607	.1710	.1804
4	.0203	.0260	.0324	.0395	.0471	.0551	.0636	.0723	.0812	.0902
5	.0045	.0062	.0084	.0111	.0141	.0176	.0216	.0260	.0309	.0361
6	.0008	.0012	.0018	.0026	.0035	.0047	.0061	.0078	.0098	.0120
7	.0001	.0002	.0003	.0005	.0008	.0011	.0015	.0020	.0027	.0034
8	.0000	.0000	.0001	.0001	.0001	.0002	.0003	.0005	.0006	.0009
9	.0000	.0000	.0000	.0000	.0000	.0000	.0001	.0001	.0001	.0002

r	2.10	2.20	2.30	2.40	λ 2.50	2.60	2.70	2.80	2.90	3.00
0	.1225	.1108	.1003	.0907	.0821	.0743	.0672	.0608	.0550	.0498
1	.2572	.2438	.2306	.2177	.2052	.1931	.1815	.1703	.1596	.1494
2	.2700	.2681	.2652	.2613	.2565	.2510	.2450	.2384	.2314	.2240
3	.1890	.1966	.2033	.2090	.2138	.2176	.2205	.2225	.2237	.2240
4	.0992	.1082	.1169	.1254	.1336	.1414	.1488	.1557	.1622	.1680
5	.0417	.0476	.0538	.0602	.0668	.0735	.0804	.0872	.0940	.1008
6	.0146	.0174	.0206	.0241	.0278	.0319	.0362	.0407	.0455	.0504
7	.0044	.0055	.0068	.0083	.0099	.0118	.0139	.0163	.0188	.0216
8	.0011	.0015	.0019	.0025	.0031	.0038	.0047	.0057	.0068	.0081
9	.0003	.0004	.0005	.0007	.0009	.0011	.0014	.0018	.0022	.0027
10	.0001	.0001	.0001	.0002	.0002	.0003	.0004	.0005	.0006	.0008
11	.0000	.0000	.0000	.0000	.0000	.0001	.0001	.0001	.0002	.0002
12	.0000	.0000	.0000	.0000	.0000	.0000	.0000	.0000	.0000	.0001

r	3.10	3.20	3.30	3.40	λ 3.50	3.60	3.70	3.80	3.90	4.00
0	.0450	.0408	.0369	.0334	.0302	.0273	.0247	.0224	.0202	.0183
1	.1397	.1304	.1217	.1135	.1057	.0984	.0915	.0850	.0789	.0733
2	.2165	.2087	.2008	.1929	.1850	.1771	.1692	.1615	.1539	.1465
3	.2237	.2226	.2209	.2186	.2158	.2125	.2087	.2046	.2001	.1954
4	.1733	.1781	.1823	.1858	.1888	.1912	.1931	.1944	.1951	.1954

r	3.10	3.20	3.30	3.40	λ 3.50	3.60	3.70	3.80	3.90	4.00
5	.1075	.1140	.1203	.1264	.1322	.1377	.1429	.1477	.1522	.1563
6	.0555	.0608	.0662	.0716	.0771	.0826	.0881	.0936	.0989	.1042
7	.0246	.0278	.0312	.0348	.0385	.0425	.0466	.0508	.0551	.0595
8	.0095	.0111	.0129	.0148	.0169	.0191	.0215	.0241	.0269	.0298
9	.0033	.0040	.0047	.0056	.0066	.0076	.0089	.0102	.0116	.0132
10	.0010	.0013	.0016	.0019	.0023	.0028	.0033	.0039	.0045	.0053
11	.0003	.0004	.0005	.0006	.0007	.0009	.0011	.0013	.0016	.0019
12	.0001	.0001	.0001	.0002	.0002	.0003	.0003	.0004	.0005	.0006
13	.0000	.0000	.0000	.0000	.0001	.0001	.0001	.0001	.0002	.0002
14	.0000	.0000	.0000	.0000	.0000	.0000	.0000	.0000	.0000	.0001

r	4.10	4.20	4.30	4.40	λ 4.50	4.60	4.70	4.80	4.90	5.00
0	.0166	.0150	.0136	.0123	.0111	.0101	.0091	.0082	.0074	.0067
1	.0679	.0630	.0583	.0540	.0500	.0462	.0427	.0395	.0365	.0337
2	.1393	.1323	.1254	.1188	.1125	.1063	.1005	.0948	.0894	.0842
3	.1904	.1852	.1798	.1743	.1687	.1631	.1574	.1517	.1460	.1404
4	.1951	.1944	.1933	.1917	.1898	.1875	.1849	.1820	.1789	.1755
5	.1600	.1633	.1662	.1687	.1708	.1725	.1738	.1747	.1753	.1755
6	.1093	.1143	.1191	.1237	.1281	.1323	.1362	.1398	.1432	.1462
7	.0640	.0686	.0732	.0778	.0824	.0869	.0914	.0959	.1002	.1044
8	.0328	.0360	.0393	.0428	.0463	.0500	.0537	.0575	.0614	.0653
9	.0150	.0168	.0188	.0209	.0232	.0255	.0281	.0307	.0334	.0363
10	.0061	.0071	.0081	.0092	.0104	.0118	.0132	.0147	.0164	.0181
11	.0023	.0027	.0032	.0037	.0043	.0049	.0056	.0064	.0073	.0082
12	.0008	.0009	.0011	.0013	.0016	.0019	.0022	.0026	.0030	.0034
13	.0002	.0003	.0004	.0005	.0006	.0007	.0008	.0009	.0011	.0013
14	.0001	.0001	.0001	.0001	.0002	.0002	.0003	.0003	.0004	.0005
15	.0000	.0000	.0000	.0000	.0001	.0001	.0001	.0001	.0001	.0002

r	5.10	5.20	5.30	5.40	λ 5.50	5.60	5.70	5.80	5.90	6.00
0	.0061	.0055	.0050	.0045	.0041	.0037	.0033	.0030	.0027	.0025
1	.0311	.0287	.0265	.0244	.0225	.0207	.0191	.0176	.0162	.0149
2	.0793	.0746	.0701	.0659	.0618	.0580	.0544	.0509	.0477	.0446
3	.1348	.1293	.1239	.1185	.1133	.1082	.1033	.0985	.0938	.0892
4	.1719	.1681	.1641	.1600	.1558	.1515	.1472	.1428	.1383	.1339
5	.1753	.1748	.1740	.1728	.1714	.1697	.1678	.1656	.1632	.1606
6	.1490	.1515	.1537	.1555	.1571	.1584	.1594	.1601	.1605	.1606
7	.1086	.1125	.1163	.1200	.1234	.1267	.1298	.1326	.1353	.1377
8	.0692	.0731	.0771	.0810	.0849	.0887	.0925	.0962	.0998	.1033
9	.0392	.0423	.0454	.0486	.0519	.0552	.0586	.0620	.0654	.0688
10	.0200	.0220	.0241	.0262	.0285	.0309	.0334	.0359	.0386	.0413
11	.0093	.0104	.0116	.0129	.0143	.0157	.0173	.0190	.0207	.0225
12	.0039	.0045	.0051	.0058	.0065	.0073	.0082	.0092	.0102	.0113
13	.0015	.0018	.0021	.0024	.0028	.0032	.0036	.0041	.0046	.0052
14	.0006	.0007	.0008	.0009	.0011	.0013	.0015	.0017	.0019	.0022
15	.0002	.0002	.0003	.0003	.0004	.0005	.0006	.0007	.0008	.0009
16	.0001	.0001	.0001	.0001	.0001	.0002	.0002	.0002	.0003	.0003
17	.0000	.0000	.0000	.0000	.0000	.0001	.0001	.0001	.0001	.0001

r	6.10	6.20	6.30	6.40	λ 6.50	6.60	6.70	6.80	6.90	7.00
0	.0022	.0020	.0018	.0017	.0015	.0014	.0012	.0011	.0010	.0009
1	.0137	.0126	.0116	.0106	.0098	.0090	.0082	.0076	.0070	.0064
2	.0417	.0390	.0364	.0340	.0318	.0296	.0276	.0258	.0240	.0223
3	.0848	.0806	.0765	.0726	.0688	.0652	.0617	.0584	.0552	.0521
4	.1294	.1249	.1205	.1161	.1118	.1076	.1034	.0992	.0952	.0912
5	.1579	.1549	.1519	.1487	.1454	.1420	.1385	.1349	.1314	.1277
6	.1605	.1601	.1595	.1586	.1575	.1562	.1546	.1529	.1511	.1490
7	.1399	.1418	.1435	.1450	.1462	.1472	.1480	.1486	.1489	.1490
8	.1066	.1099	.1130	.1160	.1188	.1215	.1240	.1263	.1284	.1304
9	.0723	.0757	.0791	.0825	.0858	.0891	.0923	.0954	.0985	.1014
10	.0441	.0469	.0498	.0528	.0558	.0588	.0618	.0649	.0679	.0710
11	.0244	.0265	.0285	.0307	.0330	.0353	.0377	.0401	.0426	.0452
12	.0124	.0137	.0150	.0164	.0179	.0194	.0210	.0227	.0245	.0263
13	.0058	.0065	.0073	.0081	.0089	.0099	.0108	.0119	.0130	.0142
14	.0025	.0029	.0033	.0037	.0041	.0046	.0052	.0058	.0064	.0071

r	6.10	6.20	6.30	6.40	λ 6.50	6.60	6.70	6.80	6.90	7.00
15	.0010	.0012	.0014	.0016	.0018	.0020	.0023	.0026	.0029	.0033
16	.0004	.0005	.0005	.0006	.0007	.0008	.0010	.0011	.0013	.0014
17	.0001	.0002	.0002	.0002	.0003	.0003	.0004	.0004	.0005	.0006
18	.0000	.0001	.0001	.0001	.0001	.0001	.0001	.0002	.0002	.0002
19	.0000	.0000	.0000	.0000	.0000	.0000	.0001	.0001	.0001	.0001

r	7.10	7.20	7.30	7.40	λ 7.50	7.60	7.70	7.80	7.90	8.00
0	.0008	.0007	.0007	.0006	.0006	.0005	.0005	.0004	.0004	.0003
1	.0059	.0054	.0049	.0045	.0041	.0038	.0035	.0032	.0029	.0027
2	.0208	.0194	.0180	.0167	.0156	.0145	.0134	.0125	.0116	.0107
3	.0492	.0464	.0438	.0413	.0389	.0366	.0345	.0324	.0305	.0286
4	.0874	.0836	.0799	.0764	.0729	.0696	.0663	.0632	.0602	.0573
5	.1241	.1204	.1167	.1130	.1094	.1057	.1021	.0986	.0951	.0916
6	.1468	.1445	.1420	.1394	.1367	.1339	.1311	.1282	.1252	.1221
7	.1489	.1486	.1481	.1474	.1465	.1454	.1442	.1428	.1413	.1396
8	.1321	.1337	.1351	.1363	.1373	.1381	.1388	.1392	.1395	.1396
9	.1042	.1070	.1096	.1121	.1144	.1167	.1187	.1207	.1224	.1241
10	.0740	.0770	.0800	.0829	.0858	.0887	.0914	.0941	.0967	.0993
11	.0478	.0504	.0531	.0558	.0585	.0613	.0640	.0667	.0695	.0722
12	.0283	.0303	.0323	.0344	.0366	.0388	.0411	.0434	.0457	.0481
13	.0154	.0168	.0181	.0196	.0211	.0227	.0243	.0260	.0278	.0296
14	.0078	.0086	.0095	.0104	.0113	.0123	.0134	.0145	.0157	.0169
15	.0037	.0041	.0046	.0051	.0057	.0062	.0069	.0075	.0083	.0090
16	.0016	.0019	.0021	.0024	.0026	.0030	.0033	.0037	.0041	.0045
17	.0007	.0008	.0009	.0010	.0012	.0013	.0015	.0017	.0019	.0021
18	.0003	.0003	.0004	.0004	.0005	.0006	.0006	.0007	.0008	.0009
19	.0001	.0001	.0001	.0002	.0002	.0002	.0003	.0003	.0003	.0004
20	.0000	.0000	.0001	.0001	.0001	.0001	.0001	.0001	.0001	.0002
21	.0000	.0000	.0000	.0000	.0000	.0000	.0000	.0000	.0001	.0001

r	8.10	8.20	8.30	8.40	λ 8.50	8.60	8.70	8.80	8.90	9.00
0	.0003	.0003	.0002	.0002	.0002	.0002	.0002	.0002	.0001	.0001
1	.0025	.0023	.0021	.0019	.0017	.0016	.0014	.0013	.0012	.0011
2	.0100	.0092	.0086	.0079	.0074	.0068	.0063	.0058	.0054	.0050
3	.0269	.0252	.0237	.0222	.0208	.0195	.0183	.0171	.0160	.0150
4	.0544	.0517	.0491	.0466	.0443	.0420	.0398	.0377	.0357	.0337
5	.0882	.0849	.0816	.0784	.0752	.0722	.0692	.0663	.0635	.0607
6	.1191	.1100	.1128	.1097	.1066	.1034	.1003	.0972	.0941	.0911
7	.1378	.1358	.1338	.1317	.1294	.1271	.1247	.1222	.1197	.1171
8	.1395	.1392	.1388	.1382	.1375	.1366	.1356	.1344	.1332	.1318
9	.1256	.1269	.1280	.1290	.1299	.1306	.1311	.1315	.1317	.1318
10	.1017	.1040	.1063	.1084	.1104	.1123	.1140	.1157	.1172	.1186
11	.0749	.0776	.0802	.0828	.0853	.0878	.0902	.0925	.0948	.0970
12	.0505	.0530	.0555	.0579	.0604	.0629	.0654	.0679	.0703	.0728
13	.0315	.0334	.0354	.0374	.0395	.0416	.0438	.0459	.0481	.0504
14	.0182	.0196	.0210	.0225	.0240	.0256	.0272	.0289	.0306	.0324
15	.0098	.0107	.0116	.0126	.0136	.0147	.0158	.0169	.0182	.0194
16	.0050	.0055	.0060	.0066	.0072	.0079	.0086	.0093	.0101	.0109
17	.0024	.0026	.0029	.0033	.0036	.0040	.0044	.0048	.0053	.0058
18	.0011	.0012	.0014	.0015	.0017	.0019	.0021	.0024	.0026	.0029
19	.0005	.0005	.0006	.0007	.0008	.0009	.0010	.0011	.0012	.0014
20	.0002	.0002	.0002	.0003	.0003	.0004	.0004	.0005	.0005	.0006
21	.0001	.0001	.0001	.0001	.0001	.0002	.0002	.0002	.0002	.0003
22	.0000	.0000	.0000	.0000	.0001	.0001	.0001	.0001	.0001	.0001

r	9.10	9.20	9.30	9.40	λ 9.50	9.60	9.70	9.80	9.90	10.00
0	.0001	.0001	.0001	.0001	.0001	.0001	.0001	.0001	.0001	.0000
1	.0010	.0009	.0009	.0008	.0007	.0007	.0006	.0005	.0005	.0005
2	.0046	.0043	.0040	.0037	.0034	.0031	.0029	.0027	.0025	.0023
3	.0140	.0131	.0123	.0115	.0107	.0100	.0093	.0087	.0081	.0076
4	.0319	.0302	.0285	.0269	.0254	.0240	.0226	.0213	.0201	.0189
5	.0581	.0555	.0530	.0506	.0483	.0460	.0439	.0418	.0398	.0378
6	.0881	.0851	.0822	.0793	.0764	.0736	.0709	.0682	.0656	.0631
7	.1145	.1118	.1091	.1064	.1037	.1010	.0982	.0955	.0928	.0901
8	.1302	.1286	.1269	.1251	.1232	.1212	.1191	.1170	.1148	.1126
9	.1317	.1315	.1311	.1306	.1300	.1293	.1284	.1274	.1263	.1251

r	9.10	9.20	9.30	9.40	λ 9.50	9.60	9.70	9.80	9.90	10.00
10	.1198	.1210	.1219	.1228	.1235	.1241	.1245	.1249	.1250	.1251
11	.0991	.1012	.1031	.1049	.1067	.1083	.1098	.1112	.1125	.1137
12	.0752	.0776	.0799	.0822	.0844	.0866	.0888	.0908	.0928	.0948
13	.0526	.0549	.0572	.0594	.0617	.0640	.0662	.0685	.0707	.0729
14	.0342	.0361	.0380	.0399	.0419	.0439	.0459	.0479	.0500	.0521
15	.0208	.0221	.0235	.0250	.0265	.0281	.0297	.0313	.0330	.0347
16	.0118	.0127	.0137	.0147	.0157	.0168	.0180	.0192	.0204	.0217
17	.0063	.0069	.0075	.0081	.0088	.0095	.0103	.0111	.0119	.0128
18	.0032	.0035	.0039	.0042	.0046	.0051	.0055	.0060	.0065	.0071
19	.0015	.0017	.0019	.0021	.0023	.0026	.0028	.0031	.0034	.0037
20	.0007	.0008	.0009	.0010	.0011	.0012	.0014	.0015	.0017	.0019
21	.0003	.0003	.0004	.0004	.0005	.0006	.0006	.0007	.0008	.0009
22	.0001	.0001	.0002	.0002	.0002	.0002	.0003	.0003	.0004	.0004
23	.0000	.0001	.0001	.0001	.0001	.0001	.0001	.0001	.0002	.0002
24	.0000	.0000	.0000	.0000	.0000	.0000	.0000	.0001	.0001	.0001

r	11.	12.	13.	14.	λ 15.	16.	17.	18.	19.	20.
0	.0000	.0000	.0000	.0000	.0000	.0000	.0000	.0000	.0000	.0000
1	.0002	.0001	.0000	.0000	.0000	.0000	.0000	.0000	.0000	.0000
2	.0010	.0004	.0002	.0001	.0000	.0000	.0000	.0000	.0000	.0000
3	.0037	.0018	.0008	.0004	.0002	.0001	.0000	.0000	.0000	.0000
4	.0102	.0053	.0027	.0013	.0006	.0003	.0001	.0001	.0000	.0000
5	.0224	.0127	.0070	.0037	.0019	.0010	.0005	.0002	.0001	.0001
6	.0411	.0255	.0152	.0087	.0048	.0026	.0014	.0007	.0004	.0002
7	.0646	.0437	.0281	.0174	.0104	.0060	.0034	.0019	.0010	.0005
8	.0888	.0655	.0457	.0304	.0194	.0120	.0072	.0042	.0024	.0013
9	.1085	.0874	.0661	.0473	.0324	.0213	.0135	.0083	.0050	.0029
10	.1194	.1048	.0859	.0663	.0486	.0341	.0230	.0150	.0095	.0058
11	.1194	.1144	.1015	.0844	.0663	.0496	.0355	.0245	.0164	.0106
12	.1094	.1144	.1099	.0984	.0829	.0661	.0504	.0368	.0259	.0176
13	.0926	.1056	.1099	.1060	.0956	.0814	.0658	.0509	.0378	.0271
14	.0728	.0905	.1021	.1060	.1024	.0930	.0800	.0655	.0514	.0387
15	.0534	.0724	.0885	.0989	.1024	.0992	.0906	.0786	.0650	.0516
16	.0367	.0543	.0719	.0866	.0960	.0992	.0963	.0884	.0772	.0646
17	.0237	.0383	.0550	.0713	.0847	.0934	.0963	.0936	.0863	.0760
18	.0145	.0256	.0397	.0554	.0706	.0830	.0909	.0936	.0911	.0844
19	.0084	.0161	.0272	.0409	.0557	.0699	.0814	.0887	.0911	.0888
20	.0046	.0097	.0177	.0286	.0418	.0559	.0692	.0798	.0866	.0888
21	.0024	.0055	.0109	.0191	.0299	.0426	.0560	.0684	.0783	.0846
22	.0012	.0030	.0065	.0121	.0204	.0310	.0433	.0560	.0676	.0769
23	.0006	.0016	.0037	.0074	.0133	.0216	.0320	.0438	.0559	.0669
24	.0003	.0008	.0020	.0043	.0083	.0144	.0226	.0329	.0442	.0557
25	.0001	.0004	.0010	.0024	.0050	.0092	.0154	.0237	.0336	.0446
26	.0000	.0002	.0005	.0013	.0029	.0057	.0101	.0164	.0246	.0343
27	.0000	.0001	.0002	.0007	.0016	.0034	.0063	.0109	.0173	.0254
28	.0000	.0000	.0001	.0003	.0009	.0019	.0038	.0070	.0117	.0181
29	.0000	.0000	.0001	.0002	.0004	.0011	.0023	.0044	.0077	.0125
30	.0000	.0000	.0000	.0001	.0002	.0006	.0013	.0026	.0049	.0083
31	.0000	.0000	.0000	.0000	.0001	.0003	.0007	.0015	.0030	.0054
32	.0000	.0000	.0000	.0000	.0001	.0001	.0004	.0009	.0018	.0034
33	.0000	.0000	.0000	.0000	.0000	.0001	.0002	.0005	.0010	.0020
34	.0000	.0000	.0000	.0000	.0000	.0000	.0001	.0002	.0006	.0012
35	.0000	.0000	.0000	.0000	.0000	.0000	.0000	.0001	.0003	.0007
36	.0000	.0000	.0000	.0000	.0000	.0000	.0000	.0001	.0002	.0004
37	.0000	.0000	.0000	.0000	.0000	.0000	.0000	.0000	.0001	.0002
38	.0000	.0000	.0000	.0000	.0000	.0000	.0000	.0000	.0000	.0001
39	.0000	.0000	.0000	.0000	.0000	.0000	.0000	.0000	.0000	.0001

r	25.0	30.0	40.0	50.0	λ 75.0	100.0
0	.0000	.0000	0	0	0	0
1	.0000	.0000	0	0	0	0
2	.0000	.0000	0	0	0	0
3	.0000	.0000	0	0	0	0
4	.0000	.0000	0	0	0	0
5	.0000	.0000	0	0	0	0
6	.0000	.0000	.0000	0	0	0
7	.0000	.0000	.0000	0	0	0
8	.0001	.0000	.0000	0	0	0
9	.0001	.0000	.0000	0	0	0
10	.0004	.0000	.0000	0	0	0
11	.0008	.0000	.0000	.0000	0	0
12	.0017	.0001	.0000	.0000	0	0
13	.0033	.0002	.0000	.0000	0	0
14	.0059	.0005	.0000	.0000	0	0
15	.0099	.0010	.0000	.0000	0	0
16	.0155	.0019	.0000	.0000	0	0
17	.0227	.0034	.0000	.0000	0	0
18	.0316	.0057	.0000	.0000	0	0
19	.0415	.0089	.0001	.0000	0	0
20	.0519	.0134	.0002	.0000	0	0
21	.0618	.0192	.0004	.0000	0	0
22	.0702	.0261	.0007	.0000	0	0
23	.0763	.0341	.0012	.0000	0	0
24	.0795	.0426	.0019	.0000	0	0
25	.0795	.0511	.0031	.0000	0	0
26	.0765	.0590	.0047	.0001	.0000	0
27	.0708	.0655	.0070	.0001	.0000	0
28	.0632	.0702	.0100	.0002	.0000	0
29	.0545	.0726	.0138	.0004	.0000	0
30	.0454	.0726	.0185	.0007	.0000	0
31	.0366	.0703	.0238	.0011	.0000	0
32	.0286	.0659	.0298	.0017	.0000	0
33	.0217	.0599	.0361	.0026	.0000	0
34	.0159	.0529	.0425	.0038	.0000	0
35	.0114	.0453	.0485	.0054	.0000	0
36	.0079	.0378	.0539	.0075	.0000	0
37	.0053	.0306	.0583	.0102	.0000	0
38	.0035	.0242	.0614	.0134	.0000	0
39	.0023	.0186	.0629	.0172	.0000	0
40	.0014	.0139	.0629	.0215	.0000	0
41	.0009	.0102	.0614	.0262	.0000	0
42	.0005	.0073	.0585	.0312	.0000	.0000
43	.0003	.0051	.0544	.0363	.0000	.0000
44	.0002	.0035	.0495	.0412	.0000	.0000
45	.0001	.0023	.0440	.0458	.0001	.0000
46	.0001	.0015	.0382	.0498	.0001	.0000
47	.0000	.0010	.0325	.0530	.0001	.0000
48	.0000	.0006	.0271	.0552	.0002	.0000
49	.0000	.0004	.0221	.0563	.0003	.0000
50	.0000	.0002	.0177	.0563	.0005	.0000
51	.0000	.0001	.0139	.0552	.0007	.0000
52	.0000	.0001	.0107	.0531	.0011	.0000
53	.0000	.0000	.0081	.0501	.0015	.0000
54	.0000	.0000	.0060	.0464	.0021	.0000
55	.0000	.0000	.0043	.0422	.0028	.0000
56	.0000	.0000	.0031	.0376	.0038	.0000
57	.0000	.0000	.0022	.0330	.0050	.0000
58	.0000	.0000	.0015	.0285	.0065	.0000
59	.0000	.0000	.0010	.0241	.0082	.0000
60	.0000	.0000	.0007	.0201	.0103	.0000
61	.0000	.0000	.0004	.0165	.0126	.0000
62	.0000	.0000	.0003	.0133	.0153	.0000
63	.0000	.0000	.0002	.0105	.0182	.0000
64	.0000	.0000	.0001	.0082	.0213	.0000
65	0	.0000	.0001	.0063	.0246	.0000
66	0	.0000	.0000	.0048	.0279	.0001
67	0	.0000	.0000	.0036	.0313	.0001
68	0	.0000	.0000	.0026	.0345	.0002
69	0	.0000	.0000	.0019	.0375	.0002

r	25.0	30.0	40.0	50.0	λ 75.0	100.0
70	.000	.0000	.0000	.0014	.0402	.0003
71	0	.0000	.0000	.0010	.0424	.0004
72	0	.0000	.0000	.0007	.0442	.0006
73	0	0	.0000	.0005	.0454	.0008
74	0	0	.0000	.0003	.0460	.0011
75	0	0	.0000	.0002	.0460	.0015
76	0	0	.0000	.0001	.0454	.0020
77	0	0	.0000	.0001	.0442	.0026
78	0	0	.0000	.0001	.0425	.0033
79	0	0	.0000	.0000	.0404	.0042
80	0	0	.0000	.0000	.0379	.0052
81	0	0	.0000	.0000	.0350	.0064
82	0	0	.0000	.0000	.0321	.0078
83	0	0	.0000	.0000	.0290	.0094
84	0	0	.0000	.0000	.0259	.0112
85	0	0	.0000	.0000	.0228	.0132
86	0	0	.0000	.0000	.0199	.0154
87	0	0	.0000	.0000	.0172	.0176
88	0	0	.0000	.0000	.0146	.0201
89	0	0	0	.0000	.0123	.0225
90	0	0	0	.0000	.0103	.0250
91	0	0	0	.0000	.0085	.0275
92	0	0	0	.0000	.0069	.0299
93	0	0	0	.0000	.0056	.0322
94	0	0	0	.0000	.0044	.0342
95	0	0	0	.0000	.0035	.0360
96	0	0	0	.0000	.0027	.0375
97	0	0	0	.0000	.0021	.0387
98	0	0	0	.0000	.0016	.0395
99	0	0	0	.0000	.0012	.0399
100	0	0	0	.0000	.0009	.0399
101	0	0	0	.0000	.0007	.0395
102	0	0	0	.0000	.0005	.0387
103	0	0	0	.0000	.0004	.0376
104	0	0	0	0	.0003	.0361
105	0	0	0	0	.0002	.0344
106	0	0	0	0	.0001	.0325
107	0	0	0	0	.0001	.0303
108	0	0	0	0	.0001	.0281
109	0	0	0	0	.0000	.0258
110	0	0	0	0	.0000	.0234
111	0	0	0	0	.0000	.0211
112	0	0	0	0	.0000	.0188
113	0	0	0	0	.0000	.0167
114	0	0	0	0	.0000	.0146
115	0	0	0	0	.0000	.0127
116	0	0	0	0	.0000	.0110
117	0	0	0	0	.0000	.0094
118	0	0	0	0	.0000	.0079
119	0	0	0	0	.0000	.0067
120	0	0	0	0	.0000	.0056
121	0	0	0	0	.0000	.0046
122	0	0	0	0	.0000	.0038
123	0	0	0	0	.0000	.0031
124	0	0	0	0	.0000	.0025
125	0	0	0	0	.0000	.0020
126	0	0	0	0	.0000	.0016
127	0	0	0	0	.0000	.0012
128	0	0	0	0	.0000	.0010
129	0	0	0	0	.0000	.0007
130	0	0	0	0	.0000	.0006
131	0	0	0	0	.0000	.0004
132	0	0	0	0	.0000	.0003
133	0	0	0	0	.0000	.0003
134	0	0	0	0	.0000	.0002
135	0	0	0	0	.0000	.0001
136	0	0	0	0	.0000	.0001
137	0	0	0	0	.0000	.0001
138	0	0	0	0	.0000	.0001

CUMULATIVE POISSON PROBABILITY DISTRIBUTION

$$P(r \geq \tilde{r} \mid \lambda) = \sum_{r=\tilde{r}}^{\infty} \frac{\lambda^r}{r!} e^{-\lambda}$$

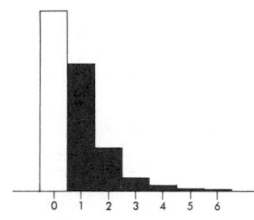

$P(r \geq 1 \mid \lambda = 0.70) = 0.5034$

r	0.1	0.2	0.3	0.4	λ 0.5	0.6	0.7	0.8	0.9	1.0
1	.0952	.1813	.2592	.3297	.3935	.4512	.5034	.5507	.5934	.6321
2	.0047	.0175	.0369	.0616	.0902	.1219	.1558	.1912	.2275	.2642
3	.0002	.0011	.0036	.0079	.0144	.0231	.0341	.0474	.0629	.0803
4	.0000	.0001	.0003	.0008	.0018	.0034	.0058	.0091	.0135	.0190
5	.0000	.0000	.0000	.0001	.0002	.0004	.0008	.0014	.0023	.0037
6	.0000	.0000	.0000	.0000	.0000	.0000	.0001	.0002	.0003	.0006
7	.0000	.0000	.0000	.0000	.0000	.0000	.0000	.0000	.0000	.0001

r	1.1	1.2	1.3	1.4	λ 1.5	1.6	1.7	1.8	1.9	2.0
1	.6671	.6988	.7275	.7534	.7769	.7981	.8173	.8347	.8504	.8647
2	.3010	.3374	.3732	.4082	.4422	.4751	.5068	.5372	.5663	.5940
3	.0996	.1205	.1429	.1665	.1912	.2166	.2428	.2694	.2963	.3233
4	.0257	.0338	.0431	.0537	.0656	.0788	.0932	.1087	.1253	.1429
5	.0054	.0077	.0107	.0143	.0186	.0237	.0296	.0364	.0441	.0527
6	.0010	.0015	.0022	.0032	.0045	.0060	.0080	.0104	.0132	.0166
7	.0001	.0003	.0004	.0006	.0009	.0013	.0019	.0026	.0034	.0045
8	.0000	.0000	.0001	.0001	.0002	.0003	.0004	.0006	.0008	.0011
9	.0000	.0000	.0000	.0000	.0000	.0000	.0001	.0001	.0002	.0002

r	2.1	2.2	2.3	2.4	λ 2.5	2.6	2.7	2.8	2.9	3.0
1	.8775	.8892	.8997	.9093	.9179	.9257	.9328	.9392	.9450	.9502
2	.6204	.6454	.6691	.6916	.7127	.7326	.7513	.7689	.7854	.8009
3	.3504	.3773	.4040	.4303	.4562	.4816	.5064	.5305	.5540	.5768
4	.1614	.1806	.2007	.2213	.2424	.2640	.2859	.3081	.3304	.3528
5	.0621	.0725	.0838	.0959	.1088	.1226	.1371	.1523	.1682	.1847
6	.0204	.0249	.0300	.0357	.0420	.0490	.0567	.0651	.0742	.0839
7	.0059	.0075	.0094	.0116	.0142	.0172	.0206	.0244	.0287	.0335
8	.0015	.0020	.0026	.0033	.0042	.0053	.0066	.0081	.0099	.0119
9	.0003	.0005	.0006	.0009	.0011	.0015	.0019	.0024	.0031	.0038
10	.0001	.0001	.0001	.0002	.0003	.0004	.0005	.0007	.0009	.0011
11	.0000	.0000	.0000	.0000	.0001	.0001	.0001	.0002	.0002	.0003
12	.0000	.0000	.0000	.0000	.0000	.0000	.0000	.0000	.0001	.0001

r	3.1	3.2	3.3	3.4	λ 3.5	3.6	3.7	3.8	3.9	4.0
1	.9550	.9592	.9631	.9666	.9698	.9727	.9753	.9776	.9798	.9817
2	.8153	.8288	.8414	.8532	.8641	.8743	.8838	.8926	.9008	.9084
3	.5988	.6201	.6406	.6603	.6792	.6973	.7146	.7311	.7469	.7619
4	.3752	.3975	.4197	.4416	.4634	.4848	.5058	.5265	.5468	.5665
5	.2018	.2194	.2374	.2558	.2746	.2936	.3128	.3322	.3516	.3712
6	.0943	.1054	.1171	.1295	.1424	.1559	.1699	.1844	.1994	.2149
7	.0388	.0446	.0510	.0579	.0653	.0733	.0818	.0909	.1005	.1107
8	.0142	.0168	.0198	.0231	.0267	.0308	.0352	.0401	.0454	.0511
9	.0047	.0057	.0069	.0083	.0099	.0117	.0137	.0160	.0185	.0214
10	.0014	.0018	.0022	.0027	.0033	.0040	.0048	.0058	.0069	.0081

r	3.1	3.2	3.3	3.4	λ 3.5	3.6	3.7	3.8	3.9	4.0
11	.0004	.0005	.0006	.0008	.0010	.0013	.0016	.0019	.0023	.0028
12	.0001	.0001	.0002	.0002	.0003	.0004	.0005	.0006	.0007	.0009
13	.0000	.0000	.0000	.0001	.0001	.0001	.0001	.0002	.0002	.0003
14	.0000	.0000	.0000	.0000	.0000	.0000	.0000	.0000	.0001	.0001

r	4.1	4.2	4.3	4.4	λ 4.5	4.6	4.7	4.8	4.9	5.0
1	.9834	.9850	.9864	.9877	.9889	.9899	.9909	.9918	.9926	.9933
2	.9155	.9220	.9281	.9337	.9389	.9437	.9482	.9523	.9561	.9596
3	.7762	.7898	.8026	.8149	.8264	.8374	.8477	.8575	.8667	.8753
4	.5858	.6046	.6228	.6406	.6577	.6743	.6903	.7058	.7207	.7350
5	.3907	.4102	.4296	.4488	.4679	.4868	.5054	.5237	.5418	.5595
6	.2307	.2469	.2633	.2801	.2971	.3142	.3316	.3490	.3665	.3840
7	.1214	.1325	.1442	.1564	.1689	.1820	.1954	.2092	.2233	.2378
8	.0573	.0639	.0710	.0786	.0866	.0951	.1040	.1133	.1231	.1334
9	.0245	.0279	.0317	.0358	.0403	.0451	.0503	.0558	.0618	.0681
10	.0095	.0111	.0129	.0149	.0171	.0195	.0222	.0251	.0283	.0318
11	.0034	.0041	.0048	.0057	.0067	.0078	.0090	.0104	.0120	.0137
12	.0011	.0014	.0017	.0020	.0024	.0029	.0034	.0040	.0047	.0055
13	.0003	.0004	.0005	.0007	.0008	.0010	.0012	.0014	.0017	.0020
14	.0001	.0001	.0002	.0002	.0003	.0003	.0004	.0005	.0006	.0007
15	.0000	.0000	.0000	.0001	.0001	.0001	.0001	.0001	.0002	.0002
16	.0000	.0000	.0000	.0000	.0000	.0000	.0000	.0000	.0001	.0001

r	5.1	5.2	5.3	5.4	λ 5.5	5.6	5.7	5.8	5.9	6.0
1	.9939	.9945	.9950	.9955	.9959	.9963	.9967	.9970	.9973	.9975
2	.9628	.9658	.9686	.9711	.9734	.9756	.9776	.9794	.9811	.9826
3	.8835	.8912	.8984	.9052	.9116	.9176	.9232	.9285	.9334	.9380
4	.7487	.7619	.7746	.7867	.7983	.8094	.8200	.8300	.8396	.8488
5	.5769	.5939	.6105	.6267	.6425	.6578	.6728	.6873	.7013	.7149
6	.4016	.4191	.4365	.4539	.4711	.4881	.5050	.5217	.5381	.5543
7	.2526	.2676	.2829	.2983	.3140	.3297	.3456	.3616	.3776	.3937
8	.1440	.1551	.1665	.1783	.1905	.2030	.2159	.2290	.2424	.2560
9	.0748	.0819	.0894	.0973	.1056	.1143	.1234	.1328	.1426	.1528
10	.0356	.0397	.0441	.0488	.0538	.0591	.0648	.0708	.0772	.0839
11	.0156	.0177	.0200	.0225	.0253	.0282	.0314	.0349	.0386	.0426
12	.0063	.0073	.0084	.0096	.0110	.0125	.0141	.0159	.0179	.0201
13	.0024	.0028	.0033	.0038	.0044	.0051	.0059	.0068	.0078	.0088
14	.0008	.0010	.0012	.0014	.0017	.0020	.0023	.0027	.0031	.0036
15	.0003	.0003	.0004	.0005	.0006	.0007	.0009	.0010	.0012	.0014
16	.0001	.0001	.0001	.0002	.0002	.0002	.0003	.0004	.0004	.0005
17	.0000	.0000	.0000	.0000	.0001	.0001	.0001	.0001	.0001	.0002
18	.0000	.0000	.0000	.0000	.0000	.0000	.0000	.0000	.0000	.0001

r	6.1	6.2	6.3	6.4	λ 6.5	6.6	6.7	6.8	6.9	7.0
1	.9978	.9980	.9982	.9983	.9985	.9986	.9988	.9989	.9990	.9991
2	.9841	.9854	.9866	.9877	.9887	.9897	.9905	.9913	.9920	.9927
3	.9423	.9464	.9502	.9537	.9570	.9600	.9629	.9656	.9680	.9704
4	.8575	.8658	.8736	.8811	.8882	.8948	.9012	.9072	.9129	.9182
5	.7281	.7408	.7531	.7649	.7763	.7873	.7978	.8080	.8177	.8270
6	.5702	.5859	.6012	.6163	.6310	.6453	.6594	.6730	.6863	.6993
7	.4098	.4258	.4418	.4577	.4735	.4892	.5047	.5201	.5353	.5503
8	.2699	.2840	.2983	.3127	.3272	.3419	.3567	.3715	.3864	.4013
9	.1633	.1741	.1852	.1967	.2084	.2204	.2327	.2452	.2580	.2709
10	.0910	.0984	.1061	.1142	.1226	.1314	.1404	.1498	.1595	.1695
11	.0469	.0514	.0563	.0614	.0668	.0726	.0786	.0849	.0916	.0985
12	.0224	.0250	.0277	.0307	.0339	.0373	.0409	.0448	.0490	.0533
13	.0100	.0113	.0127	.0143	.0160	.0179	.0199	.0221	.0245	.0270
14	.0042	.0048	.0055	.0062	.0071	.0080	.0091	.0102	.0115	.0128
15	.0016	.0019	.0022	.0026	.0030	.0034	.0039	.0044	.0050	.0057
16	.0006	.0007	.0008	.0010	.0012	.0014	.0016	.0018	.0021	.0024
17	.0002	.0003	.0003	.0004	.0004	.0005	.0006	.0007	.0008	.0010
18	.0001	.0001	.0001	.0001	.0002	.0002	.0002	.0003	.0003	.0004
19	.0000	.0000	.0000	.0000	.0000	.0001	.0001	.0001	.0001	.0001

r	7.1	7.2	7.3	7.4	λ 7.5	7.6	7.7	7.8	7.9	8.0
1	.9992	.9993	.9993	.9994	.9994	.9995	.9995	.9996	.9996	.9997
2	.9933	.9939	.9944	.9949	.9953	.9957	.9961	.9964	.9967	.9970
3	.9725	.9745	.9764	.9781	.9797	.9812	.9826	.9839	.9851	.9862
4	.9233	.9281	.9326	.9368	.9409	.9446	.9482	.9515	.9547	.9576
5	.8359	.8445	.8527	.8605	.8679	.8751	.8819	.8883	.8945	.9004
6	.7119	.7241	.7360	.7474	.7586	.7693	.7797	.7897	.7994	.8088
7	.5651	.5796	.5940	.6080	.6218	.6354	.6486	.6616	.6743	.6866
8	.4162	.4311	.4459	.4607	.4754	.4900	.5044	.5188	.5330	.5470
9	.2840	.2973	.3108	.3243	.3380	.3518	.3657	.3796	.3935	.4075
10	.1798	.1903	.2012	.2123	.2236	.2351	.2469	.2589	.2710	.2834
11	.1058	.1133	.1212	.1293	.1378	.1465	.1555	.1648	.1743	.1841
12	.0580	.0629	.0681	.0735	.0792	.0852	.0915	.0980	.1048	.1119
13	.0297	.0327	.0358	.0391	.0427	.0464	.0504	.0546	.0591	.0638
14	.0143	.0159	.0176	.0195	.0216	.0238	.0261	.0286	.0313	.0342
15	.0065	.0073	.0082	.0092	.0103	.0114	.0127	.0141	.0156	.0173
16	.0028	.0031	.0036	.0041	.0046	.0052	.0059	.0066	.0074	.0082
17	.0011	.0013	.0015	.0017	.0020	.0022	.0026	.0029	.0033	.0037
18	.0004	.0005	.0006	.0007	.0008	.0009	.0011	.0012	.0014	.0016
19	.0002	.0002	.0002	.0003	.0003	.0004	.0004	.0005	.0006	.0006
20	.0001	.0001	.0001	.0001	.0001	.0001	.0002	.0002	.0002	.0003
21	.0000	.0000	.0000	.0000	.0000	.0000	.0001	.0001	.0001	.0001

r	8.1	8.2	8.3	8.4	λ 8.5	8.6	8.7	8.8	8.9	9.0
1	.9997	.9997	.9998	.9998	.9998	.9998	.9998	.9998	.9999	.9999
2	.9972	.9975	.9977	.9979	.9981	.9982	.9984	.9985	.9986	.9988
3	.9873	.9882	.9891	.9900	.9907	.9914	.9921	.9927	.9932	.9938
4	.9604	.9630	.9654	.9677	.9699	.9719	.9738	.9756	.9772	.9788
5	.9060	.9113	.9163	.9211	.9256	.9299	.9340	.9379	.9416	.9450
6	.8178	.8264	.8347	.8427	.8504	.8578	.8648	.8716	.8781	.8843
7	.6987	.7104	.7219	.7330	.7438	.7543	.7645	.7744	.7840	.7932
8	.5609	.5746	.5881	.6013	.6144	.6272	.6398	.6522	.6643	.6761
9	.4214	.4353	.4493	.4631	.4769	.4906	.5042	.5177	.5311	.5443
10	.2959	.3085	.3212	.3341	.3470	.3600	.3731	.3863	.3994	.4126
11	.1942	.2044	.2150	.2257	.2366	.2478	.2591	.2706	.2822	.2940
12	.1193	.1269	.1348	.1429	.1513	.1600	.1689	.1780	.1874	.1970
13	.0687	.0739	.0793	.0850	.0909	.0971	.1035	.1102	.1171	.1242
14	.0372	.0405	.0439	.0476	.0514	.0555	.0597	.0642	.0689	.0738
15	.0190	.0209	.0229	.0251	.0274	.0299	.0325	.0353	.0383	.0415
16	.0092	.0102	.0113	.0125	.0138	.0152	.0168	.0184	.0202	.0220
17	.0042	.0047	.0053	.0059	.0066	.0074	.0082	.0091	.0101	.0111
18	.0018	.0021	.0023	.0027	.0030	.0034	.0038	.0043	.0048	.0053
19	.0007	.0009	.0010	.0011	.0013	.0015	.0017	.0019	.0021	.0024
20	.0003	.0003	.0004	.0005	.0005	.0006	.0007	.0008	.0009	.0011
21	.0001	.0001	.0002	.0002	.0002	.0002	.0003	.0003	.0004	.0004
22	.0000	.0000	.0001	.0001	.0001	.0001	.0001	.0001	.0001	.0002
23	.0000	.0000	.0000	.0000	.0000	.0000	.0000	.0000	.0001	.0001

r	9.1	9.2	9.3	9.4	λ 9.5	9.6	9.7	9.8	9.9	10.0
1	.9999	.9999	.9999	.9999	.9999	.9999	.9999	.9999	.9999	1.0000
2	.9989	.9990	.9991	.9991	.9992	.9993	.9993	.9994	.9995	.9995
3	.9942	.9947	.9951	.9955	.9958	.9962	.9965	.9967	.9970	.9972
4	.9802	.9816	.9828	.9840	.9851	.9862	.9871	.9880	.9889	.9897
5	.9483	.9514	.9544	.9571	.9597	.9622	.9645	.9667	.9688	.9707
6	.8902	.8959	.9014	.9065	.9115	.9162	.9207	.9250	.9290	.9329
7	.8022	.8108	.8192	.8273	.8351	.8426	.8498	.8567	.8634	.8699
8	.6877	.6990	.7100	.7208	.7313	.7416	.7515	.7612	.7706	.7798
9	.5574	.5704	.5832	.5958	.6082	.6204	.6324	.6442	.6558	.6672
10	.4258	.4389	.4521	.4651	.4782	.4911	.5040	.5168	.5295	.5421
11	.3059	.3180	.3301	.3424	.3547	.3671	.3795	.3920	.4045	.4170
12	.2068	.2168	.2270	.2374	.2480	.2588	.2697	.2807	.2919	.3032
13	.1316	.1393	.1471	.1552	.1636	.1721	.1809	.1899	.1991	.2084
14	.0790	.0844	.0900	.0958	.1019	.1081	.1147	.1214	.1284	.1355
15	.0448	.0483	.0520	.0559	.0600	.0643	.0688	.0735	.0784	.0835

r	9.1	9.2	9.3	9.4	λ 9.5	9.6	9.7	9.8	9.9	10.0
16	.0240	.0262	.0285	.0309	.0335	.0362	.0391	.0421	.0454	.0487
17	.0122	.0135	.0148	.0162	.0177	.0194	.0211	.0230	.0249	.0270
18	.0059	.0066	.0073	.0081	.0089	.0098	.0108	.0119	.0130	.0143
19	.0027	.0031	.0034	.0038	.0043	.0048	.0053	.0059	.0065	.0072
20	.0012	.0014	.0015	.0017	.0020	.0022	.0025	.0028	.0031	.0035
21	.0005	.0006	.0007	.0008	.0009	.0010	.0011	.0012	.0014	.0016
22	.0002	.0002	.0003	.0003	.0004	.0004	.0005	.0005	.0006	.0007
23	.0001	.0001	.0001	.0001	.0001	.0002	.0002	.0002	.0003	.0003
24	.0000	.0000	.0000	.0000	.0001	.0001	.0001	.0001	.0001	.0001

r	11.0	12.0	13.0	14.0	λ 15.0	16.0	17.0	18.0	19.0	20.0
1	1.0000	1.0000	1.0000	1.0000	1.0000	1.0000	1.0000	1.0000	1.0000	1.0000
2	.9998	.9999	1.0000	1.0000	1.0000	1.0000	1.0000	1.0000	1.0000	1.0000
3	.9988	.9995	.9998	.9999	1.0000	1.0000	1.0000	1.0000	1.0000	1.0000
4	.9951	.9977	.9989	.9995	.9998	.9999	1.0000	1.0000	1.0000	1.0000
5	.9849	.9924	.9963	.9982	.9991	.9996	.9998	.9999	1.0000	1.0000
6	.9625	.9797	.9893	.9945	.9972	.9986	.9993	.9997	.9998	.9999
7	.9214	.9542	.9741	.9858	.9924	.9960	.9979	.9990	.9995	.9997
8	.8568	.9105	.9460	.9684	.9820	.9900	.9946	.9971	.9985	.9992
9	.7680	.8450	.9002	.9379	.9626	.9780	.9874	.9929	.9961	.9979
10	.6595	.7576	.8342	.8906	.9301	.9567	.9739	.9846	.9911	.9950
11	.5401	.6528	.7483	.8243	.8815	.9226	.9509	.9696	.9817	.9892
12	.4207	.5384	.6468	.7400	.8152	.8730	.9153	.9451	.9653	.9786
13	.3113	.4240	.5369	.6415	.7324	.8069	.8650	.9083	.9394	.9610
14	.2187	.3185	.4270	.5356	.6368	.7255	.7991	.8574	.9016	.9339
15	.1460	.2280	.3249	.4296	.5343	.6325	.7192	.7919	.8502	.8951
16	.0926	.1556	.2364	.3306	.4319	.5333	.6285	.7133	.7852	.8435
17	.0559	.1013	.1645	.2441	.3359	.4340	.5323	.6249	.7080	.7789
18	.0322	.0630	.1095	.1728	.2511	.3407	.4360	.5314	.6216	.7030
19	.0177	.0374	.0698	.1174	.1805	.2576	.3450	.4378	.5305	.6186
20	.0093	.0213	.0427	.0765	.1248	.1877	.2637	.3491	.4394	.5297
21	.0047	.0116	.0250	.0479	.0830	.1318	.1945	.2693	.3528	.4409
22	.0022	.0061	.0141	.0288	.0531	.0892	.1385	.2009	.2745	.3563
23	.0010	.0030	.0076	.0167	.0327	.0582	.0953	.1449	.2069	.2794
24	.0005	.0015	.0040	.0093	.0195	.0367	.0633	.1011	.1510	.2125
25	.0002	.0007	.0020	.0050	.0112	.0223	.0406	.0683	.1067	.1568
26	.0001	.0003	.0010	.0026	.0062	.0131	.0252	.0446	.0731	.1122
27	.0000	.0001	.0004	.0013	.0033	.0075	.0152	.0282	.0486	.0779
28	.0000	.0001	.0002	.0006	.0017	.0041	.0088	.0173	.0313	.0525
29	.0000	.0000	.0001	.0003	.0009	.0022	.0050	.0103	.0195	.0343
30	.0000	.0000	.0000	.0001	.0004	.0011	.0027	.0059	.0118	.0218
31	.0000	.0000	.0000	.0001	.0002	.0006	.0014	.0033	.0070	.0135
32	.0000	.0000	.0000	.0000	.0001	.0003	.0007	.0018	.0040	.0081
33	.0000	.0000	.0000	.0000	.0000	.0001	.0004	.0010	.0022	.0047
34	.0000	.0000	.0000	.0000	.0000	.0001	.0002	.0005	.0012	.0027
35	.0000	.0000	.0000	.0000	.0000	.0000	.0001	.0002	.0006	.0015
36	.0000	.0000	.0000	.0000	.0000	.0000	.0000	.0001	.0003	.0008
37	.0000	.0000	.0000	.0000	.0000	.0000	.0000	.0001	.0002	.0004
38	.0000	.0000	.0000	.0000	.0000	.0000	.0000	.0000	.0001	.0002
39	.0000	.0000	.0000	.0000	.0000	.0000	.0000	.0000	.0000	.0001

r	25.0	30.0	40.0	50.0	λ 75.0	100.0
1	1.0000	1.0000	1.0000	1.0000	1.0000	1.0000
2	1.0000	1.0000	1.0000	1.0000	1.0000	1.0000
3	1.0000	1.0000	1.0000	1.0000	1.0000	1.0000
4	1.0000	1.0000	1.0000	1.0000	1.0000	1.0000
5	1.0000	1.0000	1.0000	1.0000	1.0000	1.0000
6	1.0000	1.0000	1.0000	1.0000	1.0000	1.0000
7	1.0000	1.0000	1.0000	1.0000	1.0000	1.0000
8	1.0000	1.0000	1.0000	1.0000	1.0000	1.0000
9	.9999	1.0000	1.0000	1.0000	1.0000	1.0000
10	.9998	1.0000	1.0000	1.0000	1.0000	1.0000
11	.9994	1.0000	1.0000	1.0000	1.0000	1.0000
12	.9986	.9999	1.0000	1.0000	1.0000	1.0000
13	.9969	.9998	1.0000	1.0000	1.0000	1.0000
14	.9935	.9996	1.0000	1.0000	1.0000	1.0000
15	.9876	.9991	1.0000	1.0000	1.0000	1.0000
16	.9777	.9981	1.0000	1.0000	1.0000	1.0000
17	.9623	.9961	1.0000	1.0000	1.0000	1.0000
18	.9395	.9927	1.0000	1.0000	1.0000	1.0000
19	.9080	.9871	.9999	1.0000	1.0000	1.0000
20	.8664	.9781	.9998	1.0000	1.0000	1.0000
21	.8145	.9647	.9996	1.0000	1.0000	1.0000
22	.7527	.9456	.9993	1.0000	1.0000	1.0000
23	.6825	.9194	.9986	1.0000	1.0000	1.0000
24	.6061	.8854	.9974	1.0000	1.0000	1.0000
25	.5266	.8428	.9955	1.0000	1.0000	1.0000
26	.4471	.7916	.9924	.9999	1.0000	1.0000
27	.3706	.7327	.9877	.9999	1.0000	1.0000
28	.2998	.6671	.9807	.9997	1.0000	1.0000
29	.2366	.5969	.9706	.9995	1.0000	1.0000
30	.1821	.5243	.9568	.9991	1.0000	1.0000
31	.1367	.4516	.9383	.9984	1.0000	1.0000
32	.1001	.3814	.9145	.9973	1.0000	1.0000
33	.0715	.3155	.8847	.9956	1.0000	1.0000
34	.0498	.2555	.8486	.9930	1.0000	1.0000
35	.0338	.2027	.8061	.9892	1.0000	1.0000
36	.0225	.1574	.7576	.9838	1.0000	1.0000
37	.0145	.1196	.7037	.9762	1.0000	1.0000
38	.0092	.0890	.6453	.9660	1.0000	1.0000
39	.0057	.0648	.5840	.9526	1.0000	1.0000
40	.0034	.0462	.5210	.9354	1.0000	1.0000
41	.0020	.0323	.4581	.9139	1.0000	1.0000
42	.0012	.0221	.3967	.8877	1.0000	1.0000
43	.0007	.0148	.3382	.8565	1.0000	1.0000
44	.0004	.0097	.2838	.8202	1.0000	1.0000
45	.0002	.0063	.2343	.7790	.9999	1.0000
46	.0001	.0040	.1903	.7331	.9999	1.0000
47	.0001	.0024	.1521	.6833	.9998	1.0000
48	.0000	.0015	.1196	.6303	.9996	1.0000
49	.0000	.0009	.0925	.5751	.9994	1.0000
50	.0000	.0005	.0703	.5188	.9991	1.0000
51	.0000	.0003	.0526	.4625	.9986	1.0000
52	.0000	.0002	.0387	.4073	.9979	1.0000
53	.0000	.0001	.0280	.3542	.9968	1.0000
54	.0000	.0000	.0200	.3041	.9953	1.0000
55	.0000	.0000	.0140	.2577	.9932	1.0000
56	.0000	.0000	.0097	.2155	.9904	1.0000
57	.0000	.0000	.0066	.1779	.9866	1.0000
58	.0000	.0000	.0044	.1449	.9816	1.0000
59	.0000	.0000	.0029	.1164	.9751	1.0000
60	.0000	.0000	.0019	.0923	.9669	1.0000
61	.0000	.0000	.0012	.0722	.9567	1.0000
62	.0000	.0000	.0007	.0557	.9440	1.0000
63	.0000	.0000	.0005	.0424	.9288	1.0000
64	.0000	.0000	.0003	.0318	.9106	1.0000
65	.0000	.0000	.0002	.0236	.8893	.9999
66	.0000	.0000	.0001	.0173	.8647	.9999
67	.0000	.0000	.0001	.0125	.8368	.9998
68	.0000	.0000	.0000	.0089	.8055	.9997
69	.0000	.0000	.0000	.0062	.7710	.9996
70	.0000	.0000	.0000	.0043	.7335	.9993

r	36.0	30.0	40.0	50.0	λ 75.0	100.0
71	.0000	.0000	.0000	.0030	.6934	.9990
72	.0000	.0000	.0000	.0020	.6510	.9986
73	.0000	.0000	.0000	.0013	.6068	.9980
74	.0000	.0000	.0000	.0009	.5614	.9972
75	.0000	.0000	.0000	.0006	.5153	.9960
76	.0000	.0000	.0000	.0004	.4693	.9945
77	.0000	.0000	.0000	.0002	.4239	.9926
78	.0000	.0000	.0000	.0001	.3797	.9900
79	.0000	.0000	.0000	.0001	.3372	.9867
80	.0000	.0000	.0000	.0000	.2968	.9825
81	.0000	.0000	.0000	.0000	.2589	.9774
82	.0000	.0000	.0000	.0000	.2239	.9709
83	.0000	.0000	.0000	.0000	.1918	.9631
84	.0000	.0000	.0000	.0000	.1629	.9537
85	.0000	.0000	.0000	.0000	.1370	.9425
86	.0000	.0000	.0000	.0000	.1142	.9292
87	.0000	.0000	.0000	.0000	.0943	.9139
88	.0000	.0000	.0000	.0000	.0771	.8962
89	.0000	.0000	.0000	.0000	.0625	.8762
90	.0000	.0000	.0000	.0000	.0502	.8537
91	.0000	.0000	.0000	.0000	.0399	.8286
92	.0000	.0000	.0000	.0000	.0314	.8011
93	.0000	.0000	.0000	.0000	.0245	.7712
94	.0000	.0000	.0000	.0000	.0190	.7390
95	.0000	.0000	.0000	.0000	.0145	.7048
96	.0000	.0000	.0000	.0000	.0110	.6688
97	.0000	.0000	.0000	.0000	.0083	.6313
98	.0000	.0000	.0000	.0000	.0062	.5926
99	.0000	.0000	.0000	.0000	.0046	.5532
100	.0000	.0000	.0000	.0000	.0033	.5133
101	.0000	.0000	.0000	.0000	.0024	.4734
102	.0000	.0000	.0000	.0000	.0017	.4340
103	.0000	.0000	.0000	.0000	.0012	.3953
104	.0000	.0000	.0000	.0000	.0009	.3577
105	.0000	.0000	.0000	.0000	.0006	.3216
106	.0000	.0000	.0000	.0000	.0004	.2872
107	.0000	.0000	.0000	.0000	.0003	.2547
108	.0000	.0000	.0000	.0000	.0002	.2244
109	.0000	.0000	.0000	.0000	.0001	.1963
110	.0000	.0000	.0000	.0000	.0001	.1705
111	.0000	.0000	.0000	.0000	.0000	.1471
112	.0000	.0000	.0000	.0000	.0000	.1260
113	.0000	.0000	.0000	.0000	.0000	.1072
114	.0000	.0000	.0000	.0000	.0000	.0905
115	.0000	.0000	.0000	.0000	.0000	.0759
116	.0000	.0000	.0000	.0000	.0000	.0632
117	.0000	.0000	.0000	.0000	.0000	.0522
118	.0000	.0000	.0000	.0000	.0000	.0428
119	.0000	.0000	.0000	.0000	.0000	.0349
120	.0000	.0000	.0000	.0000	.0000	.0282
121	.0000	.0000	.0000	.0000	.0000	.0227
122	.0000	.0000	.0000	.0000	.0000	.0181
123	.0000	.0000	.0000	.0000	.0000	.0143
124	.0000	.0000	.0000	.0000	.0000	.0112
125	.0000	.0000	.0000	.0000	.0000	.0088
126	.0000	.0000	.0000	.0000	.0000	.0068
127	.0000	.0000	.0000	.0000	.0000	.0052
128	.0000	.0000	.0000	.0000	.0000	.0040
129	.0000	.0000	.0000	.0000	.0000	.0030
130	.0000	.0000	.0000	.0000	.0000	.0023
131	.0000	.0000	.0000	.0000	.0000	.0017
132	.0000	.0000	.0000	.0000	.0000	.0012
133	.0000	.0000	.0000	.0000	.0000	.0009
134	.0000	.0000	.0000	.0000	.0000	.0007
135	.0000	.0000	.0000	.0000	.0000	.0005
136	.0000	.0000	.0000	.0000	.0000	.0003
137	.0000	.0000	.0000	.0000	.0000	.0002
138	.0000	.0000	.0000	.0000	.0000	.0002
139	.0000	.0000	.0000	.0000	.0000	.0001
140	.0000	.0000	.0000	.0000	.0000	.0001

AREAS AND ORDINATES OF THE NORMAL CURVE

Table of Areas
Column (2) Shows

Table of Ordinates
Column (3) Shows

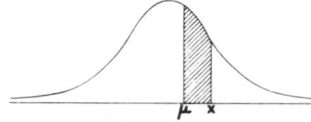

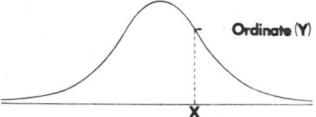

$\dfrac{X - \mu}{\sigma}$	Area under the curve between μ and X	Ordinate (Y) of the curve at X	$\dfrac{X - \mu}{\sigma}$	Area under the curve between μ and X	Ordinate (Y) of the curve at X
(1)	(2)	(3)	(1)	(2)	(3)
.00	.00000	.39894	.20	.07926	.39104
.01	.00399	.39892	.21	.08317	.39024
.02	.00798	.39886	.22	.08706	.38940
.03	.01197	.39876	.23	.09095	.38853
.04	.01595	.39862	.24	.09483	.38762
.05	.01994	.39844	.25	.09871	.38667
.06	.02392	.39822	.26	.10257	.38568
.07	.02790	.39797	.27	.10642	.38466
.08	.03188	.39767	.28	.11026	.38361
.09	.03586	.39733	.29	.11409	.38251
.10	.03983	.39695	.30	.11791	.38139
.11	.04380	.39654	.31	.12172	.38023
.12	.04776	.39608	.32	.12552	.37903
.13	.05172	.39559	.33	.12930	.37780
.14	.05567	.39505	.34	.13307	.37654
.15	.05962	.39448	.35	.13683	.37524
.16	.06356	.39387	.36	.14058	.37391
.17	.06749	.39322	.37	.14431	.37255
.18	.07142	.39253	.38	.14803	.37115
.19	.07535	.39181	.39	.15173	.36973

By permission from J. F. Kenney and E. S. Keeping, *Mathematics of Statistics*, *(Part I)*, Copyright 1954, D. Van Nostrand Company, Inc., Princeton, N. J.

AREAS AND ORDINATES OF THE NORMAL CURVE

$\frac{X - \mu}{\sigma}$	Area under the curve between μ and X	Ordinate (Y) of the curve at X	$\frac{X - \mu}{\sigma}$	Area under the curve between μ and X	Ordinate (Y) of the curve at X
(1)	(2)	(3)	(1)	(2)	(3)
.40	.15542	.36827	.90	.31594	.26609
.41	.15910	.36678	.91	.31859	.26369
.42	.16276	.36526	.92	.32121	.26129
.43	.16640	.36371	.93	.32381	.25888
.44	.17003	.36213	.94	.32639	.25647
.45	.17364	.36053	.95	.32894	.25406
.46	.17724	.35889	.96	.33147	.25164
.47	.18082	.35723	.97	.33398	.24923
.48	.18439	.35553	.98	.33646	.24681
.49	.18793	.35381	.99	.33891	.24439
.50	.19146	.35207	1.00	.34134	.24197
.51	.19497	.35029	1.01	.34375	.23955
.52	.19847	.34849	1.02	.34614	.23713
.53	.20194	.34667	1.03	.34850	.23471
.54	.20540	.34482	1.04	.35083	.23230
.55	.20884	.34294	1.05	.35314	.22988
.56	.21226	.34105	1.06	.35543	.22747
.57	.21566	.33912	1.07	.35769	.22506
.58	.21904	.33718	1.08	.35993	.22265
.59	.22240	.33521	1.09	.36214	.22025
.60	.22575	.33322	1.10	.36433	.21785
.61	.22907	.33121	1.11	.36650	.21546
.62	.23237	.32918	1.12	.36864	.21307
.63	.23565	.32713	1.13	.37076	.21069
.64	.23891	.32506	1.14	.37286	.20831
.65	.24215	.32297	1.15	.37493	.20594
.66	.24537	.32086	1.16	.37698	.20357
.67	.24857	.31874	1.17	.37900	.20121
.68	.25175	.31659	1.18	.38100	.19886
.69	.25490	.31443	1.19	.38298	.19652
.70	.25804	.31225	1.20	.38493	.19419
.71	.26115	.31006	1.21	.38686	.19186
.72	.26424	.30785	1.22	.38877	.18954
.73	.26730	.30563	1.23	.39065	.18724
.74	.27035	.30339	1.24	.39251	.18494
.75	.27337	.30114	1.25	.39435	.18265
.76	.27637	.29887	1.26	.39617	.18037
.77	.27935	.29659	1.27	.39796	.17810
.78	.28230	.29431	1.28	.39973	.17585
.79	.28524	.29200	1.29	.40147	.17360
.80	.28814	.28969	1.30	.40320	.17137
.81	.29103	.28737	1.31	.40490	.16915
.82	.29389	.28504	1.32	.40658	.16694
.83	.29673	.28269	1.33	.40824	.16474
.84	.29955	.28034	1.34	.40988	.16256
.85	.30234	.27798	1.35	.41149	.16038
.86	.30511	.27562	1.36	.41309	.15822
.87	.30785	.27324	1.37	.41466	.15608
.88	.31057	.27086	1.38	.41621	.15395
.89	.31327	.26848	1.39	.41774	.15183

AREAS AND ORDINATES OF THE NORMAL CURVE

$\dfrac{X - \mu}{\sigma}$	Area under the curve between μ and X	Ordinate (Y) of the curve at X	$\dfrac{X - \mu}{\sigma}$	Area under the curve between μ and X	Ordinate (Y) of the curve at X
(1)	(2)	(3)	(1)	(2)	(3)
1.40	.41924	.14973	1.90	.47128	.06562
1.41	.42073	.14764	1.91	.47193	.06438
1.42	.42220	.14556	1.92	.47257	.06316
1.43	.42364	.14350	1.93	.47320	.06195
1.44	.42507	.14146	1.94	.47381	.06077
1.45	.42647	.13943	1.95	.47441	.05959
1.46	.42786	.13742	1.96	.47500	.05844
1.47	.42922	.13542	1.97	.47558	.05730
1.48	.43056	.13344	1.98	.47615	.05618
1.49	.43189	.13147	1.99	.47670	.05508
1.50	.43319	.12952	2.00	.47725	.05399
1.51	.43448	.12758	2.01	.47778	.05292
1.52	.43574	.12566	2.02	.47831	.05186
1.53	.43699	.12376	2.03	.47882	.05082
1.54	.43822	.12188	2.04	.47932	.04980
1.55	.43943	.12001	2.05	.47982	.04879
1.56	.44062	.11816	2.06	.48030	.04780
1.57	.44179	.11632	2.07	.48077	.04682
1.58	.44295	.11450	2.08	.48124	.04586
1.59	.44408	.11270	2.09	.48169	.04491
1.60	.44520	.11092	2.10	.48214	.04398
1.61	.44630	.10915	2.11	.48257	.04307
1.62	.44738	.10741	2.12	.48300	.04217
1.63	.44845	.10567	2.13	.48341	.04128
1.64	.44950	.10396	2.14	.48382	.04041
1.65	.45053	.10226	2.15	.48422	.03955
1.66	.45154	.10059	2.16	.48461	.03871
1.67	.45254	.09893	2.17	.48500	.03788
1.68	.45352	.09728	2.18	.48537	.03706
1.69	.45449	.09566	2.19	.48574	.03626
1.70	.45543	.09405	2.20	.48610	.03547
1.71	.45637	.09246	2.21	.48645	.03470
1.72	.45728	.09089	2.22	.48679	.03394
1.73	.45818	.08933	2.23	.48713	.03319
1.74	.45907	.08780	2.24	.48745	.03246
1.75	.45994	.08628	2.25	.48778	.03174
1.76	.46080	.08478	2.26	.48809	.03103
1.77	.46164	.08329	2.27	.48840	.03034
1.78	.46246	.08183	2.28	.48870	.02965
1.79	.46327	.08038	2.29	.48899	.02898
1.80	.46407	.07895	2.30	.48928	.02833
1.81	.46485	.07754	2.31	.48956	.02768
1.82	.46562	.07614	2.32	.48983	.02705
1.83	.46638	.07477	2.33	.49010	.02643
1.84	.46712	.07341	2.34	.49036	.02582
1.85	.46784	.07206	2.35	.49064	.02522
1.86	.46856	.07074	2.36	.49086	.02463
1.87	.46926	.06943	2.37	.49111	.02406
1.88	.46995	.06814	2.38	.49134	.02349
1.89	.47062	.06687	2.39	.49158	.02294

AREAS AND ORDINATES OF THE NORMAL CURVE

$\frac{X - \mu}{\sigma}$	Area under the curve between μ and X	Ordinate (Y) of the curve at X	$\frac{X - \mu}{\sigma}$	Area under the curve between μ and X	Ordinate (Y) of the curve at X
(1)	(2)	(3)	(1)	(2)	(3)
2.40	.49180	.02239	2.90	.49813	.00595
2.41	.49202	.02186	2.91	.49819	.00578
2.42	.49224	.02134	2.92	.49825	.00562
2.43	.49245	.02083	2.93	.49831	.00545
2.44	.49266	.02033	2.94	.49836	.00530
2.45	.49286	.01984	2.95	.49841	.00514
2.46	.49305	.01936	2.96	.49846	.00499
2.47	.49324	.01889	2.97	.49851	.00485
2.48	.49343	.01842	2.98	.49856	.00471
2.49	.49361	.01797	2.99	.49861	.00457
2.50	.49379	.01753	3.00	.49865	.00443
2.51	.49396	.01709	3.01	.49869	.00430
2.52	.49413	.01667	3.02	.49874	.00417
2.53	.49430	.01625	3.03	.49878	.00405
2.54	.49446	.01585	3.04	.49882	.00393
2.55	.49461	.01545	3.05	.49886	.00381
2.56	.49477	.01506	3.06	.49889	.00370
2.57	.49492	.01468	3.07	.49893	.00358
2.58	.49506	.01431	3.08	.49897	.00348
2.59	.49520	.01394	3.09	.49900	.00337
2.60	.49534	.01358	3.10	.49903	.00327
2.61	.49547	.01323	3.11	.49906	.00317
2.62	.49560	.01289	3.12	.49910	.00307
2.63	.49573	.01256	3.13	.49913	.00298
2.64	.49585	.01223	3.14	.49916	.00288
2.65	.49598	.01191	3.15	.49918	.00279
2.66	.49609	.01160	3.16	.49921	.00271
2.67	.49621	.01130	3.17	.49924	.00262
2.68	.49632	.01100	3.18	.49926	.00254
2.69	.49643	.01071	3.19	.49929	.00246
2.70	.49653	.01042	3.20	.49931	.00238
2.71	.49664	.01014	3.21	.49934	.00231
2.72	.49674	.00987	3.22	.49936	.00224
2.73	.49683	.00961	3.23	.49938	.00216
2.74	.49693	.00935	3.24	.49940	.00210
2.75	.49702	.00909	3.25	.49942	.00203
2.76	.49711	.00885	3.26	.49944	.00196
2.77	.49720	.00861	3.27	.49946	.00190
2.78	.49728	.00837	3.28	.49948	.00184
2.79	.49736	.00814	3.29	.49950	.00178
2.80	.49744	.00792	3.30	.49952	.00172
2.81	.49752	.00770	3.31	.49953	.00167
2.82	.49760	.00748	3.32	.49955	.00161
2.83	.49767	.00727	3.33	.49957	.00156
2.84	.49774	.00707	3.34	.49958	.00151
2.85	.49781	.00687	3.35	.49960	.00146
2.86	.49788	.00668	3.36	.49961	.00141
2.87	.49795	.00649	3.37	.49962	.00136
2.88	.49801	.00631	3.38	.49964	.00132
2.89	.49807	.00613	3.39	.49965	.00127

AREAS AND ORDINATES OF THE NORMAL CURVE

$\frac{X - \mu}{\sigma}$	Area under the curve between μ and X	Ordinate (Y) of the curve at X	$\frac{X - \mu}{\sigma}$	Area under the curve between μ and X	Ordinate (Y) of the curve at X
(1)	(2)	(3)	(1)	(2)	(3)
3.40	.49966	.00123	3.70	.49989	.00042
3.41	.49968	.00119	3.71	.49990	.00041
3.42	.49969	.00115	3.72	.49990	.00039
3.43	.49970	.00111	3.73	.49990	.00038
3.44	.49971	.00107	3.74	.49991	.00037
3.45	.49972	.00104	3.75	.49991	.00035
3.46	.49973	.00100	3.76	.49992	.00034
3.47	.49974	.00097	3.77	.49992	.00033
3.48	.49975	.00094	3.78	.49992	.00031
3.49	.49976	.00090	3.79	.49992	.00030
3.50	.49977	.00087	3.80	.49993	.00029
3.51	.49978	.00084	3.81	.49993	.00028
3.52	.49978	.00081	3.82	.49993	.00027
3.53	.49979	.00079	3.83	.49994	.00026
3.54	.49980	.00076	3.84	.49994	.00025
3.55	.49981	.00073	3.85	.49994	.00024
3.56	.49981	.00071	3.86	.49994	.00023
3.57	.49982	.00068	3.87	.49995	.00022
3.58	.49983	.00066	3.88	.49995	.00021
3.59	.49983	.00063	3.89	.49995	.00021
3.60	.49984	.00061	3.90	.49995	.00020
3.61	.49985	.00059	3.91	.49995	.00019
3.62	.49985	.00057	3.92	.49996	.00018
3.63	.49986	.00055	3.93	.49996	.00018
3.64	.49986	.00053	3.94	.49996	.00017
3.65	.49987	.00051	3.95	.49996	.00016
3.66	.49987	.00049	3.96	.49996	.00016
3.67	.49988	.00047	3.97	.49996	.00015
3.68	.49988	.00046	3.98	.49997	.00014
3.69	.49989	.00044	3.99	.49997	.00014

Areas in One Tail of the Normal Curve at Selected Values of z

This table shows the black area:

or

$\frac{x}{s}$ or $\frac{x}{z}$	.00	.01	.02	.03	.04	.05	.06	.07	.08	.09
0.0	.5000	.4960	.4920	.4880	.4840	.4801	.4761	.4721	.4681	.4641
0.1	.4602	.4562	.4522	.4483	.4443	.4404	.4364	.4325	.4286	.4247
0.2	.4207	.4168	.4129	.4090	.4052	.4013	.3974	.3936	.3897	.3859
0.3	.3821	.3783	.3745	.3707	.3669	.3632	.3594	.3557	.3520	.3483
0.4	.3446	.3409	.3372	.3336	.3300	.3264	.3228	.3192	.3156	.3121
0.5	.3085	.3050	.3015	.2981	.2946	.2912	.2877	.2843	.2810	.2776
0.6	.2743	.2709	.2676	.2643	.2611	.2578	.2546	.2514	.2483	.2451
0.7	.2420	.2389	.2358	.2327	.2296	.2266	.2236	.2206	.2177	.2148
0.8	.2119	.2090	.2061	.2033	.2005	.1977	.1949	.1922	.1894	.1867
0.9	.1841	.1814	.1788	.1762	.1736	.1711	.1685	.1660	.1635	.1611
1.0	.1587	.1562	.1539	.1515	.1492	.1469	.1446	.1423	.1401	.1379
1.1	.1357	.1335	.1314	.1292	.1271	.1251	.1230	.1210	.1190	.1170
1.2	.1151	.1131	.1112	.1093	.1075	.1056	.1038	.1020	.1003	.0985
1.3	.0968	.0951	.0934	.0918	.0901	.0885	.0869	.0853	.0838	.0823
1.4	.0808	.0793	.0778	.0764	.0749	.0735	.0721	.0708	.0694	.0681
1.5	.0668	.0655	.0643	.0630	.0618	.0606	.0594	.0582	.0571	.0559
1.6	.0548	.0537	.0526	.0516	.0505	.0495	.0485	.0475	.0465	.0455
1.7	.0446	.0436	.0427	.0418	.0409	.0401	.0392	.0384	.0375	.0367
1.8	.0359	.0351	.0344	.0336	.0329	.0322	.0314	.0307	.0301	.0294
1.9	.0287	.0281	.0274	.0268	.0262	.0256	.0250	.0244	.0239	.0233
2.0	.0228	.0222	.0217	.0212	.0207	.0202	.0197	.0192	.0188	.0183
2.1	.0179	.0174	.0170	.0166	.0162	.0158	.0154	.0150	.0146	.0143
2.2	.0139	.0136	.0132	.0129	.0125	.0122	.0119	.0116	.0113	.0110
2.3	.0107	.0104	.0102	.00990	.00964	.00939	.00914	.00889	.00866	.00842
2.4	.00820	.00798	.00776	.00755	.00734	.00714	.00695	.00676	.00657	.00639
2.5	.00621	.00604	.00587	.00570	.00554	.00539	.00523	.00508	.00494	.00480
2.6	.00466	.00453	.00440	.00427	.00415	.00402	.00391	.00379	.00368	.00357
2.7	.00347	.00336	.00326	.00317	.00307	.00298	.00289	.00280	.00272	.00264
2.8	.00256	.00248	.00240	.00233	.00226	.00219	.00212	.00205	.00199	.00193
2.9	.00187	.00181	.00175	.00169	.00164	.00159	.00154	.00149	.00144	.00139

$\frac{x}{s}$ or $\frac{x}{z}$	.0	.1	.2	.3	.4	.5	.6	.7	.8	.9
3	.00135	$.0^3968$	$.0^3687$	$.0^3483$	$.0^3337$	$.0^3233$	$.0^3159$	$.0^3108$	$.0^4723$	$.0^4481$
4	$.0^4317$	$.0^4207$	$.0^4133$	$.0^5854$	$.0^5541$	$.0^5340$	$.0^5211$	$.0^5130$	$.0^6793$	$.0^6479$
5	$.0^6287$	$.0^6170$	$.0^7996$	$.0^7579$	$.0^7333$	$.0^7190$	$.0^7107$	$.0^8599$	$.0^8332$	$.0^8182$
6	$.0^9987$	$.0^9530$	$.0^9282$	$.0^9149$	$.0^{10}777$	$.0^{10}402$	$.0^{10}206$	$.0^{10}104$	$.0^{11}523$	$.0^{11}260$

From *Tables of Areas in Two Tails and in One Tail of the Normal Curve*, by Frederick E. Croxton. Copyright, 1949, by Prentice-Hall, Inc.

STUDENT'S *t* DISTRIBUTION

This table shows the values of black area:

d.f.	Level of Significance												
	0.9	0.8	0.7	0.6	0.5	0.4	0.3	0.2	0.1	0.05	0.02	0.01	0.001
1	.158	.325	.510	.727	1.000	1.376	1.963	3.078	6.314	12.706	31.821	63.657	636.619
2	.142	.289	.445	.617	.816	1.061	1.386	1.886	2.910	4.303	6.965	9.925	31.598
3	.137	.277	.424	.584	.765	.978	1.250	1.638	2.353	3.182	4.541	5.841	12.941
4	.134	.271	.414	.569	.741	.941	1.190	1.533	2.132	2.776	3.747	4.604	8.610
5	.132	.267	.408	.559	.727	.920	1.156	1.476	2.015	2.571	3.365	4.032	6.859
6	.131	.265	.404	.553	.718	.906	1.134	1.440	1.943	2.447	3.143	3.707	5.959
7	.130	.263	.402	.549	.711	.896	1.119	1.415	1.895	2.365	2.998	3.499	5.405
8	.130	.262	.399	.546	.706	.889	1.108	1.397	1.860	2.306	2.896	3.355	5.041
9	.129	.261	.398	.543	.703	.883	1.100	1.383	1.833	2.262	2.821	3.250	4.781
10	.129	.260	.397	.542	.700	.879	1.093	1.372	1.812	2.228	2.764	3.169	4.587
11	.129	.260	.396	.540	.697	.876	1.088	1.363	1.796	2.201	2.718	3.106	4.437
12	.128	.259	.395	.539	.695	.873	1.083	1.356	1.782	2.179	2.681	3.055	4.318
13	.128	.259	.394	.538	.694	.870	1.079	1.350	1.771	2.160	2.650	3.012	4.221
14	.128	.258	.393	.537	.692	.868	1.076	1.345	1.761	2.145	2.624	2.977	4.140
15	.128	.258	.393	.536	.691	.866	1.074	1.341	1.753	2.131	2.602	2.947	4.073
16	.128	.258	.392	.535	.690	.865	1.071	1.337	1.746	2.120	2.583	2.921	4.015
17	.128	.257	.392	.534	.689	.863	1.069	1.333	1.740	2.110	2.567	2.898	3.965
18	.127	.257	.392	.534	.688	.862	1.067	1.330	1.734	2.101	2.552	2.878	3.922
19	.127	.257	.391	.533	.688	.861	1.066	1.328	1.729	2.093	2.539	2.861	3.883
20	.127	.257	.391	.533	.687	.860	1.064	1.325	1.725	2.086	2.528	2.845	3.850
21	.127	.257	.391	.532	.686	.859	1.063	1.323	1.721	2.080	2.518	2.831	3.819
22	.127	.256	.390	.532	.686	.858	1.061	1.321	1.717	2.074	2.508	2.819	3.792
23	.127	.256	.390	.532	.685	.858	1.060	1.319	1.714	2.069	2.500	2.807	3.767
24	.127	.256	.390	.531	.685	.857	1.059	1.318	1.711	2.064	2.492	2.797	3.745
25	.127	.256	.390	.531	.684	.856	1.058	1.316	1.708	2.060	2.485	2.787	3.725
26	.127	.256	.390	.531	.684	.856	1.058	1.315	1.706	2.056	2.479	2.779	3.707
27	.127	.256	.389	.531	.684	.855	1.057	1.314	1.703	2.052	2.473	2.771	3.690
28	.127	.256	.389	.530	.683	.855	1.056	1.313	1.701	2.048	2.467	2.763	3.674
29	.127	.256	.389	.530	.683	.854	1.055	1.311	1.699	2.045	2.462	2.756	3.659
30	.127	.256	.389	.530	.683	.854	1.055	1.310	1.697	2.042	2.457	2.750	3.646
40	.126	.255	.388	.529	.681	.851	1.050	1.303	1.684	2.021	2.423	2.704	3.551
60	.126	.254	.387	.527	.679	.848	1.046	1.296	1.671	2.000	2.390	2.660	3.460
120	.126	.254	.386	.526	.677	.845	1.041	1.289	1.658	1.980	2.358	2.617	3.373
∞	.126	.253	.385	.524	.674	.842	1.036	1.282	1.645	1.960	2.326	2.576	3.291

This table is reprinted from *Table III* of Fisher and Yates: *Statistical Tables for Biological, Agricultural, and Medical Research,* published by Oliver and Boyd Ltd., Edinburgh, by permission of the authors and publishers.

CHI SQUARE PROBABILITY DISTRIBUTION

This table shows
the black area:

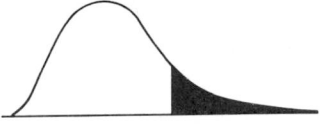

VALUES OF CHI SQUARE (χ^2)

d.f.	0.99	0.98	0.95	0.90	0.80	0.70
1	0.000157	0.000628	0.00393	0.0158	0.0642	0.148
2	0.0201	0.0404	0.103	0.211	0.446	0.713
3	0.115	0.185	0.352	0.584	1.005	1.424
4	0.297	0.429	0.711	1.064	1.649	2.195
5	0.554	0.752	1.145	1.610	2.343	3.000
6	0.872	1.134	1.635	2.204	3.070	3.828
7	1.239	1.564	2.167	2.833	3.822	4.671
8	1.646	2.032	2.733	3.490	4.594	5.527
9	2.088	2.532	3.325	4.168	5.380	6.393
10	2.558	3.059	3.940	4.865	6.179	7.267
11	3.053	3.609	4.575	5.578	6.989	8.148
12	3.571	4.178	5.226	6.304	7.807	9.034
13	4.107	4.765	5.892	7.042	8.634	9.926
14	4.660	5.368	6.571	7.790	9.467	10.821
15	5.229	5.985	7.261	8.547	10.307	11.721
16	5.812	6.614	7.962	9.312	11.152	12.624
17	6.408	7.255	8.672	10.085	12.002	13.531
18	7.015	7.906	9.390	10.865	12.857	14.440
19	7.633	8.567	10.117	11.651	13.716	15.352
20	8.260	9.237	10.851	12.443	14.578	16.266
21	8.897	9.915	11.591	13.240	15.445	17.182
22	9.542	10.600	12.338	14.041	16.314	18.101
23	10.196	11.293	13.091	14.848	17.187	19.021
24	10.856	11.992	13.848	15.659	18.062	19.943
25	11.524	12.697	14.611	16.473	18.940	20.867
26	12.198	13.409	15.379	17.292	19.820	21.792
27	12.879	14.125	16.151	18.114	20.703	22.719
28	13.565	14.847	16.928	18.939	21.588	23.647
29	14.256	15.574	17.708	19.768	22.475	24.577
30	14.953	16.306	18.493	20.599	23.364	25.508

From *Table III* of R. A. Fisher: *Statistical Methods for Research Workers*, Oliver & Boyd, Ltd., Edinburgh and London, 1936, by permission of the author and publishers.

† For larger values of *n*, the expression $\sqrt{2\chi^2} - \sqrt{2n-1}$ may be used as a normal deviate with unit variance.

VALUES OF CHI SQUARE (χ^2)

0.50	0.30	0.20	0.10	0.05	0.02	0.01
0.455	1.074	1.642	2.706	3.841	5.412	6.635
1.386	2.408	3.219	4.605	5.991	7.824	9.210
2.366	3.665	4.642	6.251	7.815	9.837	11.345
3.357	4.878	5.989	7.779	9.488	11.668	13.277
4.351	6.064	7.289	9.236	11.070	13.388	15.086
5.348	7.231	8.558	10.645	12.592	15.033	16.812
6.346	8.383	9.803	12.017	14.067	16.622	18.475
7.344	9.524	11.030	13.362	15.507	18.168	20.090
8.343	10.656	12.242	14.684	16.919	19.679	21.666
9.342	11.781	13.442	15.987	18.307	21.161	23.209
10.341	12.899	14.631	17.275	19.675	22.618	24.725
11.340	14.011	15.812	18.549	21.026	24.054	26.217
12.340	15.119	16.985	19.812	22.362	25.472	27.688
13.339	16.222	18.151	21.064	23.685	26.873	29.141
14.339	17.322	19.311	22.307	24.996	28.259	30.578
15.338	18.418	20.465	23.542	26.296	29.633	32.000
16.338	19.511	21.615	24.769	27.587	30.995	33.409
17.338	20.601	22.760	25.989	28.869	32.346	34.805
18.338	21.489	23.900	27.204	30.144	33.687	36.191
19.337	22.775	25.038	28.412	31.410	35.020	37.566
20.337	23.858	26.171	29.615	32.671	36.343	38.932
21.337	24.939	27.301	30.813	33.924	37.659	40.289
22.337	26.018	28.429	32.007	35.172	38.968	41.638
23.337	27.096	29.553	33.196	36.415	40.270	42.980
24.337	28.172	30.675	34.382	37.652	41.566	44.314
25.336	29.246	31.795	35.563	38.885	42.856	45.642
26.336	30.319	32.912	36.741	40.113	44.140	46.963
27.336	31.391	34.027	37.916	41.337	45.419	48.278
28.336	32.461	35.139	39.087	42.557	46.693	49.588
29.336	33.530	36.250	40.256	43.773	47.962	50.892

F DISTRIBUTION

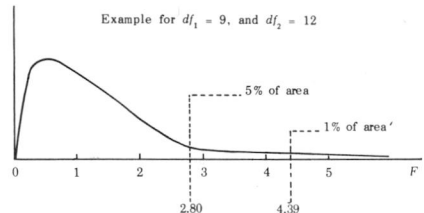

Example for $df_1 = 9$, and $df_2 = 12$

5% of area

1% of area'

2.80   4.39

PERCENTAGE POINTS OF THE F DISTRIBUTION*

df_2	P	$df_1 = 1$	2	3	4	5	6	7	8
	0.500	1.00	1.50	1.71	1.82	1.89	1.94	1.98	2.00
	0.100	39.9	49.5	53.6	55.8	57.2	58.2	58.9	59.4
	0.050	161	200	216	225	230	234	237	239
1	0.025	648	800	864	900	922	937	948	957
	0.010	4,050	5,000	5,400	5,620	5,760	5,860	5,930	5,980
	0.005	16,200	20,000	21,600	22,500	23,100	23,400	23,700	23,900
	0.001	405,284	500,000	540,379	562,500	576,405	585,937	...	598,144
	0.500	0.667	1.00	1.13	1.21	1.25	1.28	1.30	1.32
	0.100	8.53	9.00	9.16	9.24	9.29	9.33	9.35	9.37
	0.050	18.5	19.0	19.2	19.2	19.3	19.3	19.4	19.4
2	0.025	38.5	39.0	39.2	39.2	39.3	39.3	39.4	39.4
	0.010	98.5	99.0	99.2	99.2	99.3	99.3	99.4	99.4
	0.005	199	199	199	199	199	199	199	199
	0.001	998.5	999.0	999.2	999.2	999.3	999.3	...	999.4
	0.500	0.585	0.881	1.00	1.06	1.10	1.13	1.15	1.16
	0.100	5.54	5.46	5.39	5.34	5.31	5.28	5.27	5.25
	0.050	10.1	9.55	9.28	9.12	9.01	8.94	8.89	8.85
3	0.025	17.4	16.0	15.4	15.1	14.9	14.7	14.6	14.5
	0.010	34.1	30.8	29.5	28.7	28.2	27.9	27.7	27.5
	0.005	55.6	49.8	47.5	46.2	45.4	44.8	44.4	44.1
	0.001	167.5	148.5	141.1	137.1	134.6	132.8	...	130.6
	0.500	0.549	0.828	0.941	1.00	1.04	1.06	1.08	1.09
	0.100	4.54	4.32	4.19	4.11	4.05	4.01	3.98	3.95
	0.050	7.71	6.94	6.59	6.39	6.26	6.16	6.09	6.04
4	0.025	12.2	10.6	9.98	9.60	9.36	9.20	9.07	8.98
	0.010	21.2	18.0	16.7	16.0	15.5	15.2	15.0	14.8
	0.005	31.3	26.3	24.3	23.2	22.5	22.0	21.6	21.4
	0.001	74.1	61.3	56.2	53.4	51.7	50.5	...	49.0
	0.500	0.528	0.799	0.907	0.965	1.00	1.02	1.04	1.05
	0.100	4.06	3.78	3.62	3.52	3.45	3.40	3.37	3.34
	0.050	6.61	5.79	5.41	5.19	5.05	4.95	4.88	4.82
5	0.025	10.0	8.43	7.76	7.39	7.15	6.98	6.85	6.76
	0.010	16.3	13.3	12.1	11.4	11.0	10.7	10.5	10.3
	0.005	22.8	18.3	16.5	15.6	14.9	14.5	14.2	14.0
	0.001	47.0	36.6	33.2	31.1	29.8	28.8	...	27.6
	0.500	0.515	0.780	0.886	0.942	0.977	1.00	1.02	1.03
	0.100	3.78	3.46	3.29	3.18	3.11	3.05	3.01	2.98
	0.050	5.99	5.14	4.76	4.53	4.39	4.28	4.21	4.15
6	0.025	8.81	7.26	6.60	6.23	5.99	5.82	5.70	5.60
	0.010	13.7	10.9	9.78	9.15	8.75	8.47	8.26	8.10
	0.005	18.6	14.5	12.9	12.0	11.5	11.1	10.8	10.6
	0.001	35.5	27.0	23.7	21.9	20.8	20.0	...	19.0

* The 0.001 points of Table L are abridged with permission from Table V of R. A. Fisher and F. Yates, *Statistical Tables for Biological, Agricultural and Medical Research* (Edinburgh; Oliver & Boyd Ltd.). The rest of the table is abridged with permission from Maxine Merrington and Catherine M. Thompson, "Tables of Percentage Points of the Inverted Beta (F) Distribution," *Biometrika*, Vol. XXXIII, pp. 73–88.

Table L >> 163

9	10	12	15	20	24	30	60	120	∞
2.03	2.04	2.07	2.09	2.12	2.13	2.15	2.17	2.18	2.20
59.9	60.2	60.7	61.2	61.7	62.0	62.3	62.8	63.1	63.3
241	242	244	246	248	249	250	252	253	254
963	969	977	985	993	997	1,001	1,010	1,010	1,020
6,020	6,060	6,110	6,160	6,210	6,235	6,260	6,310	6,340	3,370
24,100	24,200	24,400	24,600	24,800	24,900	25,000	25,300	25,400	25,500
. . .	. . .	610,667	. . .	. . .	623,497	. . .	. . .	. . .	636,619
1.33	1.34	1.36	1.38	1.39	1.40	1.41	1.43	1.43	1.44
9.38	9.39	9.41	9.42	9.44	9.45	9.46	9.47	9.48	9.49
19.4	19.4	19.4	19.4	19.4	19.5	19.5	19.5	19.5	19.5
39.4	39.4	39.4	39.4	39.4	39.5	39.5	39.5	39.5	39.5
99.4	99.4	99.4	99.4	99.4	99.5	99.5	99.5	99.5	99.5
199	199	199	199	199	199	199	199	199	200
. . .	. . .	999.4	. .	. . .	999.5	. . .	. . .	. . .	999.5
1.17	1.18	1.20	1.21	1.23	1.23	1.24	1.25	1.26	1.27
5.24	5.23	5.22	5.20	5.18	5.18	5.17	5.15	5.14	5.13
8.81	8.79	8.74	8.70	8.66	8.64	8.62	8.57	8.55	8.53
14.5	14.4	14.3	14.3	14.2	14.1	14.1	14.0	13.9	13.9
27.3	27.2	27.1	26.9	26.7	26.6	26.5	26.3	26.2	26.1
43.9	43.7	43.4	43.1	42.8	42.6	42.5	42.1	42.0	41.8
. . .	. . .	128.3	. . .	. . .	125.9	. . .	. . .	. . .	123.5
1.10	1.11	1.13	1.14	1.15	1.16	1.16	1.18	1.18	1.19
3.94	3.92	3.90	3.87	3.84	3.83	3.82	3.79	3.78	3.76
6.00	5.96	5.91	5.86	5.80	5.77	5.75	5.69	5.66	5.63
8.90	8.84	8.75	8.66	8.56	8.51	8.46	8.36	8.31	8.26
14.7	14.5	14.4	14.2	14.0	13.9	13.8	13.7	13.6	13.5
21.1	21.0	20.7	20.4	20.2	20.0	19.9	19.6	19.5	19.3
. . .	. . .	47.4	. . .	. . .	45.8	. . .	. . .	. . .	44.1
1.06	1.07	1.09	1.10	1.11	1.12	1.12	1.14	1.14	1.15
3.32	3.30	3.27	3.24	3.21	3.19	3.17	3.14	3.12	3.11
4.77	4.47	4.68	4.62	4.56	4.56	4.53	4.43	4.40	4.37
6.68	6.62	6.52	6.43	6.33	6.28	6.23	6.12	6.07	6.02
10.2	10.1	9.89	9.72	9.55	9.47	9.38	9.20	9.11	9.02
13.8	13.6	13.4	13.1	12.9	12.8	12.7	12.4	12.3	12.1
. . .	. . .	26.4	. . .	. . .	25.1	. . .	. . .	. . .	23.8
1.04	1.05	1.06	1.07	1.08	1.09	1.10	1.11	1.12	1.12
2.96	2.94	2.90	2.87	2.84	2.82	2.80	2.76	2.74	2.72
4.10	4.06	4.00	3.94	3.87	3.84	3.81	3.74	3.70	3.67
5.52	5.46	5.37	5.27	5.17	5.12	5.07	4.96	4.90	4.85
7.98	7.87	7.72	7.56	7.40	7.31	7.23	7.06	6.97	6.88
10.4	10.2	10.0	9.81	9.59	9.47	9.36	9.12	9.00	9.88
. . .	. . .	18.0	. . .	. . .	16.9	. . .	. . .	. . .	15.8

df_2	**P**	$df_1 = 1$	2	3	4	5	6	7	8
	0.500	0.506	0.767	0.871	0.926	0.960	0.983	1.00	1.01
	0.100	3.59	3.26	3.07	2.96	2.88	2.83	2.78	2.75
	0.050	5.59	4.74	4.35	4.12	3.97	3.87	3.79	3.73
7	0.025	8.07	6.54	5.89	5.52	5.29	5.12	4.99	4.90
	0.010	12.2	9.55	8.45	7.85	7.46	7.19	6.99	6.84
	0.005	16.2	12.4	10.9	10.1	9.52	9.16	8.89	8.68
	0.001	29.2	21.7	18.8	17.2	16.2	15.5	...	14.6
	0.500	0.499	0.757	0.860	0.915	0.948	0.971	0.988	1.00
	0.100	3.46	3.11	2.92	2.81	2.73	2.67	2.62	2.59
	0.050	5.32	4.46	4.07	3.84	3.69	3.58	3.50	3.44
8	0.025	7.57	6.06	5.42	5.05	4.82	4.65	4.53	4.43
	0.010	11.3	8.65	7.59	7.01	6.63	6.37	6.18	6.03
	0.005	14.7	11.0	9.60	8.81	8.30	7.95	7.69	7.50
	0.001	25.4	18.5	15.8	14.4	13.5	12.9	...	12.0
	0.500	0.494	0.749	0.852	0.906	0.939	0.962	0.978	0.990
	0.100	3.36	3.01	2.81	2.69	2.61	2.55	2.51	2.47
	0.050	5.12	4.26	3.86	3.63	3.48	3.37	3.29	3.23
9	0.025	7.21	5.71	5.08	4.72	4.48	4.32	4.20	4.10
	0.010	10.6	8.02	6.99	6.42	6.06	5.80	5.61	5.47
	0.005	13.6	10.1	8.72	7.96	7.47	7.13	6.88	6.69
	0.001	22.9	16.4	13.9	12.6	11.7	11.1	...	10.4
	0.500	0.490	0.743	0.845	0.899	0.932	0.954	0.971	0.983
	0.100	3.29	2.92	2.73	2.61	2.52	2.46	2.41	2.38
	0.050	4.96	4.10	3.71	3.48	3.33	3.22	3.14	3.07
10	0.025	6.94	5.46	4.83	4.47	4.24	4.07	3.95	3.85
	0.010	10.0	7.56	6.55	5.99	5.64	5.39	5.20	5.06
	0.005	12.8	9.43	8.08	7.34	6.87	6.54	6.30	6.12
	0.001	21.0	14.9	12.6	11.3	10.5	9.92	...	9.20
	0.500	0.484	0.735	0.835	0.888	0.921	0.943	0.959	0.972
	0.100	3.18	2.81	2.61	2.48	2.39	2.33	2.28	2.24
	0.050	4.75	3.89	3.49	3.26	3.11	3.00	2.91	2.85
12	0.025	6.55	5.10	4.47	4.12	3.89	3.73	3.61	3.51
	0.010	9.33	6.93	5.95	5.41	5.06	4.82	4.64	4.50
	0.005	11.8	8.51	7.23	6.52	6.07	5.76	5.52	5.35
	0.001	18.6	13.0	10.8	9.63	8.89	8.38	...	7.71
	0.500	0.478	0.726	0.826	0.878	0.911	0.933	0.949	0.960
	0.100	3.07	2.70	2.49	2.36	2.27	2.21	2.16	2.12
	0.050	4.54	3.68	3.29	3.06	2.90	2.79	2.71	2.64
15	0.025	6.20	4.77	4.15	3.80	3.58	3.41	3.29	3.20
	0.010	8.68	6.36	5.42	4.89	4.56	4.32	4.14	4.00
	0.005	10.8	7.70	6.48	5.80	5.37	5.07	4.85	4.67
	0.001	16.6	11.34	9.34	8.25	7.57	7.09	...	6.47
	0.500	0.472	0.718	0.816	0.868	0.900	0.922	0.938	0.950
	0.100	2.97	2.59	2.38	2.25	2.16	2.09	2.04	2.00
	0.050	4.35	3.49	3.10	2.87	2.71	2.60	2.51	2.45
20	0.025	5.87	4.46	3.86	3.51	3.29	3.13	3.01	2.91
	0.010	8.10	5.85	4.94	4.43	4.10	3.87	3.70	3.56
	0.005	9.94	6.99	5.82	5.17	4.76	4.47	4.26	4.09
	0.001	14.8	9.95	8.10	7.10	6.46	6.02	...	5.44

Table L >> 165

9	10	12.	15	20	24	30	60	120	∞
1.02	1.03	1.04	1.05	1.07	1.07	1.08	1.09	1.10	1.10
2.72	2.70	2.67	2.63	2.59	2.58	2.56	2.51	2.49	2.47
3.68	3.64	3.57	3.51	3.44	3.41	3.38	3.30	3.27	3.23
4.82	4.76	4.67	4.57	4.47	4.42	4.36	4.25	4.20	4.14
6.72	6.62	6.47	6.31	6.16	6.07	5.99	5.82	5.74	5.65
8.51	8.38	8.18	7.97	7.75	7.65	7.53	7.31	7.19	7.08
...	...	13.7	...	...	12.7	...	...	...	11.7
1.01	1.02	1.03	1.04	1.05	1.06	1.07	1.08	1.08	1.09
2.56	2.54	2.50	2.46	2.42	2.40	2.38	2.34	2.32	2.29
3.39	3.35	3.28	3.22	3.15	3.12	3.08	3.01	2.97	2.93
4.36	4.30	4.20	4.10	4.00	3.95	3.89	3.78	3.73	3.67
5.91	5.81	5.67	5.52	5.36	5.28	5.20	5.03	4.95	4.86
7.34	7.21	7.01	6.81	6.61	6.50	6.40	6.18	6.06	5.95
...	...	11.2	...	...	10.3	...	...	...	9.34
1.00	1.01	1.02	1.03	1.04	1.05	1.05	1.07	1.07	1.08
2.44	2.42	2.38	2.34	2.30	2.28	2.25	2.21	2.18	2.16
3.18	3.14	3.07	3.01	2.94	2.90	2.86	2.79	2.75	2.71
4.03	3.96	3.87	3.77	3.67	3.61	3.56	3.45	3.39	3.33
5.35	5.26	5.11	4.96	4.81	4.73	4.65	4.48	4.40	4.31
6.54	6.42	6.23	6.03	5.83	5.73	5.62	5.41	5.30	5.19
...	...	9.57	...	...	8.72	...	...	...	7.81
0.992	1.00	1.01	1.02	1.03	1.04	1.05	1.06	1.06	1.07
2.35	2.32	2.28	2.24	2.20	2.18	2.16	2.11	2.08	2.06
3.02	2.98	2.91	2.84	2.77	2.74	2.70	2.62	2.58	2.54
3.78	3.72	3.62	3.52	3.42	3.37	3.31	3.20	3.14	3.08
4.94	4.85	4.71	4.56	4.41	4.33	4.25	4.08	4.00	3.91
5.97	5.85	5.66	5.47	5.27	5.17	5.07	4.86	4.75	4.64
...	...	8.45	...	...	7.64	...	...	...	6.76
0.981	0.989	1.00	1.01	1.02	1.03	1.03	1.05	1.05	1.06
2.21	2.19	2.15	2.10	2.06	2.04	2.01	1.96	1.93	1.90
2.80	2.75	2.69	2.62	2.54	2.51	2.47	2.38	2.34	2.30
3.44	3.37	3.28	3.18	3.07	3.02	2.96	2.85	2.79	2.72
4.39	4.30	4.16	4.01	3.86	3.78	3.70	3.54	3.45	3.36
5.20	5.09	4.91	4.72	4.53	4.43	4.33	4.12	4.01	3.90
...	...	7.00	...	...	6.25	...	...	...	5.42
0.970	0.977	0.989	1.00	1.01	1.02	1.02	1.03	1.04	1.05
2.09	2.06	2.02	1.97	1.92	1.90	1.87	1.82	1.79	1.76
2.59	2.54	2.48	2.40	2.33	2.29	2.25	2.16	2.11	2.07
3.12	3.06	2.96	2.86	2.76	2.70	2.64	2.52	2.46	2.40
3.89	3.80	3.67	3.52	3.37	3.29	3.21	3.05	2.96	2.87
4.54	4.42	4.25	4.07	3.88	3.79	3.69	3.48	3.37	3.26
...	...	5.81	...	...	5.10	...	...	...	4.31
0.959	0.966	0.977	0.989	1.00	1.01	1.01	1.02	1.03	1.03
1.96	1.94	1.89	1.84	1.79	1.77	1.74	1.68	1.64	1.61
2.39	2.35	2.28	2.20	2.12	2.08	2.04	1.95	1.90	1.84
2.84	2.77	2.68	2.57	2.46	2.41	2.35	2.22	2.16	2.09
3.46	3.37	3.23	3.09	2.94	2.86	2.78	2.61	2.52	2.42
3.96	3.85	3.68	3.50	3.32	3.22	3.12	2.92	2.81	2.69
...	...	4.82	...	...	4.15	...	...	...	3.38

df_2	P	$df_1 = 1$	2	3	4	5	6	7	8
	0.500	0.469	0.714	0.812	0.863	0.895	0.917	0.932	0.944
	0.100	2.93	2.54	2.33	2.19	2.10	2.04	1.98	1.94
	0.050	4.26	3.40	3.01	2.78	2.62	2.51	2.42	2.36
24	0.025	5.72	4.32	3.72	3.38	3.15	2.99	2.87	2.78
	0.010	7.82	5.61	4.72	4.22	3.90	3.67	3.50	3.36
	0.005	9.55	6.66	5.52	4.89	4.49	4.20	3.99	3.83
	0.001	14.0	9.34	7.55	6.59	5.98	5.55	...	4.99
	0.500	0.466	0.709	0.807	0.858	0.890	0.912	0.927	0.939
	0.100	2.88	2.49	2.28	2.14	2.05	1.98	1.93	1.88
	0.050	4.17	3.32	2.92	2.69	2.53	2.42	2.33	2.27
30	0.025	5.57	4.18	3.59	3.25	3.03	2.87	2.75	2.65
	0.010	7.56	5.39	4.51	4.02	3.70	3.47	3.30	3.17
	0.005	9.18	6.35	5.24	4.62	4.23	3.95	3.74	3.58
	0.001	13.29	8.77	7.05	6.12	5.53	5.12	...	4.58
	0.500	0.461	0.701	0.798	0.849	0.880	0.901	0.917	0.928
	0.100	2.79	2.39	2.18	2.04	1.95	1.87	1.82	1.77
	0.050	4.00	3.15	2.76	2.53	2.37	2.25	2.17	2.10
60	0.025	5.29	3.93	3.34	3.01	2.79	2.63	2.51	2.41
	0.010	7.08	4.98	4.13	3.65	3.34	3.12	2.95	2.82
	0.005	8.49	5.80	4.73	4.14	3.76	3.49	3.29	3.13
	0.001	11.97	7.76	6.17	5.31	4.76	4.37	...	3.87
	0.500	0.458	0.697	0.793	0.844	0.875	0.896	0.912	0.923
	0.100	2.75	2.35	2.13	1.99	1.90	1.82	1.77	1.72
	0.050	3.92	3.07	2.68	2.45	2.29	2.18	2.09	2.02
120	0.025	5.15	3.80	3.23	2.89	2.67	2.52	2.39	2.30
	0.010	6.85	4.79	3.95	3.48	3.17	2.96	2.79	2.66
	0.005	8.18	5.54	4.50	3.92	3.55	3.28	3.09	2.93
	0.001	11.38	7.31	5.79	4.95	4.42	4.04	...	3.55
	0.500	0.455	0.693	0.789	0.839	0.870	0.891	0.907	0.918
	0.100	2.71	2.30	2.08	1.94	1.85	1.77	1.72	1.67
	0.050	3.84	3.00	2.60	2.37	2.21	2.10	2.01	1.94
∞	0.025	5.02	3.69	3.12	2.79	2.57	2.41	2.29	2.19
	0.010	6.63	4.61	3.78	3.32	3.02	2.80	2.64	2.51
	0.005	7.88	5.30	4.28	3.72	3.35	3.09	2.90	2.74
	0.001	10.8	6.91	5.42	4.62	4.10	3.74	...	3.27

Table L >> 167

9	10	12	15	20	24	30	60	120	∞
0.953	0.961	0.972	0.983	0.994	1.00	1.01	1.02	1.02	1.03
1.91	1.88	1.83	1.78	1.73	1.70	1.67	1.61	1.57	1.53
2.30	2.25	2.18	2.11	2.03	1.98	1.94	1.84	1.79	1.73
2.70	2.64	2.54	2.44	2.33	2.27	2.21	2.08	2.01	1.94
3.26	3.17	3.03	2.89	2.74	2.66	2.58	2.40	2.31	2.21
3.69	3.59	3.42	3.25	3.06	2.97	2.87	2.66	2.55	2.43
...	...	4.39	...	...	3.74	...	...	...	2.97
0.948	0.955	0.966	0.978	0.989	0.994	1.00	1.01	1.02	1.02
1.85	1.82	1.77	1.72	1.67	1.64	1.61	1.54	1.50	1.46
2.21	2.16	2.09	2.01	1.93	1.89	1.84	1.74	1.68	1.62
2.57	2.51	2.41	2.31	2.20	2.14	2.07	1.94	1.87	1.79
3.07	2.98	2.84	2.70	2.55	2.47	2.39	2.21	2.11	2.01
3.45	3.34	3.18	3.01	2.82	2.73	2.63	2.42	2.30	2.18
...	...	4.00	...	...	3.36	...	...	...	2.59
0.937	0.945	0.956	0.967	0.978	0.983	0.989	1.00	1.01	1.01
1.74	1.71	1.66	1.60	1.54	1.51	1.48	1.40	1.35	1.29
2.04	1.99	1.92	1.84	1.75	1.70	1.65	1.53	1.47	1.39
2.33	2.27	2.17	2.06	1.94	1.88	1.82	1.67	1.58	1.48
2.72	2.63	2.50	2.35	2.20	2.12	2.03	1.84	1.73	1.60
3.01	2.90	2.74	2.57	2.39	2.29	2.19	1.96	1.83	1.69
...	...	3.31	...	...	2.69	...	...	...	1.90
0.932	0.939	0.950	0.961	0.972	0.978	0.983	0.994	1.00	1.01
1.68	1.65	1.60	1.55	1.48	1.45	1.41	1.32	1.26	1.19
1.96	1.91	1.83	1.75	1.66	1.61	1.55	1.43	1.35	1.25
2.22	2.16	2.05	1.95	1.82	1.76	1.69	1.53	1.43	1.31
2.56	2.47	2.34	2.19	2.03	1.95	1.86	1.66	1.53	1.38
2.81	2.71	2.54	2.37	2.19	2.09	1.98	1.75	1.61	1.43
...	...	3.02	...	...	2.40	...	...	...	1.56
0.927	0.934	0.945	0.956	0.967	0.972	0.978	0.989	0.994	1.00
1.63	1.60	1.55	1.49	1.42	1.38	1.34	1.24	1.17	1.00
1.88	1.83	1.75	1.67	1.57	1.52	1.46	1.32	1.22	1.00
2.11	2.05	1.94	1.83	1.71	1.64	1.57	1.39	1.27	1.00
2.41	2.32	2.18	2.04	1.88	1.79	1.70	1.47	1.32	1.00
2.62	2.52	2.36	2.19	2.00	1.90	1.79	1.53	1.36	1.00
...	...	2.74	...	...	2.13	...	...	...	1.00

VALUES OF THE CORRELATION COEFFICIENT
FOR DIFFERENT LEVELS OF SIGNIFICANCE*

d.f.	.05	.02	.01
1	.996917	.9995066	.9998766
2	.95000	.98000	.990000
3	.8783	.93433	.95873
4	.8114	.8822	.91720
5	.7545	.8329	.8745
6	.7067	.7887	.8343
7	.6664	.7498	.7977
8	.6319	.7155	.7646
9	.6021	.6851	.7348
10	.5760	.6581	.7079
11	.5529	.6339	.6835
12	.5324	.6120	.6614
13	.5139	.5923	.6411
14	.4973	.5742	.6226
15	.4821	.5577	.6055
16	.4683	.5425	.5897
17	.4555	.5285	.5751
18	.4438	.5155	.5614
19	.4329	.5034	.5487
20	.4227	.4921	.5368
25	.3809	.4451	.4869
30	.3494	.4093	.4487
35	.3246	.3810	.4182
40	.3044	.3578	.3932
45	.2875	.3384	.3721
50	.2732	.3218	.3541
60	.2500	.2948	.3248
70	.2319	.2737	.3017
80	.2172	.2565	.2830
90	.2050	.2422	.2673
100	.1946	.2301	.2540

*This table is reprinted from Table V-A of Fisher: Statistical Methods for Research Workers, published by Oliver and Boyd Ltd., Edinburgh, by permission of the author and publishers.

For simple correlation, d.f. is 2 less than the number of pairs in the sample; for partial correlation, the number of secondary subscripts also should be subtracted.

RANDOM SAMPLING NUMBERS

FIRST 1,512 RANDOM DIGITS

	A	B	C	D	E	F	G
1	345769	953810	627280	423578	353511	899906	827008
	549075	004410	059309	271243	403382	248735	972383
	423480	950812	197145	556566	655917	046169	363201
	554518	514280	950974	482196	058868	474936	724289
	797165	670995	791954	188521	950156	086813	033365
	062730	163375	602168	908350	360861	152201	966097
2	356756	519371	679389	371912	502903	936741	636775
	700770	781547	916968	136999	801855	605975	295802
	279584	733750	487151	116069	274869	416181	610911
	862434	481154	391464	021094	761599	474456	582253
	199585	167701	170778	934765	761328	275799	323046
	048736	514507	977406	158840	846761	198016	933522
3	815218	609732	629295	517386	824505	676788	304971
	643021	527212	492869	261844	914505	354436	355772
	164332	245407	517804	422658	751712	583087	286872
	174303	085157	308590	535846	503131	266915	465641
	136325	414066	452293	649359	844625	674828	953396
	117780	407444	426115	108970	621527	601599	652376
4	435697	245510	946158	934221	824917	509832	362638
	912252	579474	848845	824321	049853	151126	052643
	754438	658573	717914	040054	630638	264060	594641
	322053	924909	048177	957012	801464	833319	978384
	897199	125506	708669	408374	737887	906201	599469
	046637	642050	435779	502427	027842	515775	811203
5	721653	260190	842505	797017	157497	179041	979346
	202312	011976	373248	374293	802292	646914	171322
	354014	356787	511271	904434	068589	329862	829316
	682909	809290	793392	098004	120575	469925	112743
	897690	572456	871574	465543	486529	507767	608677
	139029	160636	417690	191242	625269	104858	020808
6	341447	723998	905614	519309	926345	240082	395043
	415603	129727	894956	780924	227496	134056	023014
	014881	496311	750082	707823	738906	157591	072396
	827235	783798	324650	485324	568156	098331	768720
	261607	730824	341940	259028	253973	145183	658110
	527920	834376	972906	627959	654790	342497	593779

Table N is abridged with the permission of the author and publisher from "New Random Sampling Numbers," *Baylor Business Studies* No. 1, by H. N. Broom, published by The School of Business, Baylor University, Waco, Texas.

SECOND 1,512 RANDOM DIGITS

	A	B	C	D	E	F	G
1	835431	206253	467521	029822	700399	554652	450184
	512651	743206	118787	587401	921517	015407	206860
	376187	189133	154812	828785	667020	998697	579598
	092530	869028	483691	165063	847894	041617	762973
	238036	016856	290105	538530	079931	412195	838814
	308168	717698	919814	092230	215657	469994	805803
2	773429	915639	900911	276895	149505	540379	224349
	171626	601259	009905	572567	441960	299704	313987
	180570	665625	424048	713009	830314	664642	521021
	558715	965963	494210	875287	488595	898691	713010
	345067	361180	989224	138905	355519	045847	746266
	583819	310956	174728	099164	118461	758000	496302
3	615026	599459	722322	555090	572720	826686	456517
	812358	389535	166779	441968	105639	632418	340890
	784592	003651	279275	055646	341897	510689	026160
	094619	636747	934082	787345	772825	603866	565688
	450908	919891	157771	114333	710179	062848	615156
	593546	728768	984323	290410	970562	906724	315005
4	873778	491131	209695	604075	783895	862911	772026
	965705	317845	169619	921361	315606	990029	745251
	311163	943589	540958	556212	760508	129963	236556
	454554	284761	269019	924179	670780	389869	519229
	124330	819763	596075	064570	495169	030185	866211
	920765	122124	423205	596357	469969	072245	359269
5	183002	540547	312909	389818	464023	768381	377241
	600135	865974	929756	162716	415598	878513	994633
	235787	023117	895285	027055	943962	381112	530492
	953379	655834	283102	836259	437761	391976	940853
	009658	521970	537626	806052	715247	808585	252503
	176570	849057	387097	311529	893745	450267	182626
6	747456	304530	931013	678688	270736	355032	400713
	486876	631985	368395	154273	959983	672523	210456
	987193	268135	867829	025419	301168	409545	131960
	358155	950977	170562	246987	884126	785621	467942
	021394	182615	049084	942153	278313	872709	693590
	735047	428941	630704	893281	716045	267529	427605

THIRD 1,512 RANDOM DIGITS

	A	B	C	D	E	F	G
1	133877	894168	670664	007673	436272	479568	247014
	909935	172305	428979	775425	004071	896108	519806
	204092	380210	589306	421798	273014	842846	750253
	906975	390605	040857	206293	173991	258115	043825
	387430	513087	738318	344565	465609	416995	943451
	045890	563165	460571	633567	481740	951614	668403
2	837159	143979	698357	219259	924875	691935	843585
	796578	982105	540570	724307	369621	562203	757320
	509998	316652	678549	468115	387469	316301	013153
	067045	238296	042458	275413	499300	680274	026351
	207634	540337	350587	013692	412939	274513	984596
	980620	875228	496017	581165	251684	275169	588760
3	347609	157545	919210	690074	532650	922600	693037
	475802	466358	379889	594832	514118	205292	371756
	818821	932102	628457	533138	655279	704197	584316
	362078	838671	765113	410097	138149	701956	928874
	072228	759522	791735	398202	162345	294805	828520
	147935	014193	536872	552021	693458	018447	788748
4	419843	160700	338910	184107	235002	024298	449135
	825546	648481	916364	607857	436970	438087	798960
	082314	418158	781469	991818	721194	358904	450970
	915221	233704	129127	767232	098851	584646	353870
	765613	354681	367568	496453	308935	131432	204643
	036236	196087	690273	453073	595160	410830	466051
5	607104	305543	705229	623194	613727	696054	758402
	308792	376543	027151	165422	560769	814957	589180
	857280	462801	434761	324058	482908	294374	976175
	959721	758687	456782	568719	404563	154205	663418
	207153	231920	518416	804920	932735	082468	322964
	403778	187984	157069	719462	053157	953043	416342
6	286108	108539	428918	149527	723573	636055	737916
	411295	291930	481424	871000	172070	273030	456317
	679313	787369	159935	164716	835268	174221	959886
	405323	376852	057589	437497	357398	838285	098772
	917458	429205	795610	905859	676942	294087	791952
	659514	078457	711589	690730	104700	912369	848269

FOURTH 1,512 RANDOM DIGITS

	A	B	C	D	E	F	G
1	142582	838531	948535	204547	621651	329695	014694
	097086	190024	666521	170674	144070	124008	702818
	358324	034739	403012	692427	208539	381841	432976
	257091	654023	191287	731088	259167	352640	004388
	928731	264667	956546	240744	769932	574832	914694
	729816	278812	119374	895490	818386	267958	560523
2	781062	721128	169905	290611	024176	160727	856247
	093549	401262	079175	117813	842686	246713	649987
	829708	656390	804223	434596	134518	401187	589048
	550416	658096	352864	576572	178144	051421	836509
	072934	572971	564253	950363	656948	923152	790087
	646941	109528	073147	354187	771592	647850	086352
3	905725	867727	033964	579862	045061	896494	589268
	727696	156430	671765	127312	335860	407661	709388
	742859	985436	487786	403118	684839	561387	985352
	095217	375204	659737	001286	046025	616072	224715
	791020	730765	212021	763149	590401	433554	462302
	824304	754426	728896	070857	137631	634735	426189
4	194358	810596	051443	917458	855114	808348	568628
	364029	285129	651482	180425	166024	465370	467021
	675894	027149	802421	058779	786349	597533	917864
	009913	955754	981235	888191	437609	131287	967580
	605600	593586	200254	365462	154578	179723	358203
	792003	304109	298794	661389	720132	741928	088924
5	357790	028381	163072	758986	302348	248362	909435
	482034	980395	236510	516007	654864	890157	740017
	319302	713745	057612	027685	180265	981029	237304
	622343	241778	137067	061429	489784	439401	438854
	870846	008446	490322	136989	703895	591878	506804
	603242	818115	746069	437465	507246	713641	936584
6	143632	031587	688275	170345	823659	049277	970129
	954182	040683	787002	775349	571341	854167	020533
	283056	857426	252542	404561	546734	822595	481604
	891730	027420	126799	821731	195465	709433	240637
	497562	204798	343671	124740	855713	016508	282359
	862867	628369	179980	851292	200332	260919	634484

FIFTH 1,512 RANDOM DIGITS

	A	B	C	D	E	F	G
1	234903	977328	426289	059916	370504	472536	882774
	827916	836545	259741	351195	318902	035302	168872
	072531	890103	176448	541124	205121	123085	068264
	632794	206625	925039	624334	820835	334348	388207
	382872	097936	071964	621400	646309	247900	281703
	808573	394741	959638	247381	610565	709873	334815
2	354309	158909	153881	424752	783022	533624	175172
	906243	726658	251267	365360	579630	586949	158133
	525936	310872	970208	973742	569370	017236	474078
	728432	994758	280372	252475	231276	574619	494115
	133451	621863	348390	098228	347511	147196	784562
	689269	313634	060291	180301	975085	894513	576965
3	724364	808577	482097	323717	715709	476280	826741
	765851	353829	719547	543741	908672	823137	326739
	947243	118331	223157	039177	794272	801545	460983
	465051	280456	629658	126148	156208	857169	911700
	257697	776781	820503	296026	088363	662042	354276
	160987	935231	747978	651684	343587	645322	393694
4	821728	950392	695858	129173	969025	203142	691811
	133820	518328	195320	802857	715239	430737	837670
	676119	543864	713556	608730	542030	267639	272313
	358288	970868	823717	086731	757257	482576	776482
	845316	824309	503518	427637	685270	957076	892133
	942548	198829	493211	149531	094630	027693	329382
5	143233	887181	055337	249805	513691	817352	538149
	458184	837904	923458	391183	608420	216957	172575
	851984	813538	640801	612417	716166	250195	429326
	229237	475843	059797	909582	874102	515272	856061
	174277	763056	492535	469927	796518	647131	871689
	295226	004417	146345	143745	642136	818246	547348
6	517593	113209	334612	395850	971896	012245	572923
	354462	698717	874151	603057	392502	494365	797795
	468647	924887	108659	220318	201989	613680	679493
	684049	465801	098284	331425	284530	486915	763950
	030205	684076	497019	283971	842047	824963	909776
	561626	489302	597504	153984	534636	703728	628141

SIXTH 1,512 RANDOM DIGITS

	A	B	C	D	E	F	G
1	131002	982802	349586	732144	263958	525852	079077
	311036	948264	757246	999074	473250	301361	287480
	117900	967359	951340	206249	750614	757637	039561
	420108	719403	373353	805621	324985	382658	144203
	817917	014186	490768	918089	827877	872212	083869
	616038	432163	024784	280541	925802	715031	276156
2	028826	878944	125967	203556	380380	530327	766136
	306466	023143	957987	389181	042380	427260	725014
	212582	401308	784251	118122	369778	672765	370624
	904481	259462	613526	296340	417190	492514	683658
	039150	872354	091965	042174	578011	508348	598921
	124093	002854	421698	620839	128047	574933	431906
3	834925	709114	753692	497162	994578	072578	603677
	420841	566312	353244	740576	491964	624527	967488
	254108	159489	952679	167533	521907	193160	031448
	664232	516971	792650	400468	647852	170913	160213
	801813	559026	527213	527566	325794	825990	363411
	395837	431769	701261	078829	386268	265427	791021
4	854672	844120	509813	735713	856045	423249	847869
	713626	401301	541542	792042	627765	708281	990385
	152815	799642	172512	408639	477833	489620	492357
	043842	288755	982207	793857	146365	511024	040649
	621103	658201	406878	049460	736146	544352	951680
	907380	479835	173615	613129	135183	290643	711999
5	183424	225589	588245	751920	670401	465815	707089
	298105	197406	800758	377629	387216	804517	358658
	461943	527038	040083	821392	886273	541711	128572
	972720	500061	802028	649938	152578	108946	530986
	386414	603406	598381	649820	614989	999197	343017
	494412	721901	997552	293068	929691	279002	315891
6	454723	636448	877080	705018	817266	157453	836959
	623403	702369	575734	705190	611039	247033	465424
	375076	190955	175613	953498	527196	205576	322834
	432061	773509	782619	795283	630640	591027	437851
	685739	934795	409662	288493	105881	770890	454989
	474534	628374	913113	927692	876136	484264	370120

SEVENTH 1,512 RANDOM DIGITS

	A	B	C	D	E	F	G
1	709185	340438	460965	942000	429134	371533	349945
	803284	731331	947821	256570	084028	969352	614616
	613774	169070	625816	991975	931215	403052	246287
	840558	798060	559201	234095	772891	331445	380446
	013254	808899	049165	733968	452613	895842	679503
	183393	890935	491001	295887	522848	409359	015274
2	566494	363359	560313	713965	287916	894109	241842
	292683	864228	833304	918761	233059	183442	875803
	946842	039669	518435	878301	615978	651693	711543
	575525	980274	825670	462213	902406	126143	846392
	240843	754519	584210	651407	182782	817765	960782
	061360	041163	550463	510178	587647	072249	144505
3	851654	517546	483230	028541	136386	893299	538661
	612690	041734	207715	711009	782971	000545	435275
	631361	686831	035875	817705	491952	281547	411735
	124565	390685	177734	180255	932667	048215	962608
	734976	936074	295263	694131	048298	627197	793249
	769343	796105	839915	395087	007383	320656	373892
4	473105	964875	036127	406564	157278	560401	316867
	710915	231828	274369	485163	561230	207294	575026
	684251	094146	619711	251828	512906	312645	878060
	845885	102203	988634	298754	063181	813840	639183
	142951	585206	545267	473025	306256	308372	951465
	769678	251601	274652	427707	075091	948539	086764
5	461383	401090	268780	785630	978687	375917	384056
	730981	428921	742860	534632	393924	005326	864520
	924260	284374	892698	701835	915905	152546	503404
	832534	694104	015167	316561	124648	319627	136572
	080431	863062	566150	287352	095985	339957	697877
	518363	342832	630574	179853	396155	152035	875703
6	812252	414982	006162	592861	532436	487925	892949
	502404	563221	894242	402606	765101	528596	728298
	731967	783719	925607	347223	146852	957104	238921
	417986	204070	595380	562870	621398	174973	497973
	210968	130088	408564	905832	645304	500685	143622
	825692	263029	728499	199860	635831	054995	708355

EIGHTH 1,512 RANDOM DIGITS

	A	B	C	D	E	F	G
1	231708	504611	968036	591223	211096	777439	724687
	238155	252763	490318	537699	018264	611205	073090
	931326	566249	372390	235417	704547	162374	780520
	096931	857162	342793	866552	120717	346535	914120
	852194	201759	860169	753632	802716	534359	489785
	607691	970406	826115	282337	450421	678673	125376
2	512691	009320	072128	762442	318685	123608	673704
	353452	717059	585926	870062	914621	739670	408454
	420746	200515	694228	153715	636001	137873	425685
	519963	174622	015409	760736	287516	840116	023615
	540173	291088	064135	529330	163618	648945	204881
	421579	960813	843108	619981	051172	203138	880776
3	364778	497155	604345	743963	465583	293902	704439
	871259	627949	619511	713169	643386	815933	006967
	181627	620419	433130	481489	711163	000670	051126
	353905	752314	400977	062539	491624	629837	814535
	657714	902036	245805	732944	809022	127178	800521
	174209	839951	538710	577605	718761	892356	084388
4	725469	413439	902346	165419	490822	390429	499075
	671938	454482	417903	621828	864990	763056	423658
	885010	491779	058320	721145	083903	642452	930942
	226151	515549	670028	511374	761253	268230	009611
	745760	151626	366821	250137	238004	973980	121307
	717283	968736	706421	790072	049558	182425	836501
5	595867	272784	268703	536973	836325	100691	681035
	875626	533691	412573	958910	639313	480796	948218
	625030	856928	206125	378086	936909	163194	066165
	835819	791654	670319	395431	734718	968282	648931
	381220	405003	710916	721794	385418	144613	960278
	628938	749139	238325	787263	175396	941612	116823
6	579020	178087	342515	975848	963673	016366	577259
	485604	168520	649429	618405	738261	716550	051737
	906267	794639	751681	098745	935692	164279	691086
	290971	390334	714535	236290	638512	817957	294169
	005257	486575	021560	713492	147317	892418	382709
	609514	345261	433729	259272	964743	089464	219955

Answers to Odd-Numbered Problems

Chapter 1

1-1. a. 3–5
    b. 2
    c. 3
    d. 5
    e. 5
    f. 3
    g. 5
    h. 5

1-3. a. 1.67
    b. 2,400
    c. 2,142.0
    d. 600
    e. 18,000
    f. 891.4

1-5. b. (1) 62 miles
    (2) 35 buses
    (3) 49.5 miles
    (4) A distance just under 74.5 miles
    (5) 25 miles

    c. Relative frequencies which represent area for each class are 0.035, 0.412, 0.235, 0.165, 0.082, 0.047, and 0.024.

    d. Relative frequencies per unit of width (25 miles) is the frequency density or height of each bar. These are 0.035, 0.412, 0.235, 0.082, 0.020, 0.008, and 0.003.

1-7. a. The frequencies are 8, 9, 22, 15, 7, and 3 for classes of 25–49, 50–99, 100–199, 200–399, 400–799, and 800 and over.

    b. The two cumulative frequency curves cross at the median.

Chapter 2

2-1. a. 7.2
    b. 4.6
    c. 4.5
    d. 2 and 5

2-3. a. $H = 2.177$. Total tables cleared in one hour times H equals total time worked by all boys.

    b. Hint: Use number of tables cleared per hour by each boy as weights.

2-5. a. 109.6
    b. 110.0
    c. 108.6

2-7. a. 18.17
    b. 18.15
    c. 19.5
    d. 13.5
    e. 22.45

2-9. a. 5.67 years, median
    b. 26.3%
    c. 8.44 years
    d. 2.33 years
    e. 2.82 and 8.44 years

Chapter 3

3-1. a. 6 to 37, or 31   e. 9.6
     b. 11 to 25, or 14   f. 50%
     c. 7   g. 37.8%
     d. 8   h. 38.9%
3-3. a. $99.50 and $49.80
     b. $56.21
     c. $69.50
     d. 9.47% and 22.28%
3-5. a. -0.89, skewed to the smaller values
     b. 2.58, slightly platykurtic

Chapter 4

4-1. 219
4-3. a. 13   e. 171
     b. 23   f. 456
     c. 24   g. 711
     d. 33   h. 2,039

Chapter 5

Because of possible variations in the preparation of the diagrams, none are shown in the Answers section. Compare your completed diagrams with the illustrations given in Chapter 5.

Chapter 6

6-1. a. 24   b. 12
6-3. a. 20   b. 20,160   c. 3,024
6-5. 10^{10}
6-7. a. 10   b. 4
6-9. 26
6-13. a. 0.72   b. 0.18   c. 0.60   d. 0.12
6-15. a. 0.12   e. 0.10
     b. 0.108   f. 0.90
     c. 0.208   g. 0.088
     d. 0.792   h. 0.12
6-17. 0.646
6-19. $-$$0.56
6-21. a. 11,860   b. $p_c = 0.50$ Produce 12,000

Chapter 7

7-1. a. $\frac{5}{72}$ b. $\frac{63}{256}$
7-3. a. 0.2852 b. 0.3231
7-5. 2, 1.34
7-7. a. 0.8725 b. 0.4044 c. 0.0746 d. 0.0473
7-9. 0.105, 0.535, 0.360
7-11. a. 0.1839 b. 0.3679 c. 0.2642 d. 0.5518
7-13. a. 0.8187 b. 0.1813 c. 0.9825 d. 0.8187
7-15. a. 0.467, 0.067 b. 0.5120, 0.0960
7-17. 0.0600
7-19. 0.0732

Chapter 8

8-1. 0.60653, 0.52704
8-3. a. 18.3 b. 31.8
8-5. a. 4,772.5 b. 0.77453 c. 6.68%
8-7. a. 18.37 b. 32.0
8-9. a. 0.2001 b. 0.21400
8-11. a. 0.6050 b. 0.42220
8-13. 0.4422
8-15. a. 0.67 b. 0.067 c. 0.67
8-17. a. 0.90 b. 0.083
8-19. a. 0.31 b. 0.026 c. 0.53
8-21. a. 0.23 b. 0.66

Chapter 9

9-1. 4635, 21483225, 23348224, 12124324, 01545049, 29702500, 49350625
9-3. 90583264, 83415052, 18546177, 26562067, 10927535
9-7. 0.44
9-9. 0.61949
9-11. 2.37, 0.97
9-13. a. 0.18 b. 0.098, 0.308 c. 0.074, 0.286
9-15. a. 1.020 b. 1.0095, 1.0305 c. 1.027
9-17. 34
9-19. 1,225
9-21. 5.17, 5.63
9-23. $UCL_{\bar{x}} = 11.421$ $LCL_{\bar{x}} = 11.031$
  The averages of subgroups 1, 3, 5, 8, 9, 11, 12, 15, 16, 19, and 20 lie beyond the control limits indicating statistical instability.
9-25. $UCL_R = 0.6104$ $LCL_R = 0$
9-27. $UCL_p = 0.0805$ $LCL_p = 0$
9-29. $UCL_c = 19.5$ $LCL_c = 0$

Chapter 10

10-1. a. 1   c. -7.14
      b. -2.53 d. -6

10-3. $26.93 \le \mu \le 28.07$

10-5. a. 5.27
      b. 0.61

10-7. $187.48 \le \mu \le 212.52$

10-9. $n_1 = 67$
      $n_2 = 44$
      $n_3 = 89$

10-11. $117.77 \le \mu \le 122.23$

10-13. 0.825

10-15. $\bar{n} = 6; \ m = 16$

Chapter 11

11-1. a. If $\bar{x} < 396.72$, do not purchase franchise.
      If $\bar{x} \ge 396.72$, purchase franchise.
      b. If $\bar{x} < 403.28$, do not purchase franchise.
      If $\bar{x} \ge 403.28$, purchase franchise.

11-3. a. $\bar{x}_{c_1} = 102.43$, and $\bar{x}_{c_2} = 105.57$.
      Tell the operator to stop and adjust his machine any time he gets a sample mean less than 102.4 or greater than 105.6. Otherwise, he should continue to operate.

11-5. $\bar{x}_{c_1} = 398.11$, and $\bar{x}_{c_2} = 401.89$.

11-7.

Sample	Value of z	Decision
A	1	Accept H_1
B	3	Reject H_1 and accept H_2
C	2	Reject H_1 and accept H_2

11-9. $t = -1.23$, accept the shipment.

11-11. $z = -1.965$, the machine was not adjusted the same on both days.

11-13. $t = 0.94$, accept the null hypothesis.

Chapter 12

12-1. a. If $p > 0.0508$, stop and adjust.
      If $p \le 0.0508$, continue.
      b. If $p > 0.1492$, stop and adjust.
      If $p \le 0.1492$, continue.

12-3. a. For 14 or more heads the value of $\alpha = 0.0577$, which is too great. For 15 or more heads, the value of α drops to 0.0207. See Appendix D for $n = 20$, $p = 0.5$, and $r = 15$.
      b. Value of $r = 14.167$ (use Formula 12.2) for $\alpha = 0.05$, so the answer is 15 or more heads.

12-5. $z = -2.28$, accept the dealer's claim.

12-7. $z = 0.57$, accept H_1.

Chapter 13

13-1. Computed value of $\chi^2 = 5.790$, accept H_1.

13-3. Computed value of $\chi^2 = 2.542$, accept H_1.
Hint: Value of $\lambda = 1.2$ customers per minute.

13-5. a. Computed value of $\chi^2 = 11.556$, reject H_1 and accept H_2.
b. Value of $D = 0.03$; accept H_1. In this case the Kolmogorov-Smirnov test is not as powerful as the χ^2 test since the differences in the observed and the expected distributions are in the tails of the two distributions.

13-7. Computed value of $\chi^2 = 13.81$, reject H_1 and accept H_2.

13-9. Computed value of $\chi^2 = 14.6$, reject H_1 and accept H_2.

13-11. Computed value of $D = 0.445$, reject H_1 and accept H_2.

13-13. Computed value of $z = 1.28$, accept H_1.

13-15. Computed value of $z = -1.13$, accept H_1.

13-17. Computed value of $z = 2.14$, reject H_1 and accept H_2.

13-19. Computed value of $z = 0.34$, accept H_1.

Chapter 14

14-1. $\chi^2 = 42.25$; $\chi^2_{0.02} = 40.27$; null hypothesis rejected.

14-3. $\sigma^2 = 0.00000105$; $\sigma^2 = 0.0000035$

14-5. $F = 1.47 < F_{0.10} = 1.78$; null hypothesis accepted.

14-7. $F = 5.68 > F_{0.05} = 3.48$; null hypothesis rejected.

14-9. $F = 3.64 > F_{0.05} = 3.10$; null hypothesis rejected.

Chapter 15

15-1. Computed value of F is 12.57, reject H_1 and accept H_2.

15-3. Computed value F_R is 9.44, reject H_1 and accept H_2.
Computed value of F_C is 17.35, reject H_1 and accept H_2.

15-5. Computed value of F_R is 0.56, accept H_1.
Computed value of F_C is 6.76, reject H_1 and accept H_2.
Computed value of F_I is 2.20, accept H_1.

15-7. Computed value of F_R is 29.71, reject H_1 and accept H_2.
Computed value of F_C is 6.14, accept H_1.
Computed value of F_{Tr} is 126.14, reject H_1 and accept H_2.

15-9. Computed value of F_A is 10.56, reject H_1 and accept H_2.
Computed value of F_B is 16.12, reject H_1 and accept H_2.
Computed value of F_C is 118.75, reject H_1 and accept H_2.
Computed value of F_{AB} is 0.33, accept H_1.
Computed value of F_{AC} is 1.79, accept H_1.
Computed value of F_{BC} is 1.79, accept H_1.
Computed value of F_{ABC} is 2.96, accept H_1.
Computed value of F_{Rp} is 0.33, accept H_1.

Chapter 16

16-1. b. $x_{1c} = -13.3077 + 13.4882x_2$ c. 43.3   d. 83.67, 62.37
16-3. 0.9384
16-5. b. $x_{1c} = 0.658405 + 15.2777x_2$ c. 1.0113
     d. $t = 14.573$, significant   e. 13.93, 22.52   f. 21.42, 15.04
16-7. a. 0.9794   b. $t = 12.88$, significant
16-9. a. $b_{12} = 2.547$ $t = 32.65$, significant
     b. $r_{12} = 0.9915$ $t = 30.878$, significant
16-11. 0.2294 $z = 3.657$, significant

Chapter 17

17-1. b. $a_{1.2} = 419.21736$ $b_{12} = -428.16796$ $c_{12} = 123.23816$
     c. 55.58   d. 4.010
17-3. b. $a_{1.2} = 0.3936$ $b_{12} = 0.14433$ $c_{12} = -0.00078$
     c. 3.923   d. 0.3519
17-5. a. 0.96057
     b. $r^2_{x_1.x_2^2 x_2} = 0.75332$
     $t = 4.281 > t_{0.05} = 2.447$, significant
17-7. a. 0.9813
     b. $r^2_{x_1.x_2^2 x_2} = 0.96278$
     $t = 13.457 > t_{0.05} = 2.365$, significant
17-9. $x_{1c.x_2 x_2^2 x_2^3} = 1,286.1907 - 2,177.7123x_2 + 1,286.9846x_2^2 - 255.2049x_2^3$
17-11. c. $(\log x_1)_c = 2.213961 + (-0.664166)x_2$ 0.1175, 1.895161
     d. 78.55
17-13. -0.808

Chapter 18

18-1. a. $x_{1c.23} = -395.9 + 109.49x_2 + 0.6207x_3$ b. 181.82, 88.52
     c. $t = 3.634$, significant $t = 1.012$, not significant
18-3. a. $x_{1c.23} = 6.58 + 0.88459x_2 - 0.27966x_3$ b. 9.61, 2.99
     c. $t = 4.507$, significant $t = 1.148$, not significant
18-5. a. 0.7782   b. $F = 8.776$, significant
18-7. a. 0.7997   b. $F = 13.977$, significant
18-9. a. $x_{1c} = -44.96 + 38.814x_2 + 1.0308x_3$ b. 86.09, 43.05
     c. $t = 2.067$, significant $t = 29.743$, significant
18-11. a. $x_{1c.234} = -39.09 + 39.822x_2 + 1.0241x_3 - 0.24577x_4$
     b. 42.52, -0.82
     c. $t = 2.096$, significant $t = 27.868$, significant
     $t = 0.584$, not significant
18-13. a. 0.961   b. $F = 577.49$, significant   c. 0.950
18-15. a. 0.961   b. $F = 379.71$, significant   c. 0.0

Chapter 19

19-1. b. $\mu_R = 19$; $\sigma_R = 2.96$; computed value of $z = -5.4$, reject H_1 and accept H_2. There is a significant trend.

19-3. a. The first five values of the three-year moving average are: 723.67, 659.33, 576.00, 509.00, and 518.67.

19-5. b. The trend equation is $y_c = 11.73 + 0.28x$; x unit is one year.
   c. The trend equation is $y_c = 12.69 + 0.14x$; x unit is six months.

19-7. c. The trend equation is log $y_c = 4.82703 + 0.06098x$; x unit is one year.

19-9. b. The second-degree polynomial trend equation is $y_c = 1,497.43 + 41.73x - 13.60x^2$; x unit is one year.

19-11.
Trend values

Year	Gompertz (b)	Logistic (c)
1954	127.64	141.28
1955	195.68	195.54
1956	273.39	262.70
1957	355.19	340.58
1958	435.93	424.32
1959	511.74	507.36
1960	580.16	583.36
1961	640.03	647.97
1962	691.17	699.55
1963	734.03	738.70
1964	769.42	767.28
1965	798.30	787.56

Chapter 20

20-1. b.

Month	Index
July	102.20
August	109.00
September	116.88
October	109.18
November	91.97
December	66.36
January	77.23
February	85.27
March	95.53
April	108.85
May	117.03
June	120.50
Total	1,200.00

20-3. a. The trend equation is: $y_c = 1,013.72 + 7.85x$; x unit is six months.

b and c.

y values	y_c values	Ratio to trend	Mov. total	Mov. average
720	738.90	97.44	...	...
732	754.61	97.00	287.79	95.93
719	770.31	93.34	257.39	85.80
527	786.01	67.05	220.51	73.50
482	801.72	60.12	190.54	63.51
518	817.42	63.37	190.23	63.41
556	833.13	66.74	203.86	67.95
626	848.83	73.75	218.68	72.89
676	864.53	78.19	227.26	75.75
663	880.24	75.32	227.07	75.69
659	895.94	73.55	229.50	76.50
735	911.65	80.62	241.42	80.47
809	927.35	87.24	276.23	92.08
1,022	943.05	108.37	328.59	109.53
1,275	958.76	132.98	378.97	126.32
1,341	974.46	137.61	417.04	139.01
1,450	990.17	146.44	452.27	150.76
1,692	1,005.87	168.21	470.69	156.90
1,594	1,021.57	156.03	469.43	156.48
1,506	1,037.28	145.19	439.02	146.43
1,451	1,052.98	137.80	411.74	137.25
1,376	1,068.69	128.76	387.36	129.12
1,310	1,084.39	120.81	362.82	120.94
1,246	1,100.09	113.26	340.45	113.48
1,187	1,115.80	106.38	328.17	109.39
1,228	1,131.50	108.53	330.49	110.16
1,326	1,147.21	115.59	343.99	114.66
1,394	1,162.91	119.87	330.99	110.33
1,126	1,178.61	95.54	298.47	99.49
992	1,194.32	83.06	257.77	85.92
958	1,210.02	79.17	239.82	79.94
951	1,225.73	77.59	230.95	76.98
921	1,241.43	74.19	223.61	74.54
903	1,257.13	71.83	216.73	72.24
900	1,272.84	70.71	214.17	71.39
923	1,288.54	71.63	...	...

20-5.

Year	Observed value x_t	Forecast for $\alpha = 0.25$ D_t	Forecast for $\alpha = 0.40$ D_t
1953	10.8	...	...
1954	11.2	11.2500	10.8720
1955	12.2	11.2450	11.2144
1956	12.1	11.9469	11.9754
1957	12.3	12.2125	12.2212
1958	11.9	12.4424	12.4184
1959	11.6	12.3878	12.2144
1960	12.2	12.1953	11.8987
1961	12.8	12.3124	12.1212
1962	13.1	12.6337	12.5979
1963	13.4	12.9561	12.9939
1964	14.4	13.2777	13.3454
1965	14.7	13.9037	14.1207
1966	15.0	14.4181	14.6365
1967	...	14.8563	15.0243

Chapter 21

21-1. a. Values of the index beginning in 1958 are: 84.7, 92.9, 100.0, 107.1, 114.4, and 123.2.

21-3. a. 103.0
b. 102.2
c. 101.4

21-5. a. 106.6
b. 106.6
c. 106.1
d. 106.3

21-7. a. 133.7
b. 124.5
c. 114.6

21-9. a. 111.4
b. 111.4
c. 110.1
d. 110.7

21-11.

Year	Index: 1958 = 100.0 (a)	Index: 1962 = 100.0 (b)
1958	100.0	72.5
1959	111.6	80.9
1960	114.7	83.2
1961	128.4	93.2
1962	137.8	100.0
1963	141.9	102.9
1964	143.1	103.8

21-13.

Year	Real wages
1960	$59.65
1961	59.26
1962	59.01
1963	59.23
1964	59.90

21-15. a. 107.3

b. 118.3

21-17. a. 101.1, 102.0, and 102.2

b. 102.0, 104.2, and 98.9

Index